# THE CHRISTIAN HYMNARY

Books 1-4

Published by The Christian Hymnary Publishers

Pinecraft, Sarasota, Florida 33578

THE CHRISTIAN HYMNARY



Sarasota, Florida 34278

Library of Congress Catalog Card Number: 72-95291

ISBN: 0-87813-109-4 Deluxe Edition

First Printing, 1972
Second Printing, 1974
Third Printing, 1977
Fourth Printing, 1980
Fifth Printing, 1984
Sixth Printing, 1985



## ACKNOWLEDGMENTS

Grateful acknowledgment is given individuals, trusts, and publishers who have granted permission for the use of copyrighted and uncopyrighted songs. A careful effort has been made to determine the copyright status of all materials compiled. Any oversight brought to our attention will be corrected in future editions. For a detailed listing of acknowledgments for hymns and songs used in this compilation, see pages 881-884.

*Dedicated to the living*
*Christ to Whom the early*
*Christians at daybreak would*
*"Sing an hymn to one . . . as God."*

# INTRODUCTION

True Christians in every generation have attempted to worship their Lord in the best and most appropriate way. The concern for the most zealous, devoted, acceptable worship of God, "in spirit and in truth" (Jn. 4:24), has in a sense been the genius of true Christian experience. Especially is this concern noticeable in worship through singing.

In writing of the Christians of the second century that, "they meet at day break to sing an hymn to one, Christ, as God," the historian Pliny unconsciously paid telling tribute to the intensity and spirituality of early Christian worship in song. Centuries later when Cardinal Cajetan said of one of the reformers, "He has conquered us by his songs," marked tribute again was paid to the potential for righteousness in, and the transcendant power of spiritual singing in worship.

## The Need for Acceptable Worship

There is an apparent need in the present hour to recover and experience again the fervor and sublimity of primitive Christian worship. Especially does this appear apparent in the area of worship in song. To do this effectively and learn to worship our God acceptably, "in psalms and hymns and spiritual songs" (Eph. 5:19), "with reverence and godly fear" (Heb. 12:28), may necessitate going to the Word of God and anew reviewing the nature of true worship as exemplified in worshipers of old.

In one of the notable examples of a life of worship recorded in the Scriptures, the martyr Stephen (Acts 6, 7), manifested a heart truly united to Christ and brought the total of his affections, appetites, and desires to the throne of God. In a life where every desire and purpose, and every act of religious worship was guided and regulated by the Word of God, he fully demonstrated worship "in spirit and in truth" (Jn. 4:24). And finally, in an act of consummate devotion he committed the keeping of his soul to Him that "judgeth righteously" (I Pet. 2:24), and prayed in faith, "Lord Jesus, receive my spirit" (Acts 7:59). May such true worship be our portion is the compiler's prayer.

*The Christian Hymnary* in recognition of this need is presented to the Christian church for the purposes of

1) contributing to a more intense, spiritual, and powerful worship of our God in song;
2) presenting the teachings of our Lord as sound and Biblical doctrine;
3) assisting in the salvation of men.

## The Need for Proper Tempo in Worship

For the realization of the first of the above purposes and objectives, a more powerful and acceptable worship of God, the compiler has been led to call attention to what he believes to be one of the first hindrances to spiritual worship in singing (providing the heart is seeking and is attuned to God). This is the practice of singing with excessive rapidity in hurried and unseemly strains. A certain writer suggests that, "God's acquaintance is not made hurriedly," and in singing this especially appears noticeable. In true worship there must of necessity be calmness, time, and deliberation, as one writer suggests. If it is unthinkable to hurry through private devotions in prayer and praise and Bible reading, then it must be equally so to hurry through the great hymns of supplication and devotion to God.

Excessive speed or tempo in singing, which appears to be largely an American phenomenon, appears therefore to be one of the first blocks to worship "with the Spirit." This does not mean that groups dragging their singing are spiritual, or that we will wish to drag hymns in a dull and insipid fashion, but it does mean that we will do our utmost to sing "with the Spirit" in a grave, reverent, and considerate manner. A knowledge of the various types of hymns in this regard may help us to achieve a more suitable tempo and contribute to more effective worship.

## Suggestions for Tempo in Worship

Lyric poetry as used in our hymnody, as others have suggested, usually consists primarily of narrative, description, praise, supplication, adoration and praise. The first two are to be sung normally in moderate tone of voice and in moderate time, except in the case of description–when it is of heaven it should be performed in a soft and tender manner. Praise ought to be sung in a spirited manner since we have great reason to praise our God for His abundant salvation. Hymns of supplication need to be sung in a slow and plaintive style befitting suppliants of the mercies of our great Creator and God. Hymns of adoration and devotion will need to be sung in a manner moderately slow and solemn, suitably expressing our deepest and most heartfelt sentiment and emotion toward our Heavenly Father, and our Lord Jesus Christ.

The compiler has introduced metronomic marks (M.M.) at the top center of each hymn page suggesting hymn speeds that may be of help in realizing singing, "with the spirit and with the understanding also (I Cor. 14:15).

## Overemphasis of Music: A Hindrance to Worship

A second hindrance or block to spiritual singing may be an overemphasis of the music (hymn tune and harmony) at the expense of the words or text. To engage in spiritual singing we will need to be thoroughly familiar with both the words and music, and then we will need to concentrate on the words lest we become pre-occupied with the vehicle (the music) and "worship music" as W. C. Hays suggests, and we fall into the condemnation of those of whom our Lord spoke, "This people . . . honoureth me with their lips; but their heart is far from me" (Matt. 15:8).

The testimony of the following is pertinent in this regard: Augustine (354-430) early church theologian, confessed, "When it befalls me to be more moved with the singing (music) than with the words which are being sung, I confess that I sin grievously . . ." Conrad Grebel, 1498-1526, leader and co-founder of the Swiss Brethren (Anabaptists), Zurich, Switzerland, 1525, wrote that he who sings poorly is vexed and he who sings well is [likely to become] conceited; therefore, he thought, if anyone wishes to sing he should sing and give thanks in his heart. In hymn No. 674, st. 4, we have included the testimony of Charles Wesley, 1707-1788, noted hymn writer:

Still let us on our guard be found,
And watch against the power of sound,
With sacred jealousy;
Lest, haply, sense should damp our zeal,
And music's charms bewitch and steal
Our hearts away from Thee.

Another contributing factor in our failure to maintain a high level of spiritual worship may be the departure from the simplicity of Christ (II Cor. 11:3), in the use of external accompaniment. It is well known and authenticated that the church of the book of Acts, of the Pauline and other Epistles sang a cappella, that is, without the accompaniment of musical instruments. The apostolic church, the primitive medieval church, the radical reformers sang a cappella. Many thousands of God's people sing a cappella today because they believe this to be the Biblical, practical, and spiritual way to worship their Lord. The chief value of this practice appears to be to help the congregation keep its sense of worship focused on the words rather than on the music, and to sing "with the Spirit."

## Spiritual Singing: The Norm for Worship

Spiritual singing is the need of the hour! If our congregations are to engage in worship of this quality and dimension, then we must truly be, above any other consideration, a people of God. Our lives must support our singing. Spiritual singing must stem from spiritual lives–from hearts keenly aware of the presence of God. It is evident that such spiritual lives stem from a new birth, being born from above, born of the Spirit, filled with the Spirit of God, walking in the Spirit, walking in love, in true holiness, and in true Christian discipleship, Jn. 3:3, 5; Eph. 5:18, 2, 8; Gal. 5:16, 25; Heb. 12:14; I Jn. 2:6.

To achieve spiritual singing is to achieve spirituality in the hearts of our people. And to obtain a new life in the Spirit there must be a discharging of our tremendous moral responsibility in repentance and faith to a moral Creator and God (Acts 20:21). This demands a return to sanity *(resipiscentia:* a growing wise again), a total change of mind, purpose, opinion, inclination, attitude, and direction, a thorough brokenness and yieldedness before God, and a casting of ourselves unreservedly in obedient faith upon Jesus Christ as Saviour and Lord, Ezek. 14:6; Lu. 15:18; Ps. 51:17; Rom. 10:9, 10.

## Suggestions for Procedure in Worship

To achieve spiritual singing may also entail some change in our method and procedure. There may need be a change of emphasis from mere formal training in song leadership or leading, to spiritual maturity and consistency, spontaneity, and dedication. There may be a need to *line hymns* in instances, that is, to read entire stanzas or sentences before singing them. There may be a need to deemphasize song leaders' beating of time in the worship service in certain instances. There may need be a giving of ourselves to prayer in serious preparation for worship if this is lacking. There may be a need for song leaders to develop a fresh consciousness of the presence of God, Father, Son, and Holy Spirit, in the gathered assembly*, as others have suggested, *and to manifest this consciousness*– a consciousness and feeling based on fact that God and ministering spirits are really there (Mt. 18:20; Heb. 1:14). There may be a need for the ministers of congregations, as those duly called to minister in the things of God, to regularly participate in the selection and leading of the hymns of worship as has been long practiced by certain denominations. There may furthermore be a need to publicly and regularly *read* the Scripture texts appearing at top of hymn page before singing hymns, as a foundational basis for spiritual singing. There may be a need to stress singing in unison when harmony is too difficult for the individual to master without undue preoccupation. There may be a need for informal classes and schools periodically for a thorough mastery of both the text and music of our hymnody, so that in worship we can fully exercise ourselves as channels in the ministry of the Spirit. May our Lord in His infinite wisdom supply that which may be lacking in our worship.

It is the prayer of the compiler that *The Christian Hymnary* under God may contribute to a more intense, spiritual, and powerful worship of our Creator in song. Where this occurs the Christian faith, in spite of adversity, will be preserved, and, as the history of the church would indicate, the prevalent liberal tendencies of the pulpit may in time be happily corrected through the presentation and preservation of Biblical doctrine in hymnody. This latter concern brings us to our second purpose or objective.

## The Place of Sound Doctrine in Hymnody and Worship

To present the teachings of our Lord as sound and Biblical doctrine in hymnody, is our second purpose in compiling *The Christian Hymnary*. This has necessitated the alteration of various texts, the recasting of others, the elimination of certain hymn texts, and the introduction of various new hymn materials. The new materials included in and appearing for the first time in *The Christian Hymnary* are written and composed by a dozen contemporary authors and composers. They include the work of the compiler, with the exception of the numerous alterations he has made, and are as follows:

| | |
|---|---|
| Recasts | 17 |
| Composites | 6 |
| New texts | 42 |
| New translations | 25 |
| New tunes | 22 |
| New arrangements of tunes and harmony | 59 |
| New arrangements of harmony | 21 |
| Tunes new to American hymnals | 12 |

[Note: In addition, the best hymn books of America and many of Europe were winnowed over a period of years in order to combine into one volume the present collection of hymns and songs.]

The compiler submits the various alterations and the compilation as a whole to the church at large with the hope that the doctrine of our Lord may be advanced.

## The Corelationship Between Doctrinal Content and Spiritual Singing in Worship

To present the doctrines of our Lord in hymnody, however, has many precedents, and to underscore the great importance of this task and to point up the corelationship between doctrinal content and spiritual singing, we cite the following statement written concerning Bishop Wordsworth, a noted English author of one hundred years ago:

> ". . . Like the Wesleys (he) looked upon hymns as a valuable means of stamping permanently upon the memory the great doctrines of the Christian church. He held it to be 'the first duty of a hymn-writer to teach sound doctrine, and thus to save souls.' He thought that the material for English church hymns should be sought 1) in the Holy Scriptures, 2) in the writings of Christian antiquity, and 3) in the poetry of the ancient church. He did not select a subject which seemed to him most adapted for poetical treatment, but felt himself bound to treat impartially every subject that is brought before us in the church's services, whether of a poetical nature or not . . . Like the Greek (Eastern) hymn-writers, (he) drew his inspiration from the Holy Scriptures . . . he sought and found Christ everywhere in the New Testament. The Gospel history was only the history of what 'Jesus *began* to do and teach' on earth; the Acts of the Apostles and all the Epistles were the history of what He

* "gathered assembly" is the Greek for church.

*continued* to do and to teach from heaven; and the Apocalypse was 'the seal and colophon (finishing stroke, summit) of all.' Naturally he presents this theory, a theory most susceptible of poetical treatment, in his hymns. . . ."

The close correlation between doctrinal content in hymnody and spiritual singing may further be seen in the universal practise of collecting and singing by true Christians of all communities, primarily those hymns which are richest in the living words of the Bible and which are in keeping with its doctrine. The universal acceptance of these hymns points up the following important principle: *The true authority and basis of public worship, including spiritual singing, is Scripture.*

The raison d'etre or foundational basis for prayer and sermon in the public assembly, as others have pointed out, is not to be found in tradition which is mundane and earthly but in the tradition and principle of God's Word. The true hymn, equally so, derives its doctrine and spirit from the words that are spirit and life. And as the singer in spiritual singing engages the text imbued with the Holy Scriptures, the Word of God becomes an instrument of good in control of the Spirit.

It is evident that there can be no working of the Holy Spirit, whether in spiritual singing or other aspect of true worship, except in close correlation to sound doctrine.

## The Ausbund: Example of Doctrine in Hymnody and Worship

One of the outstanding examples of doctrinal content in hymnody preserved for us and worthy of our emulation and duplication is found in the four-hundred-year-old Anabaptist *Ausbund.* Probably the oldest hymnal in constant use since its original compilation, (1535-1540), and first publication, 1564, the *Ausbund* abounds with doctrinal references. The following excerpts from a study of the *Ausbund* by Joseph Overholt as an unpublished thesis, bring these references to attention:

> "It is evident from the study of the theological themes expressed in the hymns of the *Ausbund* that this hymn book is an expression of the Christian faith in agreement with conservative Christian theology and with the teachings of the Bible . . . In examining the theme of the deity of Christ in the *Ausbund,* we find that the hymn writers express a faith in His deity . . . Upon studying the names of Christ, we find that nearly one half, or fifty-two, out of a total of 112 observed titles refer to Him as the Son of God. In the descending scale of importance, we find the names Lord, Truth, Way, God, Life, Door, Bread, and King of Kings . . . When we consider a second aspect of the theme of Christ's deity, namely His authority, we find seventy-eight different references to His Word, commands and teachings." (For additional information on *Ausbund* materials see ADDENDUM.)

In recognition and appreciation of the doctrine oriented hymnody of the Anabaptist *Ausbund,* the compiler has included twelve selections of his own translation and musical arrangement from this hymnal in *The Christian Hymnary* beginning with No. 408 in the section, "Hymns of Martyrs." Two translations of hymns by Menno Simons (1496-1561), and two by Dirk Philips (1504-1570), early Dutch Anabaptist leaders, are also included in this section and are found at Nos. 422, 423, 424, and Nos. 426, 427 respectively. True translations rather than paraphrases have been attempted in this endeavor, with primary concern for accurate rendering of the original languages. It is the compiler's prayer that these selections may find a ready usage and result in deepened appreciation for our Lord and the heritage He has bequeathed.

## The Essentiality of Doctrine in Hymnody and Worship

It is evident that doctrinal content in hymnody is indispensible for the practice of spiritual singing. A summarization of our concern for true doctrinal content and consistency in hymnody might be given in the following extract from an article by Wilmer D. Swope who has contributed to *The Christian Hymnary* in hymn selections and original materials:

> "To be of ultimate worth and service to God and Christians, lyrical poetry (poetry set to hymn tunes as used in our hymnody), must:
>
> 1. Be faithful to Scripture, express truth, be theologically correct and orthodox, teach sound doctrine.
> 2. Cultivate and build strong Christian qualities, hold constant the goal of Christian perfection, be a call to holiness of life and consecration.
> 3. Appeal to the spirit and soul, be a medium of corporate worship expression, be

useful in encouraging interaction in brotherhood through meeting God in company with other believers in public meeting and assembly.

4. Express attitudes of worship, inspire to worship action, teach reverence to God.
5. Speak in understandable positive words, give a call for the repentance of sinners.
6. Sustain Christian hope and consolation, be a reminder of the future home, build Christian perseverance under persecution (the outstanding quality of the lyrical poetry of the *Ausbund)*.

## The Salvation of Men: A Concern in Hymnody and Worship

The third purpose of *The Christian Hymnary* is to assist in the salvation of men. This is undertaken in the arrangement of the hymns and the Index According to Subjects and in the general hymn content referred to above. Various hymn and song selections are compiled, particularly in warning and invitation, with the object of helping souls come to the Lord. Attempt has been made to arrange the hymns and the Index According to Subjects so that the great doctrines of God as Creator, Jesus Christ as Saviour and Lord, the Holy Spirit as the holy Comforter and Guide, redemption through the blood, the Holy Scriptures, the plan of salvation, the Christian life and evidences, the church, ordinances, the commission to seek the lost, heaven, judgment, perdition, days and services, the Christian home and school, might readily be found and impressed on many minds that they by the grace of God might be brought to life in Christ, and others might be strengthened and encouraged in the Christian way.

The materials in *The Christian Hymnary* are arranged into four "books": Book One has hymns, chorales, and songs compiled for general worship with little or no repeating in the refrains; Book Two is made up of choruses and short selections with choruses; Book Three has children's selections compiled in both hymns and songs; Book Four comprises selections for occasional use largely of the Gospel hymn and song type with repeating in the refrains. (Where congregations should wish to omit any books in the above arrangement the publisher plans, D.V., to make this option available in future editions).

## Acknowledgements

The compiler pays tribute to his deceased parents, Joseph Stuckey Overholt (1876-1937), and Hannah Wagler Overholt (1879-1965), for their part in the compilation of this hymnal. As the head of a large family of children, with only a second grade formal education, father taught himself to read music, collected numerous hymnals for singing in the home, and encouraged his children to sing and to compose selections for singing. The several compositions and arrangements found in this compilation are the fruit of this early encouragement. Many of the outstanding old selections found in this hymnal have been compiled from father's personal collection.

To mother we owe an immeasurable debt for helping to lead her family to the Lord, and in encouraging her children to sing informally in the home. Her voice will always be remembered as she sang the great hymns of the church.

We are greatly indebted to everyone who has assisted with the publication of this hymnal, to those who have shared materials, have given permission to use their materials, have given counsel in the arranging of selections, have provided greatly needed financial assistance in personal loans, have given assistance in the selection of materials, have given encouragement to continue with the task of compilation–may God richly bless you is our prayer!

The compiler particularly expresses his indebtedness to nationals of Poland, Germany, France, and Holland, where he was privileged to serve in a term of relief service, for presenting as gifts, various hymnals which have become occasional sources for materials used in this collection. Indebtedness is expressed to individuals in Scandinavia, Great Britain, Switzerland and elsewhere in Europe, where the compiler was privileged to conduct Gospel services and engage in language study, for acquainting him with additional hymns and *Volkslieder* which have enriched the present compilation.

Above all we would thank our Lord and Master, Jesus Christ, for His enabling grace for the task of compilation of the past twelve years, to whom this hymnal is dedicated, and in worship of whom we would, even as the early Christians of Christendom's morn, "meet at daybreak to sing an hymn to one, Christ, as God!"

John J. Overholt
Compiler of *The Christian Hymnary*
December, 1972

SOLI DEO GLORIA

# ADDENDUM

## Examples of Spiritual Singing from the Scriptures and *Martyrs Mirror*. Additional Doctrine Content from the *Ausbund*.

### Songs in the Night

It is God who must give, and will give spiritual singing for His glory. The book of Job brings this to attention in 35:10: "Where is God my Maker which giveth songs in the night?" Stalwart and victorious, privileged and blessed have been the singers filled with the Spirit of God whose hymns and songs have rung out throughout history's night:

- Our Lord Jesus sang the Hallel (including Pss. 115-118), pashal hymn of praise and triumph in the night of Gethsemane, Calvary, and the eventual redemption of the world, Mk. 14:26.
- Paul and Silas, missionaries of our Lord, sang hymns of praise and conviction within dark prison cells in the night of spiritual destitution, persecution, and enslavement that prevailed in pagan Philippi, Acts 16:25.
- The great "cloud of witnesses," the martyr heroes and stalwarts of our Lord, sang their death chant, "Unto Him that loved us and bought us from our sins in His own blood," as they faced the lions in the arena and colosseum, in the night that over-shadowed demon-darkened Rome, Heb. 12:1; Rev. 1:5.
- The tortured Anabaptist, Hans Schmid of Aachen, martyred in 1558, wrote, "In jail . . . I began to pray and sing as loud as I was able to raise my voice . . . so that everyone outside could hear"–spiritual hymns and songs in the darkness and night of persecution and death that beclouded medieval Europe.
- The imprisoned Anabaptists of Passau Castle from 1535 to 1540 sang and wrote the hymns and songs of the *Ausbund,* oldest hymnal of the free church, during the night of suffering and martyrdom engulfing a spiritually darkened continent.
- The martyr Anabaptist, George Blaurock, Christian missionary and a leader of the Swiss Brethren, on occasions in 1525 and later, when arrested, lifted up his voice in hymns to God while being led away to torture or imprisonment; finally when facing death in 1529 he wrote and sang his Schwanenlied,

  "Darum so will ich singen,
  Zu Lob dem Namen dein,
  Und ewiglich verkünden
  Die Gnad, die mir erschien,"

  "Therefore will I be singing
  In blessing of Thy name,
  Eternally praise bringing
  Of grace that to me came,"
  *(Ausbund* No. 30; No. 417,
  *The Christian Hymnary)*

- and midst the flames of the stake that devoured his mortal body, George Blaurock glorified his Maker who "giveth songs in the night!" May God grant that we too, shall sing songs in the night!

### Spirit-Motivated Singing in *Martyr's Mirror*

In the *Martyrs Mirror,* Dutch Anabaptist classic of the seventeenth century, first published in 1660 by T. J. van Braght (1625-64), and translated into English in 1837 and 1886, are recorded the following incidents which we present as an exhibit of Spirit-motivated singing.

1) "When Babylas was sentenced . . . to be beheaded . . . he sang the comforting words of the 116th Psalm (a portion of the Jewish Hallel) on his way to the place of execution: 'Return unto thy rest, O my soul' " (A. D. 254, p. 135, 1951 Edition).
2) ". . . When they had built a great fire of wood they made her climb upon it, and there, after singing sweet psalms and hymns of praise to the honor of God, she was consumed by the flames" (Irene, A. D. 309, p. 184).
3) ". . . They were led out to punishment . . . their leader, namely, Gerard going before

them singing: 'Blessed are ye,' says the Lord, 'when men shall hate you for my sake' " (A. D. 1161, p. 295).

4) "Oh his way to the place of execution he composed and sang a hymn which is still extant" (Thomas Hermann, 1527, p. 422).

5) ". . . They sang and rejoiced in prison so that their enemies . . . were more troubled and afraid than the prisoners" (A. D. 1529, p. 437).

6) "When he was led to the place of execution, he sang joyfully on the way . . . and sang for joy that God had given him such courage and heart" (George Bauman, 1529, p. 437).

7) ". . . While the others were being drowned and executed, the rest who were yet alive and waited for death sang until the executioner took them" (350 persons, 1529, p. 437).

8) ". . . The judge remanded them to prison, in which they sang comforting hymns together and rejoiced in God" (Jerome Kels, Michael Seifensieder, Hans Oberacker, 1536, p. 446).

9) ". . . And told them that they should not pass silently through the cities and towns, but should make their faith known by singing or otherwise" (spoken to Austrian brethren on the way to the galleys, p. 452).

10) "When they were led to the stake, many of the people seeing their steadfastness, wept. But they sang for joy . . ." (Maria van Beckum and Ursula, 1544, p. 457).

11) "This lover of God also sang in the fire, in which he lived for some time, praising God by his singing, and praying for all men who were worthy that God should enlighten them" (Hans Blietel, 1545, p. 474).

12) "When they were being led out to the slaughter, they boldly and joyfully sang" (Hans Staudtach, Anthony Keyn, Blasius Beck, Leonhard Schneider, 1546, p. 475).

13) "When Fije's sentence was read . . . he sang and leaped, praising and thanking God . . . they could not prevail upon him for Fije did nothing but sing and speak, praising and thanking God" (1549, p. 485).

14) ". . . They were led back to prison where they rejoiced together and sang: 'Saligh is den man, en goet geheeten' and also the forty-first Psalm" (Govert, Gillis, 1550, p. 494).

"Anneken immediately commenced to sing: 'In Thee, O Lord, do I put my trust' [Ps. 71:1] . . . When it was thought that the old woman had been strangled at the stake, she began to sing a hymn in honor of her Bridegroom, which when Anneken heard it, she, from ardent love, sang with her. When they all stood at their stakes each with a strap around the neck . . . commending their souls into the hands of God, they fell asleep in the Lord, and were burned" (Mariken and Anneken with the above, 1550, p. 495).

15) ". . . Sentenced to death as heretics . . . Dieuwertgen came forward singing . . ." (1550, p. 495).

16) ". . . He joyfully kept singing a hymn until the last moment, that is, as long as he had breath, while he was standing at the stake at which he was burnt to ashes" (Palmken Palmen, 1550, p. 496).

17) ". . . Lijsken was undaunted and of good cheer, and commenced singing a hymn . . . And forthwith she began to sing, 'Behold, what poor sheep we are' [Rom. 8:36]. Before the hymn was finished, the lords came with the servants into the prison . . ." (1551, p. 522).

18) "On her way to the water (drowning), she sang with a joyful heart . . ." (Maria of Monjou, 1552, p. 525).

19) "When he was led to death, and having been brought from the wagon upon the scaffold, he lifted up his voice, and sang the hymn,

'Father in heaven, I call:
O strengthen now my faith'

. . . The rope with which he was to be strangled, becoming a little loose, having not been twisted well by the executioner, he again lifted up his voice, and sang the end of said hymn,

'Brethren, sisters, all, good-bye!
We must now separate,
Till we meet beyond the sky,
With Christ our only Head;
For this yourselves prepare,

And I'll await you there.' "
(Gerrit Hasepoot, 1556, p. 560).

20) "But the prisoners were valiant and comforted one another . . . and being thus of good cheer, they began to sing for joy . . . the sisters rejoiced, and sang, so that the people were astonished" (Hans Smit, a minister, and eleven others, 1558, p. 588).
"In the evening about ten o'clock they were separated again, and led away. On their way through the city, they joyfully sang, and made known their faith . . . when the minister heard that he was to die, he commenced to sing joyfully . . . Hans Smit, as the minister, was first executed. When being led through the city, he sang joyfully" (p. 589).

21) "When brought forth from prison to be taken to the place of execution . . . these people were full of gladness, and they joyfully sang with a cheerful mind" (Gotthard of Nonenberg and Peter Kramer, 1558, p. 590).

22) "As they were coming out of the court they said, 'We are not ashamed of the Gospel' [Rom. 1:16], and while walking in the street they sang, 'O Lord, forever in my thought Thou art; My soul doth long to be close to Thy heart' [Ps. 143:8] . . . They began to sing this farewell hymn, 'Farewell, brethren and sisters all' " (Joris and Joachim, 1560, p. 644).

23) "On his way to death (at the stake) he rejoiced greatly in the Lord, and sang yet as he was going into the straw in which he was burnt, the last verse of the hymn composed by himself, which begins thus, 'O Lord, Thou art forever in my thoughts' (Joost Joosten, aged 18, 1560, p. 651).

24) ". . . He was joyful, and constantly sang and praised God with a valiant heart" (Julius Klampherer on way to drowning, 1561, p. 652).

25) "Lauwerens van de Walle, Antonis Schoonvelt, and Kalleken Strings were also apprehended . . . On their way to town Kalleken commenced to sing a hymn . . . Antonis said, 'Sister, do not fear these; just sing as much as you want to' and Lauwerens helped her sing. When they came into the city, there was a great concourse of people, and they made known the Word of God by singing and speaking" (1561, p. 653).

26) ". . . Schut had been cheerful in his tribulation and had sang much in prison and on his way to death" (1561, p. 655).

27) "The sentence was that Conrad should suffer death if he did not recant. And when he had been thus sentenced twice they took him out [to the place of execution]. When he arrived there he began to sing, 'O God, how gently Thou doest chasten me.' " (Conrad Koch, 1565, p. 687).

28) "Jan van Paris, Pieter van Cleves, Hendrick Maelschalck, and Lauwerens Pieters had not yet united with the church but were novices and ready to united; hence going to hear the Word of God preached they were apprehended at Ghent, in Flanders, in the year 1568, and taken to the Count's Castle . . . When the brethren heard that they were to be burnt alive, they raised their voices and sang, 'I call upon Thee, O heavenly Father' " (p. 723).

29) ". . . We send you three new hymns as a cordial and friendly greeting . . . we think our confinement will not last much longer . . . we hope to go before . . ." (Hendrick Maelschalck [above] p. 724).

30) "Claudine was beautiful of person and a good singer, so that she moved the bystanders by her singing. Especially on the last day of her life, people stood before the prison to hear her sing with a joyful heart when death was announced to her. One who related it to me had heard her sing with a clear strong voice the 27th psalm of David, 'Le Seigneur est la clarte qui m'addresse' " (1568 p. 738).

31) ". . . Neeltgen and her daughter Trijntgen were also delivered to the lords and conducted to the Dinghuys, and came into the street on their way thither, both of them being joyful and of good courage, Trijntgen for joy began to sing, thus she was kindled in the Lord . . . Ursel said to the lords: 'And may I not sing a little, and say something now and then?' But this they would not permit her . . . the executioner had a piece of wood which he put in Ursel's mouth, and tied up her mouth with a cloth" (1570, pp. 842, 843).

32) ". . . They found nothing on his person except a hymn" (Hans van den Wege, burnt at the stake, 1570, p. 864).

33) ". . . About twelve o'clock in the night . . . the executioner . . . and others assembled and conducted him to the torture tower, whither he gladly went, singing, 'I call upon

Thee, O heavenly Father, Be pleased to strengthen my faith' " (Reytse Aysess, drowned April 23, 1574, p. 1005).

May *The Christian Hymnary* contribute to true worship and *glorify our Maker which giveth songs in the night* [Job 35:10], in a manner worthy of the martyrs of old!

## Additional Doctrinal Content in the *Ausbund*

Following is additional material on doctrinal content of the *Ausbund* from the unpublished thesis prepared by Joseph Overholt, which underscores the correlation between sound doctrine and spiritual singing.

"The *(Ausbund)* writers placed more importance upon the deity of Christ than upon His humanity. In the order in which the themes relating to His deity came, we see those referring to His authority coming first, His names, worship, second coming and judgment, and resurrection rank next in order. With regard to His humanity, they placed emphasis on His being truly man, with a number of references to His incarnation and birth. Themes relating to Soteriology (the work of Christ in providing for man's salvation), were ranked King, Priest, and Prophet.

"... As a frame of reference for a discussion of the church themes, we note the four marks of the true church, namely unity, holiness, catholicity (universality), and apostolicity, which came down from the Nicene creed ... Through a study of the names of the church as bride, flock, body, people of God, sheep, vineyard, tabernacle, we see the basic oneness of the church revealed.

"In studying the body of Christ, we note again the Christo-centric view of the hymn writers ... Eighteen general references to union with Christ include Head, Cornerstone, Foundation, Guide. The process of union with Christ is through the new birth, to which there are ten references. Holiness, the result of union with Christ, is quoted in the context of the church thirty-seven times.

"... In the *Ausbund* there are thirty-seven direct references to holiness; thirty-five references to the children of God who have holiness; ten references to the Holy Spirit as the One who brings holiness. The Holy Spirit initiates into the church, regenerates, leads, empowers, drives, brings the new birth, according to the hymns of the *Ausbund.*

"... The inevitable consequence of living a holy life is suffering, according to the themes of the *Ausbund*. The church is made up of martyrs. There are fifteen specific references to the suffering church in the hymns, and more with regard to individual Christians. Another aspect of holiness was discipleship.

"Originally, catholicity meant universality. The hymn writers would have applied it to the invisible church, the universal body of believers, and also to the total number of visible professed believers in Christ. One finds twelve references to the body of Christ, or the invisible church. Related themes were references to the new birth, redemption, witnessing, and the formation of the church. The hymn writers were interested in evangelism as the extension of the ... church ....

"... In the *Ausbund* are reflected the burning convictions ... of individuals who were interested in recapitulating (or restoring) the apostolic church. Within its pages are recorded 190 general references to discipleship; 173 to faith; 142 to conversion; 103 to love; 53 to nonresistance; 183 to joy. All of its themes were apostolic, for all were Biblical, and built upon the "foundation of the apostles and prophets, Jesus Christ himself being the chief cornerstone," Eph. 2:20. (Additional references in the *Ausbund* include the following:

| | |
|---|---|
| Christ as King | 200 references |
| Prophet | 78 |
| Intercessor | 70 |
| His sacrificial death | 120 |
| suffering | 29) |

It is our prayer that the examples of singing recorded in the Holy Scriptures, the *Martyrs Mirror,* and the *Ausbund,* including the doctrinal content of the latter, which clearly points up the correlation between sound doctrine and spiritual singing, may inspire us to sing the doctrine-oriented hymns compiled in *The Christian Hymnary* in acceptable worship. May we be inspired to worship our living Lord "with the spirit and with the understanding also" (I Cor. 14:15), "in spirit and in truth" (Jn. 4:24).

John J. Overholt

# ABBREVIATIONS AND DEFINITIONS

| | |
|---|---|
| **Adapted** | Acquired and arranged. |
| **Alt.** | Words or text altered, changed from original. |
| **Alt. by compiler** | Minor alteration of text by John J. Overholt. |
| **Anabaptists** | Reformers of the 16th century who baptized again upon confession of faith, and who in their doctrine and practice recovered the New Testament ideal. |
| **Anon.** | Anonymous, unknown. |
| **Arr.** | Music of melody and harmony arranged and changed from original. |
| **Arr. by compiler** | Minor arrangement of music by John J. Overholt. |
| **Author** | Writer of the words or text of a hymn (placed at left of page). |
| **Beating time** | Indicating and spelling out the time or tempo of a selection and noting the time signature for the number of beats in a measure. |
| **Cento** | Combination of stanzas or parts of stanzas by the same author. |
| **Chants** | Ancient form of hymnody which is to be sung without observing the written time or pulse signature. |
| **Chorale** | Hymn where four musical parts usually give effect of singing distinct melodies in harmony. |
| **Compiler** | One who compiles or collects the selections in a hymnal. |
| **Composer** | The writer of the music of a hymn (placed at the right of page). |
| **Composite** | Combination of stanzas or parts of stanzas by several authors. |
| **Composite arr.** | Arrangement of the stanzas or words of text written by several authors. |
| **Descant or obligato** | An accompanying part usually sung by sopranos. |
| **Gospel hymn** | Term coined by Ira David Sankey. Songs mainly of exhortation and testimony set to folk-like tunes (like folk tunes). |
| **Gospel song** | Term coined by D. W. Whittle and P. P. Bliss, co-workers of Dwight L. Moody and Ira David Sankey. Similar to above. Co-ordinates with exhortation primarily rather than prayer (as in a true hymn). |
| **Harmony** | The proper blending or joining of alto, bass, and tenor parts supporting the lead melody, or soprano. |
| **Harmony arr.** | Harmony arranged and changed from original. |
| **Hymn** | Lyric or word poem reverently and devotionally written expressing the worshiper's attitude toward God. It is simple and metrical in form, spiritual in quality, and engages the singer in worship of God through prayer and praise.* |

*From a Paper of the Hymn Society – "What is a Hymn?" by Carl F. Price, No. VI, copyright 1937.

**Key signature** Sharps or flats on a staff, or omission of them, designating where the key note, or do is located.

**Lyric poetry** Poetry adapted to singing. (For types see introduction.)

**Measure** Sections of musical score divided by perpendicular lines.

**M.M.** Metronomic marks indicating the suggested speed or tempo to sing a given selection with the use of a metronome. (Where a metronome is not available, speed or tempo can be approximated by using a watch with a sweep second hand. M.M. 60 equals 60 seconds in a minute approximately, and one beat equals one second. At the speed of M.M. 120 there are two beats in a second.)

**Meter** Division of syllables in a musical selection.

**Metronome** Instrument for measuring time, tempo, pulse, or speed.

**Recast** Change and reconstruction of text and words, usually with a change in meter.

**Ref.** Refrain or chorus.

**Score** Two staffs with all musical components for full width of page.

**Singing with the Spirit** Singing in the energy of the Holy Spirit, as if in the very presence of Christ, exercising both intellect and emotion.

**Staff** Five lines and spaces.

**Tempo, time, pulse speed** The speed at which a selection is sung and determined by time signature.

**Time signature** Numbers at left of score designating number of beats in a measure and the identity of note receiving one beat.

**Tr.** Translation, Translated

**Tune** The melody or lead part, usually sung by sopranos.

(Explanatory note: minor alterations of words and arrangement of music in this hymnal are designated as *altered or arranged by compiler.* Extensive alterations or arrangements by compiler are designated by *use of compiler's full name.*)

# THE CHRISTIAN HYMNARY

## CONTENTS

Complete index of Hymn Topics, pp. 874-876

# O GOTT VATER, WIR LOBEN DICH

1. O Gott Vater, wir loben dich,
Und deine Gü–te– preisen;
Die du, O Herr, so gnädiglich,
An uns neu hast– be–wiesen,
Und hast uns Herr zusammen g'führt,
Uns zu ermahnen durch– dein– Wort,
Gib uns Genad– zu– diesem.

2. Oefne den Mund, Herr, deiner Knecht,
Gib ihn'n Weisheit– dar–neben,
* Dass er dein Wort mög sprechen recht,
Was dient zum from–men– Leben,
Und nützlich ist zu deinem Preis,
Gib uns Hunger nach sol–cher– Speis,
Das ist unser– be–gehren.

3. Gib unserm Herzen auch Verstand,
Erleuchtung hie– auf– Erden,
Dass dein Wort in uns werd bekannt,
Dass wir fromm mö–gen– werden,
Und leben in Gerechtigkeit,
Achten auf dein Wort al–le–zeit,
So bleibt man un–be–trogen.

4. Dein, o Herr, ist das Reich allein,
Und auch die Macht– zu–sammen,
Wir loben dich in der Gemein,
Und danken dei–nem– Namen,
Und bitten dich aus Herzens Grund,
Wollst bey uns seyn zu die–ser– Stund,
Durch Jesum Chris–tum–, Amen.

Hymn No. 131 by Leenaerdt Clock, c. 1590, from the 16th Century Anabaptist *Ausbund*. Other settings of this hymn in exact meter may be found at Nos. 53, 54, 408, 409, 410, 411, 666.

* Daß: The phonetic spelling *ss* is used instead of the German ß in *Ausbund* translations.

**BEGINNING OF WORSHIP:** OPENING HYMN OF PRAISE AND PRAYER

# O GOD AND FATHER, THEE WE BLESS 1

*Bless the Lord, O my soul: and all that is within me, bless His holy name.* Ps. 103:1.

From the 16th century Anabaptist *Ausbund*
Hymn No. 131, Leonard Clock, c. 1590
*O Gott Vater, wir loben dich*
Tr. John J. Overholt, 1969

DIE NACHFOLGE CHRISTI
8.9.8.9.8.10.9.
M.M. 69

Claude Goudimel, 1505-1572
Arr. John J. Overholt, 1971

1. O God and Fa - ther, Thee we bless, Thy good - ness ev - er
2. O - pen Thy servants' lips, O Lord, And grant them wis - dom,
3. An un - der-stand - ing mind im - part, In - spire us, Lord, we
4. Thine on - ly is the king - dom, Lord, Thine on - ly is the
praise ad-dress - ing, That Thou, O Lord, with grac - ious - ness, A -
and Thy pow - er, That they right - ly may speak Thy Word, That
here do pray Thee, That Thy Word known with - in our hearts, In
pow - er giv - en; With - in Thy church with one ac - cord Thy
new us kind - ly man - i - fest - ing, Hast led us thus to -
ho - ly lives may spring and flow - er And glo - ri - fy Thee
ho - ly lives may ev - er praise Thee; And in true right - eous-
name we praise, and raise to heav - en! And from our heart's depth,
geth - er, Lord, To us ad - mon - ish through Thy liv - ing
for Thy good, O grant us hun - ger for such sac - red
ness, that we, Thy grac - ious Word so heed - ing con - stant -
Lord, we pray, Be with us in this hal - lowed hour to -
Word; For this grant grace and con - stant bless - ing!
food; This is our fer - vent pray'r this hour!
ly, May un - de - ceived o - bey and serve Thee!
day, Through Je - sus Christ, our Sav - ior, A - men! A - men.

# 2 COME, THY PRESENCE MANIFESTING

*Oh that Thou wouldest rend the heavens, that Thou wouldest come down.* Is. 64:1. *In Thy presence is fulness of joy.* Ps. 16:11.

John J. Overholt, 1971

DIE GEGENWART GOTTES 8.8.8.7.8.7.8.7.
M.M. 60

Wolfgang Wessnitzer, 1615-1697
Arr. John J. Overholt, 1971

1. Come, Thy pres - ence man - i - fest-ing, O our God, Thy truth at - test - ing, Wilt Thou grant our soul's re - quest-ing That we wor-ship in Thy fear; O re - move all thoughts distracting, Fix our hearts and hopes a - bove; Here Thy bless-ing e'er trans-act-ing, Fa-ther, here im-part Thy love.

2. Lord, as - sist us in our prais-ing, That we love's de - vot - ion phrasing, May true worship be up - rais - ing, And may glor - i - fy Thy name; We would ren-der thanks and blessing, For sal - va-tion thro' Christ's blood; Ev - er Thee our want con-fess-ing, Fa-ther, grant us heav'nly food.

3. Lord, Thy sac - red Word ap - ply - ing, And our hearts new sanc - ti - fy - ing, Grant that we on Thee re - ly - ing Prac-tice that which we shall hear; Bless Thy min - i - sters and preaching, May they Christ to us re - veal; May Thy Word men's hearts be reaching; Fa-ther, here men's spirits seal.

4. Lord, Thy pres - ence man - i - fest-ing, To Thy Ho - ly Word at - test-ing, Come, and grant our soul's re - quest-ing That we to Thy truth ad - here; O re - buke all de - mon striving; Sin for-give in Je - sus' name; In Thy Spir - it bring re - viv - ing, Fa-ther, that we Thee acclaim. A - men.

## COME, GREAT GOD, THY PEOPLE HEAR 3

*Arise, O Lord God, into Thy resting place.* II Chron. 6:41.

Sts. 2 and 3, John Newton, 1725-1807
Recast, and St. 1, John J. Overholt, 1970

CULBACH NEW 7.7.7.6.
M.M. 63

Scheffler's *Heilige Seelenlust*, 1657
Arr. John J. Overholt, 1970

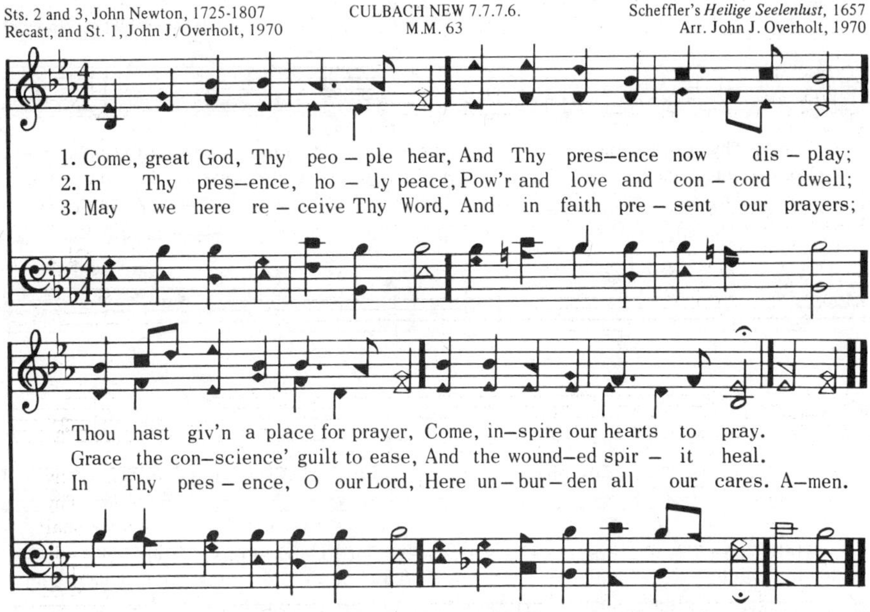
1. Come, great God, Thy peo – ple hear, And Thy pres–ence now dis – play;
2. In Thy pres–ence, ho – ly peace, Pow'r and love and con – cord dwell;
3. May we here re – ceive Thy Word, And in faith pre – sent our prayers;
Thou hast giv'n a place for prayer, Come, in–spire our hearts to pray.
Grace the con–science' guilt to ease, And the wound–ed spir – it heal.
In Thy pres – ence, O our Lord, Here un – bur – den all our cares. A–men.

## LIGHT OF LIFE! CONSUMING FIRE! 4

*Our God is a consuming fire.* Heb. 12:29. *Who among us shall dwell with the devouring fire? who among us shall dwell with everlasting burnings?* Is. 33:14.

Charles Wesley, 1707-1788
Alt. by Compiler, 1970

CAPETOWN 7.7.7.5.
M.M. 60

Frederick Filitz, 1847 (1804-1876)

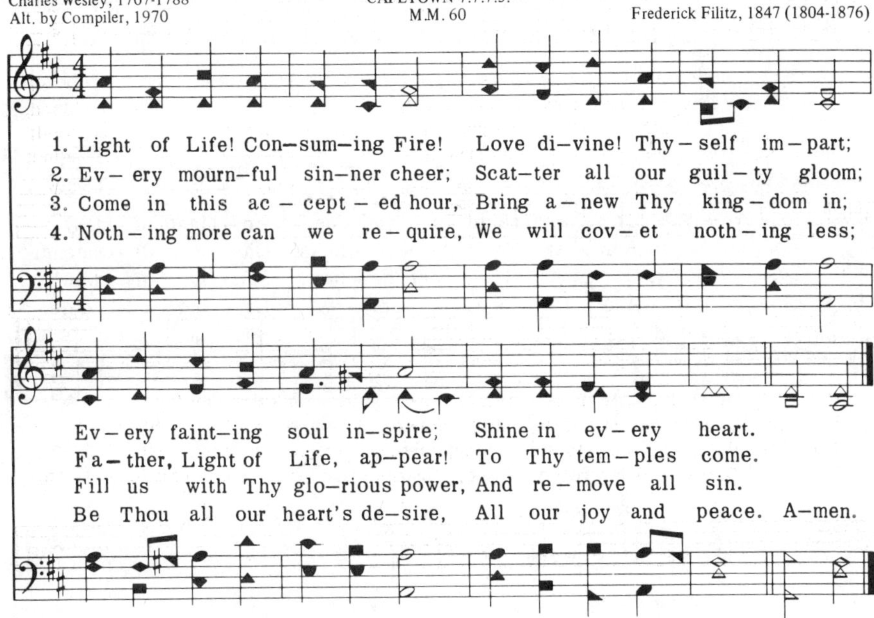
1. Light of Life! Con–sum–ing Fire! Love di–vine! Thy – self im – part;
2. Ev – ery mourn–ful sin–ner cheer; Scat–ter all our guil – ty gloom;
3. Come in this ac – cept – ed hour, Bring a – new Thy king – dom in;
4. Noth – ing more can we re – quire, We will cov – et noth – ing less;
Ev – ery faint–ing soul in–spire; Shine in ev – ery heart.
Fa – ther, Light of Life, ap–pear! To Thy tem – ples come.
Fill us with Thy glo–rious power, And re – move all sin.
Be Thou all our heart's de–sire, All our joy and peace. A–men.

# 5 COME, THOU ALMIGHTY KING

*The Lord shall be king over all the earth.* Zech. 14:9.

Anonymous
St. 3, Alt. by Compiler, 1972

ITALIAN HYMN 6.6.4.6.6.6.4.
M.M. 76

Felice de Giardini, 1769 (1716-1796)

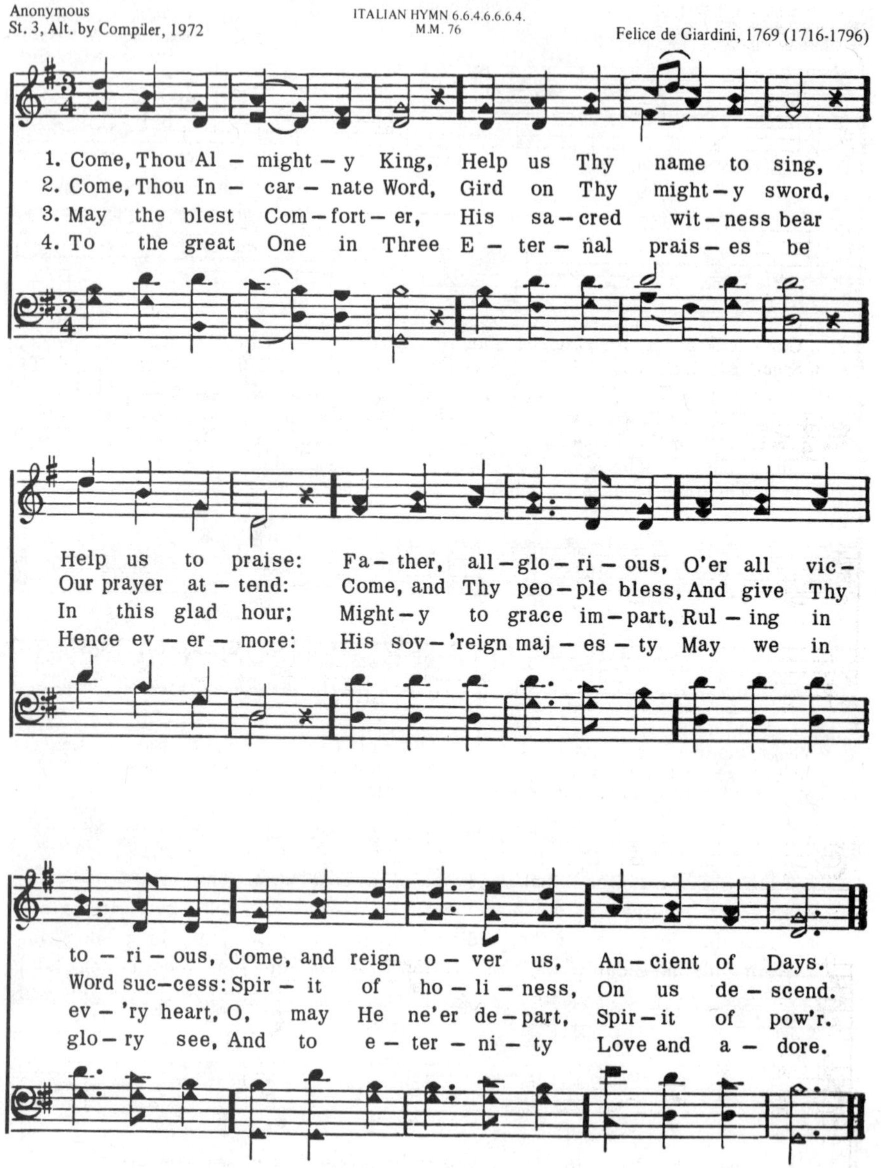
1. Come, Thou Al – might – y King, Help us Thy name to sing,
2. Come, Thou In – car – nate Word, Gird on Thy might – y sword,
3. May the blest Com – fort – er, His sa – cred wit – ness bear
4. To the great One in Three E – ter – nal prais – es be
Help us to praise: Fa – ther, all – glo – ri – ous, O'er all vic –
Our prayer at – tend: Come, and Thy peo – ple bless, And give Thy
In this glad hour; Might – y to grace im – part, Rul – ing in
Hence ev – er – more: His sov – 'reign maj – es – ty May we in
to – ri – ous, Come, and reign o – ver us, An – cient of Days.
Word suc – cess: Spir – it of ho – li – ness, On us de – scend.
ev – 'ry heart, O, may He ne'er de – part, Spir – it of pow'r.
glo – ry see, And to e – ter – ni – ty Love and a – dore.

# OPEN NOW THY GATES OF BEAUTY 6

*Open to me the gates of righteousness: I will go into them, and I will praise the Lord.* Ps. 118:19.

Benjamin Schmolck, 1732 (1672-1737)
*Tut mir auf die schöne Pforte*
Tr. Catherine Winkworth, 1836 (1827-1878)
Alt.

UNSER HERRSCHER 8.7.8.7.7.7.
M.M. 80

Joachim Neander, 1680 (1650-1680)
Descant Geoffrey Shaw

Descant

1. O - pen now thy gates of beau - ty, Zi - on, let me en - ter there,
2. Gra - cious God I come be - fore Thee, Come Thou al - so down to me;
3. Speak, O Lord, and I will hear Thee, Let Thy will be done in - deed;

Where my soul in joy - ful du - ty Waits for Him who an - swers prayer:
Where we find Thee and a - dore Thee, There a heaven on earth must be:
May I un - dis - turbed draw near Thee While Thou dost Thy peo - ple feed.

O how bless - ed is this place, Filled with sol - ace, light, and grace!
To my heart O en - ter Thou, Let it be Thy tem - ple now.
Here of life the foun - tain flows, Here is balm for all our woes. A-men.

# 7 THE LORD IS IN HIS HOLY TEMPLE

*The Lord is in His holy temple.* Hab. 2:20.

THE LORD IS IN HIS HOLY TEMPLE (Excell) 9.7.7.
M.M. 63

Edwin Othello Excell, 1851-1921

Edwin Othello Excell

The Lord is in His ho - ly tem - ple: Let all the
p
pp
earth keep si - lence, keep si - lence be - fore... Him. A - MEN.

# 8 LO, GOD IS HERE

*Though He be not far from everyone of us.* Acts 17:27.

Gerhard Tersteegen, 1697-1769
*Gott ist gegenwärtig*
Tr. John Wesley, 1703-1791
Alt. by Compiler, 1965

DUKE STREET L.M. 8.8.8.8.
M.M. 120

John Hatton, d. 1793
H. Boyd's *Psalm and Hymn Tunes*, 1793

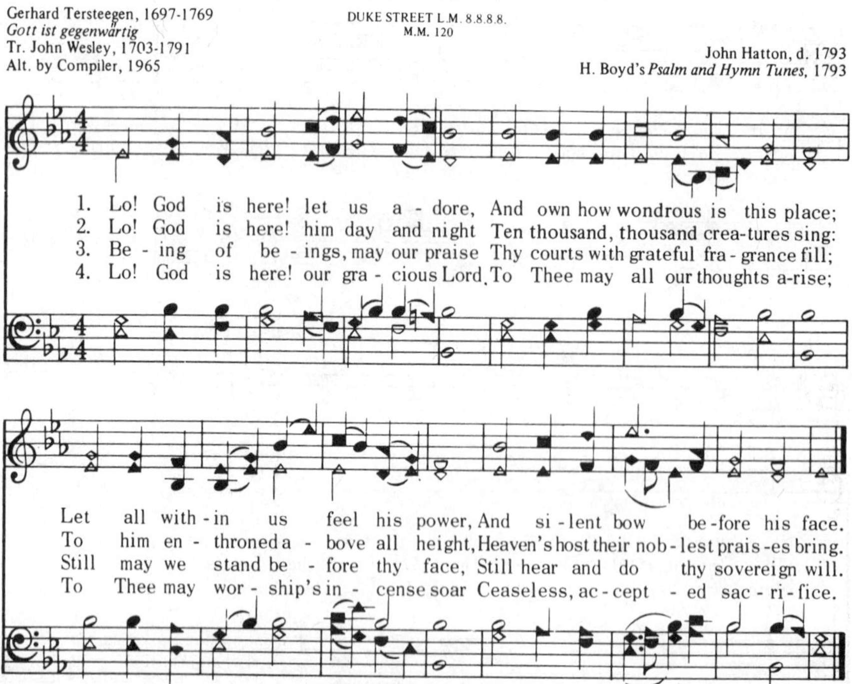
1. Lo! God is here! let us a - dore, And own how wondrous is this place;
2. Lo! God is here! him day and night Ten thousand, thousand crea-tures sing:
3. Be - ing of be - ings, may our praise Thy courts with grateful fra - grance fill;
4. Lo! God is here! our gra - cious Lord, To Thee may all our thoughts a-rise;
Let all with - in us feel his power, And si - lent bow be-fore his face.
To him en - throned a - bove all height, Heaven's host their nob - lest prais - es bring.
Still may we stand be - fore thy face, Still hear and do thy sovereign will.
To Thee may wor - ship's in - cense soar Ceaseless, ac - cept - ed sac - ri - fice.

# THE LORD IS IN HIS HOLY TEMPLE 9

*Let all the earth keep silence before Him.* Hab. 2:20.

THE LORD IS IN HIS HOLY TEMPLE (Anon.) 9.10
M.M. 66

Anonymous — Anonymous

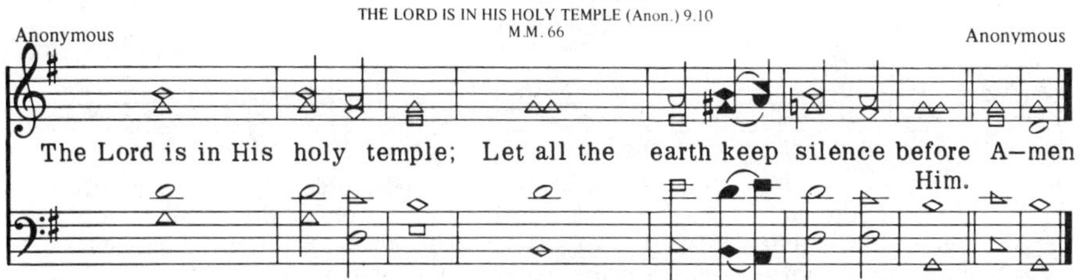
The Lord is in His holy temple; Let all the earth keep silence before Him. A–men

# GOD HIMSELF IS PRESENT 10

*Tremble, thou earth, at the presence of the Lord, at the presence of the God of Jacob.* Ps. 114:7.

Gerhard Tersteegen, 1729 (1697-1769)
*Gott ist gegenwärtig*
Tr. F. W. Foster and J. Miller. 1789, alt.

WUNDERBARER KÖNIG 6.6.8.6.6.8.3.3.6.6.
M.M. 84

Joachim Neander's *Bundes-Lieder,* 1680

1. God him - self is pres - ent, Let us now a - dore him,
And with awe ap - pear be - fore him!
God is in his tem - ple, All with - in keep si - lence,
Pros - trate lie with deep - est rev - erence. Him a - lone God we own,
Him, our God and Sav - iour; Praise His name for - ev - er!

2. God him - self is pres - ent, Hear the praise re - sound - ing!
See the host the throne sur - round - ing!
'Ho - ly, Ho - ly, Ho - ly,' Hear the hymn a - scend - ing,
An - gels, saints, their voic - es blend - ing! Bow thine ear To us here:
Hear, O Christ, the prais - es That thy Church now rais - es.

3. O thou Fount of bless - ing Pur - i - fy my spir - it,
Trust - ing on - ly in thy mer - it;
Like the ho - ly an - gels Who be - hold thy glo - ry,
May I cease - less - ly a - dore thee. Let thy will Ev - er still
Rule thy Church ter - res - trial, As the hosts ce - les - tial. A - men.

# 11 COME, LET US SING UNTO THE LORD

*O come let us sing unto the Lord: let us make a joyful noise to the Rock of our salvation.* Ps. 95:1.

Based on Psalms 95, 96
John D. Martin, 1972 (b. 1946)

MAAMME LAULU 8.6.10.10.8.6.
M.M. 66

Fredrik Pacius, 1848
Har. John D. Martin, 1972

1. Come, let us sing un - to the Lord; A joy - ful noise we'll raise. Un - to the rock of our sal - va - tion sing, Be - fore His pres - ence loud thanks - giv - ing bring, A - dore the Lord our sov - 'reign King; Pour forth a song of praise.
2. The depths of earth, hills high and strong, The wide and fer - tile land He formed at His com-mand; He made the sea, Come let us wor - ship and bow down the knee; He is our God, His peo - ple we, The sheep of His right hand.
3. Bow down your ear to hear His voice, Your op - en heart ex - pand; Re - mem - ber those who in the wil - der - ness With - stood our God and suf - fered great dis - tress, Who could not en - ter in - to rest With - in the prom -ised land.
4. Show forth sal - va - tion, praise and bless, A - mong the hea- - then say The Lord is great and great - ly to be praised; His fear a - bove the gods of earth we raise; The Mak - er of the heav - en's haze Hath hon - or, maj - es - ty.
5. The strength and beau - ty of the Lord Are with us here to - day; Give to the Lord the glo - ry due His name; Bring of - ferings to His courts and laud His fame; The God of heav'n and earth doth reign; His sov - 'reign will o - bey.
6. The Lord shall judge with right - eous - ness; The earth shall not be moved; Let heavens re - joice and let the earth be glad; Let fields be joy - ful, let them not be sad; Let roar - ing seas be not for - bade; He comes to judge with truth.

# O COME, LOUD ANTHEMS LET US SING 12

*Sing aloud unto God our strength.* Ps. 81:1

SALISBURY L.M. 8.8.8.8. with Ref.
M.M. 96

Tate and Brady's *New Version of the Psalms,* 1696

Lowell Mason's . . . *Collection,* 1822

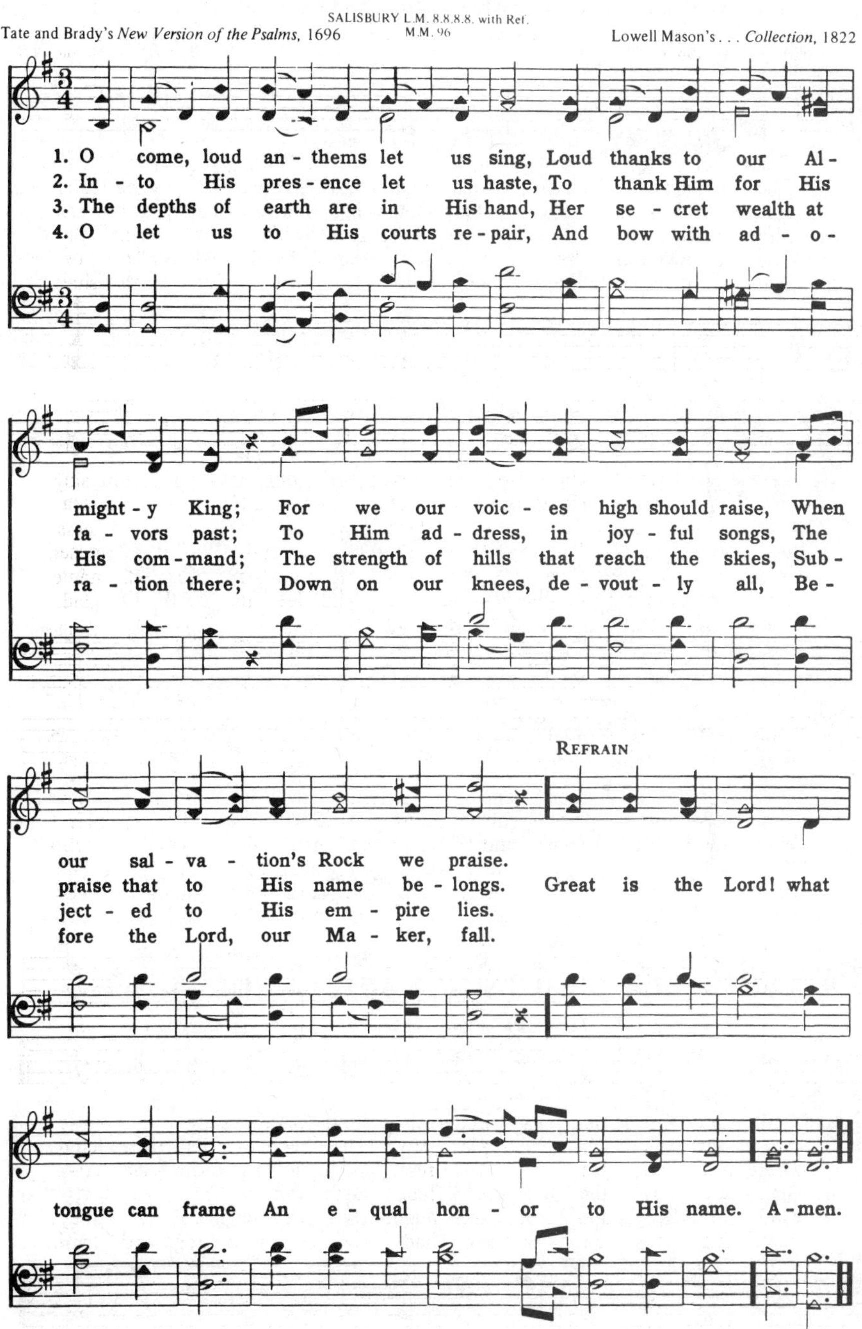

1. O come, loud anthems let us sing, Loud thanks to our Almighty King; For we our voices high should raise, When our salvation's Rock we praise.
2. Into His presence let us haste, To thank Him for His favors past; To Him address, in joyful songs, The praise that to His name belongs.
3. The depths of earth are in His hand, Her secret wealth at His command; The strength of hills that reach the skies, Subjected to His empire lies.
4. O let us to His courts repair, And bow with adoration there; Down on our knees, devoutly all, Before the Lord, our Maker, fall.
REFRAIN
Great is the Lord! what tongue can frame An equal honor to His name. Amen.

# 13 COME, YE THAT LOVE JEHOVAH'S NAME

*Let us draw near with a true heart in full assurance of faith.* Heb. 10:22.

Anne Steele, 1717-1778
Isaac Watts, 1674-1748
Ottiwell Heginbotham, 1744-1768
Composite, Arr. John J. Overholt, 1968

CAPERS NEW C.M. 8.6.8.6.
M.M. 69

R. M. McIntosh, 1836-1899
Arr. John J. Overholt, 1968

1. Come ye that love Je - ho - vah's name, And joy to make it known;
2. Come join your hymns and joy - ful songs, With an - gels round the throne;
3. "Wor thy the Lamb that died," they cry, "Sal - va - tion to ob - tain!"
4. Our God is wor - thy to re - ceive Hon - or and pow'r di - vine;
5. Let all who dwell a - bove the sky, Up - on the earth and seas,

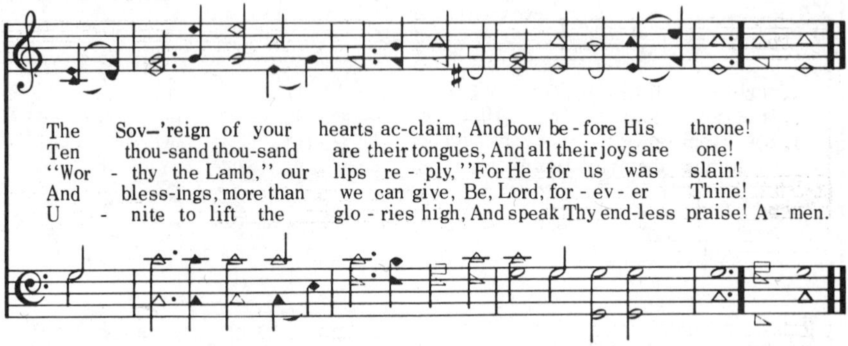

The Sov—'reign of your hearts ac-claim, And bow be - fore His throne!
Ten thou-sand thou-sand are their tongues, And all their joys are one!
"Wor - thy the Lamb," our lips re - ply, "For He for us was slain!
And bless-ings, more than we can give, Be, Lord, for - ev - er Thine!
U - nite to lift the glo - ries high, And speak Thy end-less praise! A - men.

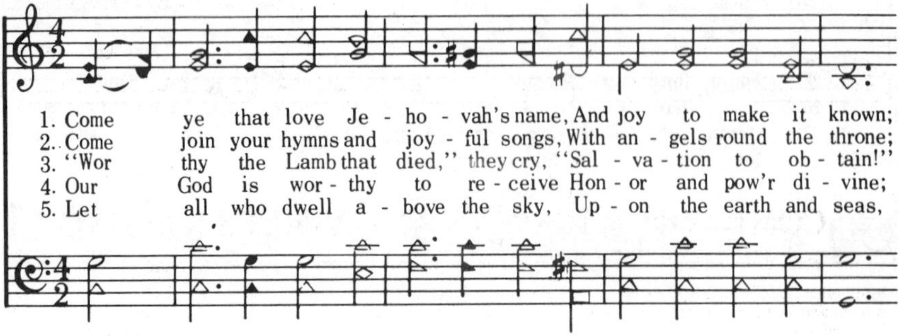

6. Let all creation join in one, to bless thy sacred name,
And glorify thee on Thy throne, and to adore the Lamb.

7. Come, shout aloud the Father's grace, And sing the Saviour's love;
Soon shall you join the glorious theme, in loftier strains above.

# 14 COME, LET US JOIN OUR CHEERFUL SONGS

*We took sweet counsel together, and walked unto the house of God in company.* Ps. 55:14.

CHESTERFIELD C.M. 8.6.8.6.
M.M. 88

Isaac Watts, 1674-1748

Thomas Haweis, 1732-1820

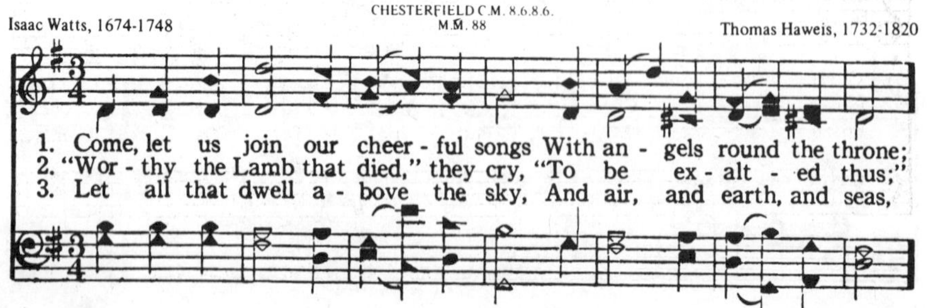
1. Come, let us join our cheer - ful songs With an - gels round the throne;
2. "Wor - thy the Lamb that died," they cry, "To be ex - alt - ed thus;"
3. Let all that dwell a - bove the sky, And air, and earth, and seas,

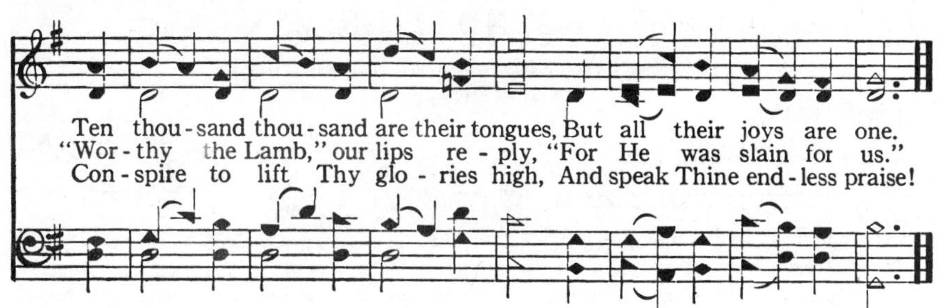
Ten thou-sand thou-sand are their tongues, But all their joys are one.
"Wor-thy the Lamb," our lips re-ply, "For He was slain for us."
Con-spire to lift Thy glo-ries high, And speak Thine end-less praise!

# COME, YOUR HEARTS AND VOICES RAISING 15

*Come thou with us and we will do thee good: for the Lord hath spoken good concerning Israel.* Num. 10:29.

Paul Gerhardt, 1667 (1607-1676)
*Kommt und lasst uns Christum ehren*
Tr. Composite,
Recast John J. Overholt, 1971

ERMAHNUNG ZUR ANDACHT 8.8.8.7.7.
M.M. 60

Franz Abt, 1819-1885
Arranged by Compiler, 1971

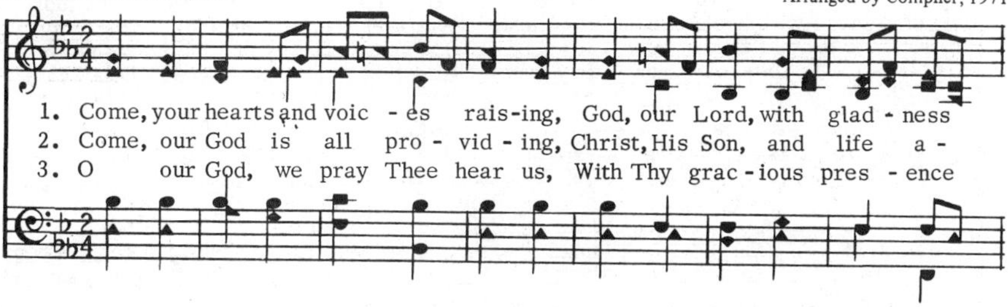

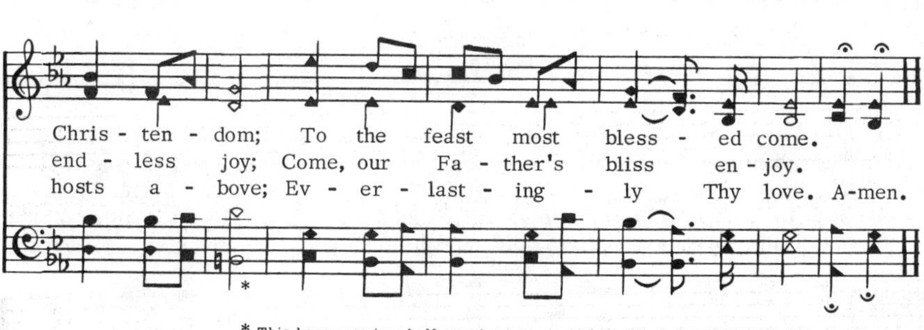

1. Come, your hearts and voic - es rais-ing, God, our Lord, with glad - ness prais-ing, Loud-ly sing His love a - maz - ing, All ye saints of Chris - ten - dom; To the feast most bless - ed come.

2. Come, our God is all pro - vid - ing, Christ, His Son, and life a - bid - ing; He the faith-ful steps is guid - ing To heav'ns light and end - less joy; Come, our Fa - ther's bliss en - joy.

3. O our God, we pray Thee hear us, With Thy grac - ious pres - ence cheer us, Gent - ly lead us and be near us, Till we praise with hosts a - bove; Ev - er - last - ing - ly Thy love. A-men.

* This bass note is a half step between so and la. Ti may also be sung.

# 16 COME, HEAVEN-BOUND PILGRIMS

*Thy statutes have been my songs in the house of my pilgrimage.* Ps. 119:54.

John M. Shenk, 1848-1935 | REBECCA 11.11.11.11. M.M. 63 | John M. Shenk

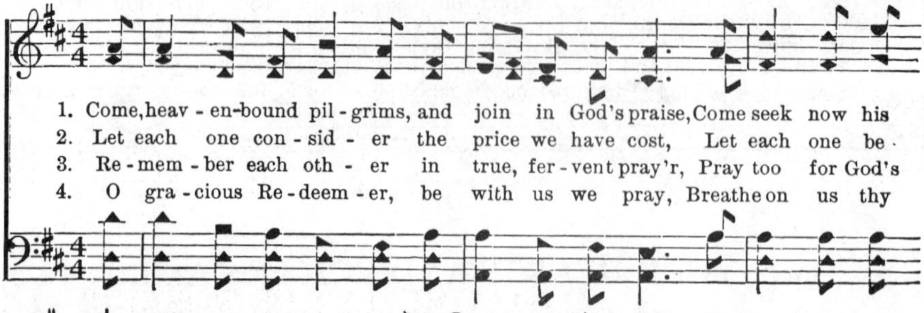

1. Come, heav - en-bound pil - grims, and join in God's praise, Come seek now his
2. Let each one con - sid - er the price we have cost, Let each one be -
3. Re - mem - ber each oth - er in true, fer - vent pray'r, Pray too for God's
4. O gra - cious Re - deem - er, be with us we pray, Breathe on us thy

bless - ing and learn of his ways, In hum - ble de - vo - tion bow
bur - dened with souls that are lost, And seek that in - fill - ing of
ser - vants that they may de - clare The mes - sage of truth with an
Spir - it to show us the way, And fill us with good - ness, with

low at his feet, In true spir - it wor - ship, his fa - vor en - treat.
pow'r from a - bove, That fits us for ser - vice and fills us with love.
anx - ious de - sire, That all be en - kin - dled with heav - en - ly fire.
peace and de - light, That all to thy glo - ry may shine as a light.

# 17 STAND UP, AND BLESS THE LORD, YOUR GOD

*Stand up and bless the Lord your God for ever and ever.* Neh. 9:5.

James Montgomery, 1771-1854
Altered by Compiler, 1970 | TALLIS' ORDINAL C.M. 8.6.8.6. M.M. 84 | Thomas Tallis, c. 1567 (1520-1585)

1. Stand up, and bless the Lord, your God, Ye peo—ple of His choice;
2. Though high a—bove all praise and fame, A—bove all bless—ing high,
3. Oh, for the liv—ing flame of fire From His own al—tar brought,
4. God is our strength and song ac—claimed And His sal—va—tion ours;
5. Stand up, and bless the Lord, and deign Your God to e'er a—dore;

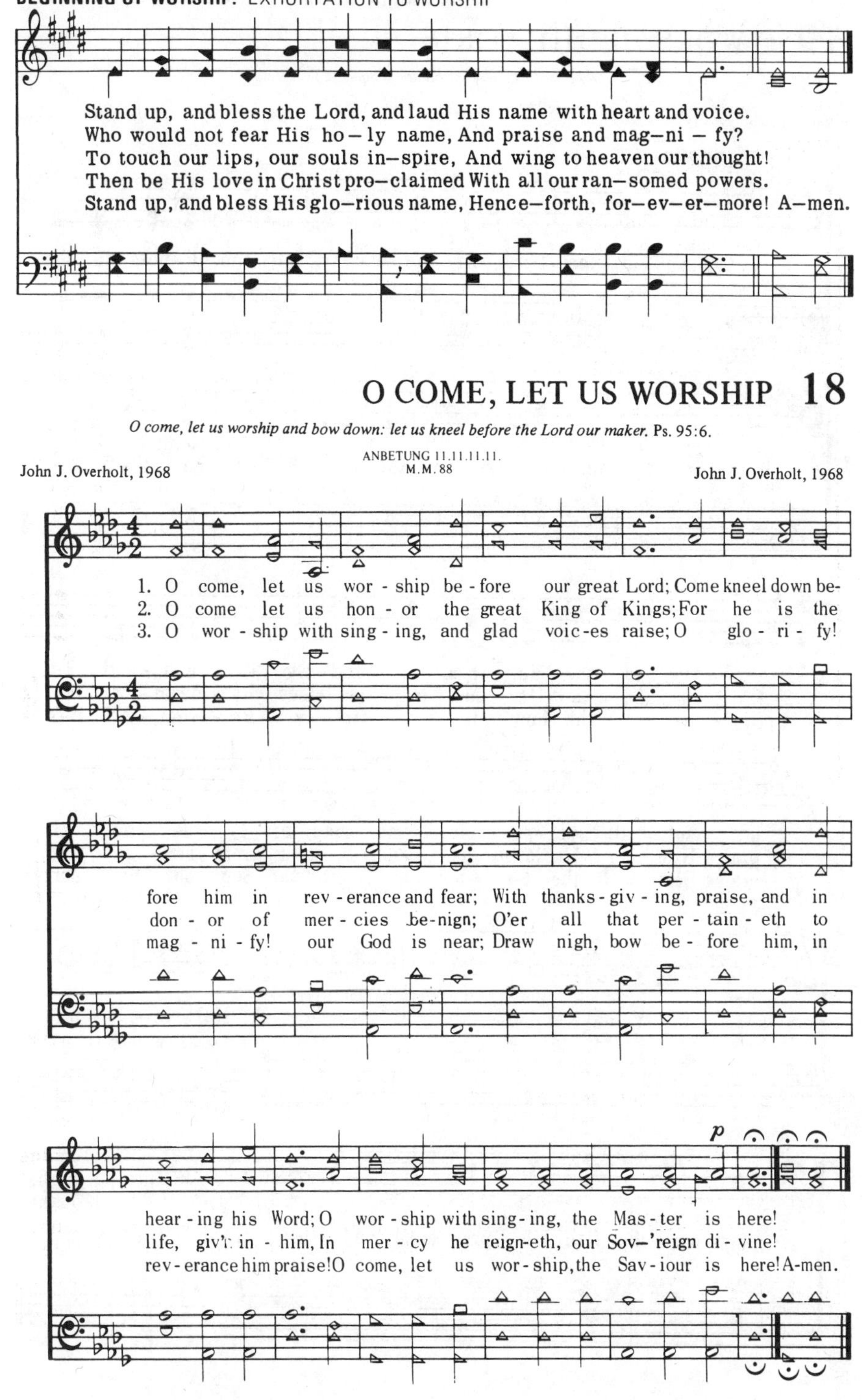
Stand up, and bless the Lord, and laud His name with heart and voice.
Who would not fear His ho–ly name, And praise and mag–ni – fy?
To touch our lips, our souls in–spire, And wing to heaven our thought!
Then be His love in Christ pro–claimed With all our ran–somed powers.
Stand up, and bless His glo–rious name, Hence–forth, for–ev–er–more! A–men.
O COME, LET US WORSHIP 18
O come, let us worship and bow down: let us kneel before the Lord our maker. Ps. 95:6.
John J. Overholt, 1968
ANBETUNG 11.11.11.11.
M.M. 88
John J. Overholt, 1968
1. O come, let us wor - ship be - fore our great Lord; Come kneel down be-
2. O come let us hon - or the great King of Kings; For he is the
3. O wor - ship with sing - ing, and glad voic-es raise; O glo - ri - fy!
fore him in rev - erance and fear; With thanks - giv - ing, praise, and in
don - or of mer - cies be-nign; O'er all that per - tain - eth to
mag - ni - fy! our God is near; Draw nigh, bow be - fore him, in
hear - ing his Word; O wor - ship with sing - ing, the Mas - ter is here!
life, giv'n in - him, In mer - cy he reign-eth, our Sov–'reign di - vine!
rev - erance him praise! O come, let us wor - ship, the Sav - iour is here! A-men.
p

# 19 O WORSHIP THE LORD

*Worship the Lord in the beauty of holiness.* Ps. 29:2.

WORSHIP THE LORD 5.8.8.8.12.7.7. with Ref.
M.M. 84

Robert Lowry, 1826-1899 | Robert Lowry

*Earnestly*

O wor-ship the Lord in the beau-ty of ho-li-ness, in the beau-ty of ho-li-ness, in the beau-ty of ho-li-ness.

*Sopranos & Altos*

1. Glo-ry to the Fa-ther, a-bound-ing in mer-cy! Be joy-ful, all ye peo-ple, and mag-ni-fy Je-ho-vah.
2. Glo-ry be to Je-sus, our gra-cious Re-deem-er! We praise Him, for He loved us, and bro't a great sal-va-tion.
3. Glo-ry to the Spir-it, the Ho-ly Re-veal-er! We praise Him with the Fa-ther and with the Son, our Sav-ior.

CHORUS

O glo-ry, hal-le-lu-jah, Hal-le-lu-jah, Hal-le-lu-jah! O come be-fore His pres-ence and glo-ri-fy His name.

# COME, O COME, AND SWEETLY JOIN 20

*O come, let us sing unto the Lord.* Ps. 95:1.

HARMONIE DU BRUDERSTADT 7.7.7.5.7.7.
M.M. 63

Charles Wesley, 1707-1788
Recast John J. Overholt, 1971

J. A. Hiller, 1817
Arr. R. D. Wetzel
Arranged by Compiler, 1971

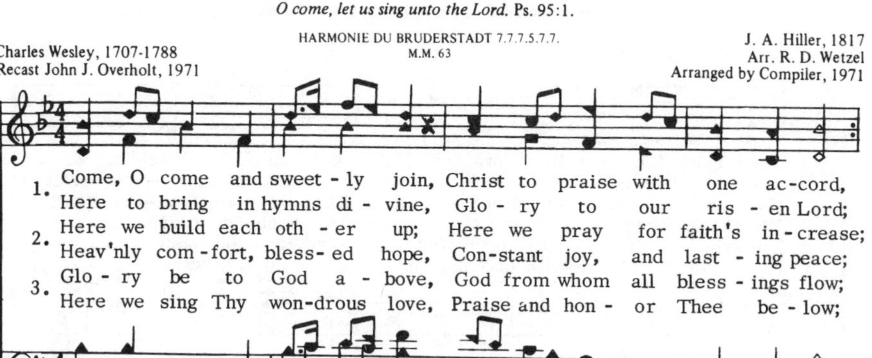
1. Come, O come and sweet - ly join, Christ to praise with one ac-cord,
Here to bring in hymns di - vine, Glo - ry to our ris - en Lord;
2. Here we build each oth - er up; Here we pray for faith's in-crease;
Heav'nly com-fort, bless-ed hope, Con-stant joy, and last - ing peace;
3. Glo - ry be to God a - bove, God from whom all bless - ings flow;
Here we sing Thy won-drous love, Praise and hon - or Thee be - low;

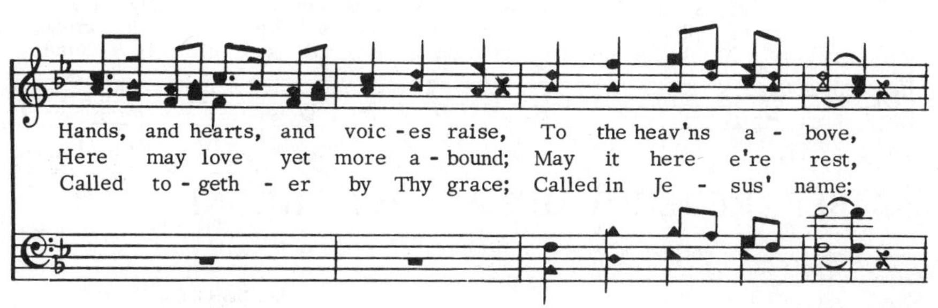
Hands, and hearts, and voic-es raise, To the heav'ns a - bove,
Here may love yet more a - bound; May it here e're rest,
Called to-geth - er by Thy grace; Called in Je - sus' name;

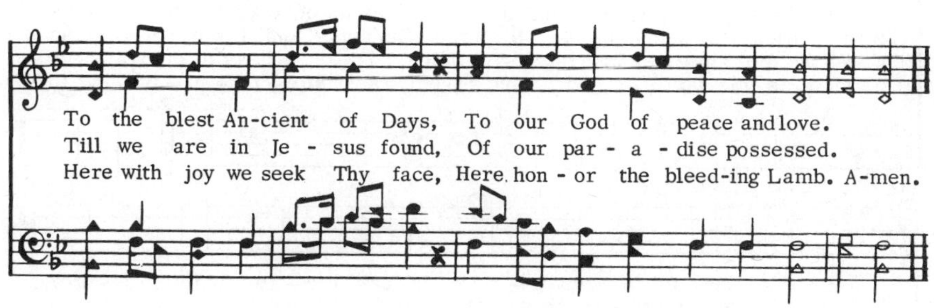
To the blest An-cient of Days, To our God of peace and love.
Till we are in Je - sus found, Of our par - a - dise possessed.
Here with joy we seek Thy face, Here hon - or the bleed-ing Lamb. A-men.

## 21 ONCE MORE WE COME BEFORE OUR GOD

*Wherewith shall I come before the Lord?* Mic. 6:6.

Joseph Hart, 1712-1768 | MARLOW C.M. 8.6.8.6. M.M. 66 | John Chetham, 1701-1760

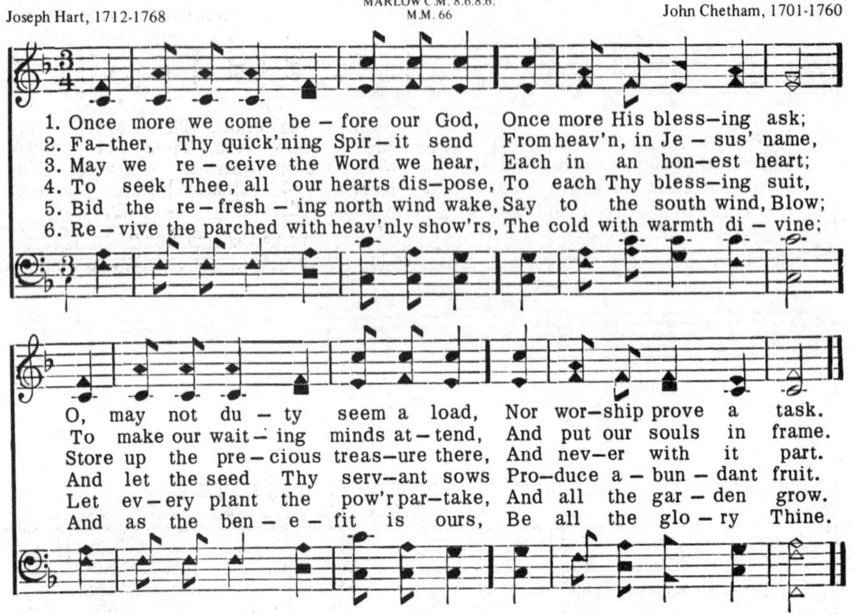
1. Once more we come be – fore our God, Once more His bless–ing ask;
2. Fa–ther, Thy quick'ning Spir – it send From heav'n, in Je – sus' name,
3. May we re – ceive the Word we hear, Each in an hon–est heart;
4. To seek Thee, all our hearts dis–pose, To each Thy bless–ing suit,
5. Bid the re – fresh – ing north wind wake, Say to the south wind, Blow;
6. Re – vive the parched with heav'nly show'rs, The cold with warmth di – vine;
O, may not du – ty seem a load, Nor wor–ship prove a task.
To make our wait – ing minds at – tend, And put our souls in frame.
Store up the pre – cious treas–ure there, And nev–er with it part.
And let the seed Thy serv–ant sows Pro–duce a – bun – dant fruit.
Let ev – ery plant the pow'r par–take, And all the gar – den grow.
And as the ben – e – fit is ours, Be all the glo – ry Thine.

## 22 BEFORE JEHOVAH'S AWEFUL THRONE

*Round about the throne . . . ten thousand times ten thousand.* Rev. 5:11.

Isaac Watts, 1719, (1674-1748)
Alt. John Wesley, 1736 (1703-1791) | WATTS L.M. 8.8.8.8. M.M. 60 | John David Brunk, 1910 (1872-1926)

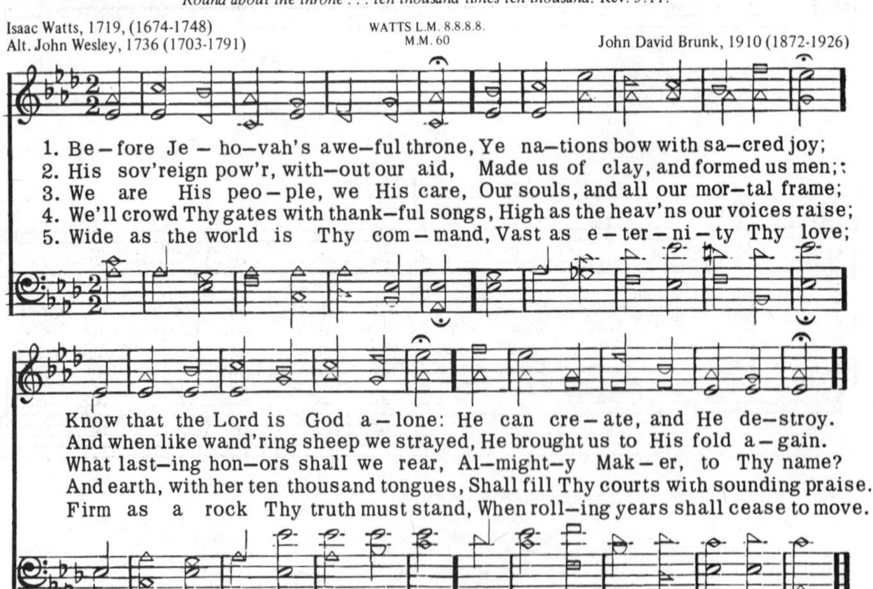
1. Be – fore Je – ho–vah's awe–ful throne, Ye na–tions bow with sa–cred joy;
2. His sov'reign pow'r, with–out our aid, Made us of clay, and formed us men;
3. We are His peo – ple, we His care, Our souls, and all our mor–tal frame;
4. We'll crowd Thy gates with thank–ful songs, High as the heav'ns our voices raise;
5. Wide as the world is Thy com – mand, Vast as e – ter – ni – ty Thy love;
Know that the Lord is God a – lone: He can cre – ate, and He de–stroy.
And when like wand'ring sheep we strayed, He brought us to His fold a – gain.
What last–ing hon–ors shall we rear, Al–might–y Mak – er, to Thy name?
And earth, with her ten thousand tongues, Shall fill Thy courts with sounding praise.
Firm as a rock Thy truth must stand, When roll–ing years shall cease to move.

# GREAT GOD, INDULGE MY HUMBLE CLAIM 23

*O God, Thou art my God.* Ps. 63:1.

HAGERSTOWN L.M. 8.8.8.8.
M.M. 80

Isaac Watts, 1674-1748

John David Brunk, 1902 (1872-1926)

1. Great God, in - dulge my hum - ble claim, Thou art my
2. Thou great and good, Thou just and wise, Thou art my
3. With read - y feet I love t' ap - pear A - mong Thy
4. I'll lift my hands, I'll raise my voice, While I have

hope, my joy, my rest; The glo - ries that com-
Fa - ther and my God; And I am Thine by
saints, and seek Thy face; Oft have I seen Thy
breath to pray or praise; This work shall make my

pose Thy name Stand all en - gaged to make me blest.
sa - cred ties, Thy son, Thy serv - ant, bought with blood.
glo - ry there, And felt the pow'r of sov - 'reign grace.
heart re - joice, Thro' - out the rem - nant of my days.

# 24 WE NOW HAVE MET TO WORSHIP THEE

*For the edifying of the body of Christ.* Eph. 4:12.

STEPHENSON L.M.D. 8.8.8.8.
M.M. 66

Joseph S. Shoemaker, 1853-1936 — Joseph S. Shoemaker

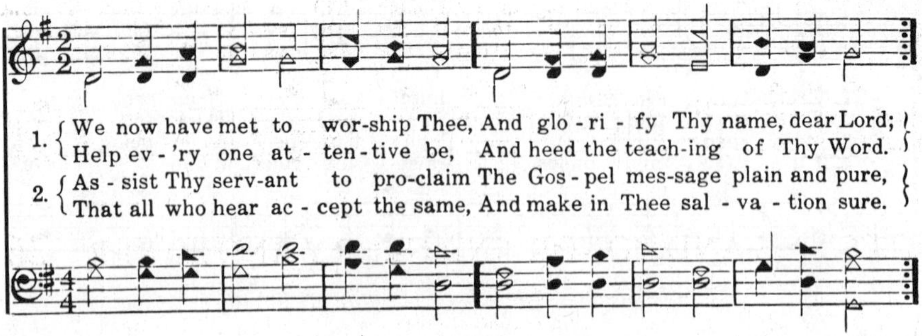

1. We now have met to worship Thee, And glo - ri - fy Thy name, dear Lord;
Help ev - 'ry one at - ten - tive be, And heed the teach-ing of Thy Word.
2. As - sist Thy serv-ant to pro-claim The Gos - pel mes-sage plain and pure,
That all who hear ac - cept the same, And make in Thee sal - va - tion sure.

Fill ev - 'ry heart with love di - vine, Teach ev - 'ry tongue Thy praise to sing;
In Thee a - lone help us to trust, And in Thy love and laws a - bide,

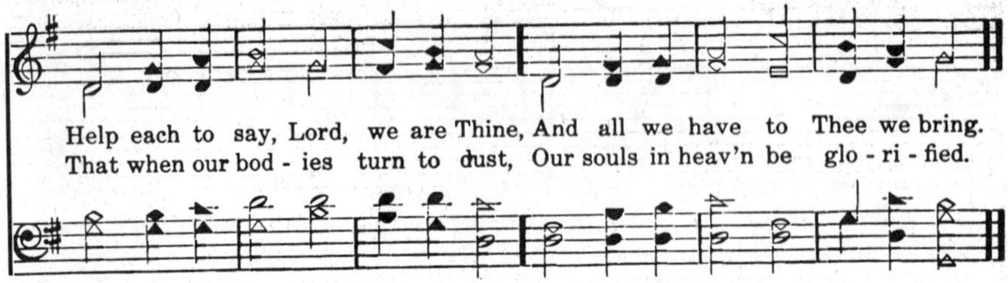

Help each to say, Lord, we are Thine, And all we have to Thee we bring.
That when our bod - ies turn to dust, Our souls in heav'n be glo - ri - fied.

# 25 LORD, WE COME BEFORE THEE NOW

*Let us therefore come boldly unto the throne of grace.* Heb. 4:16.

HENDON 7.7.7.7.7.
M.M. 63

William Hammond, 1719-1783 — Henri Alexander Cesar Malan, 1787-1864; Arr. Lowell Mason, 1792-1872

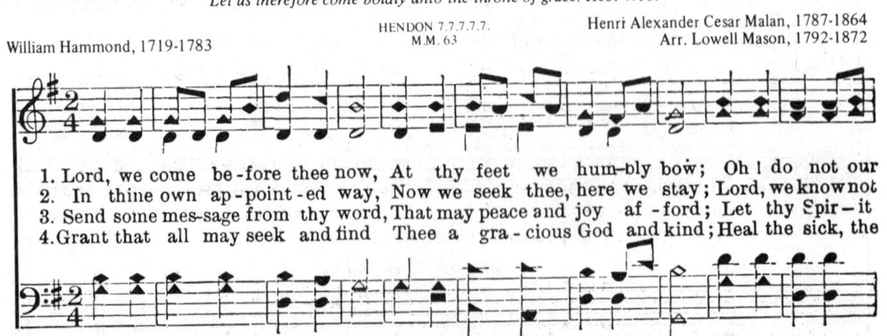
1. Lord, we come be-fore thee now, At thy feet we hum-bly bow; Oh! do not our
2. In thine own ap-point-ed way, Now we seek thee, here we stay; Lord, we know not
3. Send some mes-sage from thy word, That may peace and joy af - ford; Let thy Spir - it
4. Grant that all may seek and find Thee a gra - cious God and kind; Heal the sick, the

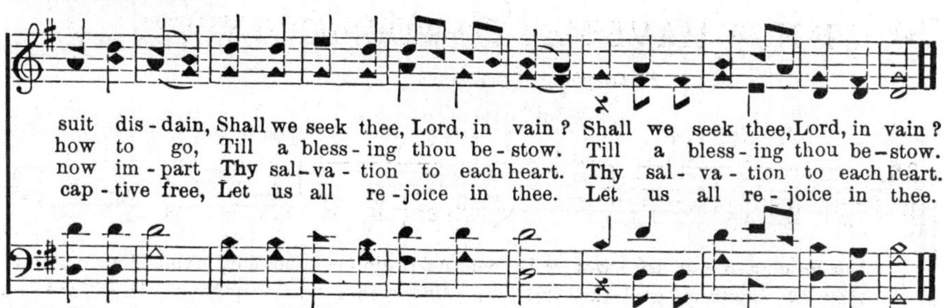
suit dis - dain, Shall we seek thee, Lord, in vain ? Shall we seek thee, Lord, in vain ?
how to go, Till a bless - ing thou be - stow. Till a bless - ing thou be - stow.
now im - part Thy sal - va - tion to each heart. Thy sal - va - tion to each heart.
cap - tive free, Let us all re - joice in thee. Let us all re - joice in thee.

## BLESSING AND HONOR AND GLORY AND POWER 26

*Blessing, and honour, and glory, and power, be unto Him.* Rev. 5:13.

Horatio Bonar, 1808-1889

AMERICAN HYMN 10.10.10.10.10.
M.M. 63

Matthias Keller, 1813-1890

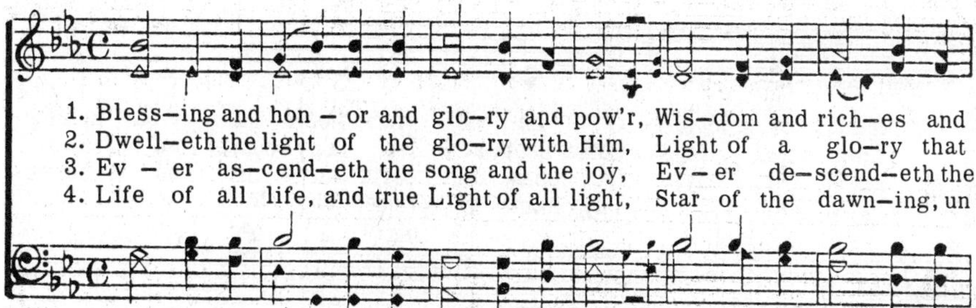

1. Bless–ing and hon – or and glo–ry and pow'r, Wis–dom and rich–es and
2. Dwell–eth the light of the glo–ry with Him, Light of a glo–ry that
3. Ev – er as–cend–eth the song and the joy, Ev – er de–scend–eth the
4. Life of all life, and true Light of all light, Star of the dawn–ing, un

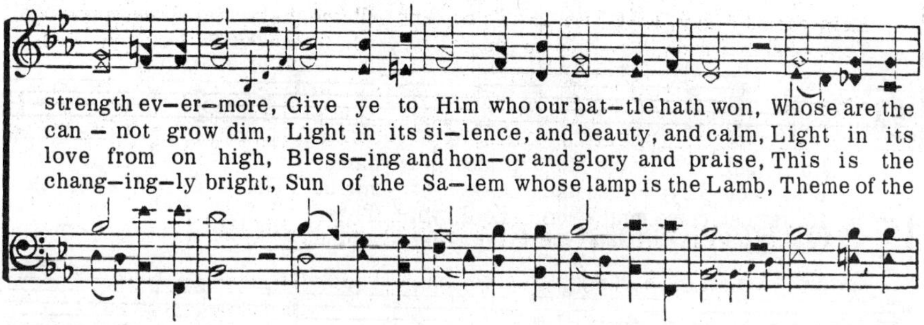

strength ev–er–more, Give ye to Him who our bat–tle hath won, Whose are the
can – not grow dim, Light in its si–lence, and beauty, and calm, Light in its
love from on high, Bless–ing and hon–or and glory and praise, This is the
chang–ing–ly bright, Sun of the Sa–lem whose lamp is the Lamb, Theme of the

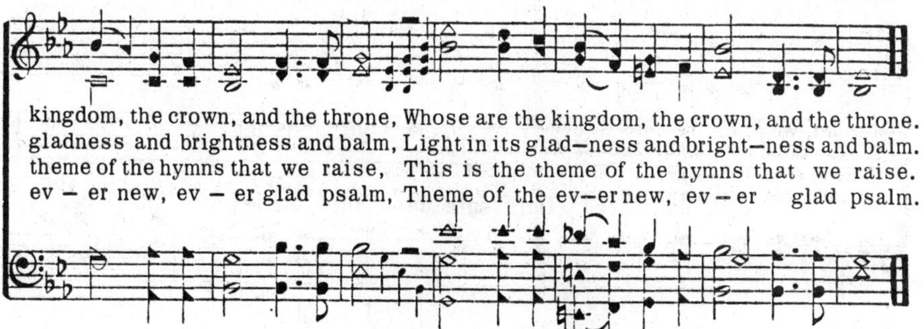

kingdom, the crown, and the throne, Whose are the kingdom, the crown, and the throne.
gladness and brightness and balm, Light in its glad–ness and bright–ness and balm.
theme of the hymns that we raise, This is the theme of the hymns that we raise.
ev – er new, ev – er glad psalm, Theme of the ev–er new, ev – er glad psalm.

# 27 GOD OF OUR STRENGTH, ENTHRONED ABOVE

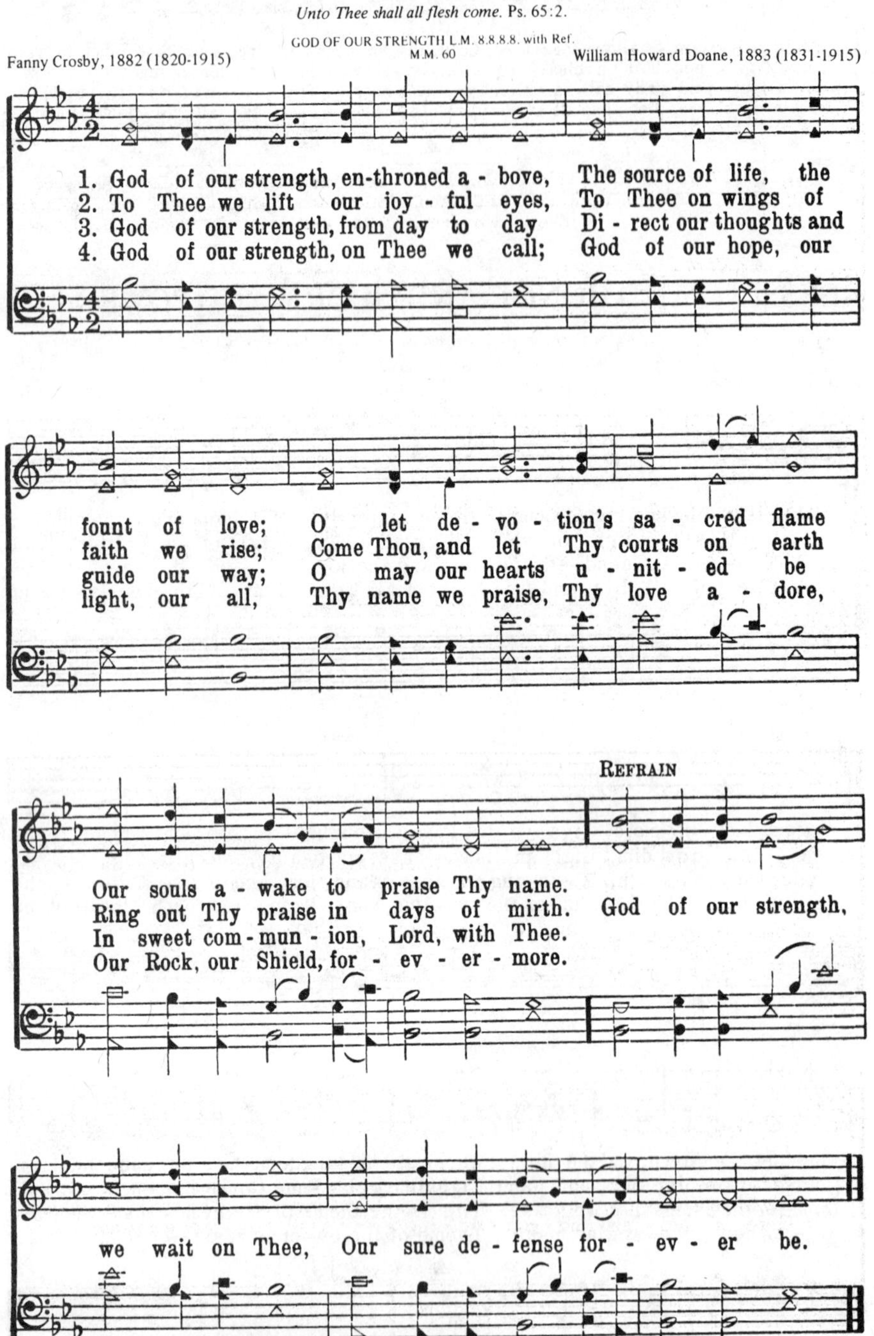
Unto Thee shall all flesh come. Ps. 65:2.
GOD OF OUR STRENGTH L.M. 8.8.8.8. with Ref.
M.M. 60
Fanny Crosby, 1882 (1820-1915)
William Howard Doane, 1883 (1831-1915)
1. God of our strength, en-throned a - bove, The source of life, the fount of love; O let de - vo - tion's sa - cred flame Our souls a - wake to praise Thy name.
2. To Thee we lift our joy - ful eyes, To Thee on wings of faith we rise; Come Thou, and let Thy courts on earth Ring out Thy praise in days of mirth.
3. God of our strength, from day to day Di - rect our thoughts and guide our way; O may our hearts u - nit - ed be In sweet com - mun - ion, Lord, with Thee.
4. God of our strength, on Thee we call; God of our hope, our light, our all, Thy name we praise, Thy love a - dore, Our Rock, our Shield, for - ev - er - more.
REFRAIN
God of our strength, we wait on Thee, Our sure de - fense for - ev - er be.

# IN THY HOLY PLACE 28

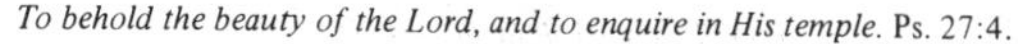

*To behold the beauty of the Lord, and to enquire in His temple.* Ps. 27:4.

IN THY HOLY PLACE 7.7.7.7.8.7.8.7.
M.M. 72

Samuel Frederick Coffman, 1901 (1872-1954)

John David Brunk, 1911 (1872-1926)

*m*

1. In Thy ho - ly place we bow, Per-fumes sweet to heav - en rise,
2. Ho - ly light doth fill this place,—Spir - it light our way to guide;
3. On Thy ho - ly bread we feed, Hun - ger nev - er-more to know:

*cres.* *dim.*

While our gold - en cen - sers glow With the fire of sac - ri - fice.
In the pres - ence of Thy face Sin and dark-ness ne'er can hide.
Thou sup - pli - est all our need; Fa - ther, whith-er shall we go?

*p* *cres.*

Saints low bend - ing, prayers as-cend-ing, Ho - ly lips and hands im-plore;—
Heav - en's gleam-ing, full - ness streaming, Life and truth for man is found;
Ne'er for - sak - ing, here par - tak - ing Bread our souls to sat - is - fy;

*m* *cres.* *dim.*

Faith be - liev - ing and re - ceiv - ing Grace from Him whom we a - dore.
Light per-vad - ing, nev - er fad - ing, Light-ing all the world a - round.
Here a - bid - ing and con - fid - ing, We shall nev - er want nor die.

# 29 HOLY, HOLY, HOLY

*I the Lord your God am holy.* Lev. 19:2.

NICAEA 11.12.12.10.
M.M. 72

Reginald Heber, 1783-1826

John Bacchus Dykes, 1861 (1823-1876)

1. Ho - ly, ho - ly, ho - ly, Lord God Al-might - y! Ear - ly in the
2. Ho - ly, ho - ly, ho - ly, all the saints a - dore Thee, Cast-ing down their
3. Ho - ly, ho - ly, ho - ly, tho' the dark-ness hide Thee, Tho' the eye of
4. Ho - ly, ho - ly, ho - ly, Lord God Al-might - y! All Thy works shall

morn - ing our song shall rise to Thee; Ho - ly, ho - ly, ho - ly,
gold-en crowns a-round the glass - y sea; Cher-u - bim and ser-a - phim,
sin - ful man Thy glo - ry may not see; On - ly Thou art ho - ly!
praise Thy name, in earth, and sky, and sea; Ho - ly, ho - ly, ho - ly,

mer - ci - ful and might-y, God in Three Per - sons, bless-ed Trin - i - ty!
fall-ing down be-fore Thee, Which wert, and art, and ev - er-more shalt be.
there is none be - side Thee, Per - fect in pow'r, in love, in pu - ri - ty.
mer - ci - ful and might-y, God in Three Per - sons, bless-ed Trin - i - ty!

# 30 HOLY, HOLY, HOLY, LORD GOD ALMIGHTY

*Thou only art holy.* Rev. 15:4.

HOLY, HOLY, HOLY, LORD Irregular
M.M. 60

Anonymous

Traditional Chant

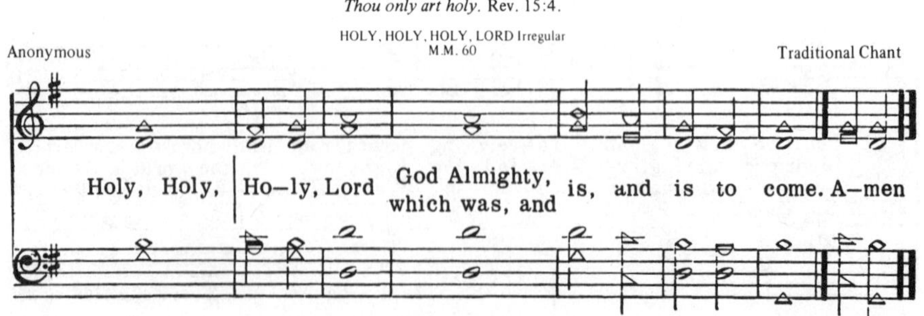
Holy, Holy,
Ho—ly, Lord
God Almighty,
which was, and
is, and is to come. A—men

# O HOLY, HOLY, HOLY LORD 31

*And they rest not day and night saying, holy, holy, holy, Lord God Almighty.* Rev. 4:8.

Josiah Conder, 1789-1855
Reginald Heber, 1783-1826
Composite, Arr. John J. Overholt, 1965

SUCH WER DER WILL EIN ANDER ZIEL 8.8.8.8.8.8.8.
M.M. 80

Johann Stobäus, 1613
Arranged by Compiler, 1965

1. O ho – ly, ho – ly, ho – ly Lord, Thou God of hosts by all a– dored; The heav'ns and earth are full of Thee, Thy light, Thy pow'r, Thy ma – jes – ty. Loud hal – le – lu – jahs to Thy name, An – gels and ser – a– phim pro–claim, E – ter – nal praise to Thee is given!

2. Ho – san – na to the liv – ing God! Ho – san – na to the in – car– nate Word! To God, Cre – a – tor, Sav – iour, King, Let earth, let heav'n ho– san – na sing. "Ho – san – na, Lord!" Thine an – gels cry, "Ho – san – na, Lord!" Thy saints re – ply; The dead and liv – ing swell the sound!

3. A – post – les join the glo – rious throng, And swell the loud tri – um– phant song; Pro–phets and mar – tyrs hear the sound, And raise their hal – le– lu – jahs 'round. Glo – ry to Thee, O God most high, Our Fa – ther, Thee we glo – ri – fy And Son and Spir – it, ev – er – more!

All praise to Thee is given!
The liv–ing swell the sound!
Thee praise for–ev–er–more!

E – ter – nal praise to Thee is given!
The liv–ing raise and swell the sound!
Thee glo–ri – fy for – ev – er – more!

# 32 ALL CREATURES OF OUR GOD AND KING

*Let everything that hath breath praise the Lord.* Ps. 150:6.

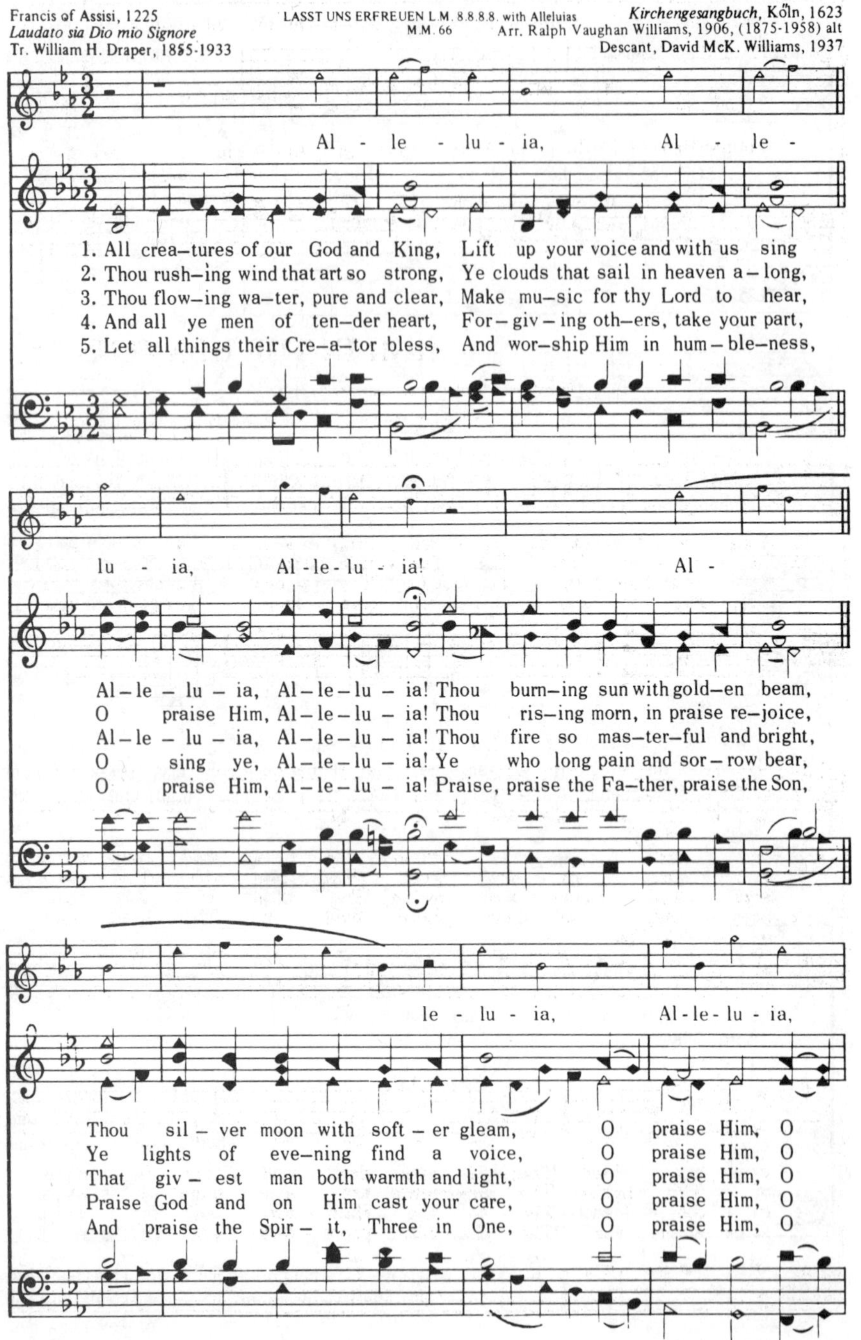
Francis of Assisi, 1225
*Laudato sia Dio mio Signore*
Tr. William H. Draper, 1855-1933
LASST UNS ERFREUEN L.M. 8.8.8.8. with Alleluias
M.M. 66
*Kirchengesangbuch,* Köln, 1623
Arr. Ralph Vaughan Williams, 1906, (1875-1958) alt
Descant, David McK. Williams, 1937
Al - le - lu - ia, Al - le - lu - ia, Al - le - lu - ia! Al - le - lu - ia, Al - le - lu - ia,
1. All crea–tures of our God and King, Lift up your voice and with us sing Al–le – lu – ia, Al–le–lu – ia! Thou burn–ing sun with gold–en beam, Thou sil – ver moon with soft – er gleam, O praise Him, O
2. Thou rush–ing wind that art so strong, Ye clouds that sail in heaven a – long, O praise Him, Al–le–lu – ia! Thou ris–ing morn, in praise re–joice, Ye lights of eve–ning find a voice, O praise Him, O
3. Thou flow–ing wa–ter, pure and clear, Make mu–sic for thy Lord to hear, Al–le – lu – ia, Al–le–lu – ia! Thou fire so mas–ter–ful and bright, That giv – est man both warmth and light, O praise Him, O
4. And all ye men of ten–der heart, For–giv – ing oth–ers, take your part, O sing ye, Al–le–lu – ia! Ye who long pain and sor – row bear, Praise God and on Him cast your care, O praise Him, O
5. Let all things their Cre–a–tor bless, And wor–ship Him in hum – ble–ness, O praise Him, Al–le–lu – ia! Praise, praise the Fa–ther, praise the Son, And praise the Spir – it, Three in One, O praise Him, O

Al-le-lu-ia, Al-le-lu-ia, Al-le-lu-ia, Al-le-lu-ia! A-men.
praise Him, Al-le-lu - ia, Al-le- lu - ia, Al-le-lu ia! A-men.

# HIGH IN THE HEAVENS 33

*Thy mercy, O Lord, is in the heavens.* Ps. 36:5.

Isaac Watts, 1674-1748

TRURO L.M. 8.8.8.8.
M.M. 66

T. William's *Psalmodia Evangelica*, 1789
Har. Arr. by Compiler, 1974

1. High in the heav'ns, E - ter - nal God, Thy good - ness
2. For - ev - er firm Thy jus - tice stands, As moun - tains
3. My God, how ex - cel - lent Thy grace, Whence all our
4. Life, like a foun - tain, rich and free, Springs from the

in full glo - ry shines; Thy truth shall break through
their foun - da - tions keep; Wise are the won - ders
hope and com - fort spring! The sons of Ad - am
pres - ence of our Lord; And in Thy light our

ev - 'ry cloud That veils and dark - ens Thy de - signs.
of Thy hands; Thy judg-ments are a might - y deep.
in dis - tress Fly to the shad - ow of Thy wing.
souls shall see The glo - ries prom - ised in Thy Word.

## 34 ETERNAL GOD, WE LOOK TO THEE

*Lord, Thou hast been our dwelling place in all generations.* Ps. 90:1.

WINCHESTER OLD C.M. 8.6.8.6.
M.M. 69

James Merrick, 1763 (1720-1796)

Thomas Este's *Psalter*, 1592

1. E - ter - nal God, we look to Thee, To Thee for help we fly;
2. Lord, let Thy fear with - in us dwell, Thy love our foot - steps guide:
3. Not what we wish, but what we want, O let Thy grace sup - ply:
Thine eye a - lone our wants can see, Thy hand a - lone sup - ply.
That love will all vain love ex - pel; That fear, all fear be - side.
The good un-asked in mer - cy grant; The ill, though asked, de - ny. A-men.

## 35 O GOD, OUR HELP

*God is our refuge and strength, a very present help in trouble.* Ps. 46:1.

ST. ANNE C.M. 8.6.8.6.
M.M. 72

Isaac Watts, 1719 (1674-1748), alt.

William Croft, 1708 (1678-1727)

1. O God, our help in a - ges past, Our hope for years to come,
2. Be - neath the shad - ow of Thy throne Still may we dwell se - cure;
3. Be - fore the hills in or - der stood, Or earth re - ceived her frame,
4. A thou - sand a - ges, in Thy sight, Are like an eve - ning gone;
5. O God, our help in a - ges past, Our hope for years to come;
Our shel - ter from the storm - y blast, And our e - ter - nal home!
Suf - fi - cient is Thine arm a - lone, And our de - fense is sure.
From ev - er - last - ing Thou art God; To end - less years the same.
Short as the watch that ends the night, Be - fore the ris - ing sun.
Be Thou our guide while life shall last, And our e - ter - nal home!

# FATHER, I STRETCH MY HANDS TO THEE 36

*I stretch forth my hands unto Thee.* Ps. 143:6.

Charles Wesley, 1741 (1707-1788)

AZMON C.M. 8.6.8.6.
M.M. 63

Carl Gotthelf Gläser, 1784-1829
Arr. Lowell Mason, 1839 (1792-1872)

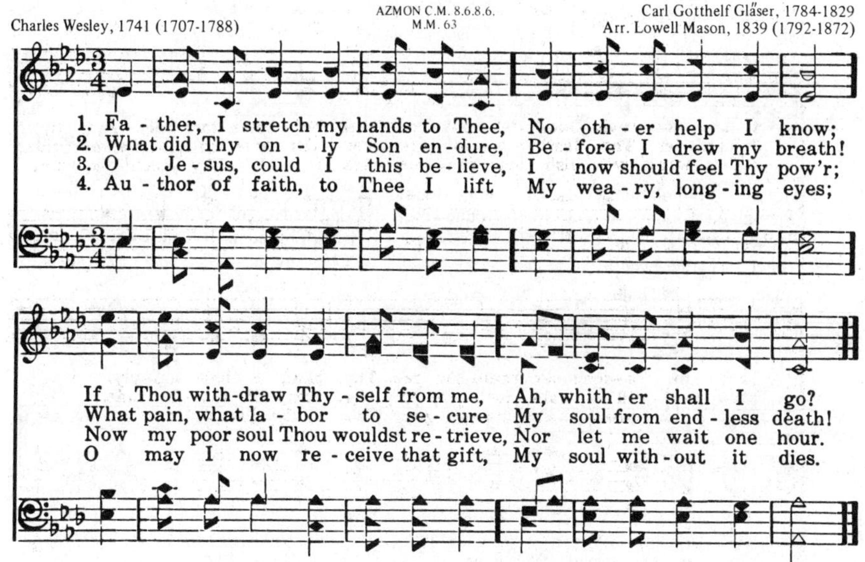

1. Fa - ther, I stretch my hands to Thee, No oth - er help I know;
2. What did Thy on - ly Son en - dure, Be - fore I drew my breath!
3. O Je - sus, could I this be - lieve, I now should feel Thy pow'r;
4. Au - thor of faith, to Thee I lift My wea - ry, long - ing eyes;
If Thou with - draw Thy - self from me, Ah, whith - er shall I go?
What pain, what la - bor to se - cure My soul from end - less dèath!
Now my poor soul Thou wouldst re - trieve, Nor let me wait one hour.
O may I now re - ceive that gift, My soul with - out it dies.

# ABOVE THE TREMBLING ELEMENTS 37

*Humble yourselves in the sight of the Lord, and He shall lift you up.* Jas. 4:10.

Anna L. Price, 1890 (1837-1924)

DUNDEE C.M. 8.6.8.6.
M.M. 54

*Scottish Psalter*, 1615

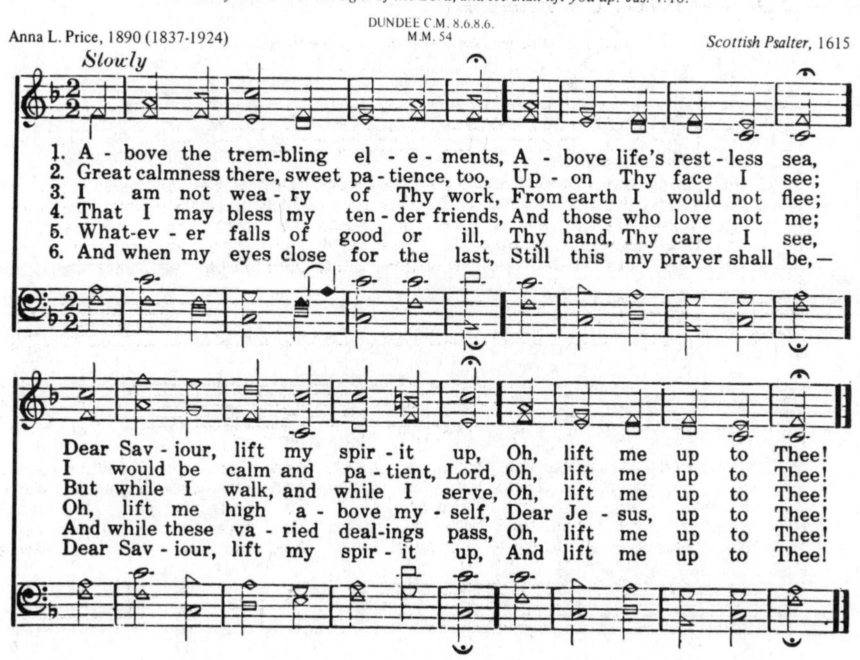

Slowly
1. A - bove the trem - bling el - e - ments, A - bove life's rest - less sea,
2. Great calmness there, sweet pa - tience, too, Up - on Thy face I see;
3. I am not wea - ry of Thy work, From earth I would not flee;
4. That I may bless my ten - der friends, And those who love not me;
5. What - ev - er falls of good or ill, Thy hand, Thy care I see,
6. And when my eyes close for the last, Still this my prayer shall be, —
Dear Sav - iour, lift my spir - it up, Oh, lift me up to Thee!
I would be calm and pa - tient, Lord, Oh, lift me up to Thee!
But while I walk, and while I serve, Oh, lift me up to Thee!
Oh, lift me high a - bove my - self, Dear Je - sus, up to Thee!
And while these va - ried deal - ings pass, Oh, lift me up to Thee!
Dear Sav - iour, lift my spir - it up, And lift me up to Thee!

# 38 GREAT JEHOVAH! GOD OF NATIONS

*If My people, which are called by My name, shall humble themselves and pray, and seek My face, and turn from their wicked ways; then will I hear from heaven . . .* II Chron. 7:14.

HAST DU JESU RUF VERNOMMEN 8.7.8.7.D.
M.M. 72
Howell E. Lewis, 1860-1953, alt.
Slowly
From Gesangbuch mit Noten
1. Great Je–ho–vah! God of na–tions! From Thy tem–ple in the skies,
2. Though our sins, our hearts con–found–ing, Long and loud for judg–ment call,
3. Great Je–ho–vah! God of pow–er! Hear Thy peop–le's falt–'ring cry;
CHO. Great Je–ho–vah! God of na–tions! From Thy tem–ple in the skies,
Hear Thy peo–ple's sup–pli – ca – tions, Now for their de–liv–'rance rise.
Thou hast mer–cy more a – bound–ing; Je – sus' blood can cleanse them all.
Save us in the need–ful hour –– Send de–liv–'rance from on high.
Hear Thy peop–le's sup – pli – ca – tions, Now for their de – liv – 'rance rise.
Lo! with deep con–tri – tion turn – ing, In thy ho – ly place we bow;
Let that mer–cy veil trans – gres – sion; Let that blood soul heal–ing give;
Save us Lord in trib – u – la – tion, May our faith Thee firm em–brace,
Hear us, fast–ing, pray–ing, mourn–ing; Hear us, spare us, save us now.
Hear our pray'r, our sins con – fes – sion; Heal our land, our sins for – give.
Till ap – pears thy great sal – va – tion, And we see Thee face to face.

# LORD OF OUR LIFE AND GOD OF OUR SALVATION 39

*Hearken Thou to the supplication of Thy servant, and of Thy people.* I Kings 8:30.

Matthäus A. von Löwenstern, 1644 (1594-1648)
*Christe du Beistand*
Tr. Philip Pusey, 1840
Alt. John J. Overholt, 1971

CHRISTE SANCTORUM
11.11.11.5.
M.M. 66

18th Century French church melody
Har. Ralph Vaughan Williams, 1872-1958
Arr. John J. Overholt, 1968

1. Lord of our life and God of our sal–va–tion, Star of our night and Hope of ev–'ry na–tion, Hear and re–ceive Thy church's sup–pli–ca–tion, Thou great Al–might–y Lord.
2. See round Thine ark the hun–gry bil–lows curl–ing; See how Thy foes their ban–ners are un–furl–ing. Lord, while their darts en–ven–omed they are hurl–ing, Thou canst pre–serve us, Lord.
3. Lord, Thou canst help when earth–ly ref–uge fail–eth; Lord, Thou canst save when dead–ly sin as–sail–eth; Lord, o'er Thy church nor death nor hell pre–vail–eth; Grant us Thy peace, O Lord. A–men.

4. Peace in our hearts, our evil thoughts assuaging;
Peace in Thy church where brothers are engaging;
Peace when the world its busy war is waging.
Calm Thy foes' raging, Lord.

5. Grant us Thy help till backward they are driven;
Grant them Thy truth that they may be forgiven;
Grant peace on earth or, after we have striven,
Peace in Thy heaven, Lord.

# 40 HUNGRY, AND FAINT, AND POOR

*The effectual prayer of a righteous man availeth much.* Jas. 5:16.

BOYLSTON S.M.
M.M. 62

John Newton, 1725-1807 | Lowell Mason, 1792-1872

1. Hun - gry, and faint, and poor, Be - hold us, Lord, a - gain
2. Thy word in - vites us nigh, Or we would starve in - deed;
3. The food our spir - its want, Thy hand a - lone can give;
As - sem - bled at Thy mer - cy's door, Thy boun - ty to ob - tain.
For we no mon - ey have to buy, Nor right-eous - ness to plead.
O hear the prayer of faith, and grant That we may eat and live!

# 41 FATHER, HEAR THE PRAYER WE OFFER

*Ask, and it shall be given you.* Matt. 7:7.

ST. SYLVESTER 8.7.8.7.
M.M. 60

Love Maria Willis, 1824 | John Bacchus Dykes, 1823-1876

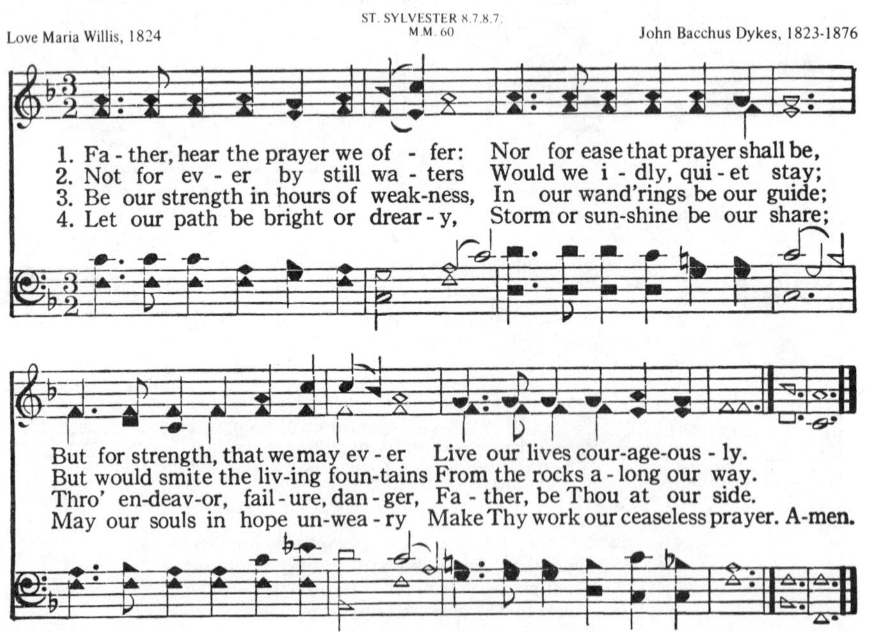
1. Fa - ther, hear the prayer we of - fer: Nor for ease that prayer shall be,
2. Not for ev - er by still wa - ters Would we i - dly, qui - et stay;
3. Be our strength in hours of weak-ness, In our wand'rings be our guide;
4. Let our path be bright or drear - y, Storm or sun-shine be our share;
But for strength, that we may ev - er Live our lives cour-age-ous - ly.
But would smite the liv-ing foun-tains From the rocks a - long our way.
Thro' en-deav-or, fail - ure, dan - ger, Fa - ther, be Thou at our side.
May our souls in hope un-wea - ry Make Thy work our ceaseless prayer. A-men.

# FATHER, TO SEEK THY FACE 42

*Thy face, Lord, will I seek.* Ps. 27:8.

James George Deck, 1855 (1802-1884)

ST. JOHN 6.6.6.6.8.8.
M.M. 60

William Havergal, 1793-1870
Harmony arr. by Compiler, 1965

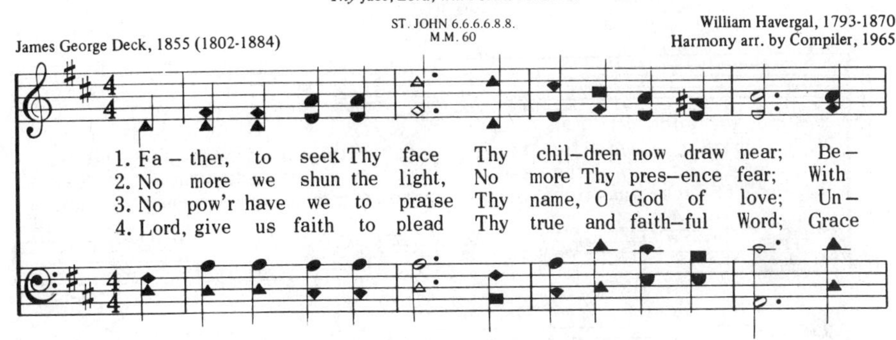
1. Fa – ther, to seek Thy face Thy chil–dren now draw near; Be –
2. No more we shun the light, No more Thy pres–ence fear; With
3. No pow'r have we to praise Thy name, O God of love; Un –
4. Lord, give us faith to plead Thy true and faith–ful Word; Grace

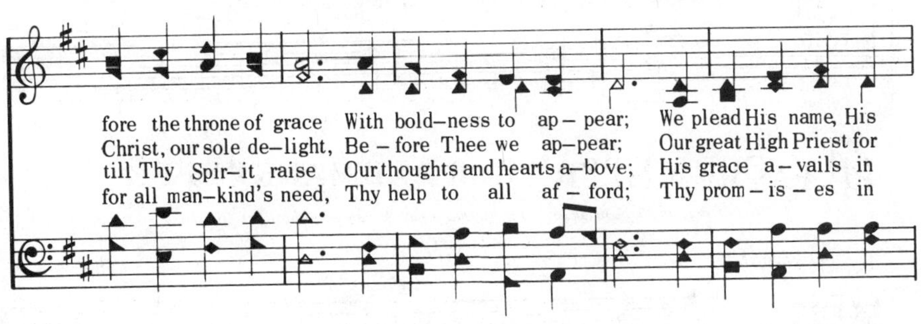
fore the throne of grace With bold–ness to ap – pear; We plead His name, His
Christ, our sole de–light, Be – fore Thee we ap–pear; Our great High Priest for
till Thy Spir–it raise Our thoughts and hearts a–bove; His grace a – vails in
for all man–kind's need, Thy help to all af – ford; Thy prom – is – es in

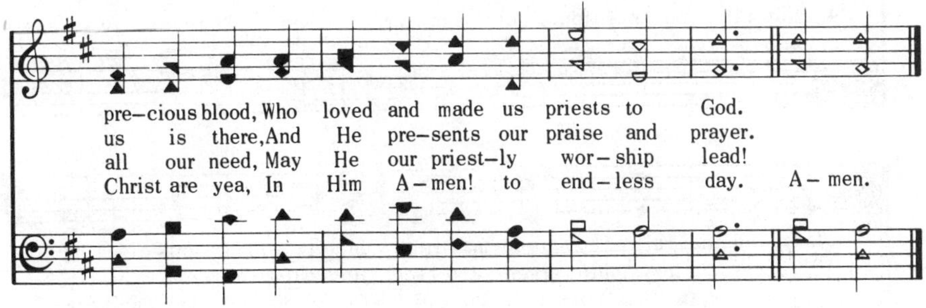
pre–cious blood, Who loved and made us priests to God.
us is there, And He pre–sents our praise and prayer.
all our need, May He our priest–ly wor – ship lead!
Christ are yea, In Him A – men! to end – less day. A – men.

# 43 LORD, WHILE FOR ALL MANKIND WE PRAY

*Supplications, prayers, intercessions, and giving of thanks, be made for all men.* I Tim. 2:1.

John R. Wreford, 1800-1881
Alt. by Compiler, 1970

LAMBETH C.M. 8.6.8.6.
M.M. 63

Wilhelm F. A. Schulthes, 1816-1879

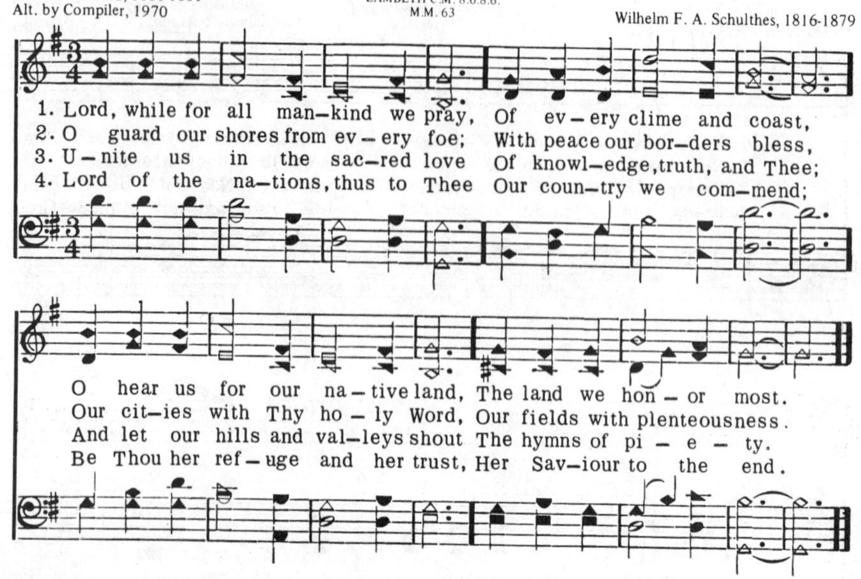
1. Lord, while for all man–kind we pray, Of ev–ery clime and coast,
2. O guard our shores from ev–ery foe; With peace our bor–ders bless,
3. U–nite us in the sac–red love Of knowl–edge, truth, and Thee;
4. Lord of the na–tions, thus to Thee Our coun–try we com–mend;
O hear us for our na–tive land, The land we hon–or most.
Our cit–ies with Thy ho–ly Word, Our fields with plenteousness.
And let our hills and val–leys shout The hymns of pi–e–ty.
Be Thou her ref–uge and her trust, Her Sav–iour to the end.

# 44 O GOD WE PRAY FOR ALL MANKIND

*Prayers . . . be made . . . for kings, and for all that are in authority.* I Tim. 2:1-2.

Howard J. Conover, 1850-1922

DALEHURST C.M. 8.6.8.6.
M.M. 80

John H. Gower, 1890

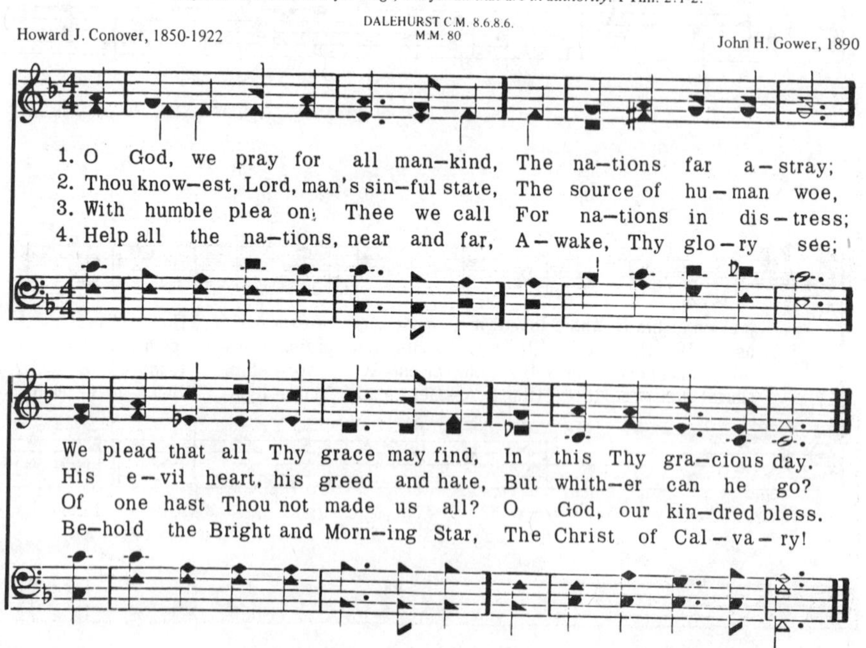
1. O God, we pray for all man–kind, The na–tions far a–stray;
2. Thou know–est, Lord, man's sin–ful state, The source of hu–man woe,
3. With humble plea on Thee we call For na–tions in dis–tress;
4. Help all the na–tions, near and far, A–wake, Thy glo–ry see;
We plead that all Thy grace may find, In this Thy gra–cious day.
His e–vil heart, his greed and hate, But whith–er can he go?
Of one hast Thou not made us all? O God, our kin–dred bless.
Be–hold the Bright and Morn–ing Star, The Christ of Cal–va–ry!

# O NATION, O OUR NATION 45

*Gather together, O nation . . . before the day of the Lord's anger come upon you. Seek ye the Lord . . .* Zech. 2:1-3.

Fannie Kreider, 1898-1971
Altered by Compiler, 1970

ST. HILDA 7.6.7.6.D.
M.M. 76

Justin Heinrich Knecht, 1752-1817
and Edward Husband, 1871 (1843-1908)

1. O na – tion, O our na – tion, Blest land that gave us birth,
2. The foe is on the thresh–old, To crush be – neath his feet
3. One ray of hope still gleam–eth, If we who own His name,
4. Then hear our cry, O Fa – ther, Though hosts of hell as – sail,
For thee are prayers as – cend–ing, To Him who rules the earth;
The faith our fa – thers cher – ished, A faith once pure and sweet.
Will hum – bly ask for – give – ness, And seek His face a – gain;
We claim Thy pre – cious prom – ise, Through prayer we shall pre – vail;
For thou, our own dear na – tion, Art sick and sore dis–tressed,
How can we grant him en – trance To pass our thresh–old o'er,
To us is prom–ise giv – en, How – ev – er small our band,
The ru – lers of our na – tion, Guide Thou with watch–ful eye;
Art trou – bled, and de – spair – ing From strife to be at rest.
And find our sons and daugh–ters En–thralled with–in his power?
That God will hear from heav – en, And heal our strick–en land.
In paths of peace us lead, till We're sum–moned to the sky.

## 46 NOW THANK WE ALL OUR GOD

*That I may publish with the voice of thanksgiving, and tell of all Thy wondrous works.* Ps. 26:7.

Martin Rinckart, 1636 (1586-1649)
*Nun danket alle Gott*
Tr. Catherine Winkworth, 1858 (1827-1878)

NUN DANKET ALLE GOTT 6.7.6.7.6.6.6.6.
M.M. 72

Johann Cruger, 1647 (1598-1662)
Harmony arr. John J. Overholt, 1970

1. Now thank we all our God With heart, and hands and voic - es,
2. Oh, may this boun - teous God Thro' all our life be near us,
3. All praise and thanks to God The Fa - ther now be giv - en,

Who won - drous things hath done, In whom His world re - joic - es,
With ev - er joy - ful hearts And bless - ed peace to cheer us;
The Son and Him who reigns With them in high - est heav - en.

Who from our moth - er's arms Hath blessed us on our way With
And keep us in His grace, And guide us when per-plexed, And
The one e - ter - nal God, Whom earth and heav'n a - dore, For

count - less gifts of love, And still is ours to - day.
free us from all ills, In this world and the next.
thus it was, is now, And shall be ev - er - more.

## 47 FATHER, WE THANK THEE

*Let us offer the sacrifice of praise to God continually . . . giving thanks to His name.* Heb. 13:15.

John J. Overholt, 1970

FATHER WE THANK THEE 5.5.7.4.
M.M. 72

Arr. from George Handel, 1685-1759

Fa—ther, we thank Thee, Fa—ther, we thank Thee,

For Thy un–speak–a–ble gift, Je–sus, our Lord. A–men.

# GREAT GOD OF NATIONS, NOW TO THEE 48

*The Lord is high above all nations.* Ps. 113:4. *Sing unto the Lord with thanksgiving.* Ps. 147:7.

Alfred Alexander Woodhull, 1829 (1810-1836)
Altered by Compiler, 1970

ROCKINGHAM OLD L.M. 8.8.8.8.
M.M. 80

A. William's *Supplement to Psalmody*
Adapted by Edward Miller, 1790 (1731-1807)
Harmony arr. by Compiler, 1970

1. Great God of na–tions, now to Thee Our hymn of thank–ful–ness we raise; With hum–ble heart, and bend–ing knee, We of–fer Thee our thanks and praise.

2. We give Thee thanks, Al–might–y God, For all the kind–ness Thou hast shown To this blest land our fa–thers trod, This land we hum–bly call our own.

3. We thank Thee that the Gos–pel's light Through all our land its ra–diance sheds; Dis–pels the shades of er–ror's night, And heaven–ly bless–ings round us spreads.

4. Great God, pre–serve us in Thy fear; And may we ev–er thank–ful be; O spread Thy truth's bright pre–cepts here, That all the peo–ple wor–ship Thee.

# 49 NOW BE PRAISE UNTO OUR GOD

*Sing forth the honour of His name: make His praise glorious.* Ps. 66:2

John J. Overholt, 1968

NUN GOTT LOB 7.8.7.8.8.7.
M.M. 63

Traditional Amish Melody
As sung by the compiler's mother,
Hannah Wagler Overholt, 1876-1965
Har. John J. Overholt, 1966, 1972

1. Now be praise un – to our God, Our Cre – a – tor,
2. Now be praise un – to our God, Our Cre – a – tor
3. Now be praise un – to our God, Our Cre – a – tor
4. Now be praise un – to our God, Now ex – tol the
we would praise Thee! God the Fa – ther, fount of love,
praise with sing – ing! To the Fa – ther grant our love,
now be prais – ed! Praise the Fa – ther, praise the Son,
great Cre – a – tor! Now the Fa – ther praise and laud,
God the Son, all life per – vad – ing, God the Spir – it,
To the Son true wor – ship bring – ing, To the Spir – it
And the Spir – it, Christ is rais – ed, Through His blood our
And the Son, our Lord and Sav–iour, And the Spir – it,
life cre – a – ting, We do praise Thee now, our God.
rev – erence wing–ing, Three in One, we praise Thee, God.
souls are sav – ed, Praise the liv – ing Three in One.
Co – Cre – a – tor, Praise be to the Tri – une God. God. A–men.
Alternate Ending

# ALL PRAISE TO GOD, WHO REIGNS ABOVE 50

*Our God, we thank Thee, and praise Thy glorious name.* I Chron. 29:13.

Johann J. Schütz, cento, 1675 (1640-1690)
*Sei Lob und Ehr' dem höchsten Gut*
Tr. Composite

MIT FREUDEN ZART
8.7.8.7.8.8.7.
M.M. 56

Adapted from *Geneva 138, Pseaulmes,* Lyon, 1547
Bohemian Brethren's *Kirchengeseng,* Berlin, 1566
Harmony arr. John J. Overholt, 1970

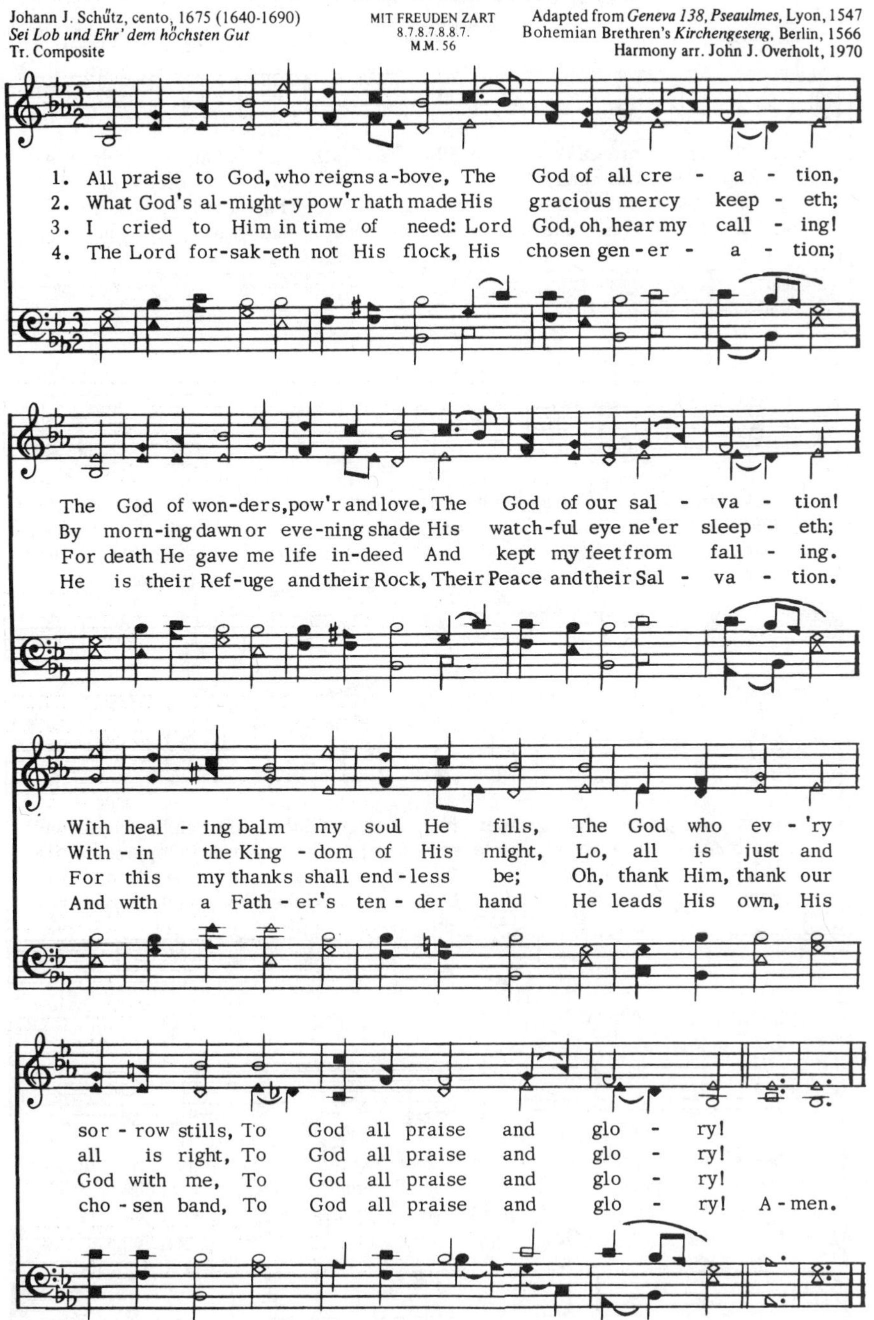
1. All praise to God, who reigns a-bove, The God of all cre - a - tion,
2. What God's al-might-y pow'r hath made His gracious mercy keep - eth;
3. I cried to Him in time of need: Lord God, oh, hear my call - ing!
4. The Lord for-sak-eth not His flock, His chosen gen-er - a - tion;
The God of won-ders, pow'r and love, The God of our sal - va - tion!
By morn-ing dawn or eve-ning shade His watch-ful eye ne'er sleep - eth;
For death He gave me life in-deed And kept my feet from fall - ing.
He is their Ref-uge and their Rock, Their Peace and their Sal - va - tion.
With heal - ing balm my soul He fills, The God who ev - 'ry
With - in the King - dom of His might, Lo, all is just and
For this my thanks shall end - less be; Oh, thank Him, thank our
And with a Fath - er's ten - der hand He leads His own, His
sor - row stills, To God all praise and glo - ry!
all is right, To God all praise and glo - ry!
God with me, To God all praise and glo - ry!
cho - sen band, To God all praise and glo - ry! A - men.

# 51 I'LL PRAISE MY MAKER

*While I live will I praise the Lord.* Ps. 146:2.

Isaac Watts, 1674-1748
Alt. John Wesley, 1703-1791

NASHVILLE 8s. 61.
M.M. 66

Day's *Psalter*
Har. Lowell Mason, 1792-1872

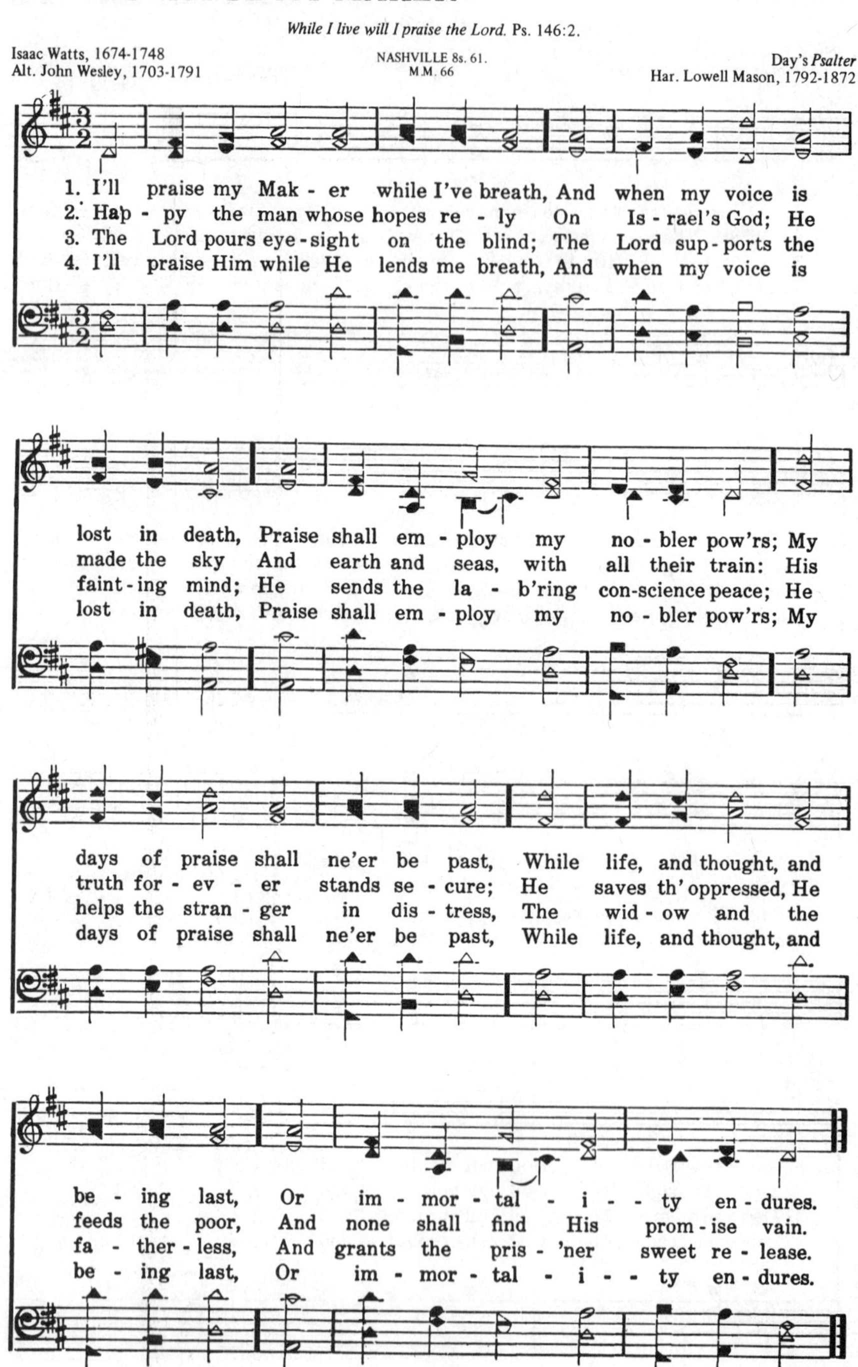
1. I'll praise my Mak - er while I've breath, And when my voice is
2. Hap - py the man whose hopes re - ly On Is - rael's God; He
3. The Lord pours eye - sight on the blind; The Lord sup - ports the
4. I'll praise Him while He lends me breath, And when my voice is
lost in death, Praise shall em - ploy my no - bler pow'rs; My
made the sky And earth and seas, with all their train: His
faint - ing mind; He sends the la - b'ring con-science peace; He
lost in death, Praise shall em - ploy my no - bler pow'rs; My
days of praise shall ne'er be past, While life, and thought, and
truth for - ev - er stands se - cure; He saves th' oppressed, He
helps the stran - ger in dis - tress, The wid - ow and the
days of praise shall ne'er be past, While life, and thought, and
be - ing last, Or im - mor - tal - i - ty en - dures.
feeds the poor, And none shall find His prom - ise vain.
fa - ther - less, And grants the pris - 'ner sweet re - lease.
be - ing last, Or im - mor - tal - i - ty en - dures.

# I'LL PRAISE MY MAKER 52

*Seven times a day do I praise Thee.* Ps. 119:164.

Isaac Watts, 1674-1748
Alt. John Wesley, 1703-1791

STRASSBURG 8.8.8.8.8.8.
M.M. 60

From the French Psalter, Strasburg, 1542

1. I'll praise my Maker while I've breath; And when my voice is lost in death, Praise shall employ my nobler powers. My days of praise shall ne'er be past, While life, and thought and being last, Or immortality endures.

2. Happy the man whose hopes rely On Is-rael's God; He made the sky And earth and seas, with all their train. His truth for ever stands secure; He saves th'oppressed, He feeds the poor; And none shall find His promise vain.

3. The Lord pours eyesight on the blind; The Lord supports the fainting mind; He sends the laboring conscience peace. He helps the stranger in distress, The widow and the fatherless, And grants the prisoner sweet release.

4. I'll praise Him while He lends me breath; And when my voice is lost in death, Praise shall employ my nobler powers. My days of praise shall ne'er be past, While life, and thought and being last, Or immortality endures.

# 53 O GOD AND FATHER, THEE WE BLESS

*Sing unto the Lord, bless His name.* Ps. 96:2.

From the 16th century Anabaptist *Ausbund*
Hymn No. 131, Leonard Clock, c. 1590
*O Gott Vater, wir loben dich*
Tr. John J. Overholt, 1969

LOBET DEN HERRN 8.7.8.7.8.8.7.
M.M. 76

Melchior Vulpius, 1609 (1560-1615)
Harmony arr. John J. Overholt, 1971

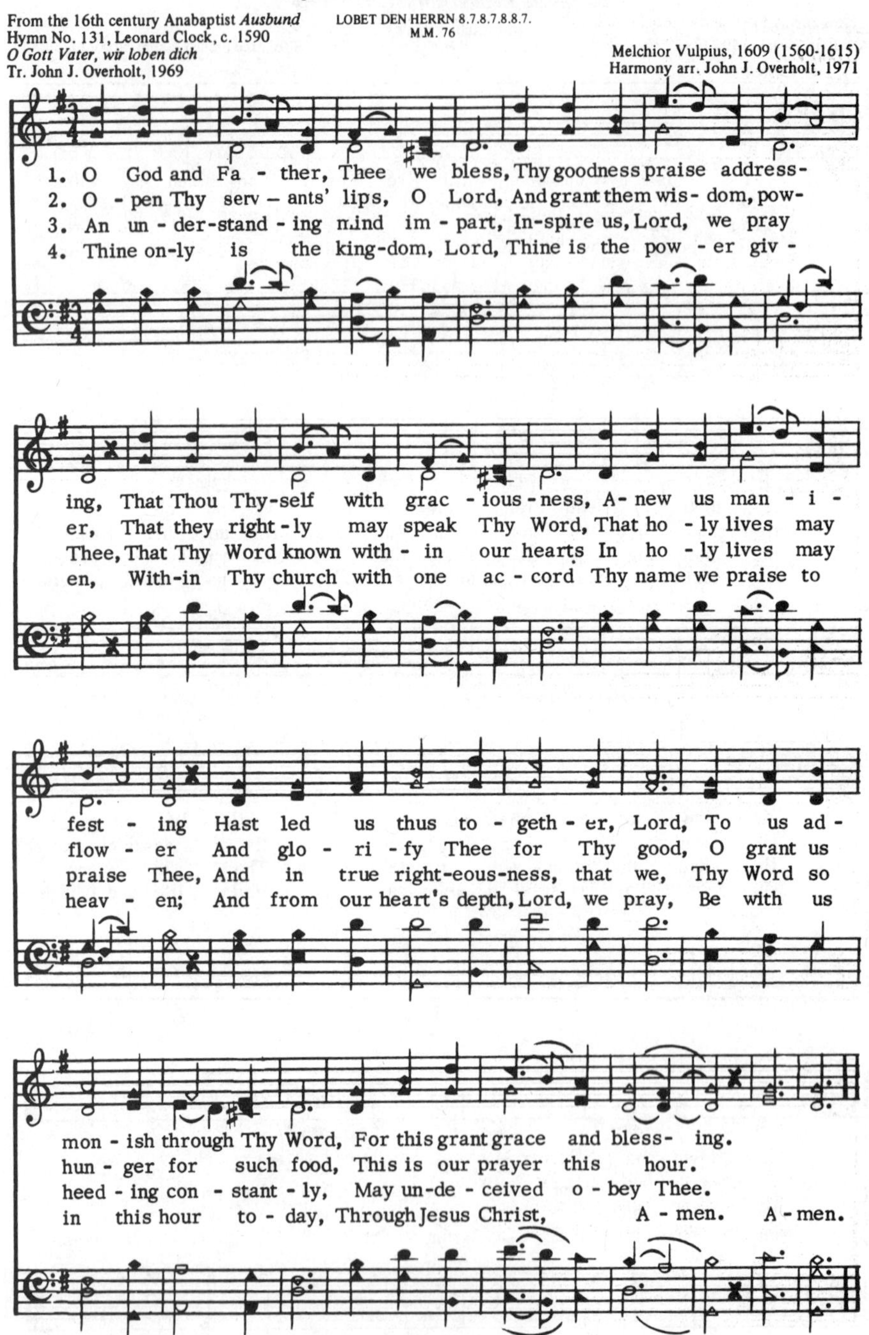
1. O God and Fa - ther, Thee we bless, Thy goodness praise address-
2. O - pen Thy serv – ants' lips, O Lord, And grant them wis - dom, pow-
3. An un - der-stand - ing mind im - part, In-spire us, Lord, we pray
4. Thine on-ly is the king-dom, Lord, Thine is the pow - er giv -
ing, That Thou Thy-self with grac - ious - ness, A- new us man - i -
er, That they right - ly may speak Thy Word, That ho - ly lives may
Thee, That Thy Word known with - in our hearts In ho - ly lives may
en, With-in Thy church with one ac - cord Thy name we praise to
fest - ing Hast led us thus to - geth - er, Lord, To us ad -
flow - er And glo - ri - fy Thee for Thy good, O grant us
praise Thee, And in true right-eous-ness, that we, Thy Word so
heav - en; And from our heart's depth, Lord, we pray, Be with us
mon - ish through Thy Word, For this grant grace and bless- ing.
hun - ger for such food, This is our prayer this hour.
heed - ing con - stant - ly, May un-de - ceived o - bey Thee.
in this hour to - day, Through Jesus Christ, A - men. A - men.

# O GOD AND FATHER, THEE WE BLESS 54

*O bless our God.* Ps. 66:8.

From the 16th century Anabaptist *Ausbund*
Hymn No. 131, Leonard Clock, c. 1590
*O Gott Vater, wir loben dich*
Tr. John J. Overholt, 1969

THE GREAT PHYSICIAN
8.7.8.7.8.8.7.
M.M. 92

John H. Stockton, 1813-1877
Harmony arr. John J. Overholt, 1971, 1974

*Slowly with feeling*

1. O God and Fa - ther, Thee we bless, Thy good - ness, praise ad–dress–ing,
2. O – pen Thy serv–ants' lips, O Lord, And grant them wis - dom, pow - er,
3. An un - der-stand - ing mind im - part, In – spire us, Lord, we pray thee,
4. Thine on - ly is the king- dom, Lord, Thine is the pow - er giv - en;

That Thou, O Lord, with gra – cious–ness A - new us man – i – fest – ing,
That they right - ly may speak Thy Word, That ho - ly lives may flow - er
That Thy Word known with - in our hearts In ho - ly lives may praise Thee;
With - in Thy church with one ac - cord Thy name we praise to hea - ven!

Hast led us thus to - geth - er, Lord, To us ad–mon–ish through Thy Word;
And glo - ri - fy Thee for Thy good, O grant us hun-ger for such food;
And in true right - eous- ness, that we, Thy Word so heed-ing con-stant-ly,
And from our heart's depth, Lord, we pray, Be with us in this hour, to - day

To us ad–mon–ish through Thy Word; For this, grant grace and bless–ing!
O grant us hun- ger for such food; This is our pray'r this hour!
Thy Word so heed- ing con - stant - ly, May un - de-ceived o - bey Thee!
Be with us in this hour, to - day, Through Je - sus Christ, A – men! A- men!

# 55 PRAISE THOU THE LORD, O MY SOUL

*O that men would praise the Lord for His goodness.* Ps. 107:8.

Johann Daniel Herrnschmidt, 1714
(1675-1723)
*Lobe den Herren, o meine Seele*
Tr. Lester Hostetler, 1938

LOBE DEN HERREN, O MEINE SEELE
10.8.10.8.8.8.8.
M.M. 92

*Neu-vermehrte Christliche*
*Seelenharf*, Ansbach, 1664

1 Praise thou the Lord, O my soul, sing prais - es! Him let me bless in
2 Praise, all ye peo - ple, His name all - glo-rious, Him who in heav'n and

life and death. All through my days His great love a - maz - es,
earth doth reign. All that hath life and breath, sound the cho - rus,

Him let me praise with ev - ery breath, Who life and light hath giv'n to me.
Sing ye His praise with glad re - frain. Ye chil-dren of our ho - ly God,

Bless, O my soul, e - ter - nal - ly. Hal - le - lu - jah! Hal - le - lu - jah!
Fa - ther and Son, and Spir - it, laud. Hal - le - lu - jah! Hal - le - lu - jah! A-men.

# PRAISE YE THE LORD 56

*Praise Him according to His excellent greatness.* Ps. 150:2.

John Kempthorne, 1775-1838
Thomas Kelley, 1769-1855
Reginald Heber, 1783-1826
Composite, arr. John J. Overholt, 1964
HERR, DIR IST NIEMAND ZU VERGLEICHEN
9.9.8.9.9.8.9.8.9.8.
M.M. 92
Justin H. Knecht, 1752-1817
1. Praise ye the Lord, ye heav'ns a - dore him, Sun, moon, and stars re - joice be - fore him, Praise him a - bove in realms of light;
Praise ye the Lord for he hath spo - ken, His laws which nev - er shall be bro - ken, His coun - sels ev - er just and right;
2. Praise ye the Lord by whom is giv - en His great sal - va - tion show'red from heav-en; His great sal - va - tion from on high;
Praise ye the Lord for won - drous bless - ing, E - ter - nal life and joy pos - sess - ing, Through Him who gave him - self to die;
3. Praise ye the Lord with voic - es sing - ing From heav'n and earth your tri - butes bring - ing, Prais - ing on high our Sav - iour's name;
Sin - ners for whom his life was giv - en, Let us ex - alt his name to heav - en, Let us ex - tol his won - drous fame;
Praise ye the God of our sal - va - tion Crea - tures on high his power pro - claim,
Praise ye the Lord in grate - ful sor - row While ye up - on his pas - sion gaze,
E - ter nal life in him pos - sess - ing Let us e're praise his won - der - ful name,
Heav - en and earth and all cre - a - tion Hon - or and glo - ri - fy his name.
He who was bruised to bone and mar - row, Whose blood was shed our souls to save.
Bless - ing and hon - or, glory and pow - er Be now and ev - er to the Lamb.

# 57 THAT MAN HATH PERFECT BLESSEDNESS

*Blessed is the man that walketh not in the counsel of the ungodly.* Ps. 1:1.

Based on Psalm 1
Nichol Grieve, 1940 (1868-1954)

DUNFERMLINE C.M. 8.6.8.6.
M.M. 80

*Scottish Psalter,* 1615

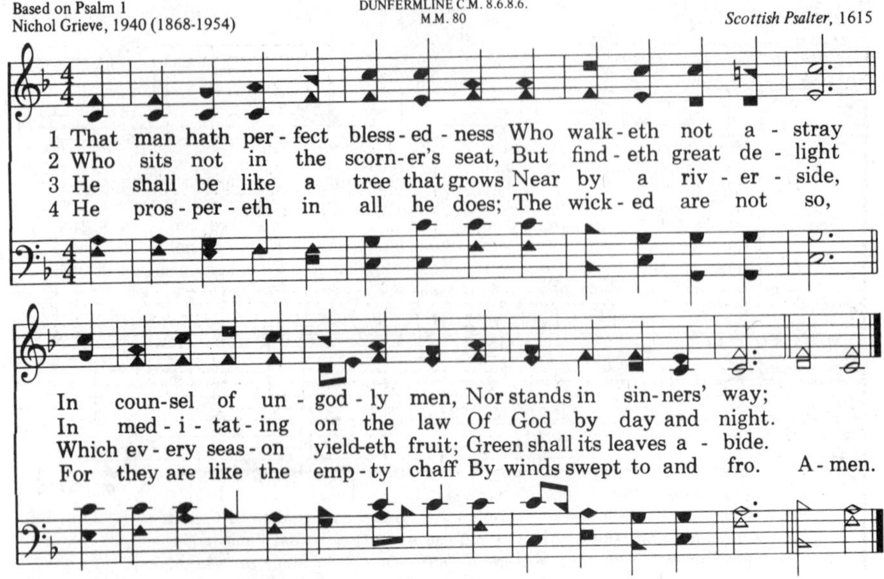
1 That man hath per - fect bless - ed - ness Who walk - eth not a - stray
2 Who sits not in the scorn - er's seat, But find - eth great de - light
3 He shall be like a tree that grows Near by a riv - er - side,
4 He pros - per - eth in all he does; The wick - ed are not so,
In coun - sel of un - god - ly men, Nor stands in sin - ners' way;
In med - i - tat - ing on the law Of God by day and night.
Which ev - ery seas - on yield - eth fruit; Green shall its leaves a - bide.
For they are like the emp - ty chaff By winds swept to and fro. A - men.

# 58 I LOVE THEE, O MY LORD

*I will love Thee, O Lord, my strength.* Ps. 18:1.

Based on Psalm 18
Anonymous

ROTHWELL L.M. 8.8.8.8.
M.M. 96

William Tans'ur, 1706-1783

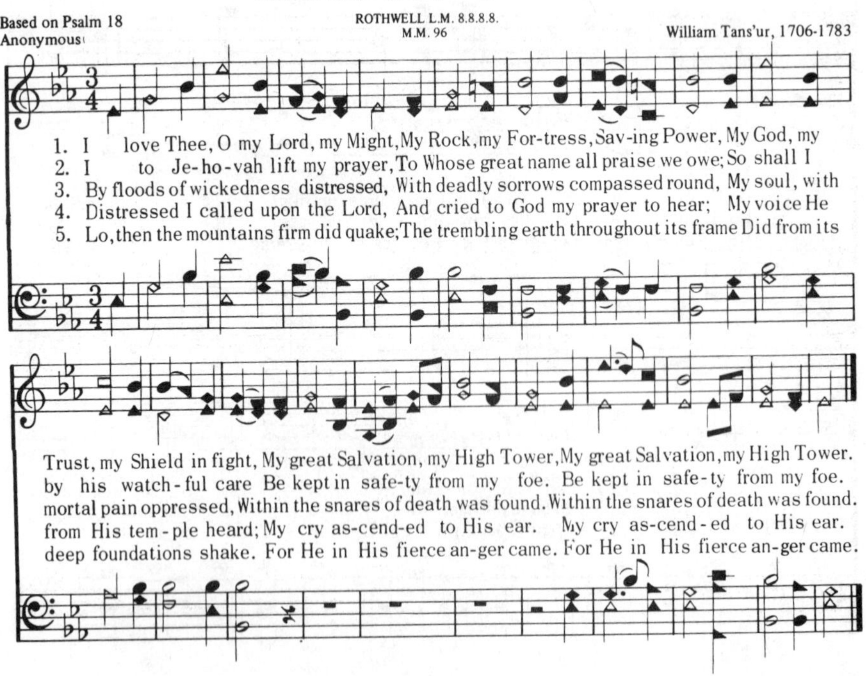
1. I love Thee, O my Lord, my Might, My Rock, my For - tress, Sav - ing Power, My God, my
2. I to Je - ho - vah lift my prayer, To Whose great name all praise we owe; So shall I
3. By floods of wickedness distressed, With deadly sorrows compassed round, My soul, with
4. Distressed I called upon the Lord, And cried to God my prayer to hear; My voice He
5. Lo, then the mountains firm did quake; The trembling earth throughout its frame Did from its
Trust, my Shield in fight, My great Salvation, my High Tower, My great Salvation, my High Tower.
by his watch - ful care Be kept in safe - ty from my foe. Be kept in safe - ty from my foe.
mortal pain oppressed, Within the snares of death was found. Within the snares of death was found.
from His tem - ple heard; My cry as - cend - ed to His ear. My cry as - cend - ed to His ear.
deep foundations shake. For He in His fierce an - ger came. For He in His fierce an - ger came.

# MY SHEPHERD IS THE HEAVENLY FATHER 59

*He maketh me to lie down in green pastues.* Ps. 23:2.

Based on Psalm 23
Wilmer D. Swope, 1969

SHEPHERD 10.4.10.4.10.10.4.
M.M. 76

Herbert C. Richert, b. 1900

1. My Shep-herd is the Heav'n-ly Fa-ther kind, I shall not want,
2. To pas-tures green, my Shep-herd lead-eth me, I feed me there,
3. He lead-eth me in paths of righ-teous-ness, For His name's sake,
4. And when my feet shall tread the vale of death, I shall not fear,
5. Thou dost a-noint my head with sa-cred oil, My cup runs o'er,
The Fa-ther from His trea-sure store shall give Rich gifts to me,
By spar-kling wa-ters clear, He lead-eth me, I slack my thirst,
My Shep-herd doth re-store my soul to life, For-gives my sins,
My Shep-herd leads me through the shad-ows dark, He gives me light,
Good-ness and mer-cy, Lord, shall fill my days, My life is blest,
With lov-ing care the Shep-herd leads His sheep,
The ver-dant mead-ows shall re-fresh my soul,
From sin and death He has re-stor'd my soul,
He leads my soul to heav'n-ly pas-tures bright,
Then when my pil-grim-age on earth is done,
My Heav'n-ly Fa-ther loves and cares for me. (He cares for me)
O pre-cious thought, my Shep-herd cares for me. (He cares for me)
O, may I al-ways heed my Shep-herd's voice. (My Shep-herd's voice)
His rod and staff they ev-er com-fort me. (They com-fort me)
With-in God's house I dwell for-ev-er-more. (For-ev-er-more)

# 60 THE LORD'S MY SHEPHERD

*The Lord is my shepherd; I shall not want.* Ps. 23:1.

CRIMOND C.M. 8.6.8.6.
M.M. 88
Jessie Seymour Irvine, 1872 (1836-1887)
Arr. David Grant, 1833-1893
Descant, W. Baird Ross
Based on Psalm 23
Scottish Psalter, 1650
Descant
1. The Lord's my Shep - herd, I'll not want; He makes me down to lie In pas - tures green; He lead - eth me The qui - et wa - ters by.
2. My soul He doth re - store a - gain; And me to walk doth make With - in the paths of right - eous - ness, E'en for His own name's sake.
3. Yea, though I walk thro' death's dark vale, Yet will I fear no ill; For Thou art with me, and Thy rod, And staff me com - fort still.
4. My ta - ble Thou hast fur - nish - ed In pres - ence of my foes; My head Thou dost with oil a - noint, And my cup o - ver - flows.
5. Good - ness and mer - cy all my life Shall sure - ly fol - low me; And in God's house for - ev - er - more My dwell - ing place shall be.

# THE LORD'S MY SHEPHERD 61

*I am the good shepherd, and know My sheep.* Jn. 10:14.

Based on Psalm 23
*Scottish Psalter,* 1650
Altered by Compiler, 1969

BAIN 8.6.8.6.4.4.6.
M.M. 69

James Leith McBeth Bain
Arr. John J. Overholt, 1969

1. The Lord's my Shepherd, I'll not want, He makes me down to lie In pastures green; He leadeth me The quiet waters by. He leadeth me, He leadeth me, The quiet waters by.
2. My soul He doth restore again; And me to walk doth make Within the paths of righteousness, Ev'n for His own name's sake. Within the paths of righteousness, Ev'n for His own name's sake.
3. Yea, though I walk in death's dark vale, Yet will I fear none ill: For Thou art with me; and Thy rod And staff me comfort still. Thy rod and staff me comfort still, They do me comfort still.
4. My table Thou hast furnished In presence of my foes; My head Thou dost with oil anoint, And my cup overflows. My head Thou dost with oil anoint, And my cup overflows.
5. Goodness and mercy all my life Shall surely follow me: And in God's house forevermore My dwelling place shall be. And in God's house forevermore My dwelling place shall be. Amen.

# 62 THE LORD OF HOSTS

*I waited patiently for the Lord; and He inclined unto me, and heard my cry.* Ps. 40:1.

Based on Psalm 40
Wilmer D. Swope, 1969

MIDWAY 10.4.10.4.10.10.
M.M. 72

John Huebert, 1969

1. The Lord of Hosts in - clines His ear to me, He sees my tears.
2. He gives a song of vic - to - ry to me, Let praise re - sound.
3. I now de - light to think and do Thy will, My king who bled.
4. Let all re - joice, be glad, who seek the Lord, Re - joice and sing.
The Lord of Hosts will purge my sin from me, He knows my fears.
He gives my heart a song of flow - ing praise, My songs re - dound.
The law of God is in my heart and mind, It is se - cured.
The great sal - va - tion of the Lord is free, Praise God the King.
From out the pit my Lord has lift - ed me;
My praise to God shall man - y see and hear;
I have not hid Thy righ - teous - ness with - in;
His lov - ing kind - ness is my bless - ing sure;
My feet He set up - on the sol - id rock.
The Lord is kind, His mer - cy ev - er sure.
Thy truth and lov - ing kind - ness I de - clare.
I mag - ni - fy and praise the name of God. A - men.

# GOD BE MERCIFUL TO ME 63

*Have mercy upon me, O God . . . according unto the multitude of Thy tender mercies blot out my transgressions.* Ps. 51:1.

Based on Psalm 51
*Psalter,* 1912, Sts. 1-4
*The Hymnbook,* 1955, St. 5

REDHEAD NO. 76 (Ajalon) 7.7.7.7.7.7.
M.M. 84

Richard Redhead, 1853 (1820-1901)

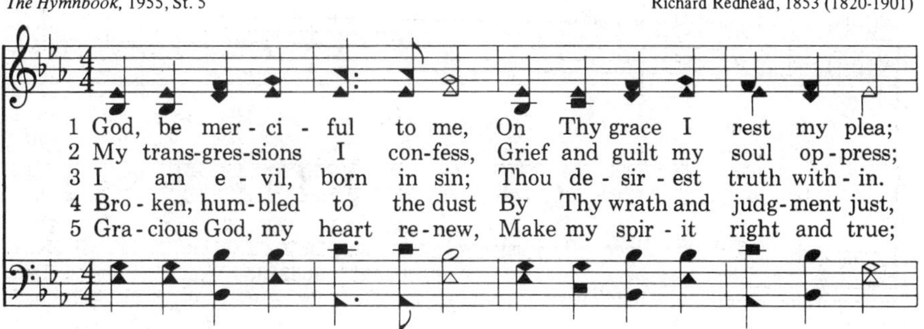
1 God, be mer - ci - ful to me, On Thy grace I rest my plea;
2 My trans-gres-sions I con-fess, Grief and guilt my soul op - press;
3 I am e - vil, born in sin; Thou de - sir - est truth with - in.
4 Bro - ken, hum-bled to the dust By Thy wrath and judg-ment just,
5 Gra - cious God, my heart re - new, Make my spir - it right and true;

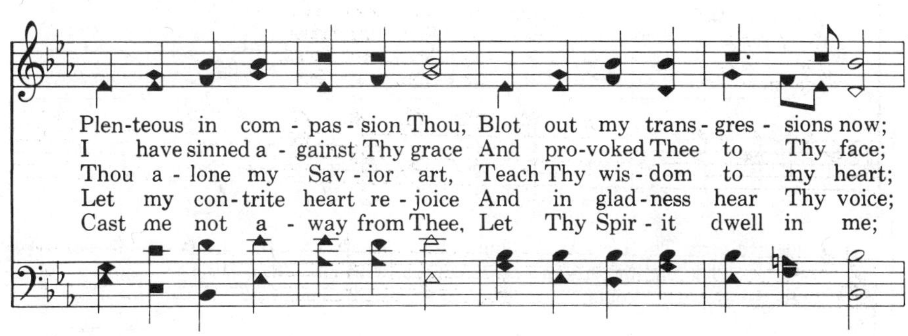
Plen-teous in com - pas - sion Thou, Blot out my trans - gres - sions now;
I have sinned a - gainst Thy grace And pro-voked Thee to Thy face;
Thou a - lone my Sav - ior art, Teach Thy wis - dom to my heart;
Let my con-trite heart re - joice And in glad-ness hear Thy voice;
Cast me not a - way from Thee, Let Thy Spir - it dwell in me;

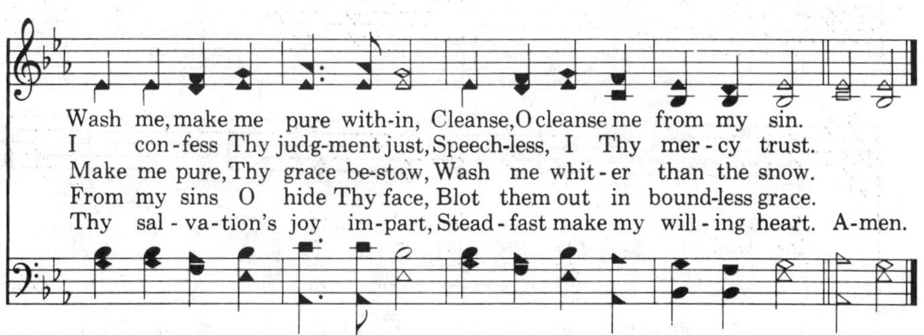
Wash me, make me pure with-in, Cleanse, O cleanse me from my sin.
I con-fess Thy judg-ment just, Speech-less, I Thy mer - cy trust.
Make me pure, Thy grace be-stow, Wash me whit - er than the snow.
From my sins O hide Thy face, Blot them out in bound-less grace.
Thy sal - va-tion's joy im-part, Stead - fast make my will - ing heart. A-men.

# 64 I WILL ABIDE IN THY DWELLING PLACE

*I will abide in Thy tabernacle for ever.* Ps. 61:4.

Based on Psalm 61
John J. Overholt, 1965

RUHESTÄTTE 12.10.12.10 with Ref.
M.M. 50

John J. Overholt, 1965

Descant to be sung with third stanza
1. I will a – bide in Thy dwell–ing place for – ev – er, I will Thee
2. For Thou hast been a safe shel – ter, a strong tow – er, From the fierce
3. We shall a – bide there be – fore our God for – ev – er, Mer – cy and
trust and e're Thy cov – ert claim, For Thou, O God, hast heard me,
en – e – my that threat – ens sore. Thou willt pro – long life man – y
truth pre–serve our souls in Him. We shall sing praise un – to His
Thou hast giv – en The her–i–tage of those that fear Thy name.
gen – er – a – tions, King, sub–ject Thou canst save who Thee im – plore.
name for – ev – er, Dai – ly per – form our vows and laud His fame.

REFRAIN

Hear my cry O God, at - tend un - to my prayer, From the
end of the earth to Thee I cry; When my heart's o'erwhelmed lead me
to the rock that's high-er, Lead me to the rock that is high - er than I.

# 65 LET THE PEOPLE PRAISE THEE

Let the people praise Thee, O God. Ps. 67:5.
Based on Psalm 67
John J. Overholt, 1965
JAUCHZEN 13.10.13.10. with Ref.
M.M. 80
John J. Overholt, 1965
1. Let the peo - ple praise thee, O God, O let them praise thee!
2. God be mer - ci - ful un - to us and bless us
3. Let the peo - ple praise thee, then shall the earth yield in - crease
4. Let the peo - ple praise thee, O God, O let them praise thee!
O let the na - tions be glad, let them sing! (sing for joy)
And cause his face up - on us to shine (us to shine)
And God even our God shall bless us with joy (with great joy)
Thy right - eous judg - ment and gov – ern – ment bring (do thou bring)
Let the peo - ple praise thee, O God O let them praise thee!
That thy way be known up - on earth to help us
Our God shall bless us and all the earth shall fear him
Let the peo - ple praise thee, O God, O let them praise thee!
REFRAIN
Praise thee, Cre - a - tor, Re - deem - er, and King! We praise thee!
Mer - cy and bless - ing are in thee com - bined. Be mer - ciful
Let the peo – ple praise Thee and prais – es em – ploy! Bless us
God of all na - tions, thy prais - es we sing! We praise thee!

(we praise thee) We praise thee! (We do praise thee)
(un - to us) And bless us (shine up - on us)
(and keep us) We praise thee! (we a - dore thee)
(we praise thee) We praise thee! (we do praise thee)
We praise thee Cre - a a - tor, Re - deem - er, and King!
Mer - cy and bless - ing are in Thee com - bined!
Let the peo - ple praise thee and prais - es em - ploy!
God of all na – tions, Thy prais – es we sing!

## HOW LOVELY ARE THY DWELLINGS FAIR 66

*How amiable are Thy tabernacles, O Lord of hosts.* Ps. 84:1.

Based on Psalm 84
John Milton, 1648 (1608-1674)

WINCHESTER OLD C.M. 8.6.8.6.
M.M. 88

T. Est's *Whole Booke of Psalmes*, 1592

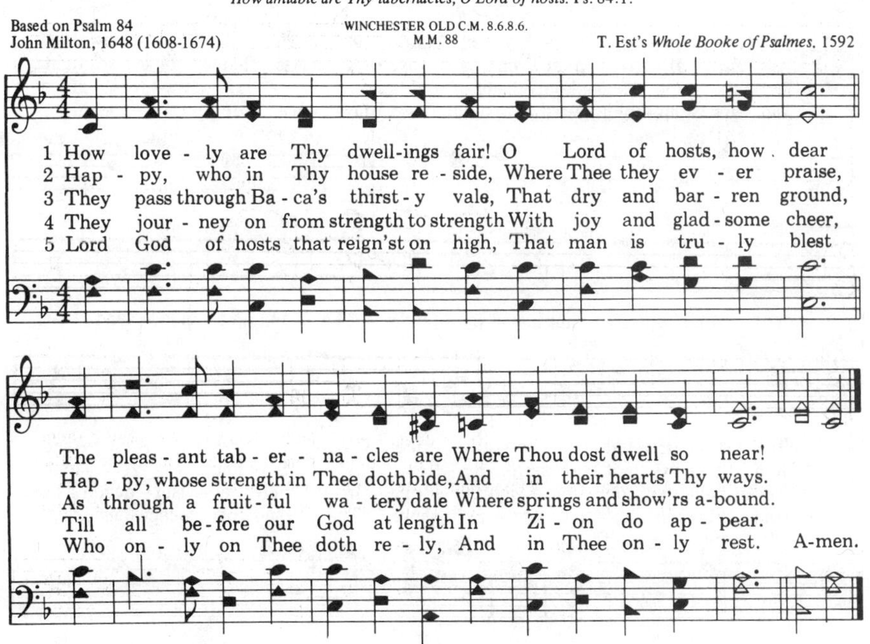
1 How love - ly are Thy dwell-ings fair! O Lord of hosts, how dear
2 Hap - py, who in Thy house re - side, Where Thee they ev - er praise,
3 They pass through Ba - ca's thirst - y vale, That dry and bar - ren ground,
4 They jour - ney on from strength to strength With joy and glad - some cheer,
5 Lord God of hosts that reign'st on high, That man is tru - ly blest
The pleas - ant tab - er - na - cles are Where Thou dost dwell so near!
Hap - py, whose strength in Thee doth bide, And in their hearts Thy ways.
As through a fruit - ful wa - tery dale Where springs and show'rs a - bound.
Till all be - fore our God at length In Zi - on do ap - pear.
Who on - ly on Thee doth re - ly, And in Thee on - ly rest. A-men.

# 67 O PRAISE OUR GREAT AND GRACIOUS LORD

*I will utter dark sayings of old: Which we have heard and known, and our fathers have told us.* Ps. 78:2-3.

Based on Psalm 78
Harriet Auber, 1773-1862
Alt. Wilmer D. Swope
Altered by Compiler, 1970

ELLACOMBE 8.6.8.6.D.
M.M. 84

Adapted from *Gesangbuch* . . .
Wúrttemberg, 1784

Descant

4. O may we faith–ful ev – er stand, And trust our heav'n–ly Guide;

1. O praise our great and gra–cious Lord, And call up– on His name;
2. He gave the shadow–ing cloud by day, The mov – ing fire by night;
3. We, too, have Man – na from a–bove, The Bread that comes from heav'n;
4. O may we faith – ful ev – er stand, And trust our heav'n–ly Guide;

Who us up – holds with power–ful hand, While ebbs life's fee–ble tide,

To strains of joy tune ev – ery chord, His might – y acts pro–claim;
To guide His Is – rael on their way, He made their dark–ness light;
To us the same kind hand of love Has liv – ing wa – ters given;
Who us up–holds with power–ful hand, While ebbs life's fee–ble tide,

And brings us to that hap – py shore, The land of peace and rest,

Tell how He led His cho–sen race To Ca–naan's prom–ised land;
And have we not a sure re – treat, A Sav–iour ev – er nigh,
We have the Rock, from which the spring In rich a – bun – dance flows;
And brings us to that hap – py shore, The land of peace and rest,

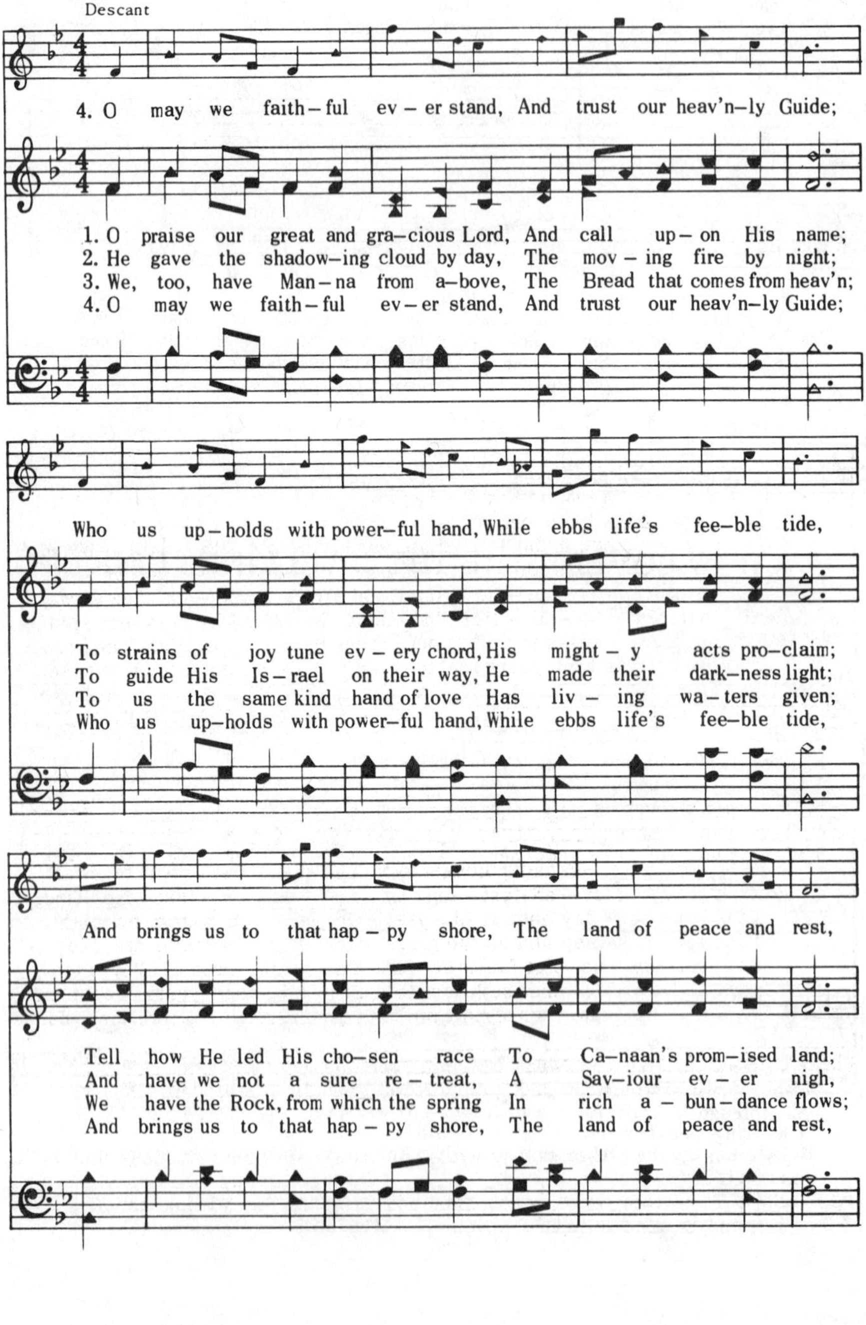

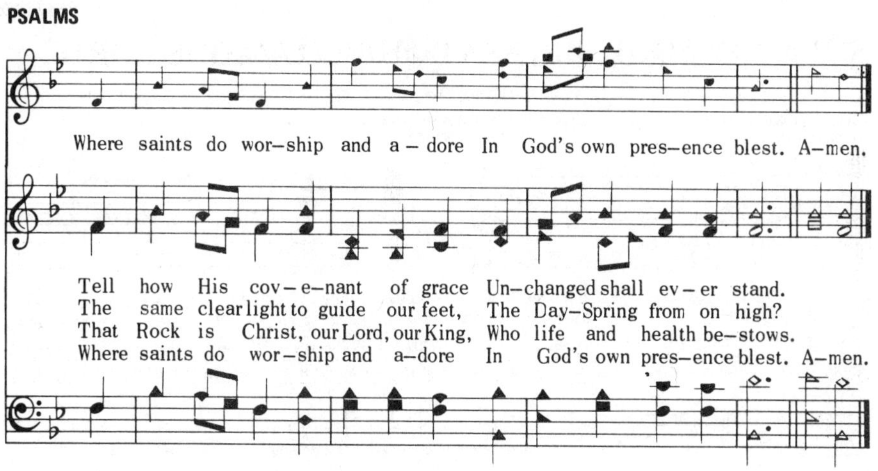
Where saints do wor–ship and a – dore In God's own pres–ence blest. A–men.
Tell how His cov – e–nant of grace Un–changed shall ev – er stand.
The same clear light to guide our feet, The Day–Spring from on high?
That Rock is Christ, our Lord, our King, Who life and health be–stows.
Where saints do wor–ship and a–dore In God's own pres–ence blest. A–men.

# LORD, THOU HAST BEEN OUR DWELLING PLACE 68

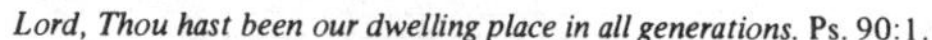
*Lord, Thou hast been our dwelling place in all generations.* Ps. 90:1.

Based on Psalm 90
Anonymous Psalter

ST. PETER C.M. 8.6.8.6.
M.M. 72

Alexander R. Reinagle, 1799-1877

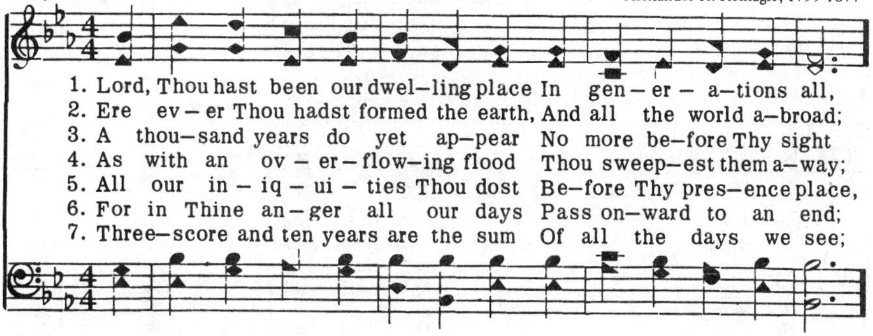

1. Lord, Thou hast been our dwel–ling place In gen – er – a–tions all,
2. Ere ev – er Thou hadst formed the earth, And all the world a–broad;
3. A thou–sand years do yet ap–pear No more be–fore Thy sight
4. As with an ov – er – flow–ing flood Thou sweep–est them a–way;
5. All our in – iq – ui – ties Thou dost Be–fore Thy pres–ence place,
6. For in Thine an – ger all our days Pass on–ward to an end;
7. Three–score and ten years are the sum Of all the days we see;

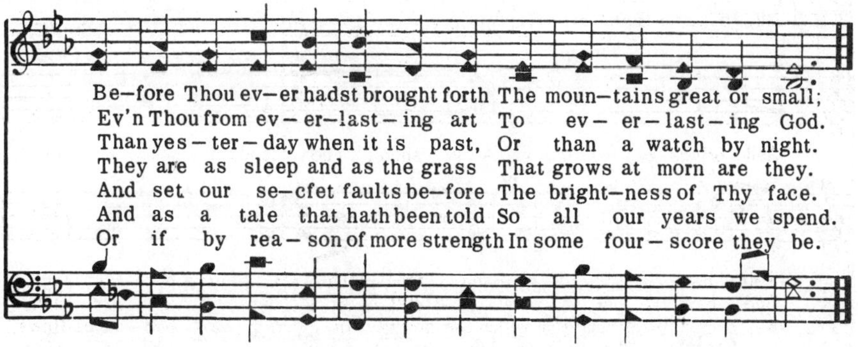

Be–fore Thou ev–er hadst brought forth The moun–tains great or small;
Ev'n Thou from ev – er–last – ing art To ev – er–last – ing God.
Than yes – ter – day when it is past, Or than a watch by night.
They are as sleep and as the grass That grows at morn are they.
And set our se–cfet faults be–fore The bright–ness of Thy face.
And as a tale that hath been told So all our years we spend.
Or if by rea – son of more strength In some four – score they be.

8. Who knows the power of Thy wrath?
According to Thy fear
So is Thy wrath; Lord, teach Thou us
Our end in mind to bear,

9. And so to count our days that we
Our hearts may still apply
To learn.Thy wisdom and Thy truth,
That we may live thereby.

# 69 O MY SOUL, BLESS THOU JEHOVAH

*Bless the Lord, O my soul.* Ps. 103:1.

Based on Psalm 103
Anonymous

BLESS JEHOVAH 8.8.8.8.L.M.D.
M.M. 72

Silas Jonas Vail, 1818-1884

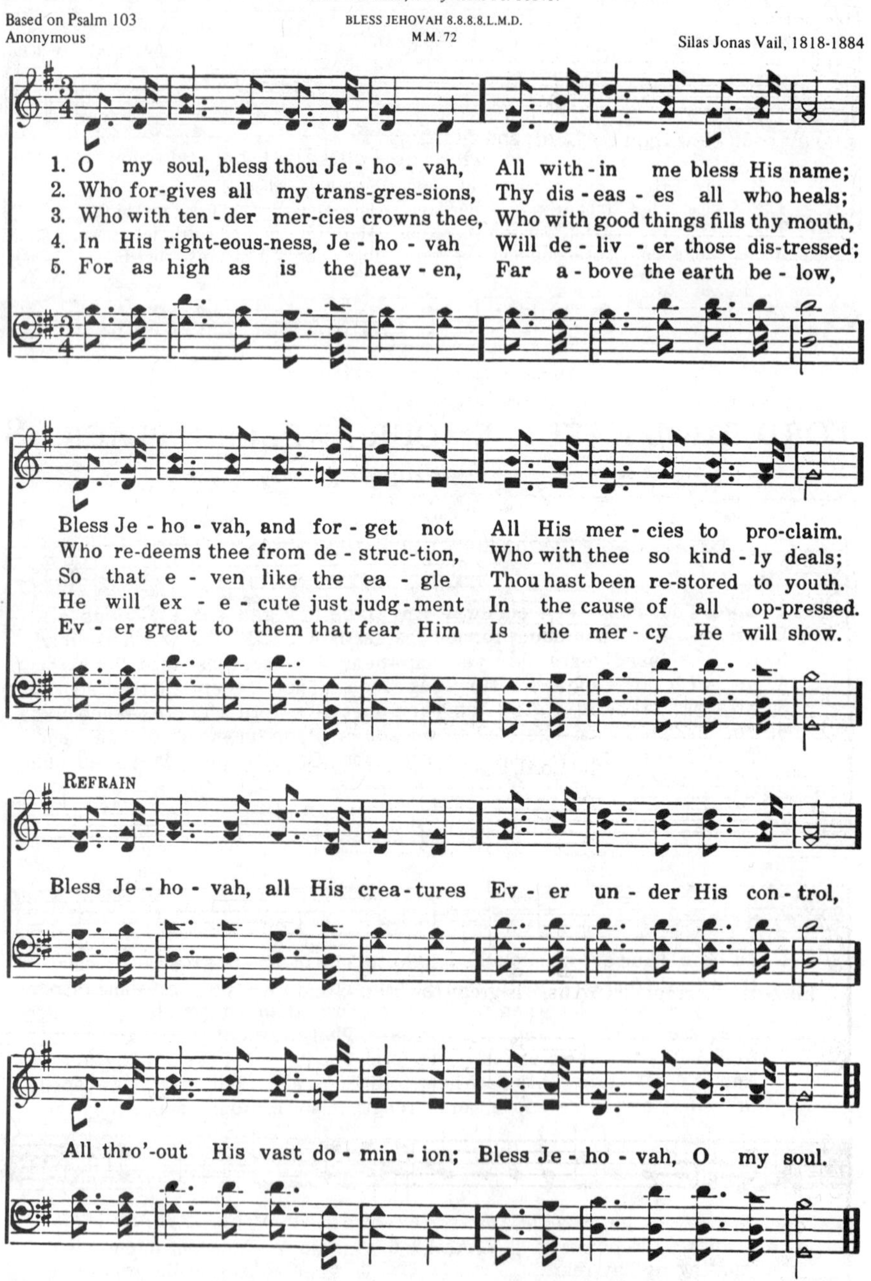
1. O my soul, bless thou Je - ho - vah, All with - in me bless His name;
2. Who for-gives all my trans-gres-sions, Thy dis - eas - es all who heals;
3. Who with ten - der mer-cies crowns thee, Who with good things fills thy mouth,
4. In His right-eous-ness, Je - ho - vah Will de - liv - er those dis-tressed;
5. For as high as is the heav - en, Far a - bove the earth be - low,
Bless Je - ho - vah, and for - get not All His mer - cies to pro-claim.
Who re-deems thee from de - struc-tion, Who with thee so kind - ly deals;
So that e - ven like the ea - gle Thou hast been re-stored to youth.
He will ex - e - cute just judg-ment In the cause of all op-pressed.
Ev - er great to them that fear Him Is the mer - cy He will show.
Refrain
Bless Je - ho - vah, all His crea-tures Ev - er un - der His con - trol,
All thro'-out His vast do - min - ion; Bless Je - ho - vah, O my soul.

# O MY SOUL, BLESS THOU THE LORD 70

*All that is within me, bless His holy name.* Ps. 103:1.

Based on Psalm 103
Anonymous

BLESS THOU THE LORD 7.7.5.
M.M. 80

Ludwig van Beethoven, 1770-1827

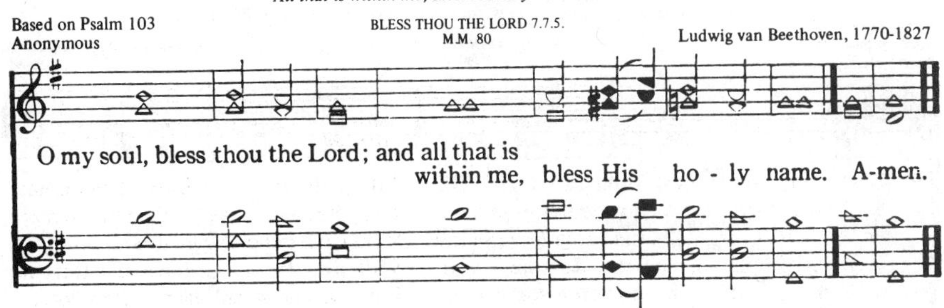
O my soul, bless thou the Lord; and all that is
within me, bless His ho - ly name. A-men.

# O PRAISE THE LORD 71

*O praise the Lord, all ye nations.* Ps. 117:1.

Based on Psalm 117
Anonymous

O PRAISE THE LORD 8.6.6.10.11.4.12.11.4.
M.M. 88

Will Hill

O praise the Lord, all ye na-tions; Praise Him, all ye peo-ple, praise Him, all ye

peo - ple. O praise the Lord, Praise Him, all ye peo - ple, For His mer - ci - ful

kind-ness is great tow'rd us, is great tow'rd us; and the truth of the Lord en-

dur-eth for ev-er, for ev - er and ev - er, ev - er and ev - er: Praise ye the Lord.

# 72 TO THE HILLS I LIFT MINE EYES

*I will lift up mine eyes unto the hills, from whence cometh my help.* Ps. 121:1.

Based on Psalm 121
Charles Wesley, 1708-1788

SEPARATION 7.6.7.6.7.7.7.6.
M.M. 60

Anonymous
Arranged

1. To the hills I lift mine eyes, The ev - er last - ing hills;
Stream-ing hence in fresh sup-plies, My soul the Spir - it feels:
2. Faith-ful soul pray al - ways; pray And still in God con - fide;
He thy fee - ble steps shall stay, Nor suf - fer Thee to slide:
3. Nei - ther sin, nor earth, nor hell, Thy Keep - er can sur-prise;
Care-less slum-bers can - not steal On His all see - ing eyes:
Will He not His help af - ford! Help, while yet I ask, is giv'n:
Lean on thy Re-deem - er's breast; He thy qui - et spir - it keeps:
He is Is - rael's sure de - fence: Is - rael all His care shall prove,
God comes down, the God and Lord Who made both earth and heav'n.
Rest in Him, se - cure - ly rest; Thy Watch - man nev - er sleeps.
Kept by watch-ful prov - i - dence, And ev - er wak - ing love.

# I WILL EXTOL THEE, O MY GOD 73

*Every day will I bless Thee; and I will praise Thy name for ever and ever.* Ps. 145:2.

Based on Psalm 145
Anonymous

EVERY DAY WILL I BLESS THEE 8.6.8.6. with Ref.
M.M. 96

James McGranahan, 1840-1907

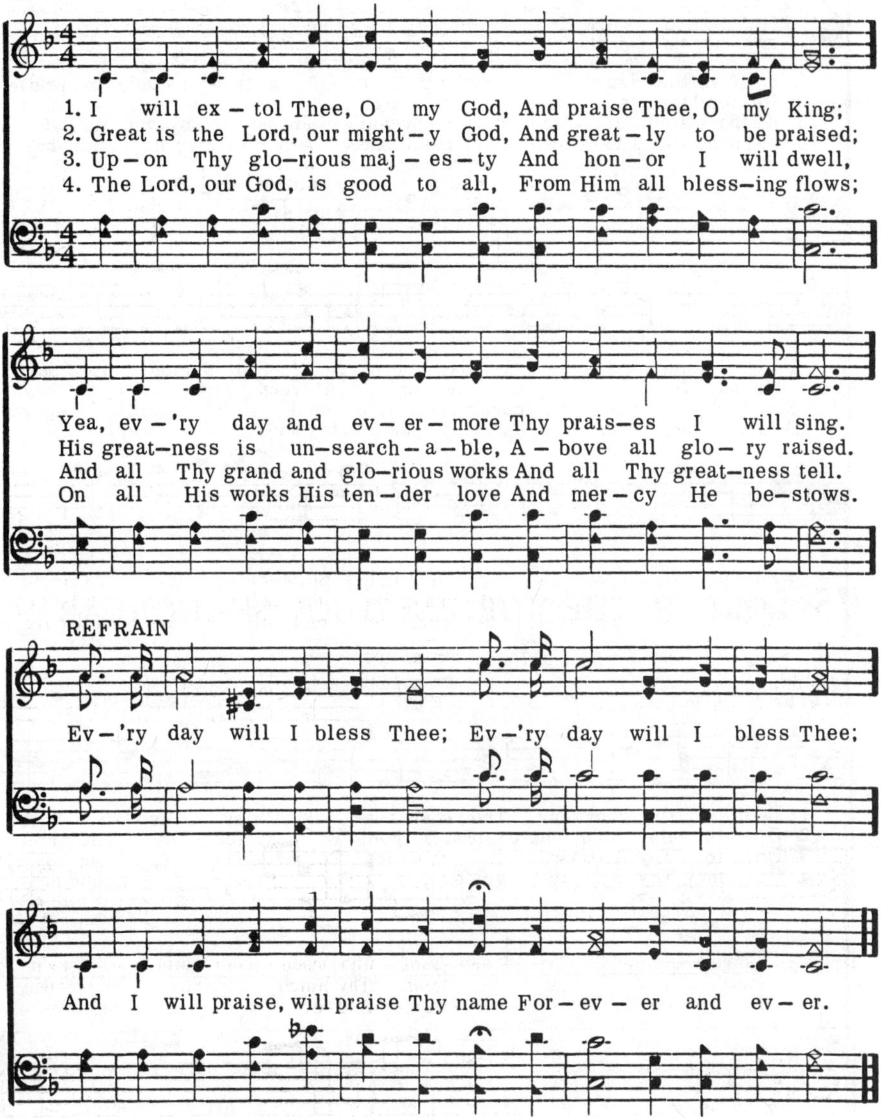

1. I will ex – tol Thee, O my God, And praise Thee, O my King;
2. Great is the Lord, our might – y God, And great – ly to be praised;
3. Up – on Thy glo–rious maj – es – ty And hon – or I will dwell,
4. The Lord, our God, is good to all, From Him all bless–ing flows;

Yea, ev – 'ry day and ev – er – more Thy prais–es I will sing.
His great–ness is un–search – a – ble, A – bove all glo – ry raised.
And all Thy grand and glo–rious works And all Thy great–ness tell.
On all His works His ten – der love And mer – cy He be–stows.

REFRAIN

Ev – 'ry day will I bless Thee; Ev – 'ry day will I bless Thee;

And I will praise, will praise Thy name For – ev – er and ev – er.

# 74 I OWE THE LORD A MORNING SONG

*I will sing aloud of Thy mercy in the morning.* Ps. 59:16.

GRATITUDE C.M. 8.6.8.6.
M.M. 88

Amos Herr, 1890 (1816-1897) — Amos Herr

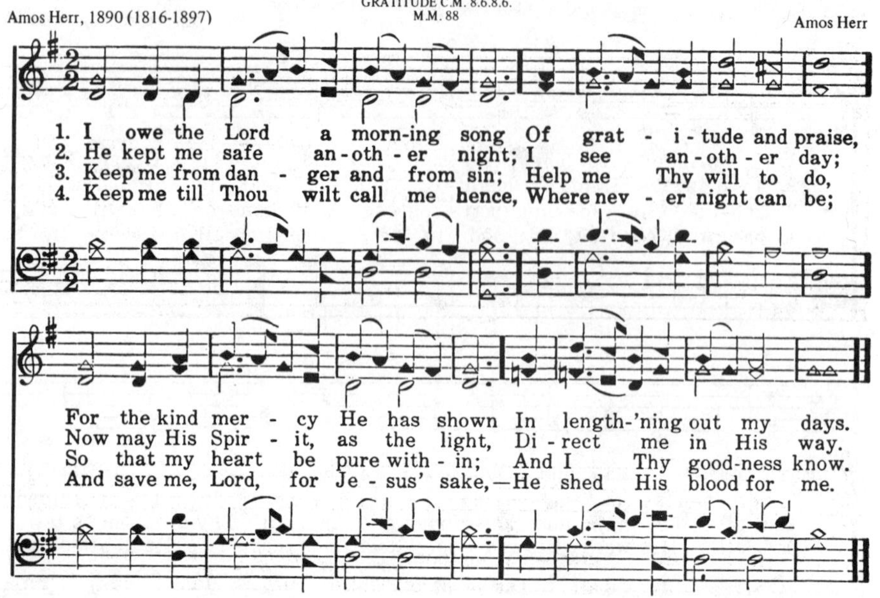
1. I owe the Lord a morn-ing song Of grat - i - tude and praise,
2. He kept me safe an-oth - er night; I see an-oth - er day;
3. Keep me from dan - ger and from sin; Help me Thy will to do,
4. Keep me till Thou wilt call me hence, Where nev - er night can be;
For the kind mer - cy He has shown In length-'ning out my days.
Now may His Spir - it, as the light, Di - rect me in His way.
So that my heart be pure with - in; And I Thy good-ness know.
And save me, Lord, for Je - sus' sake,—He shed His blood for me.

# 75 LORD, IN THE MORNING THOU SHALT HEAR

*To show forth Thy lovingkindness in the morning.* Ps. 92:2.

WARWICK C.M. 8.6.8.6.
M.M. 63

Isaac Watts, 1719 (1674-1748) — Samuel Stanley, 1800 (1767-1822)

1. Lord, in the morn-ing Thou shalt hear My voice as - cend-ing high;
2. Up to the hills where Christ is gone To plead for all His saints,
3. Un - to Thy house will I re - sort, To taste Thy mer - cies there;
4. Oh, may Thy Spir - it guide my feet In ways of right-eous-ness,
To Thee will I di - rect my prayer, To Thee lift up mine eye;
Pre - sent - ing, at His Fa-ther's throne, Our songs and our com-plaints.
I will fre - quent Thy ho - ly court, And wor - ship in Thy fear.
Make ev - 'ry path of du - ty straight And plain be - fore my face.

# O GOD, INSPIRE OUR MORNING HYMN 76

*In the morning will I direct my prayer unto Thee.* Ps. 5:3.

Daniel S. Warner, 1842-1895
NEWBOLD C.M. 8.6.8.6.6.
M.M. 80
George Kingsley, 1811-1884
1. O God, in – spire our morn – ing hymn Of
2. Thy mir – a – cle of love so sweet Pre –
3. 'Tis blest to rise, O Lord, and join Cre –
4. Sweet morn – ing is the time to pray, How
love and grat – i – tude; O bless the sac – ri –
served us all se – cure; While help – less in un –
a – tion's har – mo – nies, To hymn Thy praise at
love – ly and how meet, To send our ear – ly
fice we bring, Thou source of ev – 'ry good.
con – scious sleep, Thy pres – ence kept us pure.
ear – ly morn, And of – fer thanks to Thee.
thoughts a – way, Up to the mer – cy – seat. A – men.

# 77 DAYSPRING OF ETERNITY

*Until the day dawn, and the day star arise in your hearts.* II Pet. 1:19.

Christian Knorr von Rosenroth, 1684 (1636-1689)
*Morgenglanz der Ewigkeit*
Tr. Catherine Winkworth, 1855 and 1863 (1827-1878)

MORGENGLANZ DER EWIGKEIT
7.8.7.8.7.3.
M.M. 80

Johann Rudolph Ahle, 1662 (1625-1673)

1 Day - spring of e - ter - ni - ty! Hide no more Thy ra - diant dawn - ing!
2 Let Thy mer - cies' morn - ing dew Rouse our con - science from its blind - ness:
3 Let the glow of love de - stroy Cold o - be - dience faint - ly giv - en,
4 Through this dark and tear - ful place Nev - er be Thy light de - nied us,

Light from light's ex - haust - less sea, Shine on us a - fresh this morn - ing!
Glad - den life's dry plains a - new With the riv - ers of Thy kind - ness;
Wake our hearts to love and joy With the flush - ing east - ern heav - en;
O Thou glo - rious sun of grace, To yon world of glad - ness guide us,

And dis - pel with glo - rious might All our night.
Wa - ter dai - ly us Thy flock From the rock.
Let us tru - ly rise ere yet Life hath set.
When to joys that nev - er end We as - cend! A-men.

# 78 MY OPENING EYES WITH RAPTURE SEE

*I myself will awake early. I will praise Thee, O Lord, among the people.* Ps. 57:8-9.

James Hutton, 1713-1795

ERNAN L.M. 8.8.8.8.
M.M. 66

Lowell Mason, 1850 (1792-1872)

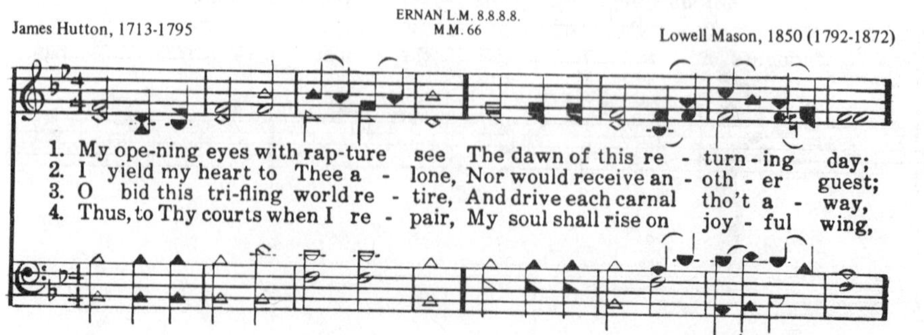
1. My ope-ning eyes with rap-ture see The dawn of this re - turn-ing day;
2. I yield my heart to Thee a - lone, Nor would receive an - oth - er guest;
3. O bid this tri-fling world re - tire, And drive each carnal tho't a - way,
4. Thus, to Thy courts when I re - pair, My soul shall rise on joy - ful wing,

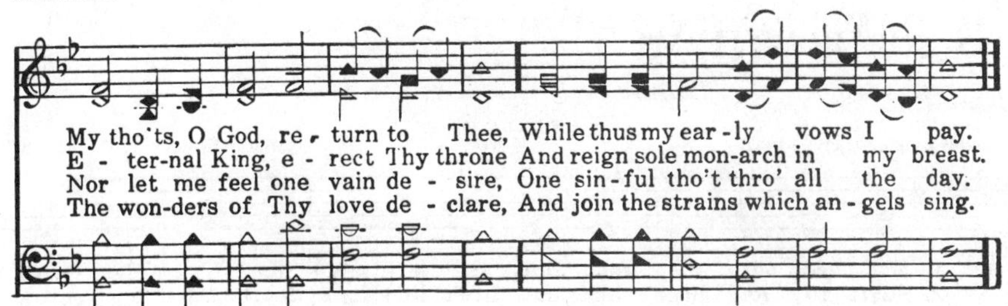
My tho'ts, O God, re - turn to Thee, While thus my ear - ly vows I pay.
E - ter-nal King, e - rect Thy throne And reign sole mon-arch in my breast.
Nor let me feel one vain de - sire, One sin - ful tho't thro' all the day.
The won-ders of Thy love de - clare, And join the strains which an - gels sing.

# WITH THE MORN IN RADIANCE BREAKING 79

*From the rising of the sun unto the going down of the same the Lord's name is to be praised.* Ps. 113:3.

Traditional Polish
*Kiedy ranne wstaja zorze*
Tr. W. J. Rose, 1922

PIESN PORANNA L.M. 8.8.8.8.
M.M. 63

Polish Melody
Arranged by Compiler, 1964

1. With the morn in radiance breaking
Earth in all her glory waking,
Sky and sea, Thine own creation,
Hymn Thee, Lord, in adoration.

2. Man whom Thou hast richly dowered,
Blessings on his head hast showered;
All ungrateful, shamed before Thee,
Man alone does not adore Thee.

3. Scarce from sleep my thoughts awaken
When to Thee my vows are taken;
Thou, whose robe is gladsome nature,
Lord of every grateful creature.

4. Death hath many captives numbered
While in peace we calmly slumbered;
Now the newborn day arriving
Summons us to noble striving.

# 80 ABIDE WITH ME

*Thou, Lord, only makest me dwell in safety.* Ps. 4:8.

EVENTIDE 10.10.10.10.
M.M. 56

Henry F. Lyte, 1847 (1793-1847) | William H. Monk, 1861 (1823-1889)

1. A - bide with me: fast falls the e - ven - tide; The dark - ness
2. Swift to its close ebbs out life's lit - tle day; Earth's joys grow
3. I need Thy pres - ence ev - 'ry pass - ing hour; What but Thy
4. I fear no foe, with Thee at hand to bless: Ills have no
5. Hold Thou Thy cross be - fore my clos - ing eyes; Shine through the
deep - ens; Lord, with me a - bide: When oth - er help - ers fail, and
dim, its glo - ries pass a - way; Change and de - cay in all a-
grace can foil the tempter's pow'r? Who like Thy - self my guide and
weight, and tears no bit - ter - ness. Where is death's sting? where, grave, thy
gloom, and point me to the skies: Heav'n's morning breaks, and earth's vain
com-forts flee, Help of the help - less, O a - bide with me.
round I see; O Thou who chang-est not, a - bide with me.
stay can be? Thro' cloud and sun - shine, O a - bide with me.
vic - to - ry? I tri - umph still, if Thou a - bide with me.
shad-ows flee: In life, in death, O Lord, a - bide with me.

# 81 SAVIOUR, AGAIN WE RAISE

*In the night His song shall be with me.* Ps. 42:8.

John Ellerton, 1826-1893
Recast John J. Overholt, 1969

TRENTHAM S.M. 6.6.8.6.
M.M. 80

Robert Jackson, 1888 (1842-1914)

1. Sav–iour, a – gain we raise Our eve–ning hymn of praise; We bless Thee
2. Grant peace up–on our way; With Thee shall end our day; Guard lips from
3. Grant peace, Lord, through the night; Turn dark–ness in–to light; From harm and
4. Grant us Thy peace through life, Thy balm in sor – row, strife; And when Thou

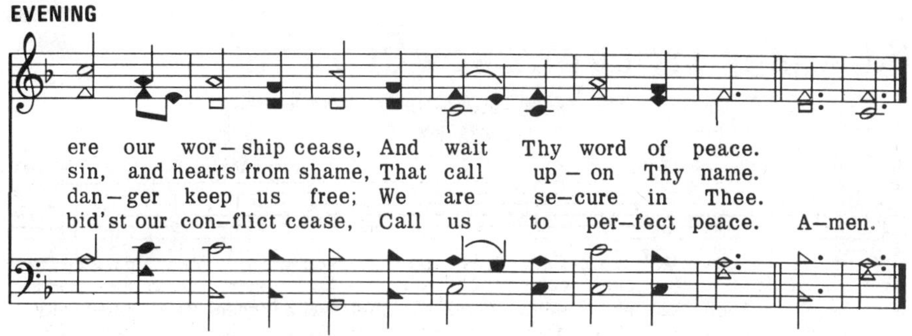
EVENING
ere our wor – ship cease, And wait Thy word of peace.
sin, and hearts from shame, That call up – on Thy name.
dan – ger keep us free; We are se – cure in Thee.
bid'st our con – flict cease, Call us to per – fect peace. A – men.

# SAVIOUR, BREATHE AN EVENING BLESSING 82

*I will both lay me down in peace and sleep.* Ps. 4:8.

EVENING SONG 8.7.8.7.
M.M. 72

James Edmeston, 1820 (1791-1867)

Jacob Henry Hall, 1855-1941)

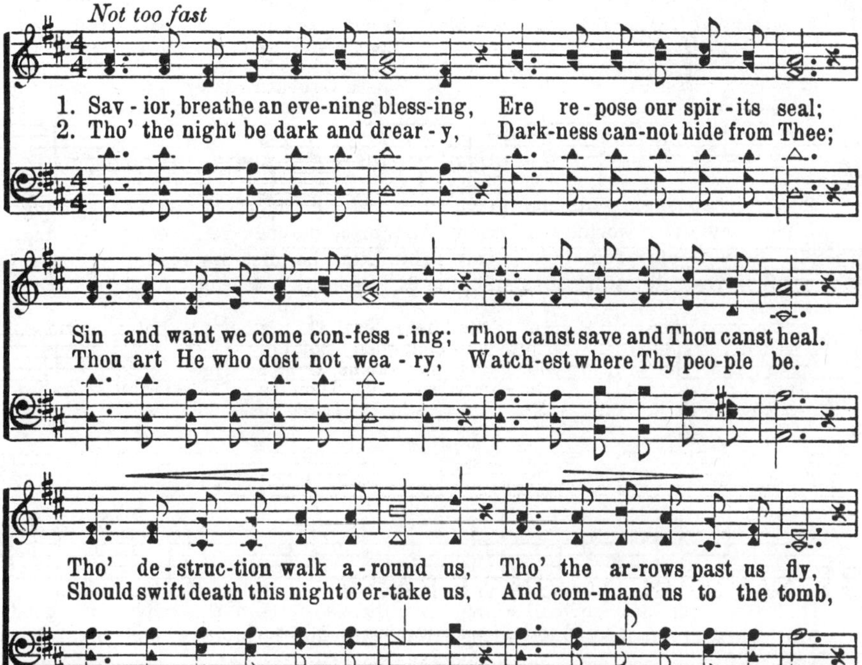

*Not too fast*

1. Sav - ior, breathe an eve-ning bless-ing, Ere re - pose our spir - its seal;
2. Tho' the night be dark and drear - y, Dark-ness can-not hide from Thee;

Sin and want we come con-fess - ing; Thou canst save and Thou canst heal.
Thou art He who dost not wea - ry, Watch-est where Thy peo-ple be.

Tho' de - struc-tion walk a - round us, Tho' the ar-rows past us fly,
Should swift death this night o'er-take us, And com-mand us to the tomb,

*m*
An - gel guards from Thee surround us; *f* We are safe, if Thou art nigh.
May the morn in heav'n a - wake us, Clad in bright e - ter - nal bloom.

# 83 THE DUTEOUS DAY NOW CLOSETH

*Yea, the darkness hideth not from Thee; but the night shineth as the day.* Ps. 139:12.

Paul Gerhardt, 1648 (1607-1676)
*Nun ruhen all Wälder*
Tr. Robert Bridges, 1899 (1844-1930)
Altered by Compiler

DER MOND IST AUFGEGANGEN 7.7.6.7.7.8.
M.M. 72

Johann Abraham Peter Schulz, 1747-1800
Har. John J. Overholt, 1971

1. The duteous day now clos - eth, Each flower and tree re - pos - eth,
2. Now all the heav'nly splen - dor Breaks forth in star-light ten - der
3. Man e're is drawn to pon – der The joys of home far yon - der;
4. Re–moved from mor-tal blind - ness Man finds God's lov-ing kind - ness,

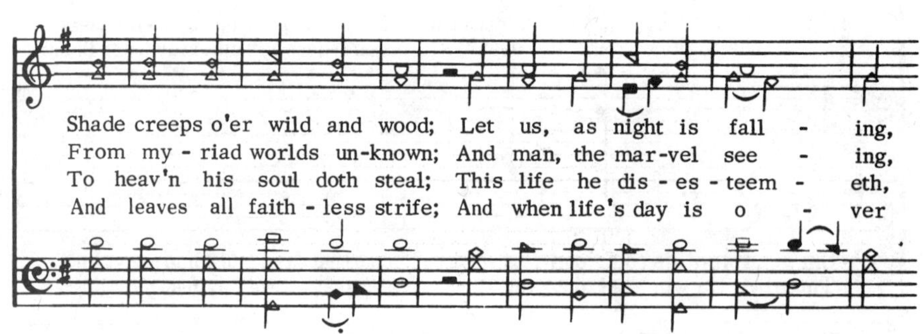
Shade creeps o'er wild and wood; Let us, as night is fall - ing,
From my - riad worlds un-known; And man, the mar-vel see - ing,
To heav'n his soul doth steal; This life he dis - es - teem - eth,
And leaves all faith - less strife; And when life's day is o - ver

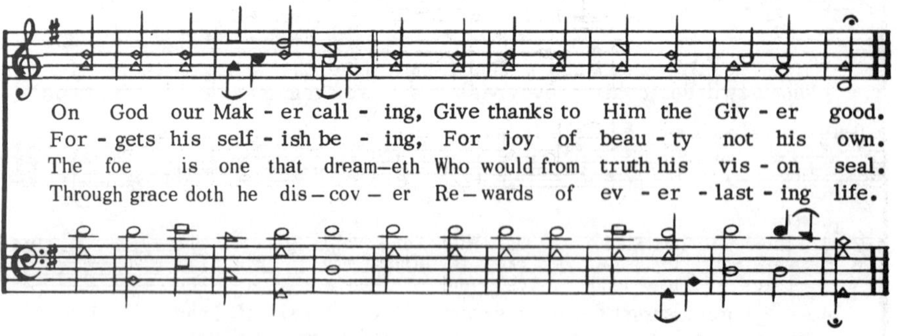
On God our Mak - er call - ing, Give thanks to Him the Giv - er good.
For - gets his self - ish be - ing, For joy of beau - ty not his own.
The foe is one that dream–eth Who would from truth his vis - on seal.
Through grace doth he dis – cov – er Re – wards of ev - er - last - ing life.

# FATHER, IN HIGH HEAVEN DWELLING 84

*I dwell in the high and holy place.* Is. 57:15.

George Rawson, 1807-1889
Altered by Compiler, 1969

EVENING HYMN 8.8.7.D.
M.M. 72

W. Jackson
Arr. John J. Overholt, 1970

1. Fa - ther, in high heav - en dwell - ing, May our ev - 'ning hymn be tell - ing Of Thy mer - cy large and free: Through the day Thy love has fed us, Thro' the day Thy care has led us, With di - vi - nest char - i - ty.

2. This day's sins, oh par - don, Sav - iour, E - vil thoughts per - verse be - hav - iour, En - vy, pride and van - i - ty: From the world, the flesh, de - liv - er-- Save us now, and save us ev - er, O Thou Lamb of Cal - va - ry.

3. From en - tice-ments of the dev - il, From the might of spir - its e - vil, Be our shield and pan - o - ply: Let Thy pow'r this night de - fend us, And a heav'n - ly peace at - tend us, And an - gel - ic com - pa - ny.

4. Whilst the night-dews are dis - till - ing, Ho - ly One, each heart be fill - ing With Thine own se - ren - i - ty: Soft - ly let the eyes be clos - ing, Lov - ing souls on Thee re - pos - ing, Ev - er bless - ed Trin - i - ty.

# 85 FATHER MOST HOLY

*Holy, holy, holy, Lord God Almighty, which was, and is, and is to come.* Rev. 4:8.

Latin Hymn c. 10th Century
*O Pater, Sancte, mitis atque pie*
Tr. Percy Dearmer, 1867-1936

CHRISTE SANCTORUM 11.11.11.5.
M.M. 60

18th Century French Church Melody
Har. Ralph Vaughan Williams 1872-1958
Arr. John J. Overholt, 1968

1. Fa - ther most ho - ly, mer - ci - ful and ten - der, Je - sus our
2. Trin - i - ty sa - cred, Un - i - ty un - shak - en; De - i - ty
3. Mak - er of all things, all thy crea - tures praise thee; Lo, all things
4. To the all rul - ing tri - une God be glo - ry; High-est and

Sav - iour, with the Fa - ther reign - ing; Spir - it all kind - ly,
per - fect, giv - ing and for - giv - ing, Light of the an - gels,
serve thee through thy whole cre - a - tion; Hear us, Al - might - y,
great - est, help thou our en - deav - er, We too would praise thee,

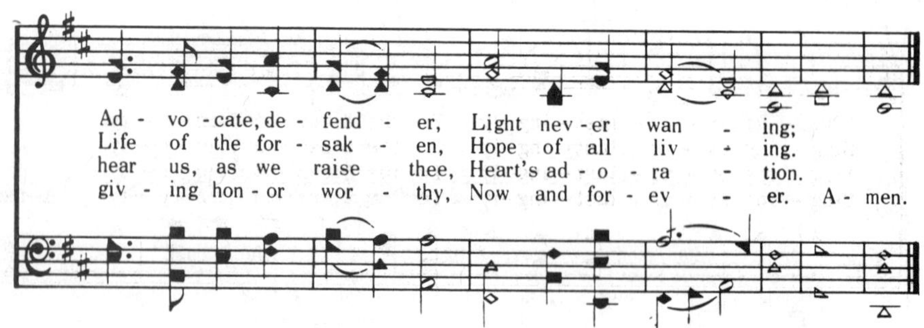
Ad - vo - cate, de - fend - er, Light nev - er wan - ing;
Life of the for - sak - en, Hope of all liv - ing.
hear us, as we raise thee, Heart's ad - o - ra - tion.
giv - ing hon - or wor - thy, Now and for - ev - er. A - men.

# HOLY, HOLY, HOLY, LORD GOD OF HOSTS 86

*Holy, holy, holy, is the Lord of hosts: the whole earth is full of His glory.* Is. 6:3.

TOPLADY 7.7.7.7.7.7.
M.M. 76

Christopher Wordsworth, 1862 (1807-1885) — Thomas Hastings, 1830 (1784-1872)

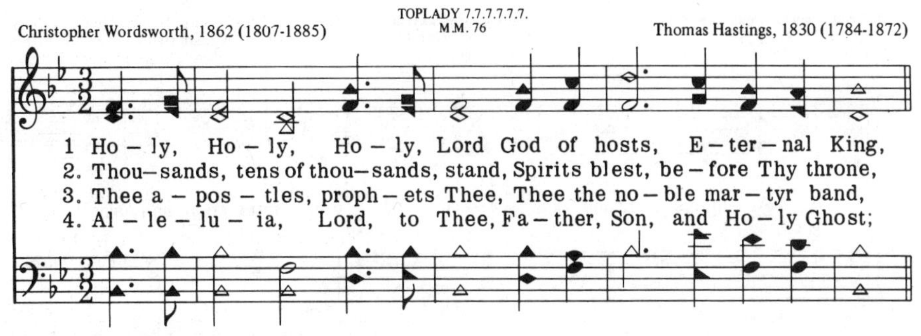
1 Ho – ly, Ho – ly, Ho – ly, Lord God of hosts, E – ter – nal King,
2. Thou – sands, tens of thou – sands, stand, Spirits blest, be – fore Thy throne,
3. Thee a – pos – tles, proph – ets Thee, Thee the no – ble mar – tyr band,
4. Al – le – lu – ia, Lord, to Thee, Fa – ther, Son, and Ho – ly Ghost;

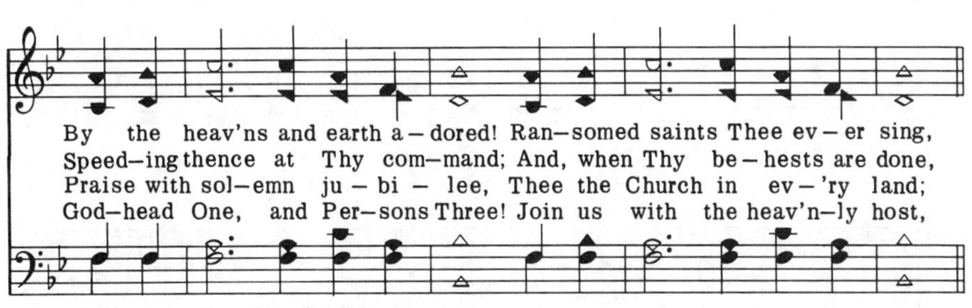
By the heav'ns and earth a – dored! Ran – somed saints Thee ev – er sing,
Speed – ing thence at Thy com – mand; And, when Thy be – hests are done,
Praise with sol – emn ju – bi – lee, Thee the Church in ev – 'ry land;
God – head One, and Per – sons Three! Join us with the heav'n – ly host,

Chant – ing ev – er – last – ing – ly To the bless – ed Trin – i – ty.
Sing – ing ev – er – last – ing – ly To the bless – ed Trin – i – ty.
Sing – ing ev – er – last – ing – ly To the bless – ed Trin – i – ty.
Sing – ing ev – er – last – ing – ly To the bless – ed Trin – i – ty. A – men.

# 87 ALL THINGS BRIGHT AND BEAUTIFUL

*In the beginning God created the heaven and the earth.* Gen. 1:1.

Cecil Frances Alexander, 1848 (1818-1895)

ALL THINGS BRIGHT AND BEAUTIFUL 7.6.7.6.D.
M.M. 78

William Henry Monk, 1823-1889

*Verse 1 and Refrain*

All things bright and beau - ti - ful, All crea - tures great and small,
All things wise and won - der - ful, The Lord God made them all.

2. Each lit - tle flower that o - pens, Each lit - tle bird that sings,
He made their glow-ing co - lours, He made their ti - ny wings:

3. The pur - ple head - ed moun - tain, The riv - er run - ning by,
The sun - set, and the morn - ing That bright - ens up the sky:

4. The cold wind in the win - ter, The pleas-ant sum - mer sun,
The ripe fruits in the gar - den, He made them ev - ery one:

5. He gave us eyes to see them, And lips that we might tell
How great is God Al - might - y Who has made all things well:

# HEAVEN AND EARTH, THE SEA AND AIR 88

*The Lord made heaven and earth, the sea, and all that in them is.* Ex. 20:11.

Joachim Neander, 1650-1680
*Himmel, Erde, Luft, und Meer*
Tr. Catherine Winkworth, 1858 (1827-1878)
and Frances Elizabeth Cox, 1841 (1812-1897)

GOTT SEI DANK 7.7.7.7.
M.M. 96

J. A. Freylinghausen's *Neues Geistreiches Gesangbuch*, 1704

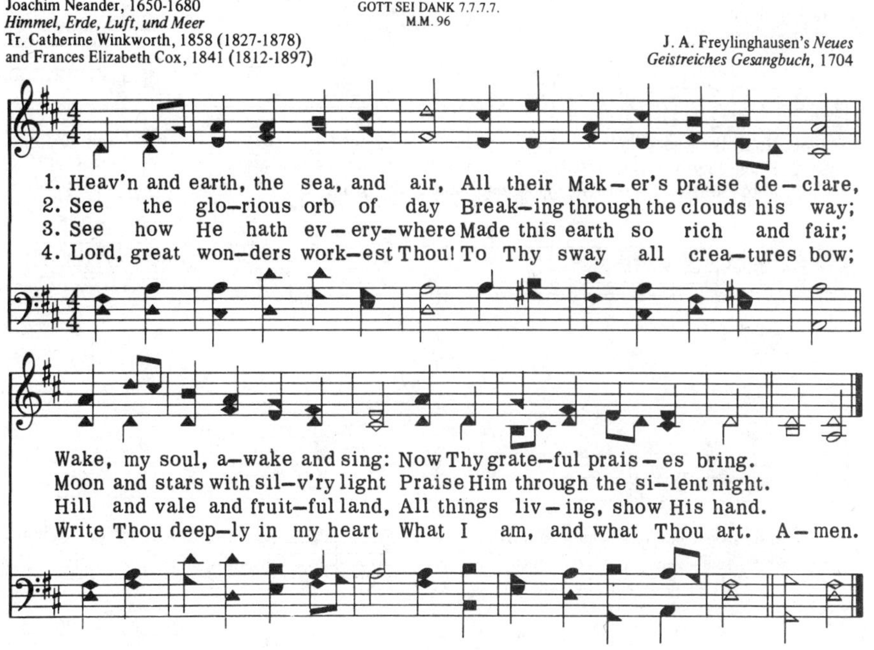
1. Heav'n and earth, the sea, and air, All their Mak-er's praise de-clare,
2. See the glo-rious orb of day Break-ing through the clouds his way;
3. See how He hath ev-ery-where Made this earth so rich and fair;
4. Lord, great won-ders work-est Thou! To Thy sway all crea-tures bow;
Wake, my soul, a-wake and sing: Now Thy grate-ful prais-es bring.
Moon and stars with sil-v'ry light Praise Him through the si-lent night.
Hill and vale and fruit-ful land, All things liv-ing, show His hand.
Write Thou deep-ly in my heart What I am, and what Thou art. A-men.

# O LORD, OUR LORD, IN ALL THE EARTH 89

*O Lord our Lord, how excellent is Thy name in all the earth!* Ps. 8:1.

Based on Psalm 8
*Psalter*, 1912

DUNFERMLINE C.M. 8.6.8.6.
M.M. 84

*Scottish Psalter*, 1615

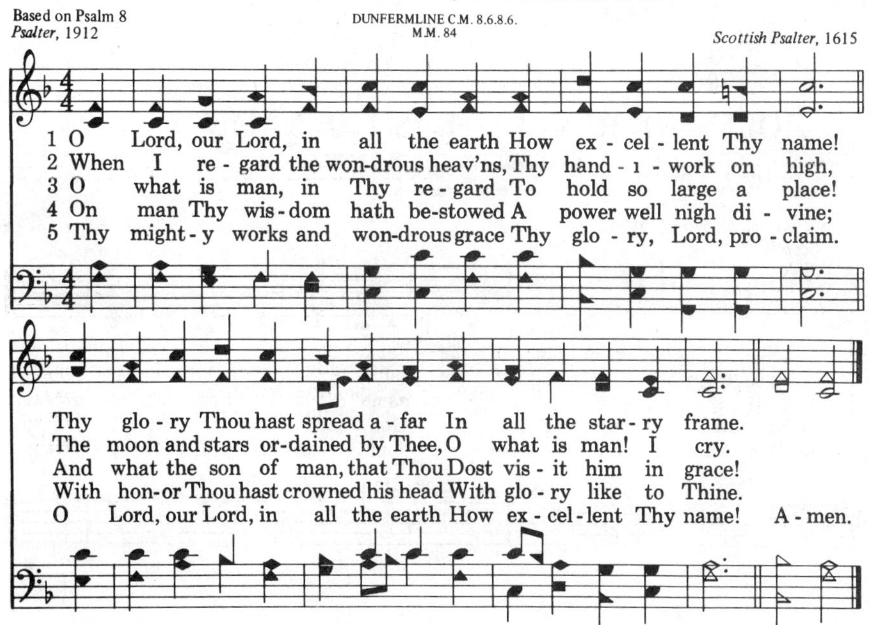
1 O Lord, our Lord, in all the earth How ex-cel-lent Thy name!
2 When I re-gard the won-drous heav'ns, Thy hand-i-work on high,
3 O what is man, in Thy re-gard To hold so large a place!
4 On man Thy wis-dom hath be-stowed A power well nigh di-vine;
5 Thy might-y works and won-drous grace Thy glo-ry, Lord, pro-claim.
Thy glo-ry Thou hast spread a-far In all the star-ry frame.
The moon and stars or-dained by Thee, O what is man! I cry.
And what the son of man, that Thou Dost vis-it him in grace!
With hon-or Thou hast crowned his head With glo-ry like to Thine.
O Lord, our Lord, in all the earth How ex-cel-lent Thy name! A-men.

# 90 HOLY AS THOU, O LORD, IS NONE

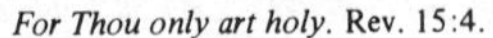

*For Thou only art holy.* Rev. 15:4.

Charles Wesley, 1707-1788
Altered by Compiler, 1969

GERICHT L.M. 8.8.8.8.
M.M. 60

John J. Overholt, 1965

1. Ho – ly as Thou, O Lord, is none; Thy ho – li – ness is all Thine own;
2. When Thy own pu – ri – ty we share, Thine on – ly glo – ry we de–clare;
3. Sole, self – ex – ist–ing God and Lord, By all Thy heav'n–ly host a – dored,

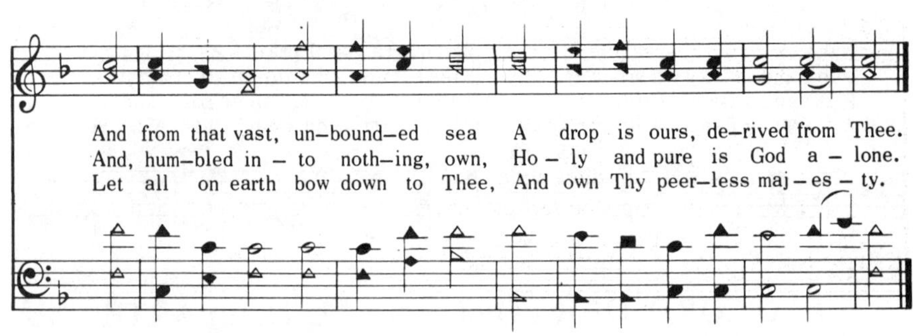
And from that vast, un–bound–ed sea A drop is ours, de–rived from Thee.
And, hum–bled in – to noth–ing, own, Ho – ly and pure is God a – lone.
Let all on earth bow down to Thee, And own Thy peer–less maj – es – ty.

# 91 HOLY AND REVEREND IS THE NAME

*Holy and reverend is His name.* Ps. 111:9.

John Needham, 1710-1787
Isaac Watts, 1674-1748
Composite, arr. John J. Overholt, 1970

DUNDEE C.M. 8.6.8.6.
M.M. 58

*Scottish Psalter*, 1615

Slowly.
1. Ho – ly and rev–erend is the name Of our e – ter – nal King;
2. The deep–est rev–erence of the mind Pay, O my soul, to God!
3. With sa – cred awe pro–nounce His name Whom words nor thoughts can reach
4. Ex – alt the Lord, our ho – ly God, And wor–ship at His feet;
5. Thou ho – ly God, pre – serve my soul From all pol – lu – tion free;

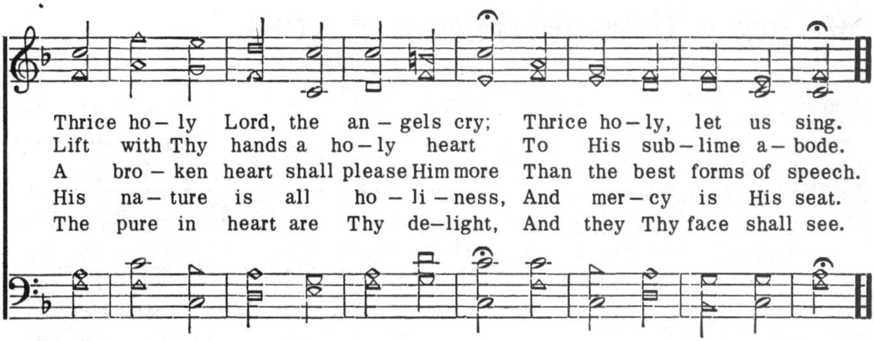

Thrice ho– ly Lord, the an – gels cry; Thrice ho – ly, let us sing.
Lift with Thy hands a ho – ly heart To His sub – lime a – bode.
A bro – ken heart shall please Him more Than the best forms of speech.
His na – ture is all ho – li – ness, And mer – cy is His seat.
The pure in heart are Thy de–light, And they Thy face shall see.

# GOD THE LORD IS KING 92

*I the Lord your God am holy.* Lev. 19:2.

George Rawson, 1807-1889

ST. THOMAS (Holywood) 8.7.8.7.4.4.7.
M.M. 92

John Francis Wade, 1711-1786

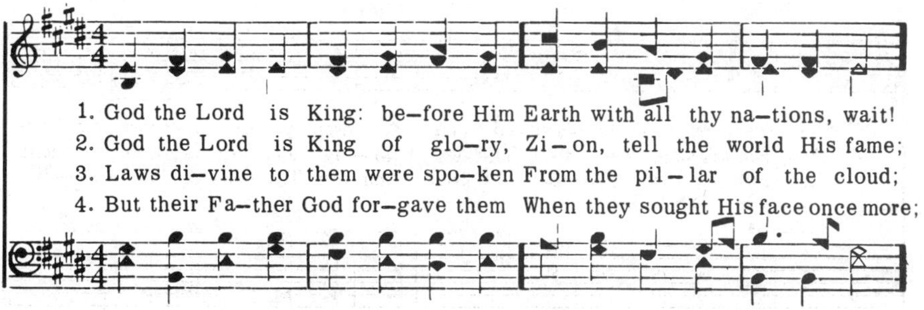

1. God the Lord is King: be–fore Him Earth with all thy na–tions, wait!
2. God the Lord is King of glo–ry, Zi – on, tell the world His fame;
3. Laws di–vine to them were spo–ken From the pil – lar of the cloud;
4. But their Fa–ther God for–gave them When they sought His face once more;

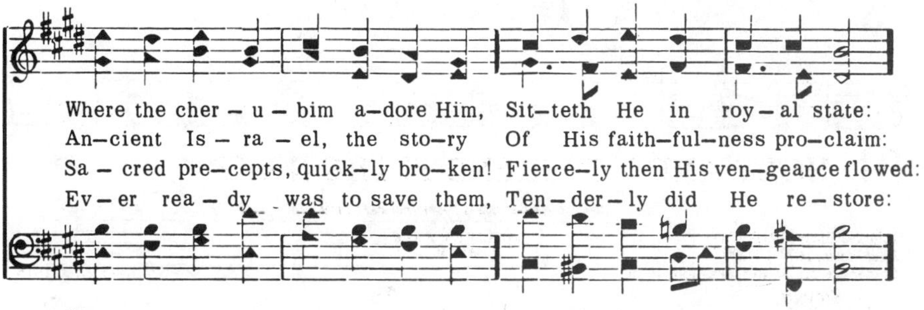

Where the cher – u – bim a–dore Him, Sit–teth He in roy – al state:
An–cient Is – ra – el, the sto–ry Of His faith–ful–ness pro–claim:
Sa – cred pre–cepts, quick–ly bro–ken! Fierce–ly then His ven–geance flowed:
Ev – er rea – dy was to save them, Ten – der – ly did He re – store:

He is ho – ly; He is ho – ly; Bless–ed, on – ly Po–ten–tate!
He is ho – ly; He is ho – ly; Ho – ly is His awe–ful name.
He is ho – ly; He is ho – ly; To the dust their hearts were bowed.
He is ho – ly; He is ho – ly; We too will His grace im–plore.

# 93 FOR GOD SO LOVED US

*For God so loved the world, that He gave His only begotten Son.* Jn. 3:16.

August Rische, 1819-1906
*Gott ist die Liebe*
Composite paraphrase, Sts. 1-3, *Youth Hymnary*
St. 4 and refrain, *The Hymnbook*

GOTT IST DIE LIEBE 10.9. with Ref.
M.M. 56

Thüringer Melody, c. 1840

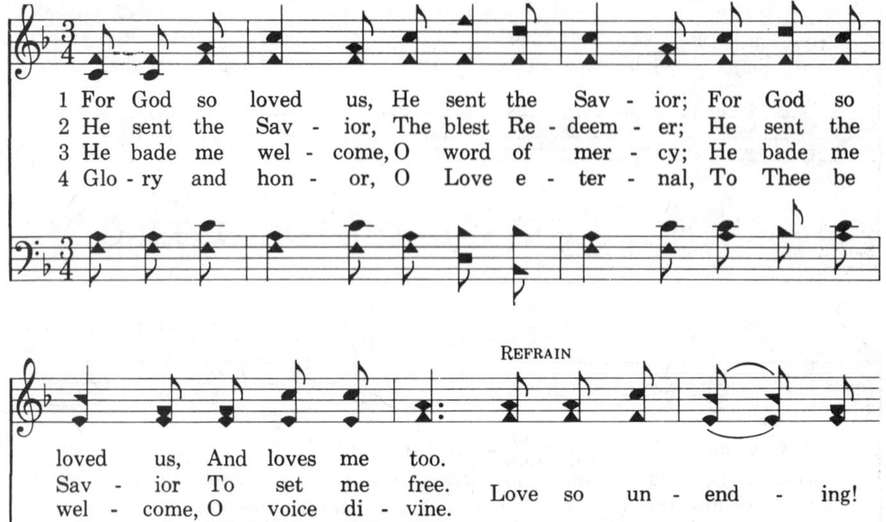
1 For God so loved us, He sent the Sav - ior; For God so
2 He sent the Sav - ior, The blest Re - deem - er; He sent the
3 He bade me wel - come, O word of mer - cy; He bade me
4 Glo - ry and hon - or, O Love e - ter - nal, To Thee be
REFRAIN
loved us, And loves me too.
Sav - ior To set me free.
wel - come, O voice di - vine.
giv - en While life shall last.
Love so un - end - ing!

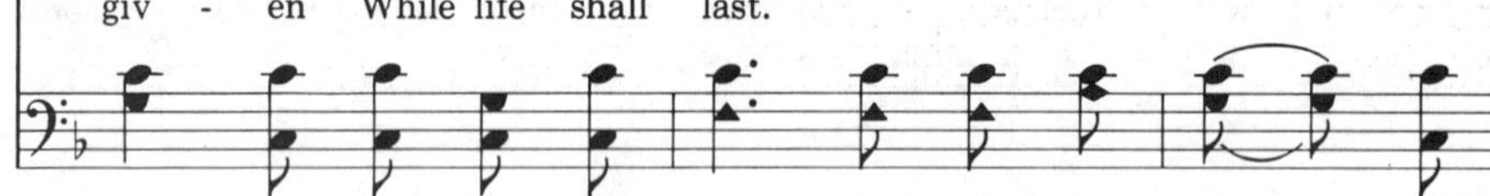

I'll sing Thy prais - es, God loves His chil - dren, Loves e - ven me.

1 Gott ist die Liebe, lässt mich erlösen;
Gott ist die Liebe, er liebt auch mich.

2 Ich lag in Banden der schnöden Sünde;
ich lag in Banden und konnt nicht los.

3 Er sandte Jesum, den treuen Heiland;
er sandte Jesum und macht mich los.

4 Jesus, mein Heiland, gab sich zum Opfer;
Jesus, mein Heiland, büsst meine Schuld.

REFRAIN Drum sag ich noch einmal:
Gott ist die Liebe,
Gott ist die Liebe,
er liebt auch mich.

# I SING THE PRAISE OF LOVE UNBOUNDED 94

*Hereby perceive we the love of God, because He laid down His life for us.* I Jn. 3:16.

Gerhard Tersteegen, 1757 (1697-1769)
*Ich bete an die Macht der Liebe*
Tr. R. A. John, 1912

ST. PETERSBURG 9.8.9.8.9.9.
M.M. 84

Dimitri S. Bortniansky, 1825 (1751-1825)

*In moderate time*

1. I sing the praise of love un - bound - ed, Which God in Christ has shown to man; I sing of love that hath been found - ed Ere yet the stars their cours - es ran; The love that of - fers free sal - va - tion To sin - ful man of ev - ery na - tion.
2. The love of God planned my sal - va - tion Be - fore I saw the light of day, And took a - way the law's dam - na - tion Of him whose feet had gone a - stray; God's love is mine, O bless-ed mor - tal! It o - pens wide the heaven - ly por - tal.
3. While life shall last, I'll sing the glo - ry Of Christ the Sav - iour and His love; With an - gel hosts I'll tell the sto - ry Of Christ, in Zi - on's home a - bove; God's love is mine, death can - not sev - er Me from that heart that loves for - ev - er. A - men.

# 95 O GOD OF WONDROUS GRACE

*God is able to make all grace abound toward you.* II Cor. 9:8.

Luther D. Reed, 1873-
Edwin H. Nevin, 1814-
Composite, arr. John J. Overholt, 1965

WIE GROSS IST DES ALMĂCHTIGEN GŬTE
9.8.9.8.9.8.
M.M. 76

Johann A. Freylingshausen, 1670-1739

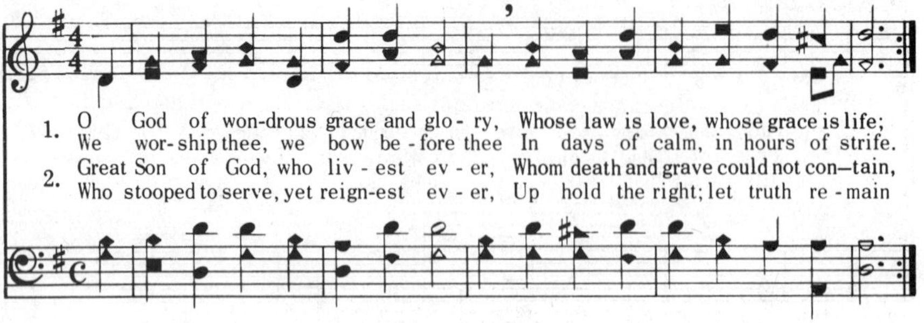

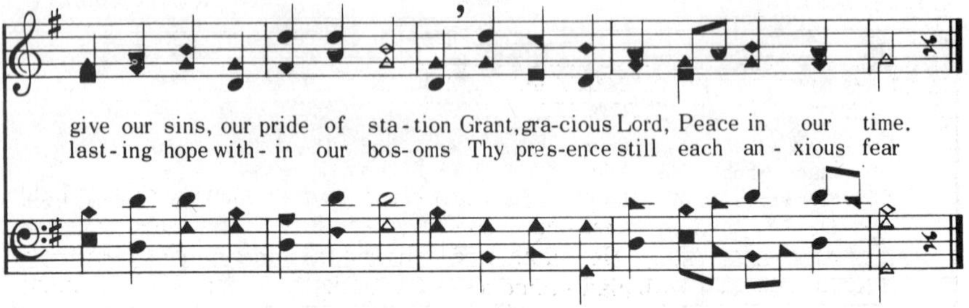

1. O God of won-drous grace and glo-ry, Whose law is love, whose grace is life;
We wor-ship thee, we bow be-fore thee In days of calm, in hours of strife.
In thee, we trust, bless thou our na-tion; Our times are in thy power-ful hand. For-
give our sins, our pride of sta-tion Grant, gra-cious Lord, Peace in our time.

2. Great Son of God, who liv-est ev-er, Whom death and grave could not con-tain,
Who stooped to serve, yet reign-est ev-er, Up hold the right; let truth re-main
Be with us when the storm is sweep-ing o-ver our path-way dark and drear. Wake
last-ing hope with-in our bos-oms Thy pres-ence still each an-xious fear

3. Creator, Who art true, and mighty,
Whose breath revives the souls of men;
Cleanse thou our hearts, inspire us rightly
To live and learn and love again.
Be with us in the darksome valley,
When we shall cross death's chilling stream;
Wilt thou light up the steps to glory
With thy sweet presence' radiant beam.

4. O God, whose grace and power supernal
Endure though time itself decay;
Our strength renew, with life eternal
Crown all who seek and find the way.
May grace divine in constant favor
Through Jesus' blood and righteousness
Endue to sacrificial labor
Our lives in servant faithfulness.

## WHEN ALL THY MERCIES, O MY GOD 96

*His mercy endureth forever.* Ps. 118:1.

ST. PETER C.M. 8.6.8.6.
M.M. 69

Joseph Addison, 1712 (1672-1719) Alexander Robert Reinagle, 1836 (1799-1877)

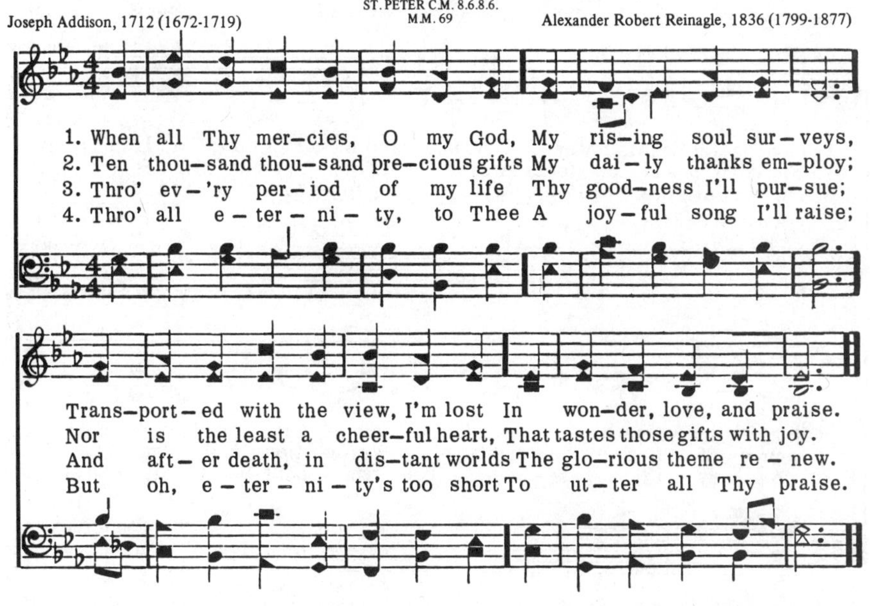
1. When all Thy mer–cies, O my God, My ris–ing soul sur–veys,
2. Ten thou–sand thou–sand pre–cious gifts My dai–ly thanks em–ploy;
3. Thro' ev–'ry per–iod of my life Thy good–ness I'll pur–sue;
4. Thro' all e–ter–ni–ty, to Thee A joy–ful song I'll raise;
Trans–port–ed with the view, I'm lost In won–der, love, and praise.
Nor is the least a cheer–ful heart, That tastes those gifts with joy.
And aft–er death, in dis–tant worlds The glo–rious theme re–new.
But oh, e–ter–ni–ty's too short To ut–ter all Thy praise.

## LET US WITH A GLADSOME MIND 97

*I will be glad and rejoice in Thee: I will sing praise to Thy name.* Ps. 9:2.

INNOCENTS 7.7.7.7.
M.M. 80

John Milton, 1608-1674 *From a Parish Hymnal,* 1850

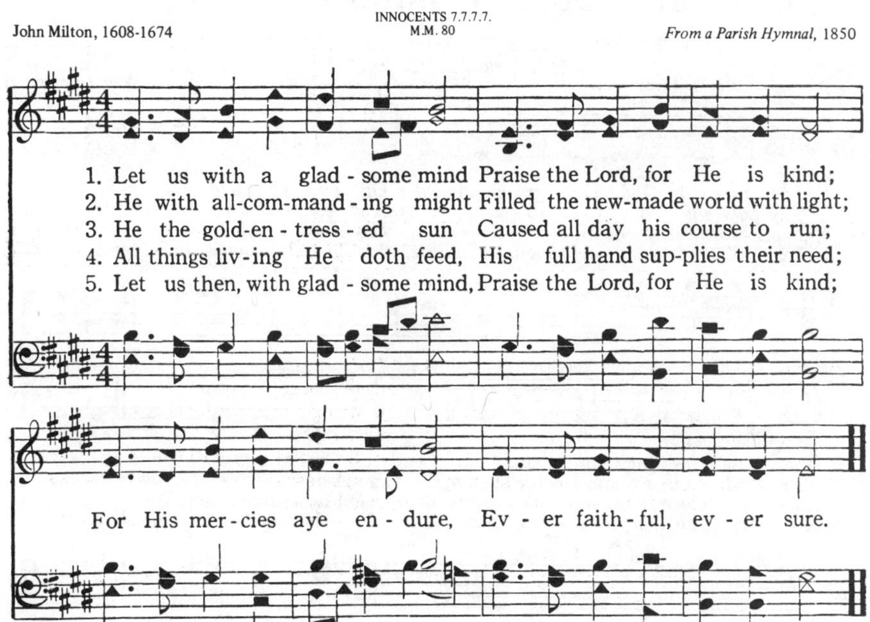
1. Let us with a glad-some mind Praise the Lord, for He is kind;
2. He with all-com-mand-ing might Filled the new-made world with light;
3. He the gold-en-tress-ed sun Caused all day his course to run;
4. All things liv-ing He doth feed, His full hand sup-plies their need;
5. Let us then, with glad-some mind, Praise the Lord, for He is kind;
For His mer-cies aye en-dure, Ev-er faith-ful, ev-er sure.

# 98 GOD IS THE FOUNTAIN WHENCE

*The eternal God is thy refuge, and underneath are the everlasting arms.* Deut. 33:27.

Benjamin Beddome, 1717-1795 — GERAR S.M. 6.6.8.6. M.M. 72 — Lowell Mason, 1792-1872

1. God is the fountain whence Ten thou - sand bless-ings flow; To Him my
2. The com-forts He af - fords Are nei - ther few nor small; He is the
3. He fills my heart with joy, My lips at - tunes for praise; And to His
life, my health, and friends, And ev - 'ry good I owe.
source of fresh de - lights, My por - tion and my all.
glo - ry I'll de - vote The rem - nant of my days.

# 99 JEHOVAH, GOD, THY GRACIOUS POWER

*Thou openest Thine hand, and satisfiest the desire of every living thing.* Ps. 145:16.

John Thomson, 1810 (1783-1818) — TEMPLE C.M. 8.6.8.6. M.M. 80 — Maro L. Bartlett

1. Je - ho - vah, God, Thy gra-cious pow'r On ev - 'ry hand we see; O
2. Thy pow'r is in the o - cean deeps, And reach-es to the skies; Thine
3. From morn till noon, till la - test eve, Thy hand, O God, we see; And
4. In all the vary - ing scenes of time, On Thee our hopes de - pend, Thro'
may the bless-ings of each hour Lead all our tho'ts to Thee.
eye of mer - cy nev - er sleeps; Thy good-ness nev - er dies.
all the bless-ings we re - ceive, Pro - ceed a - lone from Thee.
ev - 'ry age, in ev - 'ry clime, Our Fa - ther, and our Friend. A - MEN.

# GREAT IS THY FAITHFULNESS 100

*Great is Thy faithfulness.* Lam. 3:23.
GREAT IS THY FAITHFULNESS 11.10.11.10. with Ref.
M.M. 84
Thomas O. Chisholm, 1866-1960
William M. Runyan, 1870-1957
1. "Great is Thy faith-ful-ness," O God my Fa-ther, There is no shad-ow of
2. Sum-mer and win-ter, and spring-time and harvest, Sun, moon and stars in their
3. Par-don for sin and a peace that en-dur-eth, Thy own dear presence to
turn-ing with Thee; Thou chang-est not, Thy com-pas-sions, they fail not;
cours-es a-bove, Join with all na-ture in man-i-fold wit-ness,
cheer and to guide; Strength for to-day and bright hope for to-mor-row,
As Thou hast been Thou for-ev-er wilt be.
To Thy great faith-ful-ness, mer-cy and love.
Blessings all mine, with ten thou-sand be-side!
CHORUS
"Great is Thy faith-ful-ness!
Great is Thy faithfulness!" Morning by morning new mercies I see; All I have
rall.
need-ed Thy hand hath provided—"Great is Thy faithfulness," Lord, un-to me!

# 101 GUIDE ME, O THOU GREAT JEHOVAH

*Thou hast guided them in Thy strength unto Thy holy habitation.* Ex. 15:13.

ZION 8.7.8.7.4.7.4.7.
M.M. 76

William Williams, 1717-1791 — Thomas Hastings, 1784-1872

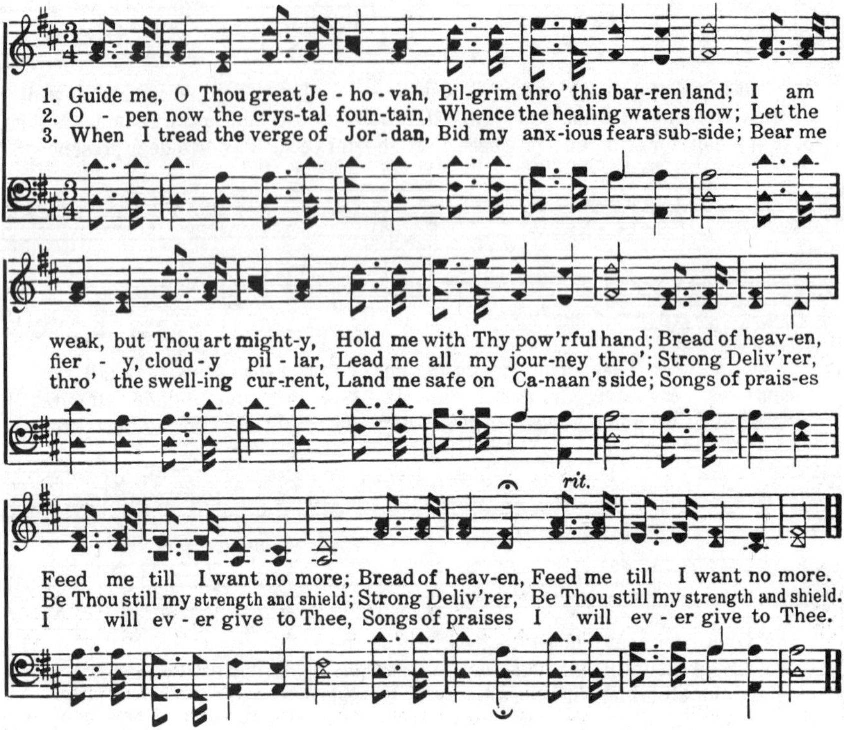

1. Guide me, O Thou great Je - ho - vah, Pil-grim thro' this bar-ren land; I am
weak, but Thou art might-y, Hold me with Thy pow'rful hand; Bread of heav-en,
Feed me till I want no more; Bread of heav-en, Feed me till I want no more.

2. O - pen now the crys-tal foun-tain, Whence the healing waters flow; Let the
fier - y, cloud - y pil - lar, Lead me all my jour-ney thro'; Strong Deliv'rer,
Be Thou still my strength and shield; Strong Deliv'rer, Be Thou still my strength and shield.

3. When I tread the verge of Jor - dan, Bid my anx-ious fears sub-side; Bear me
thro' the swell-ing cur-rent, Land me safe on Ca-naan's side; Songs of prais-es
I will ev - er give to Thee, Songs of praises I will ev - er give to Thee.

rit.

# 102 O GOD OF BETHEL

*Let us arise, and go up to Bethel; and I will make there an altar unto God.* Gen. 35:3.

ST. ANNE C.M. 8.6.8.6.
M.M. 69

Philip Doddridge, 1702-1751 — William Tansur, 1700-1783

1. O God of Beth-el, by whose hand Thy peo-ple still are fed,
Who thro' this wea-ry pil-grim-age Hast all our fa-thers led.
2. O spread Thy cov'ring wings a-round, Till all our wan-d'rings cease,
And at our Fa-ther's loved a-bode Our souls ar-rive in peace. A-men.

# TAKE THOU MY HAND, O FATHER 103

*Lead me in a plain path.* Ps. 27:11.

Julie Katharina Hausman, 1862 (1825-1901)
*So Nimm den meine Hände*
Tr. Herman Brückner, 1866-1942

SO NIMM DENN MEINE HÄNDE
7.4.7.4.D.
M.M. 92

Friedrich Silcher, 1842 (1789-1862)

1 Take Thou my hand, O Fa - ther, And lead Thou me, Un - til my
2 O cov - er with Thy mer - cy My poor, weak heart! Let ev - ery
3 Though naught of Thy great pow - er May move my soul, With Thee through
jour - ney end - eth, E - ter - nal - ly. A - lone I will not wan - der
thought re - bel - lious From me de - part. Per - mit Thy child to lin - ger
night and dark - ness I reach the goal. Take, then, my hands, O Fa - ther,
One sin - gle day; Be Thou my true com-pan - ion And with me stay.
Here at Thy feet, And blind-ly trust Thy good - ness With faith com-plete.
And lead Thou me Un - til my jour-ney end - eth E - ter - nal - ly. A-men.

1 So nimm denn meine Hände
 und führe mich
bis an mein selig Ende
 und ewiglich!
Ich kann allein nicht gehen,
 nicht einen Schritt;
wo du wirst gehn und stehen,
 da nimm mich mit.

2 In deine Gnade hülle
 mein schwaches Herz,
und mach es endlich stille
 in Freud und Schmerz.
Lass ruhn zu deinen Füssen
 dein schwaches Kind;
es will die Augen schliessen
 und folgen blind.

3 Wenn ich auch gar nichts fühle
 von deiner Macht,
du bringst mich doch zum Ziele
 auch durch die Nacht.
So nimm denn meine Hände
 und führe mich
bis an mein selig Ende
 und ewiglich!

# 104 IF THOU BUT SUFFER GOD TO GUIDE THEE

*I will guide thee with Mine eye.* Ps. 32:8.

George Neumark, 1641 (1621-1681)
*Wer nur den lieben Gott lasst walten*
Tr. Catherine Winkworth, 1863 (1827-1878)

WER NUR DEN LIEBEN GOTT LÄSST WALTEN
9.8.9.8.8.8.
M.M. 80

George Neumark, 1641

1 If thou but suffer God to guide thee, And hope in Him through all thy ways, He'll give thee strength whate'er betide thee, And bear thee through the evil days. Who trusts in God's unchanging love Builds on a rock that nought can move.

2 Only be still and wait His leisure In cheerful hope, with heart content To take whate'er thy Father's pleasure And all-deserving love hath sent, Nor doubt our inmost wants are known To Him who chose us for His own.

3 He knows the time for joy, and truly Will send it when He sees it meet, When He has tried and purged thee throughly And finds thee free from all deceit, He comes to thee all unaware And makes thee own His loving care.

4 Sing, pray, and keep His ways unswerving, So do thine own part faithfully, And trust His Word, though undiscerning Thou yet shall find it true for thee; God never yet forsook at need The soul that trusted Him indeed. Amen.

# ETERNAL FATHER 105

*I dwell in the high and holy place.* Is. 57:15.

Harvey D. Ganse, 1872 (1822-1891)

WAREHAM L.M. 8.8.8.8.
M.M. 88

William Knapp, 1738 (1698-1768)

1. E - ter - nal Fa - ther, when to Thee, Be - yond all
2. But, Sav - iour, Thou art by my side; Thy voice I
3. And Thou, great Spir - it, in my heart Dost make Thy
4. Blest Trin - i - ty, in whom a - lone All things cre-

worlds, by faith I soar, Be - fore Thy bound - less
hear, Thy face I see: Thou art my Friend, my
tem - ple day by day; The Ho - ly Ghost of
a - - ted move or rest, High in the heav'ns Thou

maj - es - ty I stand in si - lence, and a - dore.
dai - ly Guide; God o - ver all, yet God with me.
God Thou art, Yet dwell - est in this house of clay.
hast Thy throne; Thou hast Thy throne with - in my breast.

# 106 LORD, THOU HAST SEARCHED

*O Lord, Thou hast searched me, and known me.* Ps. 139:1.

BERA L.M. 8.8.8.8.
M.M. 92

Isaac Watts, 1719 (1674-1748)

John E. Gould, 1849 (1822-1875)

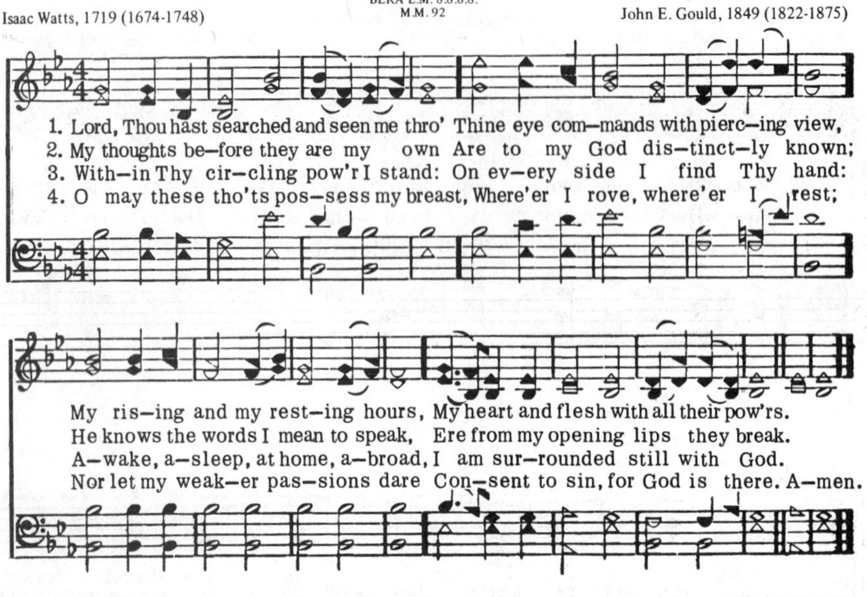
1. Lord, Thou hast searched and seen me thro' Thine eye com–mands with pierc–ing view,
2. My thoughts be–fore they are my own Are to my God dis–tinct–ly known;
3. With–in Thy cir–cling pow'r I stand: On ev–ery side I find Thy hand:
4. O may these tho'ts pos–sess my breast, Where'er I rove, where'er I rest;
My ris–ing and my rest–ing hours, My heart and flesh with all their pow'rs.
He knows the words I mean to speak, Ere from my opening lips they break.
A–wake, a–sleep, at home, a–broad, I am sur–rounded still with God.
Nor let my weak–er pas–sions dare Con–sent to sin, for God is there. A–men.

# 107 I WOULD LOVE THEE

*I will love Thee, O Lord, my strength.* Ps. 18:1.

I WOULD LOVE THEE 8.7.8.7.
M.M. 69

Jeanne Marie Guyon, 1648-1717

From *Hymns and Tunes,* 1890

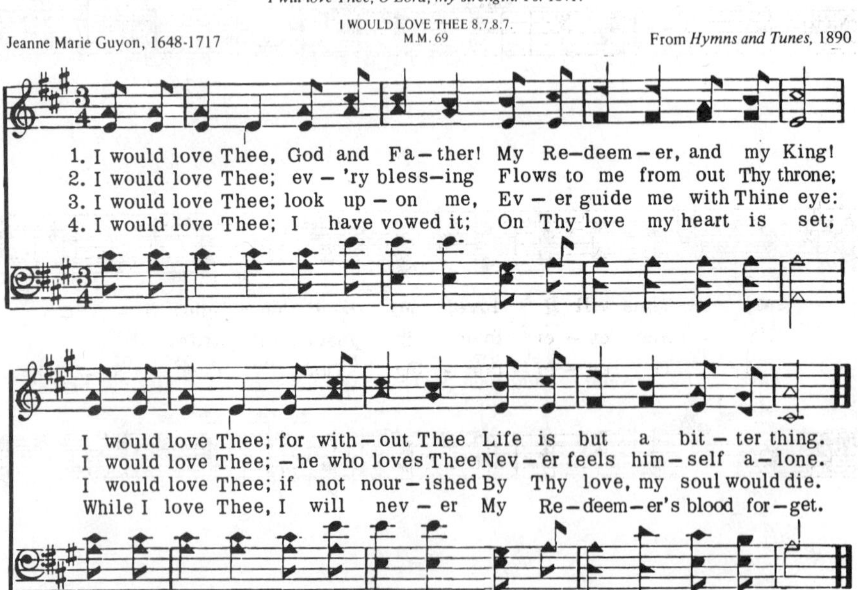
1. I would love Thee, God and Fa–ther! My Re–deem–er, and my King!
2. I would love Thee; ev – 'ry bless–ing Flows to me from out Thy throne;
3. I would love Thee; look up – on me, Ev – er guide me with Thine eye:
4. I would love Thee; I have vowed it; On Thy love my heart is set;
I would love Thee; for with–out Thee Life is but a bit – ter thing.
I would love Thee; – he who loves Thee Nev – er feels him–self a–lone.
I would love Thee; if not nour–ished By Thy love, my soul would die.
While I love Thee, I will nev – er My Re–deem–er's blood for–get.

# THEE WILL I LOVE MY LORD, MY GOD 108

*O love the Lord, all ye His saints.* Ps. 31:23.

SO LANGE JESUS BLEIBT DER HERR
L.M. 8.8.8.8.
M.M. 63

John J. Overholt, 1970

*Choralbuch der Mennoniten Gemeinden Russlands,* Halbstadt, 1914

1. Thee will I love, my Lord, my God, O Thou Cre–a – tor, Light of Light; Be–neath Thy smile or chast–'ning rod, Thee will I love, my soul's de – light!
2. Thee will I love with fil – ial fears, O ev – er–liv – ing Life of Life; Thee will I serve with grate–ful tears, And ev – er love in peace or strife!
3. Thee will I love though worlds de – cay, Though fail my flesh, its powers re – move; Thee will I love in end–less day, O ev – er – last – ing God of love! A – men.

# 109 WAKE, AWAKE, FOR NIGHT IS FLYING

*For unto you is born this day in the city of David a Saviour.* Lk. 2:11.

Philipp Nicolai, 1599 (1556-1608)
*Wachet auf, ruft uns die Stimme*
Tr. Catherine Winkworth, 1858 (1827-1878)
Altered by compiler, 1971

WACHET AUF, RUF UNS DIE STIMME
8.9.8.8.9.8.6.6.4.8.8.
M.M. 96

Philipp Nicolai
Har. Johann Sebastian Bach, 1685-1750

1. Wake, a – wake, for night is fly – ing, The
Mid – night hears the wel – come voic – es, And
watch–men on the heights are cry – ing; A –
at the lov – ing cry re – joic – es; Come
wake, Je – ru – sa – lem, at last! The Bride – groom
forth, ye vir – gins, night is past!
comes, a – wake, Your lamps with glad–ness take; Al –

le – lu – ia! And for His mar – riage feast pre –

pare, For ye must go to meet Him there.

2. Zion hears the watchmen singing,
And all her heart with joy is springing,
She wakes, she rises from her gloom;
For her Lord comes down all–glorious,
The strong in grace, in truth victorious,
Her Star is risen, her Light is come!
Ah come, Thou blessed Lord,
O Jesus, Son of God,
Alleluia!
We follow till the halls we see
Where Thou hast bid us sup with Thee.

3. Now let all the heavens adore Thee,
And men and angels praise before Thee,
With heart and voice in clearest tone;
Of one pearl each shining portal,
Where we are with the host immortal
Of saints around Thy dazzling throne;
Nor eye hath seen, nor ear
Hath yet attained to hear
What there is ours,
But we rejoice, and sing to Thee
Our hymns of joy eternally.

# 110 HAIL THE BLEST MORN

*They saw the young child with Mary His mother, and fell down, and worshipped Him.* Matt. 2:11.

Reginald Heber, 1811 (1783-1826)

ZION'S GLAD MORNING 11.10.11.10.
M.M. 100

Arranged from *Harmonia Sacra*

1. Hail the blest morn when the great Me - di - a - tor Down from the re - gions of glo - ry de - scends; Shep - herds, go wor - ship the Babe in the man - ger; Lo! for His guard the bright an - gels at - tend.
2. Bright-est and best of the sons of the morn - ing, Dawn on our dark - ness, and lend us Thine aid; Star of the East, the ho - ri - zon a - dorn - ing, Guide where our in - fant Re-deem - er is laid.
3. Cold on His cra - dle the dew-drops are shin - ing, Low lies His head with the beasts of the stall; An - gels a - dore Him in slum-ber re - clin - ing, Mak - er, and Mon - arch, and Sav - iour of all.
4. Say, shall we yield Him, in cost - ly de - vo - tion, O - dors of E - dom and of-f'rings di - vine, Gems of the moun - tain and pearls of the o - cean, Myrrh from the for - est, or gold from the mine?
5. Vain - ly we of - fer each am - ple ob - la - tion, Vain - ly with gifts would His fa - vor se - cure; Rich - er by far is the heart's ad - o - ra - tion,—Dear - er to God are the prayers of the poor.

# 111 HOW BRIGHTLY SHINES THE MORNING STAR

*When they saw the star, they rejoiced with exceeding great joy.* Matt. 2:10.

Philipp Nicolai, 1599 (1556-1608)
*Wie schön leuchtet der Morgenstern*
Recast, Johann Adolph Schlegel, 1721-1793
*Wie herrlich strahlt der Morgenstern*
Tr. John Morrison Sloan, 1865

WIE SCHÖN LEUCHTET DER MORGENSTERN
8.8.6.8.8.7.8.8.8.
M.M. 88

Philipp Nicolai

1. How bright - ly shines the morn - ing star, With mer - cy beam-ing
2. Re - joice ye heav'ns; thou earth re - ply; With praise, ye sin - ners,

from a - far, The host of heav'n re - joic - es; O right-eous branch, O
fill the sky, For this His in - car - na - tion. In - car - nate God, put
Jes - se's rod, Thou Son of Man and Son of God, We, too, will lift our
forth Thy power, Ride on, ride on, great con-quer - or, Till all know Thy sal-
voic - es. Je - sus, Je - sus, Ho - ly ho - ly, yet most low - ly,
va - tion. A - men, A - men, Hal - le - lu - jah, hal - le - lu - jah,
Draw Thou near us, Great Im - man - uel, come and hear us.
Praise be giv - en Ev - er - more by earth and heav - en.

# 112 O COME, O COME, EMMANUEL

*Behold, a virgin shall conceive, and bear a son, and shall call His name Immanuel.* Is. 7:14.

Anonymous
*Veni, Veni Emmanuel*
Tr. John Mason Neale, 1851 (1818-1866)
Altered by Compiler, 1970

THE FIRST NOEL IRREGULAR
M.M. 76

English Carol, 1833

Descant

1. O come, O come, Emmanuel, And ransom captive Israel, That mourns in lonely exile here, Until the Son of God appear.
2. O come, Thou Rod of Jesse, free Thine own from Satan's tyranny; From depths of hell Thy people save, And give them victory o'er the grave.
3. O come, Thou Dayspring, come and cheer Our spirits by Thine advent here; Disperse the gloomy clouds of night, And death's dark shadows put to flight.
4. O come, Thou Key of David, come, And open wide our heav'nly home; Make safe the way that leads on high, And close the path to misery.
5. O come, O come, Thou Lord of might, Who to Thy tribes, on Sinai's height, In ancient times didst give the law, In cloud and majesty and awe.

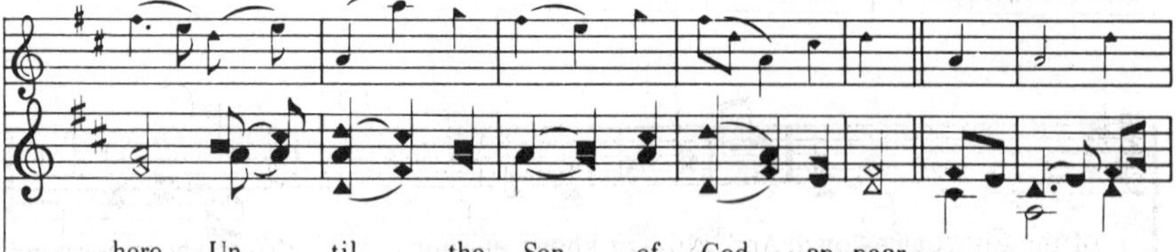

REFRAIN

Rejoice! Re-

joice! Em – man – u – el Is come to Thee, O Is – ra – el!

# WHILE SHEPHERDS WATCHED 113

*Fear not: for, behold, I bring you good tidings of great joy.* Lk. 2:10.

HANDEL C.M. 8.6.8.6.6.
M.M. 84

Nahum Tate, 1762 (1652-1715)

George Friedrich Handel, 1685-1715

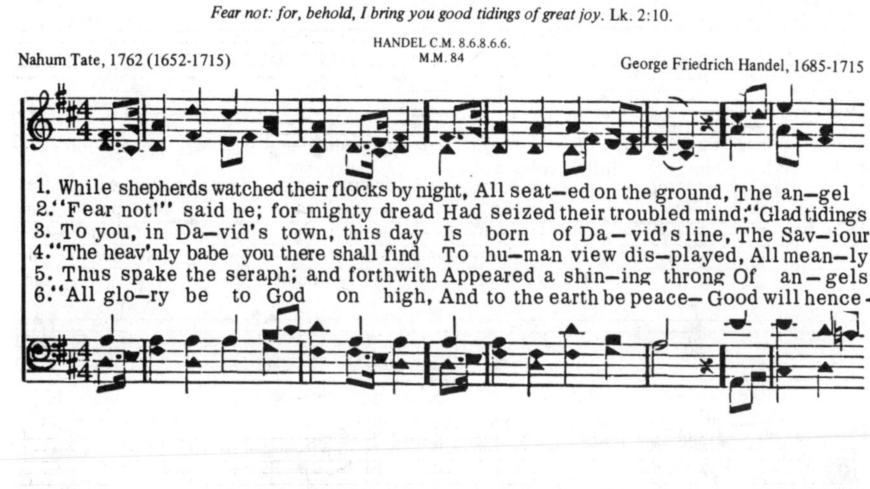
1. While shepherds watched their flocks by night, All seat–ed on the ground, The an–gel
2."Fear not!" said he; for mighty dread Had seized their troubled mind;"Glad tidings
3. To you, in Da–vid's town, this day Is born of Da – vid's line, The Sav–iour
4."The heav'nly babe you there shall find To hu–man view dis–played, All mean–ly
5. Thus spake the seraph; and forthwith Appeared a shin–ing throng Of an – gels
6."All glo–ry be to God on high, And to the earth be peace– Good will hence –

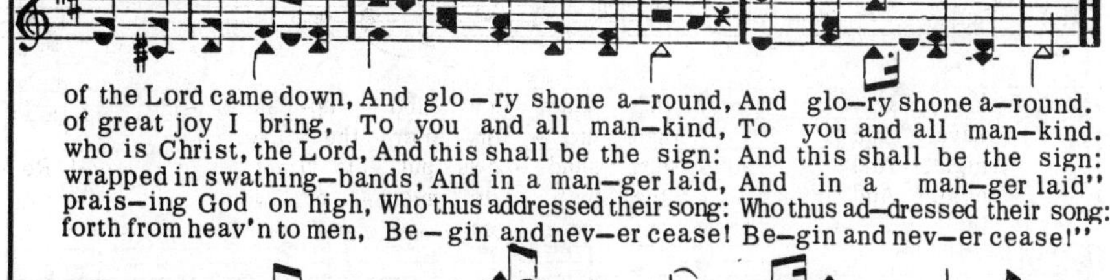
of the Lord came down, And glo – ry shone a–round, And glo–ry shone a–round.
of great joy I bring, To you and all man–kind, To you and all man–kind.
who is Christ, the Lord, And this shall be the sign: And this shall be the sign:
wrapped in swathing–bands, And in a man–ger laid, And in a man–ger laid"
prais–ing God on high, Who thus addressed their song: Who thus ad–dressed their song:
forth from heav'n to men, Be – gin and nev–er cease! Be–gin and nev–er cease!"

# 114 ONCE IN A LONELY MANGER

*And she brought forth her firstborn son, and wrapped Him in swaddling clothes, and laid Him in a manger.* Lk. 2:7.

Anonymous
Arranged by Compiler, 1965

SALVATION 7.6.D. with Ref.
M.M. 116

Anonymous
Har. John J. Overholt, 1965

1. Once in a lone - ly man - ger, hun-dreds of years a - go,
2. Jo - seph and Ma - ry wea - ry, no one would take them in,
3. Far from the east three strang-ers, led by a star their way,
A lit - tle babe so ho - ly came to this world be - low,
Slept in a sta - ble drea - ry, nigh to a crowd - ed inn,
Kept safe - ly from great dang - ers, seek-ing the Christ they say,
Near was a crowd - ed ci - ty, Beth - le - hem dark and old,
Out on the hill - sides fright - ened, shep-herds be - held a sight,
Came to the man - ger low - ly, bring - ing their gifts of love,
Here Jo - seph sought for pi - ty, chill was the night and cold.
For all the sky was bright - ened, on that e - vent - ful night.
Wor-shiped the babe so ho - ly, gift of the world a - bove.
CHORUS
An - gels sang out the sweet sto - ry, fear not, for lo, this morn,
Ref. Glo – ry to God in the high – est! Peace and good–will towards men!

Je - sus the Christ of glo - ry, a lit - tle babe is born.
*Glo – ry to God in the high – est! Ev – er A – men! A – men!*

# SILENT NIGHT 115

*They . . . found Mary, and Joseph, and the babe lying in a manger.* Lk. 2:16.

Joseph Mohr, 1818 (1792-1848)
*Stille Nacht, heilige Nacht*
Tr. John Freeman Young, 1863 (1820-1885)

STILLE NACHT 6.6.8.8.6.6.
M.M. 72

Franz Grüber, 1787-1863

1. Si - lent night! Ho - ly night! All is calm, all is bright,
Round yon vir - gin moth-er and Child; Ho - ly In - fant, so ten - der and mild,
Sleep in heav - en - ly peace, Sleep in heav - en - ly peace.

2. Si - lent night! Ho - ly night! Shep - herds quake at the sight!
Glo - ries stream from heaven a - far, Heav'nly hosts sing al - le - lu - ia.
Christ, the Sav - iour, is born! Christ, the Sav - iour, is born.

3. Si - lent night! Ho - ly night! Son of God, love's pure light
Ra - diant beams from Thy ho - ly face, With the dawn of re - deem - ing grace,
Je - sus, Lord, at Thy birth, Je - sus, Lord, at Thy birth.

# 116 BEHOLD THE GREAT CREATOR

*Glory to God in the highest, and on earth peace, good will toward men.* Lk. 2.14.

Thomas Pestel, 1584-1659
Altered by Compiler, 1970

HANDEL C.M. 8.6.8.6.6.
M.M. 80

George Friedrich Handel, 1685-1759

1. Be–hold, the great Cre–a–tor makes Him–self a house of clay; A robe of hu – man flesh he takes Which he will wear for aye, Which he will wear for aye.
2. Hark, hark, the wise e–ter–nal Word Like a weak in–fant cries! In form of serv–ant is the Lord, And God in cra – dle lies, And God in cra – dl e lies.
3. This won–der struck the world amazed, It shook the star–ry frame; Squad–rons of spir–its stood and gazed, Then down in troops they came, Then down in troops they came.
4. Glad shepherds ran to view this sight; Heav'n's host glad tidings brings, And eastern sag – es with de–light A–dore this King of Kings, A–dore this King of Kings.
5. Join then, all hearts that are not stone, And all our voic–es prove, To cel – e– brate this Ho – ly One, The God of peace and love, The God of peace and love.

# 117 FROM EAST TO WEST

*Mine eyes have seen Thy salvation.* Lk. 2:30.

Caelius Sedulius, c. 450
*A solis ortus cardine*
Tr. John Ellerton, 1826-1893
Altered by Compiler, 1970

DUKE STREET L.M. 8.8.8.8.
M.M. 69

John Hatton, 1793

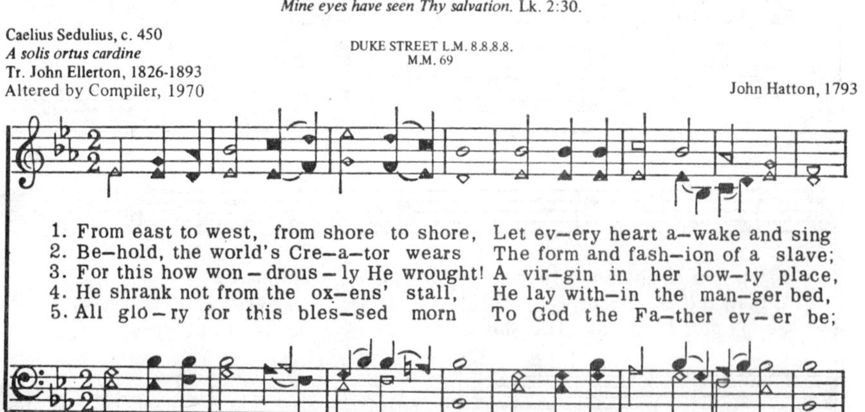
1. From east to west, from shore to shore, Let ev–ery heart a–wake and sing
2. Be–hold, the world's Cre–a–tor wears The form and fash–ion of a slave;
3. For this how won – drous – ly He wrought! A vir–gin in her low–ly place,
4. He shrank not from the ox–ens' stall, He lay with–in the man–ger bed,
5. All glo – ry for this bles–sed morn To God the Fa–ther ev – er be;

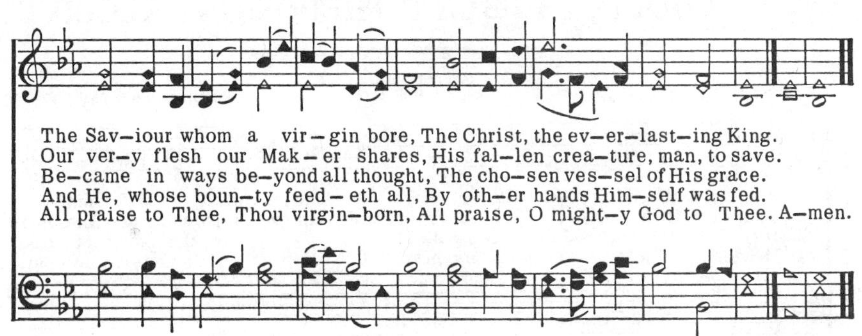
The Sav–iour whom a vir – gin bore, The Christ, the ev–er–last–ing King.
Our ver–y flesh our Mak – er shares, His fal–len crea–ture, man, to save.
Be–came in ways be–yond all thought, The cho–sen ves–sel of His grace.
And He, whose boun–ty feed – eth all, By oth–er hands Him–self was fed.
All praise to Thee, Thou virgin–born, All praise, O might–y God to Thee. A–men.

**JESUS CHRIST:** LIFE, MINISTRY OF

# MY DEAR REDEEMER AND MY LORD 118

*Let this mind be in you, which was also in Christ Jesus.* Phil. 2:5.

MISSIONARY CHANT L.M. 8.8.8.8.
M.M. 63

Isaac Watts, 1709 (1674-1748) Charles Zeuner, 1795-1857)

1. My dear Re - deem - er and my Lord, I read my
2. Such was Thy truth, and such Thy zeal, Such def - 'rence
3. Cold moun - tains and the mid - night air Wit-nessed the
4. Be Thou my pat - tern; make me bear More of Thy

du - ty in Thy Word; But in Thy life the
to Thy Fa - ther's will, Such love, and meek - ness
fer - vor of Thy prayer; The des - ert Thy temp-
gra - cious im - age here: Then God the Judge shall

law ap - pears Re - vealed in liv - ing char - ac - ters.
so di - vine, I would trans - cribe and make them mine.
ta - tions knew, Thy con - flict and Thy vic - t'ry too.
own my name A - mongst the fol - l'wers of the Lamb.

# 119 BEHOLD, THE BLIND THEIR SIGHT RECEIVE

*Jesus . . . went about doing good.* Acts 10:38.

Isaac Watts, 1674-1748

GRACE CHURCH L.M. 8.8.8.8.
M.M. 96

Ignace Joseph Pleyel, 1757-1831

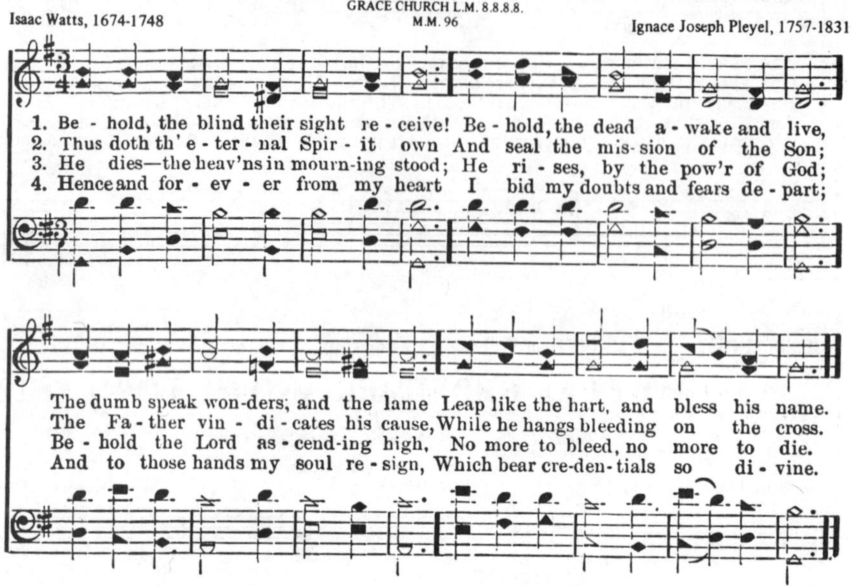
1. Be - hold, the blind their sight re - ceive! Be - hold, the dead a - wake and live,
2. Thus doth th' e - ter - nal Spir - it own And seal the mis - sion of the Son;
3. He dies—the heav'ns in mourn-ing stood; He ri - ses, by the pow'r of God;
4. Hence and for - ev - er from my heart I bid my doubts and fears de - part;
The dumb speak won-ders; and the lame Leap like the hart, and bless his name.
The Fa - ther vin - di - cates his cause, While he hangs bleeding on the cross.
Be - hold the Lord as - cend-ing high, No more to bleed, no more to die.
And to those hands my soul re - sign, Which bear cre-den - tials so di - vine.

# 120 THE SAVIOUR, WHAT A NOBLE FLAME

*He was in the world . . . and the world knew Him not.* Jn. 1:10.

William Cowper, 1731-1800
Altered by Compiler

AVON C.M. 8.6.8.6.
M.M. 92

Hugh Wilson, 1766-1824

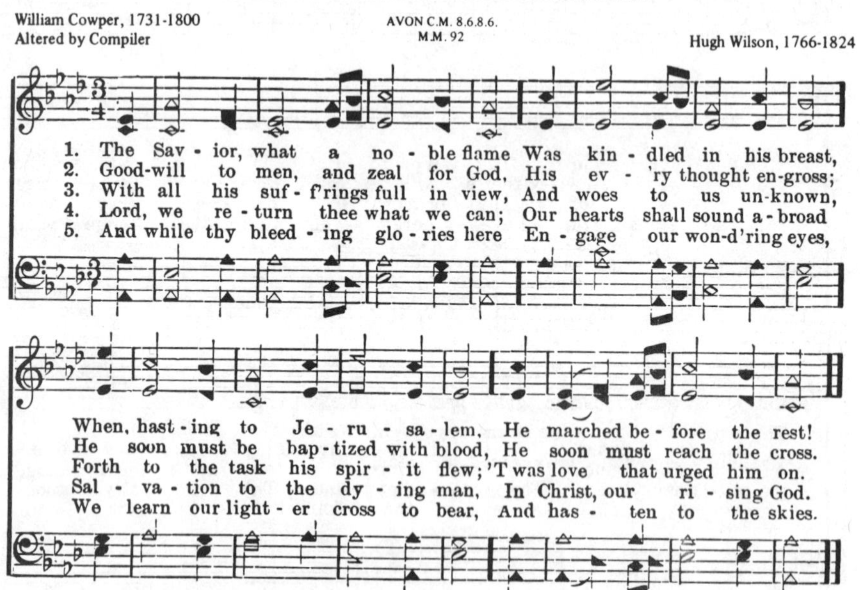
1. The Sav - ior, what a no - ble flame Was kin - dled in his breast,
2. Good-will to men, and zeal for God, His ev - 'ry thought en-gross;
3. With all his suf - f'rings full in view, And woes to us un-known,
4. Lord, we re - turn thee what we can; Our hearts shall sound a - broad
5. And while thy bleed - ing glo - ries here En - gage our won-d'ring eyes,
When, hast - ing to Je - ru - sa - lem, He marched be - fore the rest!
He soon must be bap - tized with blood, He soon must reach the cross.
Forth to the task his spir - it flew; 'T was love that urged him on.
Sal - va - tion to the dy - ing man, In Christ, our ri - sing God.
We learn our light - er cross to bear, And has - ten to the skies.

# HOW SWEETLY FLOWED THE GOSPEL SOUND 121

*They were astonished . . . for He taught them as one that had authority.* Mk. 1:22.

HEBER L.M. 8.8.8.8.
M.M. 84

John Bowring, 1792-1872 E. Barnes

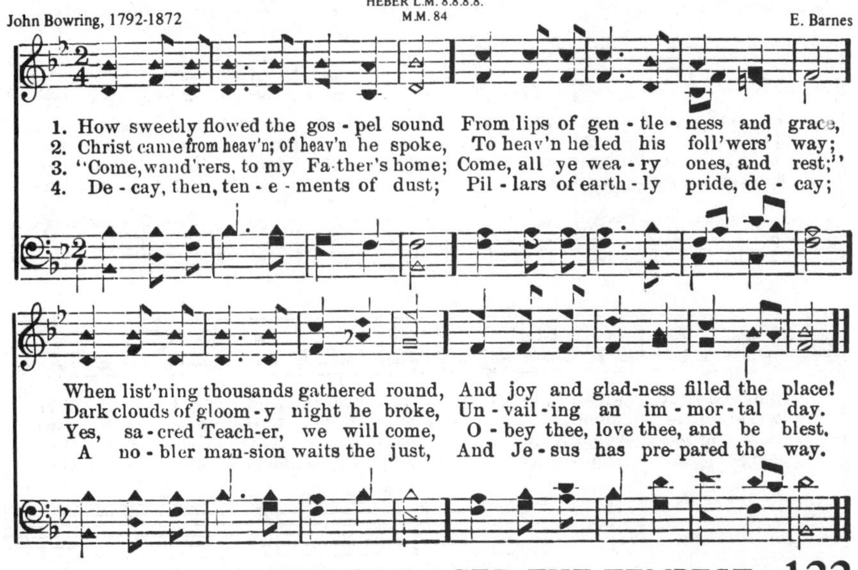
1. How sweetly flowed the gos - pel sound From lips of gen - tle - ness and grace,
2. Christ came from heav'n; of heav'n he spoke, To heav'n he led his foll'wers' way;
3. "Come, wand'rers, to my Fa-ther's home; Come, all ye wea - ry ones, and rest;"
4. De - cay, then, ten - e - ments of dust; Pil - lars of earth - ly pride, de - cay;
When list'ning thousands gathered round, And joy and glad-ness filled the place!
Dark clouds of gloom - y night he broke, Un - vail - ing an im - mor - tal day.
Yes, sa - cred Teach-er, we will come, O - bey thee, love thee, and be blest.
A no - bler man-sion waits the just, And Je - sus has pre-pared the way.

# FIERCE RAGED THE TEMPEST 122

*And He . . . rebuked the wind, and said unto the sea, Peace, be still.* Mk. 4:39.

ST. AELRED L.M. 8.8.8.3.
M.M. 100

Godfrey Thring, 1861 (1823-1903) John Bacchus Dykes, 1825-1876

1. Fierce raged the tem-pest o'er the deep, Watch did Thine anx-ious servants keep,
2. "Save, Lord, we per-ish," was their cry, "O save us in our ag - o - ny!"
3. The wild winds hushed; the an - gry deep Sank, like a lit - tle child, to sleep;
4. So, when our life is cloud - ed o'er, And storm-winds drift us from the shore,
But Thou wast wrapped in guile - less sleep, Calm and still.
Thy word a - bove the storm rose high, "Peace, be still."
The sul - len bil - lows ceased to leap, At Thy will.
Say, lest we sink to rise no more, "Peace, be still." A - men.

# 123 'TIS MIDNIGHT

*And He went forward a little, and fell on the ground, and prayed.* Mk. 14:35.

OLIVE'S BROW L.M. 8.8.8.8.
M.M. 48

William Bingham Tappan, 1744-1849 — William Batchelder Bradbury, 1816-1868

1. 'Tis mid-night, and on Ol-ive's brow The star is dimmed that late-ly shone; 'Tis mid-night, in the gar-den now The suf-f'ring Sav-iour prays a-lone.
2. 'Tis mid-night, and from all re-moved The Sav-iour wres-tles lone with fears; E'en that dis-ci-ple whom He loved Heeds not his Mas-ter's grief and tears.
3. 'Tis mid-night, and for oth-ers' guilt The Man of Sor-rows weeps in blood; Yet He who hath in an-guish knelt Is not for-sak-en by His God.
4. 'Tis mid-night, and from e-ther-plains Is borne the song that an-gels know; Un-heard by mor-tals are the strains That sweet-ly soothe the Sav-iour's woe.

# 124 O THE AGONIZING PRAYER

*If it be possible, let this cup pass from Me: nevertheless . . . as Thou wilt.* Matt. 26:39.

ALBERTSON 7.7.7.7.7.
M.M. 60

Thomas Mackeller, 1812-1899 — Mrs. Joseph F. Knapp, 1839-1908

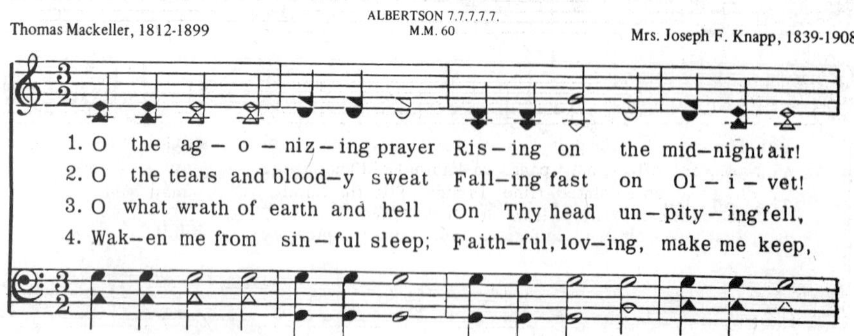
1. O the ag–o–niz–ing prayer Ris–ing on the mid–night air!
2. O the tears and blood–y sweat Fall–ing fast on Ol–i–vet!
3. O what wrath of earth and hell On Thy head un–pity–ing fell,
4. Wak–en me from sin–ful sleep; Faith–ful, lov–ing, make me keep,

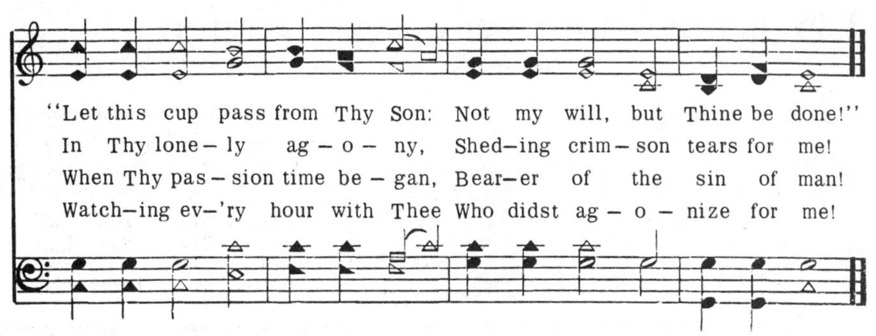
"Let this cup pass from Thy Son: Not my will, but Thine be done!"
In Thy lone – ly ag – o – ny, Shed–ing crim – son tears for me!
When Thy pas – sion time be – gan, Bear–er of the sin of man!
Watch–ing ev–'ry hour with Thee Who didst ag – o – nize for me!

# THRONED UPON THE AWFUL TREE 125

*He is despised and rejected of men; a man of sorrows, and acquainted with grief . . . Surely He hath borne our griefs, and carried our sorrows . . . He was wounded for our transgressions, He was bruised for our iniquities . . . the Lord hath laid on Him the iniquity of us all . . . He was afflicted, yet He opened not His mouth: He is brought as a lamb to the slaughter . . .* Is. 53:3-7.

John Ellerton, 1875 (1826-1893)
Sts. 1, 2, 4, Alt. by Compiler, 1972

THRONED 7.7.7.7.7.7.
M.M. 58

Welsh Hymn Melody

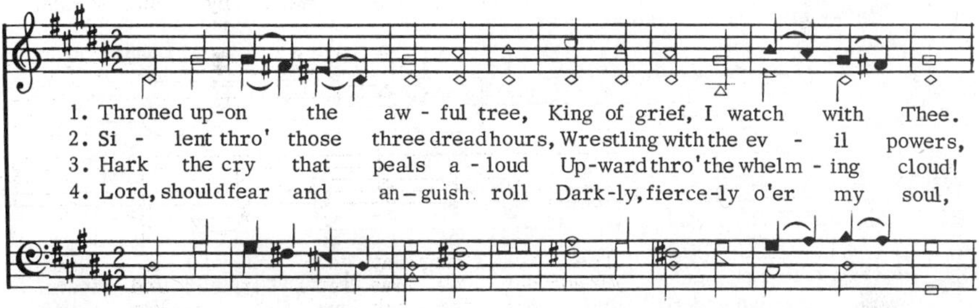

1. Throned up-on the aw - ful tree, King of grief, I watch with Thee.
2. Si - lent thro' those three dread hours, Wrestling with the ev - il powers,
3. Hark the cry that peals a - loud Up-ward thro' the whelm - ing cloud!
4. Lord, should fear and an – guish roll Dark-ly, fierce-ly o'er my soul,

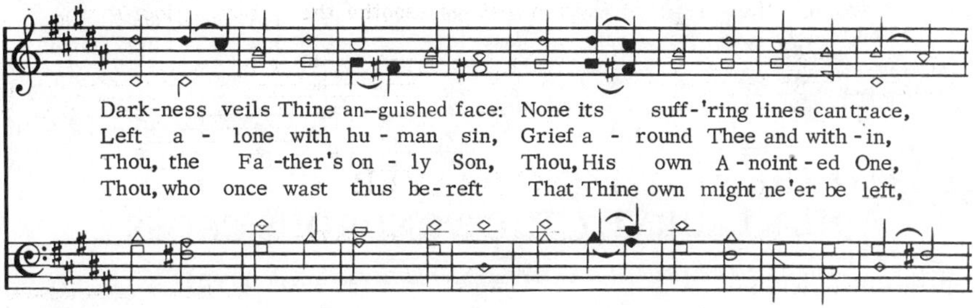

Dark-ness veils Thine an–guished face: None its suff-'ring lines can trace,
Left a - lone with hu - man sin, Grief a - round Thee and with - in,
Thou, the Fa -ther's on - ly Son, Thou, His own A - noint - ed One,
Thou, who once wast thus be - reft That Thine own might ne'er be left,

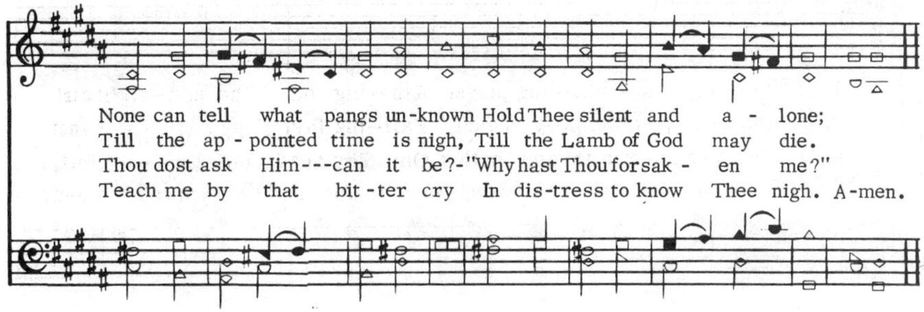

None can tell what pangs un-known Hold Thee silent and a - lone;
Till the ap - pointed time is nigh, Till the Lamb of God may die.
Thou dost ask Him---can it be?-"Why hast Thou forsak - en me?"
Teach me by that bit - ter cry In dis-tress to know Thee nigh. A-men.

# 126 BEHOLD THE SAVIOUR OF MANKIND

*Thus it behoved Christ to suffer.* Lk. 24:46.

Samuel Wesley, Sr., 1662-1735
Recast, John J. Overholt, 1968

SO LANGE JESUS BLEIBT DER HERR
L.M. 8.8.8.8.
M.M. 63

*Choralbuch der Mennoniten Gemeinden Russlands,* Halbstadt, 1914

1. Be - hold the Sav - iour of man - kind
2. Hark! how he groans while na - ture shakes,
3. 'Tis done! the pre - cious ran - som's paid!
4. But soon he'll break death's en - vious chain,

Nailed to the shame - ful, curs - ed tree; How great the
And earth's strong pil - lars wild - ly bend; The tem - ple's
"Re - ceive my soul!" he glad - ly cries; See where he
And in full glo - ry ev - er shine; O Lamb of

love that him in - clined To suf - fer, bleed and die for thee.
vail in sun - der breaks, The so - lid mar - bles clear - ly rend.
bows his sa - cred head! He bows his sa - cred head and dies.
God, was ev - er pain, Was love or sor - row e'er like thine!

# 127 WHEN I SURVEY THE WONDROUS CROSS

*God forbid that I should glory, save in the cross of our Lord Jesus Christ.* Gal. 6:14.

Isaac Watts, 1707 (1674-1748)

HAMBURG L.M. 8.8.8.8.
M.M. 72

Lowell Mason, 1792-1872

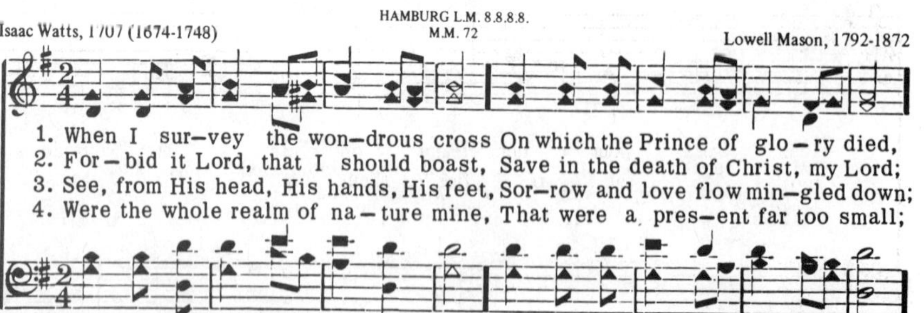
1. When I sur–vey the won–drous cross On which the Prince of glo–ry died,
2. For–bid it Lord, that I should boast, Save in the death of Christ, my Lord;
3. See, from His head, His hands, His feet, Sor–row and love flow min–gled down;
4. Were the whole realm of na–ture mine, That were a pres–ent far too small;

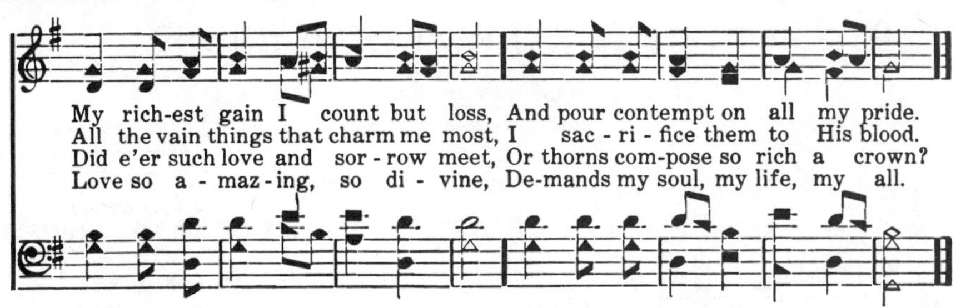
My rich-est gain I count but loss, And pour contempt on all my pride.
All the vain things that charm me most, I sac - ri - fice them to His blood.
Did e'er such love and sor - row meet, Or thorns com-pose so rich a crown?
Love so a - maz - ing, so di - vine, De-mands my soul, my life, my all.

# WHEN I SURVEY THE WONDROUS CROSS 128

*By whom the world is crucified unto me, and I unto the world.* Gal. 6:14.

ROCKINGHAM OLD
L.M. 8.8.8.8.
M.M. 76

A. William's *Supplement to Psalmody*, c. 1780
Adapted by Edward Miller, 1790 (1731-1807)
Harmony arranged by Compiler, 1965

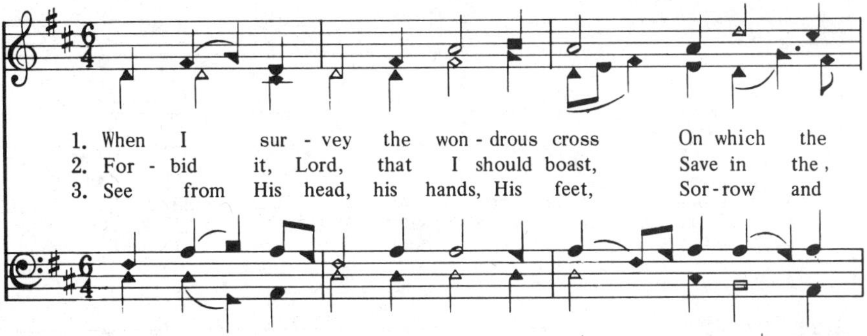

Isaac Watts, 1707 (1674-1748)

1. When I sur - vey the won - drous cross On which the
2. For - bid it, Lord, that I should boast, Save in the,
3. See from His head, his hands, His feet, Sor - row and

Prince of Glo - ry died, My rich - est gain I count but
death of Christ my Lord; All the vain things that charm me
love flow min - gled down; Did e'er such love and sor – row

loss, And pour con - tempt on all my pride.
most, I sac - ri - fice them to His blood.
meet, Or thorns com - pose so rich a crown.

# 129 O SACRED HEAD NOW WOUNDED

*And platted a crown of thorns, and put it about His head.* Mk. 15:17.

Bernard of Clairvaux, c. 1153
*Salve caput cruentatum*
Paul Gerhardt, 1656 (1607-1676)
*O Haupt voll Blut und Wunden*
Tr. Composite,
James W. Alexander, 1830 (1804-1859) and others

HERZLICHT TUT MICH VERLANGEN
7.6.7.6.D.
M.M. 60

Hans Leo Hassler, 1601 (1564-1612)
Har. Johann Sebastian Bach, 1729 (1685-1750)

1. O sa - cred Head, now wound - ed, With grief and shame weighed down!
2. O no - blest brow and dear - est, In oth - er days the world
3. What Thou, my Lord, hast suf - fered Was all for sin - ners' gain:
4. What lan-guage shall I bor - row To thank Thee, dear-est Friend,
5. Be near when I am dy - ing, O show Thy cross to me;
Now scorn-ful - ly sur - round - ed With thorns, Thine on - ly crown:
All feared when Thou ap - pear - edst; What shame on Thee is hurled!
Mine, mine was the trans - gres - sion, But Thine the dead - ly pain.
For this Thy dy - ing sor - row, Thy pit - y with - out end?
And for my suc - cor fly - ing, Come, Lord, to set me free;
O sa - cred Head, what glo - ry, What bliss till now was Thine!
How art Thou pale with an - guish, With sore a - buse and scorn;
Lo, here I fall, my Sav - iour! 'Tis I de - serve Thy place;
O make me Thine for - ev - er; And should I faint - ing be,
These eyes, new faith re - ceiv - ing, From Je - sus shall not move;
Yet, tho' de - spised and gor - y, I joy to call Thee mine.
How does that vis - age lan - guish Which once was bright as morn!
Look on me with Thy fa - vor, Vouch-safe to me Thy grace.
Lord, let me nev - er, nev - er Out - live my love to Thee.
For he who dies be - liev - ing, Dies safe - ly, thro' Thy love.

# O SACRED HEAD NOW WOUNDED 130

*He was wounded for our transgressions, He was bruised for our iniquities.* Is. 53:5.

Bernard of Clairvaux, c. 1153
*Salve caput cruentatum*
Paul Gerhardt, 1656 (1607-1676)
*O Haupt voll Blut und Wunden*
Tr. Composite,
James W. Alexander, 1830 (1804-1859) and others

KTO PODA SILU 7.6.7.6.D.
M.M. 56

Czechoslovakian melody
K. Royova
Harmony arr. by Compiler, 1971

1. O sa - cred Head, now wound-ed, With grief and shame weighed down!
2. O nob - lest brow and dear-est, In oth - er days the world
3. What Thou, my Lord, hast suffered Was all for sin - ners gain;
4. What lan-guage shall I bor - row To thank Thee, dear - est Friend,
5. Be near when I am dy - ing, O show Thy cross to me;

Now scorn - ful - ly sur - round-ed With thorns, Thine on - ly crown;
All feared when Thou ap - pear - est; What shame on Thee is hurled!
Mine, mine was the trans-gress - ion, But Thine the dead - ly pain.
For this Thy dy - ing sor - row, Thy pit - y with - out end.
And for my suc - cor fly - ing, Come, Lord, to set me free;

O sac - red Head, what glo - ry, What bliss till now was Thine!
How art Thou pale with an - guish, With sore a - buse and scorn;
Lo, here I fall, my Sav - iour! 'Tis I de - serve Thy place;
O make me Thine for - ev - er; And should I faint - ing be,
These eyes, new faith re - ceiv - ing, From Je - sus shall not move;

Yet, tho' des-pised and go - ry, I joy to call Thee mine.
How does that vis - age lan - guish Which once was bright as morn!
Look on me with Thy fav - or, Vouch - safe to me Thy grace.
Lord, let me nev - er, nev - er Out - live my love to Thee.
For he who dies be - liev - ing, Dies safe - ly, thro' Thy love. A - men.

# 131 UPON THE CROSS EXTENDED

*They crucified Him, and parted His garments.* Matt. 27:35.

Paul Gerhardt, cento, 1648 (1607-1676)
*O Welt, sieh hier dein Leben*
Tr. John Kelley, 1867, alt.

O DU LIEBE MEINER LIEBE (New)
7.7.6.7.8.
M.M. 66

Manuscript Chorale Book, Herrnhaag, 1735
Arranged by Compiler, 1970

1. Up – on the cross ex – tend – ed, See, world, thy Lord sus – pend – ed,
2. Come hith – er now and pon – der. 'Twill fill thy soul with won – der,
3. 'Tis I who should be smit – ten, My doom should here be writ – ten:
Thy Sav – iour yields His breath. The Prince of Life from heav – en
Blood streams from ev – ery pore. Through grief whose depth none knoweth,
Bound hand and foot in hell. The fet – ters and the scourg – ing,
Him – self hath free – ly giv – en To shame and blows and bit – ter death.
From His great heart there flow – eth Sigh aft – er sigh of an – guish o'er.
The floods a – round Thee surg – ing, 'Tis I who have de – served them well. A – men.

4. The load Thou takest on Thee,
That pressed so sorely on me,
It crushed me to the ground.
The cross for me enduring,
The crown for me securing,
My healing in Thy wounds is found.

5. A crown of thorns Thou wearest,
My shame and scorn Thou bearest,
That I might ransomed be.
My Bondsman, ever willing,
My place with patience filling,
From sin and guilt hast made me free.

6. Thy cords of love, my Saviour,
Bind me to Thee forever,
I am no longer mine.
To Thee I gladly tender
All that my life can render
And all I have to Thee resign.

7. Thy groaning and Thy sighing,
Thy bitter tears and dying,
With which Thou wast opprest—
They shall, when life is ending,
Be guiding and attending
My way to Thine eternal rest. Amen.

# FATHER, FORGIVE THEM 132

*Father, forgive them.* Lk. 23:34.

Thomas B. Pollock, 1870 (1836-1896)
Alt.

FATHER, FORGIVE THEM IRREGULAR
M.M. 69

William Henry Monk, 1889 (1823-1899)

1. "Father, forgive them; for they know not what they do."
2. "To-day shalt thou be with Me in Par - a - dise."
3. { "Woman, be - hold thy son!" :‖ / : "Be - hold thy moth - - - er!"
4. "My God, My God, why hast Thou for - sak - en Me?"
5. "I thirst."
6. "It is fin - ish - ed."
7. "Father, into Thy hands I com - mend My spir - - - it."

# OUT ONTO CALVARY'S HILL 133

*Let us go forth therefore unto Him without the camp, bearing His reproach.* Heb. 13:13.

*Zion's Harp*

CALVARY NEW S.M. 6.6.6.6.
M.M. 60

*Zion's Harp*
Arr. John J. Overholt, 1971

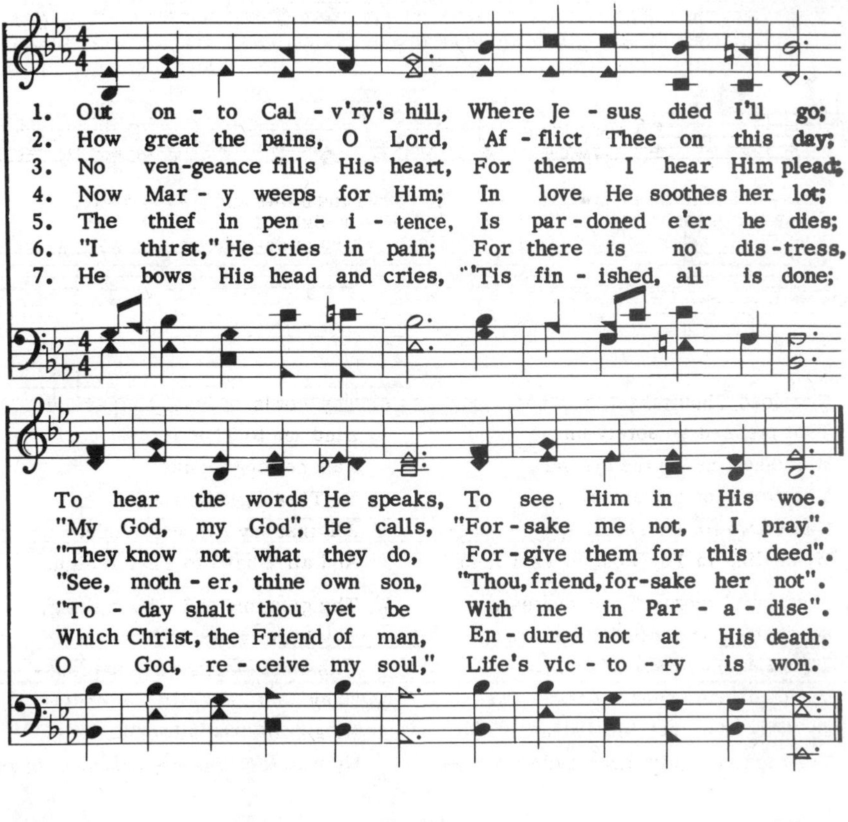

1. Out on - to Cal - v'ry's hill, Where Je - sus died I'll go;
To hear the words He speaks, To see Him in His woe.

2. How great the pains, O Lord, Af - flict Thee on this day;
"My God, my God", He calls, "For - sake me not, I pray".

3. No ven-geance fills His heart, For them I hear Him plead;
"They know not what they do, For - give them for this deed".

4. Now Mar - y weeps for Him; In love He soothes her lot;
"See, moth - er, thine own son, "Thou, friend, for - sake her not".

5. The thief in pen - i - tence, Is par - doned e'er he dies;
"To - day shalt thou yet be With me in Par - a - dise".

6. "I thirst," He cries in pain; For there is no dis - tress,
Which Christ, the Friend of man, En - dured not at His death.

7. He bows His head and cries, "'Tis fin - ished, all is done;
O God, re - ceive my soul," Life's vic - to - ry is won.

# 134 NOT WHAT THESE HANDS HAVE DONE

*Ye were . . . redeemed, with . . . the precious blood of Christ.* I Pet. 1:18-19.

Horatio Bonar, 1808-1889

MCGRANAHAN 6.6.8.6. with Ref.
M.M. 69

James McGranahan, 1840-1907

1. Not what these hands have done, Can save this guilt – y soul;
Not what this toil – ing flesh has borne, Can make my spir–it whole.

2. Not what I feel or do, Can give me peace with God;
Not all my prayers, or sighs, or tears, Can ease my aw–ful load.

3. Thy love to me, O God, Not mine, O Lord, to Thee,
Can rid me of this dark un – rest, And set my spir–it free.

4. No oth – er work save Thine, No mean – er blood, will do;
No strength, save that which is di–vine, Can bear me safe – ly through.

5. I praise the God of grace, I trust His love and might;
He calls me His, I call Him mine; My God, my joy, my light!

REFRAIN

Thy work a – lone, my Sav – iour, Can ease this weight of sin;
Thy blood a – lone, O Lamb of God, Can give me peace with–in.

# THERE IS A FOUNTAIN FILLED WITH BLOOD 135

*There shall be a fountain opened . . . for sin and for uncleanness.* Zech. 13:1.

CLEANSING FOUNTAIN 8.6.8.6.6.6.8.6.
M.M. 66

William Cowper, 1779 (1731-1800)

Early American Melody

1. There is a foun - tain filled with blood, Drawn from Im - man-uel's veins;
2. The dy - ing thief re - joiced to see That foun - tain in his day;
3. E'er since, by faith, I saw the stream Thy flow - ing wounds sup - ply,
4. And when this fee - ble, fal - t'ring tongue Lies si - lent in the grave,
And sin - ners wash - ing in that flood, Lose all their guilt - y stains;
And may I there, tho' vile as he, Wash all my sins a - way;
Re - deem - ing love has been my theme, And shall be, till I die;
Then in a no - bler, sweet - er song I'll sing thy pow'r to save;
Lose all their guilt - y stains, . . Lose all their guilt - y stains,
Wash all my sins a - way, . . Wash all my sins a - way,
And shall be, till I die, . . . And shall be, till I die,
I'll sing thy pow'r to save, . . . I'll sing thy pow'r to save,
And sin - ners, wash - ing in that flood, Lose all their guilt - y stains.
And may I there, tho' vile as he, Wash all my sins a - way.
Re - deem - ing love has been my theme, And shall be till I die.
Then in a no - bler, sweet - er song I'll sing thy pow'r to save.

# 136 HALLELUJAH! LO, HE WAKES!

*He is not here: for He is risen.* Matt. 28:6.

Benjamin Schmolck, 1672-1737
*Halleluja! Jesus lebt*
Tr. Emmanuel Cronenwett, 1878 (1841-1931)
Altered by Compiler, 1970

MORGENGLANZ DER EWIGKEIT
7.8.7.8.7.3.
M.M. 100

Johann Rudolph Ahle, 1662 (1625-1673)

1. Hal–le–lu–jah! Lo, He wakes! Lives! o'er death and hell vic–tor–ious;
2. Hal–le–lu–jah! See the tomb, Ye, who o'er his death are pin–ing:
3. Hal–le–lu–jah! Why seek ye Yet a–mong the dead the liv–ing?
4. Hal–le–lu–jah! Then I cry: Christ too will from death re–store me,

Earth in awe with tremb–ling quakes, As the He–ro ris–es glor–ious;
Dry your tears, to joy give room, While the rad–iant sun is shin–ing,
Christ is ris–en in maj–es–ty! Hence a–way with gloom–y griev–ing,
Take me to His throne on high, Whith–er He has gone be–fore me,

He who died on Gol–go–tha, Je–sus lives!
Hear the an–gels' Glor–i–a! Je–sus lives!
Join with her of Mag–da–la! Je–sus lives!
Faith ex–ults: Vic–to–ri–a! Je–sus lives! A–men

# 137 THE LORD IS RISEN INDEED

*The Lord is risen indeed.* Lk. 24:34.

Thomas Kelley, 1809 (1769-1855)
St. 5, John J. Overholt, 1970

GERAR S.M. 6.6.8.6.
M.M. 104

Lowell Mason, 1836 (1792-1872)

1. "The Lord is ris'n in–deed!" And are the ti–dings true? Yes,
2. "The Lord is ris'n in–deed!" Then jus–tice asks no more; Mer–
3. "The Lord is ris'n in–deed!" Then is His work per–formed; The
4. "The Lord is ris'n in–deed!" At–tend–ing an–gels hear; Up
5. While thousand thousands throng The Vic–tor's song to raise, We'll

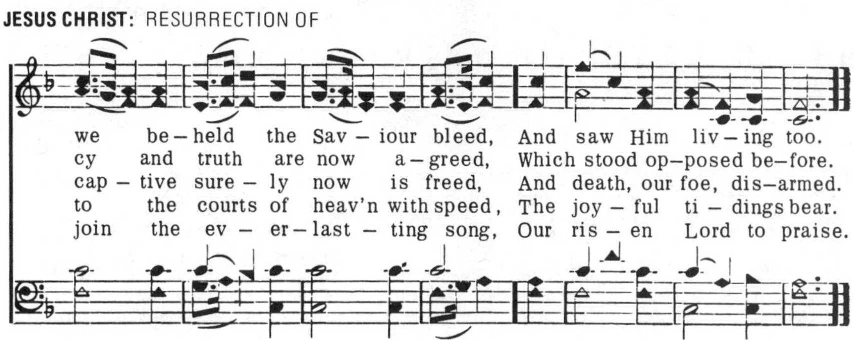
we be—held the Sav—iour bleed, And saw Him liv—ing too.
cy and truth are now a—greed, Which stood op—posed be—fore.
cap—tive sure—ly now is freed, And death, our foe, dis—armed.
to the courts of heav'n with speed, The joy—ful ti—dings bear.
join the ev—er—last—ting song, Our ris—en Lord to praise.

# LIFT YOUR GLAD VOICES 138

*Whosoever liveth and believeth in Me shall never die.* Jn. 11:26.

RESURRECTION 12.11.11.11.
M.M. 96

Henry Ware, 1794-1843

John Edgar Gould, 1822-1875

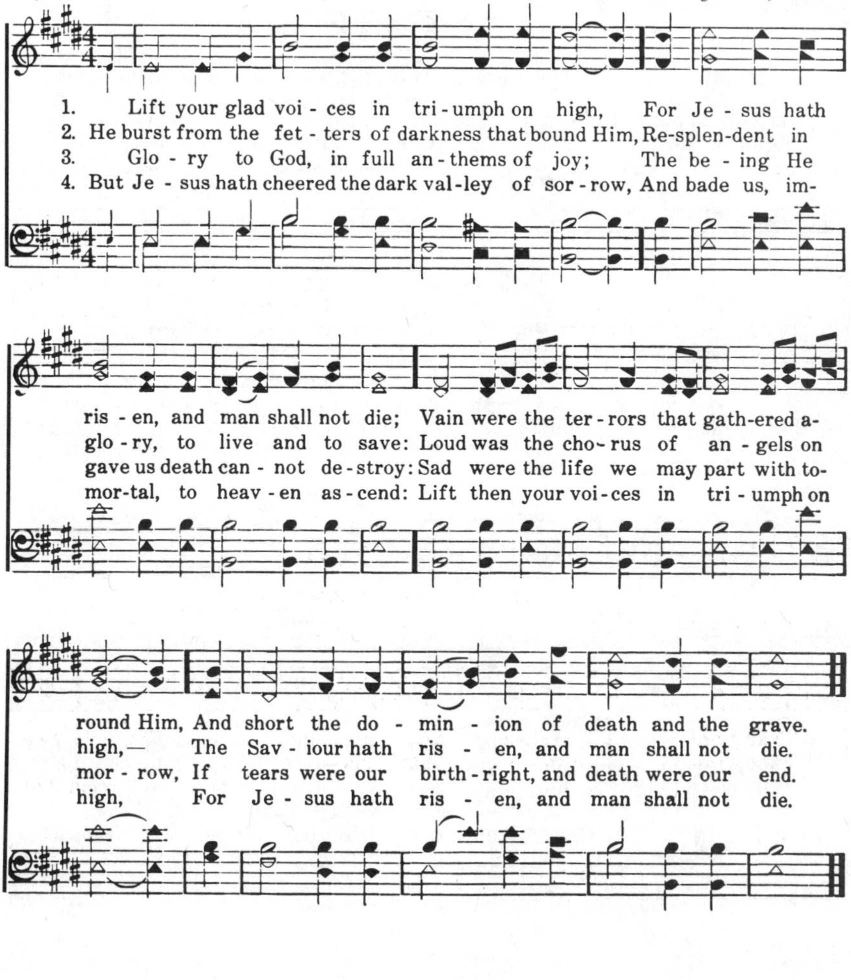

1. Lift your glad voi-ces in tri-umph on high, For Je-sus hath ris-en, and man shall not die; Vain were the ter-rors that gath-ered a-round Him, And short the do-min-ion of death and the grave.
2. He burst from the fet-ters of darkness that bound Him, Re-splen-dent in glo-ry, to live and to save: Loud was the cho-rus of an-gels on high,— The Sav-iour hath ris-en, and man shall not die.
3. Glo-ry to God, in full an-thems of joy; The be-ing He gave us death can-not de-stroy: Sad were the life we may part with to-mor-row, If tears were our birth-right, and death were our end.
4. But Je-sus hath cheered the dark val-ley of sor-row, And bade us, im-mor-tal, to heav-en as-cend: Lift then your voi-ces in tri-umph on high, For Je-sus hath ris-en, and man shall not die.

# 139 CHRIST, THE LORD, IS RISEN TODAY

*Now is Christ risen from the dead, and become the firstfruits of them that slept.* I Cor. 15:20.

Charles Wesley, 1739 (1708-1788)

WORGAN 7.4.7.4.7.4.7.4.
M.M. 76

14th century air
Revised in *Lyra Davidica*

1. Christ, the Lord, is ris'n to - day, Hal - - le - lu - jah!
2. Love's re-deem - ing work is done, Hal - - le - lu - jah!
3. Vain the stone, the watch, the seal, Hal - - le - lu - jah!
4. Lives a - gain our glo - rious King, Hal - - le - lu - jah!
Sons of men and an - gels say, Hal - - le - lu - jah!
Fought the fight, the bat - tle won, Hal - - le - lu - jah!
Christ hath burst the gates of hell, Hal - - le - lu - jah!
Where, O death, is now thy sting? Hal - - le - lu - jah!
Raise your joys and tri-umphs high, Hal - - le - lu - jah!
Lo! our sun's e - clipse is o'er, Hal - - le - lu - jah!
Death in vain for - bids His rise, Hal - - le - lu - jah!
Once He died our souls to save, Hal - - le - lu - jah!
Sing, ye heav'ns; thou earth, re - ply, Hal - - le - lu - jah!
Lo! he sets in blood no more, Hal - - le - lu - jah!
Christ hath o - pened par - a - dise, Hal - - le - lu - jah!
Where's thy vic - t'ry, boast-ing grave? Hal - - le - lu - jah!

# SEE THE CONQUEROR MOUNTS IN TRIUMPH 140

*The King of glory shall come in.* Ps. 24:7.

ST. ASAPH NEW 8.7.8.7.D.
M.M. 80

Christopher Wordsworth, 1862 (1807-1885)

William Samuel Bambridge, 1872, b. 1842
Arr. John J. Overholt, 1965

1. See the Con–qu'ror mounts in tri – umph; See the King in roy – al state,
2. Who is this that comes in glo – ry, With the trump of ju – bi – lee?
3. Thou hast raised our hu – man na – ture On the clouds to God's right hand;
Rid – ing on the clouds, His char – iot, To His heav'n–ly pal – ace gate:
Lord of bat – tles, God of ar – mies, He has gained the vic – to – ry;
There we sit in heav'n–ly plac – es, There with Thee in glo – ry stand:
Hark! ten thou – sand, thou–sand voi – ces Joy – ful Al – le – lu – ias sing,
He who on the cross did suf – fer, He who from the grave a–rose,
Je – sus reigns, a – dored by an – gels, Man with God is on the throne;
And the por – tals high are lift – ed To re – ceive their heav'n – ly King.
He has van–quished sin and Sa – tan, He by death has spoiled His foes.
Might – y Lord, in Thine as – cen–sion We by faith be – hold our own.

# 141 RISE GLORIOUS CONQUEROR

*He led captivity captive.* Eph. 4:8.

Matthew Bridges, 1848 (1800-1894)
Alt.

DORT 6.6.4.6.6.6.4.
M.M. 69

Lowell Mason, 1832 (1792-1872)

1. Rise, glo - rious Con - qu'ror, rise In - to Thy na - tive skies;
2. Vic - tor o'er death and hell, Che - ru - bic le - gions swell
3. En - ter, in - car - nate God! No feet but Thine have trod
4. Li - on of Ju - dah, hail! And let Thy name pre - vail

As - sume Thy right; And where in many a fold The clouds are
The ra - diant train: Prais - es all heav'n in - spire; Each an - gel
The ser - pent down: Blow the full trump - ets, blow, Wid - er yon
From age to age: Lord of the roll - ing years, Claim for Thine

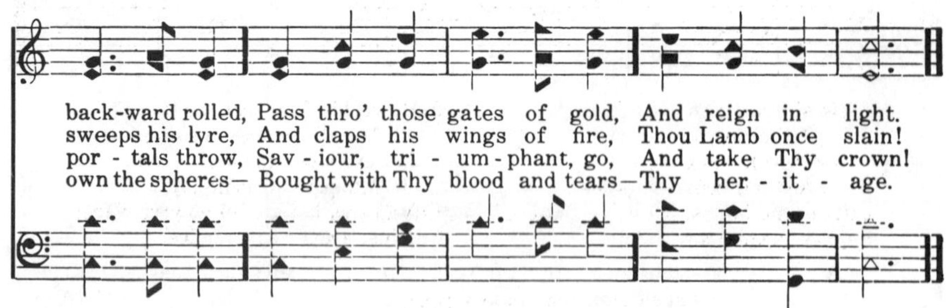
back-ward rolled, Pass thro' those gates of gold, And reign in light.
sweeps his lyre, And claps his wings of fire, Thou Lamb once slain!
por - tals throw, Sav - iour, tri - um - phant, go, And take Thy crown!
own the spheres— Bought with Thy blood and tears—Thy her - it - age.

# REJOICE, THE LORD IS KING 142

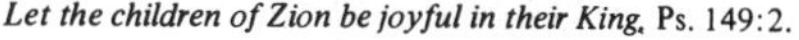

*Let the children of Zion be joyful in their King.* Ps. 149:2.

Charles Wesley, 1707-1788

ST. JOHN 6.6.6.6.8.8.
M.M. 92

William Henry Havergal, 1793-1870
Harmony arr. by Compiler, 1965

1. Rejoice, the Lord is King! Your Lord and King adore; Mortals, give thanks and sing, And triumph evermore; Lift up your hearts, lift up your voice; Rejoice, again I say, rejoice.

2. Jesus, the Saviour, reigns, The God of truth and love; When he had purged our stains, He took his seat above; Lift up your hearts, lift up your voice; Rejoice, again I say, rejoice.

3. His kingdom cannot fail, He rules o'er earth and heaven; The keys of death and hell Are to our Jesus given; Lift up your hearts, lift up your voice; Rejoice, again I say, rejoice. Amen.

4. He sits at God's right hand
Till all his foes submit,
And bow to his command,
And fall beneath his feet;
Lift up your hearts, lift up your voice;
Rejoice, again I say, rejoice.

5. He all his foes shall quell,
And all our sins destroy;
Let every bosom swell
With pure seraphic joy;
Lift up your hearts, lift up your voice;
Rejoice, again I say, rejoice.

6. Rejoice in glorious hope;
Jesus the Judge shall come,
And take his servants up
To their eternal home;
We'll soon hear the archangel's voice;
The trump of God shall sound, Rejoice!

# 143 HAIL THE DAY

*While they beheld, He was taken up.* Acts 1:9.

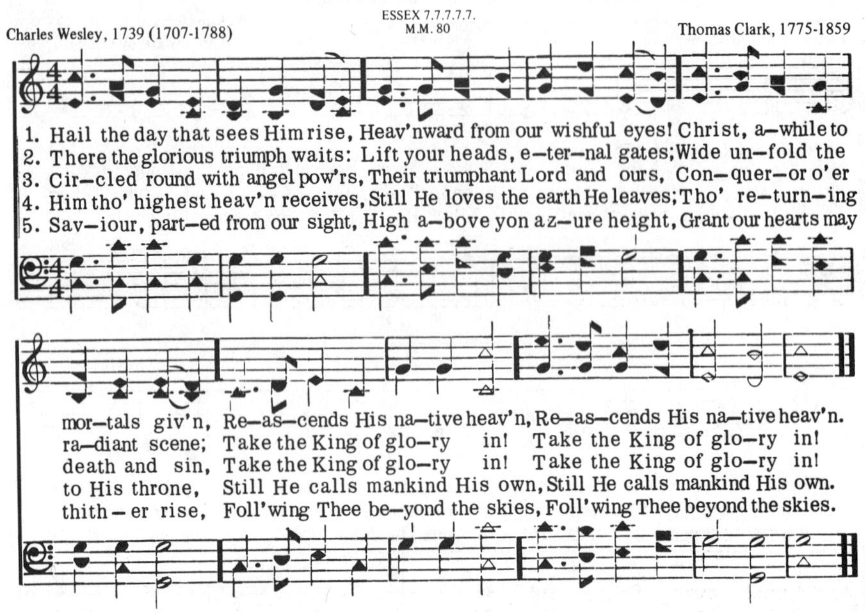
ESSEX 7.7.7.7.7.7.
M.M. 80
Charles Wesley, 1739 (1707-1788)
Thomas Clark, 1775-1859
1. Hail the day that sees Him rise, Heav'nward from our wishful eyes! Christ, a–while to
2. There the glorious triumph waits: Lift your heads, e–ter–nal gates; Wide un–fold the
3. Cir–cled round with angel pow'rs, Their triumphant Lord and ours, Con–quer–or o'er
4. Him tho' highest heav'n receives, Still He loves the earth He leaves; Tho' re–turn–ing
5. Sav–iour, part–ed from our sight, High a–bove yon az–ure height, Grant our hearts may
mor–tals giv'n, Re–as–cends His na–tive heav'n, Re–as–cends His na–tive heav'n.
ra–diant scene; Take the King of glo–ry in! Take the King of glo–ry in!
death and sin, Take the King of glo–ry in! Take the King of glo–ry in!
to His throne, Still He calls mankind His own, Still He calls mankind His own.
thith–er rise, Foll'wing Thee be–yond the skies, Foll'wing Thee beyond the skies.

# 144 CHRIST, ABOVE ALL GLORY SEATED

*He was received up into heaven, and sat on the right hand of God.* Mk. 16:19.

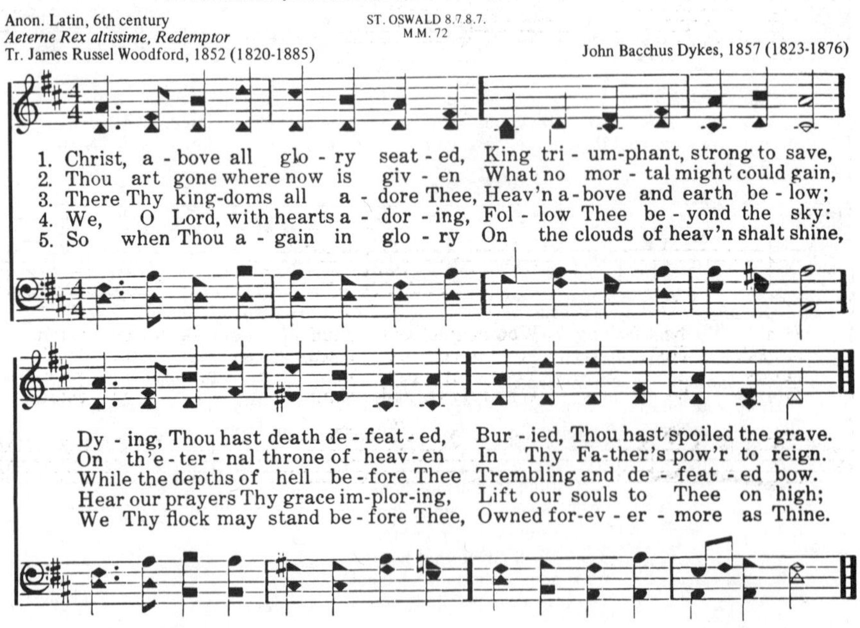
Anon. Latin, 6th century
*Aeterne Rex altissime, Redemptor*
Tr. James Russel Woodford, 1852 (1820-1885)
ST. OSWALD 8.7.8.7.
M.M. 72
John Bacchus Dykes, 1857 (1823-1876)
1. Christ, a - bove all glo - ry seat - ed, King tri - um-phant, strong to save,
2. Thou art gone where now is giv - en What no mor - tal might could gain,
3. There Thy king-doms all a - dore Thee, Heav'n a - bove and earth be - low;
4. We, O Lord, with hearts a - dor - ing, Fol - low Thee be - yond the sky:
5. So when Thou a - gain in glo - ry On the clouds of heav'n shalt shine,
Dy - ing, Thou hast death de - feat - ed, Bur - ied, Thou hast spoiled the grave.
On th'e - ter - nal throne of heav - en In Thy Fa - ther's pow'r to reign.
While the depths of hell be - fore Thee Trembling and de - feat - ed bow.
Hear our prayers Thy grace im - plor - ing, Lift our souls to Thee on high;
We Thy flock may stand be - fore Thee, Owned for - ev - er - more as Thine.

# COME, LET US TUNE OUR LOFTIEST SONG 145

*Of Him, and through Him, and to Him, are all things: to Whom be glory forever.* Rom. 11:36.

Robert A. West, 1802- | MOZART L.M. 8.8.8.8. M.M. 76 | Wolfgang Amadeus Mozart, 1756-1791

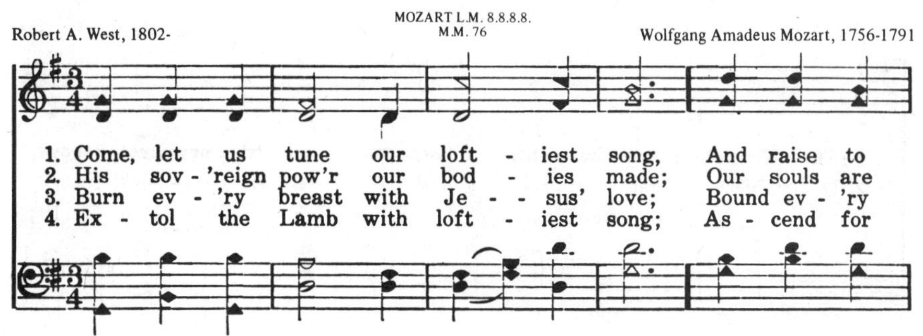
1. Come, let us tune our loft - iest song, And raise to
2. His sov - 'reign pow'r our bod - ies made; Our souls are
3. Burn ev - 'ry breast with Je - - sus' love; Bound ev - 'ry
4. Ex - tol the Lamb with loft - iest song; As - cend for

Christ our joy - ful strain; Wor - ship and thanks to
His im - mor - tal breath; And when His crea - tures
heart with rap - turous joy; And saints on earth, with
Him our cheer - ful strain; Wor - ship and thanks to

Him be - long, Who reigns, and shall for - ev - er reign.
sinned, He bled, To save us from e - ter - nal death.
saints a - bove, Your voi - ces in His praise em - ploy.
Him be - long, Who reigns, and shall for - ev - er reign.

# 146 THE KING SHALL COME WHEN MORNING DAWNS

*This same Jesus . . . shall so come in like manner as ye have seen Him go into heaven.* Acts 1:11.

Early Greek hymn
Tr. John Brownlie, 1901 (1857-1925)
JERUSALEM, JERUSALEM 8.6.8.6.D.
M.M. 72
Thomas Hastings, 1784-1872
1. The King shall come when morn - ing dawns, And light tri - um-phant breaks;
2. O bright - er than the ris - ing morn When He, vic - to - rious, rose,
3. The King shall come when morn - ing dawns, And light tri - um-phant breaks;
When beau - ty gilds the east - ern hills, And life to joy a - wakes.
And left the lone-some place of death, De - spite the rage of foes—
When beau - ty gilds the east - ern hills, And life to joy a - wakes.
Not as of old a lit - tle child To bear, and fight, and die,
O bright - er than the glo - rious morn Shall this fair morn - ing be,
The King shall come when morn - ing dawns, And light and beau - ty brings:
But crowned with glo - ry like the sun That lights the morn-ing sky.
When Christ, our King, in beau - ty comes, And we His face shall see!
Hail, Christ the Lord! Thy peo - ple pray, Come quick-ly, King of kings! A-men.

# FACE TO FACE 147

*Behold, He cometh with clouds; and every eye shall see Him.* Rev. 1:7.

TULLAR 8.7.8.7. with Ref.
M.M. 66
Mrs. Frank H. Breck, 1855-1934
Grant Colfax Tullar, 1869-1950
1. Face to face with Christ my Sav - iour, Face to face—what will it be,
2. On - ly faint - ly now I see Him, With the dark - ling veil be - tween,
3. What re - joic - ing in His pres - ence, When are ban - ished grief and pain;
4. Face to face! oh, bliss - ful mo - ment! Face to face—to see and know;
When with rap - ture I be - hold Him, Je - sus Christ, who died for me?
But a bless - ed day is com - ing, When His glo - ry shall be seen.
When the crook - ed ways are straightened, And the dark things shall be plain.
Face to face with my Re - deem - er, Je - sus Christ, who loves me so.
CHORUS
Face to face shall I be - hold Him, Far be - yond the star - ry sky;....
Face to face in all His glo - ry, I shall see Him by and by.

# 148 A WONDERFUL SAVIOUR IS JESUS MY LORD

*Hide me under the shadow of Thy wings.* Ps. 17:8.

Fanny J. Crosby, 1820-1915

KIRKPATRICK 11.8.11.8. with Ref.
M.M. 88

William James Kirkpatrick, 1838-1921

1. A wonder-ful Savior is Jesus my Lord, A wonder-ful Savior to me, He hideth my soul in the cleft of the rock, Where rivers of pleasure I see.

2. A wonder-ful Savior is Jesus my Lord, He taketh my burden away, He holdeth me up, and I shall not be moved, He giveth me strength as my day.

3. With numberless blessings each moment He crowns, And filled with His fullness divine, I sing in my rapture, oh, glory to God For such a Redeemer as mine!

4. When clothed in His brightness, transported I rise To meet Him in clouds of the sky, His perfect salvation, His wonderful love, I'll shout with the millions on high.

CHORUS

He hideth my soul in the cleft of the rock That shadows a dry, thirsty land; He hideth my life in the depths of His love, And covers me there with His hand, And covers me there with His hand.

## MAN OF SORROWS, WHAT A NAME 149

*A man of sorrows, and acquainted with grief.* Is. 53:3.

HALLELUJAH, WHAT A SAVIOUR 7.7.7.8.
M.M. 66

Philip Paul Bliss, 1875 (1838-1876) | Philip Paul Bliss

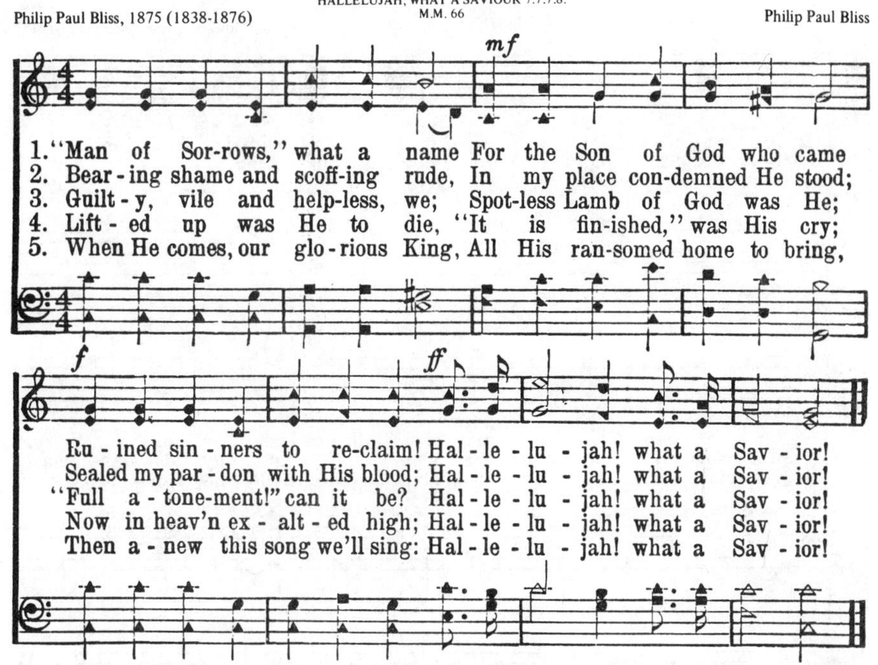

mf
1. "Man of Sor-rows," what a name For the Son of God who came
2. Bear-ing shame and scoff-ing rude, In my place con-demned He stood;
3. Guilt-y, vile and help-less, we; Spot-less Lamb of God was He;
4. Lift-ed up was He to die, "It is fin-ished," was His cry;
5. When He comes, our glo-rious King, All His ran-somed home to bring,
f
ff
Ru-ined sin-ners to re-claim! Hal-le-lu-jah! what a Sav-ior!
Sealed my par-don with His blood; Hal-le-lu-jah! what a Sav-ior!
"Full a-tone-ment!" can it be? Hal-le-lu-jah! what a Sav-ior!
Now in heav'n ex-alt-ed high; Hal-le-lu-jah! what a Sav-ior!
Then a-new this song we'll sing: Hal-le-lu-jah! what a Sav-ior!

## I AM NOT SKILLED TO UNDERSTAND 150

*The Father sent the Son to be the Saviour of the world.* I Jn. 4:14.

GREENWELL 8.7.8.7.
M.M. 66

Dora Greenwell, 1821-1882 | William James Kirkpatrick, 1838-1921

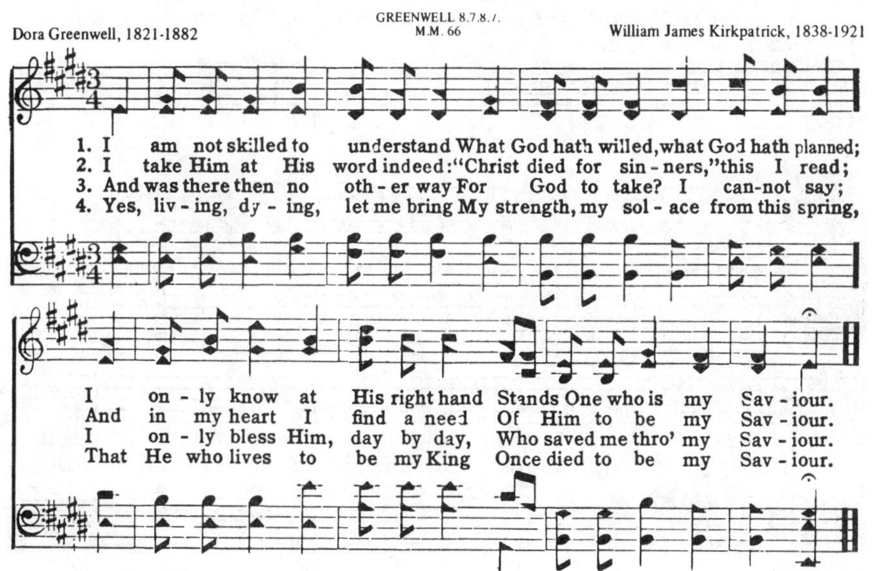

1. I am not skilled to understand What God hath willed, what God hath planned;
2. I take Him at His word indeed: "Christ died for sin-ners," this I read;
3. And was there then no oth-er way For God to take? I can-not say;
4. Yes, liv-ing, dy-ing, let me bring My strength, my sol-ace from this spring,
I on-ly know at His right hand Stands One who is my Sav-iour.
And in my heart I find a need Of Him to be my Sav-iour.
I on-ly bless Him, day by day, Who saved me thro' my Sav-iour.
That He who lives to be my King Once died to be my Sav-iour.

# 151 JESUS, THOU MIGHTY LORD

*His name shall be called Wonderful, Counsellor, the mighty God.* Is. 9:6.

Fanny Crosby, c. 1883 (1820-1915) — DOANE 6.4.6.4.D. M.M. 76 — William Howard Doane, 1883 (1831-1915)

1. Je - sus, Thou might - y Lord, Great is Thy name; Still thro' e-
2. Je - sus, Thou might - y Lord, Je - sus, our King, Praise for Thy
3. Sought by Thy mer - cy, Lord, Saved by Thy pow'r, Led by Thy

ter - nal years, Thou art the same; Change-less Thy ho - ly Word,
won-drous love Glad - ly we sing. Love in Thy di - a - dem
gra - cious hand, Kept ev - 'ry hour. Thine shall the hon - or be,

True ev - er - more; Thy name we glo - ri - fy, Thy name a - dore.
Shines ev - er - more; Thy name we glo - ri - fy, Thy name a - dore.
Thine ev - er - more; Thy name we glo - ri - fy, Thy name a - dore.

# 152 COME, YE FAITHFUL, RAISE THE ANTHEM

*Unto the King eternal, immortal, invisible, the only wise God.* I Tim. 1:17.

Job Hupton, 1805 (1762-1849)
Alt. John Mason Neale, 1867 (1818-1866) — NEANDER 8.7.8.7.8.7. M.M. 80 — Joachim Neander, 1650-1680

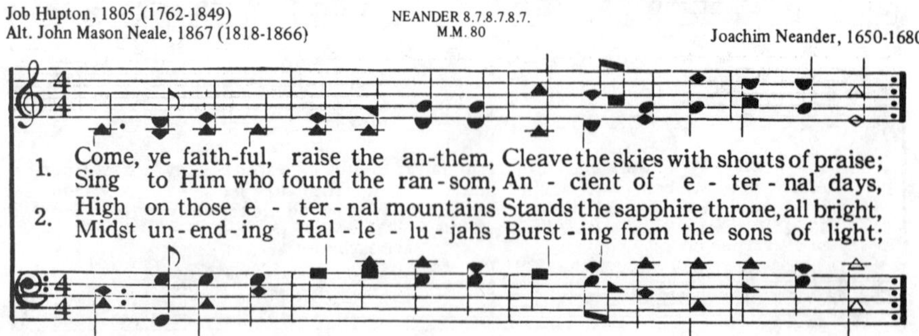
1. Come, ye faith-ful, raise the an-them, Cleave the skies with shouts of praise;
Sing to Him who found the ran - som, An - cient of e - ter - nal days,
2. High on those e - ter - nal mountains Stands the sapphire throne, all bright,
Midst un-end-ing Hal - le - lu - jahs Burst - ing from the sons of light;

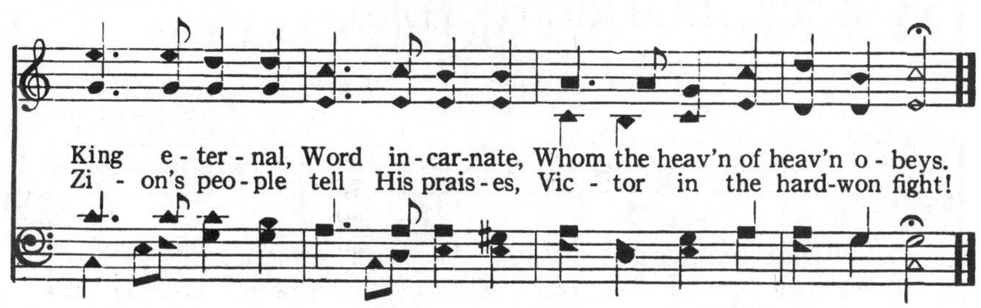
King e - ter - nal, Word in - car-nate, Whom the heav'n of heav'n o - beys.
Zi - on's peo - ple tell His prais - es, Vic - tor in the hard-won fight!

# O JESUS, KING MOST WONDERFUL 153

*He is Lord of lords, and King of kings.* Rev. 17:14.

Bernard of Clairvaux, 1091-1153
*Jesu, Rex admirabilis*
Tr. Edward Caswell, 1814-1878

ABRIDGE C.M. 8.6.8.6.
M.M. 76

Isaac Smith, 1735-1800

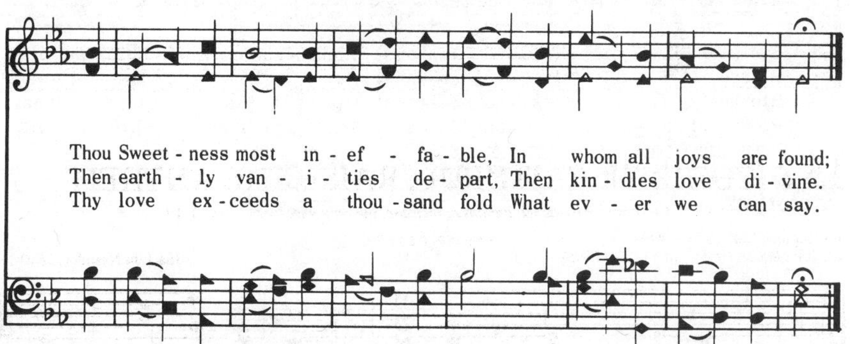

1. O Jesus, King most wonderful, Thou Conqueror renowned;
Thou Sweetness most ineffable, In whom all joys are found;

2. When once Thou visitest the heart, Then truth begins to shine;
Then earthly vanities depart, Then kindles love divine.

3. Jesus! Thy mercies are untold, Through each returning day;
Thy love exceeds a thousand fold What ever we can say.

4. May every heart confess Thy Name,
And ever Thee adore;
And, seeking Thee, itself inflame
And seek Thee more and more.

5. Thee may our tongues for ever bless;
Thee may we love alone:
And ever in our lives express
The image of Thine own.

# 154 SAVIOUR, LIKE A SHEPHERD LEAD US

*I am the good Shepherd, and know My sheep.* Jn. 10:14.

BRADBURY 8.7.8.7.D.
M.M. 63

Dorothy Anne Thrupp, 1836 (1779-1847) — William Batchelder Bradbury, 1859 (1816-1868)

1. Sav–iour, like a shep–herd lead us, Much we need Thy tend'rest care;
2. We are Thine, do Thou be–friend us, Be the guard–ian of our way;
3. Thou hast prom–ised to re–ceive us, Poor and sin–ful tho' we be;
4. Ear–ly let us seek Thy fa–vor, Ear–ly let us do Thy will;
In Thy pleas–ant pas–tures feed us, For our use Thy folds pre–pare;
Keep Thy flock, from sin de–fend us, Seek us when we go a–stray:
Thou hast mer–cy to re–lieve us, Grace to cleanse, and pow'r to free:
Bless–ed Lord and on–ly Sav–iour, With Thy love our bos–oms fill:
Bless–ed Je–sus! Bless–ed Je–sus! Thou hast bought us, Thine we are,
Bless–ed Je–sus! Bless–ed Je–sus! Hear, O hear us, when we pray,
Bless–ed Je–sus! Bless–ed Je–sus! We will ear–ly turn to Thee,
Bless–ed Je–sus! Bless–ed Je–sus! Thou hast loved us, love us still,
Bless–ed Je–sus! Bless–ed Je–sus! Thou hast bought us, Thine we are.
Bless–ed Je–sus! Bless–ed Je–sus! Hear, O hear us, when we pray.
Bless–ed Je–sus! Bless–ed Je–sus! We will ear–ly turn to Thee.
Bless–ed Je–sus! Bless–ed Je–sus! Thou hast loved us, love us still.

# SAVIOUR LIKE A SHEPHERD LEAD US 155

*He calleth His own sheep by name, and leadeth them out.* Jn. 10:3.

SAVIOUR LIKE A SHEPHERD 8.7.8.7.
M.M. 58

Dorothy Anne Thrupp, 1836 (1779-1847)

Wellington K. Jacobs, 1876

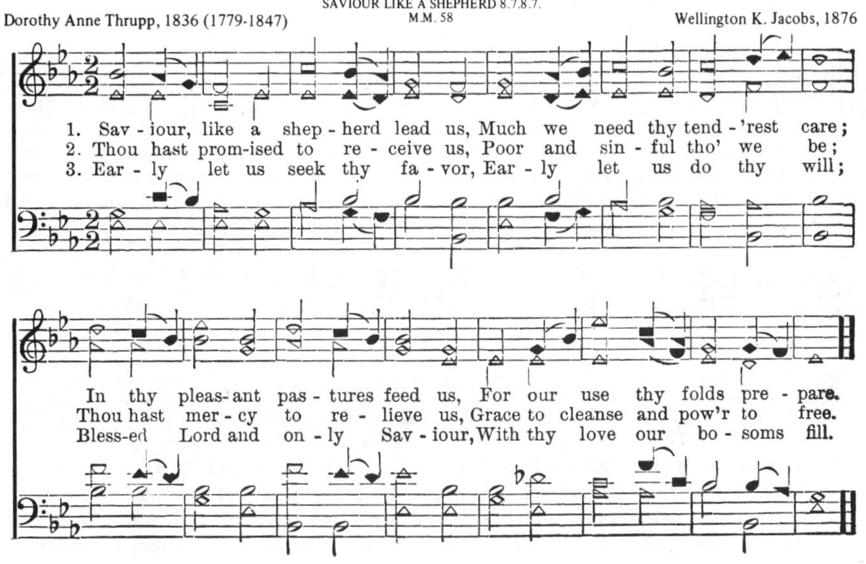
1. Sav - iour, like a shep - herd lead us, Much we need thy tend - 'rest care;
2. Thou hast prom-ised to re - ceive us, Poor and sin - ful tho' we be;
3. Ear - ly let us seek thy fa - vor, Ear - ly let us do thy will;
In thy pleas- ant pas - tures feed us, For our use thy folds pre - pare.
Thou hast mer - cy to re - lieve us, Grace to cleanse and pow'r to free.
Bless-ed Lord and on - ly Sav - iour, With thy love our bo - soms fill.

# THE LORD MY SHEPHERD IS 156

*They all shall have one shepherd.* Ezek. 37:24.

THE LORD MY SHEPHERD 6.8.6.6.
M.M. 63

Isaac Watts, 1719 (1674-1748)

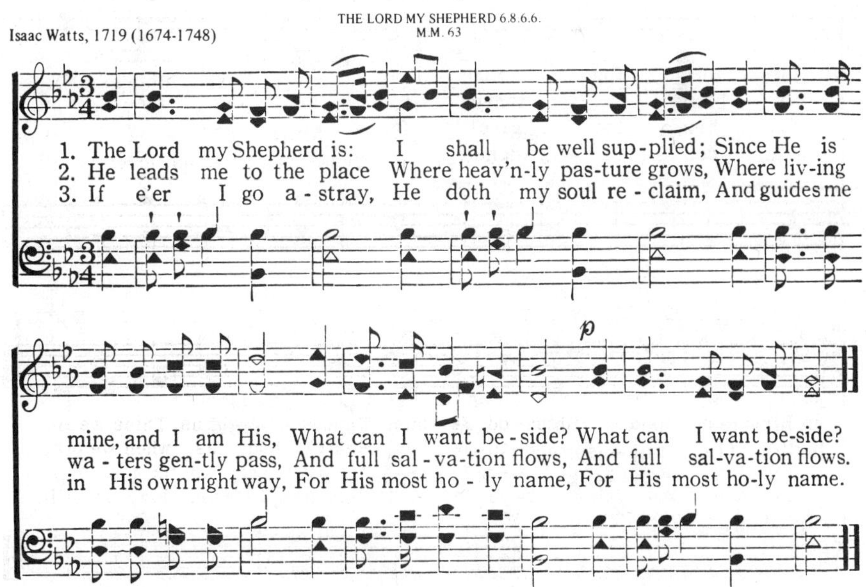
1. The Lord my Shepherd is: I shall be well sup - plied; Since He is
2. He leads me to the place Where heav'n-ly pas-ture grows, Where liv-ing
3. If e'er I go a - stray, He doth my soul re - claim, And guides me
p
mine, and I am His, What can I want be - side? What can I want be-side?
wa - ters gen-tly pass, And full sal - va-tion flows, And full sal-va-tion flows.
in His own right way, For His most ho - ly name, For His most ho-ly name.

# 157 ARISE, MY SOUL, ARISE

*He ever liveth to make intercession for them.* Heb. 7:25.

Charles Wesley, 1707-1788

DARWALL 148 6.6.6.6.8.8.
M.M. 92

John Darwall, 1770 (1731-1789)

1. A – rise, my soul, a – rise, Shake off thy guilt – y fears;
2. He ev – er lives a – bove, For me to in – ter – cede;
3. Five bleed – ing wounds He bears, Re – ceived on Cal – va – ry;
4. My God is rec – on – ciled, His par – d'ning voice I hear;
A bleed – ing Sac – ri – fice In my be – half ap – pears;
His all – re – deem – ing love, His pre – cious blood to plead;
They pour ef – fec – tual prayers, They strong – ly speak for me;
He owns me for His child, I can no lon – ger fear;
Be – fore the throne my Sure – ty stands, My
His blood a – toned for all our race, And
Oh, him for – give! for – give, they cry, Nor
With con – fi – dence I now draw nigh, And
name is writ – ten on His hands.
sprink – les now the throne of grace.
let the ran – somed sin – ner die.
Fa – ther, Ab – ba, Fa – ther, cry. A – men.

# THERE'S NOT A FRIEND LIKE THE LOWLY JESUS 158

*Ye are My friends, if ye do whatsoever I command you.* Jn. 15:14.

NO NOT ONE 10.6.10.6. with Ref.
M.M. 63
Johnson Oatman, Jr., 1856-1922
George C. Hugg, 1848-1907
Slow, and with great feeling.
1. There's not a friend like the low - ly Je - sus, No, not one! no, not one!
2. No friend like him is so high and ho - ly, No, not one! no, not one!
3. There's not an hour that he is not near us, No, not one! no, not one!
4. Did ev - er saint find this friend for - sake him? No, not one! no, not one!
5. Was e'er a gift like the Sav - iour giv - en? No, not one! no, not one!
None else could heal all our soul's dis - eas - es, No, not one! no, not one!
And yet no friend is so meek and low - ly, No, not one! no, not one!
No night so dark but his love can cheer us, No, not one! no, not one!
Or sin - ner find that he would not take him? No, not one! no, not one!
Will he re - fuse us a home in heav - en? No, not one! no, not one!
Refrain.
Je - sus knows all a - bout our struggles, He will guide till the day is done,
There's not a friend like the low - ly Je - sus, No, not one! no, not one!

# 159 I HAVE FOUND A FRIEND IN JESUS

*I am the . . . Lily of the Valleys.* Song of Sol. 2:1.

THE LILY OF THE VALLEY 8.6.11.8.6.11.
M.M. 63

J. R. Murray, c. 1887
Arr. Ira D. Sankey, 1887 (1840-1908)
Arr. John J. Overholt, 1969

Charles William Frye, 1837-1882

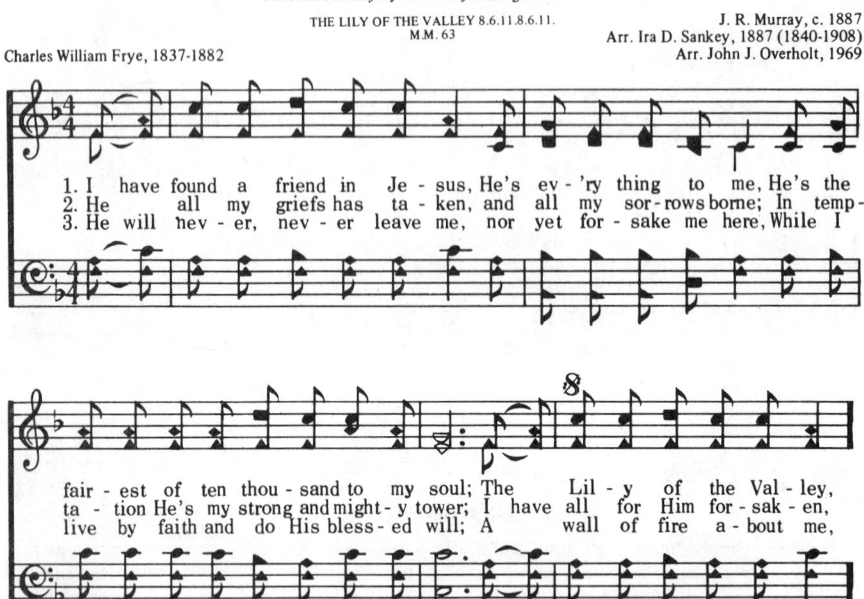
1. I have found a friend in Je - sus, He's ev - 'ry thing to me, He's the fair - est of ten thou - sand to my soul; The Lil - y of the Val - ley,
2. He all my griefs has ta - ken, and all my sor - rows borne; In temp - ta - tion He's my strong and might - y tower; I have all for Him for - sak - en,
3. He will nev - er, nev - er leave me, nor yet for - sake me here, While I live by faith and do His bless - ed will; A wall of fire a - bout me,
D. S. Lil - y of the Val - ley,

in Him a - lone I see, All I need to cleanse and make me ful - ly whole.
and all my i - dols torn From my heart, and now He keeps me by His pow'r.
I've noth - ing now to fear, With His man - na He my hun - gry soul doth feed.
the Bright and Morn - ing Star, He's the fair - est of ten thou - sand to my soul.

In sor - row He's my com - fort, in trou - ble He's my stay;
Though all the world for - sake me, and Sa - tan tempt me sore;
Then sweep - ing up to glo - ry to see His bless - ed face,

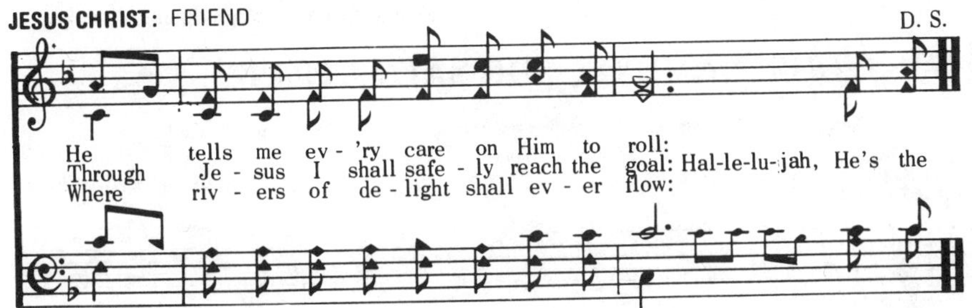
D. S.
He tells me ev - 'ry care on Him to roll:
Through Je - sus I shall safe - ly reach the goal: Hal-le-lu-jah, He's the
Where riv - ers of de - light shall ev - er flow:

# WHAT A FRIEND WE HAVE IN JESUS 160

*There is a friend that sticketh closer than a brother.* Prov. 18:24.

Joseph Medlicott Scriven, 1855 (1819-1886)

ERIE 8.7.8.7.D.
M.M. 66

Charles Crozot Converse, 1868 (1832-1918)

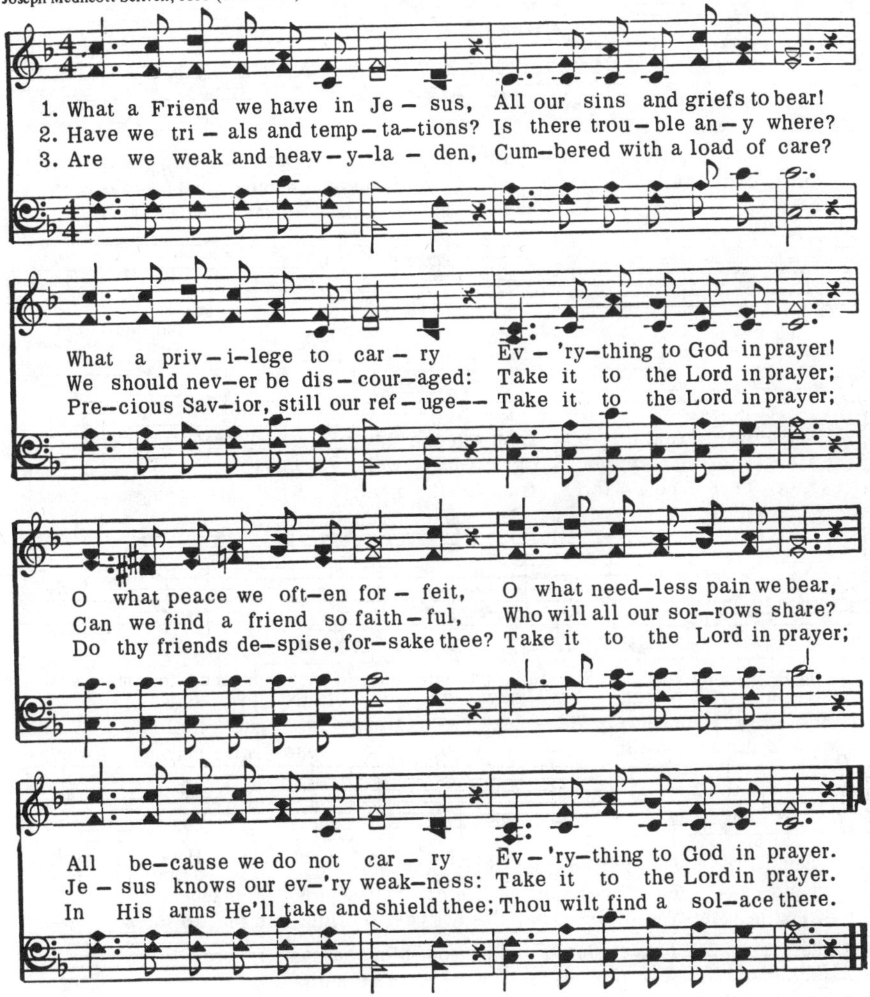

1. What a Friend we have in Je – sus, All our sins and griefs to bear!
2. Have we tri – als and temp – ta–tions? Is there trou – ble an – y where?
3. Are we weak and heav – y–la – den, Cum–bered with a load of care?

What a priv – i–lege to car – ry Ev – 'ry–thing to God in prayer!
We should nev–er be dis – cour–aged: Take it to the Lord in prayer;
Pre–cious Sav–ior, still our ref – uge–– Take it to the Lord in prayer;

O what peace we oft–en for – feit, O what need–less pain we bear,
Can we find a friend so faith – ful, Who will all our sor–rows share?
Do thy friends de–spise, for–sake thee? Take it to the Lord in prayer;

All be–cause we do not car – ry Ev – 'ry–thing to God in prayer.
Je – sus knows our ev–'ry weak–ness: Take it to the Lord in prayer.
In His arms He'll take and shield thee; Thou wilt find a sol–ace there.

# 161 JESUS, NAME OF OUR SALVATION

*There is none other name under heaven given among men, whereby we must be saved.* Acts 4:12.

Early Latin hymn
Tr. John Mason Neale, 1851 (1818-1866)
Alt, John J. Overholt, 1970

ZEUCH MICH, ZEUCH MICH 8.7.8.7.8.7.
M.M. 80

*Geistreiches Gesangbuch,*
Darmstadt, 1698

1. Je – sus, name of our sal – va – tion, Laud and hon – our
2. Je – sus is the name we treas – ure, Name be – yond what
3. 'Tis the name that who – so preach – eth Speaks like mu – sic
let us pay, Name for many – a gen – er – a – tion
words can tell; Name of glad – ness, name of pleas – ure,
to the ear; Who in prayer this name be – seech – eth
Hid in God's fore – know – ledge lay, Which with ho – ly
Ear and heart de – light – ing well; Name of sweet – ness
Sweet – est com – fort find – eth near; Who its per – fect
ex – ul – ta – tion We may sing a – loud to – day.
pass – ing meas – ure, Sav – ing us from sin and hell.
wis – dom reach – eth Heaven – ly joy pos – sess – eth here. A – men.

4. Jesus is the name exalted Over every other name;
In this name, whene'er assaulted, We can put our foes to shame;
Strength to them who else had halted, Eyes to blind, and feet to lame.

5. Therefore we, in love adoring, This most blessed name revere,
Holy Jesus, Thee imploring So to write it in us here,
That hereafter, heavenward soaring, We may praise with angels there. A–men.

# JESUS, LORD FROM HEAVEN 162

*I will . . . sing unto Thy Name.* Rom. 15:9.

John J. Overholt, 1968

KOCH 6.5.6.5.D.
M.M. 76

Mina Koch
Arranged by Compiler, 1968

1. Jesus, Lord from Heaven, Everlasting Light! (Matt 1:21; 1 Cor 15:47; Isa. 60:20)
Christ of God, the Chosen, King of Glory, Bright; (Lu 9:20; Lu 23:35; Psa 24:7-10; Rev 22:16)
Lord of dead and living, Prince of life, we bring (Rom 14:19; Acts 3:15)
Praise and adoration to our Lord and King.

2. Jesus, Lord of Glory, Living, Holy One, (1 Cor 2:8; 1 Pt 2:4; Psa 16:10)
Son of God Most Mighty, Rock, and Cornerstone; (Psa 45:3; 1 Cor 10:4; Eph 2:20)
Life and sure salvation, Lamb of God, we bring (Jn 14:16; Lu 2:30; Jn 1:29)
Praise and adoration to our Lord and King.

3. Jesus, Lord, Creator, Son of God and Man, (Rom 1:3; Gen 1:26; Heb 4:14; Matt 20:28)
Gift of God, our Saviour, Alpha and I AM; (Jn 4:10; Lu 2:11; Rev 1:8; Jn 8:58)
Prophet, Priest, Messiah, Sinner's Friend, we bring (Matt 21:11; Heb 7:17; Jn 1:41; Matt 11:19)
Praise and adoration to our Lord and King. (Matt 21:5)

*Repeat: Praise and adoration to our Lord and King.*

# 163 ALL HAIL THE POWER OF JESUS' NAME

*At the name of Jesus every knee should bow.* Phil. 2:10.

Edward Perronet, 1780 (1726-1792)

CORONATION 8.6.8.6.8.6.
M.M. 80

Oliver Holden, 1765-1844

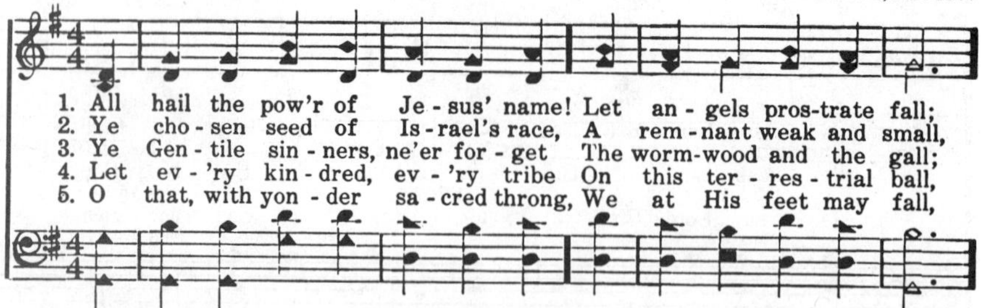

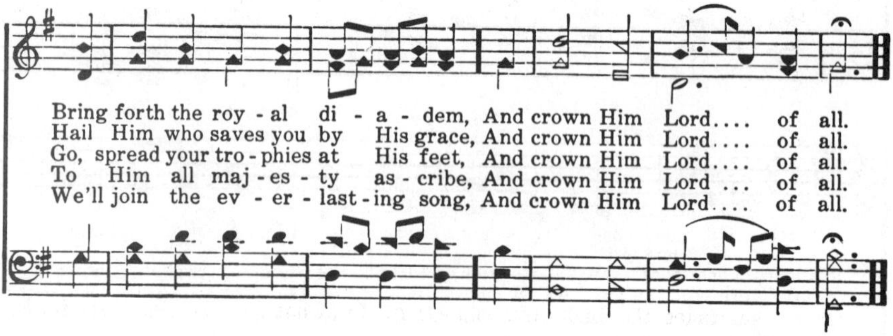

1. All hail the pow'r of Je - sus' name! Let an - gels pros-trate fall;
2. Ye cho - sen seed of Is - rael's race, A rem - nant weak and small,
3. Ye Gen - tile sin - ners, ne'er for - get The worm-wood and the gall;
4. Let ev - 'ry kin - dred, ev - 'ry tribe On this ter - res - trial ball,
5. O that, with yon - der sa - cred throng, We at His feet may fall,

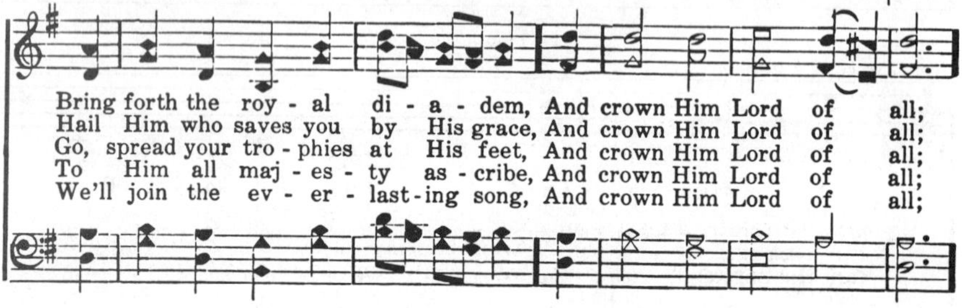

Bring forth the roy - al di - a - dem, And crown Him Lord of all;
Hail Him who saves you by His grace, And crown Him Lord of all;
Go, spread your tro - phies at His feet, And crown Him Lord of all;
To Him all maj - es - ty as - cribe, And crown Him Lord of all;
We'll join the ev - er - last-ing song, And crown Him Lord of all;

Bring forth the roy - al di - a - dem, And crown Him Lord.... of all.
Hail Him who saves you by His grace, And crown Him Lord.... of all.
Go, spread your tro - phies at His feet, And crown Him Lord.... of all.
To Him all maj - es - ty as - cribe, And crown Him Lord ... of all.
We'll join the ev - er - last - ing song, And crown Him Lord.... of all.

# 164 ALL PRAISE TO HIM WHO REIGNS ABOVE

*Wherefore God also hath highly exalted Him.* Phil. 2:9.

W. H. Clark, c. 1888

CHESTERFIELD C.M. 8.6.8.6.
M.M. 96

Thomas Haweis, 1733-1820

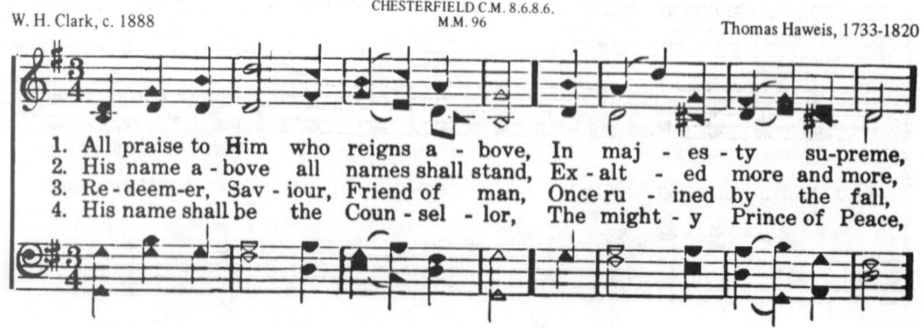
1. All praise to Him who reigns a - bove, In maj - es - ty su-preme,
2. His name a - bove all names shall stand, Ex - alt - ed more and more,
3. Re - deem-er, Sav - iour, Friend of man, Once ru - ined by the fall,
4. His name shall be the Coun - sel - lor, The might - y Prince of Peace,

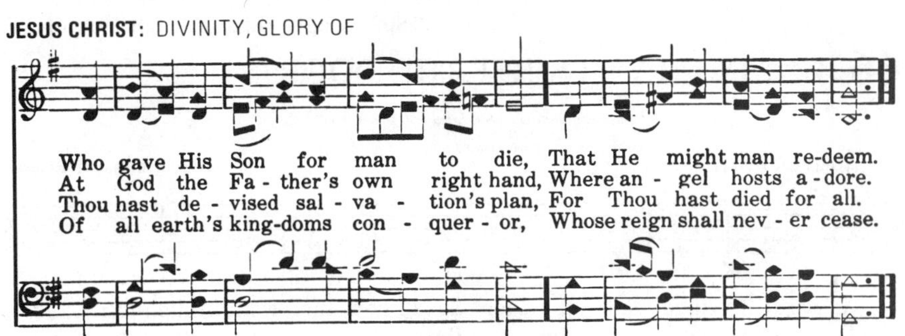
Who gave His Son for man to die, That He might man re-deem.
At God the Fa - ther's own right hand, Where an - gel hosts a - dore.
Thou hast de - vised sal - va - tion's plan, For Thou hast died for all.
Of all earth's king-doms con - quer - or, Whose reign shall nev - er cease.

# LOOK, YE SAINTS, THE SIGHT IS GLORIOUS 165

*On His head were many crowns.* Rev. 19:12.

Thomas Kelley, 1769-1855

CROWN HIM 8.7.8.7. with Ref.
M.M. 72

George Coles Stebbins, 1846-1945

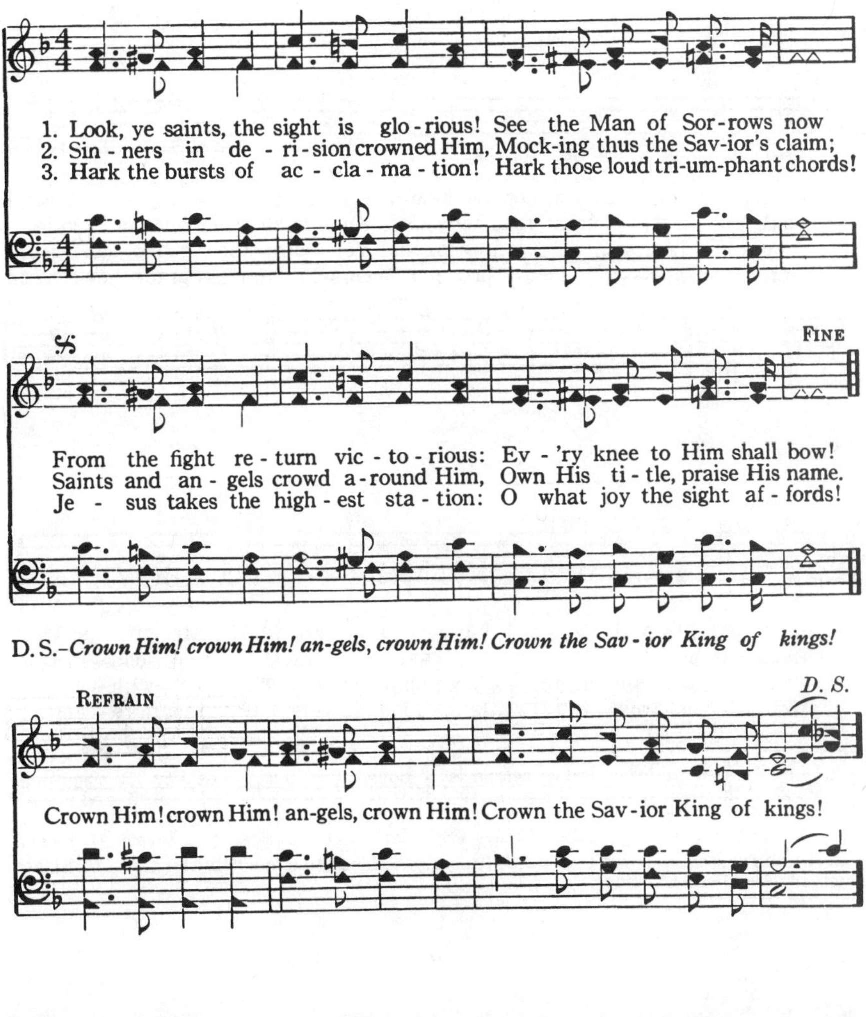

1. Look, ye saints, the sight is glo-rious! See the Man of Sor-rows now
2. Sin - ners in de - ri - sion crowned Him, Mock-ing thus the Sav-ior's claim;
3. Hark the bursts of ac - cla - ma - tion! Hark those loud tri-um-phant chords!

FINE

From the fight re - turn vic - to - rious: Ev - 'ry knee to Him shall bow!
Saints and an - gels crowd a - round Him, Own His ti - tle, praise His name.
Je - sus takes the high - est sta - tion: O what joy the sight af - fords!

D. S.-*Crown Him! crown Him! an-gels, crown Him! Crown the Sav - ior King of kings!*

REFRAIN

*D. S.*

Crown Him! crown Him! an-gels, crown Him! Crown the Sav-ior King of kings!

# 166 LORD, I HAVE SHUT THE DOOR

*I will hear what God the Lord will speak.* Ps. 85:8.

William, M. Runyan, 1870-1957

SANCTUARY 6.4.6.4.D.
M.M. 63

Willaim M. Runyan

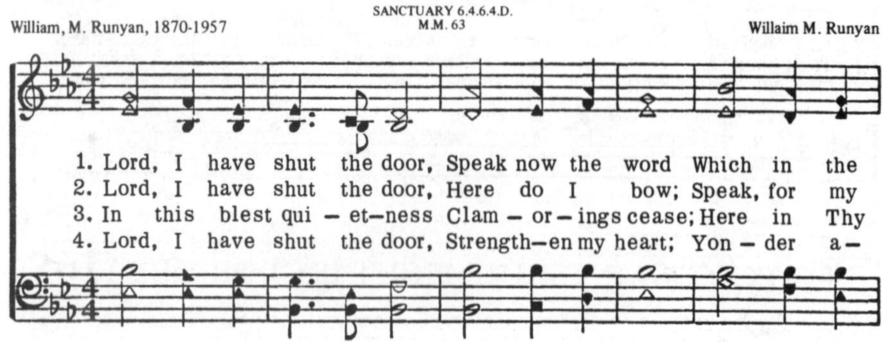
1. Lord, I have shut the door, Speak now the word Which in the
2. Lord, I have shut the door, Here do I bow; Speak, for my
3. In this blest qui – et–ness Clam – or – ings cease; Here in Thy
4. Lord, I have shut the door, Strength–en my heart; Yon – der a–

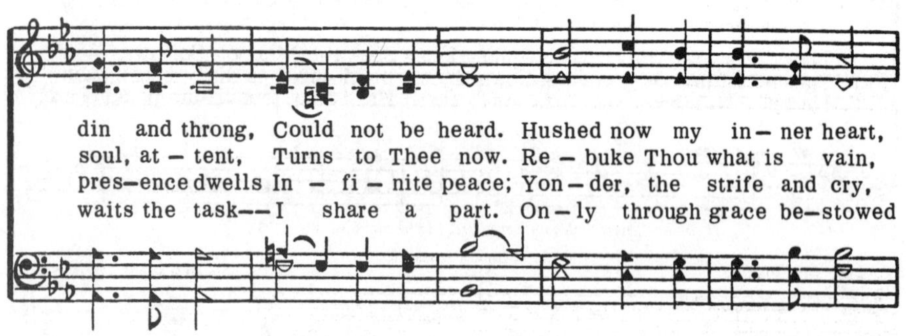
din and throng, Could not be heard. Hushed now my in – ner heart,
soul, at – tent, Turns to Thee now. Re – buke Thou what is vain,
pres–ence dwells In – fi – nite peace; Yon – der, the strife and cry,
waits the task—I share a part. On – ly through grace be–stowed

Whis–per Thy will, While I have come a–part, While all is still.
Coun–sel my soul, Thy ho – ly will re–veal, My will con – trol.
Yon – der, the sin: Lord, I have shut the door, Thou art with – in!
May I be true; Here, while a – lone with Thee, My strength re – new.

# WHEN WOUNDED SORE 167

*I will heal thee of thy wounds.* Jer. 30:17.

FOUNTAIN C.M. 8.6.8.6.
M.M. 60

Cecil Frances Alexander, 1858 (1818-1895) — Anonymous

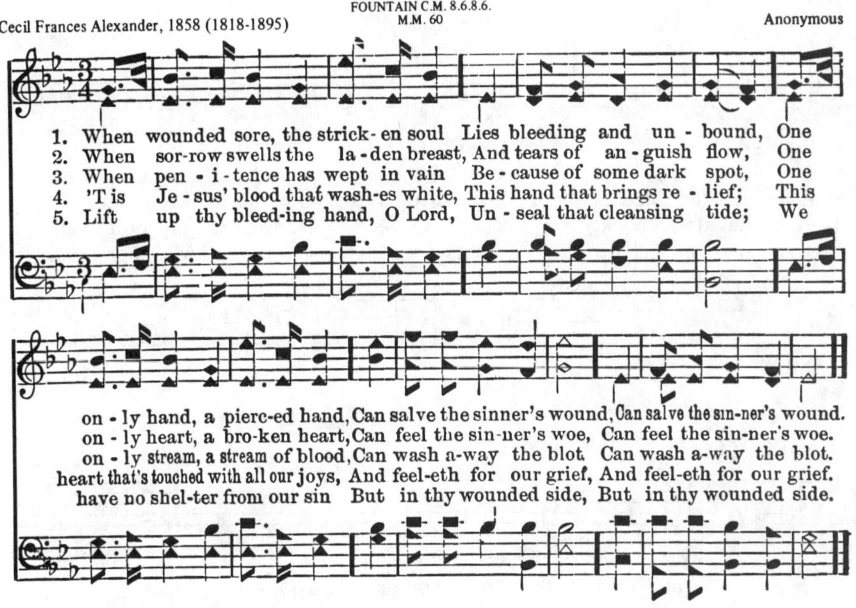
1. When wounded sore, the strick-en soul Lies bleeding and un - bound, One
2. When sor-row swells the la-den breast, And tears of an-guish flow, One
3. When pen - i - tence has wept in vain Be-cause of some dark spot, One
4. 'T is Je-sus' blood that wash-es white, This hand that brings re - lief; This
5. Lift up thy bleed-ing hand, O Lord, Un - seal that cleansing tide; We
on - ly hand, a pierc-ed hand, Can salve the sinner's wound, Can salve the sin-ner's wound.
on - ly heart, a bro-ken heart, Can feel the sin-ner's woe, Can feel the sin-ner's woe.
on - ly stream, a stream of blood, Can wash a-way the blot, Can wash a-way the blot.
heart that's touched with all our joys, And feel-eth for our grief, And feel-eth for our grief.
have no shel-ter from our sin But in thy wounded side, But in thy wounded side.

# PLUNGED IN A GULF 168

*In my distress I cried unto the Lord, and He heard me.* Ps. 120:1.

ST. NICHOLAS C.M. 8.6.8.6.
M.M. 56

Isaac Watts, 1674-1748 — Arr. William Henry Havergal, 1793-1870

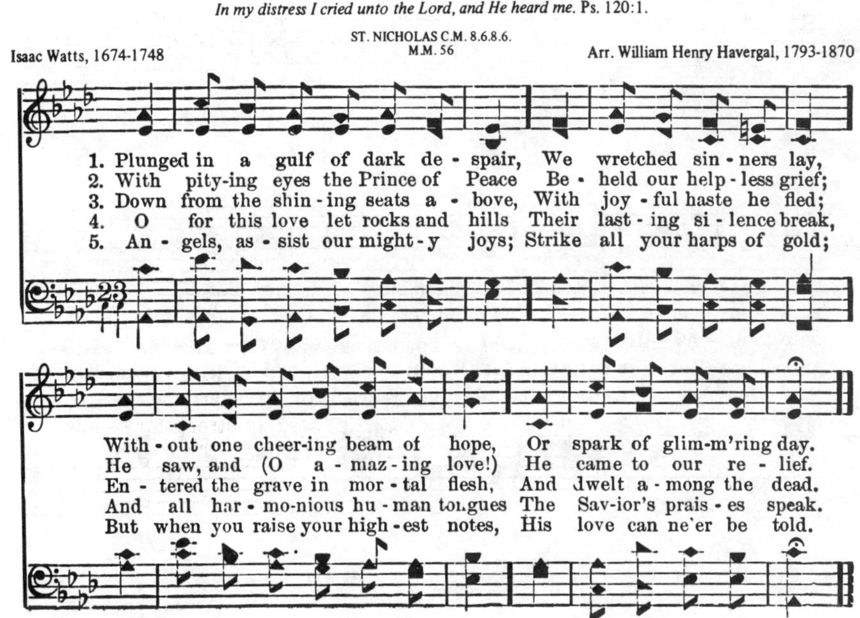
1. Plunged in a gulf of dark de - spair, We wretched sin - ners lay,
2. With pity-ing eyes the Prince of Peace Be - held our help - less grief;
3. Down from the shin - ing seats a - bove, With joy - ful haste he fled;
4. O for this love let rocks and hills Their last - ing si - lence break,
5. An - gels, as - sist our might - y joys; Strike all your harps of gold;
With - out one cheer-ing beam of hope, Or spark of glim-m'ring day.
He saw, and (O a - maz - ing love!) He came to our re - lief.
En - tered the grave in mor - tal flesh, And dwelt a - mong the dead.
And all har - mo-nious hu - man tongues The Sav-ior's prais - es speak.
But when you raise your high - est notes, His love can ne'er be told.

# 169 FOUNDATION TRUE, ART THOU, O LORD

*For other foundation can no man lay than that is laid, which is Jesus Christ.* I Cor. 3:11.

Wilmer D. Swope, 1970
Alt. John J. Overholt, 1970

PARK STREET L.M. 8.8.8.8. with Repeat
M.M. 80

Arr. from Frederick Maria Antione
Venua, 1788-1872

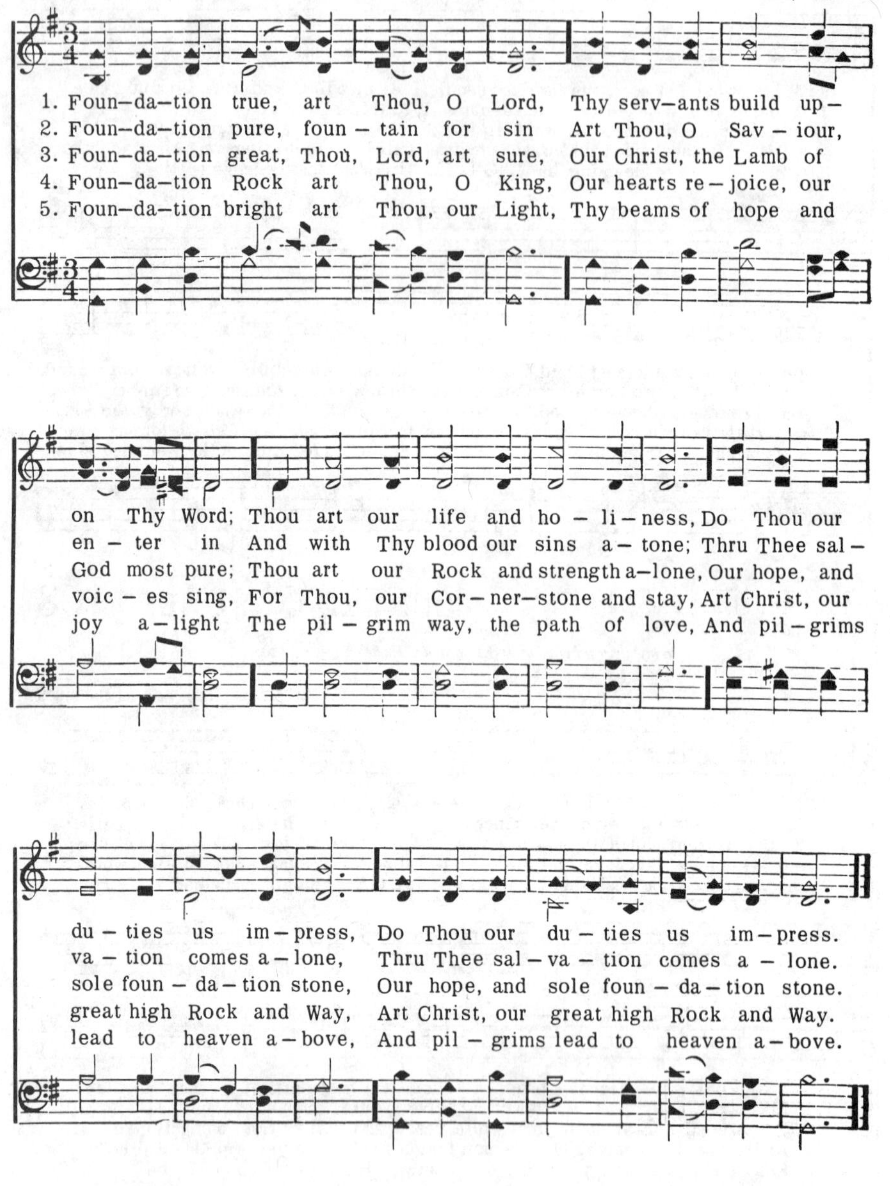
1. Foun–da–tion true, art Thou, O Lord, Thy serv–ants build up–
2. Foun–da–tion pure, foun – tain for sin Art Thou, O Sav – iour,
3. Foun–da–tion great, Thou, Lord, art sure, Our Christ, the Lamb of
4. Foun–da–tion Rock art Thou, O King, Our hearts re – joice, our
5. Foun–da–tion bright art Thou, our Light, Thy beams of hope and
on Thy Word; Thou art our life and ho – li – ness, Do Thou our
en – ter in And with Thy blood our sins a – tone; Thru Thee sal –
God most pure; Thou art our Rock and strength a–lone, Our hope, and
voic – es sing, For Thou, our Cor – ner–stone and stay, Art Christ, our
joy a – light The pil – grim way, the path of love, And pil – grims
du – ties us im – press, Do Thou our du – ties us im – press.
va – tion comes a – lone, Thru Thee sal – va – tion comes a – lone.
sole foun – da – tion stone, Our hope, and sole foun – da – tion stone.
great high Rock and Way, Art Christ, our great high Rock and Way.
lead to heaven a – bove, And pil – grims lead to heaven a – bove.

# I AM THE VINE 170

*I am the Vine, ye are the branches.* Jn. 15:5.

I AM THE VINE 10.9.10.9. with Ref.
M.M. 58
Knowles Shaw, 1834-1878
Knowles Shaw
1. "I am the vine and ye are the branch-es:" Bear pre-cious fruit for Je-sus to-day; Branch-es in Him no fruit ev-er bear-ing, Je-sus hath said, "He tak-eth a-way."
2. "Now ye are clean thro' words I have spo-ken; Liv-ing in me, much fruit ye shall bear; Dwell-ing in you, my prom-ise un-bro-ken, Glo-ry in heav'n with me ye shall share."
3. Yes, by your fruits the world is to know you, Walk-ing in love as chil-dren of day; Fol-low your Guide: He pass-eth be-fore you, Lead-ing to realms of glo-ri-ous day.
CHORUS
"I am the vine and ye are the branch-es; I am the vine, be faith-ful and true; Ask what ye will, your prayer shall be grant-ed; The Fa-ther loved me, so I have loved you."

# 171 LORD OF OUR LIFE

*In Him was life; and the life was the light of men.* Jn. 1:4.

Samuel Francis Smith, 1808-1895

LOUVAN L.M. 8.8.8.8.
M.M. 88

Virgil Corydon Taylor, 1817-1891

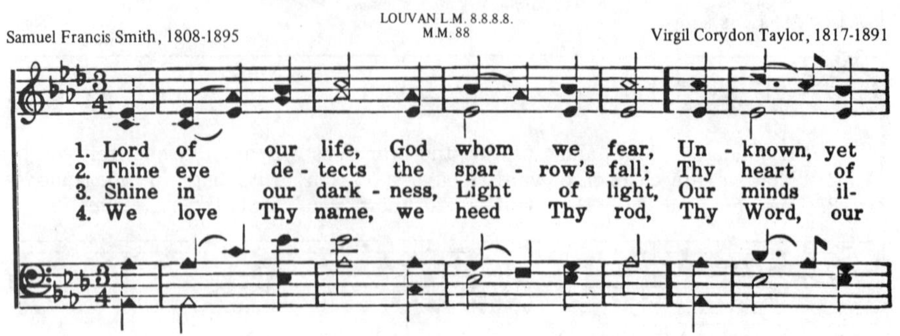
1. Lord of our life, God whom we fear, Un - known, yet
2. Thine eye de - tects the spar - row's fall; Thy heart of
3. Shine in our dark - ness, Light of light, Our minds il-
4. We love Thy name, we heed Thy rod, Thy Word, our

known; un - seen, yet near; Breath of our breath, in
love ex - pands for all; Our throb - bing life is
lume, dis - perse our night; Make us re - spon - sive
law; O gra - cious God! We wait Thy will; on

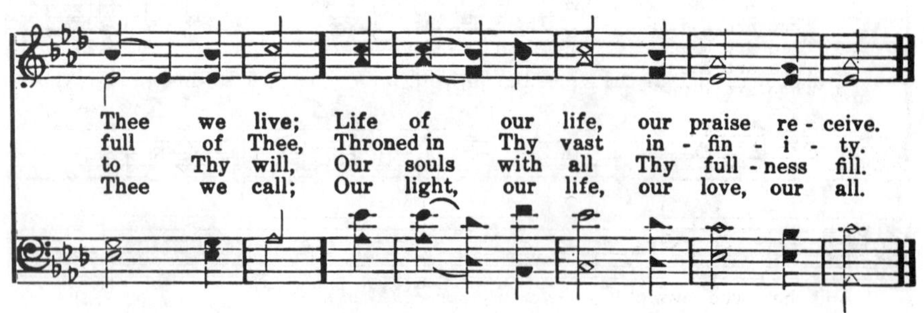
Thee we live; Life of our life, our praise re - ceive.
full of Thee, Throned in Thy vast in - fin - i - ty.
to Thy will, Our souls with all Thy full - ness fill.
Thee we call; Our light, our life, our love, our all.

# O EVERLASTING LIGHT 172

*I am the Light of the world.* Jn. 8:12.

O EVERLASTING LIGHT S.M. 6.6.8.6.
M.M. 80

Horatius Bonar, 1808-1889 — Eli S. Hallman

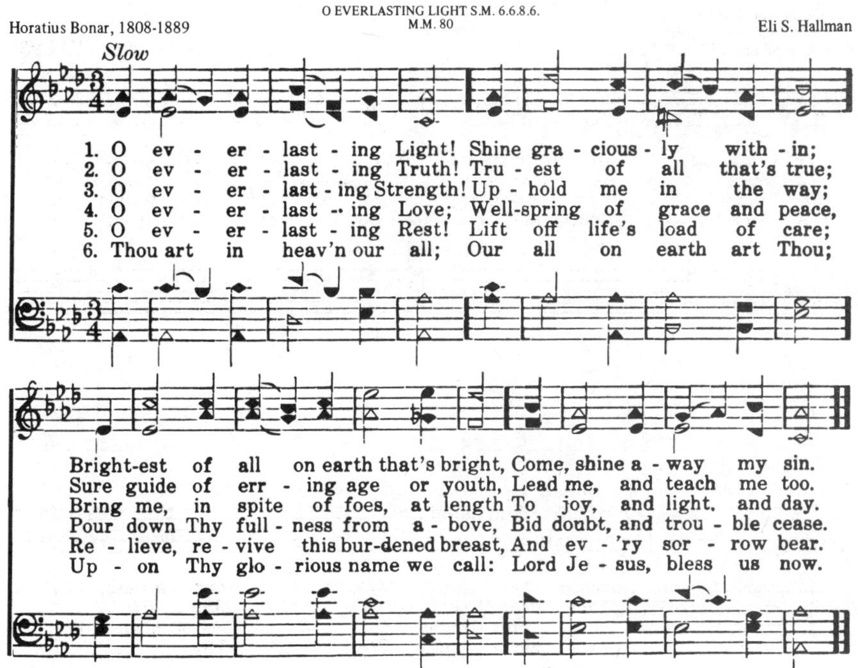
Slow
1. O ev - er - last - ing Light! Shine gra - cious - ly with - in;
2. O ev - er - last - ing Truth! Tru - est of all that's true;
3. O ev - er - last - ing Strength! Up - hold me in the way;
4. O ev - er - last - ing Love; Well-spring of grace and peace,
5. O ev - er - last - ing Rest! Lift off life's load of care;
6. Thou art in heav'n our all; Our all on earth art Thou;
Bright-est of all on earth that's bright, Come, shine a - way my sin.
Sure guide of err - ing age or youth, Lead me, and teach me too.
Bring me, in spite of foes, at length To joy, and light, and day.
Pour down Thy full - ness from a - bove, Bid doubt, and trou - ble cease.
Re - lieve, re - vive this bur-dened breast, And ev - 'ry sor - row bear.
Up - on Thy glo - rious name we call: Lord Je - sus, bless us now.

# THOU ART THE WAY 173

*I am the Way, the Truth, and the Life.* Jn. 14:6.

POLLOCK C.M. 8.6.8.6.
M.M. 66

George W. Doane, 1799-1859 — Charles Edward Pollock, b. 1853

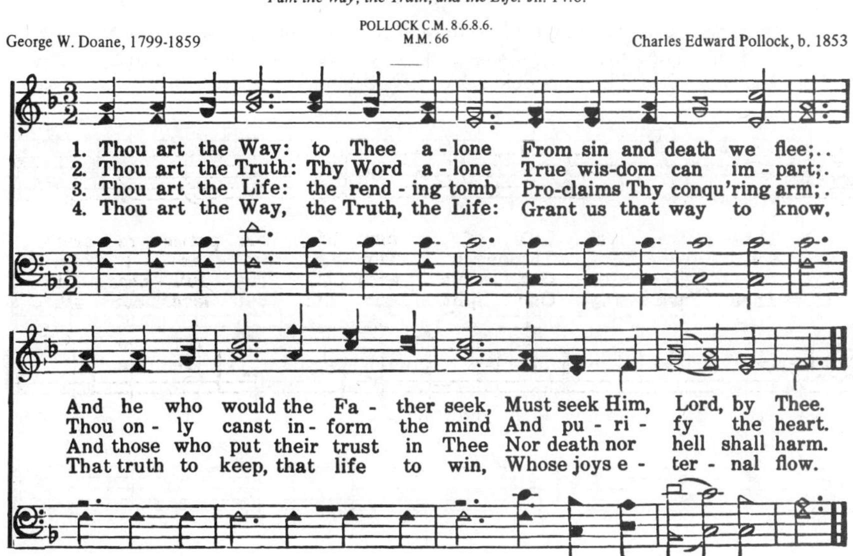
1. Thou art the Way: to Thee a - lone From sin and death we flee;
2. Thou art the Truth: Thy Word a - lone True wis-dom can im - part;
3. Thou art the Life: the rend - ing tomb Pro-claims Thy conqu'ring arm;
4. Thou art the Way, the Truth, the Life: Grant us that way to know,
And he who would the Fa - ther seek, Must seek Him, Lord, by Thee.
Thou on - ly canst in - form the mind And pu - ri - fy the heart.
And those who put their trust in Thee Nor death nor hell shall harm.
That truth to keep, that life to win, Whose joys e - ter - nal flow.

# 174 O POWER OF LOVE

*Who shall separate us from the love of Christ?* Rom. 8:35.

Gerhard Tersteegen, 1757 (1697-1769)
*Ich bete an die Macht der Liebe*
Tr. Herman Brückner, 1942 (1866-1942)

ST. PETERSBURG 9.8.9.8.9.9.
M.M. 92

Dimitri S. Bortniansky, 1825 (1751-1825)

1 O power of love, all else tran - scend - ing In Je - sus pres - ent ev - er - more, I wor - ship Thee, in hom - age bend - ing, Thy name to hon - or and a - dore: Yea, let my soul, in deep de - vo - tion, Bathe in love's might - y bound - less o - cean.
2 Thou art my rest, no earth - ly treas - ure Can sat - is - fy my yearn - ing heart, And naught can give to me the pleas - ure I find in Thee, my cho - sen part, Thy love, so ten - der, so pos - sess - ing, Is joy to me, and ev - ery bless - ing.
3 To Thee my heart and life be giv - en, Thou art in truth my high - est good; For me Thy sa - cred side was riv - en, For me was shed Thy pre - cious blood. O Thou who art the world's sal - va - tion, Be Thine my love and ad - o - ra - tion. A - men.

# JESUS, THY BOUNDLESS LOVE TO ME 175

*To know the love of Christ, which passeth knowledge.* Eph. 3:19.

Paul Gerhardt, 1666 (1607-1676)
*O Jesu Christ, mein schönstes Licht*
Tr. John Wesley, 1739 (1703-1791)
ST. PETERSBURG NEW 8.8.8.8.8.8.
M.M. 88
Dimitri S. Bortniansky, 1825 (1751-1825)
1. Je - sus, Thy bound - less love to me No tho't can reach, no
2. Thy love, how cheer - ing is its ray! All pain be - fore its
3. O draw me, Sav - iour, aft - er Thee! So shall I run and
4. Still let Thy love point out my way; How won - drous things Thy
5. In suf - f'ring be Thy love my peace, In weak - ness be Thy
tongue de - clare; U - nite my thank - ful heart to Thee, And
pres - ence flies; Care, an - guish, sor - row, melt a - way, Wher-
nev - er tire. With gra - cious words still com - fort me; Be
love hath wrought! Still lead me, lest I go a - stray; Di-
love my pow'r; And when the storms of life shall cease, Je-
reign with - out a ri - - val there. Thine whol - ly, Thine a-
e'er its heal - ing beams a - rise: O Je - sus, noth - ing
Thou my hope, my sole de - sire. Free me from ev - 'ry
rect my work, in - spire my thought; And if I fall, soon
sus, in that im - por - tant hour, In death as life be
lone I am; My soul with con - stant love a - flame.
may I see, Noth - ing de - sire or seek but Thee.
weight: nor fear Nor sin can come, if Thou art here.
may I hear Thy voice, and know that love is near.
Thou my guide, And save me, who for me hast died!

# 176 ALAS, AND DID MY SAVIOUR BLEED

*The Son of God, who loved me, and gave Himself for me.* Gal. 2:20.

Isaac Watts, 1674-1748
Response by Compiler, 1970

HE LOVES ME 8.6.8.6. with Ref.
M.M. 63

Anonymous

1. A - las! and did my Sav - iour bleed? And did my Sov - 'reign die?
2. Was it for crimes that I have done, He groaned up - on the tree?
3. Well might the sun in dark - ness hide, And shut his glo - ries in,
4. Thus might I hide my blush - ing face While His dear cross ap - pears;
5. But drops of grief can ne'er re - pay The debt of love I owe;
Would He de - vote that sa - cred head For such a worm as I?
A - maz - ing pit - y! grace un-known! And love be - yond de - gree!
When God's own Son was cru - ci - fied For man, the crea - ture's sin.
Dis - solve my heart in thank - ful - ness, And melt mine eyes to tears.
Here, Lord, I give my - self a - way; 'Tis all that I can do.
REFRAIN Faster.
He loves me, He loves me. He loves me this I know;(I know ;)
Response
I love Him, I love Him, I love Him this I know; ( I know: )
He gave Him - self to die for me, Be - cause He loves me so.
I yield my life, my all to Him, Be - cause I love Him so.

# BENEATH THE CROSS OF JESUS 177

*Who for the joy that was set before Him endured the cross, despising the shame.* Heb. 12:2.

ST. CHRISTOPHER 7.6.8.6.8.6.8.6.
M.M. 76

Elizabeth C. Clephane, 1867 (1830-1869)

Frederick Charles Maker, 1881 (1844-1927)

1. Be - neath the cross of Je - sus I fain would take my stand,—
2. Up - on that cross of Je - sus Mine eye at times can see
3. I take the cross and shad - ow For my a - bid - ing place;
The shad - ow of a might - y rock With - in a wea - ry land;
The ver - y dy - ing form of One Who suf - fered there for me;
I ask no oth - er sun - shine than The sun - shine of His face,—
A home with - in the wil - der - ness, A rest up - on the way,
And from my smit - ten heart with tears Two won - ders I con - fess,—
Con - tent to let the world go by, To know no gain nor loss,
From the burn - ing of the noon - tide heat, And the bur - den of the day.
The won - ders of His glo - rious love And my un - wor - thi - ness.
My sin - ful self my on - ly shame, My glo - ry all the cross.

# 178 ROCK OF AGES

*Who is a Rock save our God?* Ps. 18:31.

Augustus Montague Toplady, 1776 (1740-1778)
Alt. Thomas Cotterill, 1779-1823

REDHEAD 7.7.7.7.7.7.
M.M. 66

Richard Redhead, 1820-1901

1. Rock of A - ges, cleft for me, Let me hide my-
2. Not the la - bour of my hands Can ful - fil Thy
3. No - thing in my hand I bring, Sim - ply to Thy
4. While I draw this fleet - ing breath, Should mine eye - lids
self in Thee! Let the wa - ter and the blood,
law's de - mands; Could my zeal no res - pite know,
Cross I cling; Nak - ed, come to Thee for dress;
close in death, When I soar to worlds un - known,
From Thy riv - en side which flow'd, Be of sin the
Could my tears for ev - er flow, All for sin could
Help - less, look to Thee for grace; Foul, I to the
See Thee on Thy judg - ment throne, Rock of A - ges,
per — fect cure; Cleanse me from its guilt and pow'r.
not a - tone; Thou must save, and Thou a - lone.
foun - tain fly; Wash me, Sav - iour, or I die!
cleft for me, Let me hide my - self in Thee.

## ROCK OF AGES 179

*They drank of that spiritual Rock that followed them: and that Rock was Christ.* I Cor. 10:4.

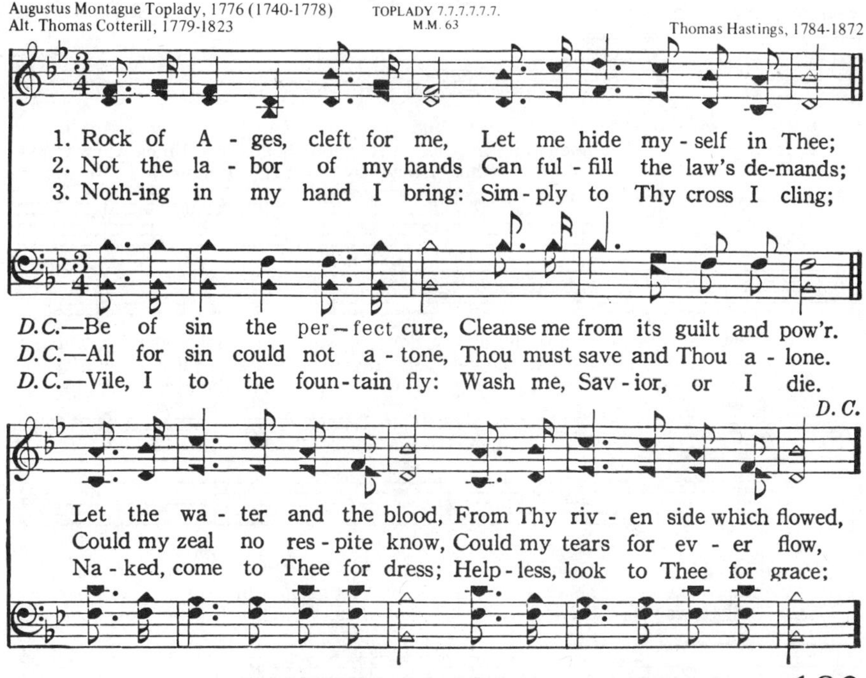
Augustus Montague Toplady, 1776 (1740-1778)
Alt. Thomas Cotterill, 1779-1823
TOPLADY 7.7.7.7.7.7.
M.M. 63
Thomas Hastings, 1784-1872
1. Rock of A - ges, cleft for me, Let me hide my - self in Thee;
2. Not the la - bor of my hands Can ful - fill the law's de-mands;
3. Noth-ing in my hand I bring: Sim - ply to Thy cross I cling;
D.C.—Be of sin the per – fect cure, Cleanse me from its guilt and pow'r.
D.C.—All for sin could not a - tone, Thou must save and Thou a - lone.
D.C.—Vile, I to the foun-tain fly: Wash me, Sav - ior, or I die.
D. C.
Let the wa - ter and the blood, From Thy riv - en side which flowed,
Could my zeal no res - pite know, Could my tears for ev - er flow,
Na - ked, come to Thee for dress; Help - less, look to Thee for grace;

## FROM EVERY STORMY WIND 180

*An hiding place from the wind, and a covert from the tempest.* Is. 32:2.

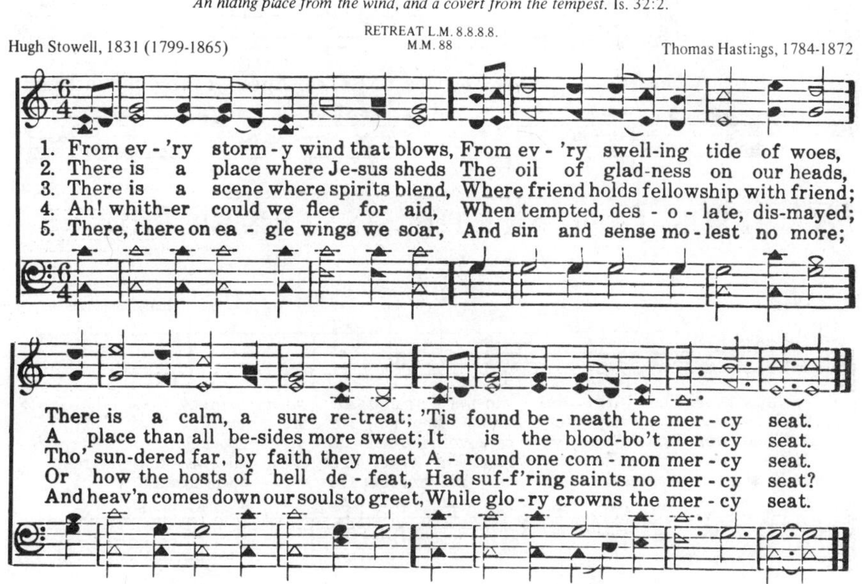
RETREAT L.M. 8.8.8.8.
M.M. 88
Hugh Stowell, 1831 (1799-1865)
Thomas Hastings, 1784-1872
1. From ev - 'ry storm - y wind that blows, From ev - 'ry swell-ing tide of woes,
2. There is a place where Je-sus sheds The oil of glad-ness on our heads,
3. There is a scene where spirits blend, Where friend holds fellowship with friend;
4. Ah! whith-er could we flee for aid, When tempted, des - o - late, dis-mayed;
5. There, there on ea - gle wings we soar, And sin and sense mo - lest no more;
There is a calm, a sure re-treat; 'Tis found be - neath the mer - cy seat.
A place than all be-sides more sweet; It is the blood-bo't mer - cy seat.
Tho' sun-dered far, by faith they meet A - round one com - mon mer - cy seat.
Or how the hosts of hell de - feat, Had suf-f'ring saints no mer - cy seat?
And heav'n comes down our souls to greet, While glo - ry crowns the mer - cy seat.

# 181 O SAFE TO THE ROCK

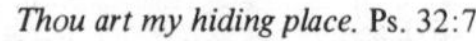

*Thou art my hiding place.* Ps. 32:7.

HIDING IN THEE 11.11.11.11. with Ref.
M.M. 60

William Orcutt Cushing, 1823-1902 — Ira David Sankey, 1840-1908

1. O safe to the Rock that is high - er than I, My soul in its
2. In the calm of the noon-tide, in sor - row's lone hour, In times when temp-
3. How oft in the con-flict, when pressed by the foe, I have fled to my

con - flicts and sor - rows would fly; So sin - ful, so wea - ry, Thine,
ta - tion casts o'er me its power; In the tem - pests of life, on its
Ref - uge and breathed out my woe; How oft - en, when tri - als like

Thine would I be; Thou blest "Rock of A - ges," I'm hid - ing in Thee.
wide, heav-ing sea, Thou blest "Rock of A - ges," I'm hid - ing in Thee.
sea - bil - lows roll, Have I hid - den in Thee, O Thou Rock of my soul.

CHORUS

Hid-ing in Thee, Hid-ing in Thee, Thou blest "Rock of Ages," I'm hid-ing in Thee.

# 182 JESUS, THOU ART THE SINNER'S FRIEND

*The Son of man . . . a friend of . . . sinners!* Lu. 7:34.

I DO BELIEVE C.M. 8.6.8.6.
M.M. 60

Richard Burham, 1749-1810 — Early American Melody

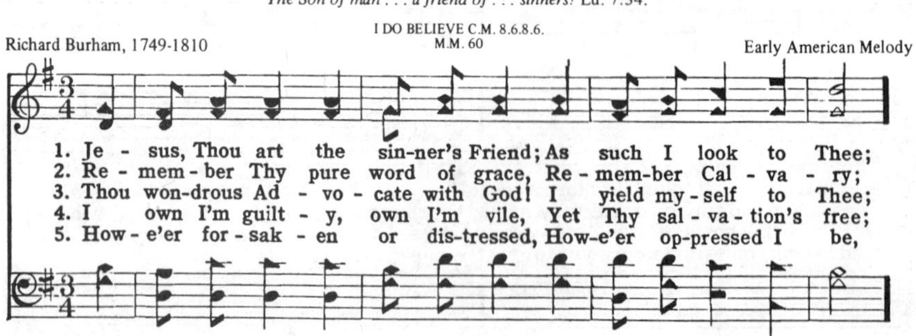
1. Je - sus, Thou art the sin-ner's Friend; As such I look to Thee;
2. Re - mem - ber Thy pure word of grace, Re - mem-ber Cal - va - ry;
3. Thou won-drous Ad - vo - cate with God! I yield my - self to Thee;
4. I own I'm guilt - y, own I'm vile, Yet Thy sal - va - tion's free;
5. How - e'er for - sak - en or dis-tressed, How-e'er op-pressed I be,

Now in the ful - ness of Thy love, O Lord! re - mem - ber me.
Re - mem-ber all Thy dy - ing groans, And then re - mem - ber me.
While Thou art sit - ting on Thy throne, O Lord! re - mem - ber me.
Then in Thy all a - bound - ing grace, O Lord! re - mem - ber me.
How - e'er af - flict - ed here on earth, Do Thou re - mem - ber me.

# WHEN STORMS AROUND ARE SWEEPING 183

*According to Thy mercy remember Thou me for Thy goodness' sake.* Ps. 25:7.

REMEMBER ME O MIGHTY ONE 7.7.7.7. with Ref.
M.M. 66

Anonymous — Johanna Kinkel, arr.

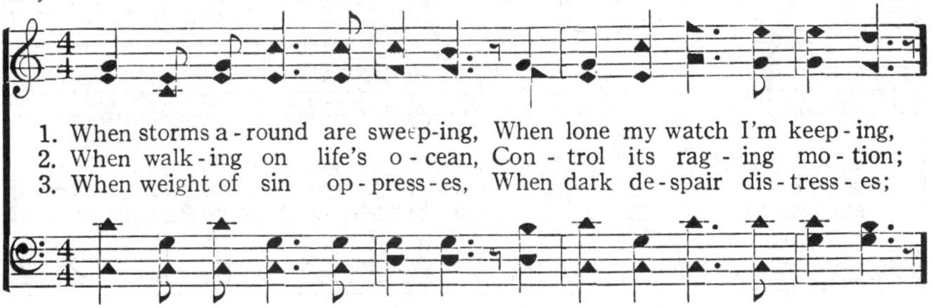

1. When storms a - round are sweep-ing, When lone my watch I'm keep - ing,
2. When walk - ing on life's o - cean, Con - trol its rag - ing mo - tion;
3. When weight of sin op - press - es, When dark de - spair dis - tress - es;

'Mid fires of e - vil fall - ing, 'Mid tempt - ers' voic - es call - ing,
When from its dan - gers shrink-ing, When in its dread deeps sink - ing,
All through the life that's mor - tal, And when I pass death's por - tal,

CHORUS

Re-mem-ber me, O might - y One! Re-mem-ber me, O might-y One!

# 184 JESUS, LOVER OF MY SOUL

*For Thou hast been a strength . . . a refuge from the storm, a shadow from the heat.* Is. 25:4.

HOLLINGSIDE 7.7.7.7.D.
M.M. 66
Charles Wesley, 1740 (1707-1788)
John Bacchus Dykes, 1861 (1823-1876)
1. Je - sus, lov - er of my soul, Let me to Thy bos - om fly,
2. Oth - er ref - uge have I none; Hangs my help-less soul on Thee;
3. Thou, O Christ, art all I want; More than all in Thee I find;
4. Plenteous grace with Thee is found, Grace to par - don all my sin;
While the near - er wa - ters roll, While the tem - pest still is high:
Leave, oh, leave me not a - lone, Still sup - port and com - fort me.
Raise the fall - en, cheer the faint, Heal the sick, and lead the blind.
Let the heal - ing streams a - bound; Make and keep me pure with - in.
Hide me, O my Sav - iour, hide, Till the storm of life is past;
All my trust on Thee is stayed, All my help from Thee I bring;
Just and ho - ly is Thy name, I am all un - right-eous-ness;
Thou of life the foun-tain art, Free - ly let me take of Thee;
Safe in - to the ha - ven guide, O re - ceive my soul at last.
Cov - er my de-fense - less head With the shad-ow of Thy wing.
False, and full of sin, I am, Thou art full of truth and grace.
Spring Thou up with - in my heart, Rise to all e - ter - ni - ty.
A - MEN.

# JESUS, LOVER OF MY SOUL 185

*The Lord . . . is my refuge and my fortress.* Ps. 91:2.

MARTYN 7.7.7.7.D.
M.M. 100
Charles Wesley, 1740 (1707-1788)
Simeon Butler Marsh, 1798-1875
1. Je - sus, lov - er of my soul, Let me to Thy bos - om fly,
2. Oth - er ref - uge have I none; Hangs my help - less soul on Thee;
3. Thou, O Christ, art all I want; More than all in Thee I find;
4. Plenteous grace with Thee is found, Grace to par - don all my sin;
While the near - er wa - ters roll, While the tem - pest still is high:
Leave, oh, leave me not a - lone, Still sup - port and com - fort me.
Raise the fall - en, cheer the faint, Heal the sick, and lead the blind.
Let the heal - ing streams abound; Make and keep me pure with - in.
Hide me, O my Sav - iour, hide, Till the storm of life is past;
All my trust on Thee is stayed, All my help from Thee I bring;
Just and ho - ly is Thy name, I am all un - right - eous - ness;
Thou of life the foun - tain art, Free - ly let me take of Thee;
Safe in - to the ha - ven guide, O re - ceive my soul at last.
Cov - er my de - fense - less head With the shad - ow of Thy wing.
False, and full of sin, I am, Thou art full of truth and grace.
Spring Thou up with - in my heart, Rise to all e - ter - ni - ty.

# 186 JESUS, LOVER OF MY SOUL

*Who loved me, and gave Himself for me.* Gal. 2:20.

Charles Wesley, 1740 (1707-1788)

REFUGE 7.7.7.7.D.
M.M. 56

Joseph Perry Holbrook, 1822-1888)

1. Je - sus, lov - er of my soul, Let me to Thy bos - om fly,
While the near - er wa - ters roll, While the tem - pest still is high:
Hide me, O my Sav - iour, hide, Till the storm of life is past;
Safe in - to the ha - ven guide, O re - ceive my soul at last.

2. Oth - er ref - uge have I none, Hangs my help - less soul on Thee;
Leave, oh, leave me not a - lone, Still sup - port and com-fort me.
All my trust on Thee is stayed, All my help from Thee I bring;
Cov - er my de - fense-less head With the shad - ow of Thy wing.

3. Thou, O Christ, art all I want; More than all in Thee I find;
Raise the fall - en, cheer the faint, Heal the sick, and lead the blind.
Just and ho - ly is Thy name, I am all un - right-eous-ness;
False, and full of sin, I am, Thou art full of truth and grace.

4. Plenteous grace with Thee is found, Grace to par - don all my sin;
Let the heal - ing streams abound; Make and keep me pure with-in.
Thou of life the foun - tain art, Free - ly let me take of Thee;
Spring Thou up with - in my heart, Rise to all e - ter - ni - ty.

# JESUS, LOVER OF MY SOUL 187

*A king shall reign . . . and . . . shall be as an hiding place.* Is. 32:1-2.

ABERYSTWYTH 7.7.7.7.D.
M.M. 60

Charles Wesley, 1740 (1707-1788)

Joseph Parry, 1879 (1841-1903)

1 Je - sus, lov - er of my soul, Let me to Thy bos - om fly,
2 Oth - er ref - uge have I none; Hangs my help - less soul on Thee;
3 Thou, O Christ, art all I want, More than all in Thee I find:
4 Plen - teous grace with Thee is found, Grace to cov - er all my sin;
While the near - er wa - ters roll, While the tem - pest still is high;
Leave, ah, leave me not a - lone, Still sup - port and com - fort me.
Raise the fall - en, cheer the faint, Heal the sick, and lead the blind,
Let the heal - ing streams a - bound, Make and keep me pure with - in.
Hide me, O my Sav - ior, hide, Till the storm of life is past;
All my trust on Thee is stayed, All my help from Thee I bring;
Just and ho - ly is Thy name, I am all un - right - eous-ness;
Thou of life the foun - tain art, Free - ly let me take of Thee;
Safe in - to the ha - ven guide, O re - ceive my soul at last.
Cov - er my de - fence-less head With the shad - ow of Thy wing.
False and full of sin I am, Thou art full of truth and grace.
Spring Thou up with - in my heart, Rise to all e - ter - ni - ty. A - men.

# 188 SHEPHERD OF TENDER YOUTH

*Thou art worthy, O Lord, to receive glory and honor and power.* Rev. 4:11.

Clemet of Alexandria, 170-220
Στόμιον πώλων ἀδαῶν
Tr. Henry Martyn Dexter, 1821-1890

BRAUN 6.6.4.6.6.6.4.
M.M. 69

Johann G. Braun, c. 1675

1. Shep - herd of ten - der youth, Guid - ing in love and truth
2. Thou art our Ho - ly Lord, The all - sub - du - ing Word,
3. Thou art the Great High Priest, Thou hast pre - pared the feast
4. Ev - er be Thou our Guide, Our Shep - herd and our Pride,
5. So now and till we die, Sound we Thy prais - es high,

Thro' de - vious ways: Christ, our tri - um - phant King, We come Thy
Heal - er of strife: Thou didst Thy - self a - base, That from sin's
Of heav'n - ly love: While in our mor - tal pain, None calls on
Our Staff and Song: Je - sus, Thou Christ of God, By Thy per-
And joy - ful sing: In - fants, and the glad throng Who to Thy

name to sing; Hith - er our chil - dren bring, To shout Thy praise.
deep dis - grace Thou might-est save our race, And give us life.
Thee in vain: Help Thou dost not dis - dain, Help from a - bove.
en - nial Word, Lead us where Thou hast trod; Make our faith strong.
Church be - long, U - nite to swell the song To Christ our King.

# 189 JESUS, THE VERY THOUGHT OF THEE

*Christ is all, and in all.* Col. 3:11.

Anonymous source prior to
Bernard of Clairvaux, 1091-1153
*Jesu, dulcis memoria*
Tr. Edward Caswall, 1849 (1814-1878)

ST. AGNES C.M. 8.6.8.6.
M.M. 80

John Bacchus Dykes, 1823-1876

1. Je - sus, the ver - y thought of Thee With sweetness fills my breast;
2. Nor voice can sing, nor heart can frame, Nor can the mem - 'ry find
3. Oh, Hope of ev - 'ry con - trite heart! Oh, Joy of all the meek!
4. And those who find Thee, find a bliss Nor tongue nor pen can show;
5. Je - sus! our on - ly joy be Thou, As Thou our prize wilt be;

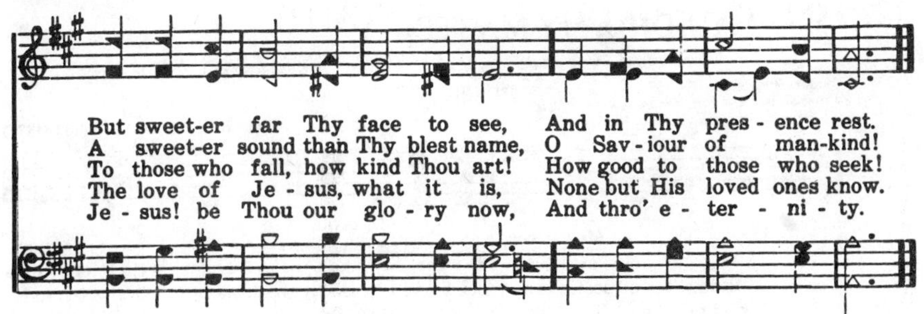
But sweet-er far Thy face to see, And in Thy pres - ence rest.
A sweet-er sound than Thy blest name, O Sav - iour of man-kind!
To those who fall, how kind Thou art! How good to those who seek!
The love of Je - sus, what it is, None but His loved ones know.
Je - sus! be Thou our glo - ry now, And thro' e - ter - ni - ty.

# MY JESUS, I LOVE THEE 190

*We love Him, because He first loved us.* I Jn. 4:19.

GORDON 11.11.11.11.
M.M. 76

*The London Hymn Book*, 1864

Adoniram Judson Gordon, 1836-1895

1. My Je - sus, I love Thee, I know Thou art mine; For Thee all the
2. I love Thee be - cause Thou hast first lov - ed me, And pur-chased my
3. I will love Thee in life, I will love Thee in death, And praise Thee as
4. In man-sions of glo - ry and end - less de - light, I'll ev - er a-

fol - lies of sin I re - sign; My gra - cious Re - deem - er, my
par - don on Cal - va - ry's tree; I love Thee for wear - ing the
long as Thou lend - est me breath; And say when the death - dew lies
dore Thee in heav - en so bright; I'll sing with the glit - ter - ing

Sav - iour art Thou, If ev - er I loved Thee, my Je - sus, 'tis now.
thorns on Thy brow; If ev - er I loved Thee, my Je - sus, 'tis now.
cold on my brow, If ev - er I loved Thee, my Je - sus, 'tis now.
crown on my brow, If ev - er I loved Thee, my Je - sus, 'tis now.

# 191 MY LORD, MY MASTER

*Our Lord and Saviour Jesus Christ. To Him be glory both now and for ever.* II Pet. 3:18.

Jacques Bridaine, 1701-1767
*Est-ce vous que je vois, o mon Maitre adorable*
Tr. Thomas Benson Pollock, b. 1836

STRENGTH AND STAY 11.10.11.10.
M.M. 58

John Bacchus Dykes, 1875 (1823-1876)

1. My Lord, my Mas - ter, at Thy feet a - dor - ing, I see Thee
2. Thine own dis - ci - ple to the Jews has sold Thee; With friendship's
3. With taunts and scoffs they mock what seems Thy weak-ness, With blows and
4. My Lord, my Sav - iour, when I see Thee wear - ing Up - on Thy
5. O Vic - tim of Thy love! O pangs most heal - ing! O sav - ing

bowed be-neath Thy load of woe: For me, a sin - ner, is Thy life-blood
kiss and loy - al word he came: How oft of faith - ful love my lips have
out - rage add - ing pain to pain: Thou art un - moved and stead-fast in Thy
bleed - ing brow the crown of thorn, Shall I for pleas - ure live, or shrink from
death! O wounds that I a - dore! O shame most glo - rious! Christ, before Thee

pour - ing; For Thee, my Sav-iour, scarce my tears will flow.
told Thee, While Thou hast seen my false-hood and my shame.
meek-ness; When I am wronged how quick-ly I com - plain.
bear - ing What-e'er my lot may be of pain or scorn?
kneel-ing, I pray Thee keep me Thine for - ev - er - more. A-MEN.

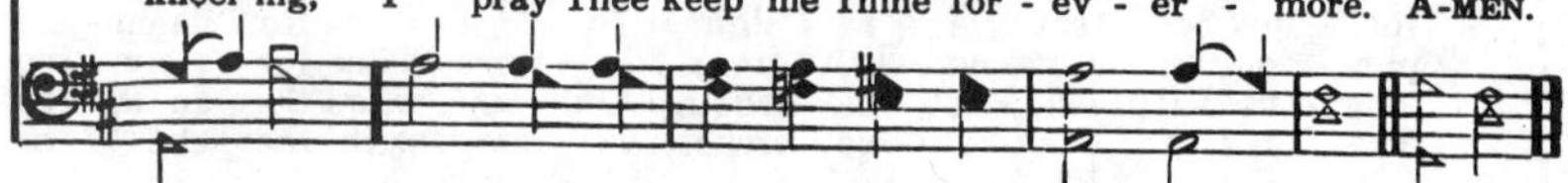

# 192 BEHOLD THE GLORIES OF THE LAMB

*Worthy is the Lamb that was slain to receive power, and riches, and wisdom, and strength, and honour, and glory, and blessing.* Rev. 5:12.

ST. MARTINS C.M. 8.6.8.6.
M.M. 58

Isaac Watts, 1706 (1674-1748)

William Tans'ur, 1735 (1706-1783)

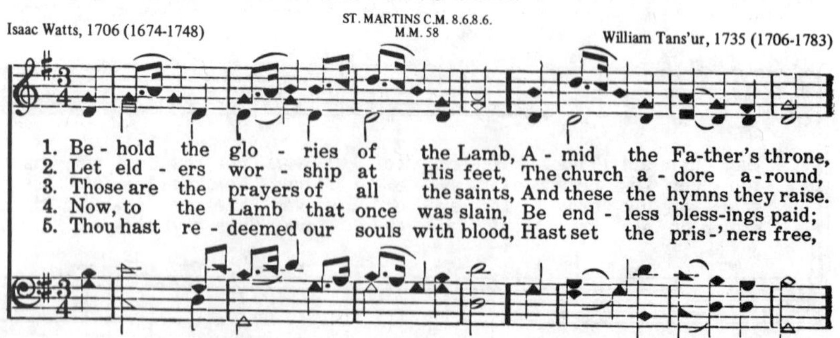
1. Be - hold the glo - ries of the Lamb, A - mid the Fa-ther's throne,
2. Let eld - ers wor - ship at His feet, The church a - dore a - round,
3. Those are the prayers of all the saints, And these the hymns they raise.
4. Now, to the Lamb that once was slain, Be end - less bless-ings paid;
5. Thou hast re - deemed our souls with blood, Hast set the pris - 'ners free,

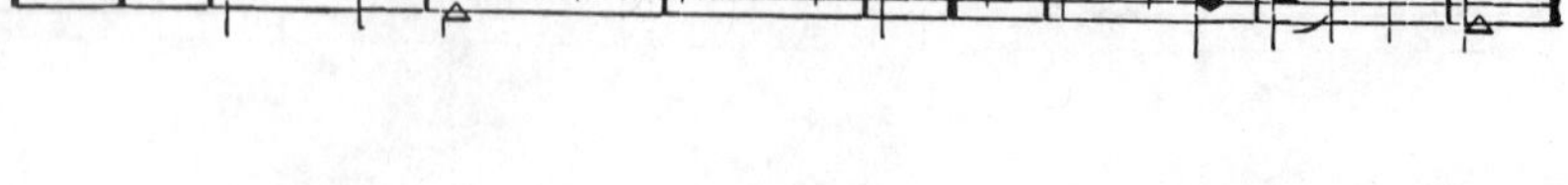

Pre-pare new hon - ors for His name, And songs be - fore un-known.
With vi - als full of o - dors sweet, And harps of sweet-er sound.
Je - sus is kind to our com-plaints, He loves to hear our praise.
Sal - va - tion, glo - ry, joy, re - main For-ev - - er on Thy head.
Hast made us kings and priests to God, And we shall reign with Thee.
BEAUTIFUL SAVIOUR 193
My beloved is . . . the chiefest among ten thousand. Song of Sol. 5:10.
Münster Gesangbuch, 1677
Schönster Herr Jesu
Tr. Joseph Augustus Seiss, 1873 (1823-1904)
SCHÖNSTER HERR JESU 5.6.8.5.5.8.
M.M. 76
Silesian Folk-song
Fallersleben's Volkslieder, 1842
Harmony arr. John J. Overholt, 1969
1. Beau - ti - ful Sav - ior! King of cre - a - tion! Son of
2. Fair are the mead - ows, Fair - er the wood - lands, Robed in
3. Fair is the sun - shine, Fair - er the moon - light And the
4. Beau - ti - ful Sav - ior! Lord of the na - tions! Son of
God and Son of man! Tru - ly I'd love Thee,
flow'rs of bloom - ing spring; Je - sus is fair - er;
spar - kling stars on high; Je - sus shines bright - er,
God and Son of man! Glo - ry and hon - or,
Tru - ly I'd serve Thee, Light of my soul, my joy my crown!
Je - sus is pur - er; He makes our sor-r'wing spir - it sing.
Je - sus shines pur - er, Than all the an - gels in the sky.
Praise, ad - o - ra - tion, Now and for - ev - er more be Thine! A - men.

# 194 I LOVE THE LORD

*Thou shalt love the Lord thy God with all thy heart, and with all thy soul, and with all thy mind.* Matt. 22:37.

Vera Sommers Overholt, 1965 LIEBE C.M. 8.6.8.6. with Refrain M.M. 52 Vera Sommers Overholt

1. I love the Lord with all my heart, He lives with me each day;
2. I love the Lord with all my heart, I'll serve Him day by day;
3. I love the Lord with all my heart, I'll bear the cross of shame;
4. I love the Lord with all my heart, And when life's course is run;
His pres - ence is so sweet to me, His will I will o - bey.
My life is His, my hands, my heart, Just use me, Lord, I pray.
I'll fol - low Him as He commands, And suf - fer for His name.
I'll hear Him say, "Well done, my child, Thou good and faith - ful one."
CHORUS
Oh, love the Lord with all your heart, With all your soul, and strength, and mind;
Oh love the Lord with all your heart, Rich bless-ings you will find.

# COME, THOU FOUNT OF EVERY BLESSING 195

*Hitherto hath the Lord helped us.* I Sam. 7:12.

NETTLETON 8.7.8.7.D.
M.M. 54

Robert Robinson, 1768 (1735-1790)

Asahel Nettleton, 1825 (1783-1844)

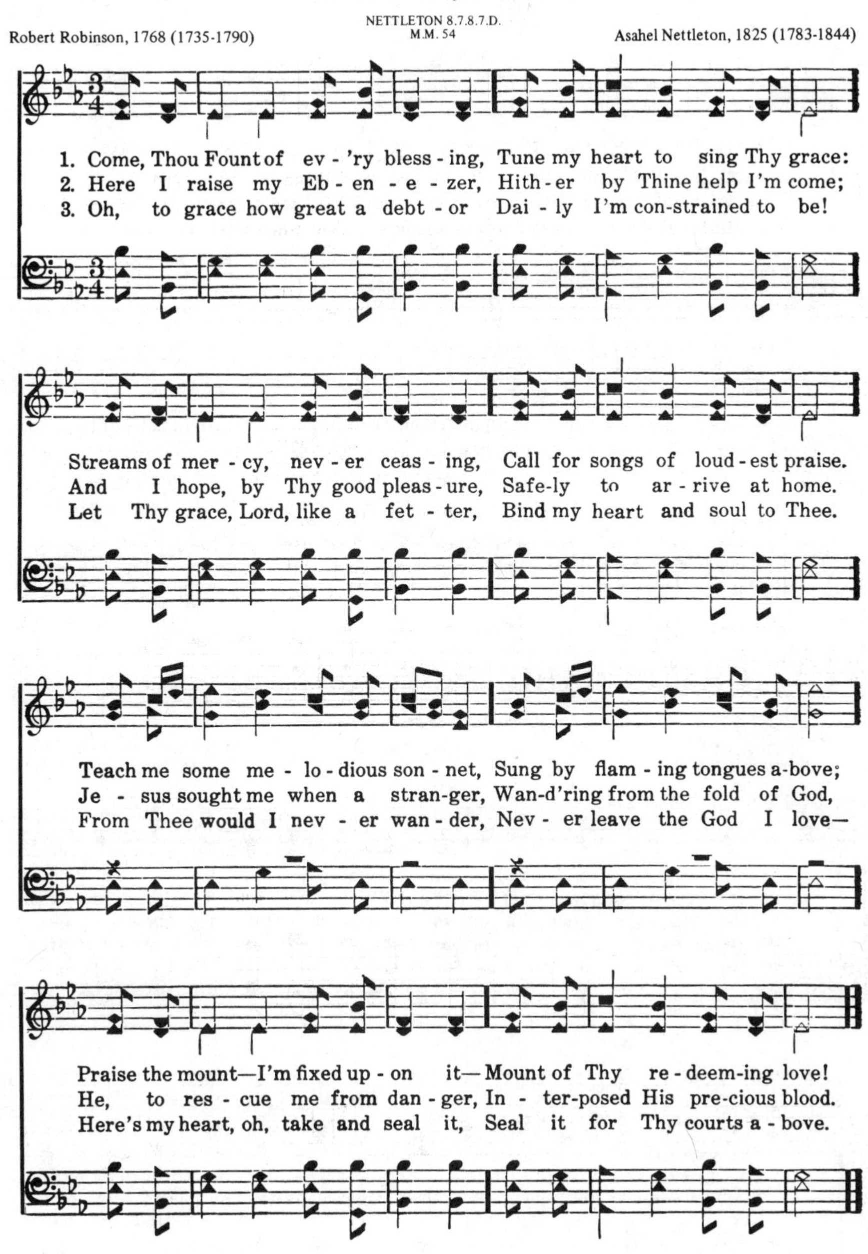
1. Come, Thou Fount of ev - 'ry bless - ing, Tune my heart to sing Thy grace:
2. Here I raise my Eb - en - e - zer, Hith - er by Thine help I'm come;
3. Oh, to grace how great a debt - or Dai - ly I'm con-strained to be!
Streams of mer - cy, nev - er ceas - ing, Call for songs of loud - est praise.
And I hope, by Thy good pleas - ure, Safe-ly to ar - rive at home.
Let Thy grace, Lord, like a fet - ter, Bind my heart and soul to Thee.
Teach me some me - lo - dious son - net, Sung by flam - ing tongues a-bove;
Je - sus sought me when a stran-ger, Wan-d'ring from the fold of God,
From Thee would I nev - er wan - der, Nev - er leave the God I love—
Praise the mount—I'm fixed up - on it—Mount of Thy re - deem-ing love!
He, to res - cue me from dan - ger, In - ter-posed His pre-cious blood.
Here's my heart, oh, take and seal it, Seal it for Thy courts a - bove.

## 196 OH FOR A THOUSAND TONGUES

*My tongue shall speak of Thy righteousness and of Thy praise all the day long.* Ps. 35:28.

Charles Wesley, 1739 (1707-1788) | FOUNTAIN C.M. 8.6.8.6. M.M. 60 | Anonymous

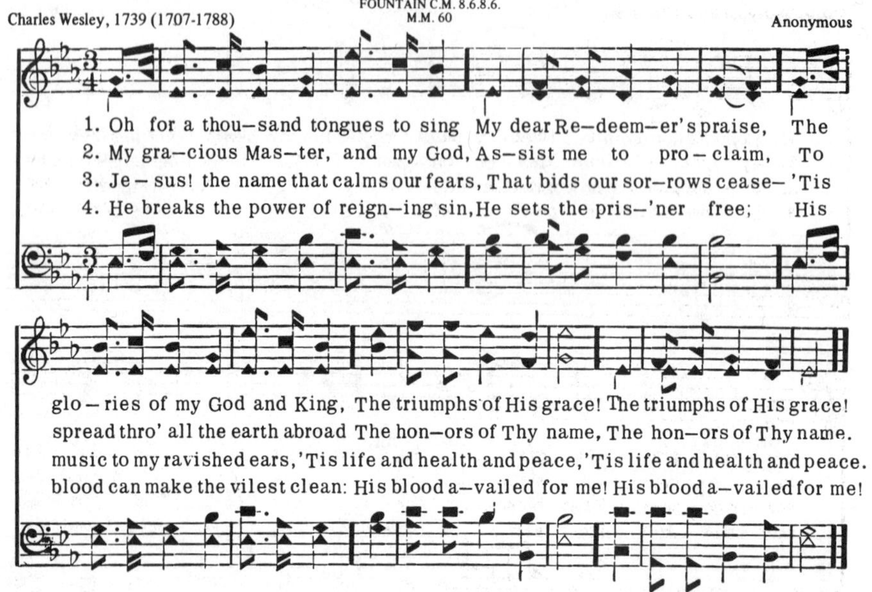
1. Oh for a thou–sand tongues to sing My dear Re–deem–er's praise, The
2. My gra–cious Mas–ter, and my God, As–sist me to pro – claim, To
3. Je – sus! the name that calms our fears, That bids our sor–rows cease– 'Tis
4. He breaks the power of reign–ing sin, He sets the pris–'ner free; His
glo – ries of my God and King, The triumphs of His grace! The triumphs of His grace!
spread thro' all the earth abroad The hon–ors of Thy name, The hon–ors of Thy name.
music to my ravished ears, 'Tis life and health and peace, 'Tis life and health and peace.
blood can make the vilest clean: His blood a–vailed for me! His blood a–vailed for me!

## 197 OH FOR A THOUSAND TONGUES

*My lips shall utter praise.* Ps. 119:171.

Charles Wesley, 1739 (1707-1788) | AZMON C.M. 8.6.8.6. M.M. 58 | Carl Gotthelf Gläser, 1734-1829 Arr. Lowell Mason, 1792-1872

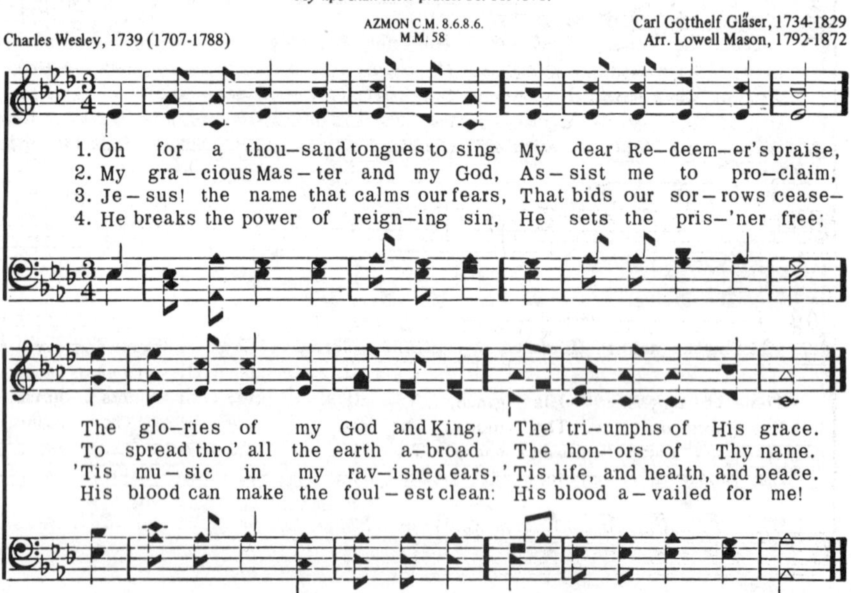
1. Oh for a thou–sand tongues to sing My dear Re–deem–er's praise,
2. My gra – cious Mas – ter and my God, As – sist me to pro–claim,
3. Je – sus! the name that calms our fears, That bids our sor – rows cease–
4. He breaks the power of reign–ing sin, He sets the pris–'ner free;
The glo–ries of my God and King, The tri–umphs of His grace.
To spread thro' all the earth a–broad The hon–ors of Thy name.
'Tis mu – sic in my rav–ished ears, 'Tis life, and health, and peace.
His blood can make the foul – est clean: His blood a – vailed for me!

# O FOR A THOUSAND TONGUES 198

*Let my mouth be filled with Thy praise and with Thy honour all the day.* Ps. 71:8.

Charles Wesley, 1739 (1707-1788)

LINGHAM C.M. D.8.6.8.6.D.
M.M. 84

Joseph Funk, 1788-1862
Arr. F.L.A.

1. O for......... a thou - sand tongues to sing My great Re -
2. My gra - cious Mas - ter and my God, As - sist me
3. Je - sus,........ the name...... that calms our fears, That bids our
4. He breaks.... the pow'r...... of a can - celled sin, He sets the

deem - er's praise, My great...... Re - deem - er's praise; The glo - ries
to pro - claim, As - sist............ me to pro - claim, To spread thro'
sor - rows cease, That bids.......... our sor - rows cease, 'Tis mu - sic
pris - 'ner free, He sets.......... the pris - 'ner free; His blood can

of......... my God..... and King, The tri - umphs of, the tri - umphs of His grace,
all........ the earth.... a - broad, The hon - ors of, the hon - ors of Thy name,
in......... the sin - ner's ears, 'Tis life and health, 'tis life and health and peace,
make... the foul - est clean, His blood a - vails, His blood a - vails for me,

The tri - umphs of His grace,.... The tri - umphs of His grace.
The hon - ors of Thy name,... The hon - ors of Thy name.
'Tis life and health and peace,...'Tis life........ and health and peace.
His blood a - vails for me,.......His blood..... a - vails for me.

# 199 ALL PRAISE TO HIM WHO REIGNS ABOVE

*Blessed be the name of the Lord.* Job 1:21.

BLESSED BE THE NAME 8.6.8.6. with Ref.
M.M. 76

W. H. Clark, c. 1888

Arr. William James Kirkpatrick, 1838-1921

1. All praise to him who reigns a - bove, In ma - jes - ty su - preme,
2. His name a - bove all names shall stand, Ex - alt - ed more and more,
3. Re - deem - er, Sav - iour, Friend of man, Once ru - ined by the fall,
4. His name shall be the Coun - sel - lor, The might - y Prince of Peace,
Who gave Him—self for man to die, That he might man re - deem.
At God the Fa - ther's own right hand, Where an - gel hosts a - dore.
Thou hast de - vised sal - va - tion's plan, For thou hast died for all.
Of all earth's king-doms con - quer - or, Whose reign shall nev - er cease.
Refrain.
Bless-ed be the name, bless-ed be the name, Blessed be the name of the Lord;
Bless - ed be tho name, blessed be the name, Blessed be the name of the Lord.

5 The ransomed hosts to thee shall bring
Their praise and homage meet;
With rapturous awe adore their King,
And worship at his feet.

6 Then shall we know as we are known,
And in that world above
Forever sing around the throne
His everlasting love.

# I GREET THEE, WHO MY SURE REDEEMER ART 200

*Thou, O Lord, art . . . our Redeemer.* Is. 63:16.

*Strasburg Psalter,* 1545
*Je Te salue, mon certain Redempteur*
Tr. Elizabeth Lee Smith, 1868 (1817-1898)

TOULON 10.10.10.10.
M.M. 84

*Geneva Psalter,* 1551
Glaude Goudimel, 1505-1572

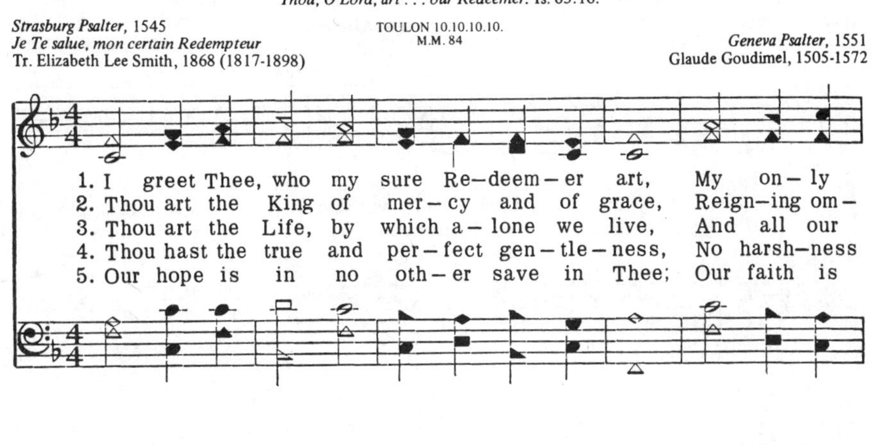
1. I greet Thee, who my sure Re–deem–er art, My on–ly
2. Thou art the King of mer–cy and of grace, Reign–ing om–
3. Thou art the Life, by which a–lone we live, And all our
4. Thou hast the true and per–fect gen–tle–ness, No harsh–ness
5. Our hope is in no oth–er save in Thee; Our faith is

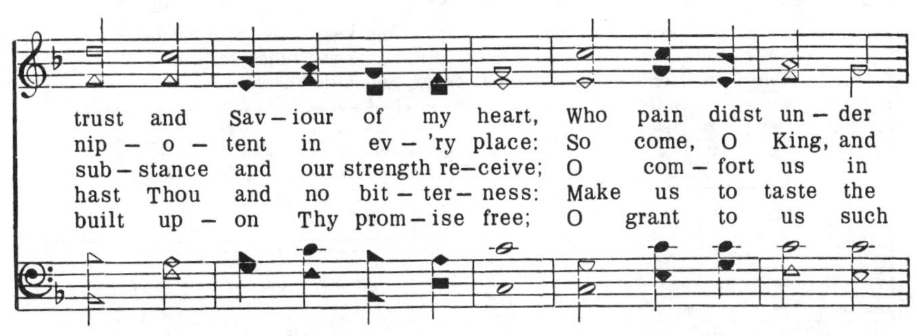
trust and Sav–iour of my heart, Who pain didst un–der
nip – o – tent in ev–'ry place: So come, O King, and
sub–stance and our strength re–ceive; O com–fort us in
hast Thou and no bit–ter–ness: Make us to taste the
built up – on Thy prom–ise free; O grant to us such

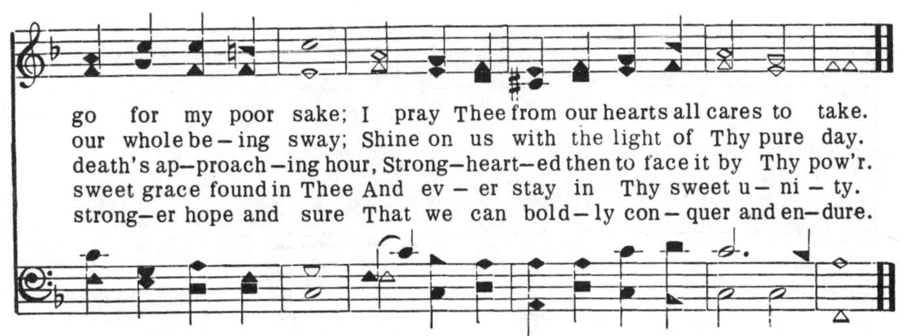
go for my poor sake; I pray Thee from our hearts all cares to take.
our whole be–ing sway; Shine on us with the light of Thy pure day.
death's ap–proach–ing hour, Strong–heart–ed then to face it by Thy pow'r.
sweet grace found in Thee And ev – er stay in Thy sweet u–ni–ty.
strong–er hope and sure That we can bold–ly con–quer and en–dure.

# 201 THY HOLY SPIRIT, LORD, ALONE

*Ye shall receive power, after that the Holy Ghost is come upon you.* Acts 1:8.

Henrietta E. Blair
Altered by Compiler, 1970

O SPIRIT OF FAITH C.M. 8.6.8.6. with Ref.
M.M. 126

William James Kirkpatrick, 1838-1921

1. Thy Ho - ly Spir - it, Lord, a - lone Can turn our hearts from sin;
His pow'r a - lone can sanc - ti - fy And keep us pure with - in.

2. Thy Ho - ly Spir - it, Lord, a - lone Can deep - er love in - spire;
His pow'r a - lone with - in our souls Can light the sa - cred fire.

3. Thy Ho - ly Spir - it, Lord, can bring The gifts we seek in pray'r;
His voice can words of com - fort speak, And still each wave of care.

4. Thy Ho - ly Spir - it, Lord, can give The grace we need this hour;
And while we wait, O Spir - it, come In sanc - ti - fy - ing power!

1-3 Thy Spir - it of Faith and Love Send in our midst, we pray,
And pur - i - fy each wait - ing heart; O fill us with pow'r to - day!

4 Thy Spir - it of Love now send In – to our midst, we pray,
That like a rush - ing, might - y wind, He sweep o'er our souls to - day!

## BAPTIZED INTO OUR SAVIOUR'S DEATH 202

*For by one Spirit are we all baptized into one body.* I Cor. 12:13.

Philip Doddridge, 1702-1751
Recast, John J. Overholt, 1967

GERICHT L.M. 8.8.8.8.
M.M. 56

John J. Overholt, 1964

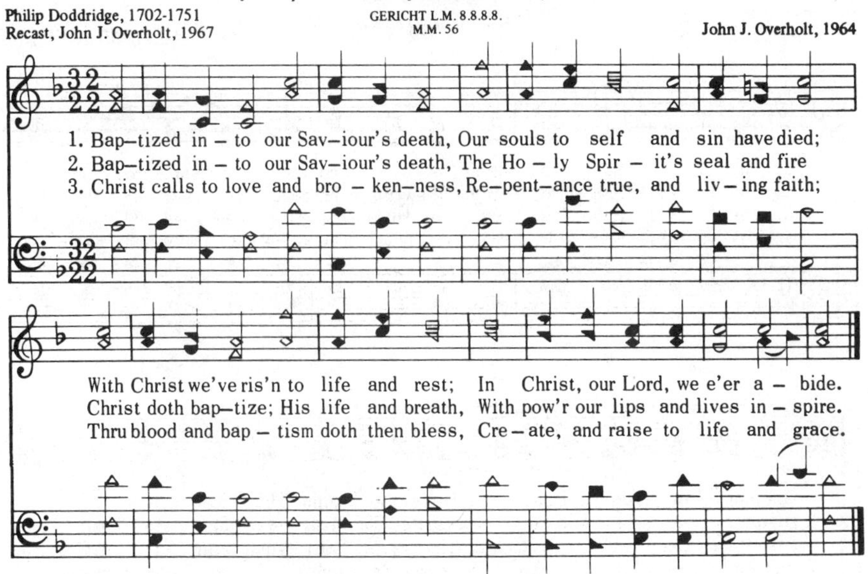
1. Bap–tized in – to our Sav–iour's death, Our souls to self and sin have died;
2. Bap–tized in – to our Sav–iour's death, The Ho – ly Spir – it's seal and fire
3. Christ calls to love and bro – ken–ness, Re–pent–ance true, and liv – ing faith;
With Christ we've ris'n to life and rest; In Christ, our Lord, we e'er a – bide.
Christ doth bap–tize; His life and breath, With pow'r our lips and lives in – spire.
Thru blood and bap – tism doth then bless, Cre – ate, and raise to life and grace.

4. Christ bids us from earth's trifles rise On wings of faith, and hope, and love;
Risen with Him, our treasure lies With Christ, our God, in heaven above.

## THE HOLY GHOST IS HERE 203

*The Holy Ghost . . . shall teach you all things.* Jn. 14:26.

BOYLSTON S.M. 6.6.8.6.
M.M. 66

Charles H. Spurgeon, 1834-1892

Lowell Mason, 1792-1872

1. The Ho - ly Ghost is here, Where saints in prayer a - gree,
2. Not far a - way is He, To be by prayer bro't nigh,
3. He dwells with - in our soul, An ev - er - wel - come guest;
4. O - be - dient to Thy will, We wait to feel Thy pow'r;
As Je - sus' part - ing Gift is near Each plead-ing com - pa - ny.
But here in pres - ent maj - es - ty, As in His courts on high.
He reigns with ab - so - lute con - trol, As mon-arch in the breast.
O Lord of life, our hopes ful - fil, And bless this hal - lowed hour. A-MEN.

# 204 LORD, POSSESS ME NOW I PRAY

*Be filled with the Holy Ghost.* Acts 9:17.

WITH THY SPIRIT FILL ME 6.6.6.6.
M.M. 69

Oswald J. Smith, b. 1890

Bently D. Ackley, 1872-1958

Legato
1. Lord, pos - sess me now, I pray, Make me whol - ly Thine to - day;
2. Lord, I yield my - self to Thee, All I am or hope to be
3. Lord, com - mis - sion me, I pray! Souls are dy - ing ev - 'ry day;
Glad - ly do I own Thy sway, With Thy Spir - it fill me.
Now and thru e - ter - ni - ty, With Thy Spir - it fill me.
Help me lead them in Thy way, With Thy Spir - it fill me.
Chorus
With Thy Spir - it fill me, With Thy Spir - it fill me;
Make me whol - ly Thine, I pray, With Thy Spir - it fill me.

## SAVIOUR AND MASTER, THEE WE OWN 205

*Be not drunk with wine . . . but be filled with the Spirit.* Eph. 5:18.

BIBLE SCHOOL HYMN C.M. 8.6.8.6.
M.M. 84

W. Graham Scroggie — George Coles Stebbins, 1846-1945

1. Sav – ior and Mas – ter, Thee we own, O may Thy Spir – it now
2. Free us, we pray, from wand'ring tho'ts, And ev – 'ry vain de – sire;
3. Let us this eve – ning hear Thy voice With pur – pose to o – bey:
4. Then, send us forth to serve Thee, Lord, With sac – ri – fi –cial grace:

Fill ev–'ry wait – ing, long – ing heart, As at Thy feet we bow.
May all our hearts be thorough–ly purged, By Thy con–sum – ing fire.
May heart and mind and will con–sent To all that Thou dost say.
Show us the work that we must do, And choose for us the place.

## WHERE TWO OR THREE WITH SWEET ACCORD 206

*And they were all filled with the Holy Ghost.* Acts 2:4.

SYKES L.M. 8.8.8.8.
M.M. 66

Samuel Stennet, 1787 (1727-1796) — Jacob Henry Hall, 1855-1941

1. " Where two or three, with sweet ac - cord, O - be-dient to their Sov-'reign Lord,
2. " There," says the Sav - iour, " will I be, A - mid this lit - tle com - pa - ny ;—
3. We meet at thy com-mand, dear Lord, Re - ly - ing on thy faith - ful word :

Meet to re-count his acts of grace, And of - fer sol - emn pray'r and praise :
To them un - veil my smil - ing face, And shed my glo - ries round the place."
Now send thy Spir - it from a - bove ; Now fill our hearts with heav'n-ly love.

# 207 O SPREAD THE TIDINGS ROUND

*I will pray the Father, and He shall give you another Comforter.* Jn. 14:16.

Frank Bottome, 1823-1894

THE COMFORTER HAS COME 6.6.6.6.D. with Ref.
M.M. 76

William James Kirkpatrick, 1838-1921

1. O spread the ti-dings 'round, wher-ev - er man is found, Wher-ev - er hu-man
2. The long, long night is past, the morn-ing breaks at last, And hushed the dreadful
3. Lo, the great King of kings, with heal-ing in His wings, To ev - 'ry cap-tive
4. O bound-less love di - vine! how shall this tongue of mine To wond'ring mor-tals
hearts and hu - man woes a-bound; Let ev-'ry Christian tongue pro-claim the joy-ful
wail and fu - ry of the blast, As o'er the gold-en hills the day ad-vanc-es
soul a full de-liv'rance brings; And thro' the va-cant cells the song of tri-umph
tell the matchless grace di-vine—That I, a child of sin, should in His im - age
Refrain
sound: The Com-fort - er has come!
fast! The Com-fort - er has come!
rings; The Com-fort - er has come!
shine! The Com-fort - er has come!
The Com-fort-er has come, the Com-fort-er has
come! The Ho - ly Ghost from heav'n, the Fa-ther's promise giv'n; O spread the
ti-dings 'round, wher-ev - er man is found—The Com - fort - er has come!

# JOYS ARE FLOWING 208

*He shall give you another Comforter, that He may abide with you forever.* Jn. 14:16.

Mrs. M. P. Ferguson
Alt.

BLESSED QUIETNESS 8.7.8.7. with Refrain
M.M. 66

Arr. J. H. F.

1. Joys are flow - ing like a riv - er, Since the Com - fort - er has come;
2. Ev - 'ry- thing is turned to glad- ness, All a-round this glo- rious Guest;
3. Like the rain that falls from heav - en, Like the sun - light from the sky,
4. What a won - der - ful sal - va - tion Where we al - ways see his face!
He a - bides with us for - ev - er, Makes the trust- ing heart his home.
Ban-ished un - be - lief and sad - ness, All is per - fect peace and rest.
So the Ho - ly Spir - it giv - en, Falls up - on us from on high.
What a peace - ful hab - i - ta - tion! What a qui - et rest - ing place!
REFRAIN.
Bless - ed qui - et- ness, ho - ly qui - et- ness, Blest as - sur - ance in my soul!
On the storm-y sea Je - sus speaks to me, And the bil-lows cease to roll.

# 209 O WONDERFUL, WONDERFUL WORD

*Thy testimonies are wonderful: therefore doth my soul keep them.* Ps. 119:129.

WONDERFUL WORD 11.8.11.8.11.8.12.8.
M.M. 84
J. L. Sterling, c. 1886
Ira David Sankey, 1886 (1840-1908)
1 O won - der - ful, won - der - ful Word of the Lord! True
2 O won - der - ful, won - der - ful Word of the Lord! The
3 O won - der - ful, won - der - ful Word of the Lord! Our
4 O won - der - ful. won - der - ful Word of the Lord! The
wis - dom its pa - ges un - fold; And though we may read them a
lamp that our Fa - ther a - bove So kind - ly has light - ed to
on - ly sal - va - tion is there; It car - ries con - vic - tion down
hope of our friends in the past; Its truth, where so firm - ly they
thou - sand times o'er, They nev - er, no nev - er, grow old!
teach us the way That leads to the arms of His love!
deep in the heart, And shows us our - selves as we are.
an - chored their trust, Through a - ges e - ter - nal shall last.
Each line hath a trea - sure, each prom - ise a pearl, That
Its warn - ings, its coun - sels, are faith - ful and just; Its
It tells of a Sav - ior, and points to the cross, Where
O won - der - ful, won - der - ful Word of the Lord! Un -
all if they will may se - cure; And we know that when time and the
judg - ments are per - fect and pure; And we know that when time and the
par - don we now may se - cure, For we know that when time and the
chang - ing, a - bid - ing and sure; For we know that when time and the

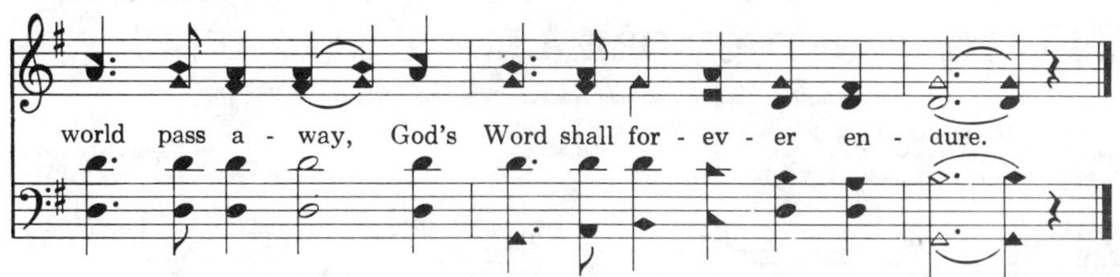
world pass a - way, God's Word shall for - ev - er en - dure.

# BREAK THOU THE BREAD OF LIFE 210

*If any man eat of this bread, he shall live forever.* Jn. 6:51.

BREAD OF LIFE 6.4.6.4.D.

Mary Artemia Lathbury, 1877 (1841-1913) Sts. 1 and 2, alt.
Alexander Groves, 1843-1909, St. 3

M.M. 58

William Fiske Sherwin, 1877 (1826-1888)

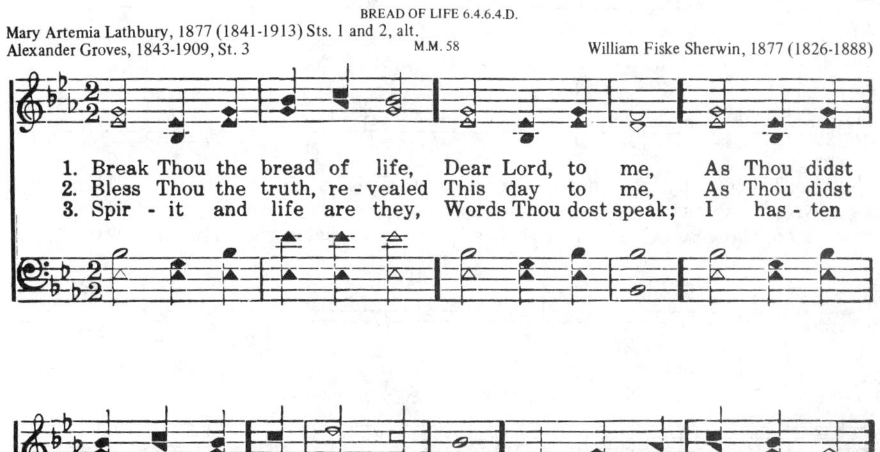
1. Break Thou the bread of life, Dear Lord, to me, As Thou didst
2. Bless Thou the truth, re - vealed This day to me, As Thou didst
3. Spir - it and life are they, Words Thou dost speak; I has - ten

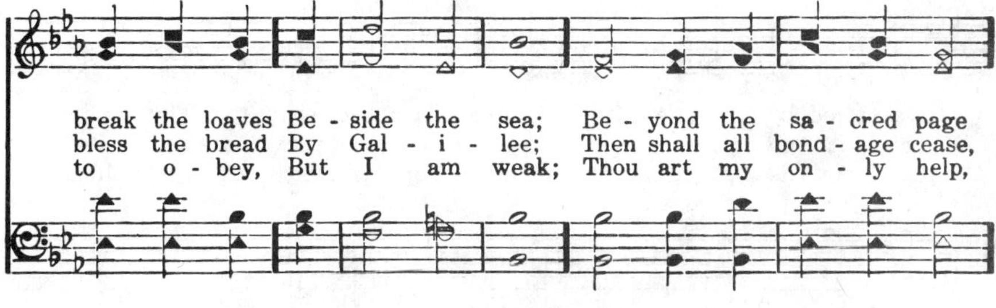
break the loaves Be - side the sea; Be - yond the sa - cred page
bless the bread By Gal - i - lee; Then shall all bond - age cease,
to o - bey, But I am weak; Thou art my on - ly help,

I seek Thee, Lord; My spir - it pants for Thee, O liv - ing Word!
All fet - ters fall; And I shall find in Thee My All - in - All!
Thou art my life; Heed - ing Thy ho - ly Word I win the strife.

# 211 THY WORD, O LORD, LIKE GENTLE DEWS

*Open Thou mine eyes, that I may behold wondrous things out of Thy law.* Ps. 119:18.

Carl Bernhard Garve, 1825 (1763-1841)
*Dein Wort, O Herr, ist milder Thau*
Tr. Catherine Winkworth, 1855 (1827-1878), and others

RELEASE C.M.D. 8.6.8.6.D.
M.M. 58

Danish Melody
From *Service Book and Hymnal*, 1958

1 Thy Word, O Lord, like gen - tle dews, Falls soft on hearts that pine;
2 Thy Word is like a flam-ing sword, A wedge that cleav - eth stone;
3 Thy Word, a won-drous guid-ing star, On pil-grim hearts doth rise,
Lord, to Thy gar - den ne'er re - fuse This heav'n-ly balm of Thine.
Keen as a fire, so burns Thy Word, And pierc-eth flesh and bone.
Leads those to God who dwell a - far, And makes the sim - ple wise.
Wa - tered by Thee, let ev - ery tree Then blos-som to Thy praise,
Let it go forth o'er all the earth To cleanse our hearts with - in,
Let not its light e'er sink in night, But in each spir - it shine,
By grace of Thine bear fruit di-vine Through all the com - ing days.
To show Thy power in Sa-tan's hour, And break the might of sin.
That none may miss heav'n's fi-nal bliss, Led by Thy light di - vine. A - men.

# WE HAVE A SURE PROPHETIC WORD 212

*We have also a more sure word of prophecy.* II Pet. 1:19.

Emanuel Cronenwett, 1880 (1841-1931)

WO GOTT ZUM HAUS L.M. 8.8.8.8.
M.M. 80

*Geistliche Lieder*
Wittenberg, 1535

1. We have a sure pro – phet – ic Word, By in – spi –
2. By powers of em – pire banned and burned, By pa – gan
3. Lo, what the Word in times of old Of fu – ture
4. A – bid – ing, stead – fast, firm, and sure, The stat – utes

ra – tion of the Lord; And tho' as – sailed on
pride re – ject – ed, spurned, The Word still stands the
days and deeds fore – told, Is all ful – filled, while
of our God en – dure: Blest he who trusts this

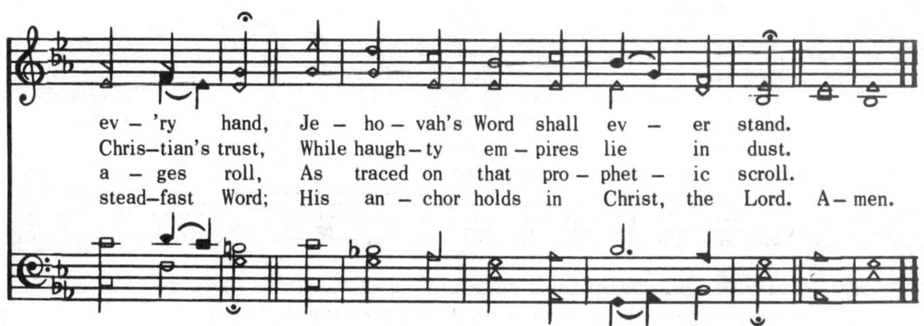
ev – 'ry hand, Je – ho – vah's Word shall ev – er stand.
Chris–tian's trust, While haugh – ty em – pires lie in dust.
a – ges roll, As traced on that pro – phet – ic scroll.
stead–fast Word; His an – chor holds in Christ, the Lord. A – men.

# 213 BLOW YE THE TRUMPET, BLOW!

*Blow ye the trumpet in Zion, and sound an alarm in My holy mountain.* Joel 2:1.

Charles Wesley, 1707-1788
Altered by Compiler, 1964

PAX DEI 10.10.10.10.
M.M. 84

Johann Bacchus Dykes, 1823-1876

1. Blow ye the trum - pet blow! The glad sol - emn sound Let all the
2. Je - sus, our great High Priest A - tone - ment hath made, Ye wea - ry
3. Ex - tol the Lamb of God The a – ton – ing Lamb, Re - demp-tion
4. Ye slaves of sin and hell Your free - dom re - ceive And safe in
5. The Gos-pel trum - pet hear The news of grace And saved from
na - tions know, To earth's far bounds, The year of glad - ness Of
spir - its rest Ye souls be glad; The year of free - dom Of
in his blood To men pro - claim; The year of rap - ture Of
Je - sus dwell In Je - sus live; The year of fa - vor Of
earth, ap - pear Be - fore His face; The year of tri - umph Of
jub - i - lee is come! Re - turn ye ran-somed sin - ners To your home.
jub - i - lee is come! Re - turn ye ran-somed sin - ners To your home.
jub - i - lee is come! Re - turn ye ran-somed sin - ners To your home.
jub - i - lee is come! Re - turn ye ran-somed sin - ners To your home.
jub - i - lee is come! Re - turn ye ran-somed sin - ners To your home.

# ALL MANKIND FELL IN ADAM'S FALL 214

*Wherefore, as by one man sin entered into the world, and death by sin . . . so by the obedience of One shall many be made righteous.* Rom. 5:12, 19.

Lazarus Spengler, cento, 1524 (1479-1534)
***Durch Adams Fall ist ganz verderbt***
**Tr. Matthias Loy, 1880, alt.**

GERICHT L.M. 8.8.8.8.
M.M. 52

John J. Overholt, 1965

1. All man–kind fell in Ad–am's fall, One com–mon sin in–fects us all;
2. Thro' all man's pow'rs cor–rup–tion creeps And him in dread–ful bond–age keeps;
3. From hearts de–praved, to e–vil prone, Flow thoughts and deeds of sin a – lone;

From sire to son the bane de–scends, And o – ver all the curse im – pends.
In guilt he draws his ear–ly breath And reaps its fruits of woe and death.
God's im – age lost, the dark–ened soul Nor seeks nor finds its heav'n–ly goal.

4. But Christ, the second Adam, came
To bear our sin and woe and shame,
To be our Life, our Light, our Way,
Our only Hope, our only Stay.

5. As by one man all mankind fell
And, born in sin, was doomed to hell,
So by one Man, who took our place,
We all received the gift of grace.

6. We thank Thee, Christ; new life is ours,
New light, new hope, new strength, new powers:
This grace our every way attend
Until we reach our journey's end!

# 215 I HEARD THE VOICE OF JESUS SAY

*If any man thirst, let him come unto Me, and drink.* Jn. 7:37.

BONAR C.M.D. 8.6.8.6.D.
M.M. 72

Horatius Bonar, 1846 (1808-1889) — John David Brunk, 1911 (1872-1926)

1. I heard the voice of Je - sus say, "Come un - to Me and rest;
2. I heard the voice of Je - sus say, "Be - hold, I free - ly give
3. I heard the voice of Je - sus say, "I am this dark world's Light;
Lay down, thou wea - ry one, lay down Thy head up - on My breast!"
The liv - ing wa - ter; thirst - y one, Stoop down and drink and live!"
Look un - to Me, thy morn shall rise And all thy day be bright!"
I came to Je - sus as I was, Wea - ry and worn and sad;
I came to Je - sus, and I drank Of that life - giv - ing stream:
I looked to Je - sus, and I found In Him my Star, my Sun;
I found in Him a rest - ing place, And He has made me glad.
My thirst was quenched, my soul re - vived, And now I live in Him.
And in that light of life I'll walk Till all my jour-ney's done.

## AMAZING GRACE 216

*That . . . He might shew the exceeding riches of His grace.* Eph. 2:7.

AMAZING GRACE C.M. 8.6.8.6.
M.M. 76

John Newton, 1779 (1725-1807) — Early American Melody

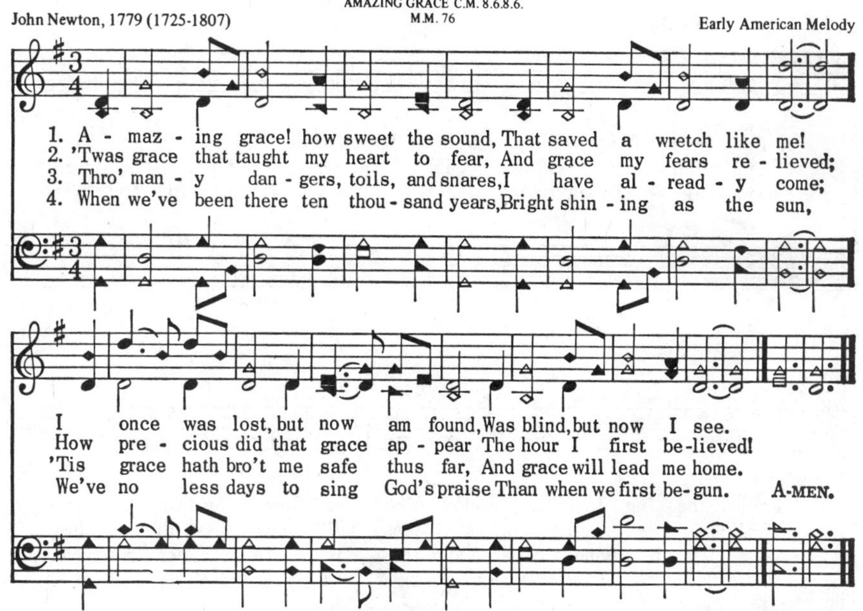

1. A - maz - ing grace! how sweet the sound, That saved a wretch like me!
2. 'Twas grace that taught my heart to fear, And grace my fears re - lieved;
3. Thro' man - y dan - gers, toils, and snares, I have al - read - y come;
4. When we've been there ten thou - sand years, Bright shin - ing as the sun,
I once was lost, but now am found, Was blind, but now I see.
How pre - cious did that grace ap - pear The hour I first be-lieved!
'Tis grace hath bro't me safe thus far, And grace will lead me home.
We've no less days to sing God's praise Than when we first be-gun.
A-MEN.

## GRACE, 'TIS A CHARMING SOUND 217

*The grace of God that bringeth salvation hath appeared to all men.* Tit. 2:11.

SILVER STREET S.M. 6.6.8.6.
M.M. 76

Philip Doddridge, 1740 (1702-1751) — Isaac Smith, 1770 (1725-1800)

1. Grace, 'tis a charm - ing sound, Har - mo - nious to mine ear;
2. Grace first con-trived the way To save re - bel - lious man;
3. Grace first in - scribed my name In God's e - ter - nal book;
4. Grace led my rov - ing feet To tread the heav'nly road;
5. Grace all the work shall crown, Thro' ev - er - last - ing days;
Heav'n with the ech - o shall re - sound, And all the earth shall hear.
And all the steps that grace dis - play Which drew the won-drous plan.
'Twas grace that gave me to the Lamb, Who all my sor - rows took.
And new sup-plies each hour I meet, While press-ing on to God.
It lays in heav'n the top - most stone, And well de - serves the praise.

# 218 I HEAR THY WELCOME VOICE

*Whosoever will, let him take the water of life freely.* Rev. 22:17.

WELCOME VOICE S.M. 6.6.8.6. with Ref.
M.M. 66

Lewis Hartsough, 1873 (1828-1919)

Lewis Hartsough

1. I hear Thy wel - come voice, That calls me, Lord, to Thee,
2. Tho' com - ing weak and vile, Thou dost my strength as - sure;
3. 'Tis Je - sus calls me on To per - fect faith and love,
For cleans - ing in Thy pre-cious blood That flowed on Cal - va - ry.
Thou dost my vile-ness ful - ly cleanse, Till spot - less all and pure.
To per - fect hope, and peace, and trust, For earth and heav'n a-bove.
CHORUS
I am com - ing, Lord! Com - ing now to Thee! Wash me,
cleanse me in the blood That flowed on Cal - va - ry!

# JESUS, THOU ART THE SINNER'S FRIEND 219

*For whosoever shall call upon the name of the Lord shall be saved.* Rom. 10:13.

Richard Burham, 1749-1810
Chorus by Asa Hull

REMEMBER ME C.M. 8.6.8.6.
M.M. 56

Asa Hull, b. 1828

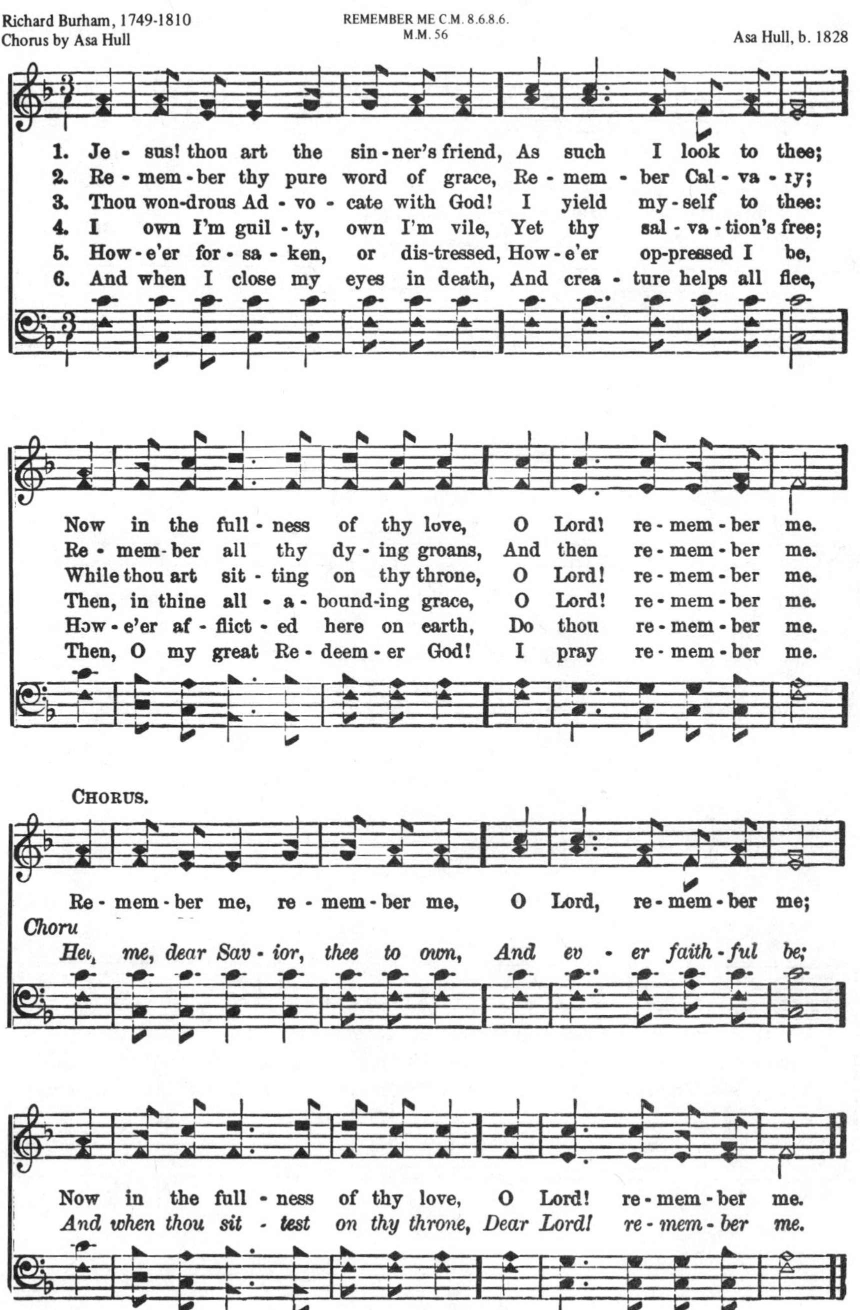

1. Je - sus! thou art the sin - ner's friend, As such I look to thee;
2. Re - mem - ber thy pure word of grace, Re - mem - ber Cal - va - ry;
3. Thou won-drous Ad - vo - cate with God! I yield my - self to thee:
4. I own I'm guil - ty, own I'm vile, Yet thy sal - va - tion's free;
5. How - e'er for - sa - ken, or dis-tressed, How - e'er op-pressed I be,
6. And when I close my eyes in death, And crea - ture helps all flee,
Now in the full - ness of thy love, O Lord! re - mem - ber me.
Re - mem - ber all thy dy - ing groans, And then re - mem - ber me.
While thou art sit - ting on thy throne, O Lord! re - mem - ber me.
Then, in thine all - a - bound-ing grace, O Lord! re - mem - ber me.
How - e'er af - flict - ed here on earth, Do thou re - mem - ber me.
Then, O my great Re - deem - er God! I pray re - mem - ber me.
CHORUS.
Re - mem - ber me, re - mem - ber me, O Lord, re - mem - ber me;
Choru
Hel, me, dear Sav - ior, thee to own, And ev - er faith - ful be;
Now in the full - ness of thy love, O Lord! re - mem - ber me.
And when thou sit - test on thy throne, Dear Lord! re - mem - ber me.

# 220 SAVIOUR, TO THEE I COME

*Thou art a God ready to pardon, gracious and merciful.* Neh. 9:17.

George P. Hott
Altered by Compiler, 1970

THY LOVE TO ME NEW 6.4.6.4.6.6.6.4.
M.M. 116

E. C. Avis
Arranged by Compiler, 1970

1. Sav – iour, to Thee I come, Bur–dened with sin; O – pen the
2. Plead–ing Thy grace a–lone, Hum – bly I bow; Thy blood for
3. I plead Thy mer – cy, Lord, Turn night to day, Ful – fill Thy

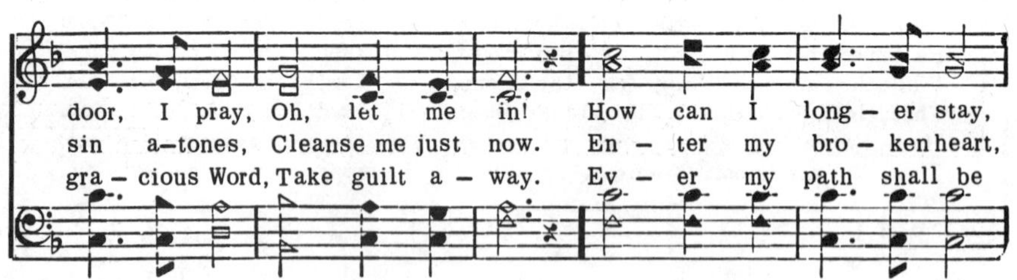
door, I pray, Oh, let me in! How can I long – er stay,
sin a–tones, Cleanse me just now. En – ter my bro – ken heart,
gra – cious Word, Take guilt a – way. Ev – er my path shall be

p
My God, from Thee a–way? Thou art the Life, the Way, In all to me.
Sav–iour, and ne'er de–part; To me Thy love im–part, Make me wholly Thine.
Where–e'er Thou leadest me; I come, O Christ, to Thee, Blest Lamb of God.

# I LAY MY SINS ON JESUS 221

*The Lord hath laid on Him the iniquity of us all.* Is. 53:6.

Horatius Bonar, 1847 (1808-1889)

ST. HILDA 7.6.7.6.D.
M.M. 66

Justin Heinrich Knecht, 1799 (1752-1817)
Edward Husband, 1871 (1843-1908)

1. I lay my sins on Je - sus, The spot - less Lamb of God;
2. I lay my wants on Je - sus; All full - ness dwells in Him;
3. I long to be like Je - sus, Meek, lov - ing, low - ly, mild;
He bears them all and frees us From the ac - curs - ed load:
He heal - eth my dis - eas - es, He doth my soul re - deem:
I long to be like Je - sus, The Fa - ther's ho - ly child:
I bring my guilt to Je - sus, To wash my crim - son stains
I lay my griefs on Je - sus, My bur - dens and my cares;
I long to be with Je - sus A - mid the heav'n - ly throng;
White in His blood most pre - cious, Till not a stain re - mains.
He from them all re - leas - es, He all my sor - rows shares.
To sing with saints His prais - es, And learn the an - gels' song.

# 222 O GOD, ACCORDING TO THY GRACE

*Create in me a clean heart, O God; and renew a right spirit within me.* Ps. 51:10.

RESIGNATION C.M.D. 8.6.8.6.D. F. Lewis' *Beauties of Harmony*, 1828

*Psalter* M.M. 76 Joseph Funk's *Genuine Church Music*, 1832 (1778-1862)

1. O God, ac – cord – ing to Thy grace Be mer – ci –
2. A – gainst Thee on – ly have I sinned, Done e – vil
3. From all pol – lu – tion make me clean, Yea, whit – er
4. From out Thy pres – ence cast me not, Thy face no
ful to me, In Thy a – bound – ing love blot out All
in Thy sight; Lord, in Thy judg – ment Thou art just, And
than the snow; O let my bro – ken heart re – joice And
more to see; Thy Ho – ly Spir – it and His grace Take
my in – iq – ui – ty; O wash me whol – ly from my
in Thy sen – tence right. Be – hold, in e – vil I was
glad – ness make me know; Blot out all my in – iq – ui –
not a – way from me. Re – store me Thy sal – va – tion's
guilt And make me clean with – in, For my trans –
formed, And I was born in sin, But Thou wilt
ties, And hide my sins from view; Cre – ate in
joy, My will – ing heart up – hold: Then sin – ners

gres– sions I con– fess, I ev – er see my sin.
make me wise in heart, Thou seek– est truth with – in.
me a spir – it right, O God, my heart re – new.
shall be turned to Thee When I Thy ways un – fold.

# WITH BROKEN HEART AND CONTRITE SIGH 223

*God be merciful to me a sinner.* Lu. 18:13.

Cornelius Elven, 1852 (1797-1873)

GERICHT L.M. 8.8.8.8.
M.M. 50

John J. Overholt, 1965

1. With bro – ken heart and con–trite sigh, A trem – bling sin – ner, Lord, I cry,
2. I smite up – on my trou–bled breast, With deep and con–scious guilt op–prest;
3. Far off I stand with tear–ful eyes Nor dare up–lift them to the skies;

Thy par–d'ning grace is rich and free, O God be mer – ci – ful to me.
Christ and His cross my on – ly plea, O God be mer – ci – ful to me.
But Thou dost all my an–guish see, O God be mer – ci – ful to me.

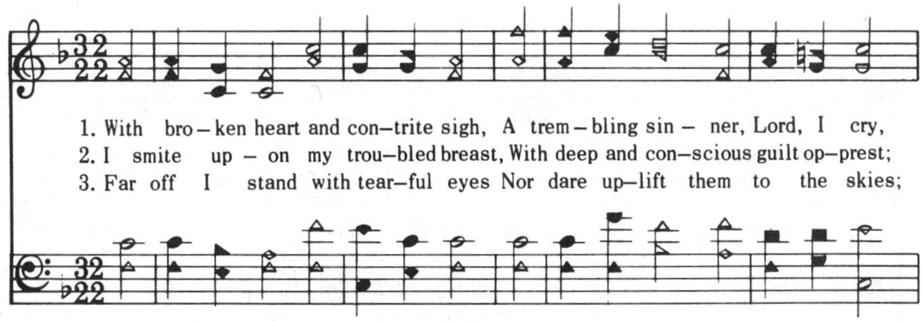

4. Nor alms nor deeds that I have done
Can for a single sin atone.
To Calvary alone I flee,
O God, be merciful to me!

5. And when redeemed from sin and hell,
With all the ransomed throng I dwell,
My raptured song shall ever be,
Thou hast been merciful to me.

# 224 SALVATION UNTO US HAS COME

*For by grace are ye saved through faith . . . not of works.* Eph. 2:8, 9.

Paul Speratus, cento, 1523 (1484-1551)
*Es ist das Heil uns kommen her*
Tr. Composite

LOBET DEN HERRN 8.7.8.7.8.8.7.
M.M. 80

Melchior Vulpius, 1609 (1560-1616)
Harmony arr. John J. Overholt

1. Sal – va – tion un – to us has come By God's free grace and fa – vor; Good works can – not a – vert our doom, They help and save us nev – er. Faith looks to Je – sus Christ a – lone, Who did for all the world a – tone; He is our one Re – deem – er.
2. What God did in His law de – mand And none to Him could ren – der Caused wrath and woe on ev – 'ry hand For man, the vile of – fend – er. Our flesh had not those pure de – sires The spir – it of the law re – quires, And lost was our con – di – tion.
3. Since Christ hath full a – tone – ment made And brought to us sal – va – tion, Each Chris – tian there – fore may be glad And build on this foun – da – tion. Thy grace a – lone, dear Lord, I plead, Thy death is now my life in – deed, For Thou hast paid my ran – som.
4. Faith clings to Je – sus' cross a – lone And rests in Him un – ceas – ing; And by its fruits true faith is known, With love and hope in – creas – ing. Yet faith a – lone doth jus – ti – fy, Works serve thy neigh – bor and sup – ply The proof that faith is liv – ing. A – men.

# I BELIEVE, O LORD, IN THEE 225

*Without faith it is impossible to please Him.* Heb. 11:6.

William H. McDonald, 1820-1901
Alteration, Sts. 1, 4, and Refrain,
John J. Overholt, 1971

TRUSTING 7.7.7.7.
M.M. 66

William Gustavus Fischer, 1835-1912

1. I be–lieve, O Lord, in Thee, In the foun–tain filled with blood,
2. Long my heart has sighed for Thee, Long has e – vil dwelt with – in;
3. Here I give my all to Thee, Tal–ents, time, and earth – ly store,
4. I re – pent and cry to Thee, Cleanse my heart from ev – ery sin;
Ref. I be–lieve, O Lord, in Thee, Bles–sed Lamb of Cal – va – ry;
D.C. for Refrain
That re–deems and sets men free, Rec – on– ciles their souls to God.
O my Lord, now par – don me, Cleanse my heart from ev – ery sin.
Soul and bod – y Thine to be, Whol–ly Thine for – ev – er – more.
O Lord Je – sus, set me free! Make me pure, with – out, with – in!
At Thy feet I hum–bly bow, O Lord Je – sus, save me now!

# FATHER, I STRETCH MY HANDS TO THEE 226

*I stretch forth my hands unto Thee.* Ps. 143:6.

MARLOW C.M. 8.6.8.6.
M.M. 60

Charles Wesley, 1707-1788

John Chetham, 1685-1763

1. Fa – ther, I stretch my hands to Thee, No oth – er help I know;
2. What did Thy on – ly Son en–dure, Be – fore I drew my breath!
3. O Je – sus, could I this be – lieve, I now should feel Thy power;
4. Au – thor of faith, to Thee I lift My wea – ry, long – ing eyes;

If Thou with–draw Thy–self from me, Ah, whith–er shall I go?
What pain, what la – bor to se – cure My soul from end–less death!
Now my poor soul Thou would'st retrieve, Nor let me wait one hour.
O may I now re – ceive that gift, My soul with – out it dies.

# 227 MY FAITH LOOKS UP TO THEE

*Looking unto Jesus the author and finisher of our faith.* Heb. 12:2.

OLIVET 6.6.4.6.6.6.4.
M.M. 76

Ray Palmer, 1808-1887 — Lowell Mason, 1832 (1792-1872)

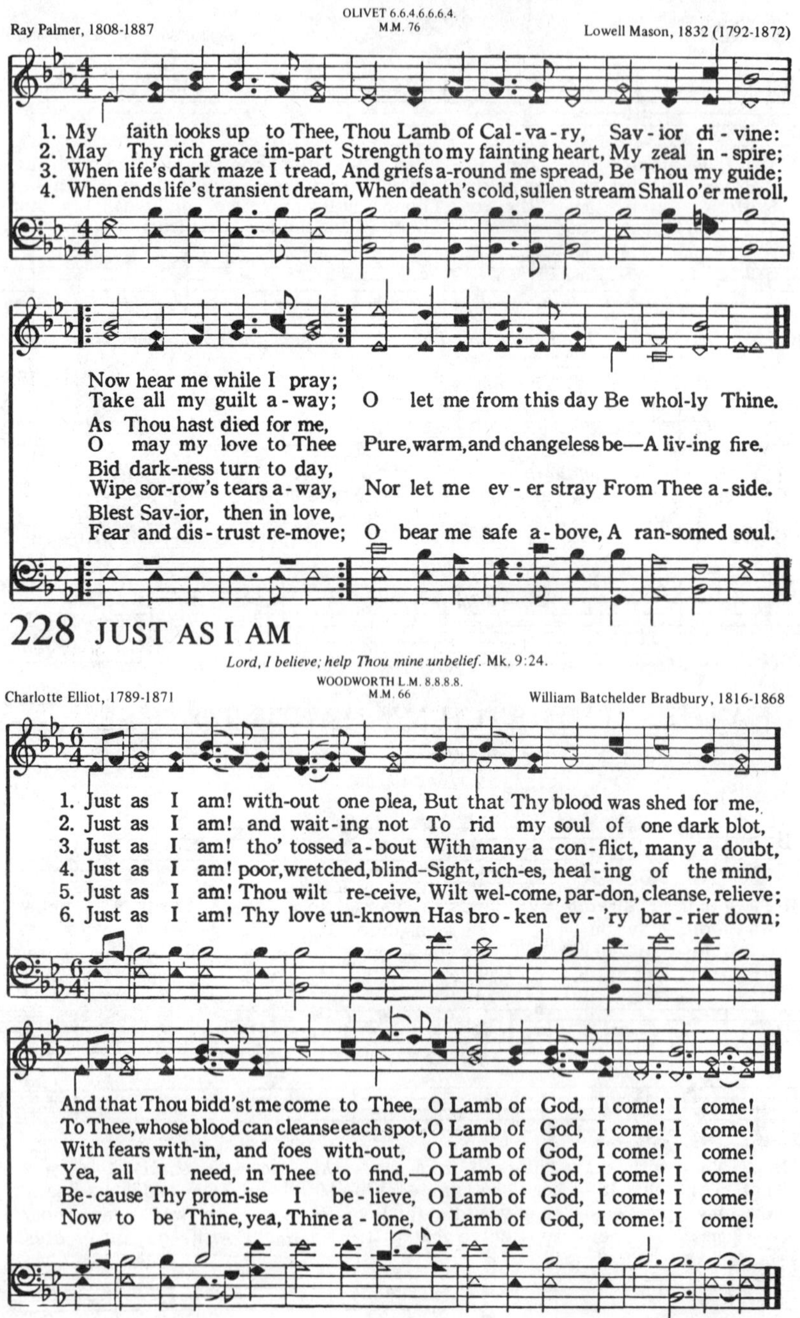
1. My faith looks up to Thee, Thou Lamb of Cal-va-ry, Sav-ior di-vine: Now hear me while I pray; Take all my guilt a-way; O let me from this day Be whol-ly Thine.
2. May Thy rich grace im-part Strength to my fainting heart, My zeal in-spire; As Thou hast died for me, O may my love to Thee Pure, warm, and changeless be—A liv-ing fire.
3. When life's dark maze I tread, And griefs a-round me spread, Be Thou my guide; Bid dark-ness turn to day, Wipe sor-row's tears a-way, Nor let me ev-er stray From Thee a-side.
4. When ends life's transient dream, When death's cold, sullen stream Shall o'er me roll, Blest Sav-ior, then in love, Fear and dis-trust re-move; O bear me safe a-bove, A ran-somed soul.

# 228 JUST AS I AM

*Lord, I believe; help Thou mine unbelief.* Mk. 9:24.

WOODWORTH L.M. 8.8.8.8.
M.M. 66

Charlotte Elliot, 1789-1871 — William Batchelder Bradbury, 1816-1868

1. Just as I am! with-out one plea, But that Thy blood was shed for me, And that Thou bidd'st me come to Thee, O Lamb of God, I come! I come!
2. Just as I am! and wait-ing not To rid my soul of one dark blot, To Thee, whose blood can cleanse each spot, O Lamb of God, I come! I come!
3. Just as I am! tho' tossed a-bout With many a con-flict, many a doubt, With fears with-in, and foes with-out, O Lamb of God, I come! I come!
4. Just as I am! poor, wretched, blind—Sight, rich-es, heal-ing of the mind, Yea, all I need, in Thee to find,—O Lamb of God, I come! I come!
5. Just as I am! Thou wilt re-ceive, Wilt wel-come, par-don, cleanse, relieve; Be-cause Thy prom-ise I be-lieve, O Lamb of God, I come! I come!
6. Just as I am! Thy love un-known Has bro-ken ev-'ry bar-rier down; Now to be Thine, yea, Thine a-lone, O Lamb of God, I come! I come!

# A RULER ONCE CAME TO JESUS BY NIGHT 229

*Except a man be born again, he cannot see the kingdom of God.* Jn. 3:3.

YE MUST BE BORN AGAIN 10.11.11.6. with Ref.
M.M. 100

William T. Sleeper, 1819-1904 — George C. Stebbins, 1846-1945

1. A rul - er once came to Je - sus by night To ask Him the way of sal - va-tion and light; The Mas-ter made an-swer in words true and plain,
2. Ye chil-dren of men, at - tend to the word So sol - emn - ly ut - tered by Je - sus the Lord; And let not this mes-sage to you be in vain,
3. O ye who would en - ter that glo - ri - ous rest, And sing with the ran-somed the song of the blest; The life ev - er - last - ing if ye would ob - tain,
"Ye must be born a - gain."...... a - gain.
REFRAIN
"Ye must be born a- gain,........ a - gain, Ye must be born a - gain;........ a - gain; I ver - i - ly, ver - i - ly say un - to thee, Ye must be born a - gain."...... a - gain.

## 230 HOW SOLEMN ARE THE WORDS

*Being born again . . . by the word of God, which liveth and abideth forever.* I Pet. 1:23.

Albert Midlane, 1825-1909 — BOYLSTON S.M. 6.6.8.6. M.M. 58 — Lowell Mason, 1792-1872

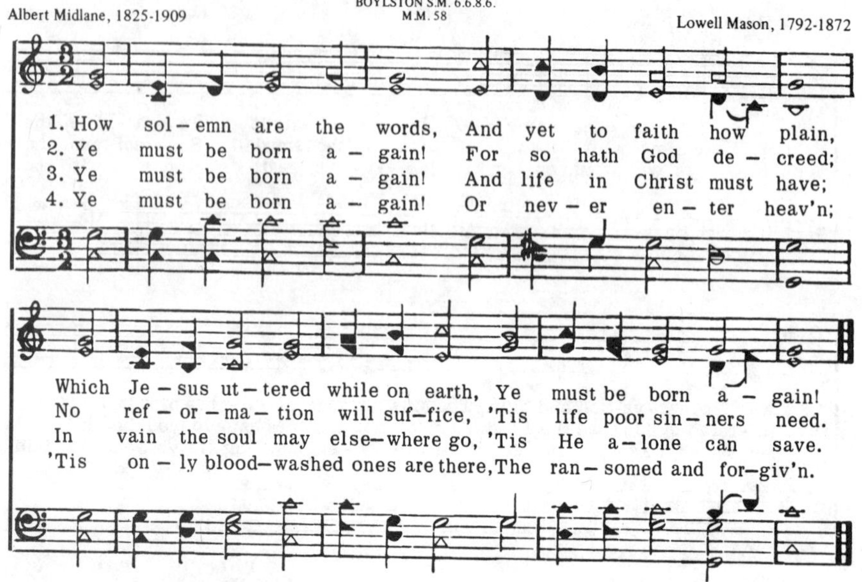
1. How sol-emn are the words, And yet to faith how plain,
2. Ye must be born a-gain! For so hath God de-creed;
3. Ye must be born a-gain! And life in Christ must have;
4. Ye must be born a-gain! Or nev-er en-ter heav'n;
Which Je-sus ut-tered while on earth, Ye must be born a-gain!
No ref-or-ma-tion will suf-fice, 'Tis life poor sin-ners need.
In vain the soul may else-where go, 'Tis He a-lone can save.
'Tis on-ly blood-washed ones are there, The ran-somed and for-giv'n.

## 231 YE MUST BE BORN AGAIN

*Except a man be born of water and of the Spirit, he cannot enter into the kingdom of God.* Jn. 3:5.

John J. Overholt, 1970 — COOPER NEW S.M. 6.6.8.6. M.M. 126 — A. B. Everett, 1828-1875; Arr. John J. Overholt, 1970

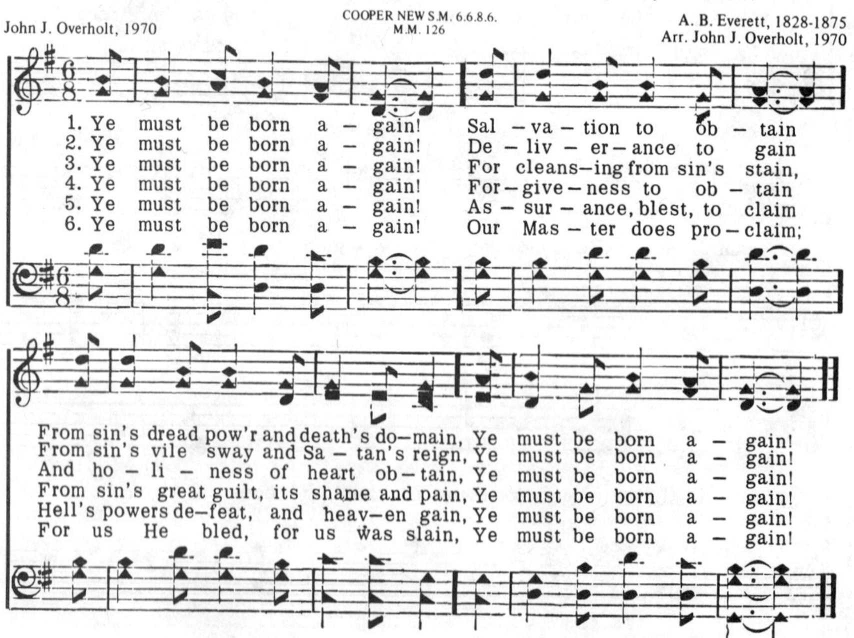
1. Ye must be born a-gain! Sal-va-tion to ob-tain
2. Ye must be born a-gain! De-liv-er-ance to gain
3. Ye must be born a-gain! For cleans-ing from sin's stain,
4. Ye must be born a-gain! For-give-ness to ob-tain
5. Ye must be born a-gain! As-sur-ance, blest, to claim
6. Ye must be born a-gain! Our Mas-ter does pro-claim;
From sin's dread pow'r and death's do-main, Ye must be born a-gain!
From sin's vile sway and Sa-tan's reign, Ye must be born a-gain!
And ho-li-ness of heart ob-tain, Ye must be born a-gain!
From sin's great guilt, its shame and pain, Ye must be born a-gain!
Hell's powers de-feat, and heav-en gain, Ye must be born a-gain!
For us He bled, for us was slain, Ye must be born a-gain!

# LOVE DIVINE, ALL LOVES EXCELLING 232

*Marvel not that I said unto thee, Ye must be born again.* Jn. 3:7.

Charles Wesley, 1707-1788

BEECHER 8.7.8.7.D.
M.M. 76

John Zundel, 1815-1882

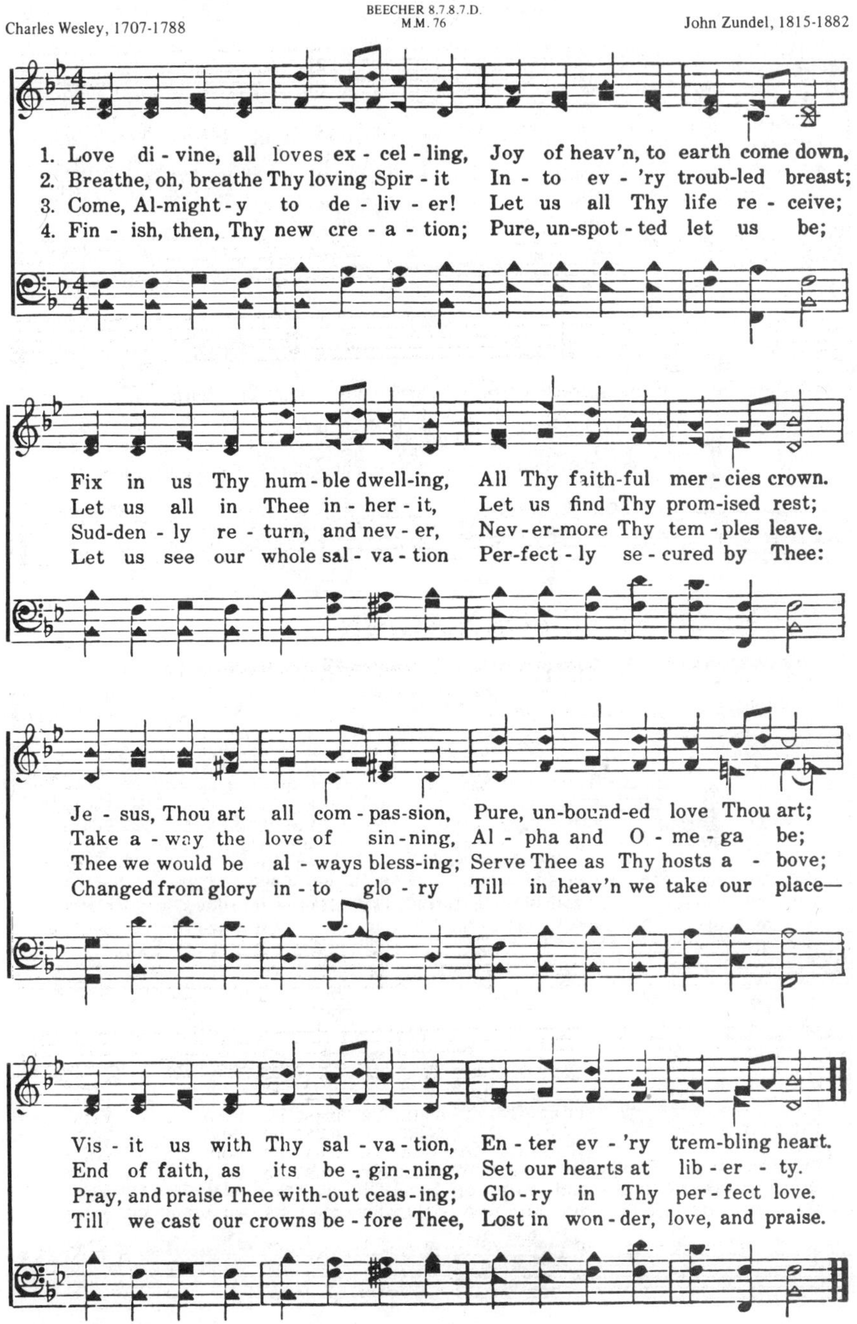
1. Love di - vine, all loves ex - cel - ling, Joy of heav'n, to earth come down,
2. Breathe, oh, breathe Thy loving Spir - it In - to ev - 'ry troub-led breast;
3. Come, Al-might - y to de - liv - er! Let us all Thy life re - ceive;
4. Fin - ish, then, Thy new cre - a - tion; Pure, un-spot - ted let us be;
Fix in us Thy hum - ble dwell-ing, All Thy faith-ful mer - cies crown.
Let us all in Thee in - her - it, Let us find Thy prom-ised rest;
Sud-den - ly re - turn, and nev - er, Nev - er-more Thy tem - ples leave.
Let us see our whole sal - va - tion Per-fect - ly se - cured by Thee:
Je - sus, Thou art all com - pas-sion, Pure, un-bound-ed love Thou art;
Take a - way the love of sin-ning, Al - pha and O - me - ga be;
Thee we would be al - ways bless-ing; Serve Thee as Thy hosts a - bove;
Changed from glory in - to glo - ry Till in heav'n we take our place—
Vis - it us with Thy sal - va - tion, En - ter ev - 'ry trem-bling heart.
End of faith, as its be - gin - ning, Set our hearts at lib - er - ty.
Pray, and praise Thee with-out ceas - ing; Glo - ry in Thy per - fect love.
Till we cast our crowns be - fore Thee, Lost in won - der, love, and praise.

# 233 TO OUR FATHER, TRUE AND KIND

*Therefore being justified by faith, we have peace with God.* Rom. 5:1.

Wilmer D. Swope, 1970
Altered by Compiler, 1970

ORIENTIS PARTIBUS 7.7.7.7.
M.M. 76

13th century French melody
Har. Richard Redhead, 1820-1901

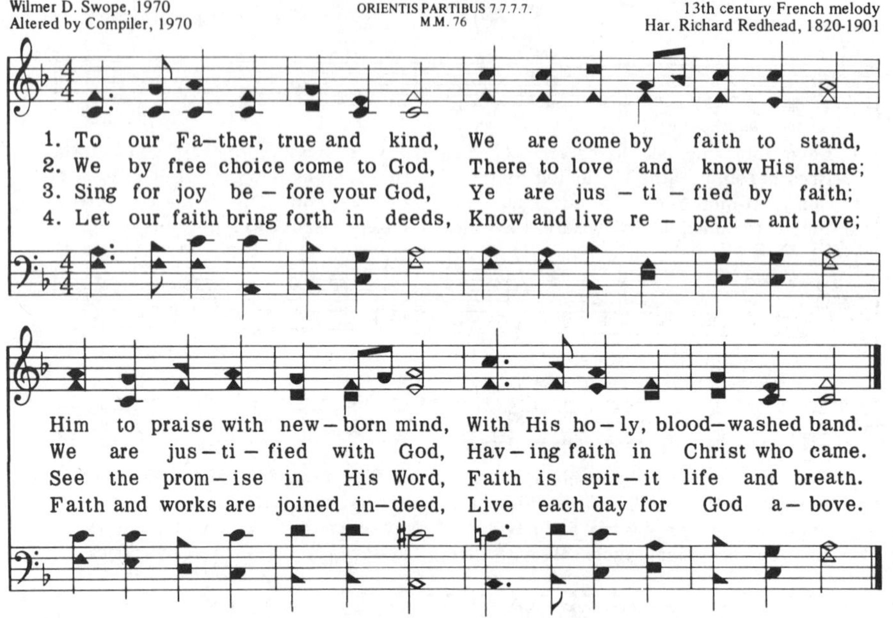
1. To our Fa–ther, true and kind, We are come by faith to stand,
2. We by free choice come to God, There to love and know His name;
3. Sing for joy be – fore your God, Ye are jus – ti – fied by faith;
4. Let our faith bring forth in deeds, Know and live re – pent – ant love;
Him to praise with new – born mind, With His ho – ly, blood–washed band.
We are jus – ti – fied with God, Hav – ing faith in Christ who came.
See the prom – ise in His Word, Faith is spir – it life and breath.
Faith and works are joined in–deed, Live each day for God a – bove.

# 234 MY SOUL COMPLETE IN JESUS STANDS

*Being now justified by His blood, we shall be saved from wrath through Him.* Rom. 5:9.

Grace W. Hinsdale, 1833
Altered by Compiler, 1970

FEDERAL STREET L.M. 8.8.8.8.
M.M. 66

Henry Kemble Oliver, 1800-1885

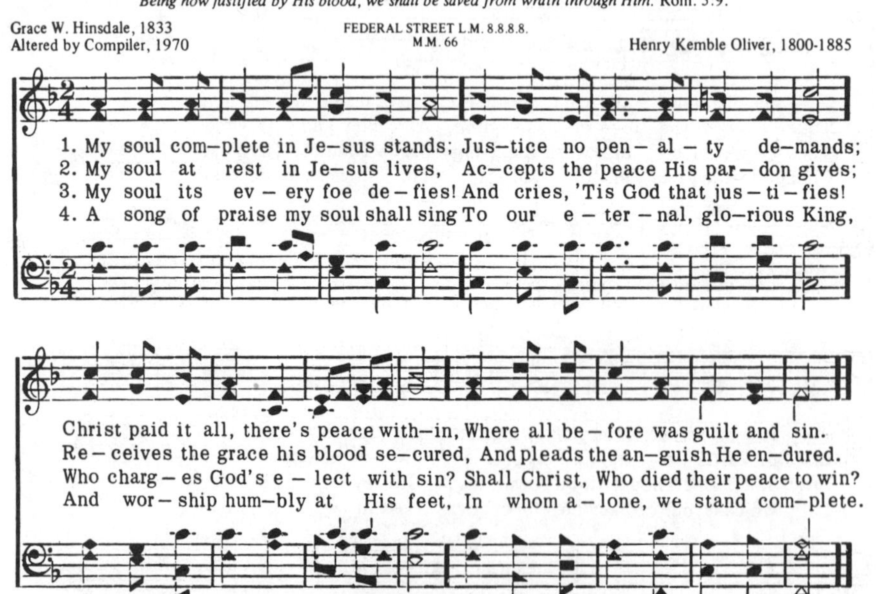
1. My soul com–plete in Je–sus stands; Jus–tice no pen – al – ty de–mands;
2. My soul at rest in Je–sus lives, Ac–cepts the peace His par – don gives;
3. My soul its ev – ery foe de – fies! And cries, 'Tis God that jus – ti – fies!
4. A song of praise my soul shall sing To our e – ter – nal, glo–rious King,
Christ paid it all, there's peace with–in, Where all be – fore was guilt and sin.
Re – ceives the grace his blood se–cured, And pleads the an–guish He en–dured.
Who charg – es God's e – lect with sin? Shall Christ, Who died their peace to win?
And wor – ship hum–bly at His feet, In whom a – lone, we stand com–plete.

## MY SOUL, REPEAT HIS PRAISE 235

*In whom we have redemption through His blood, the forgiveness of sins.* Eph. 1:7.

LOTTIE S.M. 6.6.8.6.
M.M. 63

Isaac Watts, 1719 (1674-1748)

William Batchelder Bradbury, 1816-1868

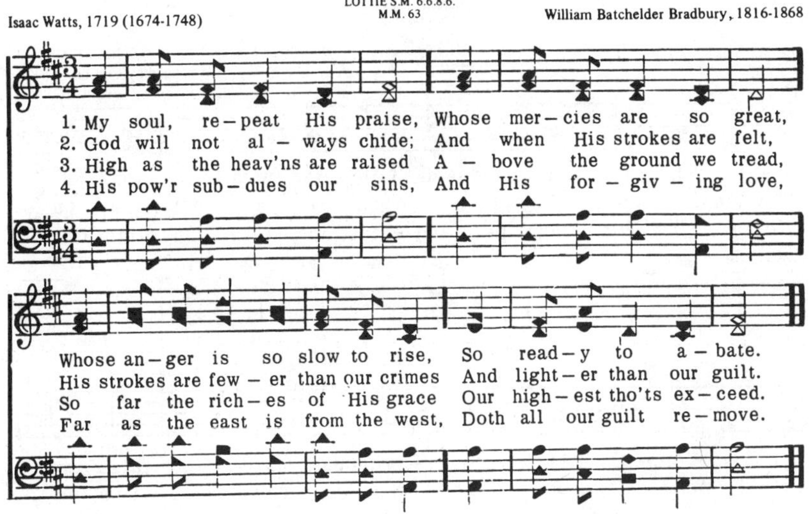
1. My soul, re-peat His praise, Whose mer-cies are so great,
2. God will not al-ways chide; And when His strokes are felt,
3. High as the heav'ns are raised A-bove the ground we tread,
4. His pow'r sub-dues our sins, And His for-giv-ing love,
Whose an-ger is so slow to rise, So read-y to a-bate.
His strokes are few-er than our crimes And light-er than our guilt.
So far the rich-es of His grace Our high-est tho'ts ex-ceed.
Far as the east is from the west, Doth all our guilt re-move.

SALVATION: ADOPTION

## ARISE, MY SOUL, ARISE 236

*Ye have received the Spirit of adoption, whereby we cry, Abba, Father.* Rom. 8:15.

LENOX 6.6.6.6.8.8.8.
M.M. 88

Charles Wesley, 1707-1788

Lewis Edson, 1748-1820

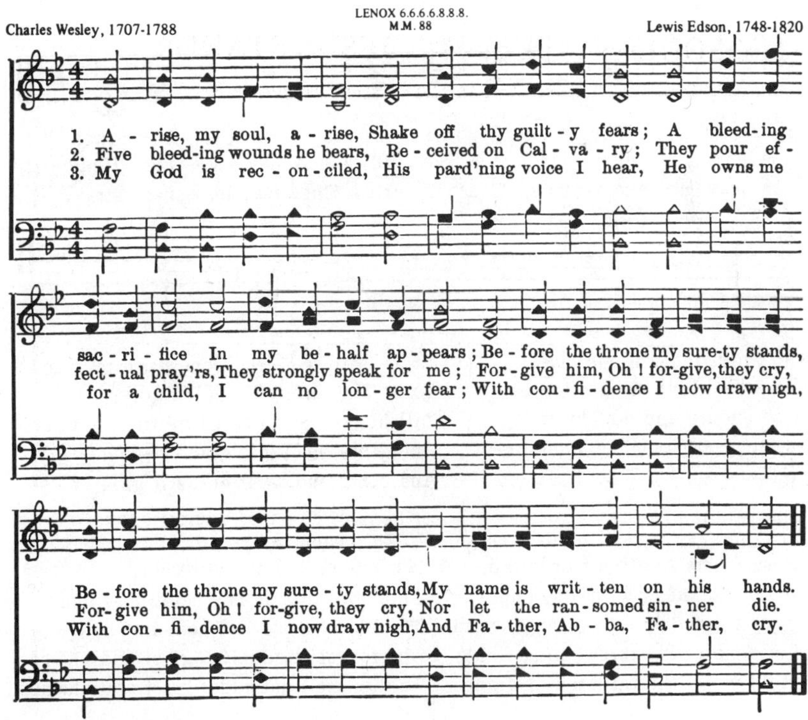
1. A-rise, my soul, a-rise, Shake off thy guilt-y fears; A bleed-ing
2. Five bleed-ing wounds he bears, Re-ceived on Cal-va-ry; They pour ef-
3. My God is rec-on-ciled, His pard'ning voice I hear, He owns me
sac-ri-fice In my be-half ap-pears; Be-fore the throne my sure-ty stands,
fect-ual pray'rs, They strongly speak for me; For-give him, Oh! for-give, they cry,
for a child, I can no lon-ger fear; With con-fi-dence I now draw nigh,
Be-fore the throne my sure-ty stands, My name is writ-ten on his hands.
For-give him, Oh! for-give, they cry, Nor let the ran-somed sin-ner die.
With con-fi-dence I now draw nigh, And Fa-ther, Ab-ba, Fa-ther, cry.

# 237 INTO THY GRACIOUS HANDS I FALL

*Your life is hid with Christ in God.* Col. 3:3.

Wolfgang Christopher Dessler, 1660-1722
*Mein Jesu dem die Seraphinen*
Tr. John Wesley, 1703-1791
St. 7, Charles Wesley, 1707-1788
Altered by Compiler, 1970

(TRADITIONAL) 8.8.8.8.8.
M.M. 100

Traditional Melody
Arranged by Compiler, 1970

1. In – to Thy gra–cious hands I fall, And with the arms of
2. Now bless–ed through Thy grace I am; No con – dem – na–tion
3. Still let Thy wis – dom be my guide, Nor take Thy flight from

faith em–brace; O King of glo – ry, hear my call; O raise me,
now I dread; I taste sal – va – tion in Thy name, A – live in
me a – way; Still with me let Thy grace a – bide, That I from

heal me by Thy grace, O raise me, heal me by Thy grace.
Thee, my liv – ing Head, A – live in Thee, my liv – ing Head.
Thee may ne – ver stray, That I from Thee may ne – ver stray.

4. Let Thy Word richly in me dwell,
Thy peace and love my portion be;
My joy to endure and do Thy will,
Till perfect I am found in Thee,
Till perfect I am found in Thee.

5. Arm me with Thy whole armor, Lord,
Support my weakness with Thy might;
Gird on my thigh Thy conquering sword,
And shield me in the threatening fight,
And shield me in the threatening fight.

6. From faith to faith, from grace to grace,
So in Thy strength shall I go on,
Till heaven and earth flee from Thy face,
And glory end what grace began,
And glory end what grace began.

7. O bliss! Accepted now I am
Through faith in Thy most holy name;
Thy blood applied, I rest in Thee,
Who for me died midst grief and shame,
Who for me died midst grief and shame.

# IN ALL THINGS GLORIFY CHRIST 238

*Whatsoever ye do, do all to the glory of God.* I Cor. 10:31.

NAUMAN 7.8.7.8.10.10.10.9.
M.M. 88

Dora Deanie Nauman — Dora Deanie Nauman

Slowly, with accents
1. In all things glo - ri - fy Christ and glo - ry not in what you've done; For you were bought with a price, and there - fore you are not your own. In His own like - ness He cre - at - ed you, His pre - cious blood He shed to pur - chase you, He lives in heav'n to in - ter - cede for you, there - fore in all things glo - ri - fy Christ.
2. In all things glo - ri - fy Christ in word and deed ex - alt God's Son; Your bod - y yield - ed and clean, a tem - ple for the Ho - ly One. To be His wit - ness is His will for you, No high - er call - ing could He of - fer you, A home in glo - ry He's pre - pared for you, there - fore in all things glo - ri - fy Christ.
cresc.
rit.

# 239 WHEN WE WALK WITH THE LORD

*Truly our fellowship is with the Father, and with His Son Jesus Christ.* I Jn. 1:3.

TRUST AND OBEY 6.6.9.D. with Ref.
M.M. 80

John H. Sammis, 1864-1919

Daniel B. Towner, 1850-1919

1. When we walk with the Lord In the light of His Word What a glo - ry He
2. Not a shad-ow can rise, Not a cloud in the skies, But His smile quickly
3. But we nev - er can prove The de-lights of His love Un - til all on the
4. Then in fel - low-ship sweet We will sit at His feet, Or we'll walk by His
sheds on our way! While we do His good will He a - bides with us still,
drives it a - way; Not a doubt nor a fear, Not a sigh nor a tear,
al - tar we lay; For the fa - vor He shows, And the joy He be - stows,
side in the way; What He says we will do, Where He sends we will go—
And with all who will trust and o - bey.
Can a - bide while we trust and o - bey.
Are for them who will trust and o - bey.
Nev - er fear, on - ly trust and o - bey.
REFRAIN
Trust and o - bey, for there's no oth-er
way To be hap - py in Je - sus, But to trust and o - bey.

# O COME THOU WOUNDED LAMB OF GOD 240

*If we say that we have fellowship with Him, and walk in darkness, we lie, and do not the truth.* I Jn. 1:6.

Nicolaus Ludwig von Zinzendorf, 1700-1760
*Ach mein verwundter Fürste!*
Johann Nitschman, 1712-1783
Anna Nitschman, 1715-1760
Composite, arr. John Wesley, 1740 (1703-1791)
Alt. George Whitefield, 1753 (1714-1770)
Altered by Compiler, 1971

WO GOTT ZUM HAUS
L.M. 8.8.8.8.
M.M. 72

*Geistliche Lieder,* Wittenberg, 1535

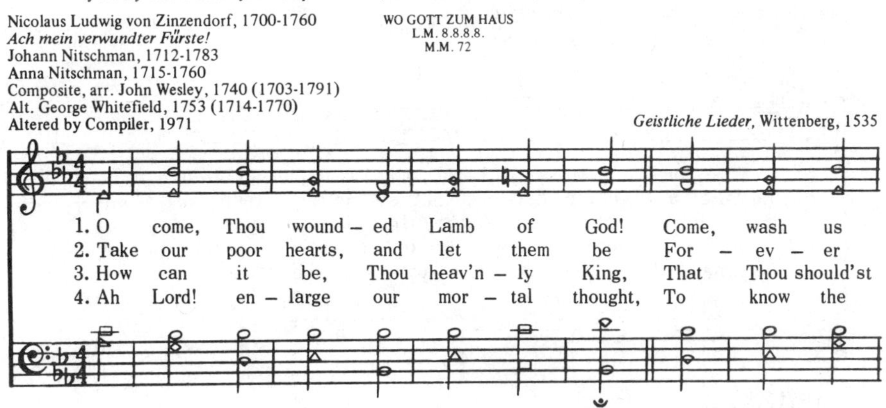

1. O come, Thou wound – ed Lamb of God! Come, wash us
2. Take our poor hearts, and let them be For – ev – er
3. How can it be, Thou heav'n – ly King, That Thou should'st
4. Ah Lord! en – large our mor – tal thought, To know the

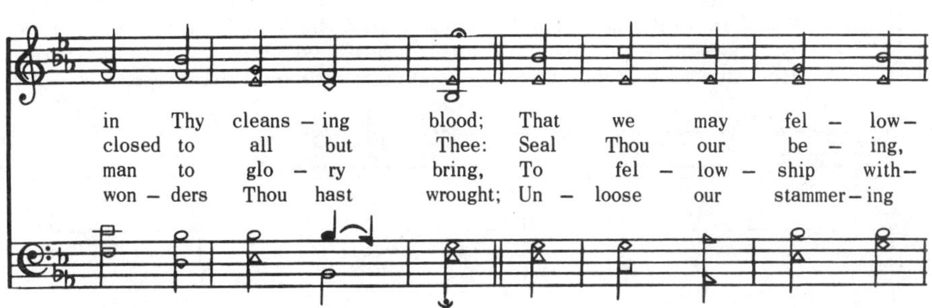

in Thy cleans – ing blood; That we may fel – low–
closed to all but Thee: Seal Thou our be – ing,
man to glo – ry bring, To fel – low – ship with–
won – ders Thou hast wrought; Un – loose our stammer – ing

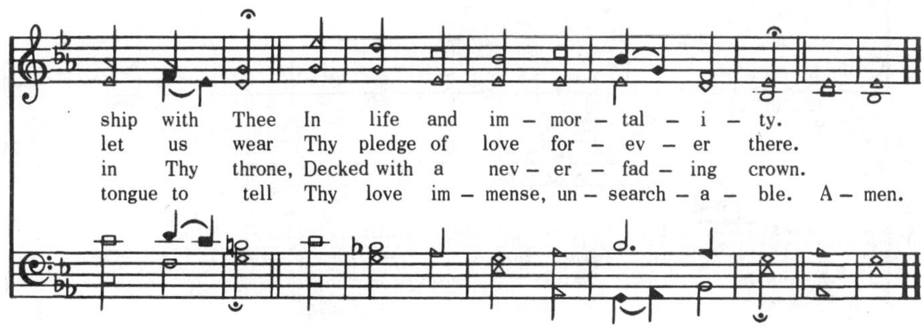

ship with Thee In life and im – mor – tal – i – ty.
let us wear Thy pledge of love for – ev – er there.
in Thy throne, Decked with a nev – er – fad – ing crown.
tongue to tell Thy love im – mense, un – search – a – ble. A – men.

# 241 RISE MY SOUL TO WATCH AND PRAY

*Watch and pray, that ye enter not into temptation.* Mt. 26:41.

Johann Burchard Freystein, cento, 1697 (1671-1718)
*Mache dich, mein Geist, bereit*
Tr. Catherine Winkworth, 1863 (1827-1878), alt.
Altered by Compiler, 1970

STRAF MICH NICHT
7.6.7.6.3.3.6.6.
M.M. 69

*Hundert Arien, Dresden,* 1694
Arranged by Compiler, 1970

1. Rise, my soul, to watch and pray, From Thy sleep a – wak – en;
2. Watch a–gainst the dev–il's snares Lest a – sleep he find Thee;
3. Watch! Let not the wick–ed world With its pow'r de – feat thee.
4. Watch a – gainst thy–self, my soul, Lest with grace thou tri – fle;
5. But while watch–ing, al – so pray To the Lord un – ceas – ing.

Be not by the e – vil day Un – a–wares o'er – tak – en.
For in–deed no pains he spares To de–ceive and blind thee.
Watch lest with her pomp un–furled She be – tray and cheat thee.
Let not self thy thoughts con–trol Nor God's mer – cy sti – fle.
He will free thee, be thy stay, Strength and faith in – creas – ing.

For the foe Well we know, Oft his har – vest
Sa – tan's prey Oft are they Who se – cure are
Watch and see Lest there be Faith – less friends to
Pride and sin Lurk with – in All thy hopes to
O Lord, bless In dis – tress And let noth – ing

reap – eth While the Chris–tian sleep – eth.
sleep – ing And no watch are keep – ing.
charm thee, Who but seek to harm thee.
scat – ter; Heed not when they flat – ter.
swerve me From the will to serve Thee. A–men.

# PILGRIM, SEEK NOT YET REPOSE 242

*Watch ye, stand fast in the faith.* I Cor. 16:13.

Charlotte Elliot, 1839 (1789-1871)
Altered by Compiler, 1970

BUCKLAND 7.7.7.7.
M.M. 66

Leighton George, 1836-1893

1. Pil–grim, seek not yet re – pose, Cast thy dreams of ease a – way;
2. Gird thy heav'n–ly ar – mor on, Wear it ev – er night and day;
3. Hear the vic – tors who o'er–came; Still they watch each war–rior's way;
4. Hear a – bove all these, thy Lord, Him thou lov – est to o – bey;
5. Watch, as if on that a – lone Hung the is – sue of the day;
Thou art in the midst of foes: Pil–grim, ev – er watch and pray!
Near thee lurks the e – vil one; Pil–grim, ev – er watch and pray!
All with one clear voice ex–claim, Pil–grim, ev – er watch and pray!
Hide with – in thy heart His word, Pil–grim, ev – er watch and pray!
Pray that help may be sent down; Pil–grim, ev – er watch and pray!

# PILGRIM, SEEK NOT YET REPOSE 243

*Let us not sleep . . . but let us watch and be sober.* I Thess. 5:6.

Charlotte Elliot, 1839 (1789-1871)
Recast, John J. Overholt, 1970

CAPETOWN 7.7.7.5.
M.M. 63

Frederich Filitz, 1847 (1804-1876)

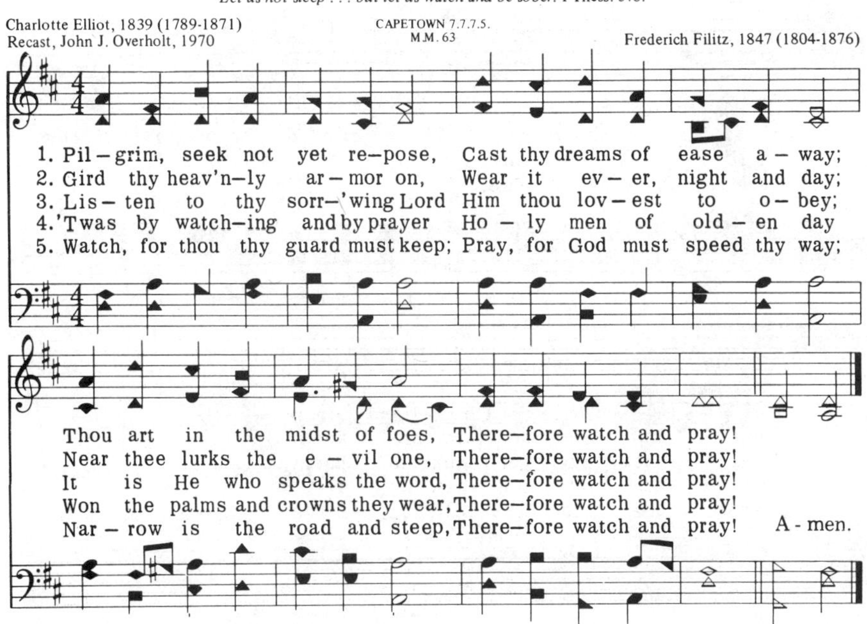
1. Pil – grim, seek not yet re–pose, Cast thy dreams of ease a – way;
2. Gird thy heav'n–ly ar – mor on, Wear it ev – er, night and day;
3. Lis – ten to thy sorr–'wing Lord Him thou lov – est to o – bey;
4.'Twas by watch–ing and by prayer Ho – ly men of old – en day
5. Watch, for thou thy guard must keep; Pray, for God must speed thy way;
Thou art in the midst of foes, There–fore watch and pray!
Near thee lurks the e – vil one, There–fore watch and pray!
It is He who speaks the word, There–fore watch and pray!
Won the palms and crowns they wear, There–fore watch and pray!
Nar – row is the road and steep, There–fore watch and pray!
A - men.

# 244 'TIS THE BLESSED HOUR OF PRAYER

*Be careful for nothing; but in every thing by prayer and supplication . . . let your requests be made known unto God.* Phil. 4:6.

BLESSED HOUR OF PRAYER 13.12.13.13. with Ref.
M.M. 76

Fanny J. Crosby, 1820-1915 — William Howard Doane, 1832-1915

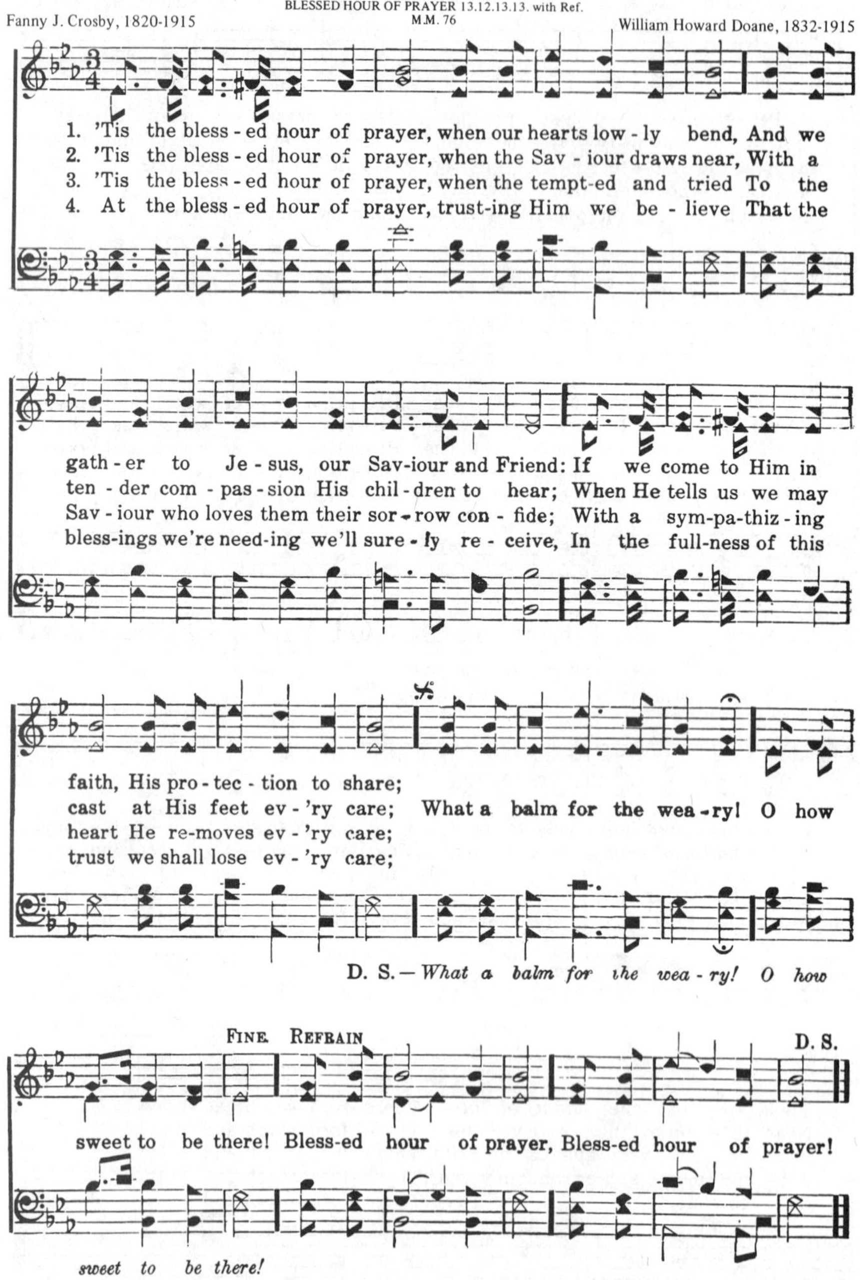

1. 'Tis the bless-ed hour of prayer, when our hearts low-ly bend, And we gath-er to Je-sus, our Sav-iour and Friend: If we come to Him in faith, His pro-tec-tion to share;
2. 'Tis the bless-ed hour of prayer, when the Sav-iour draws near, With a ten-der com-pas-sion His chil-dren to hear; When He tells us we may cast at His feet ev-'ry care;
3. 'Tis the bless-ed hour of prayer, when the tempt-ed and tried To the Sav-iour who loves them their sor-row con-fide; With a sym-pa-thiz-ing heart He re-moves ev-'ry care;
4. At the bless-ed hour of prayer, trust-ing Him we be-lieve That the bless-ings we're need-ing we'll sure-ly re-ceive, In the full-ness of this trust we shall lose ev-'ry care;
What a balm for the wea-ry! O how sweet to be there!
D. S.—What a balm for the wea-ry! O how sweet to be there!
FINE
REFRAIN
Bless-ed hour of prayer, Bless-ed hour of prayer!
D. S.

# SWEET HOUR OF PRAYER 245

*And all things, whatsoever ye shall ask in prayer, believing, ye shall receive.* Mt. 21:22.

SWEET HOUR L.M. 8.8.8.8.D.
M.M. 88

William W. Walford, c. 1842 (1772-1850) William Batchelder Bradbury, 1859 (1816-1868)

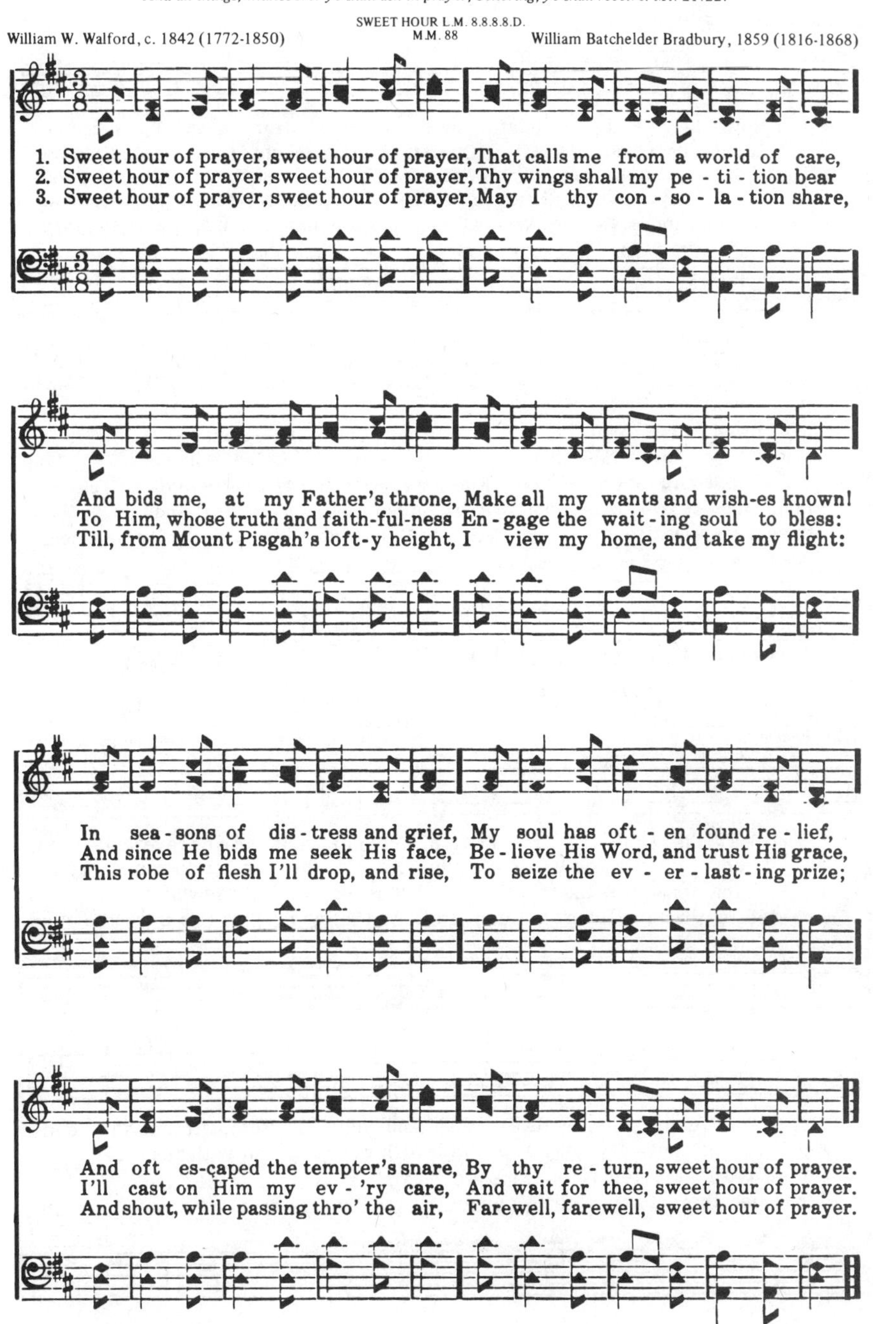
1. Sweet hour of prayer, sweet hour of prayer, That calls me from a world of care,
2. Sweet hour of prayer, sweet hour of prayer, Thy wings shall my pe - ti - tion bear
3. Sweet hour of prayer, sweet hour of prayer, May I thy con - so - la - tion share,
And bids me, at my Father's throne, Make all my wants and wish-es known!
To Him, whose truth and faith-ful-ness En - gage the wait - ing soul to bless:
Till, from Mount Pisgah's loft-y height, I view my home, and take my flight:
In sea - sons of dis - tress and grief, My soul has oft - en found re - lief,
And since He bids me seek His face, Be - lieve His Word, and trust His grace,
This robe of flesh I'll drop, and rise, To seize the ev - er - last - ing prize;
And oft es-caped the tempter's snare, By thy re - turn, sweet hour of prayer.
I'll cast on Him my ev - 'ry care, And wait for thee, sweet hour of prayer.
And shout, while passing thro' the air, Farewell, farewell, sweet hour of prayer.

# 246 OUR HEAVENLY FATHER HEAR

*The effectual fervent prayer of a righteous man availeth much.* Jas. 5:16.

James Montgomery, 1771-1854 | TRENTHAM S.M. 6.6.8.6. M.M. 76 | Robert Jackson, 1894 (1842-1914)

1. Our Heaven–ly Fa–ther, hear The prayer we of–fer now; Thy name be
2. Thy king–dom come; Thy will On earth be done in love, As saints and
3. Our dai–ly bread sup–ply, While by Thy Word we live; The guilt of
4. From dark temp–ta–tion's pow'r Our fee–ble hearts de–fend; De–liv–er
5. Thine, then, for–ev–er be Glo–ry and power di–vine; The scep–tre,
hal–lowed far and near, To Thee all na–tions bow.
ser–a–phim ful–fill Thy per–fect law a–bove.
our in–iq–ui–ty For–give, as we for–give.
in the e–vil hour, And guide us to the end.
throne, and maj–es–ty All heav'n and earth are Thine. A–men.

# 247 OUR FATHER GOD, WHO ART IN HEAV'N

*Our Father which art in heaven, Hallowed be Thy name.* Mt. 6:9.

*Minstrel of Zion* | MAINZER L.M. 8.8.8.8. M.M. 66 | Joseph Mainzer, Arranged by Compiler, 1968

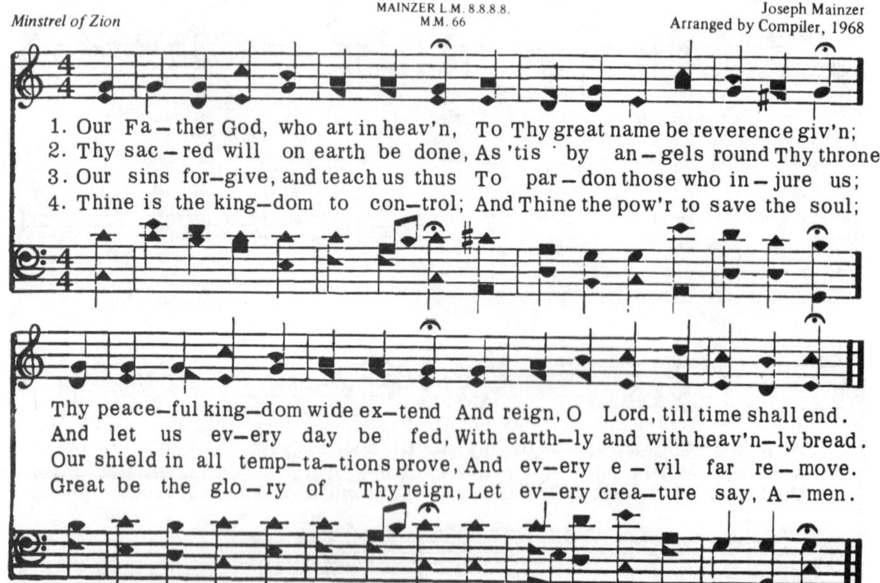
1. Our Fa–ther God, who art in heav'n, To Thy great name be reverence giv'n;
2. Thy sac–red will on earth be done, As 'tis by an–gels round Thy throne;
3. Our sins for–give, and teach us thus To par–don those who in–jure us;
4. Thine is the king–dom to con–trol; And Thine the pow'r to save the soul;
Thy peace–ful king–dom wide ex–tend And reign, O Lord, till time shall end.
And let us ev–ery day be fed, With earth–ly and with heav'n–ly bread.
Our shield in all temp–ta–tions prove, And ev–ery e–vil far re–move.
Great be the glo–ry of Thy reign, Let ev–ery crea–ture say, A–men.

## STAY, THOU INSULTED MASTER, STAY 248

*A broken and a contrite heart, O God, Thou wilt not despise.* Ps. 51:17.

Charles Wesley, 1707-1788
Altered by Compiler, 1970

WINDHAM L.M. 8.8.8.8.
M.M. 58

Daniel Read, 1785 (1757-1836)

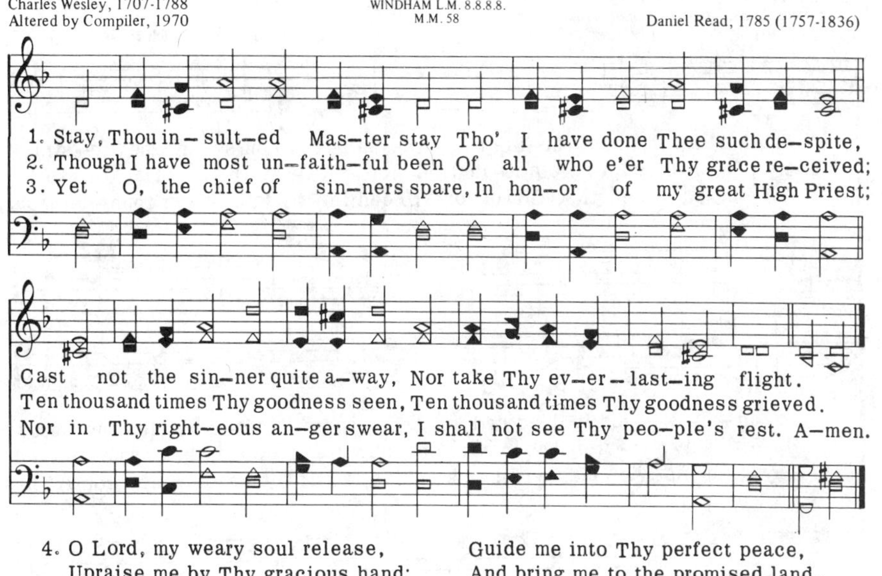
1. Stay, Thou in–sult–ed Mas–ter stay Tho' I have done Thee such de-spite,
2. Though I have most un–faith–ful been Of all who e'er Thy grace re–ceived;
3. Yet O, the chief of sin–ners spare, In hon–or of my great High Priest;
Cast not the sin-ner quite a–way, Nor take Thy ev–er–last–ing flight.
Ten thousand times Thy goodness seen, Ten thousand times Thy goodness grieved.
Nor in Thy right–eous an–ger swear, I shall not see Thy peo–ple's rest. A–men.

4. O Lord, my weary soul release,
Upraise me by Thy gracious hand;
Guide me into Thy perfect peace,
And bring me to the promised land.

## FORTY DAYS AND FORTY NIGHTS 249

*This kind can come forth by nothing, but by prayer and fasting.* Mk. 9:29.

George Hunt Smyttan, 1825-1870

MESSIAH 7.7.7.7.D.
M.M. 72

Arr. from Louis J. F. Herold, 1791-1833

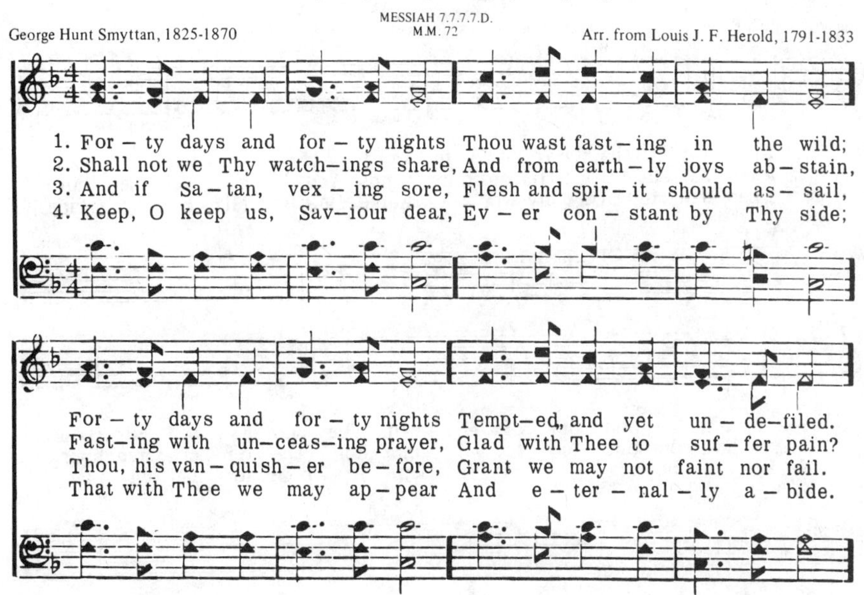
1. For – ty days and for – ty nights Thou wast fast – ing in the wild;
2. Shall not we Thy watch–ings share, And from earth – ly joys ab – stain,
3. And if Sa – tan, vex – ing sore, Flesh and spir – it should as – sail,
4. Keep, O keep us, Sav–iour dear, Ev – er con – stant by Thy side;
For – ty days and for – ty nights Tempt–ed, and yet un – de–filed.
Fast–ing with un–ceas–ing prayer, Glad with Thee to suf – fer pain?
Thou, his van – quish – er be – fore, Grant we may not faint nor fail.
That with Thee we may ap – pear And e – ter – nal – ly a – bide.

# 250 SHALL I FOR FEAR OF FEEBLE MAN

*For we cannot but speak the things which we have seen and heard.* Acts 4:20.

Johann Joseph Winckler, 1670-1722
*Sollt ich aus Furcht vor Menschenkindern*
Tr. John Wesley, 1739 (1703-1791)

SAMSON L.M. 8.8.8.8.
M.M. 72

George Friedrich Handel, 1685-1759

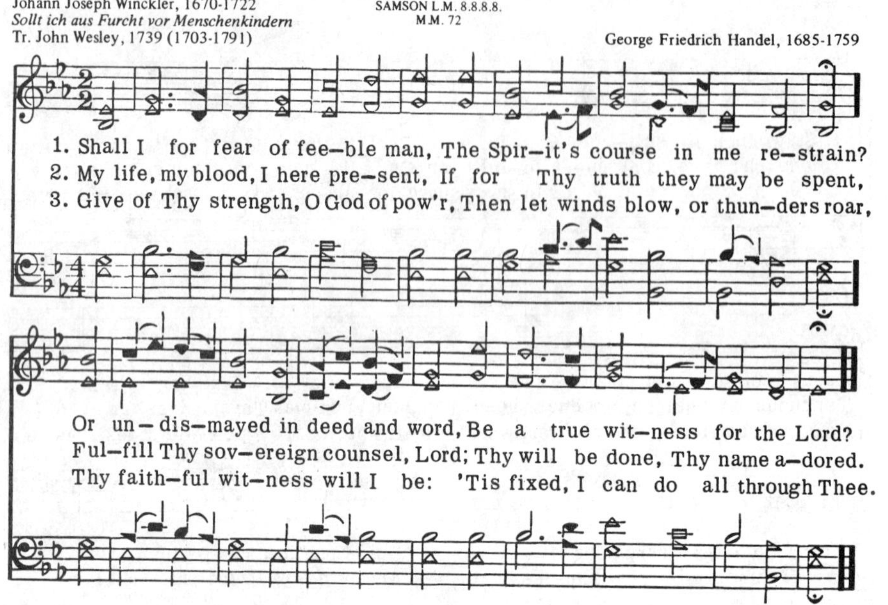
1. Shall I for fear of fee–ble man, The Spir–it's course in me re–strain?
2. My life, my blood, I here pre–sent, If for Thy truth they may be spent,
3. Give of Thy strength, O God of pow'r, Then let winds blow, or thun–ders roar,
Or un–dis–mayed in deed and word, Be a true wit–ness for the Lord?
Ful–fill Thy sov–ereign counsel, Lord; Thy will be done, Thy name a–dored.
Thy faith–ful wit–ness will I be: 'Tis fixed, I can do all through Thee.

# 251 I'M NOT ASHAMED TO OWN MY LORD

*For I am not ashamed of the gospel of Christ.* Rom. 1:16.

Isaac Watts, 1674-1748

AZMON C.M. 8.6.8.6.
M.M. 66

Carl Gotthelf Glazer, 1784-1829

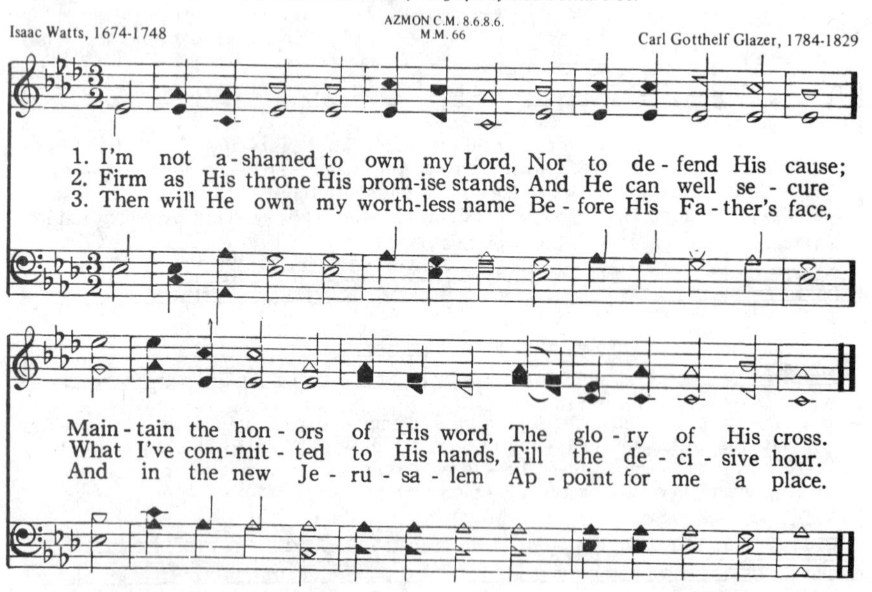
1. I'm not a-shamed to own my Lord, Nor to de-fend His cause;
2. Firm as His throne His prom-ise stands, And He can well se-cure
3. Then will He own my worth-less name Be-fore His Fa-ther's face,
Main-tain the hon-ors of His word, The glo-ry of His cross.
What I've com-mit-ted to His hands, Till the de-ci-sive hour.
And in the new Je-ru-sa-lem Ap-point for me a place.

# SHALL I FOR FEAR OF FEEBLE MAN 252

*Ye shall be witnesses unto Me.* Acts 1:8.

Johann Joseph Winckler, 1670-1722
*Sollt ich aus Furcht vor Menschenkindern*
Tr. John Wesley, 1739 (1703-1791)

SWEET HOUR L.M. 8.8.8.8.D.
M.M. 108

William Batchelder Bradbury, 1861 (1816-1868)

1. Shall I, for fear of fee–ble man, The Spir–it's course in me re–strain?
2. Shall I, to soothe the un–ho–ly throng, Sof–ten Thy truth, or smooth my tongue,
3. Yea, let men rage; since Thou wilt spread Thy shad–ow–ing wings a–round my head;
Or un–dis–mayed in deed and word, Be a true wit–ness of my Lord?
To gain earth's gild–ed toys, or flee The cross en–dured, my Lord, by Thee?
And in all pain Thy ten–der love Will still my sure re–fresh–ment prove.
Awed by a mor–tal's frown, shall I Con–ceal the Word of God most high?
What then, is he whose scorn I dread, Whose wrath or hate makes me a–fraid?
Sav–iour of men, Thy search–ing eye Doth all mine in–most thoughts descry;
How then be–fore Thee shall I dare To stand, or how thine an–ger bear?
A man! an heir of death! a slave To sin! a bub–ble on the wave!
Doth aught on earth my wish–es raise, Or the world's pleas–ures or its praise?

4. The love of Christ doth me constrain To seek the perishing souls of men;
With cries, entreaties, tears to save– To snatch them from a Christ–less grave.
For this let men revile my name; No cross I shun, I fear no shame;
All hail, reproach; and welcome, pain; Only Thy terrors, Lord, restrain.

5. My life, my blood, I here present, If for Thy truth they may be spent;
Fulfil Thy sovereign counsel, Lord; Thy will be done, Thy name adored.
Give me Thy strength, O God of power; Then let winds blow, or thunders roar,
Thy faithful witness will I be; 'Tis fixed; I can do all through Thee.

# 253 I LOVE TO TELL THE STORY

*For the love of Christ constraineth us.* II Cor. 5:14.

HANKEY 7.6.7.6.D. with Ref.
M.M. 80

Catherine G. Hankey, 1834-1911 — William Gustavus Fischer, 1835-1912

1. I love to tell the sto - ry Of un-seen things a-bove, Of Je - sus and His glo - ry, Of Je - sus and His love; I love to tell the sto - ry Be-cause I know 'tis true; It sat - is-fies my long-ings As nothing else can do.
2. I love to tell the sto - ry: More won-der-ful it seems Than all the gold-en fan-cies Of all my golden dreams; I love to tell the sto - ry: It did so much for me; And that is just the rea-son I tell it now to thee.
3. I love to tell the sto - ry: 'Tis pleas-ant to re - peat What seems, each time I tell it, More won-der-ful-ly sweet; I love to tell the sto - ry, For some have never heard The message of sal-va-tion From God's own holy word.
4. I love to tell the sto - ry, For those who know it best Seem hun - ger-ing and thirst-ing To hear it like the rest; And when, in scenes of glo-ry, I sing the new, new song, 'Twill be the old, old sto - ry That I have loved so long.
CHORUS
I love to tell the sto - ry! 'Twill be my theme in glo - ry
To tell the old, old sto - ry Of Je - sus and His love.

## YE MESSENGERS OF CHRIST 254

*Go out into the highways and hedges, and compel them to come in.* Lu. 14:23.

FESTAL SONG S.M. 6.6.8.6.
M.M. 96

Mrs. Vokes

William Henry Walter, 1894 (1825-1893)

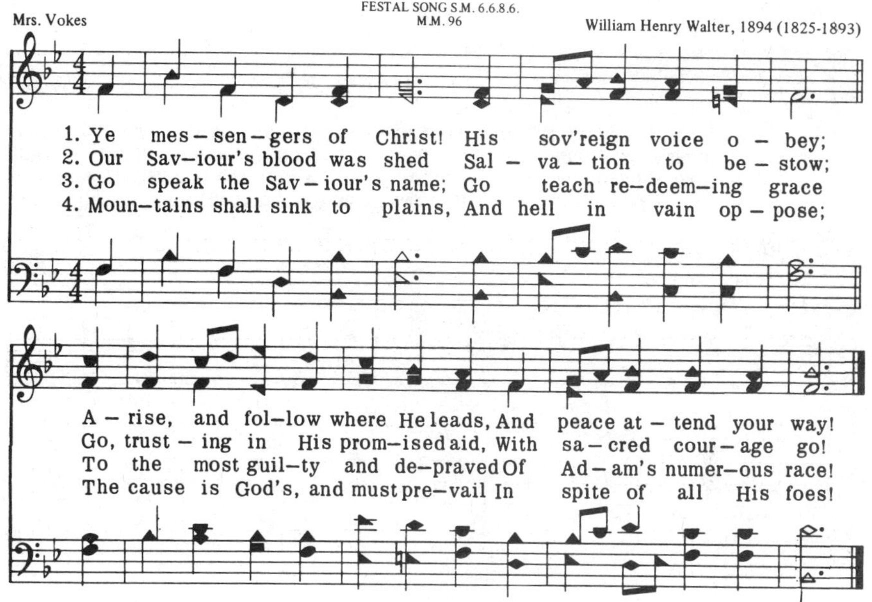
1. Ye mes-sen-gers of Christ! His sov'reign voice o-bey;
2. Our Sav-iour's blood was shed Sal-va-tion to be-stow;
3. Go speak the Sav-iour's name; Go teach re-deem-ing grace
4. Moun-tains shall sink to plains, And hell in vain op-pose;
A-rise, and fol-low where He leads, And peace at-tend your way!
Go, trust-ing in His prom-ised aid, With sa-cred cour-age go!
To the most guil-ty and de-praved Of Ad-am's numer-ous race!
The cause is God's, and must pre-vail In spite of all His foes!

## HE THAT GOETH FORTH WITH WEEPING 255

*He that goeth forth and weepeth, bearing precious seed, shall doubtless come again . . . bringing his sheaves with him.* Ps. 126:6.

STOCKWELL 8.7.8.7.
M.M. 66

Thomas Hastings, 1784-1872

Darius Elliot Jones, 1815-1881

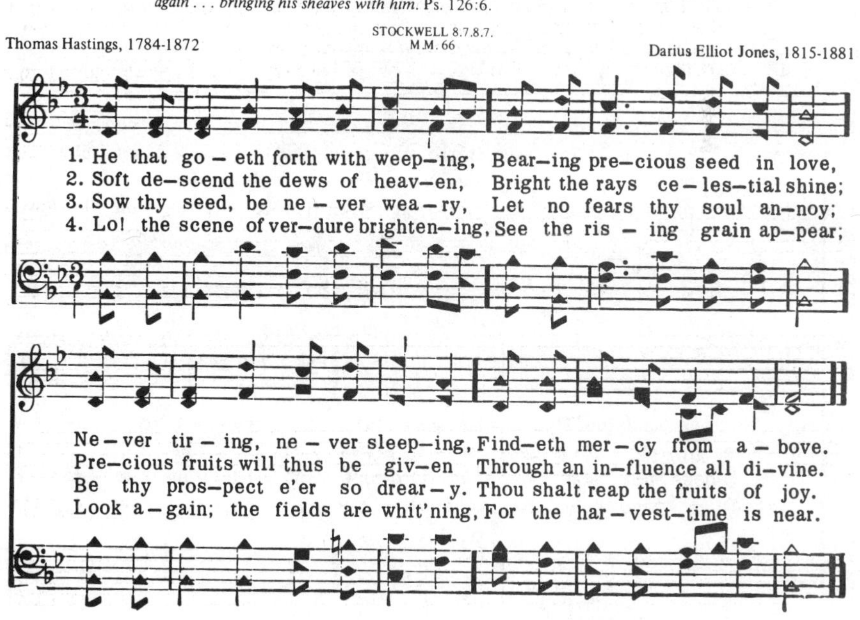
1. He that go-eth forth with weep-ing, Bear-ing pre-cious seed in love,
2. Soft de-scend the dews of heav-en, Bright the rays ce-les-tial shine;
3. Sow thy seed, be ne-ver wea-ry, Let no fears thy soul an-noy;
4. Lo! the scene of ver-dure brighten-ing, See the ris-ing grain ap-pear;
Ne-ver tir-ing, ne-ver sleep-ing, Find-eth mer-cy from a-bove.
Pre-cious fruits will thus be giv-en Through an in-fluence all di-vine.
Be thy pros-pect e'er so drear-y. Thou shalt reap the fruits of joy.
Look a-gain; the fields are whit'ning, For the har-vest-time is near.

# 256 DEAR LORD AMID THE THRONG

*Thanks be unto God, which always causeth us to triumph in Christ.* II Cor. 2:14.

Edward Denny, 1848 (b. 1796)
Altered by Compiler, 1970

ENDURANCE L.M. 8.8.8.8.
M.M. 69

Adaline Hohf Beery, 1859-1929
Arranged by Compiler, 1970

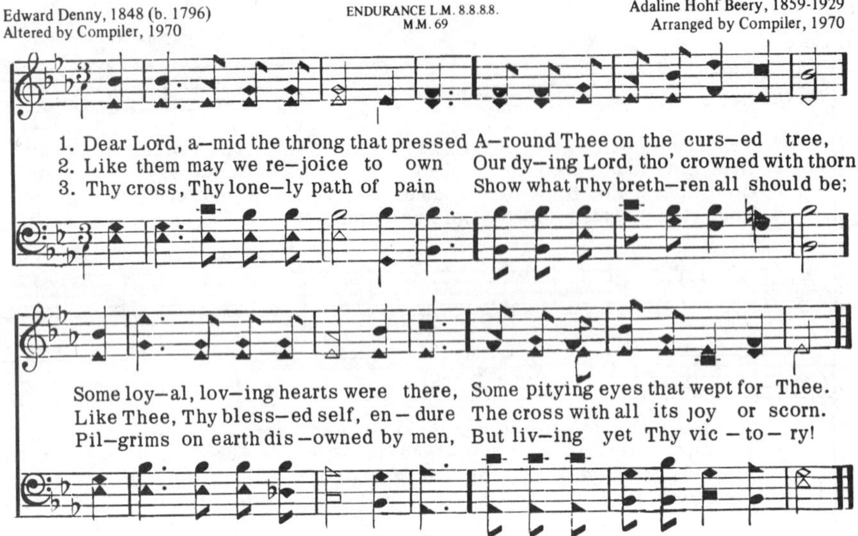
1. Dear Lord, a–mid the throng that pressed A–round Thee on the curs–ed tree,
2. Like them may we re–joice to own Our dy–ing Lord, tho' crowned with thorn;
3. Thy cross, Thy lone–ly path of pain Show what Thy breth–ren all should be;
Some loy–al, lov–ing hearts were there, Some pitying eyes that wept for Thee.
Like Thee, Thy bless–ed self, en – dure The cross with all its joy or scorn.
Pil–grims on earth dis –owned by men, But liv–ing yet Thy vic – to – ry!

# 257 THERE'S PERFECT LOVE THAT CASTS OUT FEAR

*Perfect love casteth out fear.* I Jn. 4:18.

Rudolph P. Blosser, 1873-1950

MARKELL C.M. 8.6.8.6.
M.M. 69

Aldine Silliman Kieffer, 1840-1904

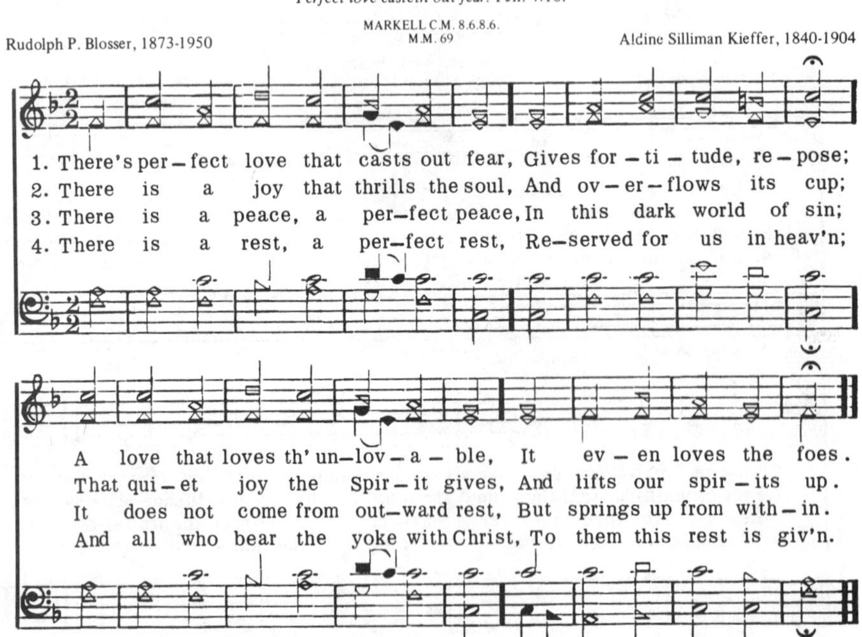
1. There's per – fect love that casts out fear, Gives for – ti – tude, re – pose;
2. There is a joy that thrills the soul, And ov – er – flows its cup;
3. There is a peace, a per–fect peace, In this dark world of sin;
4. There is a rest, a per–fect rest, Re–served for us in heav'n;
A love that loves th' un–lov – a – ble, It ev – en loves the foes.
That qui – et joy the Spir – it gives, And lifts our spir – its up.
It does not come from out–ward rest, But springs up from with – in.
And all who bear the yoke with Christ, To them this rest is giv'n.

## FOR ME TO LIVE IS CHRIST 258

*For to me to live is Christ.* Phil. 1:21.

M. Vulpius's *Ein Schön Geistlich Gesangbuch*, Jena, 1609
*Christus der ist mein Leben*
Tr. Charles Seymour Robinson, 1829-1899

HEROLD NEW S.M. 6.6.8.6.
M.M. 66

J. Henry Showalter, 1864-1947
Arranged by Compiler, 1970

1. For me to live is Christ, To die is end–less gain;
2. A pil–grim–age my lot, My home is in the skies;
3. I fare with Christ, my Lord, His path the path I choose;
4. The dawn on dis–tant hills, Shines o'er the vales be–low;
5. My jour–ney soon will end, My scrip and staff laid down;
6. Faith–ful may I en–dure, And hear my Sav–iour say,
For Him I glad–ly bear the cross, And wel–come grief and pain.
I night–ly pitch my tent be–low, And dai–ly high–er rise.
They joy who suf–fer most with Him, They win who with Him lose.
The shad–ows of this world are lost, In light to which I go.
O, tempt me not with earth–ly toys! I go to wear a crown.
Thrice wel–come home, be–lov–ed child, In–her–it end–less day!

## FOR ME TO LIVE IS CHRIST 259

*Ye are dead, and your life is hid with Christ in God.* Col. 3:3.

Elva Yoder, 1969 (b. 1903)

FERGUSON S.M. 6.6.8.6.
M.M. 80

George Kingsley, 1843 (1811-1884)

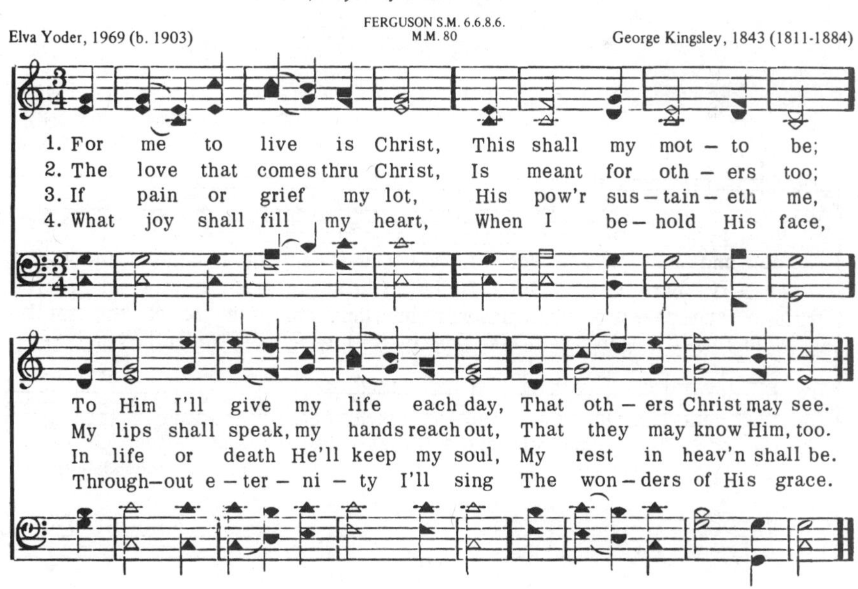

1. For me to live is Christ, This shall my mot–to be;
2. The love that comes thru Christ, Is meant for oth–ers too;
3. If pain or grief my lot, His pow'r sus–tain–eth me,
4. What joy shall fill my heart, When I be–hold His face,
To Him I'll give my life each day, That oth–ers Christ may see.
My lips shall speak, my hands reach out, That they may know Him, too.
In life or death He'll keep my soul, My rest in heav'n shall be.
Through–out e–ter–ni–ty I'll sing The won–ders of His grace.

# 260 NOT I BUT CHRIST BE HONORED

*He must increase, but I must decrease.* Jn. 3:30.

GERRISH CHANT
M.M. 69

A. A. F. Gerrish chant

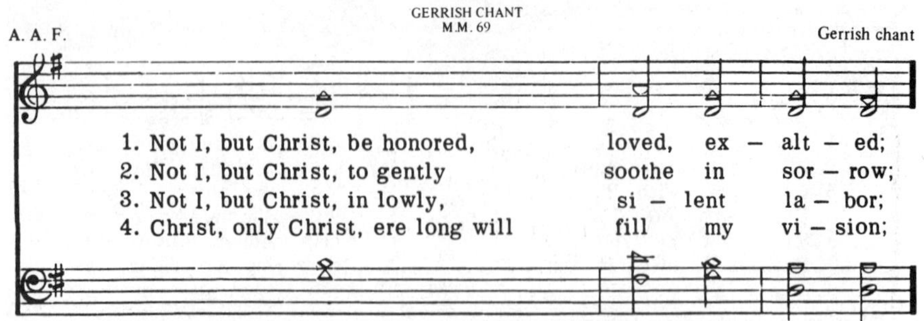
1. Not I, but Christ, be honored, loved, ex – alt – ed;
2. Not I, but Christ, to gently soothe in sor – row;
3. Not I, but Christ, in lowly, si – lent la – bor;
4. Christ, only Christ, ere long will fill my vi – sion;

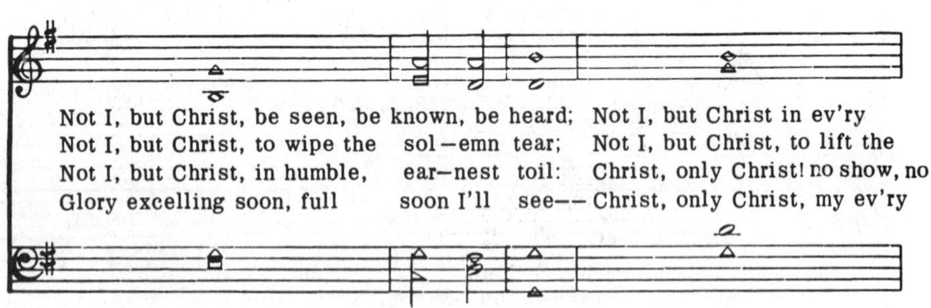
Not I, but Christ, be seen, be known, be heard; Not I, but Christ in ev'ry
Not I, but Christ, to wipe the sol–emn tear; Not I, but Christ, to lift the
Not I, but Christ, in humble, ear–nest toil: Christ, only Christ! no show, no
Glory excelling soon, full soon I'll see–– Christ, only Christ, my ev'ry

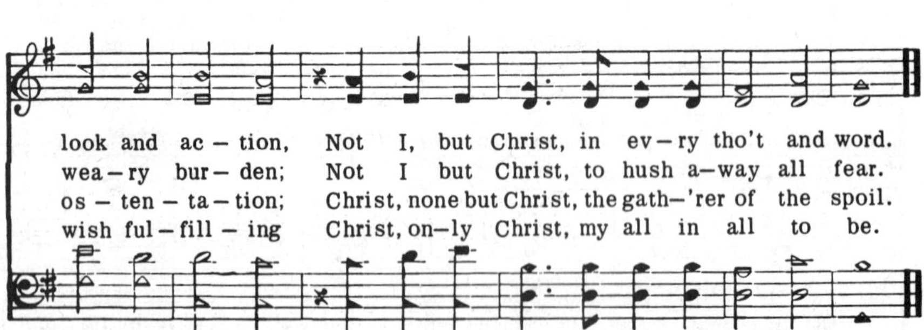
look and ac – tion, Not I, but Christ, in ev – ry tho't and word.
wea – ry bur – den; Not I but Christ, to hush a–way all fear.
os – ten – ta – tion; Christ, none but Christ, the gath–'rer of the spoil.
wish ful – fill – ing Christ, on–ly Christ, my all in all to be.

# DYING WITH JESUS 261

*I am crucified with Christ: nevertheless I live.* Gal. 2:20.

MOMENT BY MOMENT 10.10.10.9. with Ref.
M.M. 84
Daniel Webster Whittle, 1840-1901
May Whittle Moody
1. Dy - ing with Je - sus, by death reck-oned mine; Liv-ing with Je - sus, a new life di - vine; Look-ing to Je - sus till glo - ry doth shine, Mo-ment by mo - ment, O Lord, I am Thine.
2. Nev - er a tri - al that He is not there, Nev-er a bur - den that He doth not bear, Nev - er a sor - row that He doth not share, Mo-ment by mo - ment I'm un - der His care.
3. Nev - er a heart-ache and nev - er a groan, Nev-er a tear-drop and nev - er a moan; Nev - er a dan - ger but there on the throne, Mo-ment by mo - ment He thinks of His own.
4. Nev - er a weak-ness that He doth not feel, Nev-er a sick-ness that He can - not heal; Mo - ment by mo - ment, in woe or in weal, Je - sus, my Sav - ior, a - bides with me still.
CHORUS
Mo-ment by mo-ment I'm kept in His love; Mo-ment by mo-ment I've life from a - bove; Look-ing to Je - sus till glo - ry doth shine: Mo-ment by mo-ment, O Lord, I am Thine.

# 262 COME BRETHREN, LET US GO

*Come out from among them, and be ye separate.* II Cor. 6:17.

Gerhard Tersteegen, 1697-1769
*Kommt, Kinder lasst uns gehen*
Tr. Catherine Winkworth, 1827-1878

LEBANON S.M. 6.6.8.6.D.
M.M. 104

John Zundel, 1865 (1815-1882)

1. Come, breth–ren let us go! The even–ing clos–eth round.
'Tis per–il–ous to ling–er here, On this wild des–ert ground,
Take cour–age as ye wend, On towards e–ter–ni–ty,
From strength to strength your course shall be, And blest at last your end.

2. We shall not grieve our choice, Though strait our path and steep,
We know that He who called us here His Word shall ev–er keep;
Then fol–low trust–ing; come, And let each set his face
Toward yon–der fair and bless–ed place, In–tent to reach our home.

3. The bo–dy and the house, Deck not but deck the heart,
With all your powers; we are but guests Ere long we must de–part,
Ease brings dis–ease; con–tent, How–e'er his lot may fall,
A pil–grim bears and bows to all, For soon the time is spent.

4. Come, child–ren let us go! Our Fath–er is our Guide;
And when the way grows steep and dark, He jour–neys at our side;
Our spir–its He would cheer, The sun–shine of His love,
Re–vives and helps us as we rove, Ah, blest our lot e'en here.

5. O hasten bravely on, Nor yet our goal is near;
Look to the fiery pillar oft, That tells the Lord is here;
Onward your glances fend, Love beckons us, nor think,
That they who follow chance to sink, Shall miss their journey's end.

6. For this all things we dare,' Tis worth the risk, I know,
Renouncing all that blocks our course, Or weighs us down below;
O world, thou art too small; We seek another way,
Where Christ doth guide us day by day, And God is all in all!

## COME, SAVIOUR JESUS FROM ABOVE 263

*Come out of her my people, that ye be not partakers of her sins.* Rev. 18:4.

Antoinette Bourignon, 1640 (1616-1680)
*Venez Jesus, mon salutaire*
Tr. John Byrom, 1691-1763
Altered by Compiler, 1970

BISHOP L.M. 8.8.8.8.
M.M. 66

Joseph Perry Holbrook, 1822-1888

1. Come, Saviour, Jesus, from above! Assist me with Thy heavenly grace; Empty my heart of earthly love, And for Thyself prepare the place.
2. O let Thy sacred presence fill, And set my longing spirit free; Which pants to have no other will, But night and day to feast with Thee.
3. While in this region here below, No other good, will I pursue; I'll bid this world of noise and show, With all its glit-t'ring snares adieu.
4. That path with humble speed I'll seek, In which my Saviour's footsteps shine, Nor will I hear, nor will I speak, Of any other love but Thine.
5. Henceforth may no profane delight, Divide this consecrated soul; Possess it Thou, who hast the right, As Lord and Master of the whole.
6. Nothing on earth do I desire, But Thy pure love within my heart, This, only this will I require, And gladly with all others part.

# 264 LOVE NOT THE WORLD

*Love not the world, neither the things that are in the world.* I Jn. 2:15.

LOVE NOT THE WORLD C.M. 8.6.8.6. with Ref.
M.M. 58
Gertrude A. Flory
George B. Holsinger, 1857-1908
1. Love not the world! Its daz-zling show Con-ceals a snare of death; The sweet-est joy earth can be-stow, Dies as a wast-ed breath.
2. Love not the world! Its wealth, re-nown, The blood-bought soul en-slaves; Oh, strive to win a heav'n-ly crown, Which plumes of glo-ry wave.
3. Love not the world! Its sin and strife Ex-ceed the good and true; Oh, con-se-crate to Christ your life! He drained death's cup for you.
4. Love not the world! Pure joys a-bove All earth-ly things tran-scend; In Je-sus lose each i-dol love, And ev-er up-ward tend.
5. Love not the world! O Chris-tian, hear, In shin-ing words im-pearled, Shall on your ho-ly brow ap-pear, "He did not love the world."
Refrain.
Love not the world is Je-sus' plea, Sweet life to you he brought; A-lone with death on Cal-va-ry, Your sin-lost soul he sought.

## DRAW NIGH O LORD AND ON US SHINE 265

*All that is in the world, the lust of the flesh, and the lust of the eyes, and the pride of life . . . is of the world.* I Jn. 2:16.

John Newman, 1801-1890
Altered by Compiler, 1970

DALEHURST C.M. 8.6.8.6.
M.M. 72

Arthur Cottman, 1874 (1842-1879)

1. Draw nigh, O Lord, and on us shine In glo – ry and in grace;
2. Till Thou art seen, the world ap–pears To be a pleas–ure ground,
3. But when Thy keen – er, pu – rer light Is beamed up – on our sight,
4. All world–ly aims are but the scourge Which made Thy blood to flow;
5. Dear Lord, we will re–nounce for Thee All world – ly aims and fears;
6. Small is our sac – ri – fice, we turn From world – ly cares set free;
The gaud – y world grows pale be – fore The beau–ty of Thy face.
Where suns un – set–ting light the sky, And earth – ly joys a – bound.
The world its power to charm will lose, And what was day is night.
Its joys are but the treacher–ous thorns Which cir–cled 'round Thy brow.
All sel–fish memo–ries of the past, All hopes of com–ing years.
What we have ceased to love we spurn, And leave to fol – low Thee.

## BEHOLD, THE MASTER PASSETH BY 266

*Be not conformed to this world: but be ye transformed by the renewing of your mind.* Rom. 12:2.

William Walsham How, 1871 (1823-1897)
Altered by Compiler, 1970

RETREAT L.M. 8.8.8.8.
M.M. 100

Thomas Hastings, 1784-1872

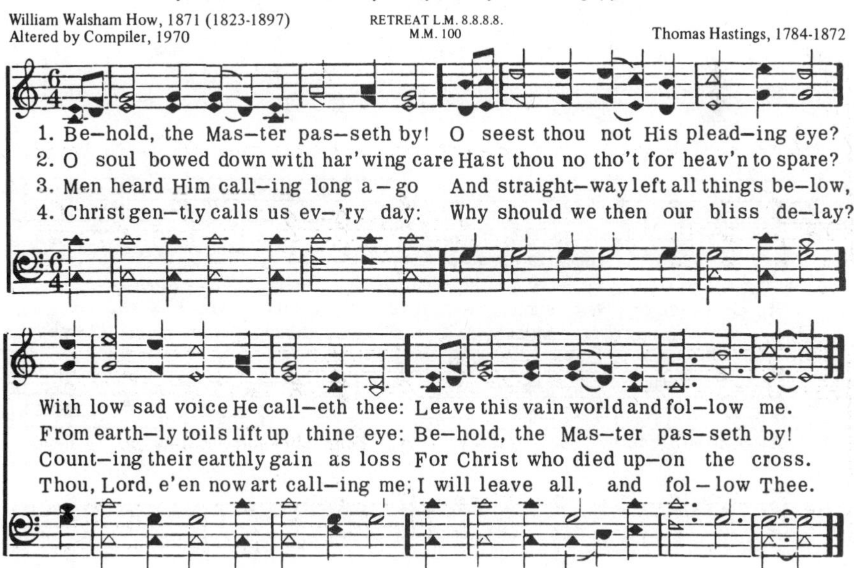
1. Be–hold, the Mas–ter pas–seth by! O seest thou not His plead–ing eye?
2. O soul bowed down with har'wing care Hast thou no tho't for heav'n to spare?
3. Men heard Him call–ing long a – go And straight–way left all things be–low,
4. Christ gen–tly calls us ev–'ry day: Why should we then our bliss de–lay?
With low sad voice He call–eth thee: Leave this vain world and fol–low me.
From earth–ly toils lift up thine eye: Be–hold, the Mas–ter pas–seth by!
Count–ing their earthly gain as loss For Christ who died up–on the cross.
Thou, Lord, e'en now art call–ing me; I will leave all, and fol – low Thee.

# 267 RENEW ME, O ETERNAL LIGHT

*They that are Christ's have crucified the flesh with the affections and lusts.* Gal. 5:24.

Johann F. Ruopp, 1714
*Erneure mich, o ew'ges Licht*
Tr. August Crull, 1923, alt.

WO GOTT ZUM HAUS NICHT GIBT SEIN GUNST
L.M. 8.8.8.8.
M.M. 80

*Geistliche Lieder,* Wittenberg, 1535

1. Re - new me O e - ter - nal Light, And let my
2. De - stroy in me the lust of sin, From all im -
3. Cre - ate in me a new heart, Lord, That glad - ly
4. Grant that I on - ly Thee may love And seek those

heart and soul be bright, Il - lum - ined with the
pure - ness make me clean. Oh, grant me pow'r and
I o - bey Thy Word And naught but what Thou
things which are a - bove Till I be - hold Thee

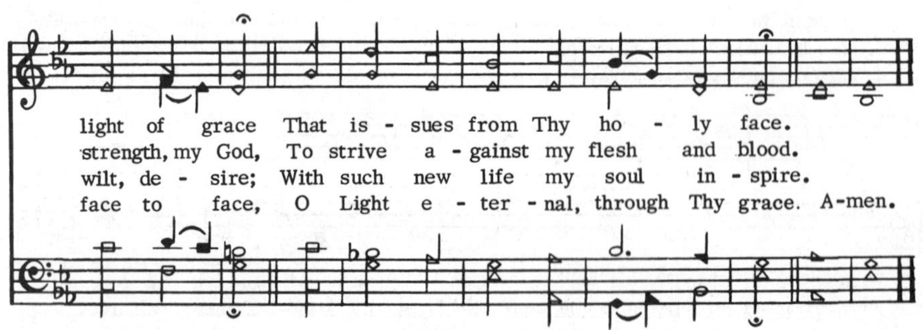
light of grace That is - sues from Thy ho - ly face.
strength, my God, To strive a - gainst my flesh and blood.
wilt, de - sire; With such new life my soul in - spire.
face to face, O Light e - ter - nal, through Thy grace. A-men.

# KEEP MY HEART PURE, O GOD 268

*Approving ourselves as the ministers of God . . . by pureness.* II Cor. 6:4, 6.

KEEP MY HEART PURE 8.8.8. with Ref.
M.M. 104

Alfred Barrot, b. 1879

William Lee Higgins, 1898-1953

1. Keep my heart pure, O God, I pray, Help me to live for Thee each day, Be Thou my guide where'er I go,
2. Keep my heart pure and free from sin, O come, dear Lord, and dwell within, Thy match-less grace on me be-stow, Keep my heart pure and white as snow.
3. Keep my heart pure, with-out al-loy, And fill me with Thy peace and joy, Di-rect my path in weal or woe,
4. Keep my heart pure, it is Thine own, O make it now Thy roy-al throne, Let me Thy love to oth-ers show,

Refrain

Keep my heart pure and white as snow, Let all my words and ac-tions glow, Guid-ing my path-way as I go, Keep my heart pure and white as snow.

# 269 PURER IN HEART

*The wisdom that is from above is first pure.* Jas. 3:17.

PURER IN HEART 6.4.6.4.6.6.4.4.
M.M. 88
Fannie Estelle Davison, 1851-1887
James H. Filmore, 1849-1936
1. Pur - er in heart, O God, Help me to be; May I de-
2. Pur - er in heart, O God, Help me to be; Teach me to
3. Pur - er in heart, O God, Help me to be; That I Thy
vote my life Whol - ly to Thee. Watch Thou my way - ward feet,
do Thy will Most lov - ing - ly. Be Thou my Friend and Guide,
ho - ly face One day may see. Keep me from se - cret sin,
Guide me with coun - sel sweet; Pur - er in heart, Help me to be.
Let me with Thee a - bide; Pur - er in heart, Help me to be.
Reign Thou my soul with - in; Pur - er in heart, Help me to be.

# 270 BLEST ARE THE PURE IN HEART

*Blessed are the pure in heart: for they shall see God.* Matt. 5:8.

John Keble, 1792-1866
And others, 1819 and 1836

FRANCONIA S.M. 6.6.8.6.
M.M. 84

*Harmonischer Liederschatz*, 1738
William Henry Havergal, 1847 (1793-1870)

1 Blest are the pure in heart, For they shall see our God;
2 The Lord, who left the heav'ns Our life and peace to bring,
3 Still to the low - ly soul He doth Him - self im - part,
4 Lord, we Thy pres - ence seek; May ours this bless - ing be:

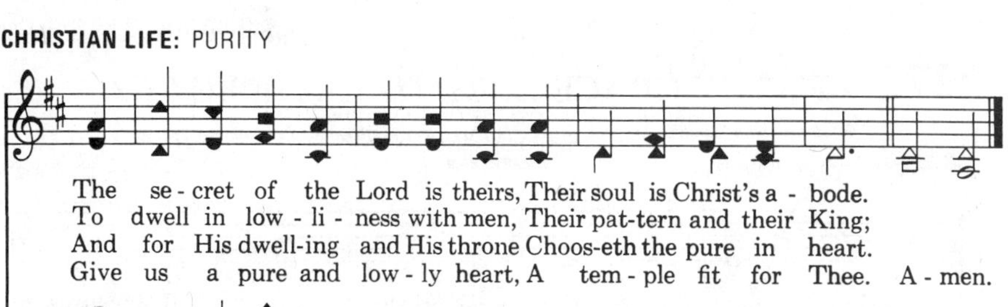
The se - cret of the Lord is theirs, Their soul is Christ's a - bode.
To dwell in low - li - ness with men, Their pat-tern and their King;
And for His dwell-ing and His throne Choos-eth the pure in heart.
Give us a pure and low - ly heart, A tem - ple fit for Thee. A - men.

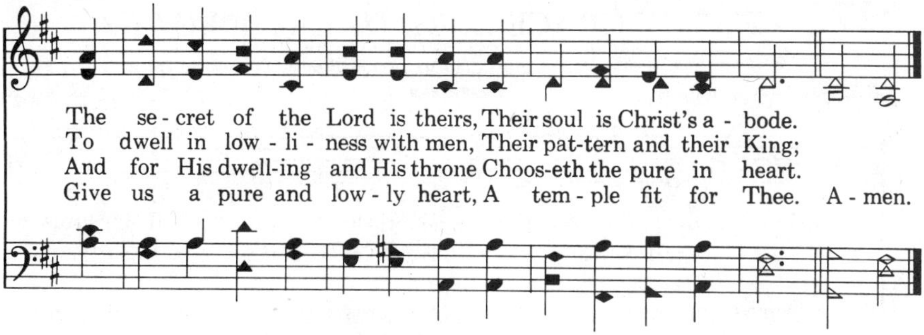

# KEEP THYSELF PURE 271

*Neither be partaker of other men's sins: keep thyself pure.* I Tim. 5:22.

Adelaide Mary Plumtre, c. 1908 — PENTECOST L.M. 8.8.8.8. M.M. 92 — William Boyd, 1868 (1847-1928)

1. Keep thy - self pure! Christ's sol - dier, hear, Thro' life's loud
2. Keep thy - self pure! thrice bless - ed he Whose heart from
3. Keep thy - self pure! for He who died, Him - self for
4. O Ho - ly Spir - it, keep us pure, Grant us Thy

strife, the call rings clear. Thy Cap - tain speaks: His
taint of sin is free; His feet shall stand where
thy sake sanc - ti - fied; Then hear Him speak - ing
strength when sins al - lure; Our bod - ies are Thy

word o - bey; So shall thy strength be as thy day.
saints have trod, He with rapt eyes shall see his God.
from the skies, And vic - tor o'er temp - ta - tion rise.
tem - ple, Lord; Be Thou in thought and act a - dored.

# 272 LET THY GRACE LORD MAKE ME LOWLY

*Be clothed with humility: for God resisteth the proud, and giveth grace to the humble.* I Pet. 5:5.

From Psalm 81
William Goode, 1812 (1762-1816)

MABYN 8.7.8.7.
M.M. 88

Thomas Hastings, 1784-1872

1. Let Thy grace, Lord, make me low–ly, Hum – ble all my swell–ing pride;
Fall – en, guilt–y, and un – ho – ly, Great–ness from mine eyes I'll hide;

2. Weaned from earth's de–lu–sive pleas–ures In Thy love I'll seek for mine;
Placed in heav'n my no–bler treasures, Earth I qui – et – ly re – sign;

D.C. No am–bi–tious heights de–sir–ing Far a – bove my hum–ble claim.
D.C. Thus my joys from Him a – ris – ing Like Him–self shall nev–er die.

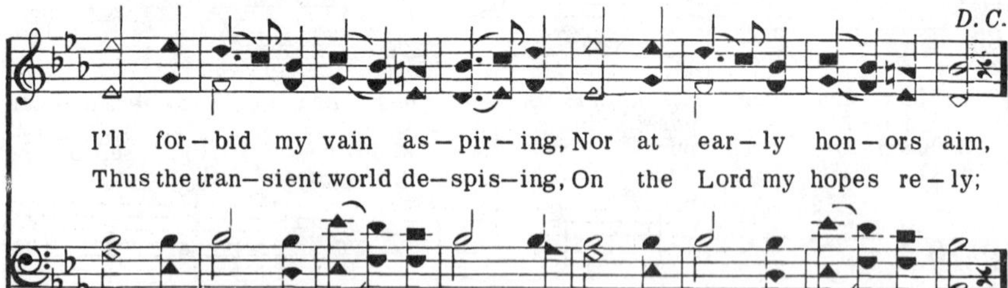
D. C.
I'll for – bid my vain as – pir – ing, Nor at ear – ly hon – ors aim,
Thus the tran– sient world de– spis– ing, On the Lord my hopes re – ly;

# 273 TAKE MY HEART O FATHER

*Humble yourselves in the sight of the Lord, and He shall lift you up.* Jas. 4:10.

Anonymous

CARRINGTON 8.7.8.7.
M.M. 63

Charles Edward Pollock, b. 1853

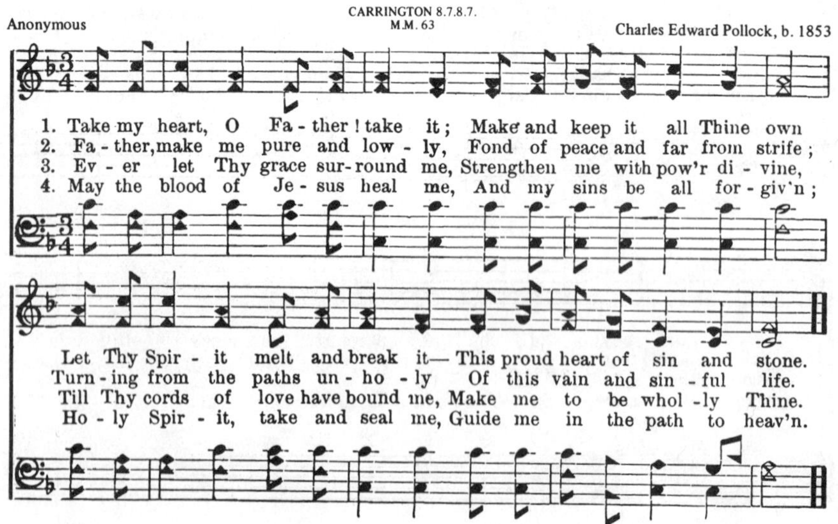
1. Take my heart, O Fa - ther ! take it ; Make and keep it all Thine own
2. Fa - ther, make me pure and low - ly, Fond of peace and far from strife ;
3. Ev - er let Thy grace sur - round me, Strengthen me with pow'r di - vine,
4. May the blood of Je - sus heal me, And my sins be all for - giv'n ;
Let Thy Spir - it melt and break it— This proud heart of sin and stone.
Turn - ing from the paths un - ho - ly Of this vain and sin - ful life.
Till Thy cords of love have bound me, Make me to be whol - ly Thine.
Ho - ly Spir - it, take and seal me, Guide me in the path to heav'n.

# LOOKING UPWARD 274

*Perfecting holiness in the fear of God.* II Cor. 7:1. *This is the will of God, even your sanctification.* I Thess. 4:3.

ST. KEVIN 7.6.7.6.D.
M.M. 100
Mary Butler, 1881
Authur Seymour Sullivan, 1872 (1842-1900)
1. Look–ing up–ward ev–ery day, Sun–shine on our fa–ces;
2. Walk–ing ev–ery day more close To our Eld–er Broth–er;
3. Leav–ing ev–ery day be–hind Some–thing which might hin–der;
Press–ing on–ward ev–ery day Toward the heaven–ly pla–ces;
Grow–ing ev–ery day more true Un–to one an–oth–er;
Run–ning swift–er ev–ery day, Grow–ing pur–er, kind–er–
Grow–ing ev–ery day in awe, For Thy name is ho–ly;
Ev–ery day more grate–ful–ly Kind–ness–es re–ceiv–ing;
Lord, so pray we ev–ery day, Hear us in Thy pit–y,
Learn–ing ev–ery day to love With a love more low–ly;
Ev–ery day more read–i–ly In–ju–ries for–giv–ing;
That we en–ter in at last To the ho–ly cit–y. A–men.

# 275 HELP ME TO BE HOLY!

*Be ye holy in all manner of conversation [walk].* I Pet. 1:15.

Adoniram Judson Gordon, 1836-1895 | TOWNER 11.11.11.11. M.M. 126 | Daniel Brink Towner, 1850-1919

1. Help me to be ho - ly, O Fa-ther of light; Guilt - bur-dened and low - ly, I bow in Thy sight; How shall a stained con-science Dare gaze on Thy face, E'en tho' in Thy pres-ence Thou grant me a place?
2. Help me to be ho - ly, O Sav-iour di - vine; Why con-quer so slow - ly This na - ture of mine? Stamp deep - ly Thy like - ness Where Satan's hath been; Ex - pel with Thy brightness My darkness and sin!
3. Help me to be ho - ly, O Spir - it di - vine; Come, sanc - ti - fy whol - ly This tem - ple of Thine; Now cast out each i - dol, Here set up Thy throne, Reign, reign without ri - val, Su - preme and a - lone!

# 276 STRIVE ARIGHT WHEN GOD DOTH CALL

*Follow peace with all men, and holiness, without which no man shall see the Lord.* Heb. 12:14.

Johann Joseph Winckler, 1714 (1670-1722)
*Ringe recht, wenn Gottes Gnade*
Tr. Catherine Winkworth, 1827-1878, alt.

RINGE RECHT 8.7.8.7.
M.M. 88

*Erbaulicher Musicalischer Christen-Schatz*, 1745

1. Strive a - right when God doth call thee, When He draws thee by His grace;
2. Per - fect truth will love to fol - low Watch - ful - ly our Mas - ter's ways;
3. Sol - diers of the cross take cour - age! Watch and war 'mid fear and pain;

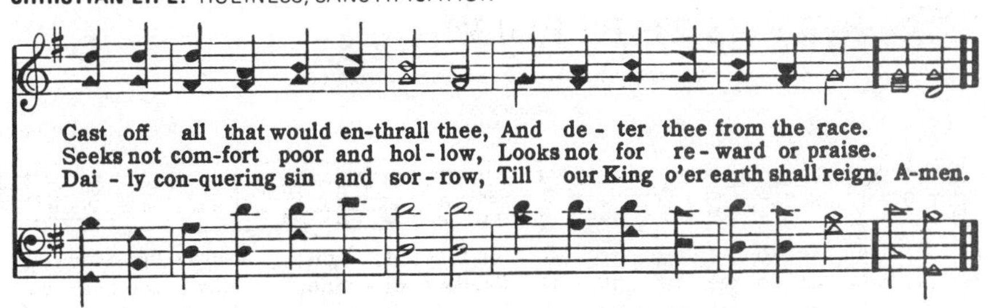
Cast off all that would en-thrall thee, And de - ter thee from the race.
Seeks not com-fort poor and hol - low, Looks not for re - ward or praise.
Dai - ly con-quering sin and sor - row, Till our King o'er earth shall reign. A-men.

## TAKE TIME TO BE HOLY 277

*We should be holy and without blame before Him in love.* Eph. 1:4.

TAKE TIME TO BE HOLY 11.11.11.11.
M.M. 104

William D. Longstaff, 1822-1894 | George Coles Stebbins, 1846-1945

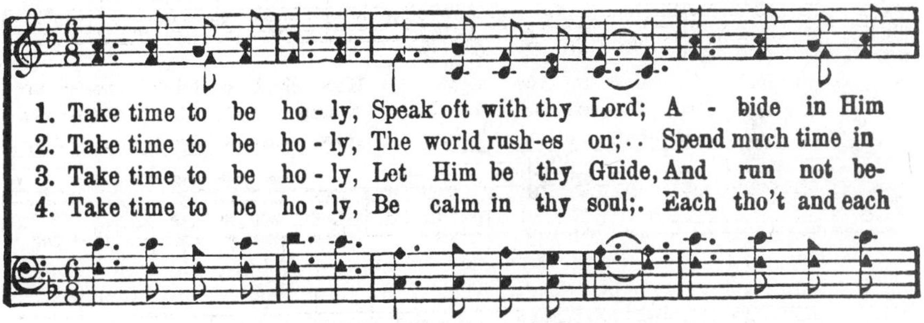

1. Take time to be ho - ly, Speak oft with thy Lord; A - bide in Him
2. Take time to be ho - ly, The world rush-es on;.. Spend much time in
3. Take time to be ho - ly, Let Him be thy Guide, And run not be-
4. Take time to be ho - ly, Be calm in thy soul;. Each tho't and each

al - ways, And feed on His Word. Make friends of God's chil - dren;
se - cret With Je - sus a - lone— By look - ing to Je - sus,
fore Him, What - ev - er be - tide;.. In joy or in sor - row,
mo - tive Be - neath His con - trol;.. Thus led by His Spir - it

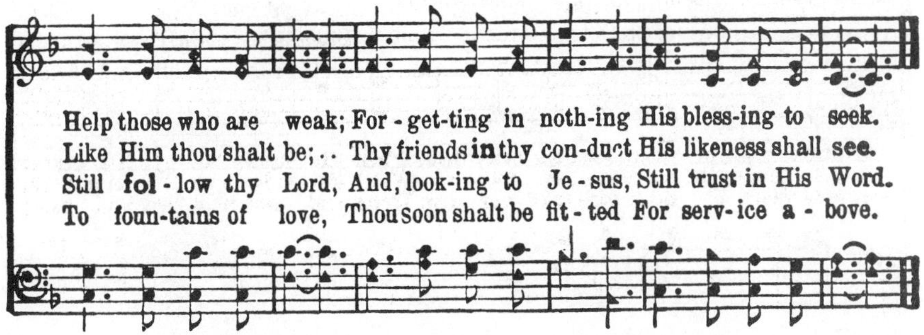

Help those who are weak; For - get-ting in noth-ing His bless-ing to seek.
Like Him thou shalt be;.. Thy friends in thy con-duct His likeness shall see.
Still fol - low thy Lord, And, look-ing to Je - sus, Still trust in His Word.
To foun-tains of love, Thou soon shalt be fit - ted For serv-ice a - bove.

# 278 TAKE UP THY CROSS! THE SAVIOUR SAID

*If any man will come after Me, let him deny himself, and take up his cross and follow Me.* Mt. 16:24.

QUEBEC L.M. 8.8.8.8.
M.M. 100

Charles William Everest, 1833 (1814-1877)

Henry Baker, 1862 (1835-1910)

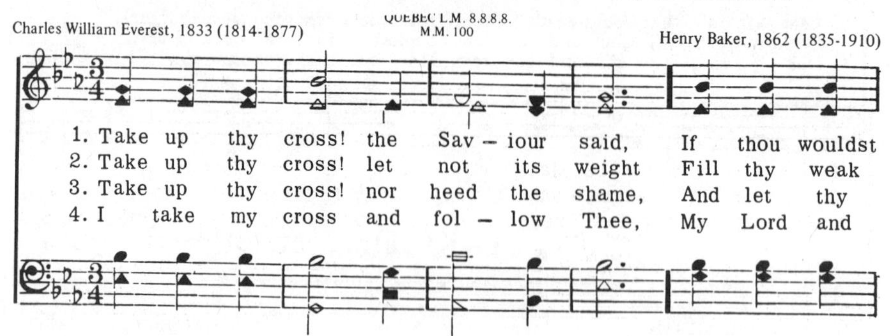
1. Take up thy cross! the Sav – iour said, If thou wouldst
2. Take up thy cross! let not its weight Fill thy weak
3. Take up thy cross! nor heed the shame, And let thy
4. I take my cross and fol – low Thee, My Lord and

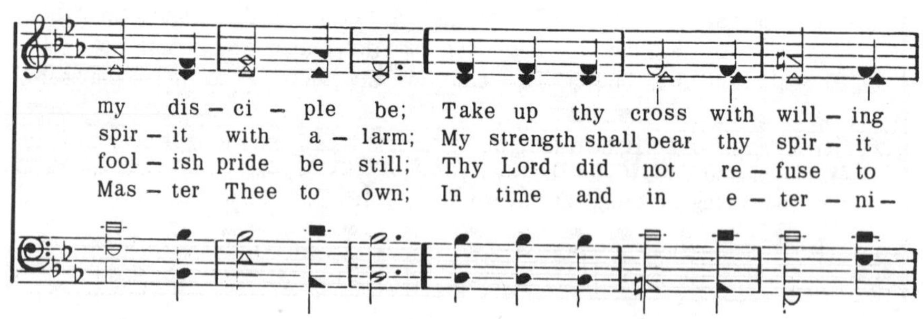
my dis – ci – ple be; Take up thy cross with will – ing
spir – it with a – larm; My strength shall bear thy spir – it
fool – ish pride be still; Thy Lord did not re – fuse to
Mas – ter Thee to own; In time and in e – ter – ni–

heart, And hum – bly fol – low af – ter me.
up, And brace thy heart and move thine arm.
die Up – on the cross on Cal – v'ry's hill.
ty, Thee e'er to serve and Thee a – lone. A–men.

# RISE, FOLLOW ME, OUR MASTER SAITH 279

*My sheep hear My voice, and I know them, and they follow Me.* Jn. 10:27.

Johann Scheffler, 1653 (1624-1677)
*Mir nach, spricht Christus, unser Held*
Tr. Catherine Winkworth, 1827-1878

LOVING KINDNESS 8.8.8.8.8.8
M.M. 72

William Caldwell, 1830
Arr. by Compiler, 1970

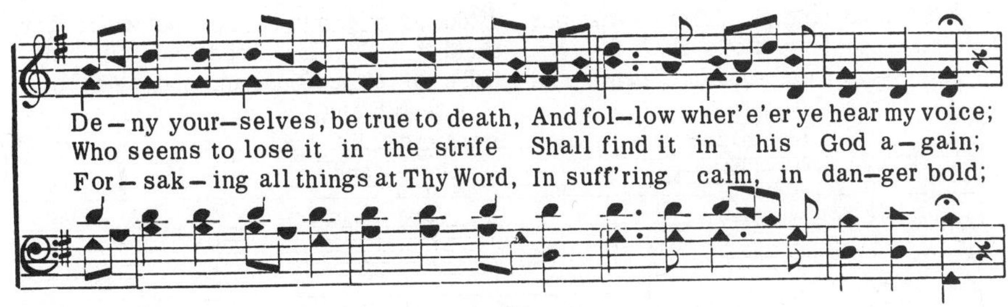
1. Rise, fol–low me! our Mas–ter saith, All ye who make my yoke your choice.
2. For he who seeks to save his life Shall find his care with–out me vain;
3. O help us fol–low Thee, dear Lord, As Thy true serv–ants did of old,

De – ny your–selves, be true to death, And fol–low wher'e'er ye hear my voice;
Who seems to lose it in the strife Shall find it in his God a – gain;
For – sak – ing all things at Thy Word, In suff'ring calm, in dan–ger bold;

For–sake the world, nor count it loss, O tread in my steps and bear the cross.
Who fol–lows not my cross through all, He can not be worth – y of my call.
'Tis on – ly he who wins the fight May e'er hope to wear the crown of light.

# 280 GUIDE ME O THOU GREAT JEHOVAH

*God . . . will be our guide even unto death.* Ps. 48:14.

William Williams 1745 (1717-1791)
*Arglwydd arwain trwy'r anialwch*
Tr. Peter Williams, 1723-1796
And others, 1771-72

CWM RHONDDA 8.7.8.7.8.7.
M.M. 69

John Hughes, 1907 (1873-1932)

1 Guide me, O Thou great Je - ho - vah, Pil - grim through this
2 O - pen now the crys - tal foun - tain, Whence the heal - ing
3 When I tread the verge of Jor - dan, Bid my anx - ious

bar - ren land; I am weak, but Thou art might-y; Hold me with Thy
streams do flow; Let the fi - ery cloud-y pil - lar Lead me all my
fears sub-side; Death of death, and hell's de - struc-tion, Land me safe on

power - ful hand; Bread of heav - en, bread of heav - en,
jour - ney through; Strong de - liv - erer, strong de - liv - erer,
Ca - naan's side; Songs of prais - es, songs of prais - es,

Feed me now and ev - er - more, Feed me now and ev - er - more.
Be Thou still my strength and shield, Be Thou still my strength and shield.
I will ev - er give to Thee, I will ev - er give to Thee. A-men.

# I WILL PRESS ON TO PERFECTION 281

*I press toward the mark for the prize of the high calling of God in Christ Jesus.* Phil. 3:14.

Philipp Friedrich Hiller, 1699-1769
*Ich will streben nach dem Leben*
Tr. John J. Overholt, 1970

GÜTERSLOH 8.5.8.5.7.7.8.5.
M.M. 72

Melody from Würtemberg, c. 1853

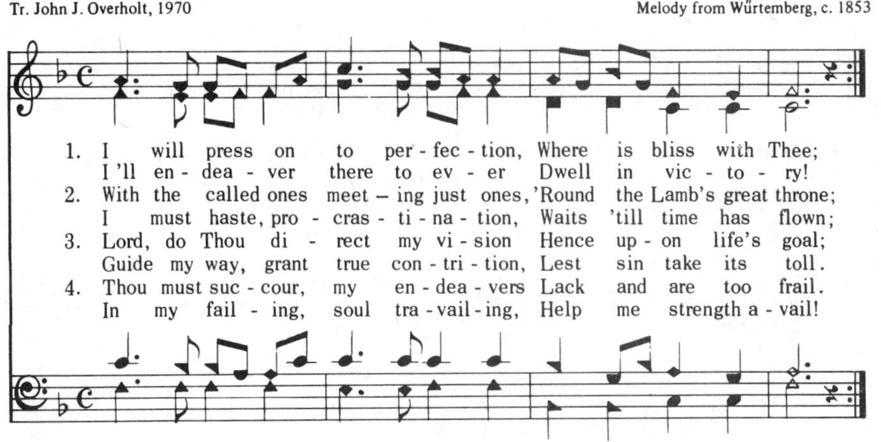

1. I will press on to per - fec - tion, Where is bliss with Thee;
I 'll en - dea - ver there to ev - er Dwell in vic - to - ry!
2. With the called ones meet – ing just ones, 'Round the Lamb's great throne;
I must haste, pro - cras - ti - na - tion, Waits 'till time has flown;
3. Lord, do Thou di - rect my vi - sion Hence up - on life's goal;
Guide my way, grant true con - tri - tion, Lest sin take its toll.
4. Thou must suc - cour, my en - dea - vers Lack and are too frail.
In my fail - ing, soul tra - vail - ing, Help me strength a - vail!

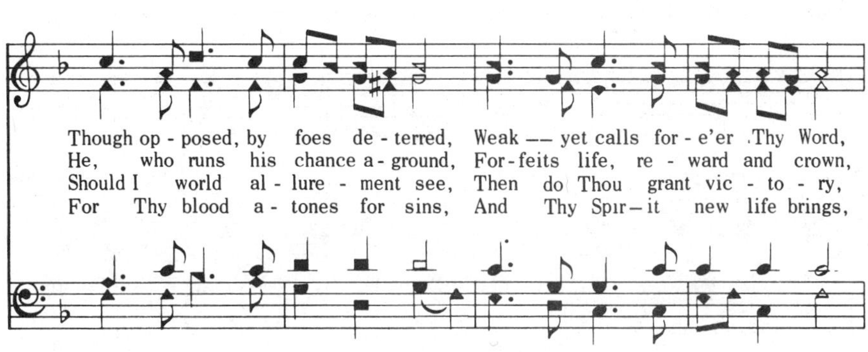

Though op - posed, by foes de - terred, Weak — yet calls for - e'er Thy Word,
He, who runs his chance a - ground, For - feits life, re - ward and crown,
Should I world al - lure - ment see, Then do Thou grant vic - to - ry,
For Thy blood a - tones for sins, And Thy Spir – it new life brings,

"Fear thou not for I am with thee... I will strength - en thee"!
Hence let base re - solves all per - ish, Sin, I will have none!
In Thy mer – cy lead me safe - ly, To Thy heav'n - ly fold.
Lord, Thy crown - ing day a - waits me, Help me ne'er to fail!

# 282 AWAKE MY SOUL

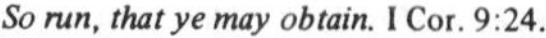

*So run, that ye may obtain.* I Cor. 9:24.

Philip Doddridge, 1755 (1702-1751), Alt.

WINCHESTER OLD C.M. 8.6.8.6.
M.M. 76

Thomas Est's *Whole Booke of Psalmes,* 1592

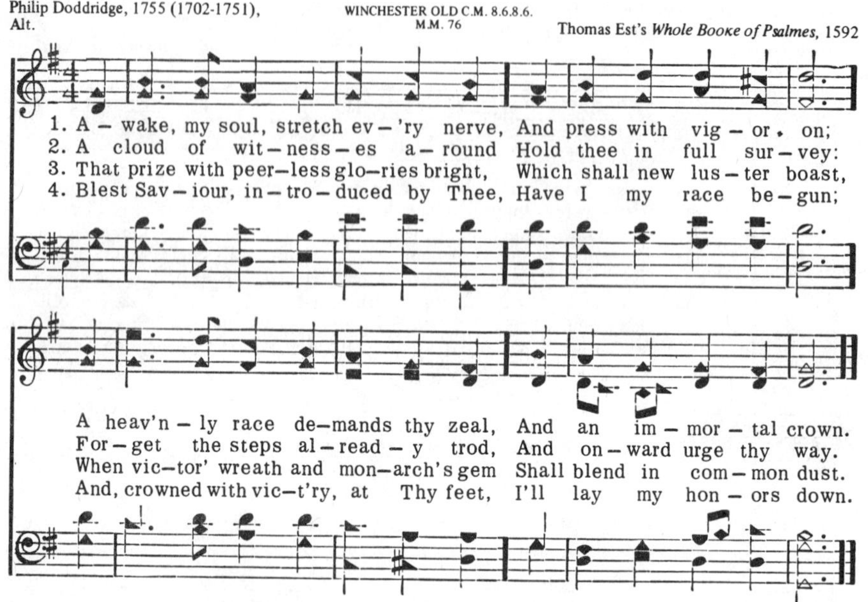
1. A – wake, my soul, stretch ev – 'ry nerve, And press with vig – or on;
2. A cloud of wit – ness – es a – round Hold thee in full sur – vey:
3. That prize with peer – less glo – ries bright, Which shall new lus – ter boast,
4. Blest Sav – iour, in – tro – duced by Thee, Have I my race be – gun;
A heav'n – ly race de – mands thy zeal, And an im – mor – tal crown.
For – get the steps al – read – y trod, And on – ward urge thy way.
When vic – tor' wreath and mon – arch's gem Shall blend in com – mon dust.
And, crowned with vic – t'ry, at Thy feet, I'll lay my hon – ors down.

# 283 RISE, O MY SOUL

*Let us run with patience the race that is set before us.* Heb. 12:1.

John Needham, 1768 (1710-1787)

PATMOS C.M. 8.6.8.6.
M.M. 72

From a Gregorian Chant

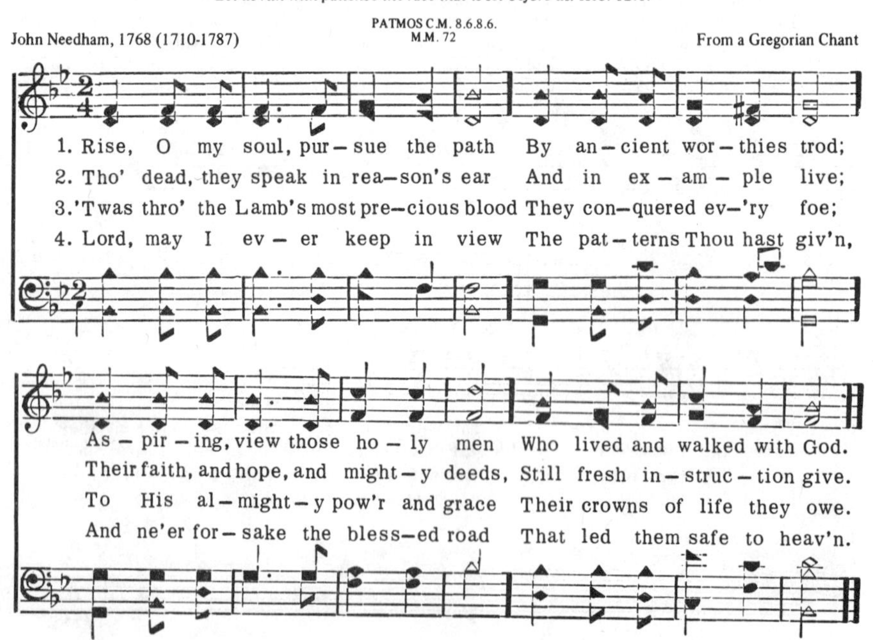
1. Rise, O my soul, pur – sue the path By an – cient wor – thies trod;
2. Tho' dead, they speak in rea – son's ear And in ex – am – ple live;
3. 'Twas thro' the Lamb's most pre – cious blood They con – quered ev – 'ry foe;
4. Lord, may I ev – er keep in view The pat – terns Thou hast giv'n,
As – pir – ing, view those ho – ly men Who lived and walked with God.
Their faith, and hope, and might – y deeds, Still fresh in – struc – tion give.
To His al – might – y pow'r and grace Their crowns of life they owe.
And ne'er for – sake the bless – ed road That led them safe to heav'n.

# O GOD, WHAT OFFERING SHALL I GIVE? 284

*I beseech you therefore, brethren . . . that ye present your bodies a living sacrifice, holy, acceptable unto God.* Rom. 12:1.

Joachim Lange, 1697 (1670-1744)
*O Jesu, süsses Licht*
Tr. John Wesley, 1739 (1703-1791)
Altered by Compiler, 1970

ST. PETERSBURG NEW 8.8.8.8.8.8.
M.M. 76

Dimitri S. Bortniansky, 1751-1825

1. O God, what offer–ing shall I give To Thee, the Lord of
2. My Lord and God, Thou hast my soul, No lon – ger mine, but
3. Thou hast my bod – y, 'tis Thy shrine, De – vo – ted sole – ly

earth and skies? My spir – it, soul, and flesh re – ceive, A
Thine I am; Guard Thou Thine own, pos – sess it whole; Cheer
to Thy will; Here let Thy light for – ev – er shine; This

ho – ly, liv – ing sac – ri – fice; I would for – ev – er
it with hope, with love in – flame, Thou hast my spir – it,
house still let Thy pres – ence fill; O Source of life! live,

Thee a – dore, Would love Thee, serve Thee more and more.
there dis – play Thy glo – ry to the per – fect day.
dwell, and move In me, that all my life be love.

# 285 LORD THOU LOV'ST THE CHEERFUL GIVER

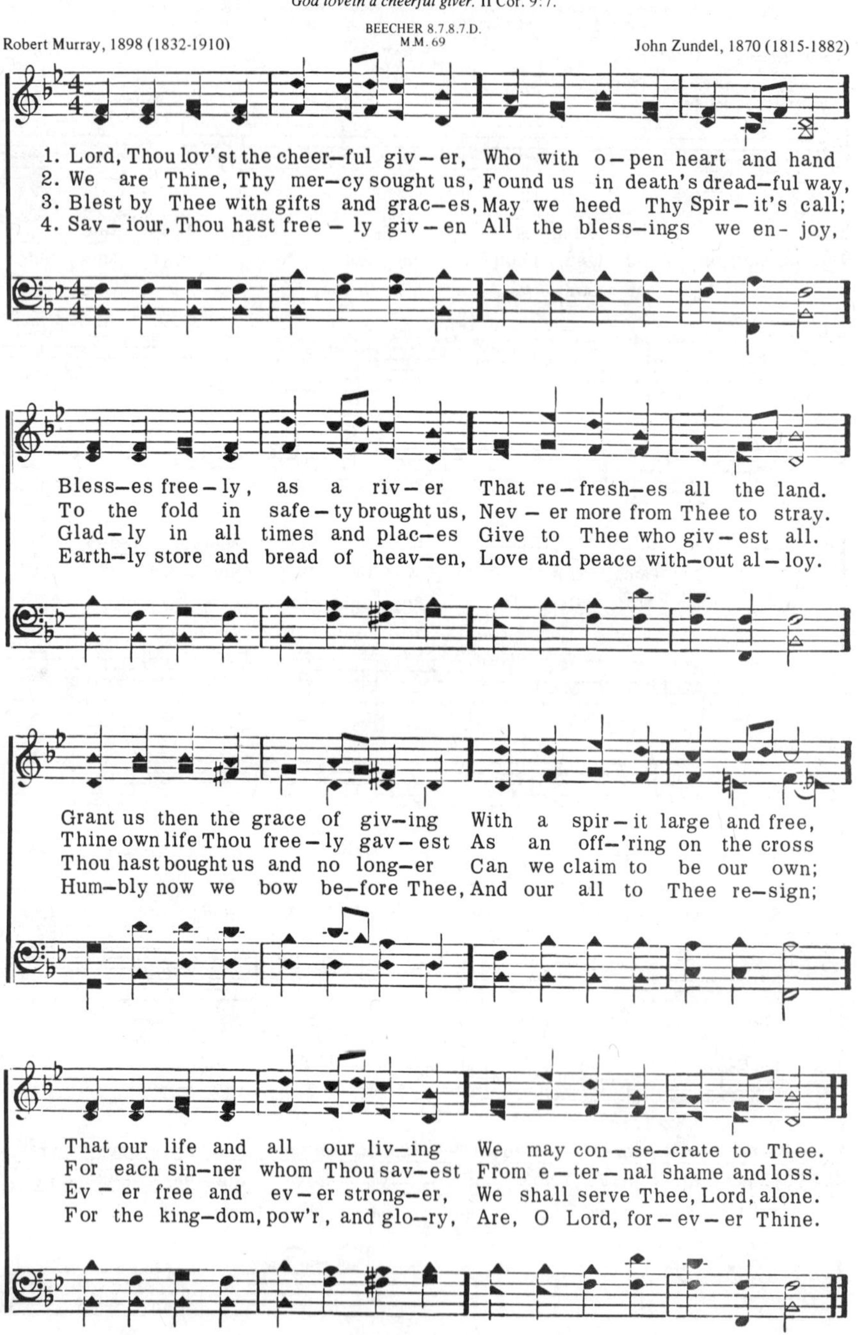
*God loveth a cheerful giver.* II Cor. 9:7.
BEECHER 8.7.8.7.D.
M.M. 69
Robert Murray, 1898 (1832-1910)
John Zundel, 1870 (1815-1882)
1. Lord, Thou lov'st the cheer–ful giv – er, Who with o – pen heart and hand
2. We are Thine, Thy mer–cy sought us, Found us in death's dread–ful way,
3. Blest by Thee with gifts and grac–es, May we heed Thy Spir – it's call;
4. Sav – iour, Thou hast free – ly giv – en All the bless–ings we en- joy,
Bless–es free – ly, as a riv – er That re – fresh–es all the land.
To the fold in safe – ty brought us, Nev – er more from Thee to stray.
Glad – ly in all times and plac–es Give to Thee who giv – est all.
Earth–ly store and bread of heav–en, Love and peace with–out al – loy.
Grant us then the grace of giv–ing With a spir – it large and free,
Thine own life Thou free – ly gav – est As an off–'ring on the cross
Thou hast bought us and no long–er Can we claim to be our own;
Hum–bly now we bow be–fore Thee, And our all to Thee re–sign;
That our life and all our liv–ing We may con – se–crate to Thee.
For each sin–ner whom Thou sav–est From e – ter – nal shame and loss.
Ev – er free and ev – er strong–er, We shall serve Thee, Lord, alone.
For the king–dom, pow'r, and glo–ry, Are, O Lord, for – ev – er Thine.

# HELP US, O LORD, THY YOKE TO WEAR 286

*The disciples, every man according to his ability, determined to send relief unto the brethren.* Acts 11:29.

QUEBEC L.M. 8.8.8.8.
M.M. 84

Thomas Cotterill, 1819 (1779-1823)
Alt. by Compiler, 1970

Henry Baker, 1835-1910

1. Help us, O Lord, Thy yoke to wear, De – light – ing
2. He that hath pi – ty on the poor Lend – eth his
3. Teach us with glad, un – grudg – ing heart, As Thou hast
4. To Thee our all de – vo – ted be, In whom we

in Thy per – fect will; Each oth—er's bur – dens learn to
sub—stance to the Lord; And, lo! his rec – om – pense is
blest our var – ious store, From our a – bun – dance to im-
breathe, and move, and live; Free – ly we have re – ceived from

bear, And thus Thy law of love ful – fill.
sure, For more than all shall be re – stored.
part Re – lief and suc – cor to the poor.
Thee; Free – ly may we re – joice to give. A—men.

# 287 LORD OF GLORY, THOU HAST BOUGHT US

*It is more blessed to give than to receive.* Acts 20:35.

Eliza S. Alderson, 1864 (1818-1889)

HYFRYDOL 8.7.8.7.D.
M.M. 92

Rowland Huge Prichard, 1830 (1811-1887)
Har. Ralph Vaughan Williams, 1951 (1872-1958)

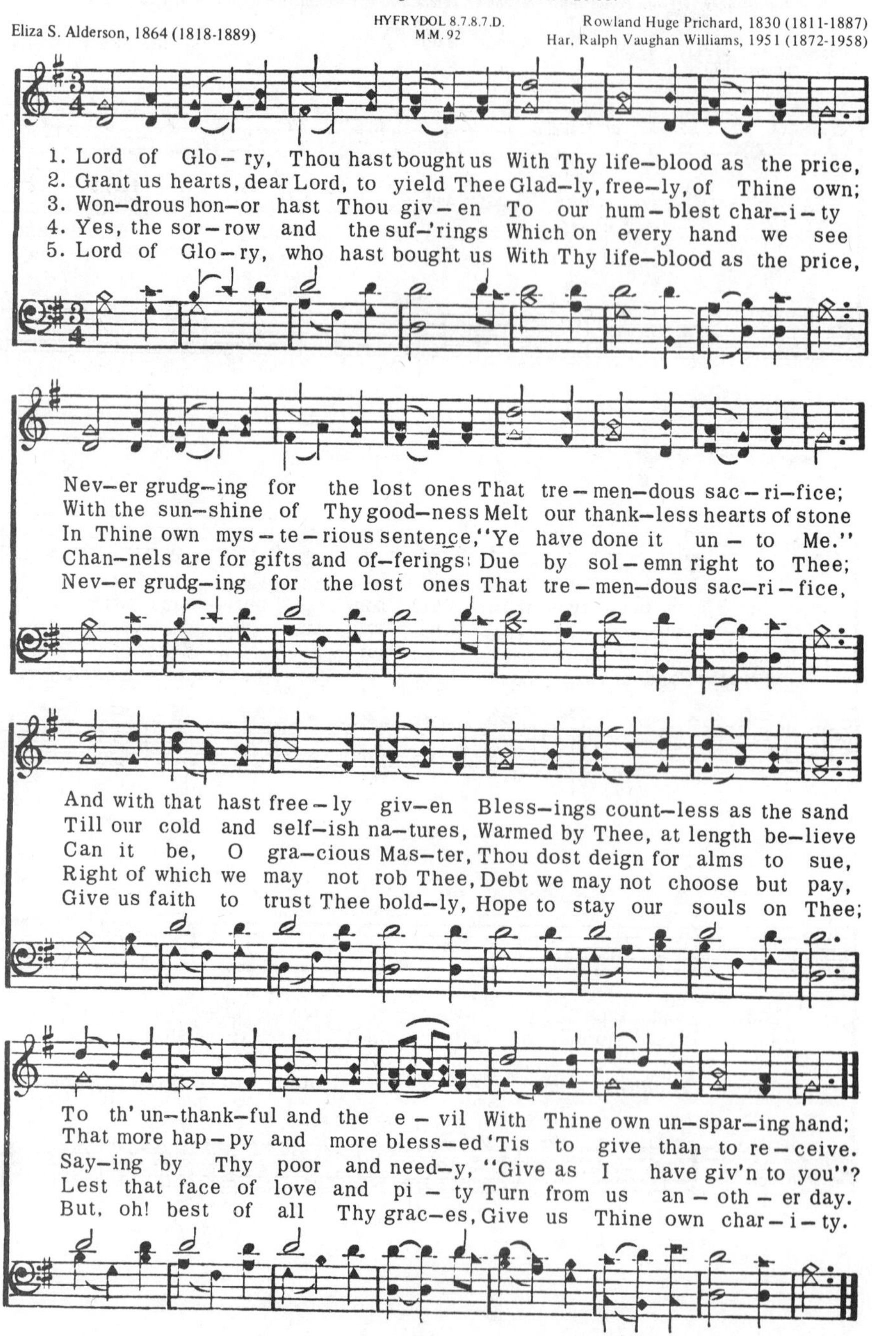
1. Lord of Glo–ry, Thou hast bought us With Thy life–blood as the price,
2. Grant us hearts, dear Lord, to yield Thee Glad–ly, free–ly, of Thine own;
3. Won–drous hon–or hast Thou giv–en To our hum–blest char–i–ty
4. Yes, the sor–row and the suf–'rings Which on every hand we see
5. Lord of Glo–ry, who hast bought us With Thy life–blood as the price,
Nev–er grudg–ing for the lost ones That tre–men–dous sac–ri–fice;
With the sun–shine of Thy good–ness Melt our thank–less hearts of stone
In Thine own mys–te–rious sentence, "Ye have done it un–to Me."
Chan–nels are for gifts and of–ferings: Due by sol–emn right to Thee;
Nev–er grudg–ing for the lost ones That tre–men–dous sac–ri–fice,
And with that hast free–ly giv–en Bless–ings count–less as the sand
Till our cold and self–ish na–tures, Warmed by Thee, at length be–lieve
Can it be, O gra–cious Mas–ter, Thou dost deign for alms to sue,
Right of which we may not rob Thee, Debt we may not choose but pay,
Give us faith to trust Thee bold–ly, Hope to stay our souls on Thee;
To th' un–thank–ful and the e–vil With Thine own un–spar–ing hand;
That more hap–py and more bless–ed 'Tis to give than to re–ceive.
Say–ing by Thy poor and need–y, "Give as I have giv'n to you"?
Lest that face of love and pi–ty Turn from us an–oth–er day.
But, oh! best of all Thy grac–es, Give us Thine own char–i–ty.

# O GOD OF MERCY! HEARKEN NOW 288

*Inasmuch as ye have done it unto one of the least of these my brethren, ye have done it unto Me.* Mt. 25:40.

HESPERUS L.M. 8.8.8.8.
M.M. 80

E. S. Clark — Henry Baker, 1866 (1835-1910)

1. O God of mer - cy! heark - en now; Be - fore Thy
2. We seek Thee where Thou dwell'st on high, Be - yond the
3. Be ours the hearts and hands to bless The sor - r'wing
4. Where pov - er - ty in pain must lie, Where lit - tle
5. Be Thou, O God e - ter - nal, blest, Thy ho - ly

throne we hum - bly bow; With heart and voice to Thee we
glit - t'ring, star - ry sky: We find Thee where Thou dwell'st be-
sons of wretch - ed - ness; Send Thou the help we can - not
suf - f'ring chil - dren cry, Bid us haste forth as called by
name on earth con - fest! Ech - o Thy praise from ev - 'ry

cry, For all on earth who suf - f'ring lie.
low Be - side the beds of want and woe.
give; Bid dy - ing souls a - rise and live.
Thee, And in Thy poor, Thy - self to see.
shore For - ev - er and for - ev - er - more. A - MEN.

# 289 LET THERE BE LIGHT, LORD GOD OF HOSTS

*I say unto you, That ye resist not evil.* Mt. 5:39.

MISSIONARY CHANT L.M. 8.8.8.8.
M.M. 58

William Merrell Vories, 1908 (b. 1880)

Heinrich Charles Zeuner, 1795-1857

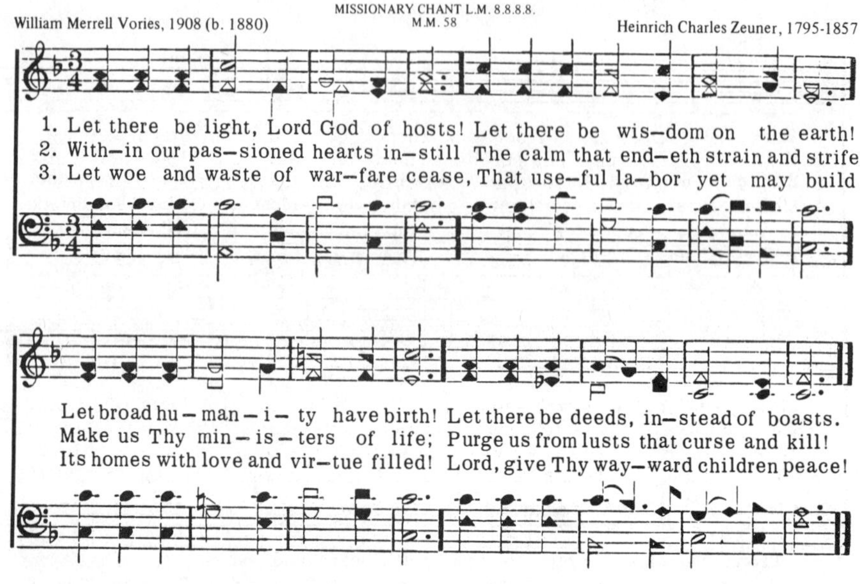
1. Let there be light, Lord God of hosts! Let there be wis–dom on the earth!
2. With–in our pas–sioned hearts in–still The calm that end–eth strain and strife;
3. Let woe and waste of war–fare cease, That use–ful la–bor yet may build
Let broad hu – man – i – ty have birth! Let there be deeds, in–stead of boasts.
Make us Thy min – is – ters of life; Purge us from lusts that curse and kill!
Its homes with love and vir–tue filled! Lord, give Thy way–ward children peace!

# 290 LORD, AS TO THY DEAR CROSS WE FLEE

*Love your enemies, bless them that curse you, do good to them that hate you.* Mt. 5:44.

GREEN HILL C.M. 8.6.8.6.
M.M. 69

John Hampden Gurney, 1838 (1802-1862)

Albert Lister Peace, 1885 (1844-1912)

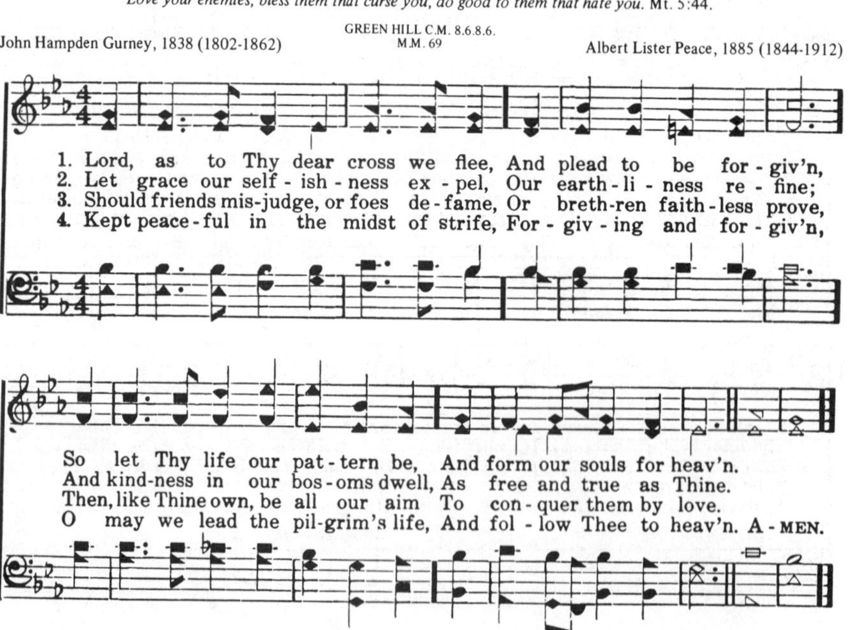
1. Lord, as to Thy dear cross we flee, And plead to be for - giv'n,
2. Let grace our self - ish - ness ex - pel, Our earth - li - ness re - fine;
3. Should friends mis-judge, or foes de - fame, Or breth-ren faith - less prove,
4. Kept peace - ful in the midst of strife, For - giv - ing and for - giv'n,
So let Thy life our pat - tern be, And form our souls for heav'n.
And kind-ness in our bos - oms dwell, As free and true as Thine.
Then, like Thine own, be all our aim To con - quer them by love.
O may we lead the pil-grim's life, And fol - low Thee to heav'n. A - MEN.

# WHAT GRACE, O LORD, AND BEAUTY 291

*Avenge not yourselves, but rather give place unto wrath: for it is written, Vengeance is mine; I will repay, saith the Lord.* Rom. 12:19.

ST. ANNE C.M. 8.6.8.6.
M.M. 88

Edward Denny, 1839 (1796-1889)

William Croft, 1708 (1678-1727)

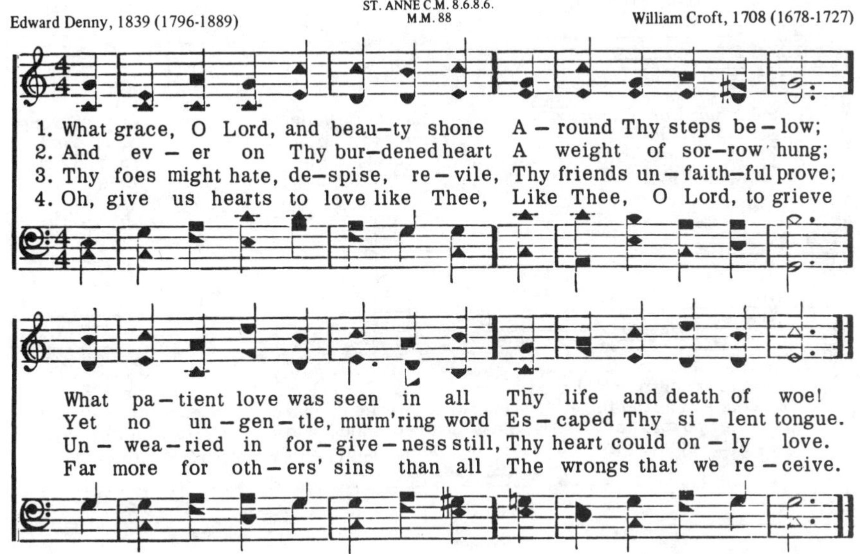
1. What grace, O Lord, and beau–ty shone A–round Thy steps be–low;
2. And ev–er on Thy bur–dened heart A weight of sor–row hung;
3. Thy foes might hate, de–spise, re–vile, Thy friends un–faith–ful prove;
4. Oh, give us hearts to love like Thee, Like Thee, O Lord, to grieve
What pa–tient love was seen in all Thy life and death of woe!
Yet no un–gen–tle, murm'ring word Es–caped Thy si–lent tongue.
Un–wea–ried in for–give–ness still, Thy heart could on–ly love.
Far more for oth–ers' sins than all The wrongs that we re–ceive.

# JESUS, MY SAVIOUR 292

*Whosoever shall smite thee on thy right cheek, turn to him the other also.* Mt. 5:39.

WAYLAND L.M. 8.8.8.8.
M.M. 63

Benjamin Beddome (1717-1795)

George Blackburn Holsinger, 1857-1908

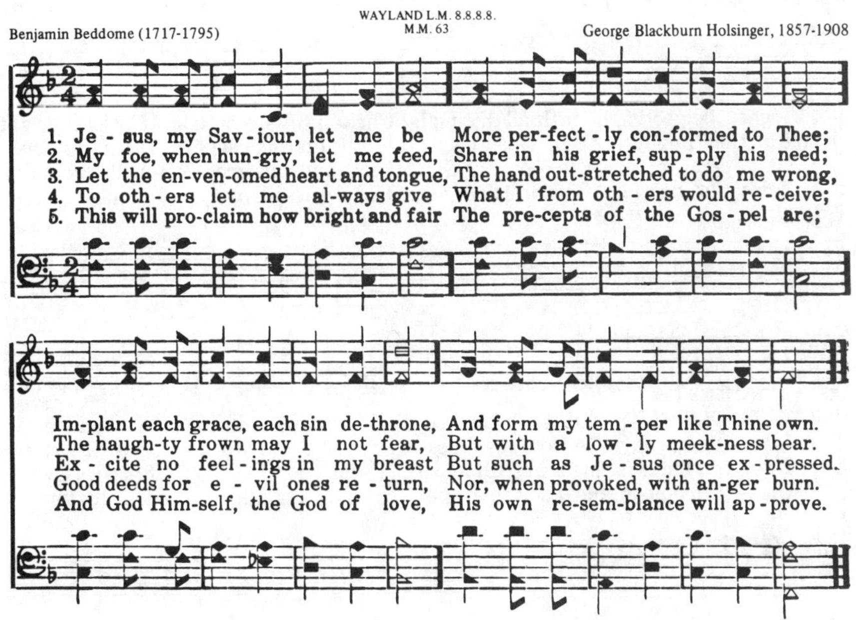
1. Je-sus, my Sav-iour, let me be More per-fect-ly con-formed to Thee;
2. My foe, when hun-gry, let me feed, Share in his grief, sup-ply his need;
3. Let the en-ven-omed heart and tongue, The hand out-stretched to do me wrong,
4. To oth-ers let me al-ways give What I from oth-ers would re-ceive;
5. This will pro-claim how bright and fair The pre-cepts of the Gos-pel are;
Im-plant each grace, each sin de-throne, And form my tem-per like Thine own.
The haugh-ty frown may I not fear, But with a low-ly meek-ness bear.
Ex-cite no feel-ings in my breast But such as Je-sus once ex-pressed.
Good deeds for e-vil ones re-turn, Nor, when provoked, with an-ger burn.
And God Him-self, the God of love, His own re-sem-blance will ap-prove.

# 293 SOLDIERS OF CHRIST, ARISE

*The weapons of our warfare are not carnal, but mighty through God to the pulling down of strongholds.* II Cor. 10:4.

SILVER STREET S.M. 6.6.8.6.
M.M. 72

Charles Wesley, 1749 (1707-1788)

Isaac Smith, 1735-1800

1. Sol - diers of Christ, a - rise, And put your ar - mor on; Strong
2. Strong in the Lord of Hosts, And in His might-y pow'r: Who
3. From strength to strength go on, Wres-tle, and fight, and pray: Tread
4. That, hav-ing all things done, And all your con - flicts past, Ye
in the strength which God sup - plies, Thro' His e - ter - nal Son.
in the strength of Je - sus trusts Is more than con - quer - or.
all the pow'rs of dark - ness down, And win the well-fought day.
may o'er - come, thro' Christ a - lone, And stand com-plete at last.

# 294 FIGHT THE GOOD FIGHT

*Fight the good fight of faith.* I Tim. 6:12.

PENTECOST L.M.
M.M. 104

John Samuel Monsell, 1811-1875

William Boyd, 1847-1928

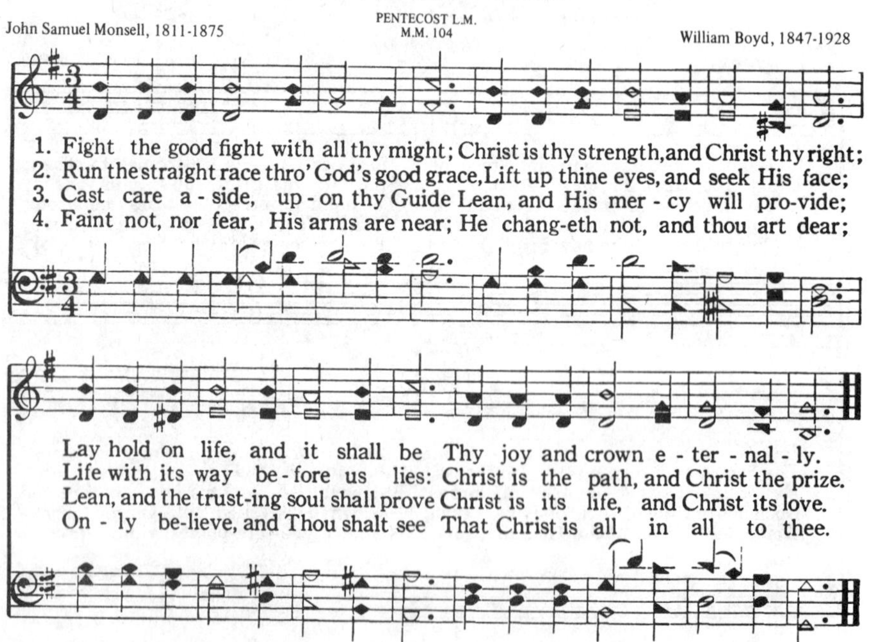
1. Fight the good fight with all thy might; Christ is thy strength, and Christ thy right;
2. Run the straight race thro' God's good grace, Lift up thine eyes, and seek His face;
3. Cast care a - side, up - on thy Guide Lean, and His mer - cy will pro-vide;
4. Faint not, nor fear, His arms are near; He chang-eth not, and thou art dear;
Lay hold on life, and it shall be Thy joy and crown e - ter - nal - ly.
Life with its way be - fore us lies: Christ is the path, and Christ the prize.
Lean, and the trust-ing soul shall prove Christ is its life, and Christ its love.
On - ly be-lieve, and Thou shalt see That Christ is all in all to thee.

## AM I A SOLDIER OF THE CROSS 295

*Watch ye, stand fast in the faith, quit you like men, be strong.* I Cor. 16:13.

ARLINGTON C.M. 8.6.8.6.
M.M. 66

Isaac Watts, 1720 (1674-1748) — Thomas Augustine Arne, 1710-1778

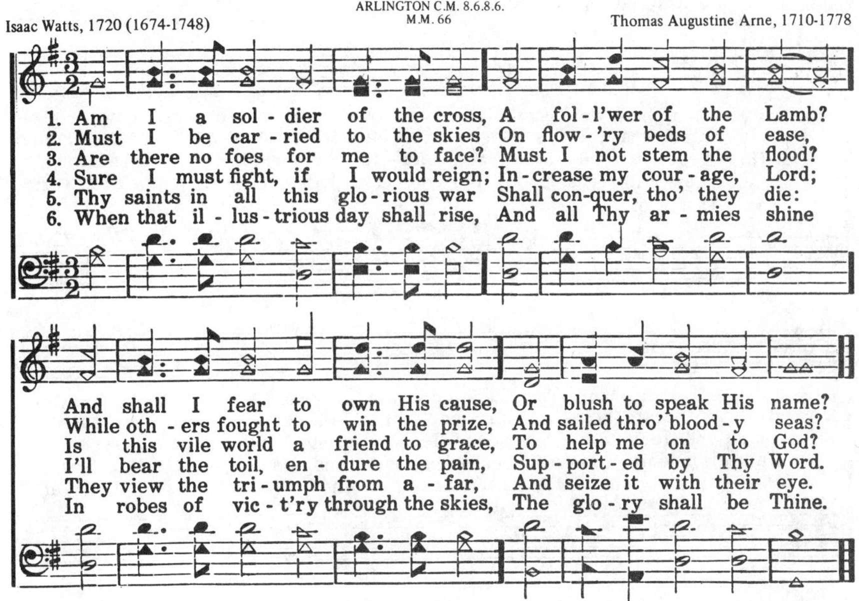
1. Am I a sol - dier of the cross, A fol - l'wer of the Lamb?
2. Must I be car - ried to the skies On flow - 'ry beds of ease,
3. Are there no foes for me to face? Must I not stem the flood?
4. Sure I must fight, if I would reign; In - crease my cour - age, Lord;
5. Thy saints in all this glo - rious war Shall con - quer, tho' they die:
6. When that il - lus - trious day shall rise, And all Thy ar - mies shine
And shall I fear to own His cause, Or blush to speak His name?
While oth - ers fought to win the prize, And sailed thro' blood - y seas?
Is this vile world a friend to grace, To help me on to God?
I'll bear the toil, en - dure the pain, Sup - port - ed by Thy Word.
They view the tri - umph from a - far, And seize it with their eye.
In robes of vic - t'ry through the skies, The glo - ry shall be Thine.

## MY SOUL, BE ON THY GUARD 296

*Endure hardness, as a good soldier of Jesus Christ.* II Tim. 2:3.

LABAN S.M. 6.6.8.6.
M.M. 80

George Heath, 1781 (1750-1822) — Lowell Mason, 1830 (1792-1872)

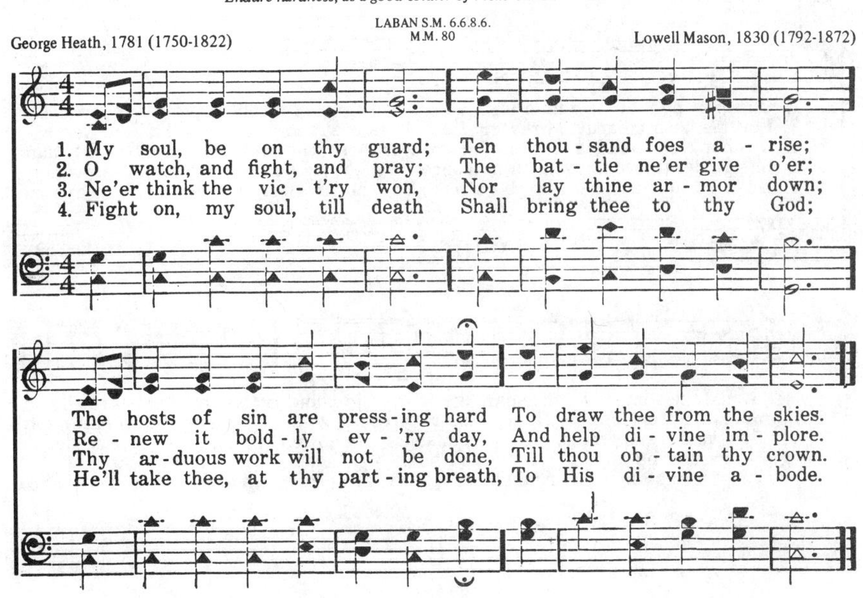
1. My soul, be on thy guard; Ten thou - sand foes a - rise;
2. O watch, and fight, and pray; The bat - tle ne'er give o'er;
3. Ne'er think the vic - t'ry won, Nor lay thine ar - mor down;
4. Fight on, my soul, till death Shall bring thee to thy God;
The hosts of sin are press - ing hard To draw thee from the skies.
Re - new it bold - ly ev - 'ry day, And help di - vine im - plore.
Thy ar - duous work will not be done, Till thou ob - tain thy crown.
He'll take thee, at thy part - ing breath, To His di - vine a - bode.

# 297 MY GOD, HOW WONDERFUL THOU ART

*Holy and reverend is His name.* Ps. 111:9.

Frederick William Faber, 1848 (1814-1863)
Altered by Compiler, 1970

GREEN HILL C.M. 8.6.8.6.
M.M. 76

Albert Lister Peace, 1885 (1844-1912)

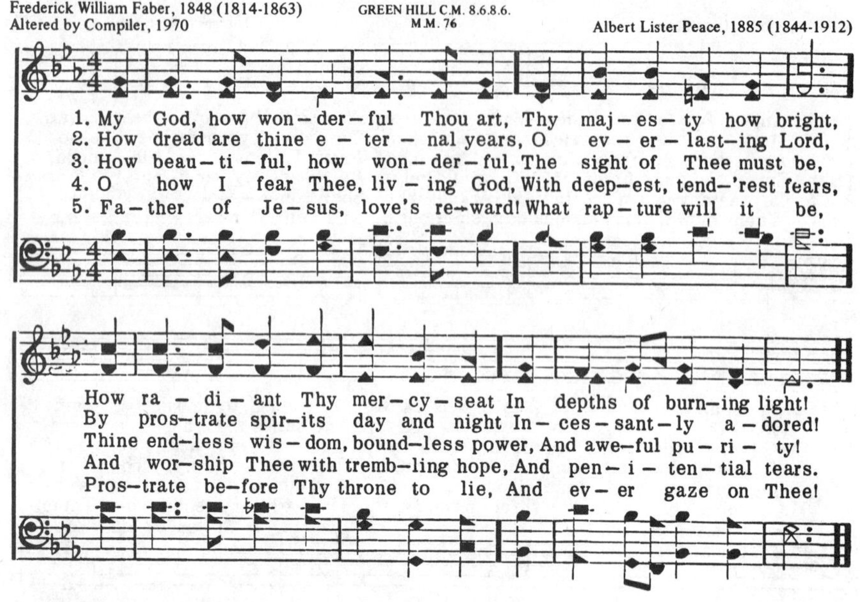

1. My God, how won-der-ful Thou art, Thy maj-es-ty how bright, How ra-di-ant Thy mer-cy-seat In depths of burn-ing light!
2. How dread are thine e-ter-nal years, O ev-er-last-ing Lord, By pros-trate spir-its day and night In-ces-sant-ly a-dored!
3. How beau-ti-ful, how won-der-ful, The sight of Thee must be, Thine end-less wis-dom, bound-less power, And awe-ful pu-ri-ty!
4. O how I fear Thee, liv-ing God, With deep-est, tend-'rest fears, And wor-ship Thee with tremb-ling hope, And pen-i-ten-tial tears.
5. Fa-ther of Je-sus, love's re-ward! What rap-ture will it be, Pros-trate be-fore Thy throne to lie, And ev-er gaze on Thee!

# 298 OH, HAPPY IS THE MAN

*Wisdom is the principal thing; therefore get wisdom.* Prov. 4:7.

Michael Bruce, 1764 (1746-1767)

MATTIE 8.6.8.6.6.
M.M. 63

L. C. Everett, 1818-1867

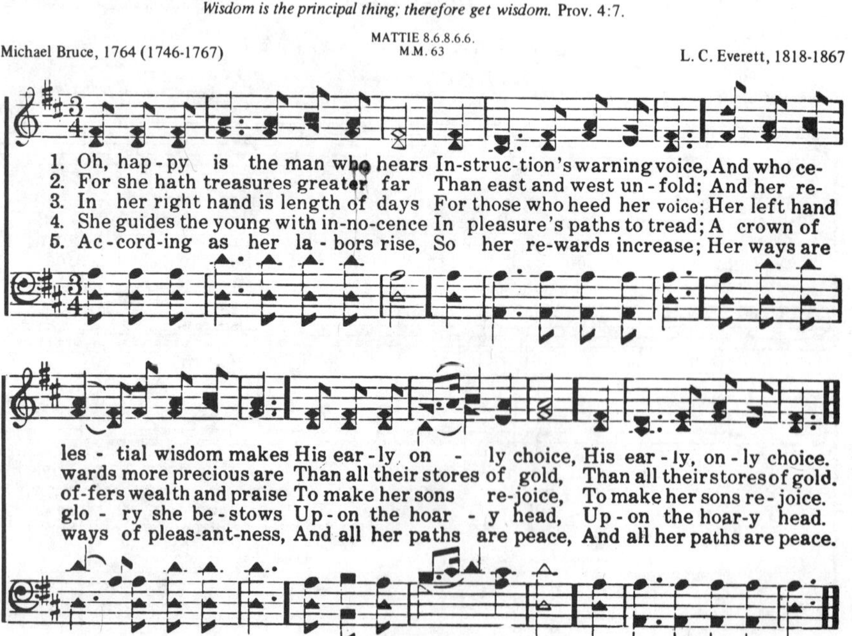

1. Oh, hap-py is the man who hears In-struc-tion's warning voice, And who ce-les-tial wisdom makes His ear-ly on-ly choice, His ear-ly, on-ly choice.
2. For she hath treasures greater far Than east and west un-fold; And her re-wards more precious are Than all their stores of gold, Than all their stores of gold.
3. In her right hand is length of days For those who heed her voice; Her left hand of-fers wealth and praise To make her sons re-joice, To make her sons re-joice.
4. She guides the young with in-no-cence In pleasure's paths to tread; A crown of glo-ry she be-stows Up-on the hoar-y head, Up-on the hoar-y head.
5. Ac-cord-ing as her la-bors rise, So her re-wards increase; Her ways are ways of pleas-ant-ness, And all her paths are peace, And all her paths are peace.

## AND MUST WE BE TO JUDGMENT BROUGHT 299

*Every idle word that men shall speak, they shall give account thereof in the day of judgment.* Mt. 12:36.

Charles Wesley, 1763 (1708-1788)
Altered by Compiler, 1970

PATMOS NEW C.M. 8.6.8.6.
M.M. 66

From a Gregorian chant
Arranged by Compiler, 1970

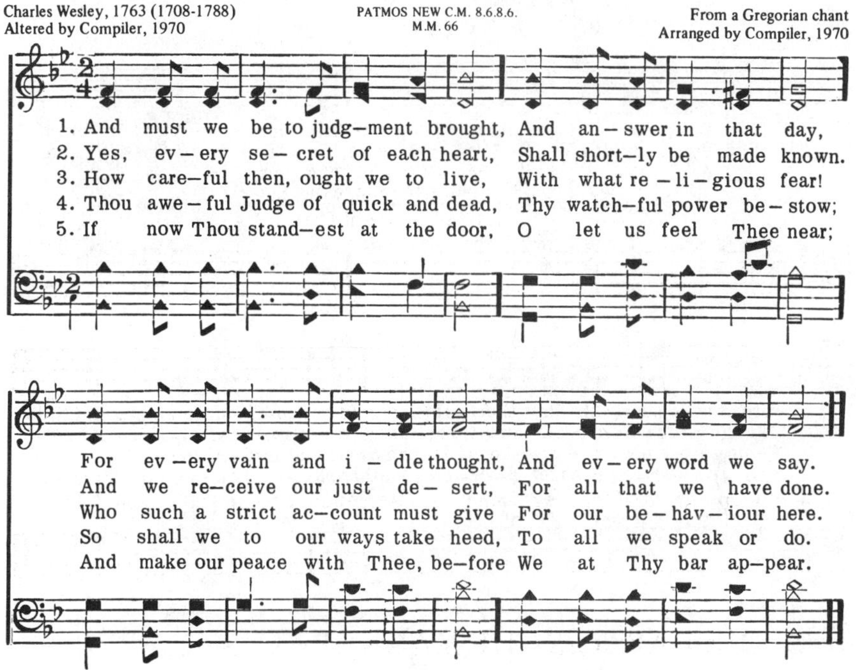

1. And must we be to judg–ment brought, And an–swer in that day,
2. Yes, ev–ery se–cret of each heart, Shall short–ly be made known.
3. How care–ful then, ought we to live, With what re–li–gious fear!
4. Thou awe–ful Judge of quick and dead, Thy watch–ful power be–stow;
5. If now Thou stand–est at the door, O let us feel Thee near;
For ev–ery vain and i–dle thought, And ev–ery word we say.
And we re–ceive our just de–sert, For all that we have done.
Who such a strict ac–count must give For our be–hav–iour here.
So shall we to our ways take heed, To all we speak or do.
And make our peace with Thee, be–fore We at Thy bar ap–pear.

## LET THE WORDS OF MY MOUTH 300

*Let the words of my mouth, and the meditation of my heart, be acceptable in Thy sight.* Ps. 19:14.

From Psalm 19:14

PRAYER FOR ACCEPTANCE 15.8.9.
M.M. 66

Adolph Baumbach, 1862 (1830-1880)

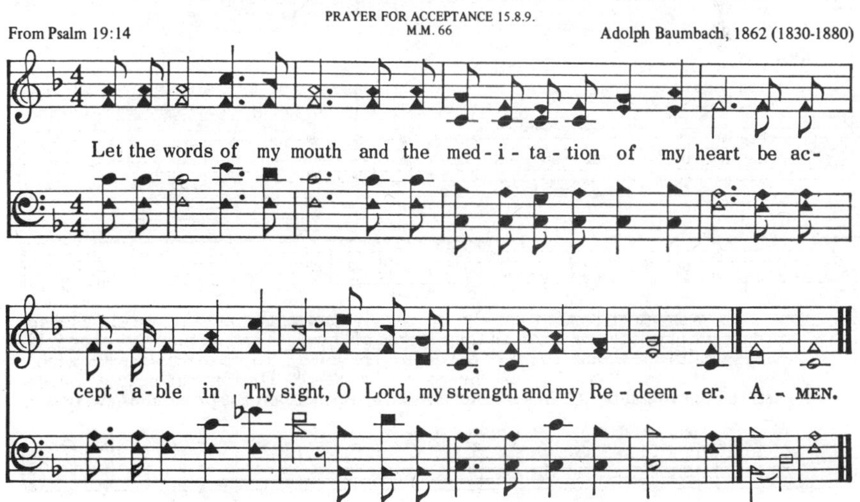

Let the words of my mouth and the med-i-ta-tion of my heart be ac-
cept-a-ble in Thy sight, O Lord, my strength and my Re-deem-er. A-MEN.

# 301 I WAS WANDERING IN A WILDERNESS

*Whereby are given unto us exceeding great and precious promises: that by these ye might be partakers of the divine nature.* II Pet. 1:4.

I BELIEVE THE PROMISES 15.11. 7.7.12 with Ref.
M.M. 69

Lanta Wilson Smith — William James Kirkpatrick, 1838-1921

1. I was wan-d'ring in a wil-der-ness of deep de-spair and sin, And my feet were grow-ing wea-ry of the road; But my sor-row, doubt and care Fled, when Je-sus met me there, And I learned to trust the prom-is-es of God.
2. I was fol-low'd by the tempt-er, as he watch'd me day by day, While I sought the shin-ing path my Sav-iour trod; But with pan-o-ply and shield, And the Spir-it's sword to wield, I have con-quer'd thro' the prom-is-es of God.
3. Aft-er days of joy-ful dream-ing came a time of grief and care, When I sank be-neath the heav-y chasten-ing rod; And the heart so torn by grief Found its com-fort and re-lief, On-ly thro' the bless-ed prom-is-es of God.
4. So I pave the way be-fore me with the prom-is-es of God; They have brightened ev-'ry step my feet have trod; And this shin-ing hap-py way Brightens in-to per-fect day, Thro' the nev-er fail-ing prom-is-es of God.
REFRAIN
I be-lieve the prom-is-es of God, I can trust His nev-er fail-ing Word; When earthly hopes shall fail, Or hosts of sin as-sail, I rest up-on the prom-is-es of God.

# IT MAY BE AT MORN 302

*Watch therefore: for ye know not what hour your Lord doth come.* Mt. 24:42.

CHRIST RETURNETH 12.12.12.7. with Ref.
M.M. 80
H. L. Turner, 1878
James McGranahan, 1878 (1840-1907)
1. It may be at morn, when the day is a - wak-ing, When sunlight thro'
2. It may be at mid - day, it may be at twi-light, It may be, per-
3. While its hosts cry Hosanna, from heaven de-scend-ing, With glo - ri - fied
4. Oh, joy! oh, de-light! should we go with-out dy - ing, No sick-ness, no
dark - ness and shad-ow is break-ing, That Je - sus will come in the
chance, that the black-ness of mid-night Will burst in - to light in the
saints and the an - gels at - tend-ing, With grace on His brow, like a
sad - ness, no dread and no cry - ing, Caught up thro' the clouds with our
full - ness of glo - ry, To re - ceive from the world "His own."
blaze of His glo - ry, When Je - sus re - ceives "His own."
ha - lo of glo - ry, Will Je - sus re - ceive "His own."
Lord in - to glo - ry, When Je - sus re - ceives "His own."
CHORUS
O Lord Je - sus, how long, how long Ere we shout the glad song, Christ re-
rit.
turn-eth! Hal - le - lu - jah! hal-le-lu - jah! A - men, Hal-le - lu - jah! A-men.

# 303 I AM WAITING FOR THE DAWNING

*And to wait for His Son from heaven, whom He hath raised from the dead, even Jesus, which delivered us from the wrath to come.* I Thess. 1:10.

S. Trevor Francis
Alt. 1873

I NEED THEE PRECIOUS JESUS 7.6.7.6.D.
M.M. 76

J. Henry Showalter, 1864-1947

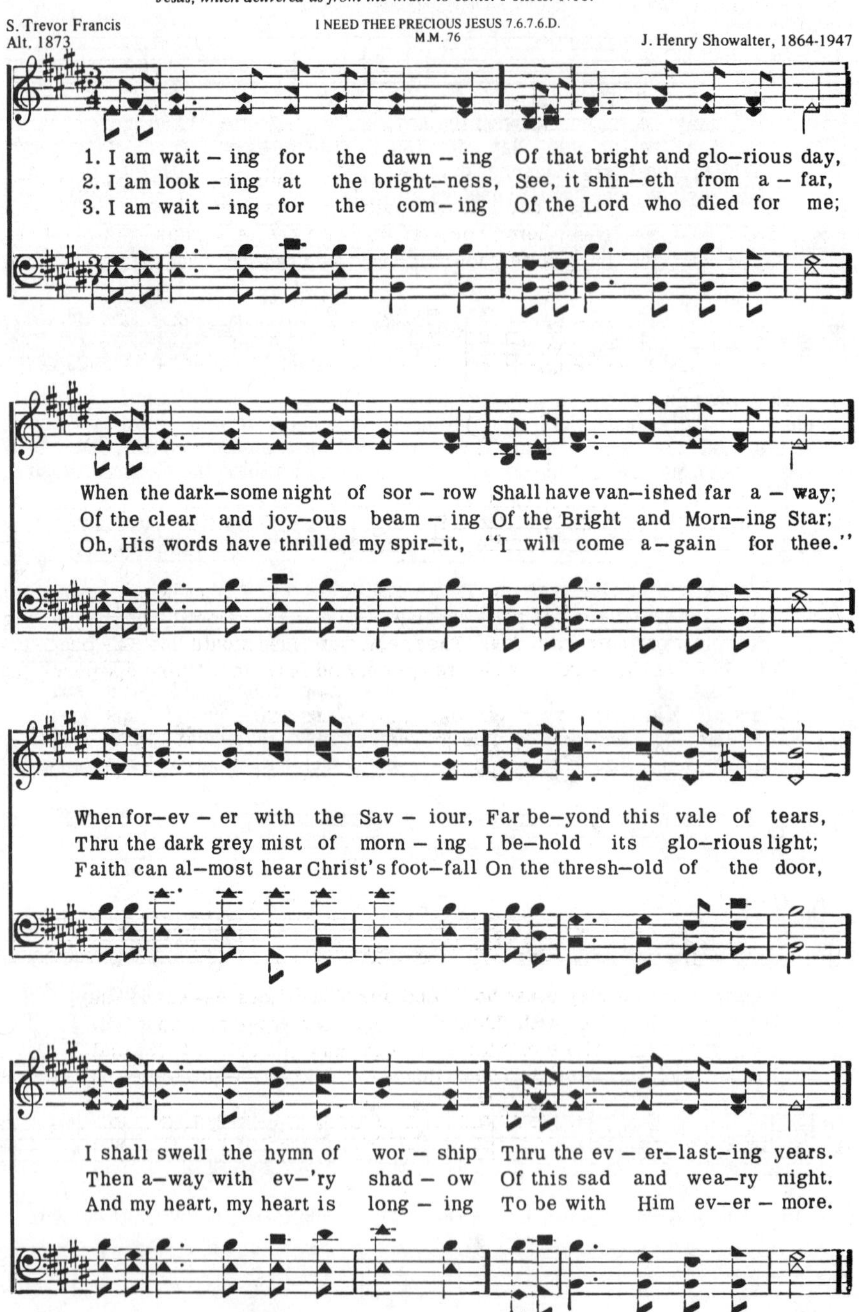

1. I am wait – ing for the dawn – ing Of that bright and glo–rious day,
2. I am look – ing at the bright–ness, See, it shin–eth from a – far,
3. I am wait – ing for the com – ing Of the Lord who died for me;
When the dark–some night of sor – row Shall have van–ished far a – way;
Of the clear and joy–ous beam – ing Of the Bright and Morn–ing Star;
Oh, His words have thrilled my spir–it, "I will come a – gain for thee."
When for–ev – er with the Sav – iour, Far be–yond this vale of tears,
Thru the dark grey mist of morn – ing I be–hold its glo–rious light;
Faith can al–most hear Christ's foot–fall On the thresh–old of the door,
I shall swell the hymn of wor – ship Thru the ev – er–last–ing years.
Then a–way with ev–'ry shad – ow Of this sad and wea–ry night.
And my heart, my heart is long – ing To be with Him ev–er – more.

# OH SON OF GOD, WE WAIT FOR THEE 304

*Waiting for the coming of our Lord Jesus Christ.* I Cor. 1:7.

Philipp Friedrich Hiller, 1699-1769
*Wir warten dein, O Gottes Sohn*
Tr. Joseph Augustus Seiss, 1890 (1823-1904)
Recast, John J. Overholt, 1970

MEINE HOFFNUNG NEW 8.7.8.7.3.3.7.
M.M. 66

Joachim Neander, 1680 (1650-1680)
Arranged by Compiler, 1970

1. Oh Son of God, we wait for Thee, In love for thine ap–pear–ing;
2. We wait for Thee, 'mid toil and pain, In wea–ri–ness and sigh–ing;
3. We wait for Thee, here Thou hast won Our hearts to hope and du – ty;
4. We wait for Thee, sure Thou wilt come; The time is swift–ly near–ing;
We know Thou sit–test on Thy throne, And we Thy name are bear–ing,
But glad that Thou our guilt hast borne And can–celed it by dy–ing,
But while our spir–its feel Thee near, Our eyes would see Thy beau–ty;
In this we al–so now re–joice, And long for Thine ap–pear–ing,
Who trusts Thee, May blest be, And see Thee, Lord, de–scend–ing.
Cheer–ful–ly, We with Thee Take up our cross and bear it.
We would be There with Thee In life and peace e–ter–nal.
Bliss 'twill be Thee to see, Home–ward Thy peo–ple bring–ing. A–men.

# 305 WAIT ON GOD AND TRUST HIM

*Commit thy way unto the Lord; trust also in Him; and He shall bring it to pass.* Ps. 37:5.

Johann Friedrich Räder, 1815-1872
*Harre, meine Seele*
Tr. J. H. Horstman, 1908
J. C. Hansen, 1916

HARRE MEINE SEELE 10.11.10.11.9.10.
M.M. 80

Henri Alexander Cesar Malan, 1787-1864

1. Wait on God, and trust Him through all thy days; Cast thy cares up - on Him
2. Wait on God, and trust Him through all thy days; Cast thy cares up - on Him
3. Wait on God, and trust Him through all thy days; Cast thy cares up - on Him
4. Wait on God, and trust Him through all thy days; Cast thy cares up - on Him

who guides all thy ways. Do not de - spair; as the morn - ing fair
who guides all thy ways. Per - ish what will, God is ref - uge still;
who guides all thy ways. Take up Thy cross; count it not a loss,
who guides all thy ways. On bend - ed knee, Lord, I cry to Thee;

Scat - ters fog and dark - ness, God re - moves thy care. 'Midst all thy tri - als,
Great - er than the Help - er is not an - y ill. Faith - ful, e - ter - nal
For the heat of sor - row melts a - way the dross. Je - sus, dear Sav - iour,
Shield my soul from e - vil; to Thy cross I flee. Gra - cious Re - deem - er,

in all thy care God re - mains thy faith - ful Friend ev - ery - where.
Sav - iour and Friend, Save my soul from e - vil un - to the end.
pa - tient and mild, Let me be o - be - dient, a trust - ing child.
might - y and strong, Let me sing re - joic - ing the vic - tor's song.

# I AM A STRANGER HERE 306

*Now then we are ambassadors for Christ, as though God did beseech you by us: we pray you in Christ's stead, be ye reconciled to God.* II Cor. 5:20.

E. Taylor Cassel, 1849-1930
THE KING'S BUSINESS 12.12.12.8. with Ref.
M.M. 60
Flora Hamilton Cassel, 1852-1911
1. I am a stran - ger here, with - in a for - eign land; My home is far a - way, up - on a gold - en strand; Am - bas - sa - dor to be of realms be - yond the sea, I'm here on business for my King.
2. This is the King's com - mand: that all men, ev - 'ry - where, Re - pent and turn a - way from sin's se - duc - tive snare; That all who will o - bey, with Him shall reign for aye, And that's my business for my King.
3. My home is bright - er far than Shar - on's ro - sy plain, E - ter - nal life and joy thro'-out its vast do - main; My Sov'reign bids me tell how mor - tals there may dwell, And that's my business for my King.
CHORUS
This is the mes - sage that I bring, A message angels fain would sing; "Oh, be ye reconciled," Thus saith my Lord and King, "Oh, be ye rec - on - ciled to God."

# 307 JESUS, I LIVE TO THEE

*For to me to live is Christ, and to die is gain.* Phil. 1:21.

DENNIS S.M. 6.6.8.6.
M.M. 72

Henry Harbaugh, 1817-1867

Johann Georg Nägeli, 1773-1836

1. Je – sus, I live to Thee, The love – li – est and best; To
2. Je – sus, I die to Thee When – ev – er death shall come; To
3. Wheth–er to live or die, I know not which is best; To
4. Liv – ing or dy – ing, Lord, I ask but to be Thine; My
live in Thee is life to me, In Thy blest love I rest.
die in Thee is life to me In my e – ter – nal home.
live in Thee is bliss to me, To die is end–less rest.
life in Thee, Thy life in me, Makes heav'n for – ev – er mine.

# 308 THOU THE GRACE OF LIFE SUPPLYING

*And this is life eternal, that they might know Thee the only true God, and Jesus Christ, whom Thou hast sent.* Jn. 17:3.

I WOULD LOVE THEE 8.7.8.7.
M.M. 63

John Samuel Bewley Monsell, 1811-1875

From *Hymns and Tunes*, 1890

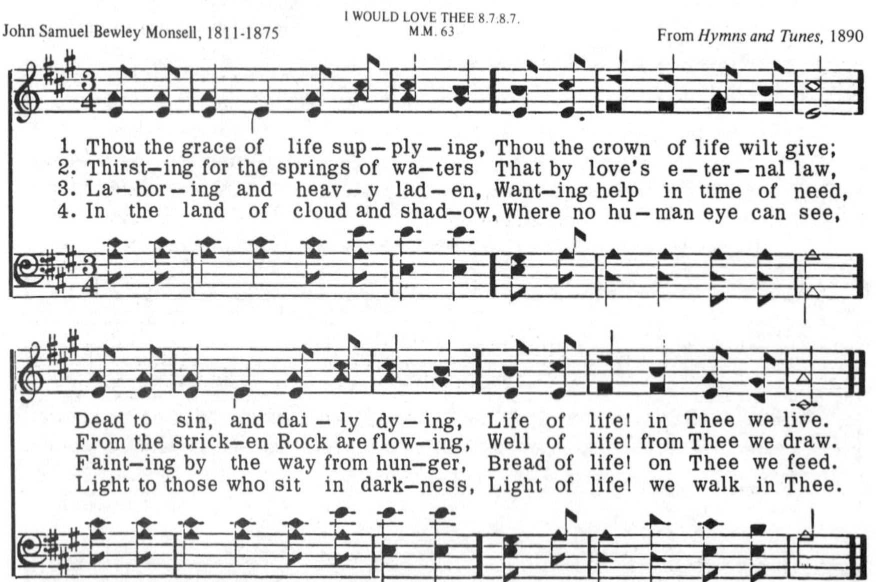
1. Thou the grace of life sup – ply – ing, Thou the crown of life wilt give;
2. Thirst–ing for the springs of wa–ters That by love's e – ter – nal law,
3. La – bor – ing and heav – y lad – en, Want–ing help in time of need,
4. In the land of cloud and shad–ow, Where no hu – man eye can see,
Dead to sin, and dai – ly dy – ing, Life of life! in Thee we live.
From the strick–en Rock are flow–ing, Well of life! from Thee we draw.
Faint–ing by the way from hun–ger, Bread of life! on Thee we feed.
Light to those who sit in dark–ness, Light of life! we walk in Thee.

# OUR GOD IS LOVE 309

*Let us love one another: for love is of God; and everyone that loveth is born of God, and knoweth God.* I Jn. 4:7.

COWPER C.M. 8.6.8.6.
M.M. 60

Anonymous — Lowell Mason, 1792-1872

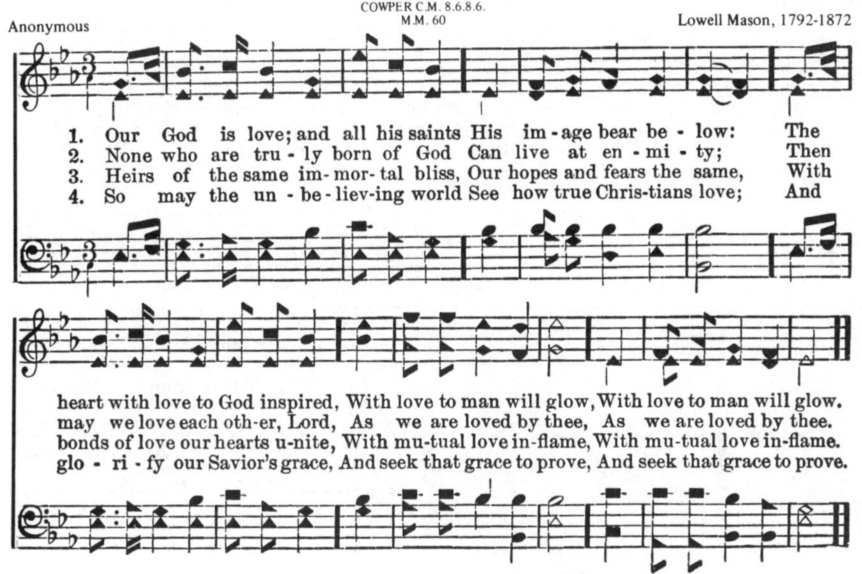
1. Our God is love; and all his saints His im-age bear be-low: The
2. None who are tru-ly born of God Can live at en-mi-ty; Then
3. Heirs of the same im-mor-tal bliss, Our hopes and fears the same, With
4. So may the un-be-liev-ing world See how true Chris-tians love; And
heart with love to God inspired, With love to man will glow, With love to man will glow.
may we love each oth-er, Lord, As we are loved by thee, As we are loved by thee.
bonds of love our hearts u-nite, With mu-tual love in-flame, With mu-tual love in-flame.
glo-ri-fy our Savior's grace, And seek that grace to prove, And seek that grace to prove.

# LOVE IS THE FOUNTAIN WHENCE 310

*God is love; and he that dwelleth in love dwelleth in God, and God in him.* I Jn. 4:16.

GERAR S.M. 6.6.8.6.
M.M. 72

Benjamin Beddome, 1717-1795 — Lowell Mason, 1792-1872

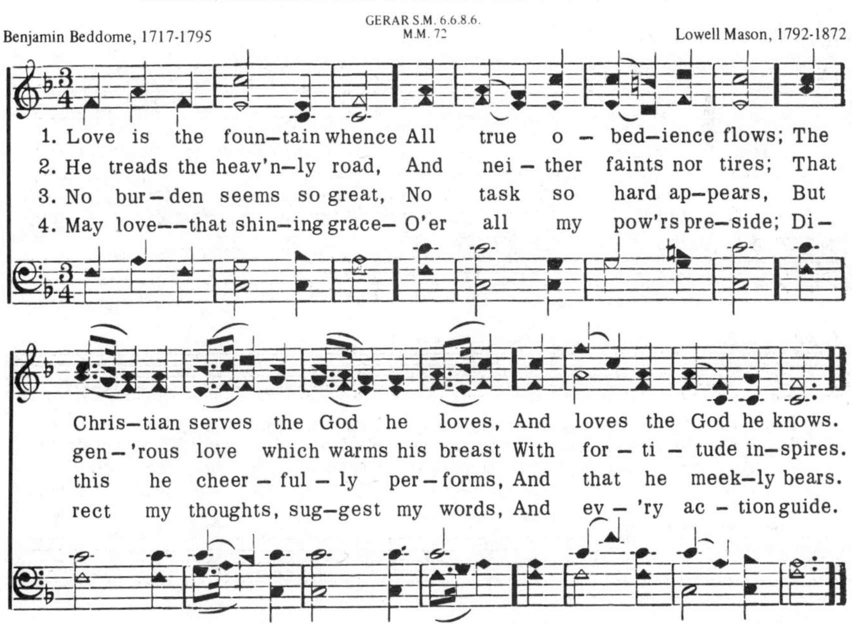
1. Love is the foun-tain whence All true o-bed-ience flows; The
2. He treads the heav'n-ly road, And nei-ther faints nor tires; That
3. No bur-den seems so great, No task so hard ap-pears, But
4. May love—that shin-ing grace— O'er all my pow'rs pre-side; Di-
Chris-tian serves the God he loves, And loves the God he knows.
gen-'rous love which warms his breast With for-ti-tude in-spires.
this he cheer-ful-ly per-forms, And that he meek-ly bears.
rect my thoughts, sug-gest my words, And ev-'ry ac-tion guide.

# 311 JESUS JOY OF LIVING

*The fruit of the Spirit is love, joy . . .* Gal. 5:22.

Gotthold Schmid
*Jesu, meine Freude*
Tr. John J. Overholt, 1968

JESU MEINE FREUDE 6.5.11.6.6.7.6.6.
M.M. 76

Gerhard Schmeling

1. Je - sus, joy of liv - ing, Je - sus, joy the best!
2. Thou thy - self hast giv - en in - to bit - 'rest death,
3. There - fore do we wor - ship, Lord, be - fore thy throne,
Soprano:
1. Com - fort peace and rest;
2. Stems our life and breath;
3. To Thee, God's own Son;
In our sor - rows giv - ing com - fort, peace, and rest;
From Thy side, blood riv – en, stems our life and breath;
Bring - ing hymns, thanks - giv - ing, to thee, God's own Son,
Thou art ho - ly unc - tion, our sal - va - tion's deep de -
Thou a - gain art ris - en from death's dread and cru - el
Heart and life and feel - ing con - se - crat - ing, Lord, to
sire Thou art plen – teous re - demp - tion, pil - lar and
night! Thou hast o - pened death's pris - on and free - dom
Thee, All we have and are, our be – ing, for all e –

tongues of fire, Pil - lar and tongues of fire!
brought and light, And free - dom brought and light!
ter – ni – ty! For all e - ter - ni - ty!

# REJOICE! REJOICE! YE SAINTS, REJOICE! 312

*Rejoice evermore.* I Thess. 5:16.

ZION'S COURTS C.M. 8.6.8.6.
M.M. 76

C. R. Hurditch

Wilmer D. Swope, 1970
Har. John J. Overholt, 1970

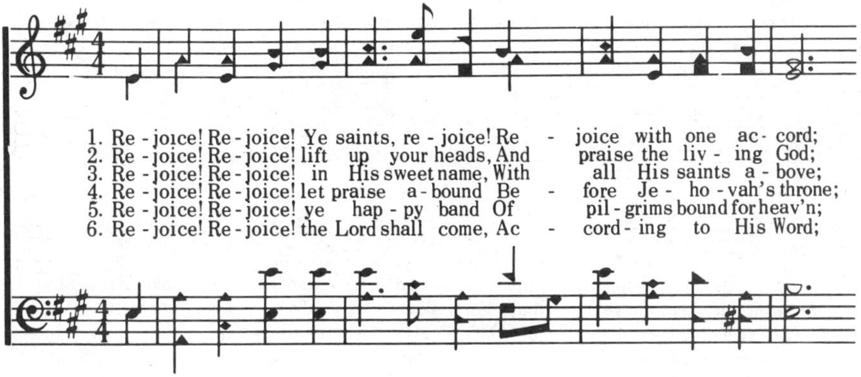

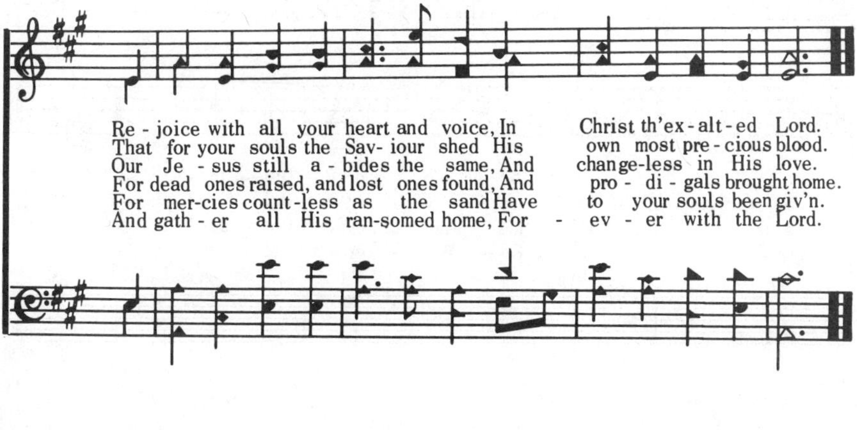

1. Re - joice! Re - joice! Ye saints, re - joice! Re - joice with one ac - cord;
Re - joice with all your heart and voice, In Christ th'ex - alt - ed Lord.

2. Re - joice! Re - joice! lift up your heads, And praise the liv - ing God;
That for your souls the Sav - iour shed His own most pre - cious blood.

3. Re - joice! Re - joice! in His sweet name, With all His saints a - bove;
Our Je - sus still a - bides the same, And change-less in His love.

4. Re - joice! Re - joice! let praise a - bound Be - fore Je - ho - vah's throne;
For dead ones raised, and lost ones found, And pro - di - gals brought home.

5. Re - joice! Re - joice! ye hap - py band Of pil - grims bound for heav'n;
For mer - cies count - less as the sand Have to your souls been giv'n.

6. Re - joice! Re - joice! the Lord shall come, Ac - cord - ing to His Word;
And gath - er all His ran - somed home, For - ev - er with the Lord.

# 313 IN THEE IS GLADNESS

*Thou hast put gladness in my heart.* Ps. 4:7.

Johann Lindemann, c. 1550-c. 1634
*In Dir ist Freude*
Tr. John J. Overholt, 1964

IN DIR IST FREUDE 10.7.10.9.9.
M.M. 80

Giovanni Gastoldi, 1556-1622

1. In Thee is glad – ness in ev – ery sad – ness, Je – sus,
In Thee pos – sess – ing heav – en – ly bless – ing, All our
2. If Thee we have when our day a – wak – ens, Nought can
Thou art sus – tain – ing, dost help the faint – ing, Meet – ing
sweet and love – ly Lord, Help – ing from shame and
joys Thou dost af – ford. In Thy great good – ness
harm us, sin nor death; We there – fore hon – or
needs of all with breath; We are re – joic – ing,
sav – ing from pris – on, All who Thee trust and make right de –
stands our sal – va – tion, For death and life Thy pro – pi – ti –
with praise, the Do – nor Of all our bless – ing, with joy pos –
and tri – umph voic – ing, Lov – ing and prais – ing, heart, mouth up –
cis – ion, Shall live for – ev – er, Hal – le – lu – jah!
a – tion, Thou fail – est nev – er, Hal – le – lu – jah!
sess – ing Our hearts this ho – ur, Hal – le – lu – jah!
rais – ing Thee, our En – dow – er, Hal – le – lu – jah!

# THOU WILT KEEP HIM IN PERFECT PEACE 314

*Thou wilt keep him in perfect peace, whose mind is stayed on Thee.* Is. 26:3.

# 315 PEACE, PERFECT PEACE

*Therefore being justified by faith, we have peace with God.* Rom. 5:1.

Edward Henry Bickersteth, 1875 (1825-1906)

PAX TECUM 10.10.
M.M. 60

George Thomas Caldbeck, 1852-1918
Arr. Charles John Vincent, 1876 (1852-1934)

1. Peace, per – fect peace, in this dark world of sin:
2. Peace, per – fect peace, by throng – ing du – ties pressed:
3. Peace, per – fect peace, with sor – rows surg – ing round:
4. Peace, per – fect peace, with loved ones far a – way:
5. Peace, per – fect peace, our fu – ture all un – known:
6. Peace, per – fect peace, death shad – 'wing us and ours:
7. It is e – nough; earth's strug–gles soon shall cease,

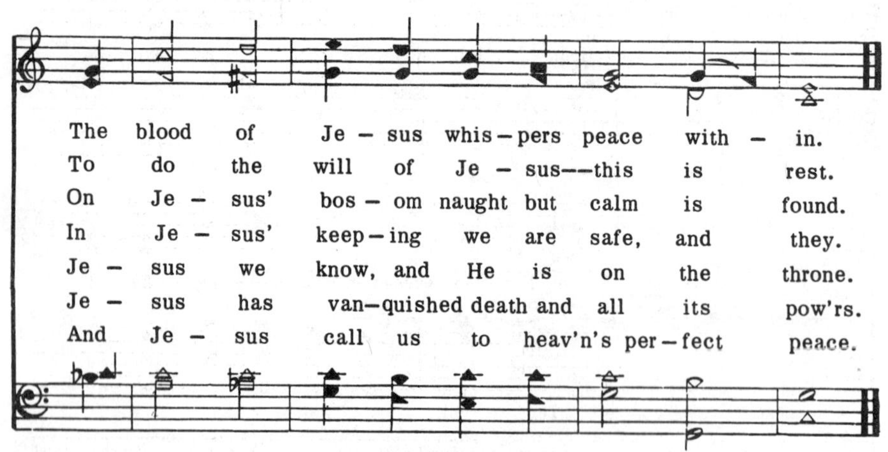
The blood of Je – sus whis – pers peace with – in.
To do the will of Je – sus—this is rest.
On Je – sus' bos – om naught but calm is found.
In Je – sus' keep – ing we are safe, and they.
Je – sus we know, and He is on the throne.
Je – sus has van–quished death and all its pow'rs.
And Je – sus call us to heav'n's per – fect peace.

# I AM SATISFIED WITH JESUS 316

*My soul shall be satisfied as with marrow and fatness; and my mouth shall praise Thee with joyful lips.* Ps. 63:5.

Benjamin Baylus McKinney, 1886-1952 | ROUTH 8.7.8.7. with Ref. M.M. 56 | Benjamin Baylus McKinney

1. I am sat - is - fied with Je - sus, He has done so much for me:
2. He is with me in my tri - als, Best of friends of all is He;
3. I can hear the voice of Je - sus, Call - ing out so plead - ing - ly,
4. When my work on earth is end - ed, And I cross the mys - tic sea,
He has suf - fered to re - deem me, He has died to set me free.
I can al - ways count on Je - sus, Can He al - ways count on me?
"Go and win the lost and stray - ing;" Is He sat - is - fied with me?
Oh, that I could hear Him say - ing, "I am sat - is - fied with thee."
REFRAIN
I am sat - is - fied, I am sat - is - fied, I am sat - is -
fied with Je - sus, But the ques - tion comes to me, As I
think of Cal - va - ry, Is my Mas - ter sat - is - fied with me?

# 317 I AM UNWORTHY TO SUFFER

*We are unprofitable servants.* Lk. 17:10. *Rejoicing that they were counted worthy to suffer shame for His name.* Acts 5:41.

John J. Overholt, 1967 | LEIDEN 10.10.D. with Ref. M.M. 100 | John J. Overholt, 1967

1. I am un-wor-thy to suf-fer with thee, I am un-wor-
2. I am un-wor-thy of grace to con-ceive, I am un-wor-
3. I am un-wor-thy to suf-fer with thee, I am un-wor-
4. I am un-wor-thy from sin to be free, I am un-wor-
thy of dark Cal-va-ry, I am un-wor-thy the dread
thy death's sorrows to leave, I am un-wor-thy by faith
thy of Geth-sem-na-ae, I am un-wor-thy thy serv-
thy thy glo-ry to see, I am un-wor-thy in heav-
ag-o-ny Thou, Lord, hast suf-fered to set sin-ners free!
to be-lieve Won-drous sal-va-tion from thee to re-ceive.
ant to be I am un-wor-thy to set sin-ners free!
en to be To praise and hon-our and glo-ri-fy thee!
REFRAIN
Lord, make me wor-thy to suf-fer with thee, I would be wor-
Lord, make me wor-thy of grace to con-ceive, I would be wor-
Lord make me wor-thy to suf-fer with thee, I would be wor-
Lord, make me wor-thy from sin to be free, I would be wor-

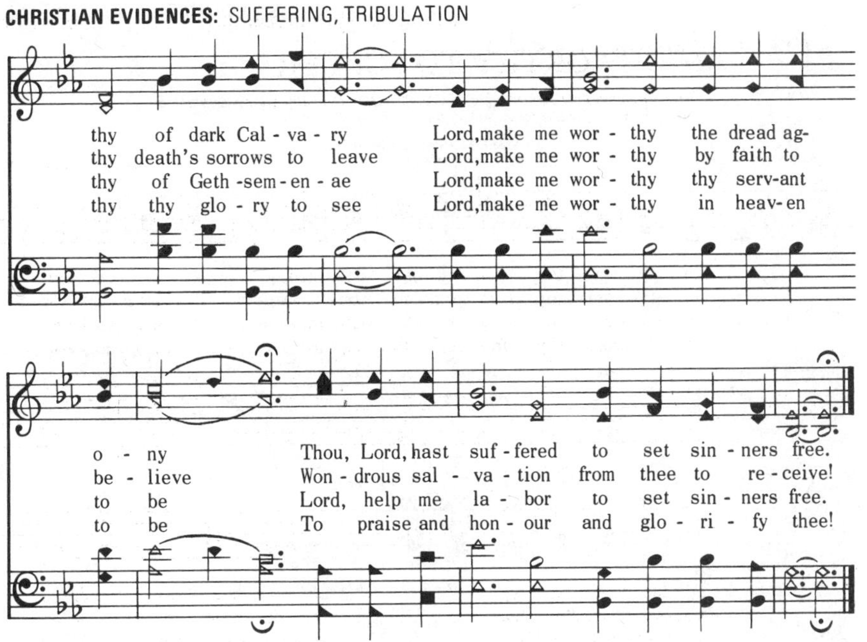
thy of dark Cal - va - ry Lord, make me wor - thy the dread ag-
thy death's sorrows to leave Lord, make me wor - thy by faith to
thy of Geth - sem - en - ae Lord, make me wor - thy thy serv-ant
thy thy glo - ry to see Lord, make me wor - thy in heav-en
o - ny Thou, Lord, hast suf - fered to set sin - ners free.
be - lieve Won - drous sal - va - tion from thee to re - ceive!
to be Lord, help me la - bor to set sin - ners free.
to be To praise and hon - our and glo - ri - fy thee!

CHRISTIAN EVIDENCES: PATIENCE

# O THOU FROM WHOM SWEET PATIENCE FLOWS 318

*The trying of your faith worketh patience. But let patience have her perfect work, that ye may be perfect and entire, wanting nothing.* Jas. 1:3-4.

Thomas Haweis, 1791 (1732-1820), alt.
Altered by Compiler, 1970

NAOMI C.M. 8.6.8.6.
M.M. 60

Johann Georg Nägeli, 1826 (1773-1836)
Arr. Lowell Mason, 1836 (1792-1872)

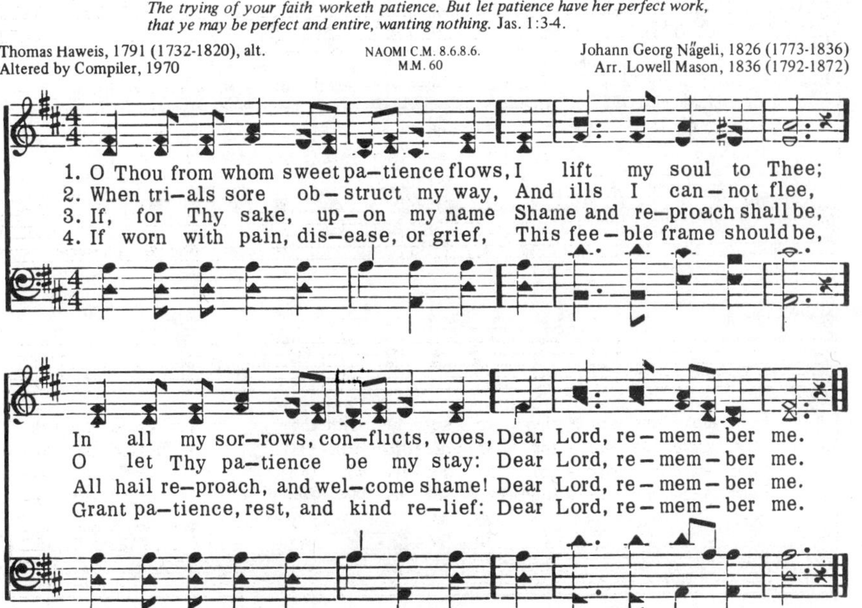
1. O Thou from whom sweet pa-tience flows, I lift my soul to Thee;
2. When tri-als sore ob-struct my way, And ills I can-not flee,
3. If, for Thy sake, up-on my name Shame and re-proach shall be,
4. If worn with pain, dis-ease, or grief, This fee-ble frame should be,
In all my sor-rows, con-flicts, woes, Dear Lord, re-mem-ber me.
O let Thy pa-tience be my stay: Dear Lord, re-mem-ber me.
All hail re-proach, and wel-come shame! Dear Lord, re-mem-ber me.
Grant pa-tience, rest, and kind re-lief: Dear Lord, re-mem-ber me.

# 319 BLESSED ASSURANCE

*And he that keepeth His commandments dwelleth in Him, and He in him. And hereby we know that He abideth in us, by the Spirit which He hath given us.* I Jn. 3:24.

Fanny J. Crosby, 1873 (1820-1915) | BLESSED ASSURANCE 9.10.9.9. with Ref. M.M. 108 | Mrs. Joseph Fairfield Knapp, 1873 (1839-1908)

1. Bless-ed as-sur-ance, Je-sus is mine! Oh, what a fore-taste of glo-ry di-vine! Heir of sal-va-tion, pur-chase of God, Born of His Spir-it, washed in His blood.
2. Per-fect sub-mis-sion, per-fect de-light, Vi-sions of rap-ture now burst on my sight; An-gels de-scend-ing bring from a-bove Ech-oes of mer-cy, whis-pers of love.
3. Per-fect sub-mis-sion, all is at rest, I in my Sav-iour am hap-py and blest; Watch-ing and wait-ing, look-ing a-bove, Filled with His good-ness, lost in His love.
REFRAIN
This is my sto-ry, this is my song, Prais-ing my Sav-iour all the day long; This is my sto-ry, this is my song, Prais-ing my Sav-iour all the day long.

# JESUS THY BLOOD AND RIGHTEOUSNESS 320

*In whom we have redemption through His blood, even the forgiveness of sins.* Col. 1:14.

Nicholas Ludwig von Zinzendorf, 1700-1760
*Christe Blut und Gerechtigkeit* (cento)
Tr. John Wesley, 1703-1791

WAREHAM L.M. 8.8.8.8.
M.M. 76

William Knapp, 1738 (1698-1768)

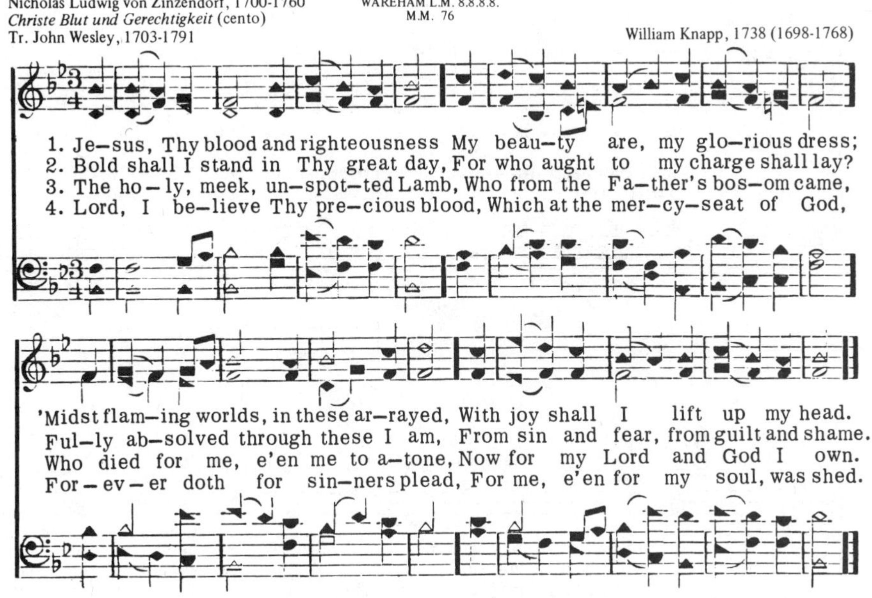
1. Je–sus, Thy blood and righteousness My beau–ty are, my glo–rious dress;
2. Bold shall I stand in Thy great day, For who aught to my charge shall lay?
3. The ho–ly, meek, un–spot–ted Lamb, Who from the Fa–ther's bos–om came,
4. Lord, I be–lieve Thy pre–cious blood, Which at the mer–cy–seat of God,
'Midst flam–ing worlds, in these ar–rayed, With joy shall I lift up my head.
Ful–ly ab–solved through these I am, From sin and fear, from guilt and shame.
Who died for me, e'en me to a–tone, Now for my Lord and God I own.
For–ev–er doth for sin–ners plead, For me, e'en for my soul, was shed.

# I KNOW THAT MY REDEEMER LIVES 321

*I know that my Redeemer liveth.* Job 19:25.

Charles Wesley, 1707-1788

BRADFORD C.M. 8.6.8.6.
M.M. 76

George Friedrich Handel, 1685-1759

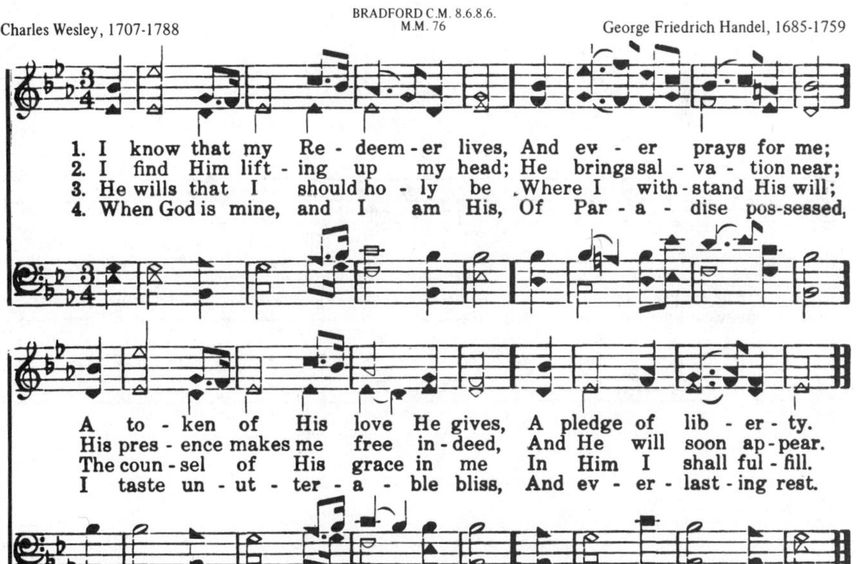
1. I know that my Re - deem - er lives, And ev - er prays for me;
2. I find Him lift - ing up my head; He brings sal - va - tion near;
3. He wills that I should ho - ly be Where I with - stand His will;
4. When God is mine, and I am His, Of Par - a - dise pos-sessed,
A to - ken of His love He gives, A pledge of lib - er - ty.
His pres - ence makes me free in - deed, And He will soon ap - pear.
The coun - sel of His grace in me In Him I shall ful - fill.
I taste un - ut - ter - a - ble bliss, And ev - er - last - ing rest.

# 322 HOW FIRM A FOUNDATION

*Fear not, I am with thee.* Gen. 26:24.

"K" in John Rippon's *Selection of Hymns,* 1787 — HUGER 11.11.11.11. M.M. 60 — Anonymous

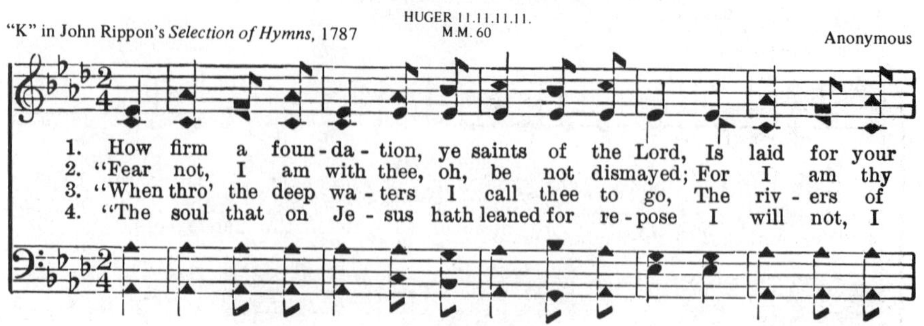
1. How firm a foun-da-tion, ye saints of the Lord, Is laid for your
2. "Fear not, I am with thee, oh, be not dismayed; For I am thy
3. "When thro' the deep wa-ters I call thee to go, The riv-ers of
4. "The soul that on Je-sus hath leaned for re-pose I will not, I

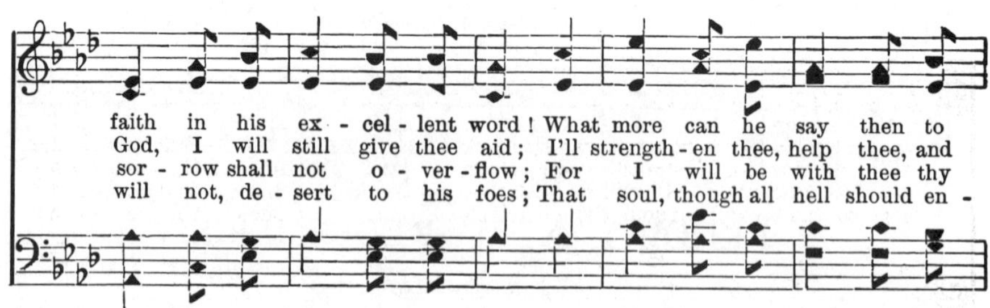
faith in his ex-cel-lent word! What more can he say then to
God, I will still give thee aid; I'll strength-en thee, help thee, and
sor-row shall not o-ver-flow; For I will be with thee thy
will not, de-sert to his foes; That soul, though all hell should en-

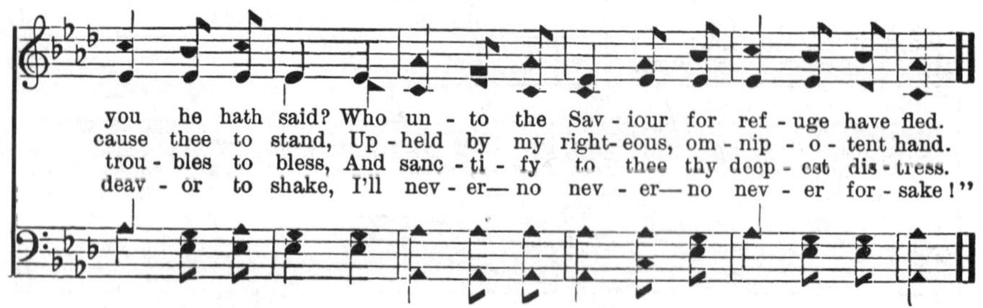
you he hath said? Who un-to the Sav-iour for ref-uge have fled.
cause thee to stand, Up-held by my right-eous, om-nip-o-tent hand.
trou-bles to bless, And sanc-ti-fy to thee thy deep-est dis-tress.
deav-or to shake, I'll nev-er—no nev-er—no nev-er for-sake!"

# HOW FIRM A FOUNDATION 323

*Jesus Christ the same yesterday, and today, and forever.* Heb. 13:8.

ADESTE FIDELES 11.11.11.11.
M.M. 84

"K" in John Rippon's *Selection of Hymns,* 1787

John Reading, 1677-1764

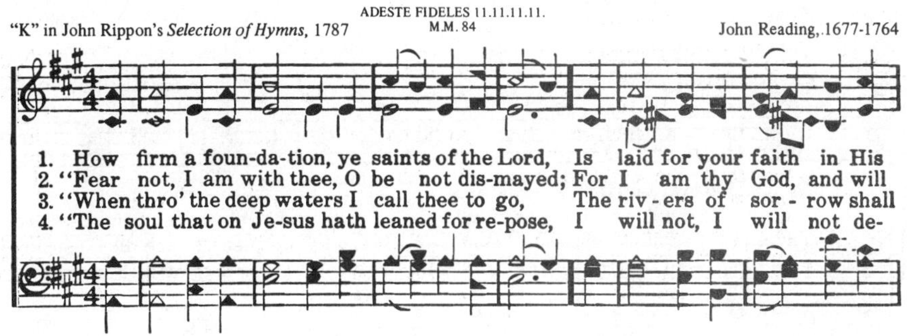
1. How firm a foun-da-tion, ye saints of the Lord, Is laid for your faith in His
2. "Fear not, I am with thee, O be not dis-mayed; For I am thy God, and will
3. "When thro' the deep waters I call thee to go, The riv-ers of sor-row shall
4. "The soul that on Je-sus hath leaned for re-pose, I will not, I will not de-

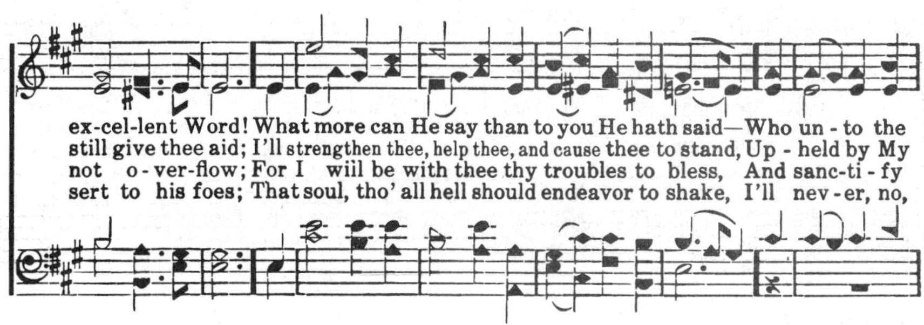
ex-cel-lent Word! What more can He say than to you He hath said—Who un-to the
still give thee aid; I'll strengthen thee, help thee, and cause thee to stand, Up-held by My
not o-ver-flow; For I will be with thee thy troubles to bless, And sanc-ti-fy
sert to his foes; That soul, tho' all hell should endeavor to shake, I'll nev-er, no,

Sav-iour for ref-uge have fled? Who un-to the Sav-iour for ref-uge have fled?
righteous, om-nip-o-tent hand, Up-held by My righteous, om-nip-o-tent hand.
to thee thy deepest dis-tress, And sanc-ti-fy to thee thy deep-est dis-tress.
nev-er, no, nev-er for-sake, I'll nev-er, no, nev-er, no, nev-er, for-sake."

# 324 IN CHRIST MY SAVIOUR'S WOUNDS SECURE

*Much more then, being now justified by His blood, we shall be saved from wrath through Him.* Rom. 5:9.

Johann Andreas Rothe, 1727 (1688-1758)
*Ich habe nun den Grund gefunden*
Tr. Anon.
Recast John J. Overholt, 1970

GEWISSHEIT 8.8.9.9.8.8.8.8.
M.M. 63

Ancient Hungarian Chorale
Arranged by Compiler, 1970

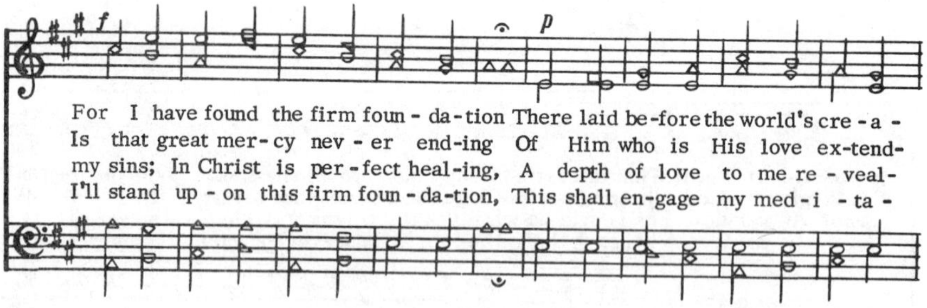

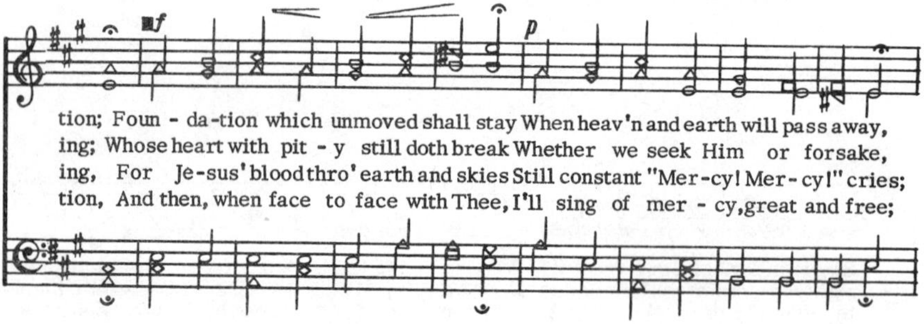

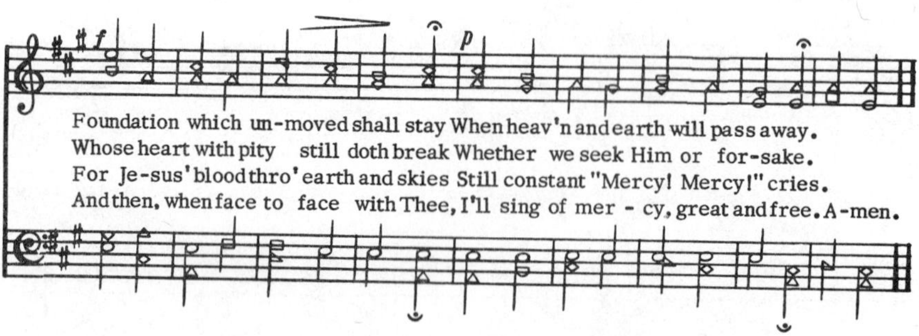

p mf f p mf p f p

1. In Christ my Sav-iour's wounds secure I rest; my an - chor there is sure, For I have found the firm foun - da - tion There laid be - fore the world's cre - a - tion; Foun - da - tion which unmoved shall stay When heav'n and earth will pass away, Foundation which un-moved shall stay When heav'n and earth will pass away.

2. That which man's wisdom far trancends, To wretched sin-ners con-des-cends, Is that great mer - cy nev - er end-ing Of Him who is His love ex-tend-ing; Whose heart with pit - y still doth break Whether we seek Him or forsake, Whose heart with pity still doth break Whether we seek Him or for-sake.

3. There is no con-dem - na - tion here; There is a sea where dis-ap-pear my sins; In Christ is per - fect heal-ing, A depth of love to me re - veal-ing, For Je-sus' blood thro' earth and skies Still constant "Mer-cy! Mer-cy!" cries; For Je-sus' blood thro' earth and skies Still constant "Mercy! Mercy!" cries.

4. As long as I on earth re-main, While I the breath of life re-tain, I'll stand up - on this firm foun - da-tion, This shall en-gage my med - i - ta - tion, And then, when face to face with Thee, I'll sing of mer - cy, great and free; And then, when face to face with Thee, I'll sing of mer - cy, great and free. A-men.

# MY HOPE IS BUILT ON NOTHING LESS 325

*Which hope we have as an anchor of the soul, both sure and steadfast, and which entereth into that within the veil.* Heb. 6:19.

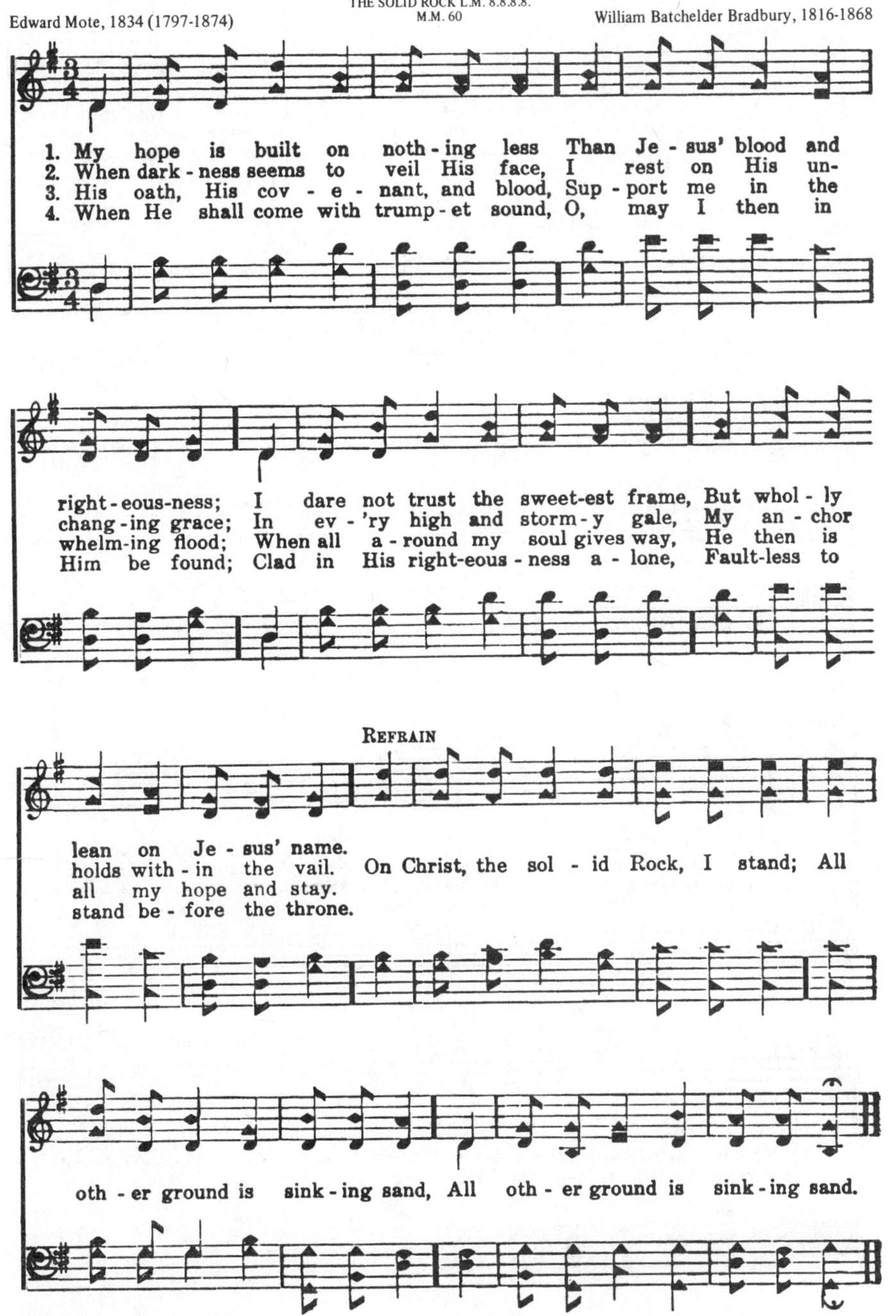
THE SOLID ROCK L.M. 8.8.8.8.
M.M. 60
Edward Mote, 1834 (1797-1874)
William Batchelder Bradbury, 1816-1868
1. My hope is built on noth-ing less Than Je-sus' blood and right-eous-ness; I dare not trust the sweet-est frame, But whol-ly lean on Je-sus' name.
2. When dark-ness seems to veil His face, I rest on His un-chang-ing grace; In ev-'ry high and storm-y gale, My an-chor holds with-in the vail.
3. His oath, His cov-e-nant, and blood, Sup-port me in the whelm-ing flood; When all a-round my soul gives way, He then is all my hope and stay.
4. When He shall come with trump-et sound, O, may I then in Him be found; Clad in His right-eous-ness a-lone, Fault-less to stand be-fore the throne.
Refrain
On Christ, the sol-id Rock, I stand; All oth-er ground is sink-ing sand, All oth-er ground is sink-ing sand.

# 326 O HOLY SAVIOUR

*The Lord is my portion, saith my soul, therefore will I hope in Him.* Lam. 3:24.

FLEMMING 8.8.8.6.
M.M. 80
Charlotte Elliott, 1836 (1789-1871)
Friedrich Ferdinand Flemming, 1778-1813
1. O Ho-ly Sav-iour, Friend un - seen, Since on Thine arm Thou bidd'st me lean,
2. Blest with communion so di - vine, Take what Thou wilt, shall I re - pine,
3. What tho' the world de-ceit-ful prove, And earthly friends and hopes re - move;
4. Tho' faith and hope are oft-en tried, I ask not, need not, aught be - side;
Help me thro'-out life's chang-ing scene, By faith to cling to Thee.
When, as the branch is to the vine, My soul may cling to Thee?
With patient, un - com-plain-ing love, Still would I cling to Thee.
So safe, so calm, so sat - is - fied, The soul that clings to Thee.
A-MEN.

# 327 WE WALK BY FAITH

*For we walk by faith, not by sight.* II Cor. 5:7.

HERMANN C.M. 8.6.8.6.
M.M. 76
Henry Alford, 1844 (1810-1871)
Nicholas Hermann, c. 1485-1561
1. We walk by faith, and not by sight; No gra-cious words we hear
2. We may not touch His hands and side, Nor fol - low where He trod;
3. Help then, O Lord, our un - be - lief; And may our faith a - bound,
4. That, when our life of faith is done, In realms of clear - er light
From Him who spake as man ne'er spake; But we be - lieve Him near.
But in His prom - ise we re - joice, And cry, "My Lord and God!"
To call on Thee when Thou art near, And seek where Thou art found:
We may be - hold Thee as Thou art, With full and end - less sight.

# WE SAW THEE NOT 328

*In whom, though now ye see Him not, yet believing, ye rejoice.* I Pet. 1:8. *I believe that Thou art the Christ, the Son of God.* Jn. 11:27.

ST. PETERSBURG NEW 8.8.8.8.8.8.
M.M. 72
Anne Richter, d. 1857
Dimitri S. Bortniansky, 1751-1825
1. We saw Thee not when Thou didst come To this poor world of
2. We saw Thee not when lift – ed high, A – mid that wild and
3. We gazed not in the o – pen tomb, Where once Thy man – gled
4. We walked not with the cho – sen few, Who saw Thee from the
sin and death; Nor yet be – held Thy cot – tage home, In
sav – age crew; Nor heard we that im – plor – ing cry, "For-
bod – y lay; Nor saw Thee in that up – per room, Nor
earth as – cend; Who raised to heav'n their won – d'ring view, Then
that de – spis – ed Naz – a – reth; But we be – lieve Thy
give, they know not what they do!" But we be – lieve the
met Thee on the o – pen way; But we be – lieve that
low to earth all pros – trate bend; But we be – lieve that
foot – steps trod Its streets and plains, Thou Son of God.
deed was done, That shook the earth and veiled the sun.
an – gels said, "Why seek the liv – ing with the dead?"
hu – man eyes Be – held the jour – ney to the skies.

# 329 I KNOW NOT WHY GOD'S WONDROUS GRACE

*I know whom I have believed, and am persuaded that He is able to keep that which I have committed unto Him against that day.* II Tim. 1:12.

Daniel Webster Whittle, 1840-1901
EL NATHAN C.M. 8.6.8.6. with Ref.
M.M. 66
James McGranahan, 1840-1907
1. I know not why God's won-drous grace To me he hath made known,
2. I know not how this sav - ing faith To me he did im - part,
3. I know not how the Spir - it moves, Con - vinc - ing men of sin.
4. I know not what of good or ill May be re - served for me,
5. I know not when my Lord may come, At night or noon- day fair,
Nor why— un - wor - thy—Christ in love Re- deemed me for his own.
Nor how be - liev - ing in his word Wrought peace with - in my heart.
Re - veal - ing Je - sus through the word, Cre - at - ing faith in him.
Of wea - ry ways or gol - den days, Be - fore his face I see.
Nor if I'll walk the vale with him, Or "meet him in the air."
REFRAIN.
But "I know whom I have be- liev - ed, And am per-suad - ed that he is a - ble
To keep that which I've com - mit - ted un - to him a-gainst that day."

# FAITH IS A LIVING POW'R 330

*Without faith it is impossible to please Him: for he that cometh to God must believe that He is, and that He is a rewarder of them that diligently seek Him.* Heb. 11:6.

HESPERUS L.M. 8.8.8.8.
M.M. 80
Petrus Herbert, 1566 (d. 1571)
Henry Baker, 1866 (1835-1910)
1. Faith is a liv – ing pow'r from heav'n Which grasps the prom – ise God has giv'n; Se – cure – ly fixed on Christ a – lone, A trust that can – not be o'er–thrown.
2. Faith finds in Christ what–e'er we need To save and strength–en, guide and feed; Strong in His grace it joys to share His cross, in hope His crown to wear.
3. Faith to the con–science whis–pers peace; And bids the mourn–er's sigh – ing cease; By faith the chil – dren's right we claim, And call up – on our Fa – ther's name.
4. Such faith in us, O God, im – plant, And to our prayers Thy fa – vor grant, In Je – sus Christ, Thy sav – ing Son, Who is our fount of health a – lone. A–men.

# 331 UNDER HIS WINGS

*In the shadow of Thy wings will I make my refuge.* Ps. 57:1.

William Orcutt Cushing, 1823-1902

UNDER HIS WINGS 11.10.11.10. with Ref.
M.M. 76

Ira David Sankey, 1840-1908

1. Un - der His wings I am safe - ly a - bid - ing; Though the night deep - ens and tem - pests are wild, Still I can trust Him; I know He will keep me; He has re-deemed me, and I am His child.
2. Un - der His wings, what a ref - uge in sor - row! How the heart yearn - ing - ly turns to His rest! Oft - en when earth has no balm for my heal - ing, There I find com-fort, and there I am blest.
3. Un - der His wings, O what pre - cious en - joy - ment! There will I hide till life's tri - als are o'er; Shel - tered, pro - tect - ed, no e - vil can harm me; Rest-ing in Je - sus I'm safe ev - er - more.
CHORUS
Un - der His wings, un - der His wings, Who from His love can sev - er?
Un - der His wings my soul shall a - bide, Safe - ly a - bide for - ev - er.

# I MUST TELL JESUS 332

*Casting all your care upon Him; for He careth for you.* I Pet. 5:7.

I MUST TELL JESUS 10.9.10.9. with Ref.
M.M. 116

Elisha Albright Hoffman, 1839-1929 — Elisha Albright Hoffman

1. I must tell Je - sus all of my tri - als; I can - not bear these bur-dens a - lone; In my dis-tress he kind - ly will help me; He ev - er loves and cares for his own.
2. I must tell Je - sus all of my trou - bles; He is a kind, com - pas- sion - ate Friend; If I but ask him, he will de - liv - er, Make of my trou - bles quick- ly an end.
3. Tempted and tried I need a great Sav - iour, One who can help my bur-dens to bear; I must tell Je - sus, I must tell Je - sus, He all my cares and sor- rows will share.
4. O how the world to e - vil al - lures me! O how my heart is tempt- ed to sin! I must tell Je - sus, and he will help me O - ver the world the vic - t'ry to win.
D.S.—I must tell Je - sus, I must tell Je - sus, Je - sus can help me, Je - sus a - lone.
FINE. REFRAIN.
I must tell Je - sus! I must tell Je - sus! I can - not bear my bur- dens a - lone;
D.S.

# 333 BE NOT DISMAYED WHATE'ER BETIDE

*Underneath are the everlasting arms.* Deut. 33:27.

GOD WILL TAKE CARE OF YOU C.M. 8.6.8.6. with Ref.
M.M. 104

Civilla D. Martin, 1866-1948

W. Stillman Martin, 1862-1935

1. Be not dis-mayed what-e'er be-tide, God will take care of you;
2. Thro' days of toil when heart doth fail God will take care of you;
3. All you may need He will pro-vide, God will take care of you;
4. No mat-ter what may be the test, God will take care of you;
Be-neath His wings of love a-bide, God will take care of you.
When dan-gers fierce your path as-sail, God will take care of you.
Noth-ing you ask will be de-nied, God will take care of you.
Lean, wea-ry one, up-on His breast, God will take care of you.
CHORUS
God will take care of you, Thro' ev-'ry day, O'er all the way;
He will take care of you, God will take care of you . . . .
take care of you.

# O THOU IN WHOSE PRESENCE 334

*In Thy presence is fulness of joy.* Ps. 16:11.

BELOVED 11.8.11.8.
M.M. 58

Joseph Swain, 1762-1796

Freeman Lewis, 1813 (1780-1859)

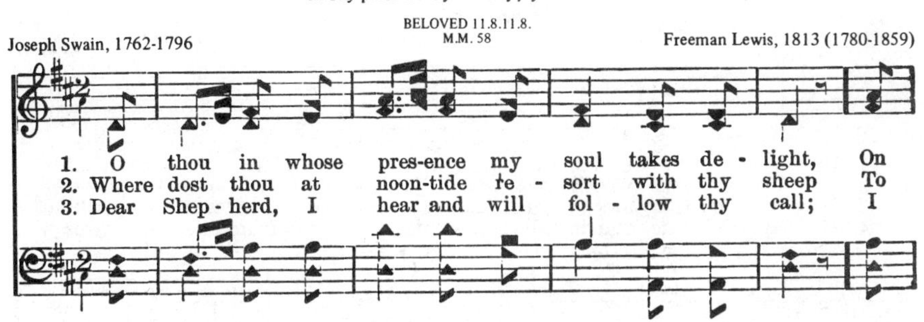
1. O thou in whose pres-ence my soul takes de - light, On
2. Where dost thou at noon-tide re - sort with thy sheep To
3. Dear Shep - herd, I hear and will fol - low thy call; I

whom in af - flic - tion I call, My com - fort by day and my
feed on the pas - tures of love? O why in the val - ley of
know the sweet sound of thy voice; Re - store and de - fend me, for

song in the night, My hope, my sal - va - tion, my all.
death should I weep, Or a - lone in the wil - der - ness rove?
thou art my all, And in thee I will ev - er re - joice.

## 335 HOW GENTLE GOD'S COMMANDS

*His commandments are not grievous.* I Jn. 5:3.

DENNIS S.M. 6.6.8.6.
M.M. 72

Philip Doddridge, 1755 (1702-1751) — Johann Georg Nägeli, 1773-1836

1. How gen - tle God's com-mands! How kind His pre - cepts are!
2. Be - neath His watch - ful eye His saints se - cure - ly dwell;
3. Why should this anx - ious load Press down your wea - ry mind?
4. His good - ness stands ap-proved, Un - changed from day to day;
Come, cast your bur - dens on the Lord, And trust His con - stant care.
That hand which bears all na - ture up, Shall guard His chil - dren well.
Haste to your heav'n-ly Fa - ther's throne, And sweet re - fresh-ment find.
Come, drop your bur - den at His feet, And bear a song a - way.

## 336 GOD MOVES IN A MYSTERIOUS WAY

*How unsearchable are His judgments, and His ways past finding out!* Rom. 11:33.

DUNFERMLINE C.M. 8.6.8.6.
M.M. 76

William Cowper, 1774 (1731-1800) — *Scottish Psalter,* 1615

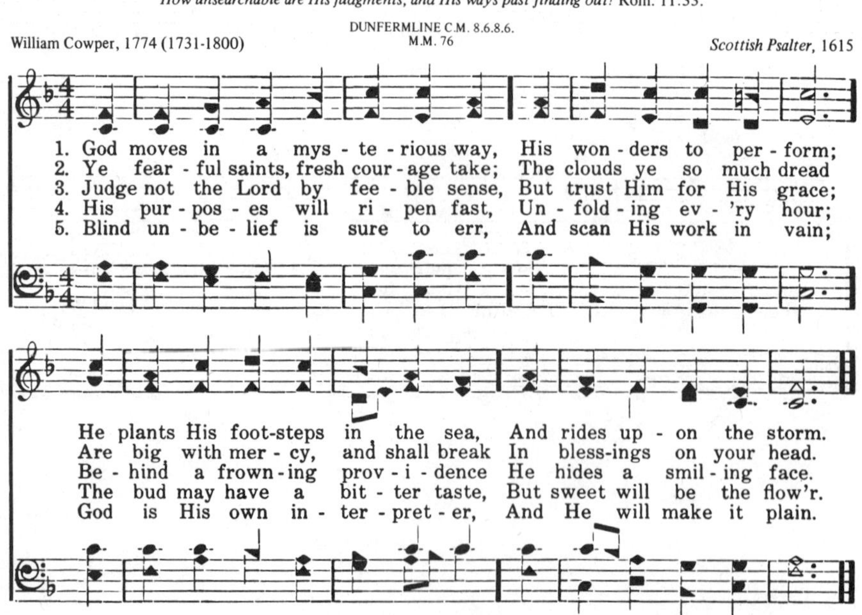
1. God moves in a mys - te - rious way, His won - ders to per - form;
2. Ye fear - ful saints, fresh cour - age take; The clouds ye so much dread
3. Judge not the Lord by fee - ble sense, But trust Him for His grace;
4. His pur - pos - es will ri - pen fast, Un - fold - ing ev - 'ry hour;
5. Blind un - be - lief is sure to err, And scan His work in vain;
He plants His foot-steps in the sea, And rides up - on the storm.
Are big with mer - cy, and shall break In bless-ings on your head.
Be - hind a frown - ing prov - i - dence He hides a smil - ing face.
The bud may have a bit - ter taste, But sweet will be the flow'r.
God is His own in - ter - pret - er, And He will make it plain.

# THE LORD OF GLORY 337

*The Lord God is my Strengeth.* Hab. 3:19.

THE LORD OF GLORY C.M. 8.6.8.6.
M.M. 80

Isaac Watts, 1674-1748

T. B. Mosley

1. The Lord of glo - ry is my light, And my sal - va - tion too;
2. One priv - i - lege my heart de - sires, Oh, grant me an a - bode
3. There shall I of - fer my re - quests, And see thy beau - ty still;

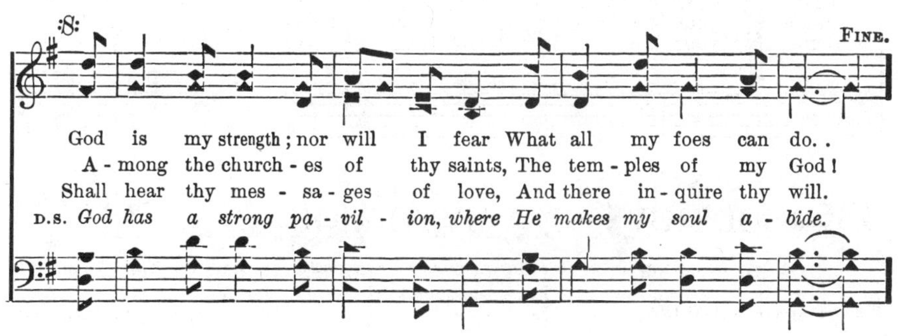
Fine.
God is my strength; nor will I fear What all my foes can do..
A - mong the church - es of thy saints, The tem - ples of my God!
Shall hear thy mes - sa - ges of love, And there in - quire thy will.
D.S. God has a strong pa - vil - ion, where He makes my soul a - bide.

Refrain.
D.S.
When trou - bles rise and storms ap - pear, There may his chil - dren hide..

# 338 YIELD NOT TO TEMPTATION

*God . . . .will with the temptation also make a way to escape.* I Cor. 10:13.

YIELD NOT TO TEMPTATION 6.5.6.5. with Ref.
M.M. 132

Horatio Richmond Palmer, 1868 (1834-1907) | Horatio Richmond Palmer

1. Yield not to temp-ta-tion, For yield-ing is sin; Each vic-t'ry will help you Some oth-er to win; Fight man-ful-ly on-ward, Dark pas-sions sub-due, Look ev-er to Je-sus, He'll car-ry you through.
2. Shun e-vil com-pan-ions, Bad lan-guage dis-dain, God's name hold in rev-'rence Nor take it in vain; Be thought-ful and ear-nest, Kind-heart-ed and true, Look ev-er to Je-sus, He'll car-ry you through.
3. To him that o'er-com-eth, God giv-eth a crown; Thro' faith we shall con-quer, Tho' oft-en cast down; He who is our Sav-iour, Our strength will re-new, Look ev-er to Je-sus, He'll car-ry you through.
CHORUS
Ask the Sav-iour to help you, Com-fort, strengthen and keep you; He is will-ing to aid you, He will car-ry you through.

# O FOR A FAITH THAT WILL NOT SHRINK 339

*Be ye steadfast, unmoveable, always abounding in the work of the Lord, forasmuch as ye know that your labour is not in vain in the Lord.* I Cor. 15:58.

William H. Bathurst, 1831 (1796-1877) | DOWNS C.M. 8.6.8.6. M.M. 66 | Lowell Mason, 1792-1872

1. O for a faith that will not shrink Tho' pressed by many a foe,
2. That will not mur – mur or com-plain Be-neath the chas–t'ning rod,
3. A faith that keeps the nar–row way Till life's last spark is fled,
4. Lord, give me such a faith as this, And then, what–e'er may come,
That will not trem–ble on the brink Of an – y earth – ly woe;
But in the hour of grief or pain Can lean up – on its God;
And with a pure and heav'n–ly ray Lights up a dy – ing bed.
I'll taste e'en here the hal–lowed bliss Of an e – ter – nal home.

# OFT IN DANGER, OFT IN WOE 340

*Be sober, be vigilant; because your adversary the devil, as a roaring lion, walketh about, seeking whom he may devour: Whom resist steadfast in the faith.* I Pet. 5:8-9.

Henry K. White, 1806, alt.
Francis Sara Colquhoun, 1827 (1809-1877)

CULBACH NEW 7.7.7.7 M.M. 80

Scheffler's *Heilige Seelenlust,* 1657
Arr. John J. Overholt, 1970

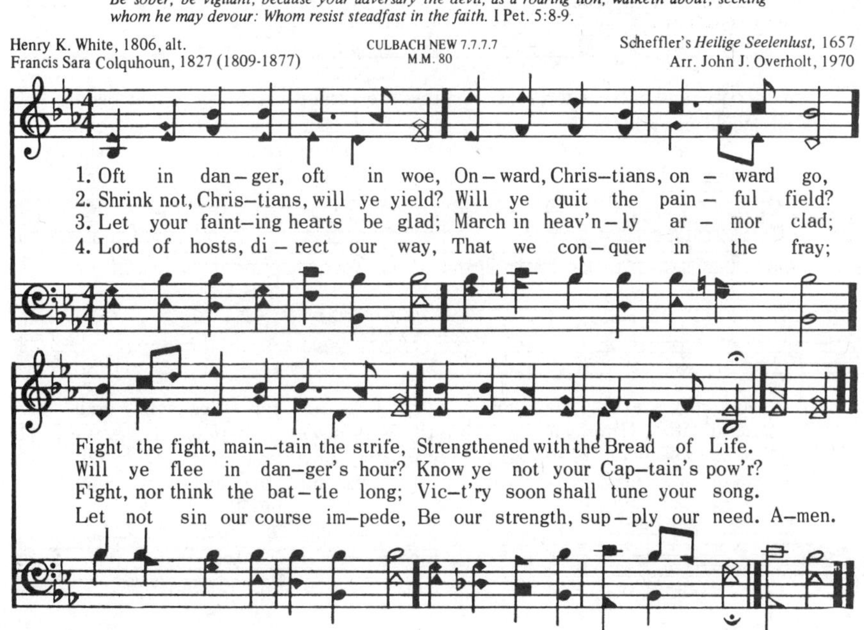
1. Oft in dan – ger, oft in woe, On – ward, Chris–tians, on – ward go,
2. Shrink not, Chris–tians, will ye yield? Will ye quit the pain – ful field?
3. Let your faint–ing hearts be glad; March in heav'n – ly ar – mor clad;
4. Lord of hosts, di – rect our way, That we con – quer in the fray;
Fight the fight, main–tain the strife, Strengthened with the Bread of Life.
Will ye flee in dan–ger's hour? Know ye not your Cap–tain's pow'r?
Fight, nor think the bat – tle long; Vic–t'ry soon shall tune your song.
Let not sin our course im–pede, Be our strength, sup – ply our need. A–men.

# 341 THY WAY AND ALL THY SORROWS

*Let them that suffer according to the will of God commit the keeping of their souls to Him in well doing, as unto a faithful Creator.* I Pet. 4:19. *Commit thy way unto the Lord.* Ps. 37:5.

Paul Gerhardt, 1656 (1607-1676)
Befiehl du deine Wege
Tr. Arthur Tozer Russel, 1851 (1806-1874)
BEFIEHL DU DEINE WEGE
7.6.7.6.D.
M.M. 63
Johann Michael Haydn, 1737-1806
1 Thy way and all thy sor - rows, Give thou in - to His hand,
2 On Him be thy re - li - ance, As thou wouldst pros-per well;
3 Leave all to His di - rec - tion; In wis - dom He doth reign;
4 Give, Lord, the con - sum - ma - tion To all our hearts' dis - tress;
His gra-cious care un - fail - ing, Who doth the heav'ns com-mand.
To make thy work en - dur - ing Thy mind on His must dwell.
Thy won - der far ex - ceed - ing, He will His course main - tain;
Our hands, our feet, O strength-en; In death our spir - its bless.
Their course and path He giv - eth To clouds and air and wind;
God yield-eth nought to sor - row And self - tor - ment - ing care;
So He as Him be - seem - eth, With won - der - work - ing skill,
Thy truth and Thy pro - tec - tion For ev - er - more we pray:
A way thy feet may fol - low, He too for thee will find.
For nought with Him a - vail - eth, No power save that of prayer.
Shall put a - way the sor - rows That now thy spir - it fill.
With these in heav'n - ly glo - ry Shall end our cer - tain way.

# FATHER, TO THEE WE LOOK 342

*Why art thou cast down, O my soul? and why art thou disquieted within me? hope thou in God: for I shall yet praise Him, who is the health of my countenance, and my God.* Ps. 42:11.

ST. BARNABAS 11.10.11.10.
M.M. 80

Frederick Homer, 1881 — John Bacchus Dykes, 1875 (1823-1876)

1. Fa - ther, to Thee we look in all our sor - row,
2. When fond hopes fail and skies are dark be - fore us,
3. Nought shall af - fright us on Thy good - ness lean - ing,
4. Pa - tient, O heart, though heav - y be thy sor - rows!
Thou art the foun - tain whence our heal - ing flows;
When the vain cares that vex our life in - crease—
Low in the heart faith sing - eth still her song;
Be not cast down, dis - qui - et - ed in vain;
Dark though the night, joy com - eth with the mor - row;
Comes with its calm the thought that Thou art o'er us,
Chas - tened by pain we learn life's deep - er mean - ing,
Yet shalt thou praise Him when these dark - ened fur - rows,
Safe - ly they rest who on Thy love re - pose.
And we grow qui - et, fold - ed in Thy peace.
And in our weak - ness Thou dost make us strong.
Where now He plow - eth, wave with gold - en grain. A - men.

# 343 LORD, THY BLESSED WORD OBEYING

*Whoso keepeth His word, in him verily is the love of God perfected: hereby know we that we are in Him.* I Jn. 2:5.

Daniel S. Warner, 1842-1895
Altered by Compiler, 1970

MABYN 8.7.8.7.D.
M.M. 88

Thomas Hastings, 1784-1872

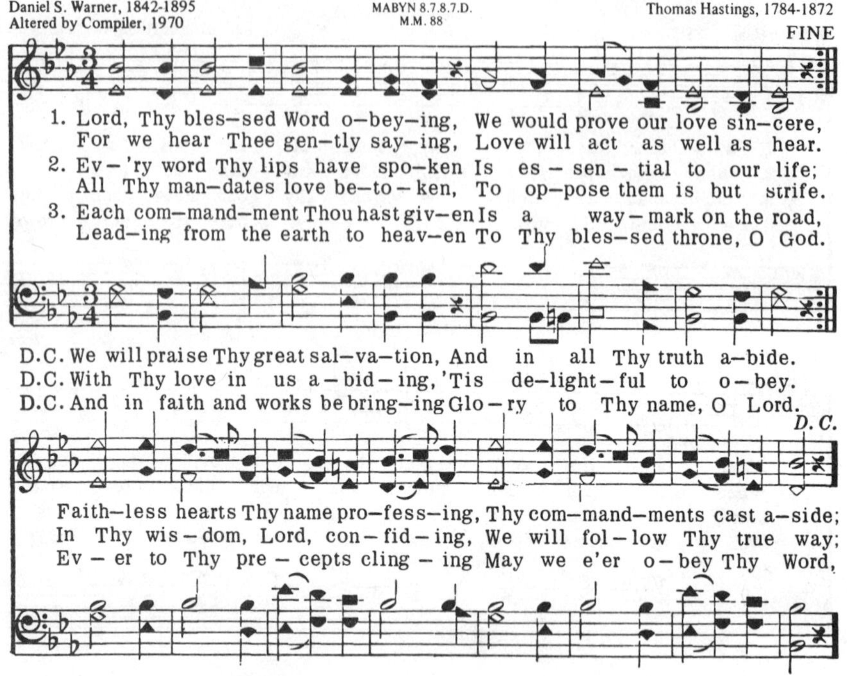
FINE
1. Lord, Thy bles–sed Word o–bey–ing, We would prove our love sin–cere,
For we hear Thee gen–tly say–ing, Love will act as well as hear.
2. Ev–'ry word Thy lips have spo–ken Is es–sen–tial to our life;
All Thy man–dates love be–to–ken, To op–pose them is but strife.
3. Each com–mand–ment Thou hast giv–en Is a way–mark on the road,
Lead–ing from the earth to heav–en To Thy bles–sed throne, O God.
D.C. We will praise Thy great sal–va–tion, And in all Thy truth a–bide.
D.C. With Thy love in us a–bid–ing, 'Tis de–light–ful to o–bey.
D.C. And in faith and works be bring–ing Glo–ry to Thy name, O Lord.
D. C.
Faith–less hearts Thy name pro–fess–ing, Thy com–mand–ments cast a–side;
In Thy wis–dom, Lord, con–fid–ing, We will fol–low Thy true way;
Ev–er to Thy pre–cepts cling–ing May we e'er o–bey Thy Word,

# 344 THOU ART MY PORTION, O MY GOD

*Thou art my portion, O Lord.* Ps. 119:57.

Isaac Watts, 1719 (1674-1748)

BOARDMAN C.M. 8.6.8.6.
M.M. 84

L. Devereux
Arr. George Kingsley, 1811-1844

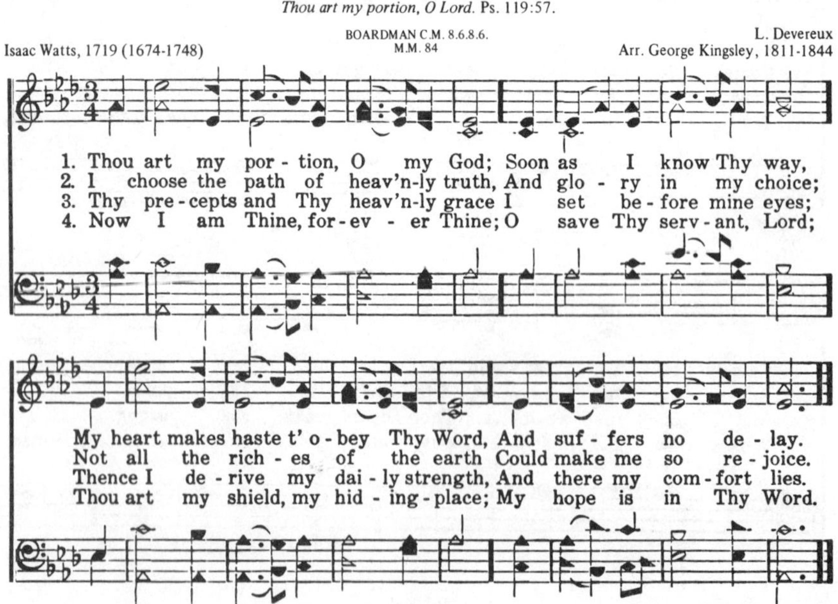
1. Thou art my por-tion, O my God; Soon as I know Thy way,
2. I choose the path of heav'n-ly truth, And glo-ry in my choice;
3. Thy pre-cepts and Thy heav'n-ly grace I set be-fore mine eyes;
4. Now I am Thine, for-ev-er Thine; O save Thy serv-ant, Lord;
My heart makes haste t' o-bey Thy Word, And suf-fers no de-lay.
Not all the rich-es of the earth Could make me so re-joice.
Thence I de-rive my dai-ly strength, And there my com-fort lies.
Thou art my shield, my hid-ing-place; My hope is in Thy Word.

## LO, WHAT A PLEASING SIGHT 345

*That ye may be perfectly joined together.* I Cor. 1:10.

GERAR S.M. 6.6.8.6.
M.M. 88

Isaac Watts, 1719 (1674-1748) | Lowell Mason, 1792-1872

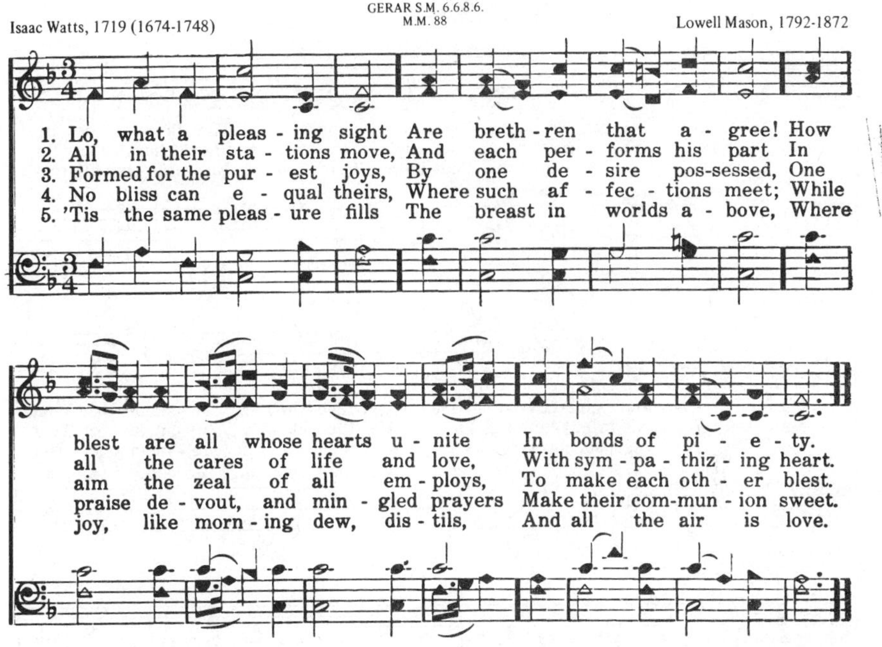
1. Lo, what a pleas - ing sight Are breth - ren that a - gree! How blest are all whose hearts u - nite In bonds of pi - e - ty.
2. All in their sta - tions move, And each per - forms his part In all the cares of life and love, With sym - pa - thiz - ing heart.
3. Formed for the pur - est joys, By one de - sire pos-sessed, One aim the zeal of all em - ploys, To make each oth - er blest.
4. No bliss can e - qual theirs, Where such af - fec - tions meet; While praise de - vout, and min - gled prayers Make their com-mun - ion sweet.
5. 'Tis the same pleas - ure fills The breast in worlds a - bove, Where joy, like morn - ing dew, dis - tils, And all the air is love.

## HOW PLEASANT AND HOW GOOD 346

*Behold, how good and how pleasant it is for brethren to dwell together in unity!* Ps. 133:1.

INVITATION C.M. 8.6.8.6.
M.M. 72

*Psalter*, 1911 | Wallace, 1814-1865, arr.

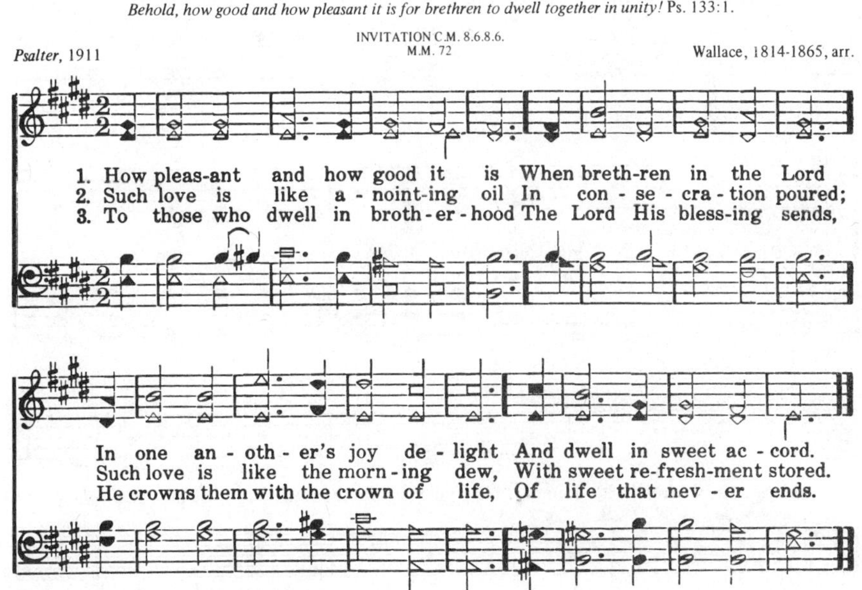
1. How pleas-ant and how good it is When breth-ren in the Lord In one an - oth - er's joy de - light And dwell in sweet ac - cord.
2. Such love is like a - noint-ing oil In con - se - cra - tion poured; Such love is like the morn - ing dew, With sweet re-fresh-ment stored.
3. To those who dwell in broth - er - hood The Lord His bless-ing sends, He crowns them with the crown of life, Of life that nev - er ends.

# 347 I WONDER, OFTEN WONDER

*The desire of our soul is to Thy name, and to the remembrance of Thee.* Is. 26:8.

I WONDER 7.6.7.6.D. with Ref.
M.M. 76

Elisha Hoffman, 1839-1929

Charles Edward Pollock, c. 1902 (b. 1853)

1. I wonder, often wonder, Just how it came to be That there is up in heaven, A mansion fair for me; And then do I remember That the dear Son of God Once shed for rebel sinners His own atoning blood.
2. I wonder, often wonder, Just why his tender love Brought down the dear Redeemer From his bright home above; And then do I remember That on the shameful tree The Saviour made atonement For tender love of me.
3. I wonder, often wonder, That he can bear with me, Enduring all my follies, And yet so gracious be; And then do I remember His grace is rich and free, And that he is so patient Because he so loves me.
Refrain.
For-ever at his feet I'll sit, And wonder at the grace So large and free it found for me In heav'n a dwelling-place.

## WE GIVE THEE BUT THINE OWN 348

*All things come of Thee, and of Thine own have we given Thee.* I Chron. 29:14.

William Walsham How, 1864 (1823-1897) DETROIT S.M. 6.6.8.6. M.M. 72 E. P. Hastings

1. We give Thee but Thine own, What-e'er the gift may be;
2. May we Thy boun-ties thus As stew-ards true re-ceive,
3. O hearts are bruised and dead, And homes are bare and cold,
4. And we be-lieve Thy Word, Though dim our faith may be,
All that we have is Thine a-lone, A trust, O Lord, from Thee.
And glad-ly, as Thou bless-est us, To Thee our first-fruits give.
And lambs for whom the Shep-herd bled Are stray-ing from the fold.
What-e'er for Thine we do, O Lord, We do it un-to Thee.

## FATHER, NOW THY SINFUL CHILD 349

*Forgive us our debts, as we forgive our debtors.* Mt. 6:12.

Josiah Conder, 1789-1855 UNIVERSITY COLLEGE 7.7.7.7. M.M. 76 Henry John Gauntlett, 1852 (1806-1876)

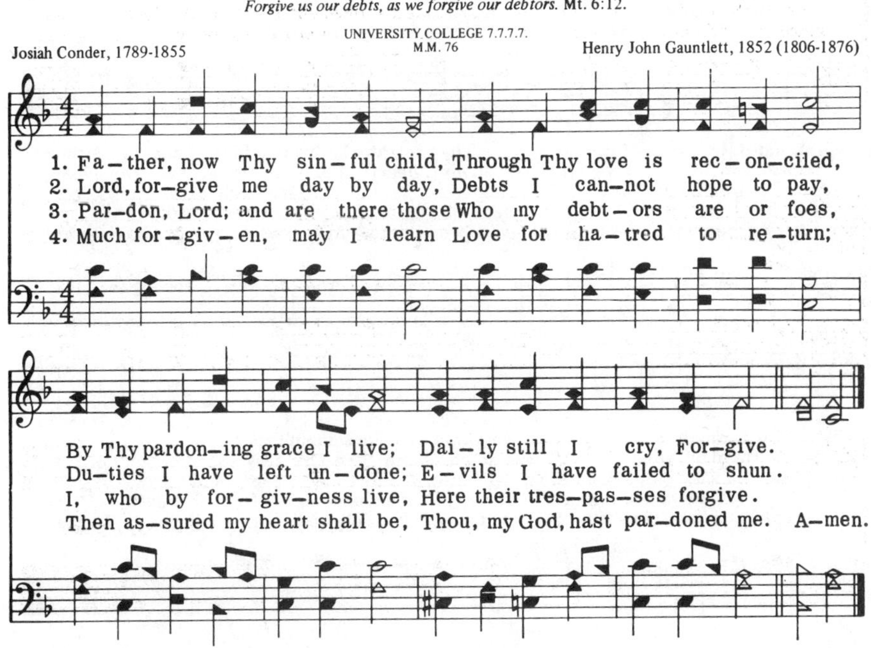

1. Fa-ther, now Thy sin-ful child, Through Thy love is rec-on-ciled,
2. Lord, for-give me day by day, Debts I can-not hope to pay,
3. Par-don, Lord; and are there those Who my debt-ors are or foes,
4. Much for-giv-en, may I learn Love for ha-tred to re-turn;
By Thy pardon-ing grace I live; Dai-ly still I cry, For-give.
Du-ties I have left un-done; E-vils I have failed to shun.
I, who by for-giv-ness live, Here their tres-pas-ses forgive.
Then as-sured my heart shall be, Thou, my God, hast par-doned me. A-men.

# 350 DID CHRIST O'ER SINNERS WEEP

*He beheld the city and wept over it.* Lk. 19:41. *O Jerusalem, Jerusalem . . . how often would I have gathered thy children together . . . and ye would not!* Mt. 23:37.

Benjamin Beddome, 1787 (1717-1795)
Alt. John J. Overholt, 1970

DULCE DOMUM S.M. 6.6.8.6.
M.M. 66

R. S. Ambrose, 1824-1908

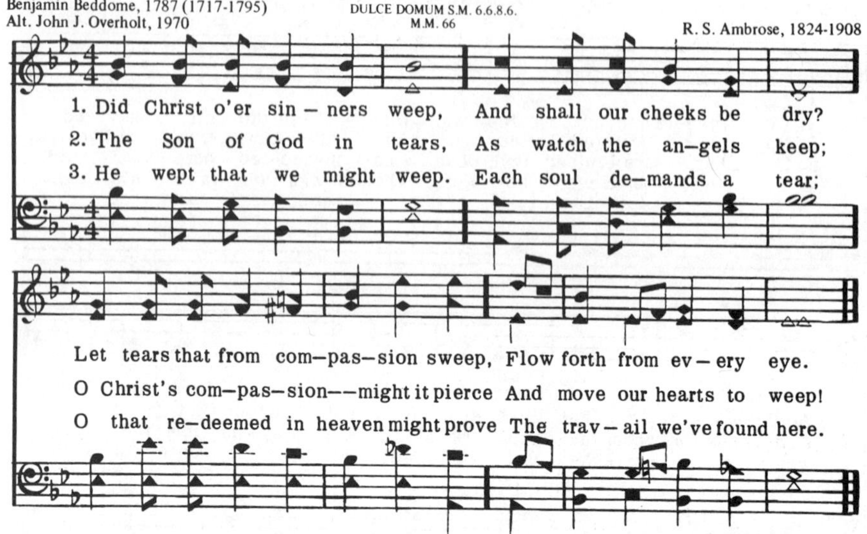
1. Did Christ o'er sin – ners weep, And shall our cheeks be dry?
2. The Son of God in tears, As watch the an–gels keep;
3. He wept that we might weep. Each soul de–mands a tear;
Let tears that from com–pas–sion sweep, Flow forth from ev – ery eye.
O Christ's com–pas–sion––might it pierce And move our hearts to weep!
O that re–deemed in heaven might prove The trav – ail we've found here.

# 351 LORD, IN THE FULLNESS OF THY MIGHT

*Be strong and of a good courage . . . Only be thou strong and very courageous, that thou mayest observe to do according to all the law.* Josh. 1:6-7.

Thomas H. Gill
Altered by Compiler, 1971

ES IST EIN BORN C.M. 8.6.8.6.
M.M. 84

C. E. Miller

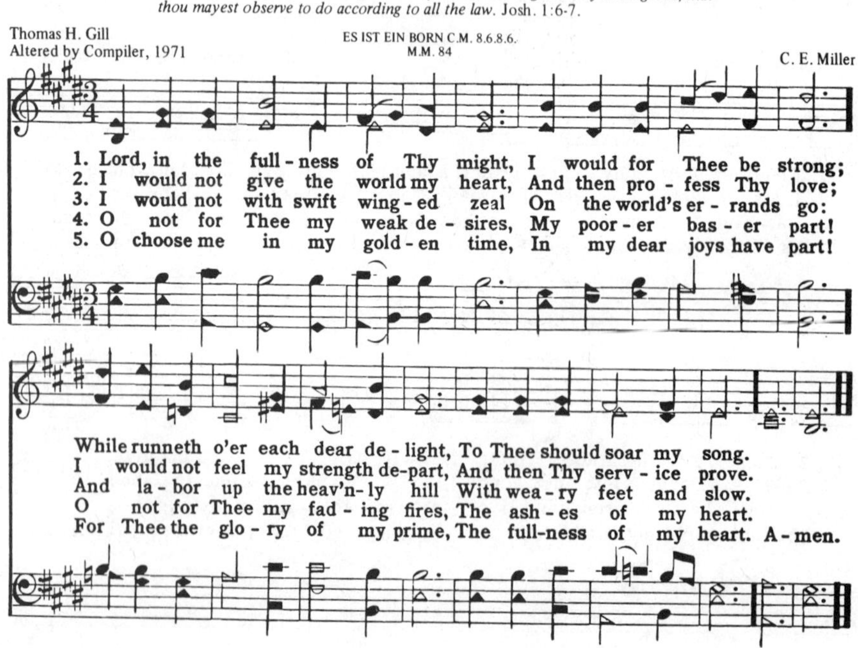
1. Lord, in the full - ness of Thy might, I would for Thee be strong;
2. I would not give the world my heart, And then pro - fess Thy love;
3. I would not with swift wing - ed zeal On the world's er - rands go:
4. O not for Thee my weak de - sires, My poor - er bas - er part!
5. O choose me in my gold - en time, In my dear joys have part!
While runneth o'er each dear de - light, To Thee should soar my song.
I would not feel my strength de-part, And then Thy serv - ice prove.
And la - bor up the heav'n - ly hill With wea - ry feet and slow.
O not for Thee my fad - ing fires, The ash - es of my heart.
For Thee the glo - ry of my prime, The full-ness of my heart. A - men.

# O TO BE LIKE THEE 352

*So now also Christ shall be magnified in my body, whether it be by life, or by death.* Phil. 1:20.

O TO BE LIKE THEE 10.9.10.9. with Ref.
M.M. 50

Thomas O. Chisholm, 1866-1960 William James Kirkpatrick, 1838-1921

1. O to be like Thee! bless-ed Re-deem-er: This is my con-stant long-ing and prayer; Glad-ly I'll for-feit all of earth's treas-ures, Je-sus, Thy per-fect like-ness to wear.
2. O to be like Thee! full of com-pas-sion, Lov-ing, for-giv-ing, ten-der and kind, Help-ing the help-less, cheer-ing the faint-ing, Seek-ing the wan-d'ring sin-ner to find.
3. O to be like Thee! low-ly in spir-it, Ho-ly and harm-less, pa-tient and brave; Meek-ly en-dur-ing cru-el re-proach-es, Will-ing to suf-fer, oth-ers to save.
4. O to be like Thee! Lord, I am com-ing, Now to re-ceive th' a-noint-ing di-vine; All that I am and have I am bring-ing; Lord, from this mo-ment all shall be Thine.
CHORUS
O to be like Thee! O to be like Thee! bless-ed Re-deem-er, pure as Thou art; Come in Thy sweet-ness, come in Thy full-ness; Stamp Thine own im-age deep on my heart.
rit.

# 353 MY SAVIOUR AND MY LORD

*Let us not love in word neither in tongue; but in deed and in truth.* I Jn. 3:18.

Alexander Rodolphe Vinet, 1828 (1799-1847)
*O Seigneur, o Sauveur*
Tr. R. Birch Hoyle
Altered by Compiler, 1964

NEW GREENLAND 7.6.7.6.D.
M.M. 84

Johann Michael Haydn, 1737-1806

1. My Sav - iour and my Lord, let our lips now ac - claim Thee,
2. When Thou, the Lamb of God, in Thy love, pure and ten - der,
3. For - bid it, Lord, that I, who ac - cept Thy great of - fers
But let our works and words in har - mo - ny ac - cord. Our
For sin - ful souls dis - tressed didst die on Cal - va - ry, Was
Should give a poor re - sponse when or - ders Thou didst give; Be
deeds must match our songs: false praise would on - ly shame Thee, Be
love for ev - er slain when life Thou didst sur - ren - der? No!
swift to taste the boons Thy love to me now prof - fers, Yet
emp - ty sounds, all vain and dead, un - wor - thy of the Lord, Both
love was shown in grief and pain, and won the vic - to - ry. And
slow to keep Thy ho - ly law by which the soul doth live. Sav -

hand and heart must take their part, to gain Thy great re - ward.
still it lives, it - self it gives to heal man's mis - er - y.
iour di - vine, I all re - sign, my err – ing soul for - give.

# I NEED THEE EVERY HOUR 354

*Mine eyes are ever toward the Lord.* Ps. 25:15.

I NEED THEE 6.4.6.4. with Ref.
M.M. 69

Annie S. Hawks, 1872 (1835-1918)

Robert Lowry, 1826-1899

1. I need Thee ev - 'ry hour, Most gra - cious Lord; No ten - der voice like Thine Can peace af - ford.
2. I need Thee ev - 'ry hour, Stay Thou near by; Temp-ta-tions lose their pow'r When Thou art nigh.
3. I need Thee ev - 'ry hour, In joy or pain; Come quick-ly and a- bide, Or life is vain.
4. I need Thee ev - 'ry hour, Teach me Thy will; And Thy rich prom-is- es In me ful - fill.
5. I need Thee ev - 'ry hour, Most Ho - ly One; Oh, make me Thine in- deed, Thou bless - ed Son.

REFRAIN

I need Thee, oh, I need Thee; Ev - 'ry hour I need Thee; O bless me now, my Sav - iour! I come to Thee.

# 355 O SON OF GOD, ALL LOVES EXCELLING

*Lord, to whom shall we go? Thou hast the words of eternal life.* Jn. 6:68.

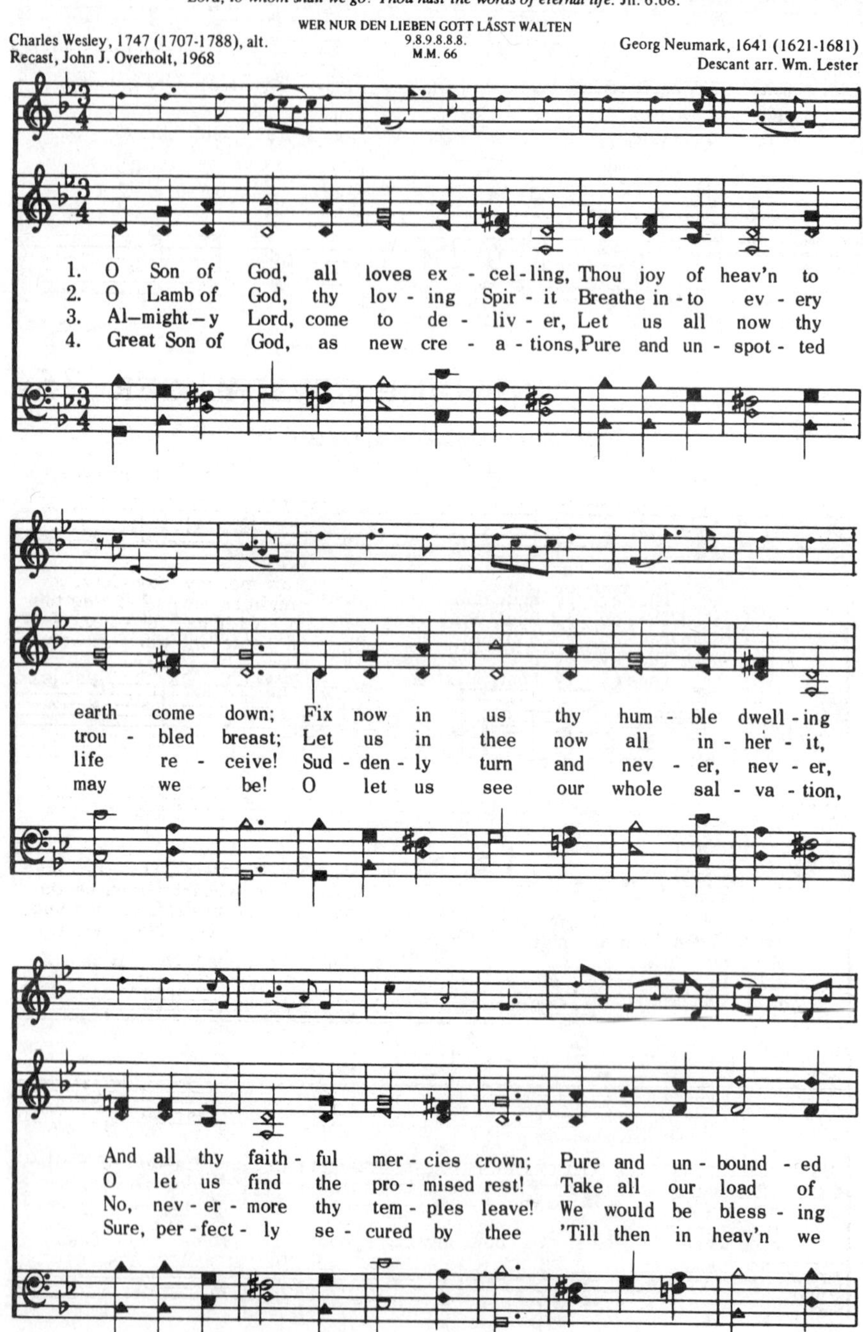
WER NUR DEN LIEBEN GOTT LÄSST WALTEN
9.8.9.8.8.8.
M.M. 66
Charles Wesley, 1747 (1707-1788), alt.
Recast, John J. Overholt, 1968
Georg Neumark, 1641 (1621-1681)
Descant arr. Wm. Lester
1. O Son of God, all loves ex - cel-ling, Thou joy of heav'n to
2. O Lamb of God, thy lov - ing Spir - it Breathe in - to ev - ery
3. Al–might – y Lord, come to de - liv - er, Let us all now thy
4. Great Son of God, as new cre - a - tions, Pure and un - spot - ted
earth come down; Fix now in us thy hum - ble dwell - ing
trou - bled breast; Let us in thee now all in - her - it,
life re - ceive! Sud - den - ly turn and nev - er, nev - er,
may we be! O let us see our whole sal - va - tion,
And all thy faith - ful mer - cies crown; Pure and un - bound - ed
O let us find the pro - mised rest! Take all our load of
No, nev - er - more thy tem - ples leave! We would be bless - ing
Sure, per - fect - ly se - cured by thee 'Till then in heav'n we

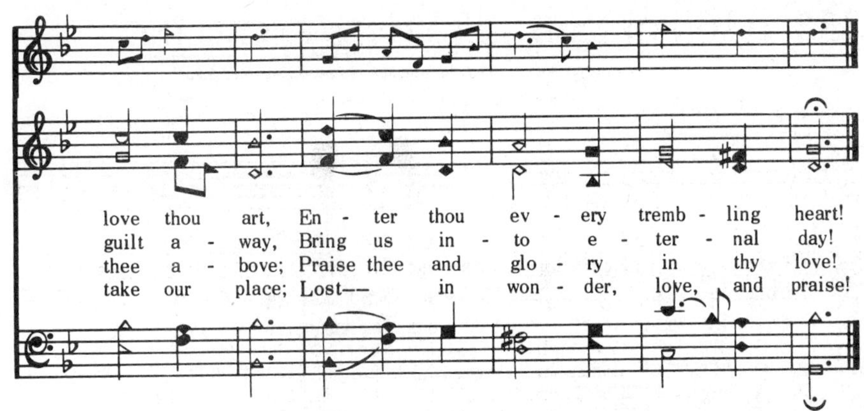
love thou art, En - ter thou ev - ery tremb - ling heart!
guilt a - way, Bring us in - to e - ter - nal day!
thee a - bove; Praise thee and glo - ry in thy love!
take our place; Lost— in won - der, love, and praise!

## NEARER, STILL NEARER 356

*Let us draw near with a true heart in full assurance of faith.* Heb. 10:22.

Leila Naylor Morris, 1862-1929 | MORRIS 9.10.9.10. M.M. 69 | Leila Naylor Morris

1. Near-er, still near - er, close to Thy heart, Draw me, my Sav - iour, so
2. Near-er, still near - er, noth - ing I bring, Naught as an of - f'ring to
3. Near-er, still near - er, Lord, to be Thine, Sin, with its fol - lies, I
4. Near-er, still near - er, while life shall last, Till safe in glo - ry my

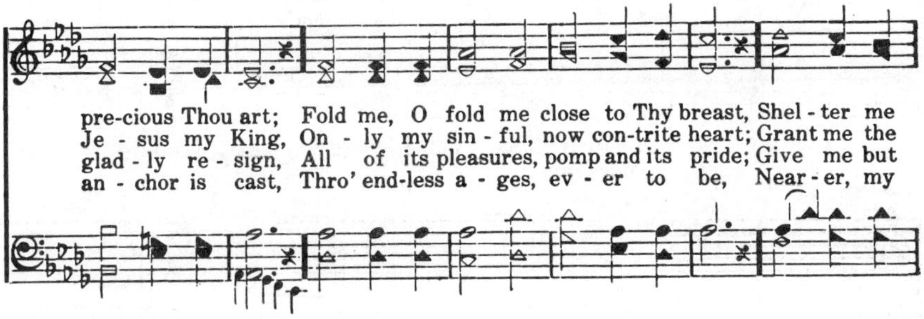

pre-cious Thou art; Fold me, O fold me close to Thy breast, Shel - ter me
Je - sus my King, On - ly my sin - ful, now con-trite heart; Grant me the
glad - ly re - sign, All of its pleasures, pomp and its pride; Give me but
an - chor is cast, Thro' end-less a - ges, ev - er to be, Near - er, my

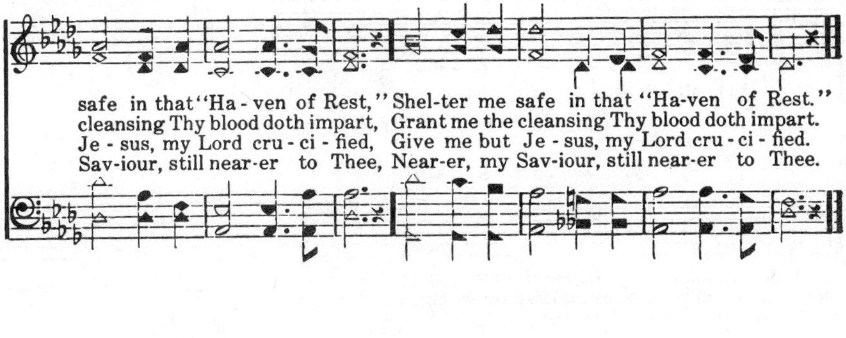

safe in that "Ha - ven of Rest," Shel-ter me safe in that "Ha-ven of Rest."
cleansing Thy blood doth impart, Grant me the cleansing Thy blood doth impart.
Je - sus, my Lord cru - ci - fied, Give me but Je - sus, my Lord cru - ci - fied.
Sav-iour, still near-er to Thee, Near-er, my Sav-iour, still near-er to Thee.

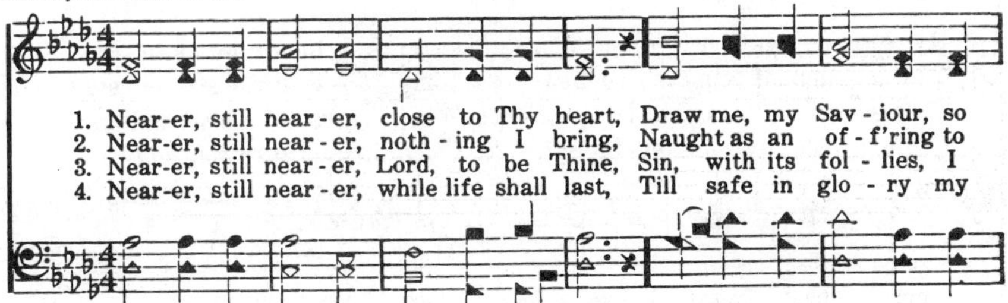

# 357 COME INTO MY HEART

*Behold, I stand at the door, and knock: if any man hear my voice, and open the door, I will come in to him, and will sup with him, and he with me.* Rev. 3:20.

Harry D. Clark, b. 1888

INTO MY HEART 9.7.9.7. with Ref.
M.M. 104

Harry D. Clark

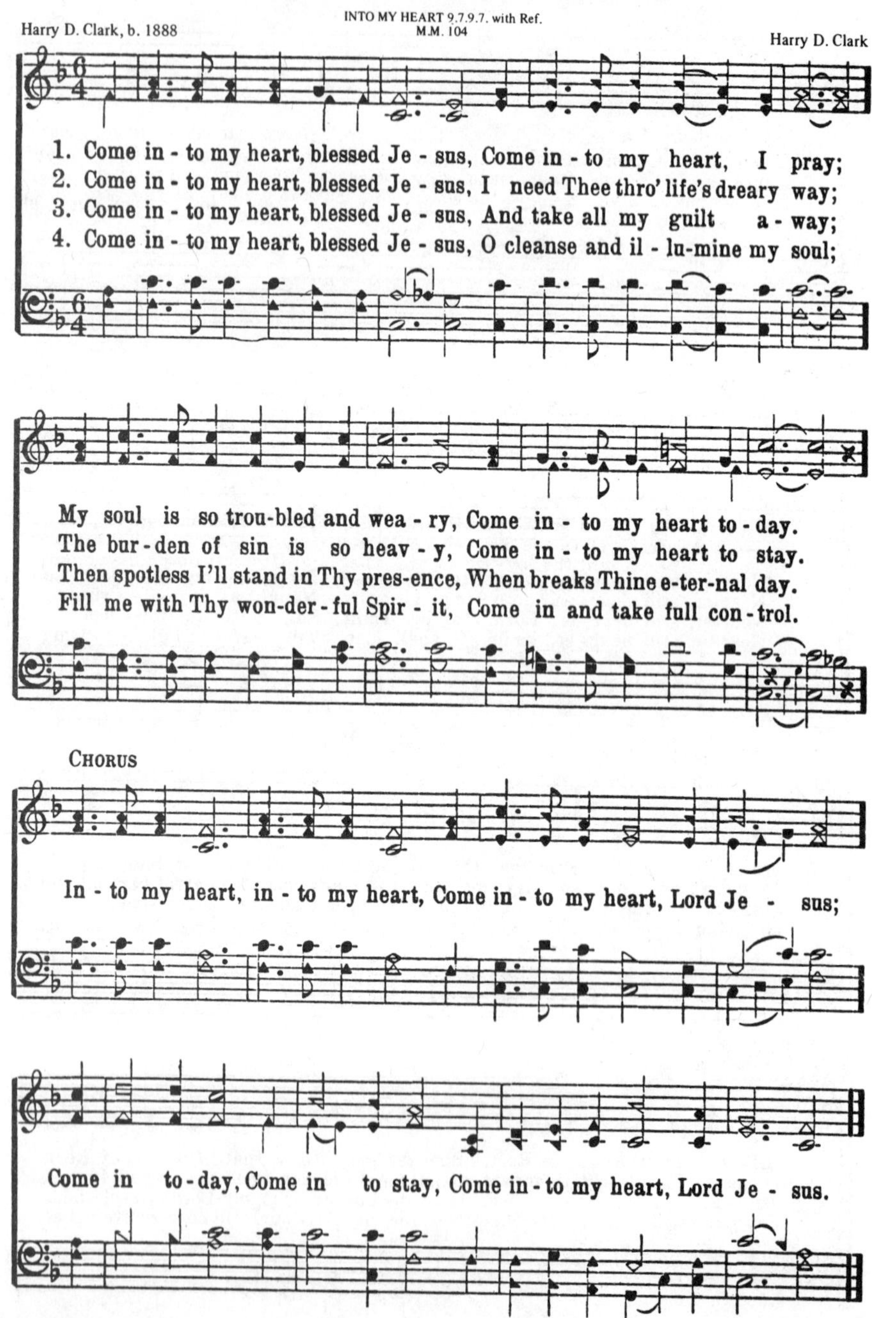
1. Come in - to my heart, blessed Je - sus, Come in - to my heart, I pray;
2. Come in - to my heart, blessed Je - sus, I need Thee thro' life's dreary way;
3. Come in - to my heart, blessed Je - sus, And take all my guilt a - way;
4. Come in - to my heart, blessed Je - sus, O cleanse and il - lu-mine my soul;
My soul is so trou-bled and wea - ry, Come in - to my heart to - day.
The bur - den of sin is so heav - y, Come in - to my heart to stay.
Then spotless I'll stand in Thy pres-ence, When breaks Thine e-ter-nal day.
Fill me with Thy won-der - ful Spir - it, Come in and take full con - trol.
CHORUS
In - to my heart, in - to my heart, Come in - to my heart, Lord Je - sus;
Come in to-day, Come in to stay, Come in - to my heart, Lord Je - sus.

# I'M PRESSING ON THE UPWARD WAY 358

*Create in me a clean heart, O God; and renew a right spirit within me.* Ps. 51:10.

HIGHER GROUND L.M.D. 8.8.8.8.D.
M.M. 76

Johnson Oatman Jr., 1856-1922

Charles H. Gabriel, 1856-1932

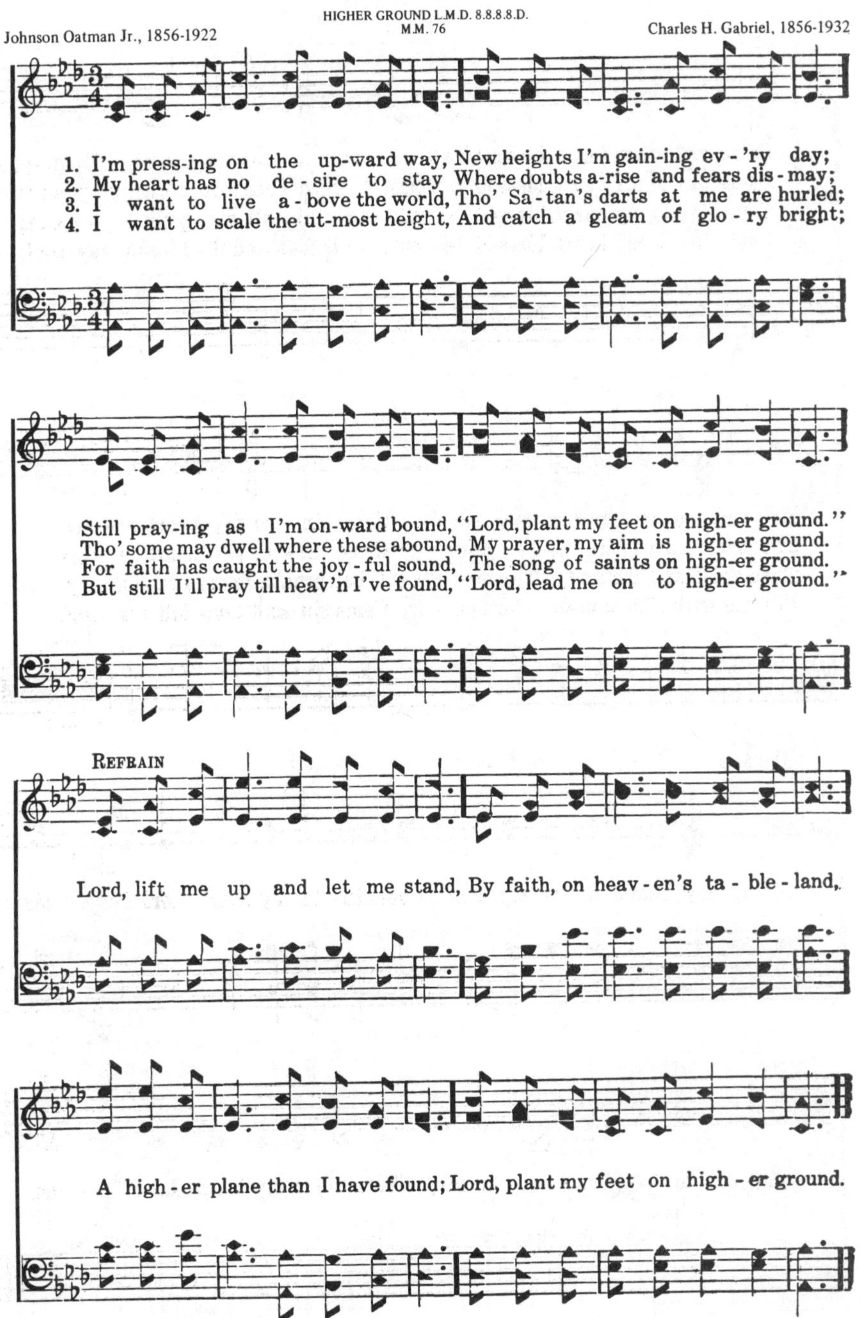
1. I'm press-ing on the up-ward way, New heights I'm gain-ing ev - 'ry day;
2. My heart has no de - sire to stay Where doubts a-rise and fears dis - may;
3. I want to live a - bove the world, Tho' Sa - tan's darts at me are hurled;
4. I want to scale the ut-most height, And catch a gleam of glo - ry bright;
Still pray-ing as I'm on-ward bound, "Lord, plant my feet on high-er ground."
Tho' some may dwell where these abound, My prayer, my aim is high-er ground.
For faith has caught the joy - ful sound, The song of saints on high-er ground.
But still I'll pray till heav'n I've found, "Lord, lead me on to high-er ground."
Refrain
Lord, lift me up and let me stand, By faith, on heav - en's ta - ble - land,
A high - er plane than I have found; Lord, plant my feet on high - er ground.

# 359 NEARER MY GOD TO THEE

*Call ye upon Him while He is near.* Is. 55:6.

Sarah F. Adams, 1841 (1805-1848) | BETHANY 6.4.6.4.6.6.4. M.M. 100 | Lowell Mason, 1792-1872

1. Near - er, my God, to Thee, Near - er to Thee; E'en though it
2. Tho' like a wan - der - er, Day - light all gone, Dark - ness be
3. There let the way ap - pear, Steps up to heav'n; All that Thou
4. Then with my wak - ing tho'ts Bright with Thy praise, Out of my
5. Or if on joy - ful wing, Cleav - ing the sky, Caught up to

be a cross That rais - eth me; Still all my song shall be,
o - ver me, My rest a stone, Yet in my dreams I'd be,
send - est me In mer - cy giv'n; An - gels to beck - on me,
sto - ny griefs Beth - el I'll raise; So by my woes to be,
meet my King, Swift - ly I fly. Still all my song shall be

Near - er, my God, to Thee, Near - er, my God, to Thee, Near - er to Thee.

# 360 O FOR A CLOSER WALK WITH GOD

*That ye might walk worthy of the Lord unto all pleasing.* Col. 1:10.

William Cowper, 1769 (1731-1800) | ELIZABETHTOWN C.M. 8.6.8.6. M.M. 69 | George Kingsley, 1838 (1811-1884)

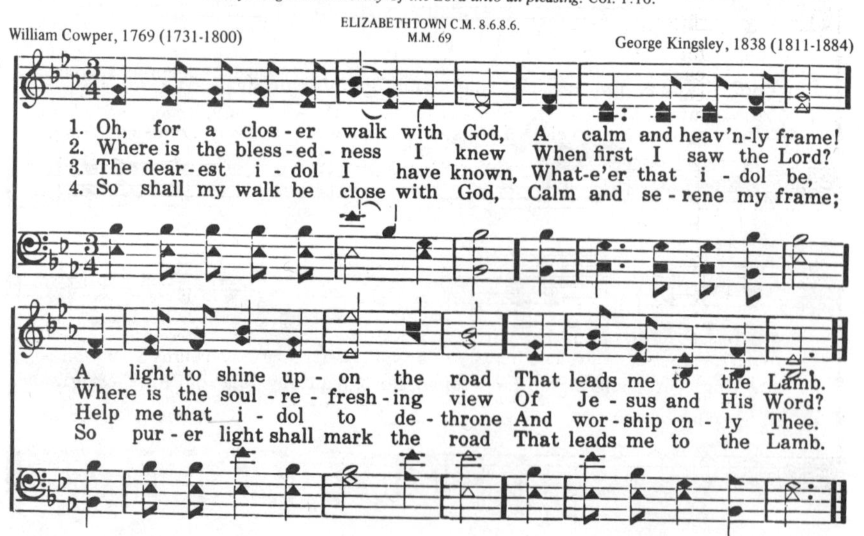
1. Oh, for a clos - er walk with God, A calm and heav'n - ly frame!
2. Where is the bless - ed - ness I knew When first I saw the Lord?
3. The dear - est i - dol I have known, What - e'er that i - dol be,
4. So shall my walk be close with God, Calm and se - rene my frame;
A light to shine up - on the road That leads me to the Lamb.
Where is the soul - re - fresh - ing view Of Je - sus and His Word?
Help me that i - dol to de - throne And wor - ship on - ly Thee.
So pur - er light shall mark the road That leads me to the Lamb.

## O LOVE THAT CASTS OUT FEAR 361

*Perfect love casteth out fear.* I Jn. 4:18.

ST. DENYS 6.6.6.6.
M.M. 80
Horatius Bonar, 1861 (1808-1889)
Frank S. Spinney, 1850-1888
1. O love that casts out fear, O love that casts out sin,
2. True sun - light of the soul, Sur-round me as I go;
3. Great love of God, come in, Well-spring of heav'n - ly peace;
4. Love of the liv - ing God, Of Fa - ther, and of Son,
Tar - ry no more with - out, But come and dwell with - in.
So shall my way be safe, My feet no stray - ing know.
Thou liv - ing wa - ter, come, Spring up, and nev - er cease.
Love of the Ho - ly Ghost, Fill Thou each need - - y one. A - MEN.

## OH, FOR A HEART TO PRAISE MY GOD 362

*I will praise Thee, O Lord, with my whole heart.* Ps. 9:1.

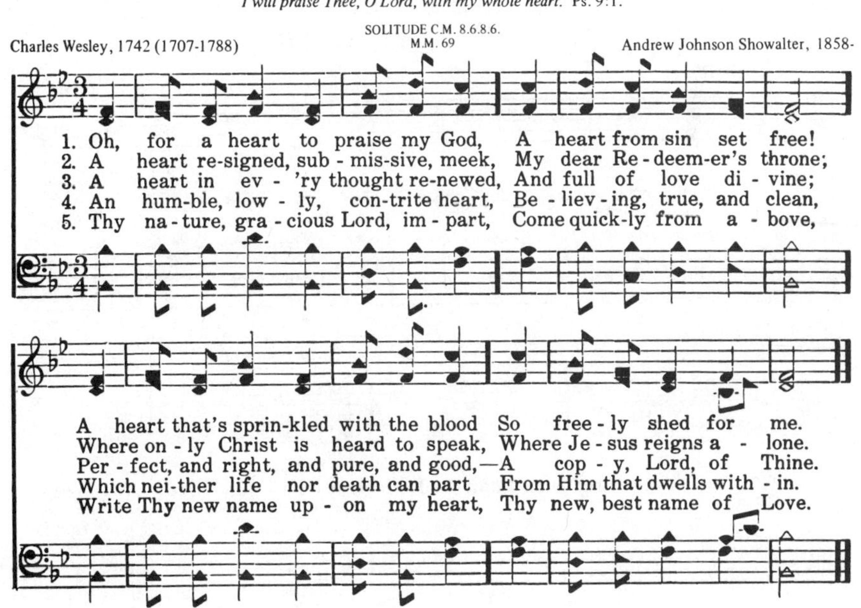
SOLITUDE C.M. 8.6.8.6.
M.M. 69
Charles Wesley, 1742 (1707-1788)
Andrew Johnson Showalter, 1858-
1. Oh, for a heart to praise my God, A heart from sin set free!
2. A heart re-signed, sub - mis-sive, meek, My dear Re - deem-er's throne;
3. A heart in ev - 'ry thought re-newed, And full of love di - vine;
4. An hum-ble, low - ly, con-trite heart, Be - liev - ing, true, and clean,
5. Thy na-ture, gra - cious Lord, im - part, Come quick-ly from a - bove,
A heart that's sprin-kled with the blood So free - ly shed for me.
Where on - ly Christ is heard to speak, Where Je - sus reigns a - lone.
Per - fect, and right, and pure, and good,—A cop - y, Lord, of Thine.
Which nei-ther life nor death can part From Him that dwells with - in.
Write Thy new name up - on my heart, Thy new, best name of Love.

# 363 JESUS, KEEP ME NEAR THE CROSS

*God forbid that I should glory, save in the cross of our Lord Jesus Christ.* Gal. 6:14.

NEAR THE CROSS 7.6.7.6. with Ref.
M.M. 96

Fanny J. Crosby, 1820-1915

William Howard Doane, 1869 (1832-1915)

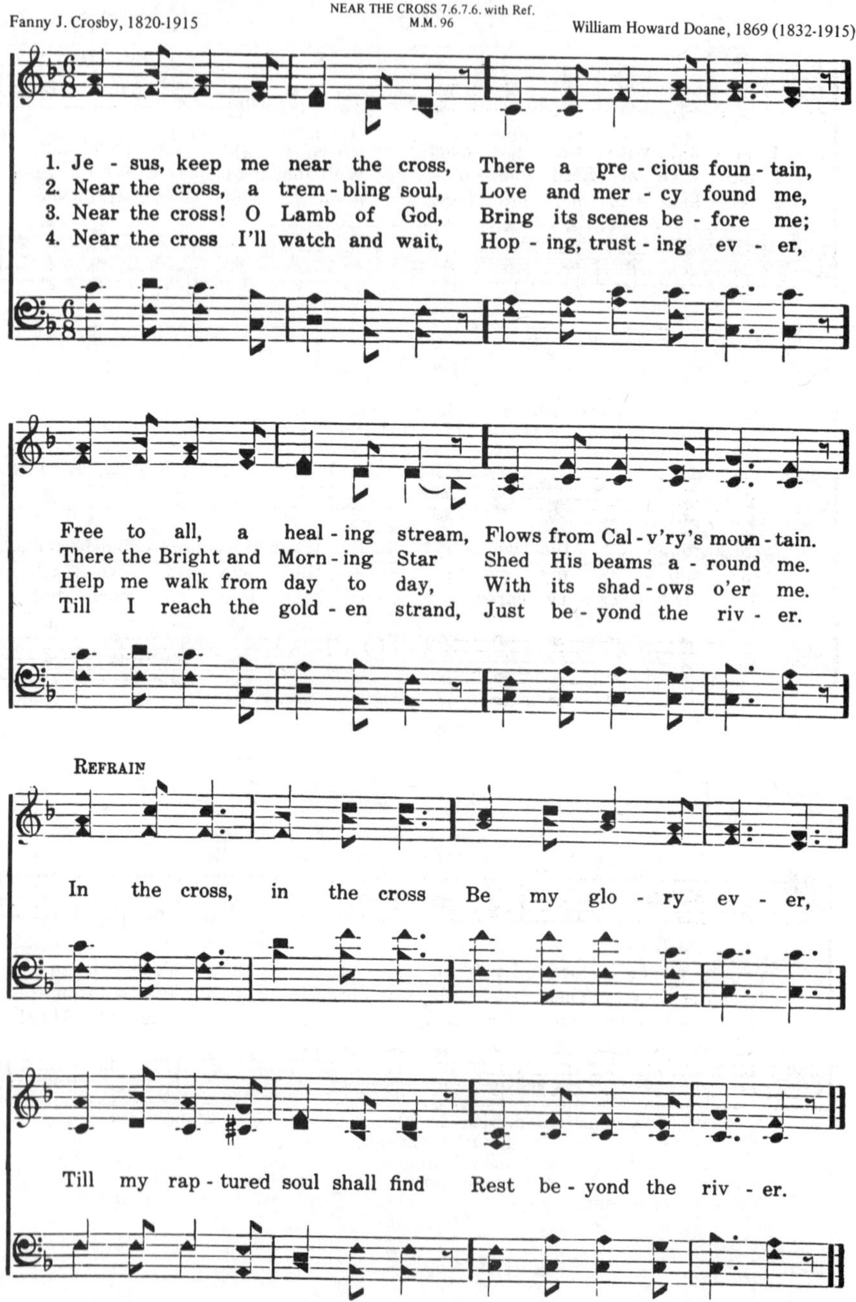
1. Je - sus, keep me near the cross, There a pre - cious foun - tain,
2. Near the cross, a trem - bling soul, Love and mer - cy found me,
3. Near the cross! O Lamb of God, Bring its scenes be - fore me;
4. Near the cross I'll watch and wait, Hop - ing, trust - ing ev - er,
Free to all, a heal - ing stream, Flows from Cal - v'ry's moun - tain.
There the Bright and Morn - ing Star Shed His beams a - round me.
Help me walk from day to day, With its shad - ows o'er me.
Till I reach the gold - en strand, Just be - yond the riv - er.
REFRAIN
In the cross, in the cross Be my glo - ry ev - er,
Till my rap - tured soul shall find Rest be - yond the riv - er.

# ABIDE WITH ME, I NEED THEE 364

*Abide with us: for it is toward evening, and the day is far spent.* Lk. 24:29.

ABIDE WITH ME 10.10.10.10.
M.M. 58

Emma G. Dietrick

Charles Edward Pollock, 1902 (b. 1853)

Slow
1. A - bide with me, I need Thee ev - 'ry day, To lead me
2. Be with me, Lord, wher - e'er my path may lead, Ful - fil Thy
3. A - bide with me, my Lord, and when at last This earth and

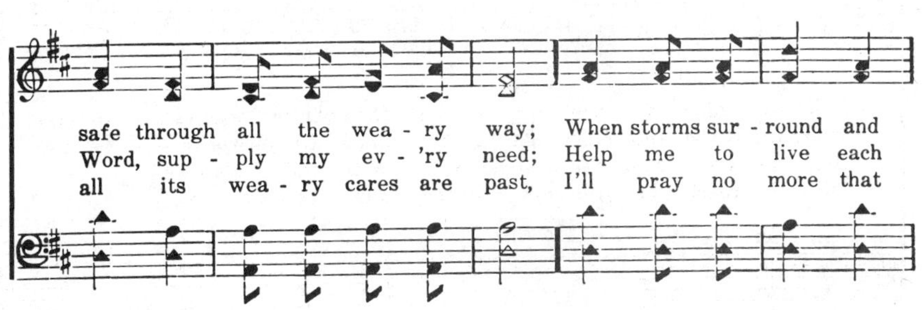
safe through all the wea - ry way; When storms sur - round and
Word, sup - ply my ev - 'ry need; Help me to live each
all its wea - ry cares are past, I'll pray no more that

on - ly clouds I see, Lord, be my com - fort and a - bide with me!
day more close to Thee, And oh, dear Lord, I pray, a - bide with me!
Thou a - bide with me, For then, at last, I shall a - bide with Thee!

# 365 I HAVE YIELDED MYSELF

*Not with eyeservice, as men-pleasers; but as the servants of Christ, doing the will of God from the heart.* Eph. 6:6.

MY HEART SAYS AMEN 10.9.10.9. with Ref.
M.M. 72

Charles W. Naylor, 1874-1950

Clarence E. Hunter, 1869-1945

1. I have yield - ed my - self to Thy serv - ice, And Thy pres - ence my bos - om doth fill; O my Sav - iour, I haste to o - bey Thee, And my heart says a - men to Thy will.
2. All the heart - ties of earth may be sun-dered, So that I may Thy pur - pose ful - fill; Help me glad - ly sub-mit and not mur - mur, Ev - er say - ing a - men to Thy will.
3. Tho' my plans and my hopes may seem blight-ed, I will love Thee and trust in Thee still, For I know all is well that Thou do - est, And my heart says a - men to Thy will.
4. When I pass to that heav - en - ly coun - try, And my soul with its glo - ry doth thrill, This for - ev - er shall be my re - joic - ing, That my heart said a - men to Thy will.
CHORUS
Yes, my heart says a - men to Thy will, Lord, And I know that Thou lov - est me still, While I bow low in hum - ble sub - mis - sion, And my heart says a - men to Thy will.

# FULLY SURRENDERED, LORD DIVINE 366

*Moreover it is required in stewards, that a man be found faithful.* I Cor. 4:2.

I WILL BE TRUE TO THEE C.M. 8.6.8.6. with Ref.
M.M. 138

Leila Naylor Morris, 1862-1929 — Leila Naylor Morris

1. Ful - ly sur - ren-dered, Lord di - vine, I will be true to Thee;
2. Tho' it may cost me friends and home, I will be true to Thee;
3. Now to the world I bid fare - well, I will be true to Thee;
4. I will go with Thee all the way, I will be true to Thee;
All that I am or have is Thine, I will be true to Thee.
Cause me in lands a - far to roam, I will be true to Thee.
Bro - ken for - ev - er its deep spell, I will be true to Thee.
All of Thy bid - ding will o - bey, I will be true to Thee.
CHORUS
I will be true to Thee, Lord, I will be true to Thee;
Where Thou lead-est me, I will fol - low Thee, I will be true to Thee.

# 367 I GAVE MY LIFE FOR THEE

*For ye are bought with a price: therefore glorify God in your body, and in your spirit, which are God's.* I Cor. 6:20.

I GAVE MY LIFE 6.6.6.6.8.6.8.6.
M.M. 120
Frances Ridley Havergal, 1852 (1836-1879)
Philip Paul Bliss, 1838-1876
1. I gave my life for thee,...... My precious blood I shed,
2. My Father's house of light,...... My glory-circled throne
3. I suffered much for thee,...... More than thy tongue can tell,
4. And I have brought to thee,...... Down from my home above,
That thou might'st ransomed be,....... And quickened from the dead;
I left, for earthly night,.... For wand'rings sad and lone;
Of bit-t'rest agony,....... To rescue thee from hell;
Salvation full and free,...... My pardon and my love;
f
I gave, I gave my life for thee, What hast thou giv'n for me?
I left, I left it all for thee, Hast thou left aught for me?
I've borne, I've borne it all for thee, What hast thou borne for me?
I bring, I bring rich gifts to thee, What hast thou brought to me?
f
I gave, I gave my life for thee, What hast thou giv'n for me?
I left, I left it all for thee, Hast thou left aught for me?
I've borne, I've borne it all for thee, What hast thou borne for me?
I bring, I bring rich gifts to thee, What hast thou brought to me?

# READY TO SUFFER 368

*I am ready not to be bound only, but also to die at Jerusalem for the name of the Lord Jesus.* Acts 21:13. *I am now ready to be offered.* II Tim. 4:6.

READY C.M. 8.6.8.6. with Ref.
M.M. 144

Ascribed to A. C. Palmer

Charles D. Tillman, 1861-1943

1. Read - y to suf-fer grief or pain, Read - y to stand the test;
2. Read - y to go, read-y to bear, Read - y to watch and pray;
3. Read - y to speak, read-y to think, Read - y with heart and brain;
4. Read - y to speak, read-y to warn, Read - y o'er souls to yearn;
Read - y to stay at home and send Oth - ers, if He sees best.
Read - y to stand a - side and give, Till He shall clear the way.
Read - y to stand where He sees fit, Read - y to bear the strain.
Read - y in life, read-y in death, Read - y for His re - turn.
CHORUS
Read - y to go, read - y to stay, Read - y my place to fill;
Read - y for serv - ice low - ly or great, Read - y to do His will.

# 369 MY LIFE, MY LOVE, I GIVE TO THEE

*I am crucified with Christ: nevertheless I live; yet not I, but Christ liveth in me.* Gal. 2:20.

I'LL LIVE FOR HIM 8.8.8.6.D.
M.M. 66

R. E. Hudson, 1834-1901

C. R. Dunbar

1. My life, my love I give to Thee, Thou Lamb of God, who died for me;
2. I now be-lieve Thou dost re-ceive, For Thou hast died that I might live;
3. Oh, Thou who died on Cal-va-ry To save my soul and make me free,
Oh, may I ev-er faith-ful be, My Sav-iour and my God!
And now hence-forth I'll trust in Thee, My Sav-iour and my God!
I'll con-se-crate my life to Thee, My Sav-iour and my God!
REFRAIN
I'll live for Him who died for me, How hap-py then my life shall be!
I'll live for Him who died for me, My Sav-iour and my God!

# HOW I PRAISE THEE 370

*For we are members of His body, of His flesh, and of His bones.* Eph. 5:30.

CHANNELS ONLY 8.7.8.7. with Ref.
M.M. 76
Mary E. Maxwell
Ada Rose Gibbs
1. How I praise Thee, pre-cious Sav - iour, That Thy love laid hold of me;
2. Emp - tied that Thou should-est fill me, A clean ves - sel in Thy hand;
3. Wit - ness-ing Thy power to save me, Set - ting free from self and sin;
4. Je - sus, fill now with Thy Spir - it Hearts that full sur - ren - der know;
Thou hast saved and cleansed and filled me That I might Thy chan-nel be.
With no power but as Thou giv - est Gra - cious-ly with each command.
Thou who bought - est to pos - sess me, In Thy full - ness, Lord, come in.
That the streams of liv - ing wa - ter From our in - ner man may flow.
CHORUS
Chan-nels on - ly, bless-ed Mas - ter, But with all Thy won-drous pow'r
Flow-ing thro' us, Thou canst use us Ev - ery day and ev - ery hour.

# 371 HAVE THINE OWN WAY, LORD

*O Lord, Thou art our Father; we are the clay, and Thou our potter; and we all are the work of Thy hand.* Is. 64:8.

HAVE THINE OWN WAY 9.9.5.4.9.
M.M. 112

Adelaide Pollard, 1862-1934 — George Coles Stebbins, 1846-1945

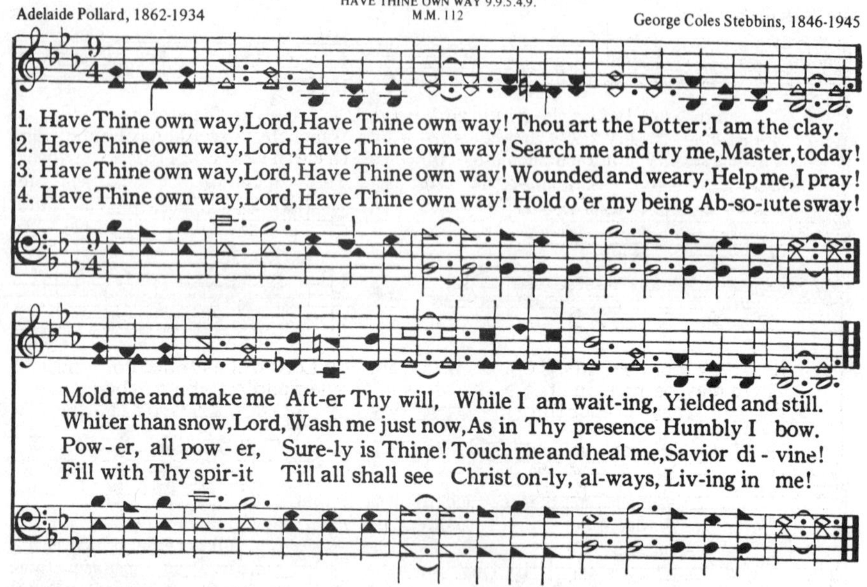
1. Have Thine own way, Lord, Have Thine own way! Thou art the Potter; I am the clay.
2. Have Thine own way, Lord, Have Thine own way! Search me and try me, Master, today!
3. Have Thine own way, Lord, Have Thine own way! Wounded and weary, Help me, I pray!
4. Have Thine own way, Lord, Have Thine own way! Hold o'er my being Ab-so-lute sway!
Mold me and make me Aft-er Thy will, While I am wait-ing, Yielded and still.
Whiter than snow, Lord, Wash me just now, As in Thy presence Humbly I bow.
Pow-er, all pow-er, Sure-ly is Thine! Touch me and heal me, Savior di-vine!
Fill with Thy spir-it Till all shall see Christ on-ly, al-ways, Liv-ing in me!

# 372 I CAN HEAR MY SAVIOUR CALLING

*I will follow Thee whithersoever Thou goest.* Lk. 9:57.

NORRIS 8.8.8.9. with Ref.
M.M. 66

E. W. Blandy — John S. Norris, 1844-1907

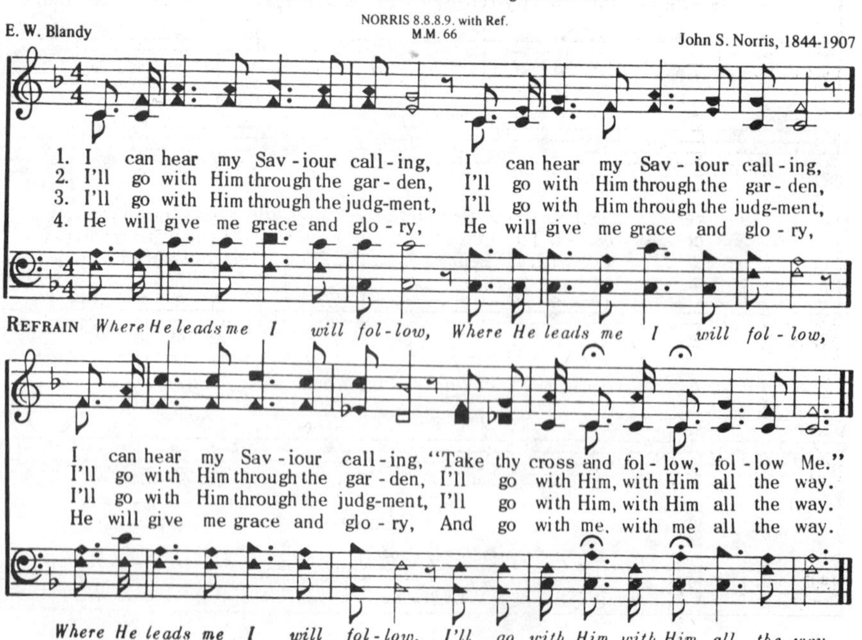
1. I can hear my Sav-iour call-ing, I can hear my Sav-iour call-ing,
2. I'll go with Him through the gar-den, I'll go with Him through the gar-den,
3. I'll go with Him through the judg-ment, I'll go with Him through the judg-ment,
4. He will give me grace and glo-ry, He will give me grace and glo-ry,
REFRAIN Where He leads me I will fol-low, Where He leads me I will fol-low,
I can hear my Sav-iour call-ing, "Take thy cross and fol-low, fol-low Me."
I'll go with Him through the gar-den, I'll go with Him, with Him all the way.
I'll go with Him through the judg-ment, I'll go with Him, with Him all the way.
He will give me grace and glo-ry, And go with me, with me all the way.
Where He leads me I will fol-low, I'll go with Him, with Him all the way.

# IT MAY NOT BE ON THE MOUNTAIN'S HEIGHT 373

*Who then is willing to consecrate his service this day unto the Lord?* I Chron. 29:5.

I'LL GO WHERE YOU WANT ME TO GO 9.7.9.7.7.9.10.8. with Ref.
M.M. 116

Charles H. Gabriel, 1859-1932 — Carrie E. Rounsefell, 1861-1930

1. It may not be on the mountain's height, Or o - ver the storm-y sea;
2. Per - haps to-day there are lov - ing words Which Jesus would have me speak;
3. There's sure-ly somewhere a low - ly place, In earth's harvest fields so wide,
It may not be at the bat-tle's front My Lord will have need of me;
There may be now in the paths of sin Some wand'rer whom I should seek;
Where I may la-bor thro' life's short day For Je - sus, the Cru - ci - fied;
But if, by a still small voice, He calls To paths that I do not know,
O Sav-ior, if Thou wilt be my guide, Tho' dark and rug-ged the way,
So trust-ing my all to Thy ten-der care, And knowing Thou lov - est me,
FINE.
I'll an-swer, dear Lord, with my hand in Thine, I'll go where you want me to go.
My voice shall ech - o Thy mes-sage sweet, I'll say what you want me to say.
I'll do Thy will with a heart sin-cere, I'll be what you want me to be.
D.S.—I'll say what you want me to say, dear Lord, I'll be what you want me to be.
CHORUS
D. S.
I'll go where you want me to go, dear Lord, O - ver mountain, or plain, or sea;

# 374 TAKE MY LIFE AND LET IT BE

*Consecrate yourselves today to the Lord.* Ex. 32:29.

HENDON 7.7.7.7.7.
M.M. 72

Frances Ridley Havergal, 1874 (1836-1879) — Abraham Henry Caesar, 1787-1864

1. Take my life, and let it be Con - se - crat - ed, Lord, to
2. Take my feet, and let them be Swift and beau - ti - ful for
3. Take my lips, and let them be Filled with mes - sag - es from
4. Take my will and make it Thine; It shall be no long - er
5. Take my love; my Lord, I pour At Thy feet its treas - ure -

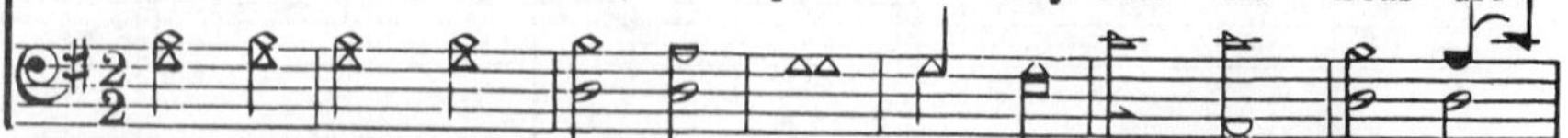

Thee; Take my hands, and let them move At the im - pulse
Thee; Take my voice, and let me sing Al - ways, on - ly,
Thee; Take my sil - ver and my gold, Not a mite would
mine; Take my heart, it is Thine own! It shall be Thy
store; Take my - self, and I will be, Ev - er, on - ly,

of Thy love, At the im - pulse of Thy love.
for my King, Al - ways, on - ly, for my King.
I with - hold, Not a mite would I with - hold.
roy - al throne, It shall be Thy roy - al throne.
all for Thee, Ev - er, on - ly, all for Thee. A - men.

# 375 TAKE MY LIFE AND LET IT BE

*Yield yourselves unto God . . . and your members as instruments of righteousness unto God.* Rom. 6:13.

YARBROUGH 7.7.7.7.7.
M.M. 138

Frances Ridley Havergal, 1874 (1836-1879) — William Batchelder Bradbury (1816-1868)

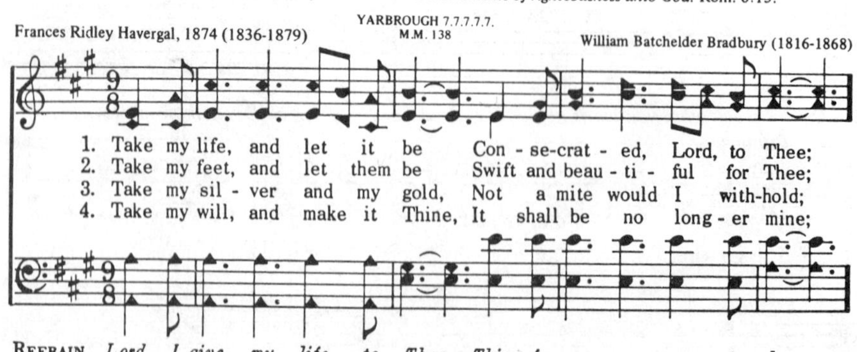
1. Take my life, and let it be Con - se-crat - ed, Lord, to Thee;
2. Take my feet, and let them be Swift and beau - ti - ful for Thee;
3. Take my sil - ver and my gold, Not a mite would I with-hold;
4. Take my will, and make it Thine, It shall be no long - er mine;
REFRAIN Lord, I give my life to Thee, Thine for-ev - er - more to be;

D. C.
Take my hands and let them move At the im-pulse of Thy love.
Take my voice and let me sing Al - ways, on - ly, for my King.
Take my mo-ments and my days, Let them flow in cease-less praise.
Take my heart, it is Thine own, It shall be Thy roy - al throne.
Lord, I give my life to Thee, Thine for-ev - er - more to be.

# SAVIOUR, WHO DIED FOR ME 376

*Who His own self bare our sins in His own body on the tree, that we, being dead to sins, should live unto righteousness.* I Pet. 2:24.

I GIVE MYSELF TO THEE 6.6.6.4.6.6.6.4.
M.M. 84

Mary Jane Mason, b. 1822 — Daniel Brink Towner, 1850-1919

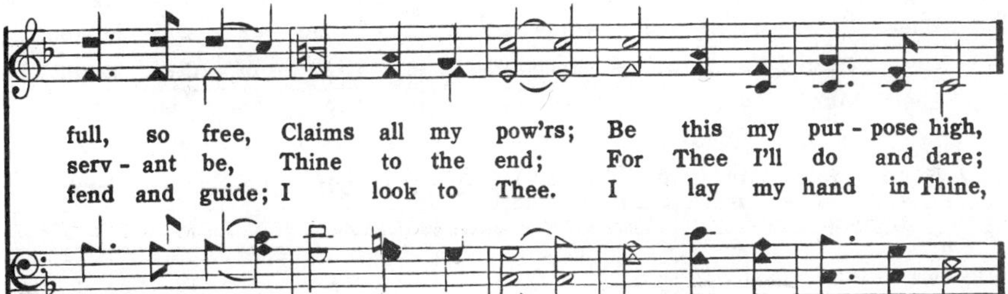

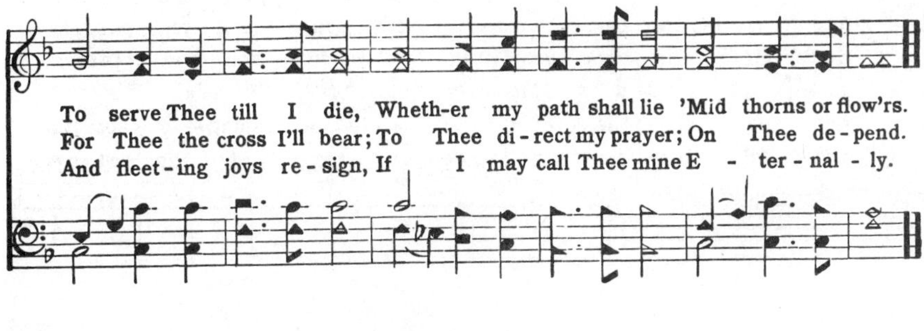

1. Sav - iour, who died for me, I give my-self to Thee; Thy love so full, so free, Claims all my pow'rs; Be this my pur - pose high, To serve Thee till I die, Wheth-er my path shall lie 'Mid thorns or flow'rs.

2. May it be joy to me To fol - low on - ly Thee; Thy faith-ful serv - ant be, Thine to the end; For Thee I'll do and dare; For Thee the cross I'll bear; To Thee di - rect my prayer; On Thee de - pend.

3. Sav - iour, with me a - bide; Be ev - er near my side; Sup - port, de - fend and guide; I look to Thee. I lay my hand in Thine, And fleet - ing joys re - sign, If I may call Thee mine E - ter - nal - ly.

# 377 O COME TO MOUNT ZION

*We are journeying unto the place of which the Lord said, I will give it you: come thou with us, and we will do thee good: for the Lord hath spoken good concerning Israel.* Num. 10:29.

S. C. E.
*Hymns of Zion,* 1841
Alt., John J. Overholt, 1970

IHR KINDERLEIN KOMMET 11.11.11.11.
M.M. 72

Johann Abraham Peter Schulz, 1747-1800

1. O come to Mount Zi – on, the mount of the Lord!
Come breathe of the o – dour of Sha – ron's bright rose,
Where ol – ives and vines spread their branch – es a – broad,
And hal – low its beau – ty with peace and re – pose.

2. Come ye that are thirst – y, and drink of the fount!
Come wor – ship in beau – ty of ho – li – ness here;
Our Christ all – tri – um – phant, is King of the mount!
Come, yield Him the heart in de – vo – tion and fear.

3. The Lamb slain at Cal – v'ry, whose blood can make white
The robes of all na – tions be – neath the broad skies,
Shall lead you to wa – ters of life and de – light,
And God shall wipe soft – ly the tears from all eyes.

4. Ye who are an hun–gered, in thank – ful – ness come,
And free – ly par – take of the life – giv – ing bread;
In man – sions of mer – cy there ev – er is room,
And ev – er the feast is a – bun – dant – ly spread.

5. O come to Mount Zi – on, the ho – ly of God!
And sing the new song of sal – va – tion and praise;
Come walk in the path – way our Sav – iour hath trod,
And fol – low in meek – ness the least of His ways.

# CHURCH OF GOD, THOU SPOTLESS VIRGIN 378

*I will build my church.* Mt. 16:18. *The church of the living God, the pillar and ground of the truth.* I Tim. 3:15
*They were all with one accord in one place.* Acts 2:1. . . . *The Lord added to the church daily. . .* Acts 2:47.

Frances Ridley Havergal, 1873 (1836-1879)
Alt. Daniel S. Warner, 1842-1895
Altered by Compiler, 1970

CHURCH OF GOD 8.7.8.7.D.
M.M. 76

Benjamin Carl Unseld, 1843-1923

1. Church of God, thou spot–less vir–gin, Church of Christ, for whom He died,
2. God him–self has set the mem–bers In his bod – y all com–plete,
3. Church of God, "be–lov–ed cit – y," Thou art of ce–les–tial mold;
4. God's own ho – li – ness with–in Thee, His own beau – ty on thy brow;
5. Church of God, in heav–en writ–ten, Thine the ris – en life of Christ,
Thou hast known no hu – man found – er, Je – sus bought thee for his bride;
Or – gan – ized by Je–sus on – ly, Oh, the un – ion pure and sweet;
Lo! from God and out of heav – en, Came the cit – y of pure gold;
Glo – ri – fied in his own im – age, This thy won–drous por–tion now;
And the treas – ures to thee giv – en, Nev – er, nev – er can be priced;
Sanc – ti – fied by God the Fa – ther, Built by Je–sus Christ, the Son,
Church of God, the an–gels mar – vel At the mu – sic of thy song;
Stones of jas - per, clear as crys–tal Is the build – ing of thy wall;
In thee dwells the tri – une full–ness, Bless–ing all thy pil–grim days;
Far a – bove this world's con–fu – sion, Walk – ing close by Je – sus' side,
Tem–pered by the Ho – ly Spir – it, Like the Ho – ly Three in One.
Earth and hell in ter – ror trem – ble, As thy ar – my moves a–long.
And the Lamb, thy light for – ev – er, Je – sus, Je – sus, all in all.
All a – round thee his sal – va – tion, And be–fore thee gates of praise.
Lean–ing on his lov – ing bos–om, Is the church, his chos–en bride.

# 379 THE CHURCH'S ONE FOUNDATION

*For other foundation can no man lay than that is laid, which is Jesus Christ.* I Cor. 3:11.

Samuel John Stone, 1865 (1839-1900) AURELIA 7.6.7.6.D. M.M. 108 Samuel Sebastian Wesley, 1864, (1810-1876)

1. The Church's one Foun - da - tion Is Je - sus Christ her Lord;
2. E - lect from ev - 'ry na - tion, Yet one o'er all the earth,
3. 'Mid toil and trib - u - la - tion, And tu - mult of her war,
4. Yet she on earth hath un - ion With God the Three in One,
She is His new cre - a - tion By wa - ter and the Word:
Her char - ter of sal - va - tion One Lord, one faith, one birth:
She waits the con - sum - ma - tion Of peace for - ev - er - more;
And mys - tic, sweet com - mun - ion With those whose rest is won:
From heav'n He came and sought her To be His ho - ly Bride;
One ho - ly name she bless - es, Par-takes one ho - ly food,
Till with the vi - sion glo - rious Her long - ing eyes are blest,
O hap - py ones and ho - ly! Lord, give us grace that we
With His own blood He bought her, And for her life He died.
And to one hope she press - es, With ev - 'ry grace en - dued.
And the great Church vic - to - rious Shall be the Church at rest.
Like them, the meek and low - ly, On high may dwell with Thee.

# CHRIST IS OUR CORNERSTONE 380

*Built upon the foundation of the apostles and prophets, Jesus Christ Himself being the chief corner stone.* Eph. 2:20.

Anonymous Latin, 6th century
*Angularis fundamentum*
Tr. John Chandler, 1837 (1806-1876)

DARWALL 148 6.6.6.6.8.8.
M.M. 96

John Darwall, 1770 (1731-1789)

1 Christ is our cor - ner - stone, On Him a - lone we build;
2 O then with hymns of praise These hal - low'd courts shall ring;
3 Here, gra - cious God, do Thou For ev - er - more draw nigh;
4 Here may we gain from heav'n The grace which we im - plore;
With His true saints a - lone The courts of heav'n are filled:
Our voic - es we will raise The three in one to sing;
Ac - cept each faith - ful vow, And mark each sup - pliant sigh;
And may that grace, once given, Be with us ev - er - more,
On His great love our hopes we place Of
And thus pro - claim in joy - ful song Both
In co - pious shower on all who pray Each
Un - til that day when all the blest To
pres - ent grace and joys a - bove.
loud and long that glo - rious name.
ho - ly day Thy bless - ings pour!
end - less rest are called a - way! A - men.

# 381 GLORIOUS THINGS OF THEE ARE SPOKEN

*Glorious things are spoken of thee, O city of God.* Ps. 87:3.

GLORIOUS THINGS 8.7.8.7.D.
M.M. 72

John Newton, 1779 (1725-1807)
Jacob Henry Hall, 1855-1941
Not too fast.
1. Glo-rious things of thee are spo-ken, Zi - on, cit - y of our God;
2. See the streams of liv - ing wat-ers, Springing from e - ter - nal Love,
3. Round each hab - i - ta - tion hov'ring, See the cloud and fire ap - pear
4. Sav - iour, if of Zi - on's cit - y I, through grace, a mem - ber am,
He whose word can - not be bro-ken Formed thee for His own a - bode:
Well sup-ply thy sons and daughters, And all fear of want re-move:
For a glo - ry and a cov'ring, Show - ing that the Lord is near:
Let the world de - ride or pit - y, I will glo - ry in Thy name:
On the Rock of A - ges found-ed, What can shake thy sure re - pose?
Who can faint while such a riv - er Ev - er flows their thirst to assuage;
Thus de - riv - ing from their ban - ner Light by night and shade by day,
Fad - ing is the world-ling's pleas-ure, All his boast - ed pomp and show:
m
f
With sal - va - tion's walls sur-round-ed, Thou mayst smile at all thy foes.
Grace which, like the Lord the Giv - er, Nev - er fails from age to age?
Safe they feed up - on the man - na Which He gives them when they pray.
Sol - id joys and last - ing treas-ure None but Zi - on's chil - dren know.

# ZION STANDS WITH HILLS SURROUNDED 382

*Like as the lion and the young lion roaring on his prey . . . so shall the Lord of hosts come down to fight for mount Zion.* Is. 31:4. *He that toucheth you toucheth the apple of His eye.* Zech. 2:8.

Thomas Kelley, 1806 (1769-1855)
ZION 8.7.8.7.4.7.
M.M. 66
Thomas Hastings, 1784-1872
1. Zi - on stands with hills sur-round - ed, Zi - on, kept by pow'r di - vine;
2. Ev - 'ry hu - man tie may per - ish; Friend to friend un - faith - ful prove;
3. In the fur - nace God may prove thee, Thence to bring thee forth more bright,
All her foes shall be con-found - ed, Tho' the world in arms com - bine:
Moth - ers cease their own to cher - ish; Heav'n and earth at last re - move;
But can nev - er cease to love thee: Thou art pre - cious in His sight:
Hap - py Zi - on, What a fa - vor'd lot is thine!
But no chang - es Can at - tend Je - ho - vah's love;
God is with thee, God thine ev - er - last - ing light;
Hap - py Zi - on, What a fa - vor'd lot is thine.
But no chang - es Can at - tend Je - ho - vah's love.
God is with thee, God thine ev - er - last - ing light. A-MEN.

# 383 UNTO THY TEMPLE, LORD, WE COME

*Ye are the temple of God.* I Cor. 3:16. *In whom all the building fitly framed together groweth unto an holy temple in the Lord.* Eph. 2:21.

Robert Collyer, 1873 (1823-1912) — MENDON L.M. 8.8.8.8. M.M. 104 — Samuel Dryer, 1828 (1785-1853)

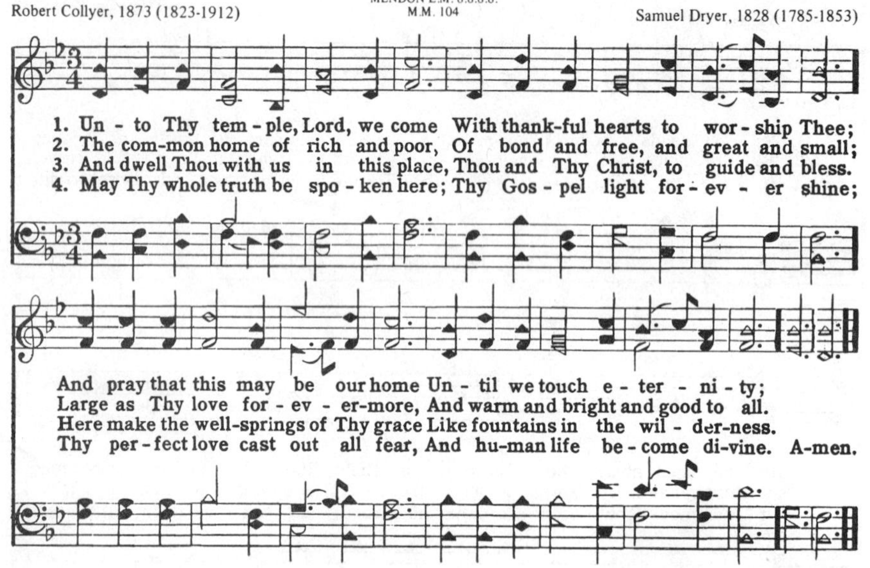

1. Un - to Thy tem - ple, Lord, we come With thank-ful hearts to wor - ship Thee;
2. The com-mon home of rich and poor, Of bond and free, and great and small;
3. And dwell Thou with us in this place, Thou and Thy Christ, to guide and bless.
4. May Thy whole truth be spo - ken here; Thy Gos - pel light for - ev - er shine;
And pray that this may be our home Un - til we touch e - ter - ni - ty;
Large as Thy love for - ev - er-more, And warm and bright and good to all.
Here make the well-springs of Thy grace Like fountains in the wil - der-ness.
Thy per - fect love cast out all fear, And hu-man life be - come di-vine. A-men.

# 384 UNTO THY CHURCH, THY BODY, LORD

*So we, being many, are one body in Christ, and every one members one of another.* Rom. 12:5.

Samuel Francis Smith, 1843 (1808-1895)
Altered by Compiler, 1971 — JAZER C.M. 8.6.8.6. M.M. 100 — William Batchelder Bradbury, 1816-1868

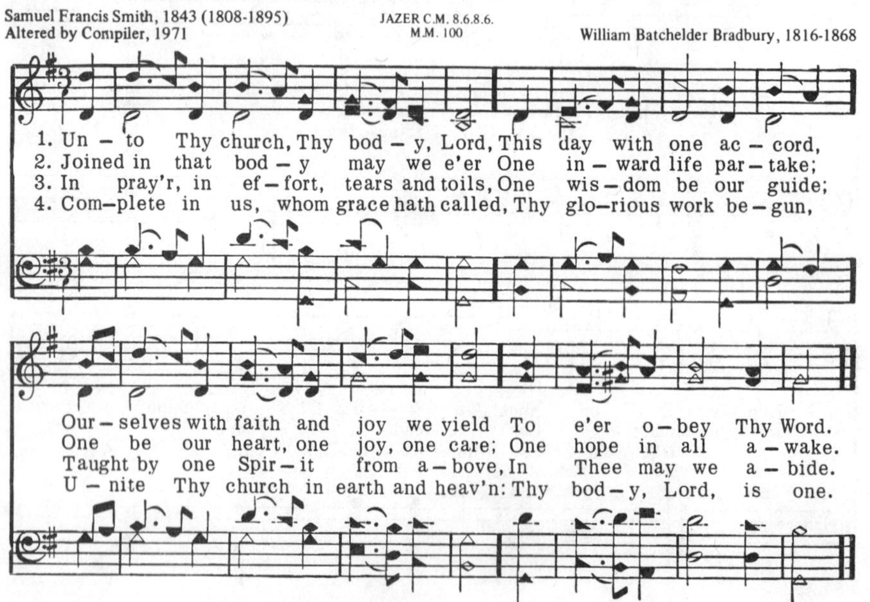

1. Un – to Thy church, Thy bod – y, Lord, This day with one ac – cord,
2. Joined in that bod – y may we e'er One in – ward life par – take;
3. In pray'r, in ef – fort, tears and toils, One wis – dom be our guide;
4. Com–plete in us, whom grace hath called, Thy glo–rious work be – gun,
Our – selves with faith and joy we yield To e'er o – bey Thy Word.
One be our heart, one joy, one care; One hope in all a – wake.
Taught by one Spir – it from a – bove, In Thee may we a – bide.
U – nite Thy church in earth and heav'n: Thy bod – y, Lord, is one.

## OUR BLEST REDEEMER 385

*In whom ye also are builded together for an habitation of God through the Spirit.* Eph. 2:22. *Your body is the temple of the Holy Ghost.* I Cor. 6:19.

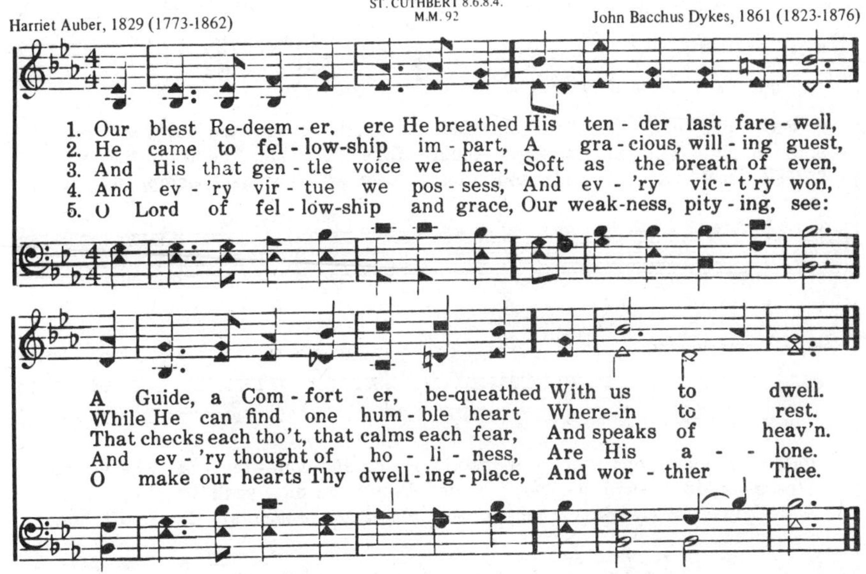
ST. CUTHBERT 8.6.8.4.
M.M. 92
Harriet Auber, 1829 (1773-1862)
John Bacchus Dykes, 1861 (1823-1876)
1. Our blest Re-deem - er, ere He breathed His ten - der last fare - well,
2. He came to fel - low-ship im - part, A gra - cious, will - ing guest,
3. And His that gen - tle voice we hear, Soft as the breath of even,
4. And ev - 'ry vir - tue we pos - sess, And ev - 'ry vic - t'ry won,
5. O Lord of fel - low-ship and grace, Our weak-ness, pity - ing, see:
A Guide, a Com - fort - er, be-queathed With us to dwell.
While He can find one hum - ble heart Where-in to rest.
That checks each tho't, that calms each fear, And speaks of heav'n.
And ev - 'ry thought of ho - li - ness, Are His a - - lone.
O make our hearts Thy dwell - ing - place, And wor - thier Thee.

## WITHIN THY TABERNACLE, LORD 386

*Judgment must begin at the house of God.* I Pet. 4:17. *Ye are the temple of the living God.* II Cor. 6:16.

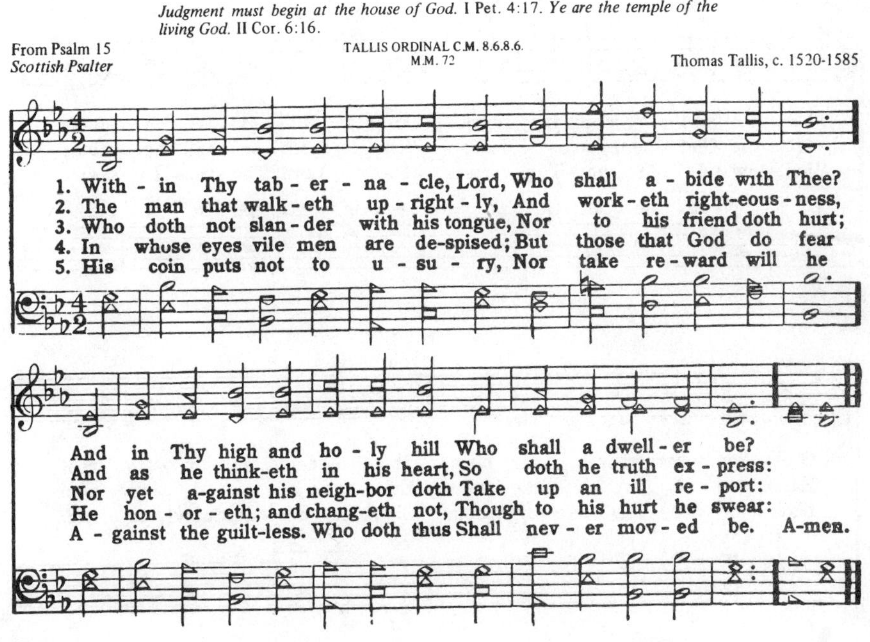
From Psalm 15
*Scottish Psalter*
TALLIS ORDINAL C.M. 8.6.8.6.
M.M. 72
Thomas Tallis, c. 1520-1585
1. With - in Thy tab - er - na - cle, Lord, Who shall a - bide with Thee?
2. The man that walk - eth up - right - ly, And work - eth right-eous - ness,
3. Who doth not slan - der with his tongue, Nor to his friend doth hurt;
4. In whose eyes vile men are de-spised; But those that God do fear
5. His coin puts not to u - su - ry, Nor take re - ward will he
And in Thy high and ho - ly hill Who shall a dwell - er be?
And as he think-eth in his heart, So doth he truth ex - press:
Nor yet a-gainst his neigh-bor doth Take up an ill re - port:
He hon - or - eth; and chang-eth not, Though to his hurt he swear:
A - gainst the guilt-less. Who doth thus Shall nev - er mov - ed be. A-men.

# 387 PEOPLE OF THE LIVING GOD

*Fellow citizens with the saints, and of the household of God.* Eph. 2:19.

James Montgomery, 1829 (1771-1854)

ENNIUS 7.7.7.7.D.
M.M. 72

*Harmonia Sacra*

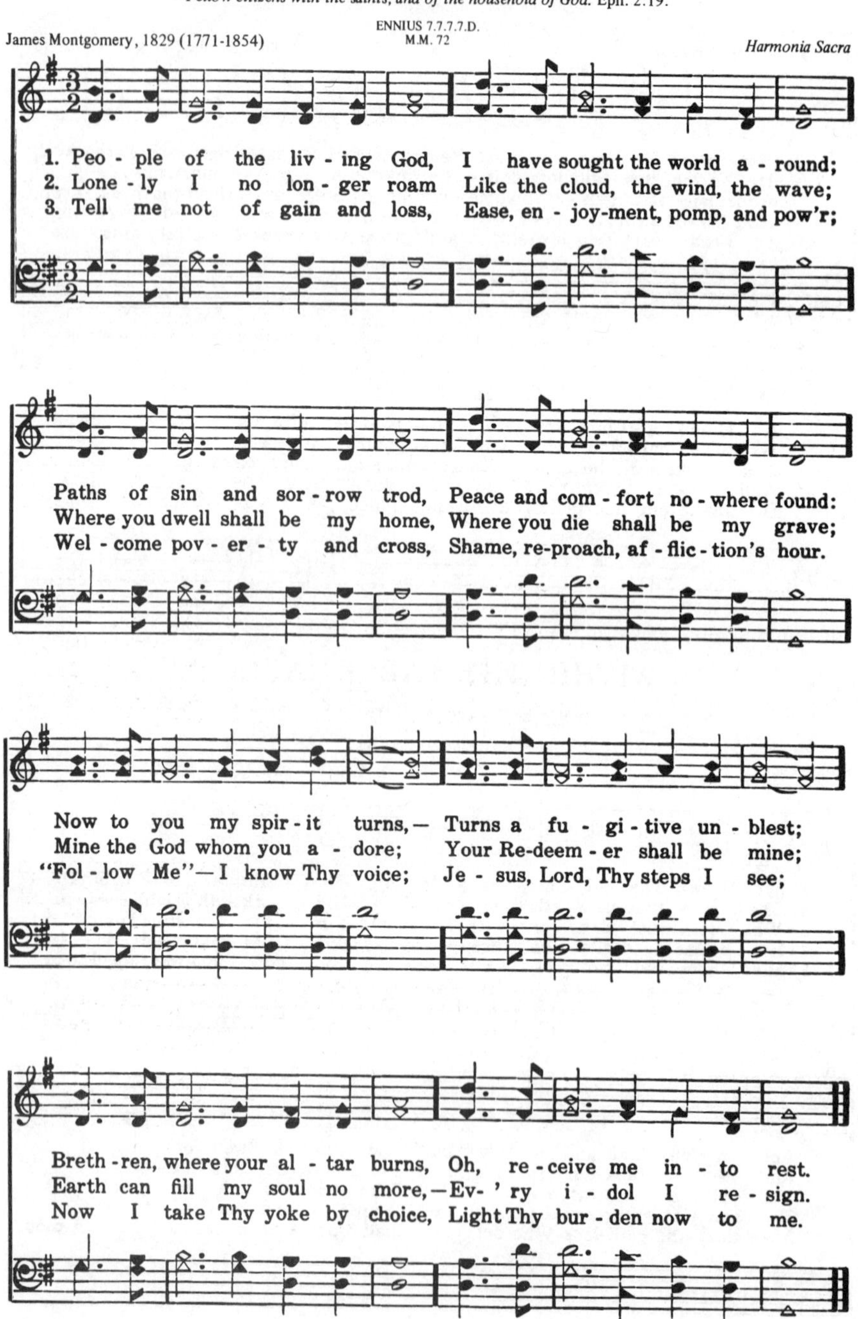
1. Peo - ple of the liv - ing God, I have sought the world a - round;
2. Lone - ly I no lon - ger roam Like the cloud, the wind, the wave;
3. Tell me not of gain and loss, Ease, en - joy-ment, pomp, and pow'r;
Paths of sin and sor - row trod, Peace and com - fort no - where found:
Where you dwell shall be my home, Where you die shall be my grave;
Wel - come pov - er - ty and cross, Shame, re-proach, af - flic - tion's hour.
Now to you my spir - it turns,— Turns a fu - gi - tive un - blest;
Mine the God whom you a - dore; Your Re-deem - er shall be mine;
"Fol - low Me"—I know Thy voice; Je - sus, Lord, Thy steps I see;
Breth - ren, where your al - tar burns, Oh, re - ceive me in - to rest.
Earth can fill my soul no more,—Ev- 'ry i - dol I re - sign.
Now I take Thy yoke by choice, Light Thy bur - den now to me.

# COME, LET US RISE WITH CHRIST 388

*If ye then be risen with Christ, seek those things which are above.* Col. 3:1.

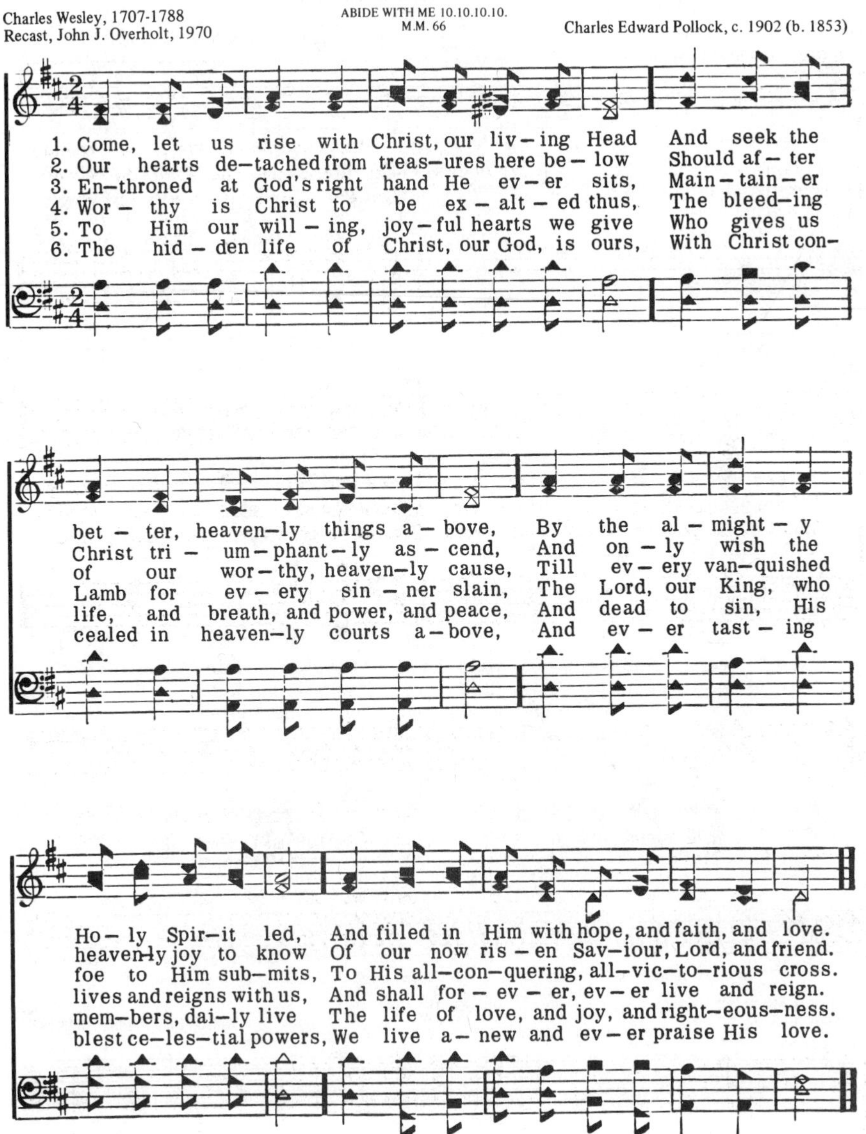
Charles Wesley, 1707-1788
Recast, John J. Overholt, 1970
ABIDE WITH ME 10.10.10.10.
M.M. 66
Charles Edward Pollock, c. 1902 (b. 1853)
1. Come, let us rise with Christ, our liv–ing Head And seek the
2. Our hearts de–tached from treas–ures here be–low Should af–ter
3. En–throned at God's right hand He ev–er sits, Main–tain–er
4. Wor–thy is Christ to be ex–alt–ed thus, The bleed–ing
5. To Him our will–ing, joy–ful hearts we give Who gives us
6. The hid–den life of Christ, our God, is ours, With Christ con-
bet–ter, heaven–ly things a–bove, By the al–might–y
Christ tri–um–phant–ly as–cend, And on–ly wish the
of our wor–thy, heaven–ly cause, Till ev–ery van–quished
Lamb for ev–ery sin–ner slain, The Lord, our King, who
life, and breath, and power, and peace, And dead to sin, His
cealed in heaven–ly courts a–bove, And ev–er tast–ing
Ho–ly Spir–it led, And filled in Him with hope, and faith, and love.
heaven–ly joy to know Of our now ris–en Sav–iour, Lord, and friend.
foe to Him sub–mits, To His all–con–quering, all–vic–to–rious cross.
lives and reigns with us, And shall for–ev–er, ev–er live and reign.
mem–bers, dai–ly live The life of love, and joy, and right–eous–ness.
blest ce–les–tial powers, We live a–new and ev–er praise His love.

# 389 THE CHURCH OF GOD A KINGDOM IS

*Who . . . hath translated us into the kingdom of His dear Son.* Col. 1:13. *Your brother and companion in tribulation, and in the kingdom and patience of Jesus Christ.* Rev. 1:9.

SO LANGE JESUS BLEIBT DER HERR
L.M. 8.8.8.8.
M.M. 66

Lionel Muirhead, 1845-1925
Alt. John J. Overholt, 1970

*Choralbuch der Mennoniten Gemeinden Russlands*
Halbstadt, 1914

1. The church of God a king–dom is, Where Christ in pow'r doth live and reign; Where ho–ly sub–jects dwell in bliss, And fruits of right–eous–ness at–tain.
2. Glad com–pa–nies of saints pos–sess This glor–ious church be–low, a–bove; And God's per–pet–ual calm doth bless This par–a–dise of won–drous love.
3. Our Sav–iour lives with–in this shrine, Our Lord, for sin once sac–ri–ficed; Our King, im–mac–u–late, di–vine, The Lamb of God, the liv–ing Christ.
4. Here rich and poor, from count–less lands, Praise God, the giv–er of all good; Here na–tions reach forth ho–ly hands, To bless and take God's ho–ly food. A–men

5. Here pure life–giving streams o'erflow
The Sower's fruitful garden–ground;
And faith and hope fair blossoms show,
And fruits of love grow and abound.

6. O King, O Christ, this endless grace
Do Thou to us and all men bring;
Thy great salvation to embrace,
And own Thee ever, Lord and King.

# 390 GLORIOUS KINGDOM OF OUR GOD

*That ye would walk worthy of God, Who hath called you into His kingdom and glory.* I Thess. 2:12.

Wilmer D. Swope, 1970
Alt. John J. Overholt, 1970

INNOCENTS 7.7.7.7.
M.M. 84

From a Parish Hymnal
William Henry Monk, 1823-1889

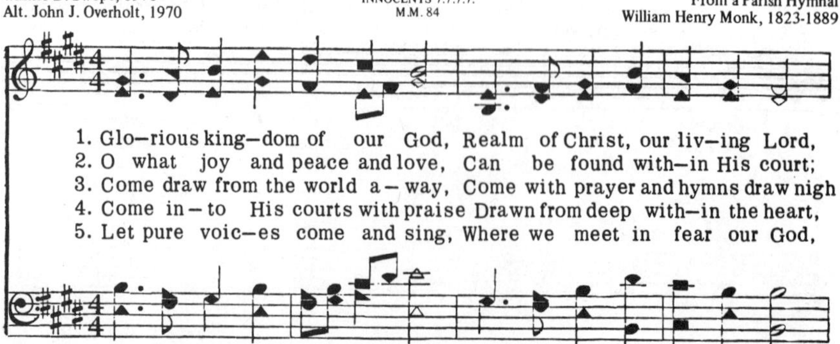
1. Glo–rious king–dom of our God, Realm of Christ, our liv–ing Lord,
2. O what joy and peace and love, Can be found with–in His court;
3. Come draw from the world a–way, Come with prayer and hymns draw nigh
4. Come in–to His courts with praise Drawn from deep with–in the heart,
5. Let pure voic–es come and sing, Where we meet in fear our God,

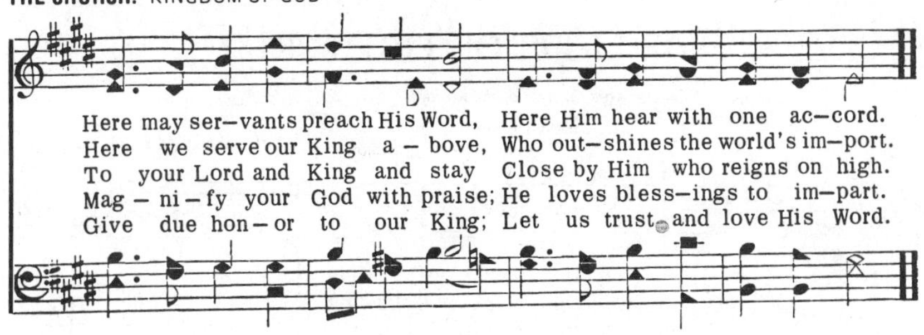
Here may ser–vants preach His Word, Here Him hear with one ac–cord.
Here we serve our King a – bove, Who out–shines the world's im–port.
To your Lord and King and stay Close by Him who reigns on high.
Mag – ni – fy your God with praise; He loves bless–ings to im–part.
Give due hon – or to our King; Let us trust and love His Word.

**THE CHURCH:** CHRIST'S GARDEN

# CHRIST HATH A GARDEN WALLED AROUND 391

*Thou shalt be like a watered garden, and like a spring of water, whose waters fail not.* Is. 58:11.

LOUVAN L.M. 8.8.8.8.
M.M. 80

Isaac Watts, 1674-1748

Virgil Corydon Taylor, 1817-1891

1. Christ hath a gar – den walled a – round, A Par – a – dise of fruit – ful ground, Cho – sen by love and fenced by grace From out the world's wide wil – der – ness.
2. Like trees of spice His serv – ants stand, There plant – ed by His might – y hand; By E – den's gra – cious streams that flow To feed their beau – ty where they grow.
3. A – wake, O wind of heav'n, and bear Their sweet – est per – fume through the air; Stir up, O south, the boughs that bloom, Till the be – lov – ed Mas – ter come.
4. That He may come, and lin – ger yet A – mong the trees that He hath set; That He may ev – er – more be seen To walk a – mid the spring–ing green.

# 392 YE ARE THE LIGHT OF THE WORLD

*Ye are the light of the world.* Mt. 5:14.
YE ARE THE LIGHT 7.7.7.7.D.
M.M. 80
R. J. Craig
John David Brunk, 1872-1926
1. Ye are the light of the world, Driv - ing the dark-ness a - way,
2. Ye are the light of the world, Caus - ing the clouds to de - part,
3. Ye are the light of the world; Thro' you the true light must shine,
Shed-ding your beams on the lost, Chang-ing their night in - to day.
Throw-ing the sun - shine of peace Down on the poor bur-dened heart.
Call - ing the lost sons of men Home to the Fa - ther di - vine.
Then let your light ev - er shine, Show - ing the right way to go;
Then let your light ev - er shine; Loved ones are pant - ing for rest;
Then let your light ev - er shine, Hal - low the name that is love;
Glad - ly the lost ones will see— God's bound-less love they will know.
Sun-shine their souls will re - vive, Lift - ing them up to the blest.
You will each shine as a star, Fixed in the or - bit a - bove.

# FORWARD FLOCK OF JESUS 393

*Ye are the salt of the earth.* Mt. 5:13.

Henry Alford, 1871 (1810-1871)
Alt. John J. Overholt, 1969

ST. GERTRUDE 6.5.6.5.D. with Ref.
M.M. 88

Arthur Seymour Sullivan, 1842-1900

1. For–ward, flock of Je–sus, Salt of all the earth, Till our yearning pur–pose
2. For–ward! be our watch–word, Steps and voices join'd; Seeking things before us,
3. Glor–ies up–on glor–ies, Hath our God pre–pared, For those who o–bey him,
4. Far o'er yon hor–i–zon, Rise the ci–ty towers Where our God a–bid–eth;

Springs to glor–ious birth; Sick, men ask for heal–ing, Blind, they grope for day;
To all else dis–joined, Burns the fie–ry pil–lar, At our van–guard's head;
One day to be shared; Eye hath not be–held them, Ear hath ne–ver heard;
That fair home is ours; Flash the streets with jasper, Shine the gates with gold;

Shine up–on the nat–ions salvation's lov–ing ray, Forward, heal–ing er–ror,
Who shall dream of shrink–ing, By Je–ho–vah led? Forward, till the des–ert,
And of these hath ut–tered, Hardly speech a word; Forward, marching heav'nward,
Flows the glad'–ning ri–ver, Shedding joys un–told; Pilgrims, upward trav–ling,

Faith dis–pel–ing night! Forward, through the darkness! Forward into light!
Yields to salt and light, Jordan flows be–fore us, Zi–on crowns the fight!
Liv–ing salt and light, Till the veil is lift–ed, Till our faith is sight!
In Je–ho–vah's might; Pilgrims, to your coun–try, For–ward in–to light!

# 394 LEADER OF FAITHFUL SOULS

*These all died in faith . . . and confessed that they were strangers and pilgrims on the earth.* Heb. 11:13.

Charles Wesley, 1747 (1797-1788)
Altered by Compiler, 1970

STELLA 8.8.8.8.8.8.
M.M. 84

*Easy Tunes*, 1852

1. Lead – er of faith – ful souls, and Guide Of all that
2. Stran – gers and pil – grims here be – low, This earth, we
3. We've no a – bid – ing cit – y here, But seek a
4. Pa – tient the ap – point – ed race to run, This wea – ry
5. Through Thee, who all our sins hast borne, Free – ly and
6. Raised by the breath of love di – vine, We urge our
trav – el to the sky, Come and with us, e'en us a – bide,
know, is not our place; But has – ten through the vale of woe,
cit – y out of sight; Thith – er our stead – y course we steer,
world we cast be – hind; From strength to strength we trav – el on,
gra – cious – ly for – given, With songs to Zi – on we re – turn,
way with strength re – newed; The church of the first – born to join,
Thy pil – grims who on Thee re – ly; On Thee a –
And rest – less to be – hold Thy face, Swift to our
As – pir – ing to the plains of light, Je – ru – sa –
The New Je – ru – sa – lem to find; Our on – ly
Con – tend – ing for our na – tive heaven; That pal – ace
We trav – el to the mount of God; With joy up –
lone our spir – its stay, While held in life's un – ev – en way.
heaven – ly coun – try move Our ev – er – last – ing home a – bove.
lem, the saints' a bode, Whose found – er is the liv – ing God.
aim, our la – bor this, To bring man – kind to Christ and bliss.
of our glo – rious King, We find it near – er while we sing.
on our heads we rise, And meet our Sav – iour in the skies. A – men.

# WE ARE PILGRIMS ON THE EARTH 395

*For we are strangers before Thee, and sojourners, as were all our fathers: our days on the earth are as a shadow, and there is none abiding.* I Chron. 29:15.

John J. Overholt, 1971 — CAPETOWN 7.7.7.7. M.M. 80 — Frederick Filitz, 1847 (1804-1876)

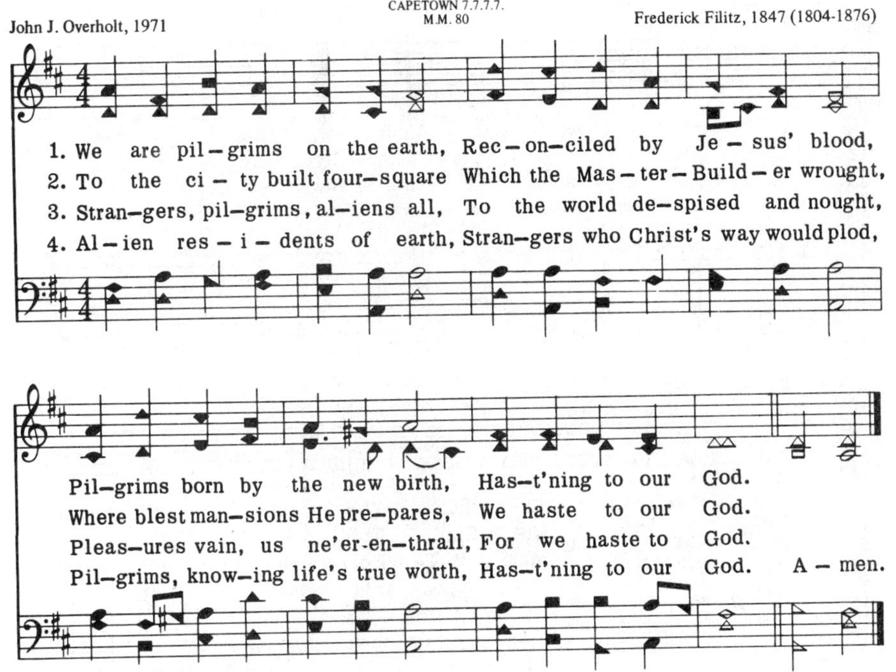
1. We are pil–grims on the earth, Rec–on–ciled by Je – sus' blood,
2. To the ci – ty built four–square Which the Mas – ter – Build – er wrought,
3. Stran–gers, pil–grims, al–iens all, To the world de–spised and nought,
4. Al – ien res – i – dents of earth, Stran–gers who Christ's way would plod,
Pil–grims born by the new birth, Has–t'ning to our God.
Where blest man–sions He pre–pares, We haste to our God.
Pleas–ures vain, us ne'er-en–thrall, For we haste to God.
Pil–grims, know–ing life's true worth, Has–t'ning to our God. A – men.

5. As we Christ our lives conform,
Are we pilgrims bought with blood;
We Christ's mandates will perform
While we haste to God.

6. Lord of pilgrims, Lord of heav'n,
We Thy pilgrims here would be;
O, may help and grace be giv'n
While we haste to Thee.

# 396 PILGRIM, AWAKE TO NEW-BORN LIFE

*Dearly beloved, I beseech you as strangers and pilgrims, abstain from fleshly lusts, which war against the soul.* I Pet. 2:11.

Wilmer D. Swope, 1971
Alt. John J. Overholt, 1971

WARRINGTON L.M. 8.8.8.8.
M.M. 88

Ralph Harrison, 1784 (1748-1810)

1. Pil – grim, a – wake! to new – born life, A – wake and
2. Pil – grim, a – rise! walk with thy Lord, For He shall
3. Pil – grim, ad – vance! the nar – row way Is that which
4. Pil – grim, re – flect! sal – va – tion's light Now shines, dis –
gird thee for the strife; The Mas – ter call – eth
guide thee with His Word, From all the de – vious
leads to heav'n – ly day; Fol – low thy Mas – ter's
pel – ling er – ror's night, For pure and ho – ly
thee from sin, From world – ly throng and e – vil din.
snares of earth, To life, the gift of Spir – it birth.
own true path, Let not thy feet stray in – to wrath.
is our Lord, Who gives new life: Oh be re–stored!

# A PILGRIM AND A STRANGER 397

*Hear my prayer, O Lord, and give ear unto my cry; hold not Thy peace at my tears: for I am a stranger with Thee, and a sojourner, as all my fathers were.* Ps. 39:12.

Paul Gerhardt, 1666 (1607-1676)
*Ich bin ein Gast auf Erden*
Tr. Jane Laurie Borthwick, 1858 (1813-1897)

I NEED THEE PRECIOUS JESUS 7.6.D.
M.M. 84

J. Henry Showalter, 1864-1947

1. A pil – grim and a stran – ger, I jour – ney here be – low;
2. There still my thoughts are dwell – ing, 'Tis there I long to be;
3. There I shall dwell for – ev – er, No more a stran–ger guest,
Far dis – tant is my coun – try, The home to which I go.
Come, Lord, and call Thy serv – ant To bless – ed–ness with Thee!
With all Thy blood–bought child–ren, In ev – er – last – ing rest;
Here I must toil and trav – ail, Oft wea – ry and op – prest,
Come, bid my toils be end – ed, Let all my wan–d'rings cease;
The pil – grim toils for – got – ten, The pil – grim con – flicts o'er,
But there my God shall lead me To ev – er – last – ing rest.
Call from the way – side lodg – ing To the sweet home of peace!
All earth – ly griefs be – hind us, E – ter – nal joys be–fore!

# 398 JESUS, JESUS, LIFE THE FOUNTAIN

*The Lord is my light and my salvation . . . the Lord is the strength of my life.* Ps. 27:1.

Hieronymus Annoni, 1697-1770
*Jesu, Jesu, Brunn des Lebens*
Tr. John J. Overholt, 1970

GREENVILLE NEW 8.7.8.7.8.7.
M.M. 69

Jean Jacques Rousseau, 1750 (1712-1778)
Arr. John J. Overholt, 1970

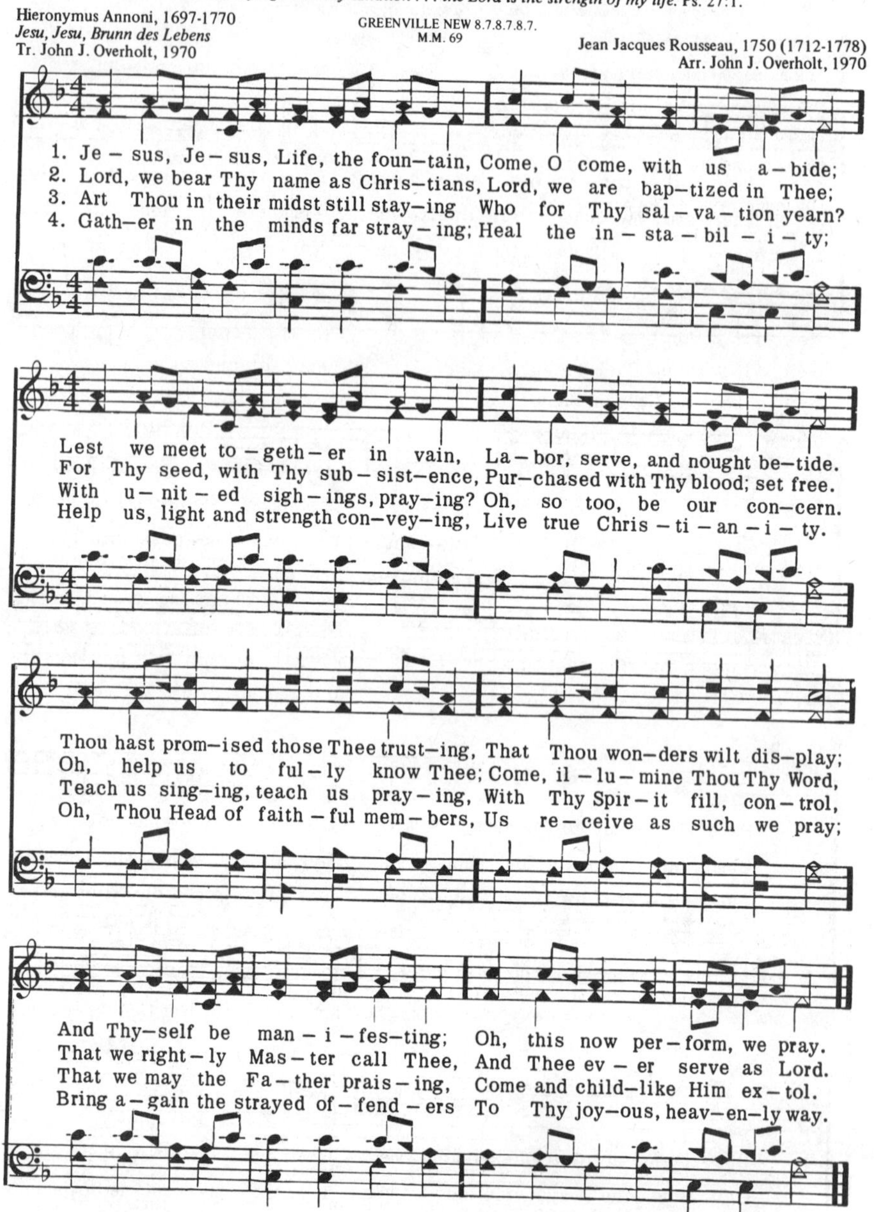
1. Je – sus, Je – sus, Life, the foun–tain, Come, O come, with us a–bide;
2. Lord, we bear Thy name as Chris–tians, Lord, we are bap–tized in Thee;
3. Art Thou in their midst still stay–ing Who for Thy sal – va – tion yearn?
4. Gath–er in the minds far stray – ing; Heal the in – sta – bil – i – ty;
Lest we meet to – geth – er in vain, La – bor, serve, and nought be–tide.
For Thy seed, with Thy sub – sist–ence, Pur–chased with Thy blood; set free.
With u – nit – ed sigh – ings, pray–ing? Oh, so too, be our con–cern.
Help us, light and strength con–vey–ing, Live true Chris – ti – an – i – ty.
Thou hast prom–ised those Thee trust–ing, That Thou won–ders wilt dis–play;
Oh, help us to ful – ly know Thee; Come, il – lu – mine Thou Thy Word,
Teach us sing–ing, teach us pray – ing, With Thy Spir – it fill, con – trol,
Oh, Thou Head of faith – ful mem – bers, Us re – ceive as such we pray;
And Thy–self be man – i – fes–ting; Oh, this now per – form, we pray.
That we right – ly Mas – ter call Thee, And Thee ev – er serve as Lord.
That we may the Fa – ther prais – ing, Come and child–like Him ex – tol.
Bring a – gain the strayed of – fend – ers To Thy joy–ous, heav–en–ly way.

5. Grant us seeing, grant us hearing, Grant us hearts, Lord, like Thine own;
Make us new–born, true, God–fearing, For Thy kingdom, Lord, alone.
Yea, do help us to be Christians, Christians ever this world's light;
Christians, salt in all earth's distance; Yea, Lord, pleasing in Thy sight!

# JESU, JESU, BRUNN DES LEBENS 399

*Der Herr ist mein Licht und mein Heil . . . der Herr ist meines Lebens Kraft.* Ps. 27:1.

Hieronymus Annoni, 1697-1770

GREENVILLE NEW 8.7.8.7.8.7.
M.M. 66

Jean Jacques Rousseau, 1750 (1712-1778)
Arr. John J. Overholt, 1970

1. Jesu, Jesu, Brunn des Lebens,
Stell, ach stell Dich bei uns ein!
Dass wir jetzund nicht vergebens
Wirken und beisammen sein.

Du verheissest ja den Deinen,
Dass Du wollest Wunder tun,
Und in ihnen willst erscheinen,
Ach, erfüll's, erfüll's auch nun!

2. Herr, wir tragen Deinen Namen,
Herr, wir sind auf Dich getauft,
Und Du hast zu Deinem Samen
Uns mit Deinem Blut erkauft.

O, so lass uns Dich erkennen,
Komm, erkläre selbst Dein Wort,
Dass wir Dich recht Meister nennen,
Und Dir dienen immerfort.

3. Bist Du mitten unter denen,
Welche sich nach Deinem Heil
Mit vereintem Seufzen sehnen,
O, so sei auch unser Teil!

Lehr uns singen, lehr uns beten,
Hauch uns an mit Deinem Geist,
Dass wir vor den Vater treten,
Wie es kindlich ist und heisst.

4. Sammle die zerstreuten Sinnen,
Stör die Flatterhaftigkeit,
Lass uns Licht und Kraft gewinnen,
Zu der Christen Wesenheit.

O Du Haupt der rechten Glieder!
Nimm auch uns zu solchen an;
Bring das Abgewich'ne wieder
Auf die frohe Himmelsbahn!

5. Gieb uns Augen, gieb uns Ohren,
Gieb uns Herzen, die Dir gleich,
Mach uns redlich neugeboren,
Herr, zu Deinem Himmelreich!

Ach ja! lehr uns Christen werden,
Christen, die ein Licht der Welt,
Christen, die ein Salz der Erden;
Ach ja, Herr, wie's Dir gefällt!

# LORD, BLESS THY SAINTS 400

*Where two or three are gathered together in my name, there am I in the midst of them.* Mt. 18:20.

Anonymous

ZEPHYR L.M. 8.8.8.8.
M.M. 69

William Batchelder Bradbury, 1844 (1816-1868)

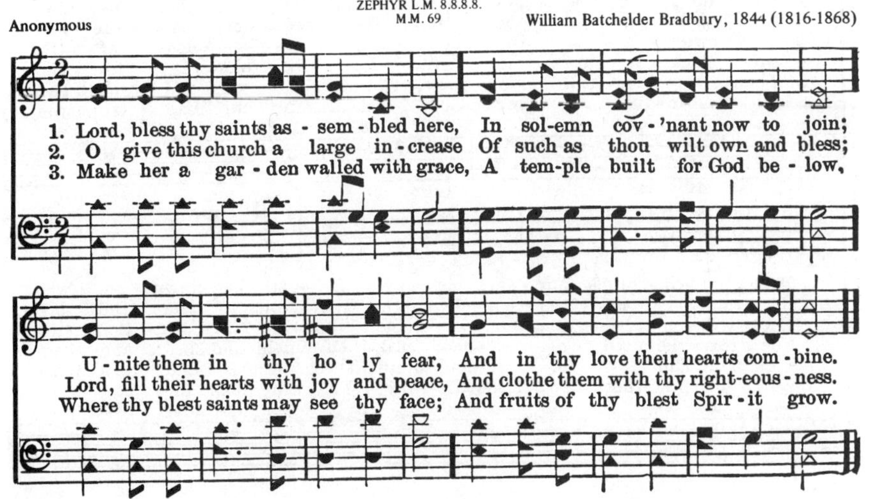
1. Lord, bless thy saints as - sem - bled here, In sol-emn cov - 'nant now to join;
2. O give this church a large in - crease Of such as thou wilt own and bless;
3. Make her a gar - den walled with grace, A tem-ple built for God be - low,
U - nite them in thy ho - ly fear, And in thy love their hearts com - bine.
Lord, fill their hearts with joy and peace, And clothe them with thy right-eous - ness.
Where thy blest saints may see thy face; And fruits of thy blest Spir - it grow.

# 401 NOT TO THE TERRORS OF THE LORD

*That they may rest from their labours.* Rev. 14:13.

COLESHILL C.M. 8.6.8.6.
M.M. 80

Isaac Watts, 1674-1748 Kirby

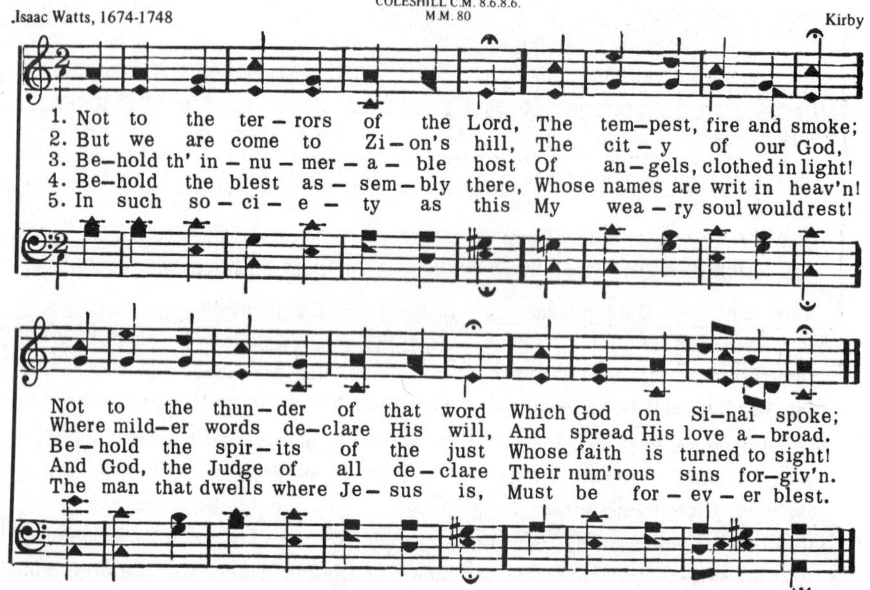
1. Not to the ter – rors of the Lord, The tem–pest, fire and smoke;
2. But we are come to Zi – on's hill, The cit – y of our God,
3. Be–hold th' in – nu – mer – a – ble host Of an–gels, clothed in light!
4. Be–hold the blest as – sem – bly there, Whose names are writ in heav'n!
5. In such so – ci – e – ty as this My wea – ry soul would rest!
Not to the thun – der of that word Which God on Si–nai spoke;
Where mild–er words de–clare His will, And spread His love a – broad.
Be – hold the spir – its of the just Whose faith is turned to sight!
And God, the Judge of all de – clare Their num'rous sins for–giv'n.
The man that dwells where Je – sus is, Must be for – ev – er blest.

# 402 FAR DOWN THE AGES NOW

*Now thanks be unto God, which always causeth us to triumph in Christ.* II Cor. 2:14.

BROADWAY S.M. 6.6.8.6.
M.M. 63

Horatius Bonar, 1808-1889 C. W. Roller

1. Far down the a ges now, Much of her jour ney done,
2. No wi - der is the gate, No broad - er is the way,
3. No sweet - er is the cup, Nor less our lot of ill;
4. No slack - er grows the fight, No fee - bler is the foe,
5. Thus on - ward still we press, Through e - vil and through good–
6. Still faith - ful to our God, And to our Cap - tain true,
The pil - grim church pur - sues her way, Un - til her crown be won.
No smooth-er is the an - cient path That leads to life and day.
'T was trib - u - la - tion a - ges since, 'T is trib - u - la - tion still.
Nor less the need of ar - mor tried, Of shield, and spear, and bow.
Thro' pain, and pov - er - ty, and want, Thro' per - il and thro' blood.
We fol - low where he leads the way; The king - dom in our view.

# HARK! THE SOUND OF HOLY VOICES 403

*To the general assembly and church of the firstborn . . . spirits of just men made perfect.* Heb. 12:23.
*Saying, Alleluiah: for the Lord God omnipotent reigneth.* Rev. 19:6.

Christopher Wordsworth, 1862 (1807-1885) | MABYN 8.7.8.7. M.M. 84 | Thomas Hastings, 1784-1872

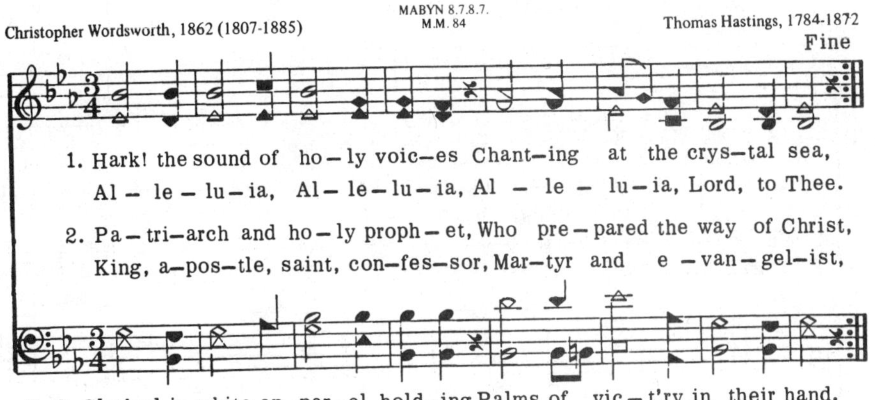
Fine
1. Hark! the sound of ho – ly voic – es Chant – ing at the crys – tal sea,
Al – le – lu – ia, Al – le – lu – ia, Al – le – lu – ia, Lord, to Thee.
2. Pa – tri – arch and ho – ly proph – et, Who pre – pared the way of Christ,
King, a – pos – tle, saint, con – fes – sor, Mar – tyr and e – van – gel – ist,

D. C. Clothed in white ap – par – el, hold – ing Palms of vic – t'ry in their hand.
D. C. Joined in ho – ly con – cert, sing – ing To the Lord of all, are there.

D. C.
Mul – ti – tudes which none can num – ber Like the stars in glo – ry stand,
Saint – ly maid – en, god – ly ma – tron, Wid – ows who have watched to pray'r,

3. They have come from tribulation
And have washed their robes in blood,
Washed them in the blood of Jesus;
Tried they were, and firm they stood,
Mocked, imprisoned, stoned, tormented,
Sawn asunder, slain with sword,
They have conquered death and Satan
By the might of Christ the Lord.

4. In Thy cross, their hope and glory,
They have triumphed, following
Thee, the Captain of salvation,
Thee, their Saviour and their King.
Gladly, Lord, with Thee they suffered,
Gladly, Lord, with Thee they died,
And by death to life immortal
They were born and glorified.

5. Now they reign in heavenly glory,
Now they walk in golden light,
Now they drink as from a river,
Holy bliss and infinite.
Love and peace they taste forever
And all truth and knowledge see
In the beatific vision
Of the blessed Trinity.

6. God of God, the One–begotten,
Light of Light, Emmanuel,
In whose body, joined together,
All the saints forever dwell,
Pour upon us of Thy fulness
That we may forevermore
God the Father, God the Spirit,
One with Thee on high, adore.

# 404 AWAKE, THOU SPIRIT OF THE MARTYRS

*Awake and sing, ye that dwell in dust.* Is. 26:19. *Awake, awake, stand up, O Jerusalem.* Is. 51:17. *Awake, awake; put on thy strength, O Zion.* Is. 52:1. *Awake thou that sleepest, and arise from the dead, and Christ shall give thee light.* Eph. 5:14.

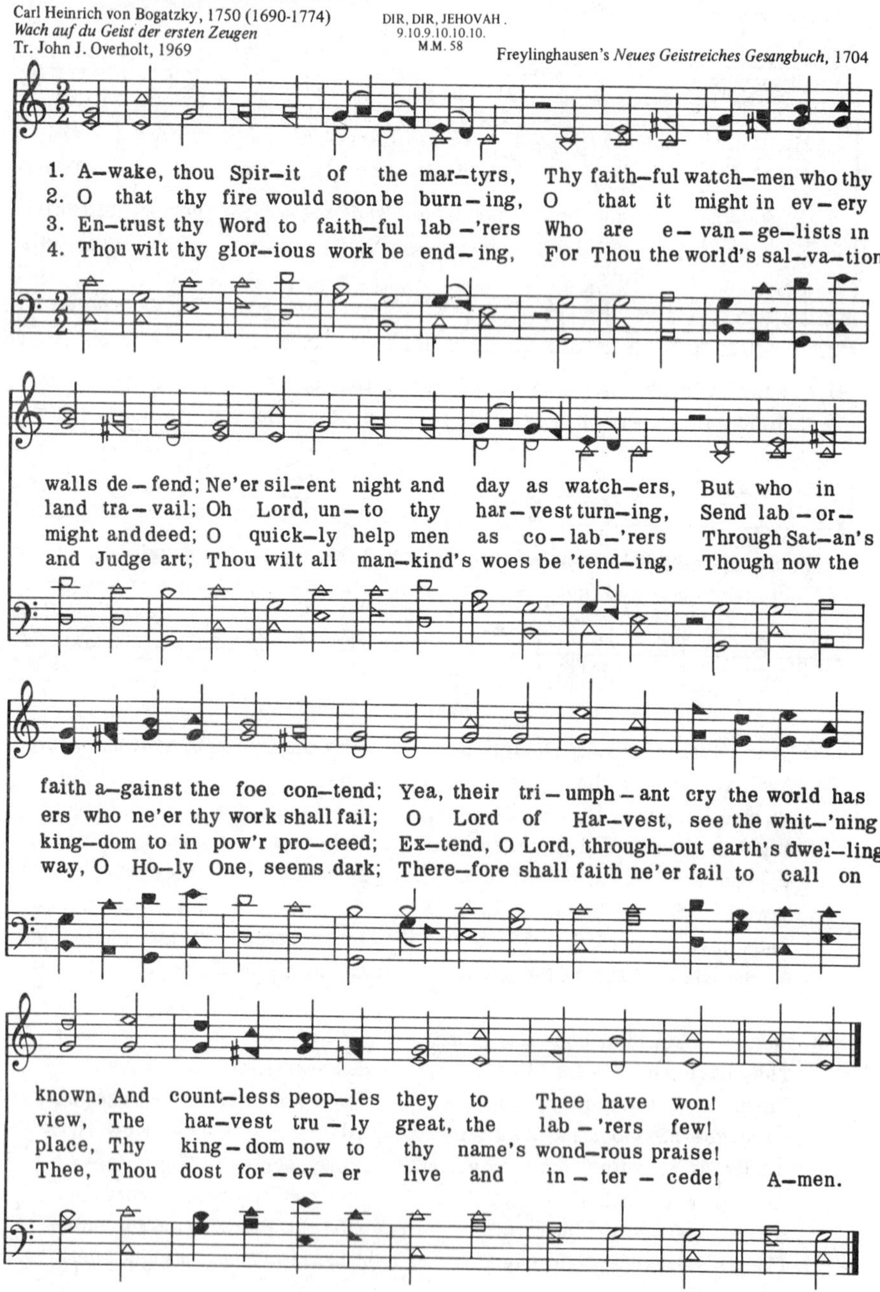
Carl Heinrich von Bogatzky, 1750 (1690-1774)
*Wach auf du Geist der ersten Zeugen*
Tr. John J. Overholt, 1969
DIR, DIR, JEHOVAH.
9.10.9.10.10.10.
M.M. 58
Freylinghausen's *Neues Geistreiches Gesangbuch*, 1704
1. A–wake, thou Spir–it of the mar–tyrs, Thy faith–ful watch–men who thy
2. O that thy fire would soon be burn – ing, O that it might in ev – ery
3. En–trust thy Word to faith–ful lab – 'rers Who are e – van – ge–lists in
4. Thou wilt thy glor–ious work be end – ing, For Thou the world's sal–va–tion
walls de – fend; Ne'er sil–ent night and day as watch–ers, But who in
land tra – vail; Oh Lord, un – to thy har – vest turn–ing, Send lab – or–
might and deed; O quick–ly help men as co – lab – 'rers Through Sat–an's
and Judge art; Thou wilt all man–kind's woes be 'tend–ing, Though now the
faith a–gainst the foe con–tend; Yea, their tri – umph – ant cry the world has
ers who ne'er thy work shall fail; O Lord of Har–vest, see the whit–'ning
king–dom to in pow'r pro–ceed; Ex–tend, O Lord, through–out earth's dwel–ling
way, O Ho–ly One, seems dark; There–fore shall faith ne'er fail to call on
known, And count–less peop–les they to Thee have won!
view, The har–vest tru – ly great, the lab – 'rers few!
place, Thy king – dom now to thy name's wond–rous praise!
Thee, Thou dost for – ev – er live and in – ter – cede! A–men.

# YE LION-HEARTED, RISE AGAIN 405

*The righteous are bold as a lion.* Prov. 28:1. *The remnant of Jacob shall be among the Gentiles . . . as a lion among the beasts of the forest.* Mic. 5:8. . . . *Men of might, and men of war . . . whose faces were like the faces of lions.* I Chron. 12:8.

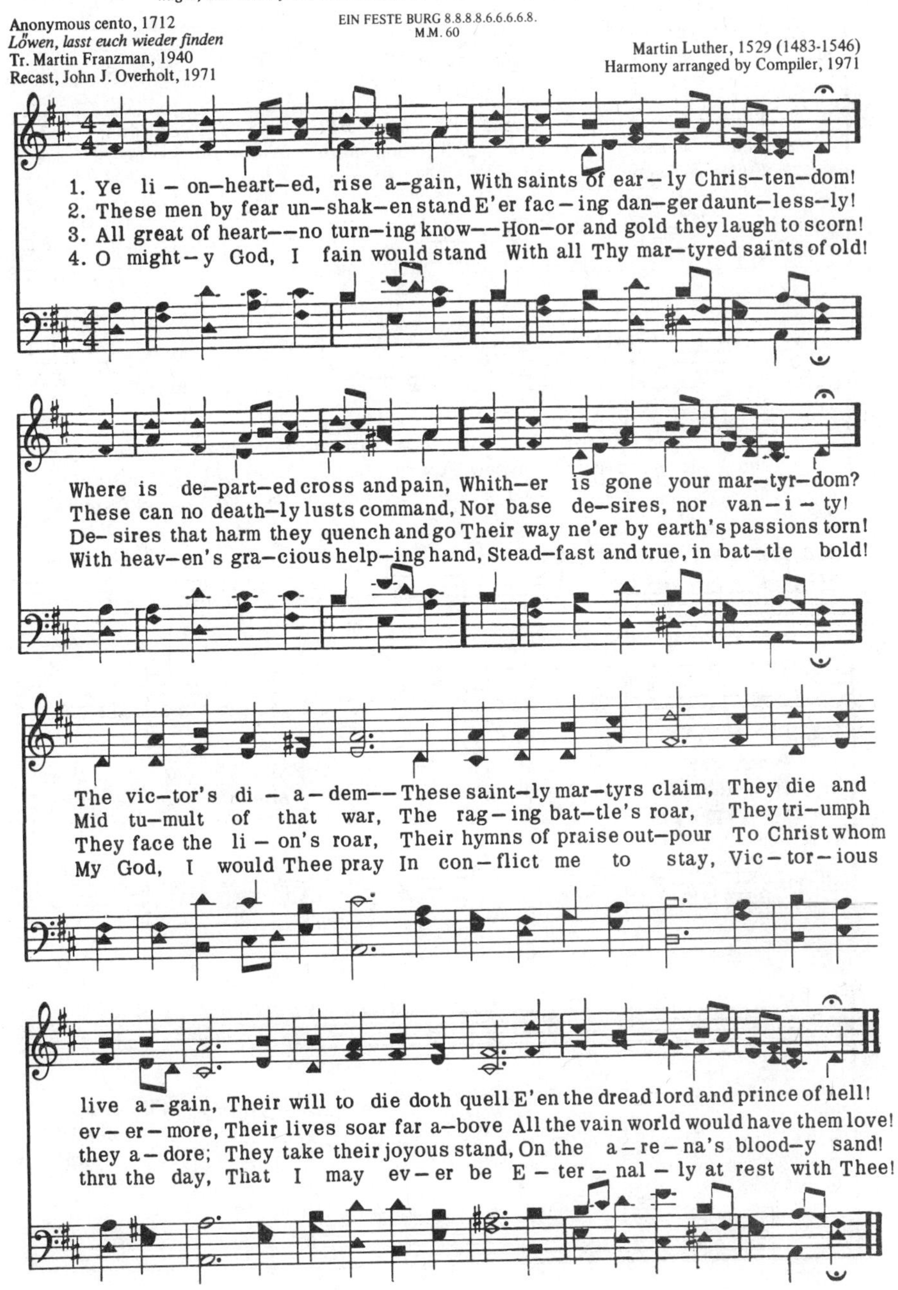
Anonymous cento, 1712
*Löwen, lasst euch wieder finden*
Tr. Martin Franzman, 1940
Recast, John J. Overholt, 1971
EIN FESTE BURG 8.8.8.8.6.6.6.6.8.
M.M. 60
Martin Luther, 1529 (1483-1546)
Harmony arranged by Compiler, 1971
1. Ye li – on–heart–ed, rise a–gain, With saints of ear – ly Chris–ten–dom!
2. These men by fear un–shak–en stand E'er fac – ing dan–ger daunt–less–ly!
3. All great of heart––no turn–ing know––Hon–or and gold they laugh to scorn!
4. O might – y God, I fain would stand With all Thy mar–tyred saints of old!
Where is de–part–ed cross and pain, Whith–er is gone your mar–tyr–dom?
These can no death–ly lusts command, Nor base de–sires, nor van – i – ty!
De– sires that harm they quench and go Their way ne'er by earth's passions torn!
With heav–en's gra–cious help–ing hand, Stead–fast and true, in bat–tle bold!
The vic–tor's di – a – dem–– These saint–ly mar–tyrs claim, They die and
Mid tu–mult of that war, The rag – ing bat–tle's roar, They tri–umph
They face the li – on's roar, Their hymns of praise out–pour To Christ whom
My God, I would Thee pray In con – flict me to stay, Vic – tor – ious
live a – gain, Their will to die doth quell E'en the dread lord and prince of hell!
ev – er – more, Their lives soar far a–bove All the vain world would have them love!
they a – dore; They take their joyous stand, On the a – re – na's blood–y sand!
thru the day, That I may ev – er be E – ter – nal – ly at rest with Thee!

# 406 FAITH OF OUR FATHERS

*Earnestly contend for the faith which was once delivered unto the saints.* Jude 3.

Frederick W. Faber, 1849 (1814-1863)

ST. CATHERINE 8.8.8.8.8.8.
M.M. 72

Henri Frederick Hemy, 1864
Adapted James George Walton, 1874 (1821-1905)

1. Faith of our fa - thers! liv - ing still In spite of dun - geon,
2. Our fa - thers, chained in pris - ons dark, Were still in heart and
3. Faith of our fa - thers! we will love Both friend and foe in
fire, and sword; O how our hearts beat high with joy
con - science free: How sweet would be their chil - dren's fate,
all our strife; And preach thee, too, as love knows how,
When-e'er we hear that glo - rious word! Faith of our fa - thers!
If they, like them, could die for thee! Faith of our fa - thers!
By kind - ly words and vir - tuous life: Faith of our fa - thers!
ho - ly faith! We will be true to thee till death!
ho - ly faith! We will be true to thee till death!
ho - ly faith! We will be true to thee till death!

# LET OUR HEARTS NEW ANTHEMS RAISE 407

*Who through faith . . . wrought righteousness . . . stopped the mouths of lions . . . out of weakness were made strong, waxed valiant in fight.* Heb. 11:33, 34.

Joseph the Hymnographer, 9th century
Early Greek Hymn
Tr. John Mason Neale, 1862 (1818-1866), alt.
St. 1, Alt. by Compiler, 1970

ST. KEVIN 7.8.7.8.D.
M.M. 84

Arthur Seymour Sullivan, 1842-1900

1. Let our hearts new an – thems raise, Wake the morn with glad – ness;
2. Nev – er flinched they from the flame, From the tor – ture nev – er;
3. Faith they had that knew not shame, Love that could not lan – guish;

God Him – self to joy and praise Turns the mar – tyrs' sad – ness:
Vain the foe – man's sharp – est aim, Sa – tan's best en – dea – vor:
And e – ter – nal hope o'er – came Mo – men – ta – ry an – guish.

Bright the day that won their crown, O – pened heav'n's bright por – tal,
For by faith they saw the land Decked in all its glo – ry,
Up and fol – low, Chris – tian men! Press through toil and sor – row;

As they laid the mor – tal down And put on th' im – mor – tal.
Where tri – um – phant now they stand With the vic – tor's sto – ry.
Spurn the night of fear, and then, O the glo – rious mor – row! A – men.

# 408 O GOD AND FATHER, THEE WE BLESS

*The earth is the Lord's, and the fulness thereof; the world, and they that dwell therein.* Ps. 24:1. *Unto thee, O Lord, do I lift up my soul.* Ps. 25:1.

From the 16th century Anabaptist *Ausbund*
Hymn No. 131, Leonard Clock, c. 1590
*O Gott Vater, wir loben dich*
Tr. John J. Overholt, 1969

AUS TIEFER NOT 8.7.8.7.8.8.7.
M.M. 48

*Kirchenampt,* Strassburg, 1525

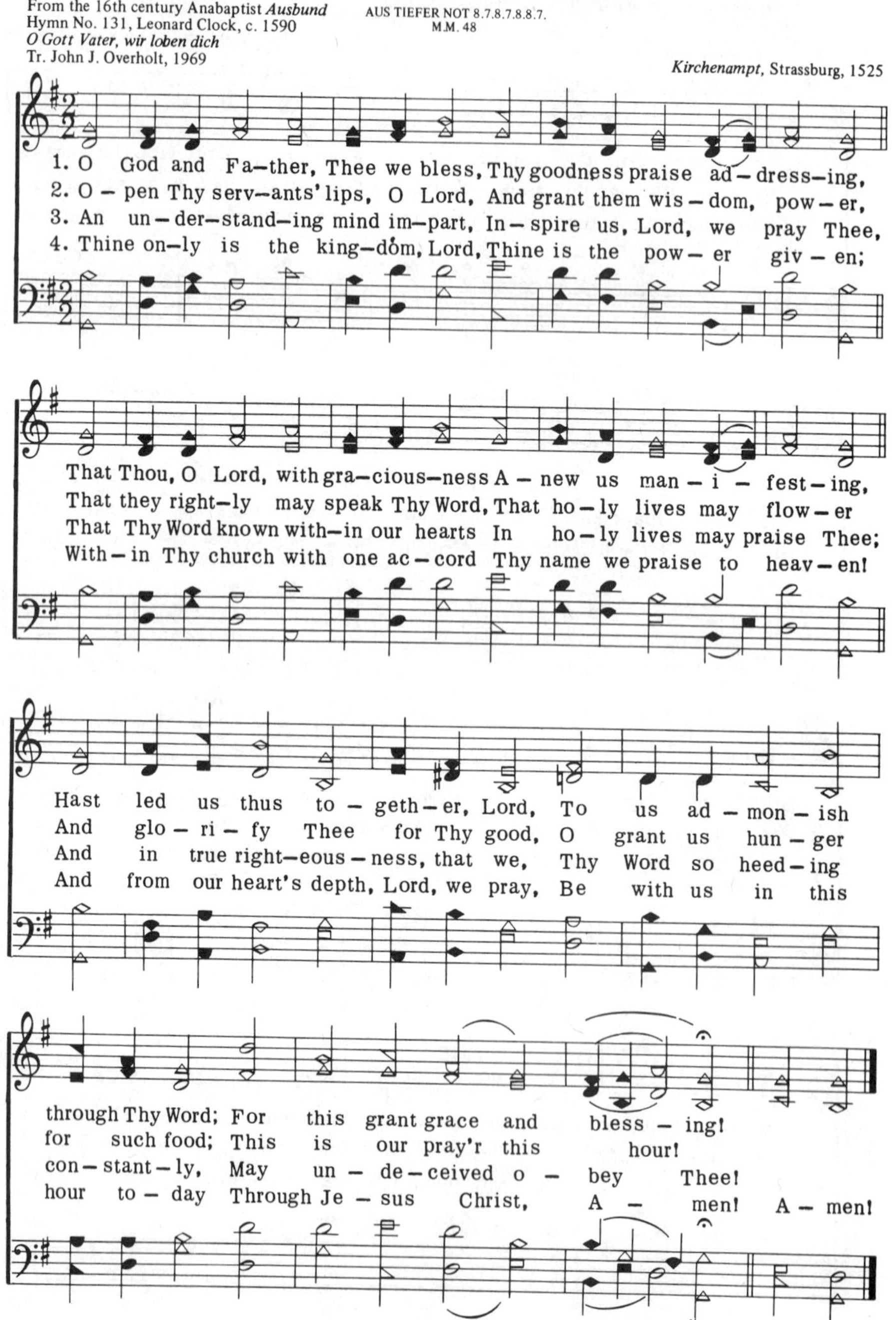
1. O God and Fa-ther, Thee we bless, Thy goodness praise ad-dress-ing,
2. O-pen Thy serv-ants' lips, O Lord, And grant them wis-dom, pow-er,
3. An un-der-stand-ing mind im-part, In-spire us, Lord, we pray Thee,
4. Thine on-ly is the king-dom, Lord, Thine is the pow-er giv-en;
That Thou, O Lord, with gra-cious-ness A-new us man-i-fest-ing,
That they right-ly may speak Thy Word, That ho-ly lives may flow-er
That Thy Word known with-in our hearts In ho-ly lives may praise Thee;
With-in Thy church with one ac-cord Thy name we praise to heav-en!
Hast led us thus to-geth-er, Lord, To us ad-mon-ish through Thy Word; For this grant grace and bless-ing!
And glo-ri-fy Thee for Thy good, O grant us hun-ger for such food; This is our pray'r this hour!
And in true right-eous-ness, that we, Thy Word so heed-ing con-stant-ly, May un-de-ceived o-bey Thee!
And from our heart's depth, Lord, we pray, Be with us in this hour to-day Through Je-sus Christ, A-men! A-men!

# O GOD, FATHER, THEE DO WE BLESS 409

*O bless our God, ye people, and make the voice of His praise to be heard.* Ps. 66:8.

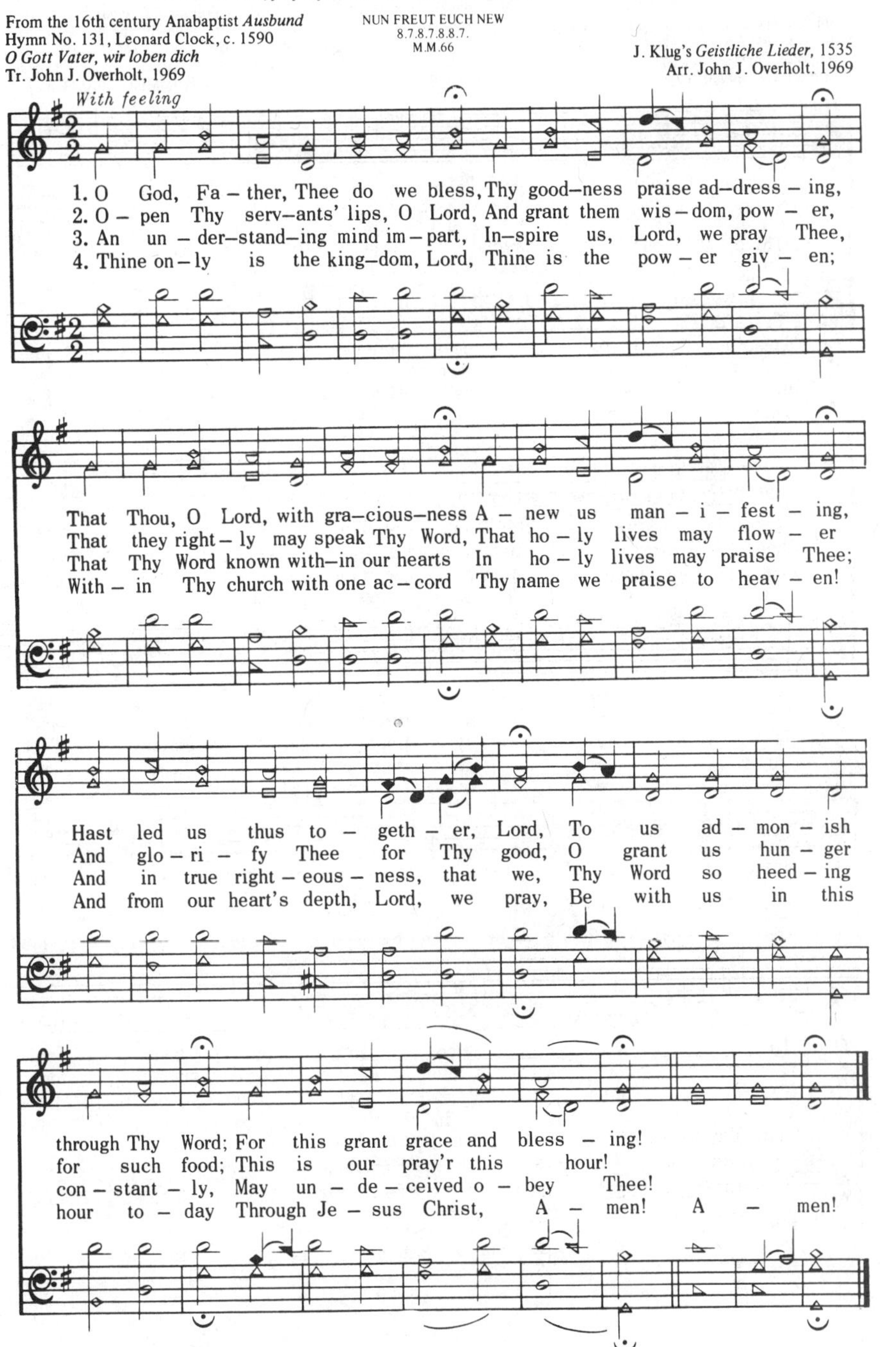
From the 16th century Anabaptist *Ausbund*
Hymn No. 131, Leonard Clock, c. 1590
*O Gott Vater, wir loben dich*
Tr. John J. Overholt, 1969
NUN FREUT EUCH NEW
8.7.8.7.8.8.7.
M.M.66
J. Klug's *Geistliche Lieder,* 1535
Arr. John J. Overholt, 1969
*With feeling*
1. O God, Fa – ther, Thee do we bless, Thy good–ness praise ad–dress – ing,
2. O – pen Thy serv–ants' lips, O Lord, And grant them wis – dom, pow – er,
3. An un – der–stand–ing mind im – part, In–spire us, Lord, we pray Thee,
4. Thine on – ly is the king–dom, Lord, Thine is the pow – er giv – en;
That Thou, O Lord, with gra–cious–ness A – new us man – i – fest – ing,
That they right – ly may speak Thy Word, That ho – ly lives may flow – er
That Thy Word known with–in our hearts In ho – ly lives may praise Thee;
With – in Thy church with one ac – cord Thy name we praise to heav – en!
Hast led us thus to – geth – er, Lord, To us ad – mon – ish
And glo – ri – fy Thee for Thy good, O grant us hun – ger
And in true right – eous – ness, that we, Thy Word so heed – ing
And from our heart's depth, Lord, we pray, Be with us in this
through Thy Word; For this grant grace and bless – ing!
for such food; This is our pray'r this hour!
con – stant – ly, May un – de – ceived o – bey Thee!
hour to – day Through Je – sus Christ, A – men! A – men!

# 410 O GOD, FATHER, THEE DO WE BLESS

*Bless the Lord, O my soul: and all that is within me, bless His holy name.* Ps. 103:1.

From the 16th Century Anabaptist *Ausbund*
Hymn No. 131, Leonard Clock, c. 1590
*O Gott Vater, wir loben dich*
Tr. John J. Overholt, 1969

LOBSANG 8.7.8.7.8.8.7.
M.M. 58

German Volkslied, *Es wollt ein* . . . , 1534
Traditional *Lobsang,* as sung by the Amish brethren,
Atlee D. Miller, Daniel J. Bontrager, Atlee A. Troyer,
David E. M. Miller, and later by Roman J. Coblentz
Arr. John J. Overholt, Millersburg, Ohio, 1970

1. O God, Fa–ther, Thee do we bless,
2. O – pen Thy serv – ants' lips, O Lord,
3. An un – der–stand – ing mind im – part,
4. Thine on – ly is the king–dom, Lord,

Thy good – ness praise ad – dress – ing,
And grant them wis – dom, pow – er,
In – spire us, Lord, we pray Thee,
Thine is the pow – er giv – en;

That Thou, O Lord, with gra–cious – ness
That they right–ly may speak Thy Word,
That Thy Word known with – in our hearts
With in Thy church with one ac – cord

A – new us man – i – fest – ing,
That ho – ly lives may flow – er
In ho – ly lives may praise Thee;
Thy name we praise to heav – en!

Hast led us thus to – geth – er, Lord,
And glo – ri – fy Thee for Thy good,
And in true right – eous – ness, that we,
And from our heart's depth, Lord, we pray,

To us ad – mon – ish through Thy Word;
O grant us hun – ger for such food;
Thy Word so heed – ing con – stant – ly,
Be with us in this hour to – day

For this grant grace and bless – ing!
This is our pray'r this ho – ur!
May un – de – ceived o – bey Thee!
Through Je – sus Christ, our Lord, A – men!

# O GOTT VATER WIR LOBEN DICH 411

*Lobe den Herrn, meine Seele, und was in mir ist, seinen heiligen Namen!* Ps. 103:1.

LOBSANG 8 7.8.7.8.8.7
M.M. 58

German Volkslied, *Es wollt ein* . . . , 1534
Traditional *Lobsang*, as sung by the Amish brethren,
Atlee D. Miller, Daniel J. Bontrager, Atlee A. Troyer,
David E. M. Miller, and later by Roman J. Coblentz
Arr. John J. Overholt, Millersburg, Ohio, 1970

From the 16th century Anabaptist *Ausbund*
Hymn No. 131, Leonard Clock, c. 1590

1. O Gott , Va-ter , wir lo-ben dich
2. Oef - ne den Mund Herr dei-ner Knecht,
3. Gib un - serm Her - zen auch Ver - stand,
4. Dein, O Herr, ist das Reich al - lein,
Und dei - ,ne Gü - ,te ,prei - sen;
Gib ihn'n Weis - heit dar - ne - ben,
Er - leuch - tung hie auf Er - den,
Und auch die Macht zu - sam - men,
Die du O Herr, so gnä-dig - lich,
Dass er dein Wort mög spre-chen recht,
Dass dein Wort in uns werd be - kannt,
Wir lo - ben dich in der Ge - mein,
An uns ,neu hast be - ,wie - sen,
Was dient zum from - men Le - ben,
Dass wir fromm mö - gen wer - den,
Und dan - ken dei - nem Na - men,
Und hast ,uns Herr ,zu - sam - men g'führt,
Und nütz - lich ist zu dei - nem Preis,
Und le - ben in Ge - rech - tig - keit,
Und bit - ten dich aus Her - zens Grund,
Uns zu er - mah - nen ,durch ,dein Wort,
Gib uns Hun - ger nach sol - cher Speis,
Ach - ten auf dein Wort al - le - zeit,
Wollst bey uns seyn zu die - ser Stund,
Gib uns Ge - ,nad zu ,die - sem.
Das ist un - ser Be - geh - ren.
So bleibt man un -- be - tro - gen.
Durch Je - sum Chris - tum .A - men.

Note: Commas in first stanza mark breathing intervals.

# 412 COME UNTO ME, SAITH GOD'S OWN SON

*Come unto Me, all ye that labour and are heavy laden, and I will give you rest. Take My yoke upon you, and learn of Me . . . and ye shall find rest unto your souls. For My yoke is easy, and My burden is light.* Mt. 28-30.

Ein eifriger Wiedertäufer
Georg Grünwald, burnt at the stake, 1530
Kommt her zu mir, spricht Gottes Sohn
Tr. John J. Overholt, 1972
GRÜNWALD 8.8.7.8.8.7.
M.M. 66
In seiner eigenen Melodie
Georg Grünwald, d. 1530
May be sung in 2/2 time also
1. Come un - to me, saith God's own Son, Ye heav - y lad- en and un - done, With sin's hard bur - den deal - ing; Ye youth and eld - ders, wom-en, men, I want to help you, for I can Soon all your ills be heal - ing.
2. My yoke is sweet, my bur - den light, Who - e'er it bears with me a - right, The fires of hell shall flee from; I'll help him faith - ful - ly, it bear, That through my-self he gain as heir, Th' e - ter - nal heav'n - ly king - dom.
3. What I did, what I suf - fered here, In life, ear - ly and late did bear, That shall you too be do - ing; Yes, what men think, and say and do, That shall work out for good a - new, When God's will they're pur-su - ing.
1. Kommt her zu mir, spricht Got - tes Sohn, All die ihr seid be - schwe - ret nun, Mit Sün - den fast be - lad - en. Ihr Jun - gen, Al - ten, Frau und Mann, Ich will euch hel - fen, denn ich kann Bald hei - len eu - ren Scha - den.
2. Mein Joch ist süss, mein Bürd ge - ring, Dass wer's nach-trägt in dem Be - ding Der Höl - len - gluth ent - wei - che: Ich helf ihm treu - lich, dass er's trag, Und durch mich selbst ge - lan - gen mag Zum ew' - gen Him - mel - rei - che.
3. Was ich that, was ich lit - te hie, In mei - nem Le - ben spat und früh, Das sollt ihr auch er - fül - len; Ja, was der Mensch denkt, red't und thut, Das kommt ihm al - les wohl zu gut, Wenn's ist nach Got - tes Wil - len.

4. Gladly the world would too be saved
If scorn and pain need not be braved,
Which all true Christians suffer;
Nor can it, may it other be;
Therefore yield himself willingly,
Who'd shun hell's pangs forever.

4. Gern wollt die Welt auch selig sein,
Wenn nur nicht wär die Schmach und Pein,
Die alle Christen leiden;
So kann und mag's nicht anders sein,
Darum ergeb sich willig drein,
Der ewig Pein will meiden.

**Note: This selection may also be sung with No. 111, Wie schön leuchtet der Morgenstern.**

5. Therefore, mark well, ye Christian band,
Ye who to God committed stand,
Your effort ne'er be ruing;
To God's most holy Word adhere,
This is the soul's treasure most dear;
God is your joy renewing.

5. Darum so merkt, ihr Christen Leut
Die ihr jetzt Gott ergeben sey'd,
Lasst euch die Müh nicht reuen;
Halt't stets am heil'gen Gottes Wort,
Das ist der Seelen höchster Hort,
Gott wird euch schon erfreuen.

# THE FATHER WE WILL EVER PRAISE 413

*Let us offer the sacrifice of praise to God continually, that is, the fruit of our lips giving thanks to His name.* Heb. 13:15.

From the 16th century Anabaptist *Ausbund*
Hymn No. 34, Georg Wagner, burnt 1527
*Den Vater woll'n wir loben*
Tr. John J. Overholt, 1970

VOX DILECTI NEW C.M.D.
8.6.8.6.D.
M.M. 66

John Bacchus Dykes, 1823-1876
Arranged by Compiler, 1970

1. The Fa - ther we will ev - er praise, Who us re - demp - tion brought;
2. In His Son, God has left us here Ex - am - ple we should heed,
1. Den Va - ter woll'n wir lo – ben, Der uns er - lö - set hat,
2. Im Sohn hat er uns g'las - sen Ein Vor - bild, mer - ket wie,
In heav - en high our thanks we'll raise, through Christ's death we are bought,
That in like fash - ion, we with fear, Should suf - fer pa - tient - ly,
Im Him - mel hoch dort o - ben, Durch sei - nes Sohn - es Tod,
Dass wir auch sol - cher mas - sen Ge - dul - dig lei - den hie,
Whom God hath us in mer - cy giv'n From sin to re - con - cile;
As us en - joins the Word of God, To help Christ bear re - proach;
Wel - chen er hat ge - ge - ben. Zu ver–söh – nen un - ser Sünd,
Ihm die Schmach hel - fen tra - gen, Wie uns die Schrift be - weisst,
That we by faith should live in Him, As His o - be - dient child.
In He-brews it to us is taught, Through God, the Ho - ly Ghost.
Dass wir im Glau - ben le - ben Als sein ge - hor - sam Kind.
Zu'n He – brä – ern thut sa - gen Durch den Hei - li - gen Geist.

# 414 GOD WILL HIS RIGHTEOUS JUDGMENT METE

*. . . The day of wrath and revelation of the righteous judgment of God; Who will render to every man according to his deeds.* Rom. 2:5-6.

From the 16th century Anabaptist *Ausbund*
Hymn No. 5, Georg Blaurock, burnt 1529
*Gott führt ein recht Gericht*
Tr. John J. Overholt, 1969

BEIRUT 6.7.8.7.
M.M. 58

Ancient Chant
Har. John J. Overholt, 1969

1. God will His righ - teous judg - ment mete, And no one this may e'er al - ter;
2. Gra - cious art Thou, O Lord, and just, In kind - ness great, and mer - cy, mild;
1. Gott - führt - ein recht Ge - richt, Und nie - mand mags ihm - brech - en.
2. Gnä - dig bist du, O Herr, und gut, Gü - tig - lich lässt dich - find - en.

All to His will, will not
Who e'er Thy will o - beys,
Wer hie thut sei - nen Will -
Wer hie auf Erd dein Will -

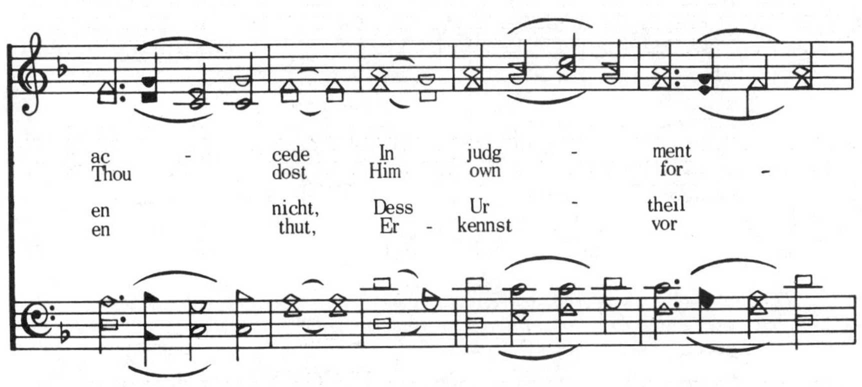
ac - cede In judg - ment
Thou dost Him own for -
en nicht, Dess Ur - theil
en thut, Er - kennst vor

sore mourn here - af - ter!
ev - er as Thy child!
wird er sprech - en.
dei - ne Kind - en.

# 415 O GOD DO THOU SUSTAIN ME

*Preserve me, O God: for in Thee do I put my trust.* Ps. 16:1. *Preserve me from the violent man.* Ps. 140:1. *He shall sustain thee.* Ps. 55:22.

Leonhart Sommer, Anabaptist
Died in prison December 25, 1573
*O Gott, thun mich erhalten*
Tr. John J. Overholt, 1970

HOHENWITTLINGEN 7.6.7.6.7.6.7.7.6.
M.M. 66

From the *Philharmonia*
Arr. John J. Overholt, 1970

1. O God, do Thou sus–tain me, In grief and sore du–ress; Pride coun – ter
2. Thou wilt nev–er for–sake me, This firm – ly I be–lieve; Thy blood Thou
1. O Gott, thun mich er–hal–ten, In min – er trawerikeit; Den hoch – mut
2. Du wirst mich nicht ver–las–sen, Das glaub ich ves–tig–lich; Dein blut hast

which disdains Thee, And com – fort my dis–tress; O Lord, let me find mer–cy
hast shed free – ly, And with it wash – ed me: There–in my trust is rest–ing,
thu zer – spal – ten, Trost mich in min – em leid, Ach, Herr, las mich gnad finden
du ver – gos – sen, Dar – mit ge–wasch–en mich. Da–ruff stehet mein ver–traw–en

In bonds and pris – on bed; Men would seek to de – vour me,
In Christ, God's on – ly Son; On Him I am now build – ing,
In band ge – fāng–nus schwer, Sie wol – len mich ver – schlin – den,
In Chris – to, Gott–es sohn; Auf den so will ich bau – wen,

With guile and con – tro – ver – sy; Save me from dan – ger dread!
In trib – u – la – tion trust – ing, God will me not dis – own!
Mit ihr – en list und find – en, Helf mir aus angest und ge – fahr.
In trűb – sal uff in schau – wen, Gott wird mich nicht ver – lohn.

3. Thy Word to us was given
To bring salvation nigh;
Who doth from evil hasten,
His flesh will then deny;
For we see not our failing
Until God's Word, so clear,
Through grace this is revealing,
Our sins removes, and healing,
Redeems from want and fear.

4. My heart is overjoying
(5) With suffering's scorn and pain;
May God me grace deploying,
Find worthy for His train,
My cross to carry with Him,
'Till life shall consumate;
From Him's no separation
Through plague or tribulation;
Lord, patient I Thee 'wait.

5. With joy I would be moving
(6) In suffering here and there;
With Abraham removing
In lands both far and near,
Until I shall have gained
The mark of the high prize;
Therewith the crown is waited,
When sufferings have abated,
And we great joy apprize.

6. To die and to be living,
(8) Until my end I see,
To Thee my trust I'm giving,
Thou wilt my helper be;
Soul, body, child, companion
Herewith commit I Thee;
Come soon, Lord, come and take me
From ruthless men do save me;
Be honor e'er to Thee. Amen.

---

3. Dein wort war uns gesendet
Zu unserer sӓligkeit;
Wer sich vom bӧsen wendet,
Der bringt sein fleisch in leid.
Dann es nicht sieht den schaden
Bis Gottes wort so klahr;
Das offenbahret aus gnaden,
Thut uns der sűnd entladen,
Erlӧst aus noht und gefahr.

5. Von hӓrtzen mich thut frewen
Der trűbsal schmach und pein;
Gott wӧll mir gnad verlichen,
Das ich mӧg wűrdig sein.
Ihm das creűtz nachzutragen
Bis an das ende min;
Mich soll von ihm nicht yagen,
Trűbsal noch andere plagen,
Mit gedult, Herr, wart ich din.

6. Mit freuden will ich ziechen
Im elӓnd hin und hӓr;
Mit Aberham auch fliechen
In landen wit und fer.
Bis ich es thun erlangen
Das fűrgesteckte zil,
Daran die cron thut hangen,
Wan trűbsal ist vergangen,
Wird sein der frewden vil.

8. Zu stӓrben und zu lӓben
Bis an das ende min;
Gott bin ich dir ergӓben,
Du wirst min hӓlfer sein.
Dir sei hiemit befohlen
Mein seel, lib, kind, und weib;
Kom bald, Herr, thun mich hollen,
Erlӧs mich von den tollen,
Dir ehr die ewig bleib. Amen.

# 416 I WILL DELIGHT IN SINGING

*I will sing of Thy power; yea, I will sing aloud . . . for Thou hast been my defence and refuge in the day of my trouble.* Ps. 59:16.

From the 16th century Anabaptist *Ausbund*
Hymn No. 6, Felix Mantz, drowned 1527
*Mit Lust so will ich singen*
Tr. John J. Overholt, 1969

FOUNDLAND NEW 7.6.7.6.8.7.6.
M.M. 63

From the *Philharmonia*
Arr. by Compiler, 1969

1. I will de-light in sing-ing, In God o'er-joys my heart;
2. Him God to me is send-ing, Ex-am-ple and true light,
1. Mit Lust so will ich sin-gen, Mein Herz freut sich in Gott,
2. Den mir Gott thut zu-sen-den Zu ein'm Vor-bild und Licht,
For grace He is me bring-ing, That I from death de-part
Who me, e'er my life's end-ing, Doth to His king-dom cite;
Der mir viel Kunst thut brin-gen, Dass ich en-trinn dem Tod,
Der mich vor mein-em En-de, Zu sei-nem Reich be-ruft,
Which last-ing ev-er, hath no end;
That I with Him have end-less bliss,
Der e-wig-lich nim-met kein End,
Dass ich mit ihm hab e-wig Freud,
I praise Thee Christ from heav-en, Who dost my grief at-tend.
And from my heart may love Him, And all His right-eous-ness.
Ich preiss dich Christ vom Him-mel, Der mir mein Kum-mer wend.
Und lie-be ihn von Her-zen, Auch all sein G'rech-tig-keit.

3. Christ, then, would I be praising,
(7) Who patience shows to all,
With friendship us embracing,
Moved by His grace withal;
His love to all men shows He, too,
In likeness to His Father,
Which no one false will do.

4. Christ no one is co–ercing
(9) His glory–world to share;
They heaven are traversing
Who willingly prepare,
Through faith and baptism rightly wrought,
Repentance, with hearts holy;
For them is heaven bought.

5. Christ, in His blood thus shedding,
(10) Which He did willingly,
And His great task not dreading,
This would He have us see,
Us with His holy power endows;
For who Christ's love constraineth,
In holy likeness grows.

6. Where Christ's love is abiding,
(12) Is spared the enemy,
And Christ proclaims this tiding
To all who heirs would be;
That who shows mercy lovingly
And keeps His Lord's clear teaching,
Is glad eternally.

7. Those hate and envy harb'ring,
(15) Cannot true Christians be;
And those who evil, inj'ring,
Fists strike in enmity;
Before our Lord to kill and thieve,
Blood innocent they're shedding
In base hypocrisy.

8. Thus shall men be apprizing
(16) Those who with Christ are not,
Who Christian rules despising,
With Belial's kind do plot,
Ev'n as did Cain in sin o'erthrow,
When God owned Abel's offering;
And hence must suffer woe.

9. Herewith shall I be closing;
(17) Observe, saints, one and all,
It is not indisposing
To notice Adam's fall,
Who, too, received the tempter's voice,
His God was disobedient,
And death became His choice.

10. So those who Christ withstanding,
(18) Whom worldly lust ensnares,
Shall likewise find their ending;
No godly love is theirs.
So closeth here this hymn, indeed;
With Christ I am remaining,
Who knows and meets my need. Amen.

---

7. Christum den will ich preisen,
Der alle G'dult erzeigt,
Thut uns gar freundlich weisen
Mit seiner Gnad geneigt,
Beweisst die Lieb an jedermann,
Nach seines Vaters Arte,
Welch's kein falscher thun kann.

9. Christus thut niemand zwingen
Zu seiner Herrlichkeit,
Allein wird's dem gelingen,
Der willig ist bereit,
Durch rechten Glaub und wahre Tauff
Würkt Buss mit reinem Herzen,
Dem ist der Himmel kauft.

10. Durch Christi Blutvergiessen,
Welch's er hat willig thon,
Es thät ihn nicht verdriessen,
Welch's er uns weist gar schon,
Begabet uns mit heilger Kraft.
Dann wen sein Lieb thut treiben,
Der wächst in Gottes Saft.

12. Die Lieb in Christum reine,
Verschonet hie den Feind,
Wer mit ihm Erb will seyne,
Dem wird auch das verkündt,
Dass er beweiss Barmherzigkeit,
Nach seines Herren Lehre,
So wird er ewig erfreut.

15. Die Neid und Hass erzeigen,
Mögen nicht Christen seyn,
Und sich zum Bösen neigen,
Schlagen mit Fäusten drein.
Laufen vor Christo wie Mörder und Dieb,
Unschuldig Blut vergiessen,
Ist alles falsche Lieb.

16. Dabey soll mans erkennen,
Die nicht mit Christo sind,
Die Christlich Ordnung trennen,
Wie alle Belials Kind.
Als Cain seinem Bruder that,
Als Gott zu Abels Opfer thät kehren,
Bracht ihn in grosse Noth.

17. Hiemit will ichs beschliessen,
Merkt auf ihr Frommen all,
Es soll uns nicht verdriessen,
Zu betrachten Adams Fall,
Der auch annahm der Schlangen Rath.
Thät Gott ungehorsam bleiben,
Drum folget ihm der Tod.

18. So wirds den'n auch geschehen,
Die Christo widerstohn,
Weltliche Lüst ansehen,
Kein göttlich Lieb nicht hon.
Also hat dieses Lied ein End,
Bey Christo will ich bleiben,
Der all mein Noth erkennt. Amen.

# 417 LORD GOD! TO THEE BE BLESSING

*The Lord stood with me, and strengthened me; that by me the preaching might be fully known . . . I was delivered out of the mouth of the lion.* II Tim. 4:17.

From the 16th century Anabaptist *Ausbund*
Hymn No. 30, Georg Blaurock, burnt 1529
*Herr Gott! dich will ich loben*
Tr. John J. Overholt, 1971

SCHWANENLIED 7.6.7.6.8.7.6.
M.M. 66

Arr. John J. Overholt, 1971

1. Lord God! to Thee be bless - ing From hence un-til my end,
That I Thy faith possess - ing Thee know and appre-hend; Thy Ho-ly Word
2. Thy Word received I from Thee, As Thou, O Lord, dost know;
It shall not void re - turn Thee, I hope; strength me bestow That I may
1. Herr Gott! dich will ich lo - ben, Von jetzt bis an mein End,
Dass du mir gabst den Glau-ben, Durch den ich dich er-kennt. Dein heil 'ges Wort
2. Von dir hab ichs ge - nom - men, Wie du, o Herr, wohl weisst,
Nicht leer wirds wie-der kom- men, Hoff ich, und stark mein'n Geist, Dass ich er-kenn

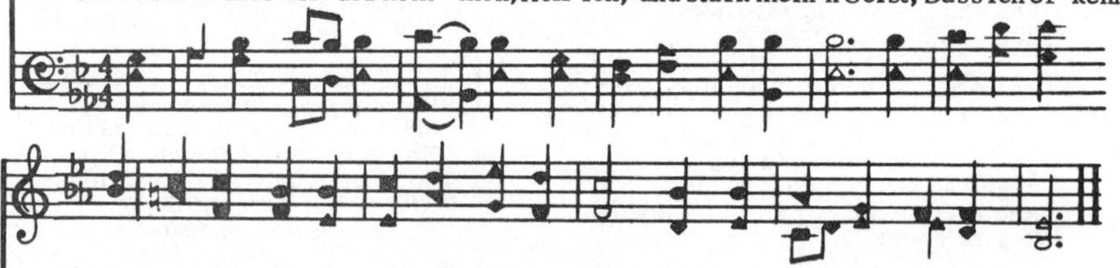

Thou send-est me Which I thro' grace and mer - cy Possess and prize from Thee.
know Thy will, not mine, In this is my rejoic-ing, Ev - er in my heart's shrine.
send - st du zu mir, Welch's ich aus lau-ter Gna-den Bey mir be-find und spühr.
den Wil - len dein, Dess thu ich mich er - freu-en In meines Her-zens Schrein.

3. What dread, when inward trifling
I found, and greatly feared
A burden was me stifling;
Hadst Thou not soon appeared
That I Thy Word of grace obtain,
Then must I be enduring
And suff'ring lasting pain.

4. Therefore will I be blessing
And ever praising Thee,
Thy name in heav'n addressing,
That Thou art shown to be
E'er as a father it behoove,
Wilt me ne'er be forsaking;
For Thy child me approve.

5. To Thee, Lord, I am crying,
Help, God and Father, mine,
That I in love complying,
Be child and heir of Thine;
O Lord, my faith make mightier,
Lest fall the house to ruins,
Where Thy help absent were.

6. O Lord, forget me never,
For e'er with me abide;
Thy Spirit teach me ever,
Protect, in suffering hide
That I may know Thy comfort rife,
And valiantly may conquer,
With vict'ry in the strife.

3. Gar sehr thäts mich erschröcken,
Da ich's befand in mir,
Ein Bürd wollt mich ersticken,
Wärst du nicht kommen schier
Mit deinem Wort der Gnaden schein,
Hätt ich müssen erliegen,
Und leiden ewig Pein.

4. Hierauf so will ich loben
Und preisen ewiglich
Dein'n Namen hoch dort oben,
Dass du erzeigest dich
Allzeit wie sichs ein'm Vater ziemt,
Wollst mich doch nicht verstossen,
Wähl mich zu deinem Kind.

5. Zu dir, Herr, thu ich schreyen,
Hilf, Gott und Vater, mein,
Dass ich aus Lieb und Treuen
Ein Kind und Erb sey dein,
O Herr, stärk mir den Glauben sehr,
Sonst gieng der Bau zu Trümmern,
Wo dein Hülf nicht da wär.

6. Vergiss mein nicht, O Herre,
Wollst allzeit bey mir seyn,
Dein Geist mich schütz und lehre,
Dass ich im Leiden mein
Getröstet werd zu aller Zeit,
Und ritterlich erobre
Den Sieg in diesem Streit.

7. The foe beat hard upon me
Where in the field I lay;
He fain from it would drive me,
Lord, Thou didst vict'ry stay;
With weapon sharp he on me pressed,
That all my body trembled,
From force and falsehood stressed.

8. In this, Thou Lord, hadst mercy,
Through Thy grace, help, and pow'r,
Help'st Thy poor son to vict'ry;
Triumphant didst empow'r;
O Lord, how soon Thou heard'st my plight,
Didst come in help so mighty,
The foe Thyself didst fight.

9. Therefore will I be singing
In blessing of Thy name,
Eternally praise bringing
Of grace that to me came;
Before Thy children hence I pray
That Thou wilt keep us ever
From foes without delay.

10. In flesh I am distrusting,
It is too weak revealed;
In Thy Word I am trusting,
This comfort is and shield,
Dependent on it though hard–pressed
That Thou wilt from disasters
Me help into Thy rest.

11. Our latest hour is nearing
So must we now it man;
Help us, O Lord, in bearing
The cross after Thy plan;
Come with Thy grace boundless, unspanned,
That we may be committing
Our spirits in Thy hand.

12. I earnestly do pray Thee
Before all of our foes,
Lord, those mislead* before Thee,
So many thus are those,
That Thou them charge of evil void,
Yet be this after Thy will,
This pray I Thee, O God.

13. So will I then be parting
With comrades mine, indeed,
May God us grace imparting,
Into His kingdom lead;
That we in faith all doubt transcend,
His holy work fulfilling,
This grant He in the end.

7. Der Feind hat auf mich g'schlagen,
Im Feld, darin ich lieg,
Wollt mich daraus verjagen.
Herr, du gabst mir den Sieg.
Mit scharfer Wehr er auf mich drang,
Dass all mein Leib thät zittern,
Vor falscher Lehr und Zwang.

8. Dess lies'st dich, Herr, erbarmen.
Durch dein Gnad, Hilf und Kraft,
Hälfst deinem Sohn mir armen,
Und machest mich sieghaft.
O Herr, wie bald du mich erhörtst,
Kommst stark mit deiner Hülfe,
Den Feinden selber wehrst.

9. Darum so will ich singen,
Zu Lob dem Namen dein,
Und ewiglich verkünden
Die Gnad, die mir erschien.
Nun bitt ich dich vor all dein Kind,
Wollst uns ewig bewahren
Vor allen Feinden g'schwind.

10. Auf Fleisch kann ich nicht bauen,
Es ist zu schwacher Art:
In dein Wort will ich trauen,
Das sey mein Trost und Hort,
Darauf ich mich verlassen thu,
Wirst mir aus allen Nöthen
Helfen zu deiner Ruh.

11. Die Stund des letzten Tagen,
So wir nun müssen dran,
Wollst uns, Herr, helfen tragen,
Das Creutz wohl auf dem Plan,
Mit aller Gnad dich zu uns wend,
Dass wir mögen befehlen
Den Geist in deine Händ.

12. Hertzlich thu ich dich bitten
Vor alle uns're Feind,
Wollst ihn'n, o Herr, mit Sitten,
Wie viel doch deren seynd,
Nicht rechnen ihre Missethat,
Das g'scheh nach deinem Willen,
Dess bitt ich dich, o Gott.

13. Also will ich mich scheiden,
Sammt den Gefährten mein,
In Gnad woll uns Gott leiten
Wohl in das Reiche sein.
Dass wir im Glauben ohn Zweifel seynd
Sein heil'ges Werk vollenden,
Der geb uns Kraft ins End.

* Sitten: manners, morals, propriety

# 418 WHO CHRIST WILL FOLLOW

*All that will live godly in Christ Jesus shall suffer persecution.* II Tim. 3:12.

From the 16th century Anabaptist *Ausbund*
Hymn No. 11, J'org Wagner, burnt 1527
*Wer Christo jetzt will folgen nach*
Tr. John J. Overholt, 1970
ANGELUS NEW 8.8.7.8.7.
M.M. 84
Scheffler's *Heilige Seelenlust*, 1657
Arr. John J. Overholt, 1970
1. Who Christ will fol – low now, new–born, Dare not be moved by this world's scorn, The cross must bear sin – cere – ly;
2. This did George Wag – ner, too, as – pire, He went to heav'n 'mid smoke and fire, The cross his test and prov – ing,
1. Wer Chris – to jetzt will fol – gen nach, Muss ach – ten nich – te der Welt Schmach, Das Creutz er auch muss tra – gen.
2. Al – so thăt Jörg der Wag–ner auch, Gen Him – mel fuhr er in dem Rauch, Durchs Creutz ward er be – wăh – ret,
No oth – er way to heav–en leads, From childhood we're taught clear–ly.
As gold is in the fur–nace tried, His heart's de–sire ap – prov – ing.
Kein an – der Weg in Him–mel geht, Hőrt ich von Ju–gend sa – gen.
Gleich wie man thut dem kla–ren Gold, Von Her–zen ers be – geh – ret. A – men.

3. The falcon tower became his lease,
It brought about his soul's release,
No human sorrowing swerved him,
Nor was he moved by his small child,
Nor had his wife unnerved him.

4. They no more his could be to aid,
Though he gladly with them had stayed,
His love and sorrow welling;
No labor spared he on his part,
As righteous partners dwelling.

3. Der Falkenthurm ward ihm zu Theil,
Es galt ihm seiner Seelen Heyl,
Er acht kein's Menschen Trauren,
Er acht auch nicht sein kleine Kind,
Noch seiner Ehlichen Frauen.

4. Wiewohl sie ihm nicht war'n nunmehr,
Und er gern bey ihn'n blieben wăr,
Hat Liebs und Leids gelitten,
Kein Arbeit an seim Leib gespart,
Nach frommer Ehleut Sitten.

| | |
|---|---|
| 5. Although he from them must depart,<br>No meanly sacrifice of heart,<br>That he from them be parting,<br>No prince with all his princely gain<br>Could him from this be thwarting. | 5. Gleichwohl er sie verlassen muss,<br>Es war ihm kein geringe Buss,<br>Dass er von ihn'n musst scheiden.<br>Kein Fürst mit seinem Fürstenthum,<br>Hätts ihm mögen erleiden. |
| 6. Two barefoot monks in grey array,<br>George Wagner's sorrows would allay,<br>They would him be converting;<br>He waved them to their cloister home,<br>Their speech he'd be averting. | 6. Zween Baarfüss–Mönch in grauem Kleid<br>Jörg Wagner trösten in seim Leid,<br>Sie wollten ihn bekehren.<br>Er wiess sie in ihr Klösterlein,<br>Ihr Red wollt er nicht hören. |
| 7. The hangman him with rope interned,<br>In the town hall four counts he learned,<br>Upon which hinged his living;<br>Before he one truth would deny,<br>His life would he be giving. | 7. Der Henker führt ihn an ein'm Strick,<br>Im Rathhaus las man ihm vier Stück,<br>Darauf stund ihm sein Leben:<br>Eh er eins widerrufen wollt,<br>In Tod thät er sich geben. |
| 8. The article which first would weigh,<br>With the confession it did lay,<br>No priest could be forgiving,<br>For against God would he have sinned,<br>Who'd only be grace giving. | 8. Der erst Artikel war nicht leicht,<br>Traff an die mündlich Ohrenbeicht,<br>Kein Pfaff mocht ihm verzeihen,<br>Dieweil er wider Gott gethan,<br>Der ihn allein konnt freyen. |
| 9. Baptism is right as Christ has taught,<br>When this ord'nance is not distraught,<br>Portends his bitter dying,<br>In symbol washes us from sins,<br>And grace us signifying. | 9. Der Tauff ist recht wie Christus lehrt,<br>Wenn die Ordnung nicht wird verkehrt,<br>Bedeut sein bitter Sterben,<br>Ist ein Abwäschung unser Sünd,<br>Dadurch wir Gnad erwerben. |
| 10. Of our Lord Christ's own sacrament,<br>George Wagner testified intent,<br>A symbol, it esteem I,<br>Of Christ's own body offered free;<br>No flattery spake he hereby. | 10. Vons Herren Christi Sacrament<br>Jörg Wagner ihn'n auch frey bekennt,<br>Ich halt es vor ein Zeichen,<br>Vor Christi hingegebnen Leib,<br>Redt er ohn alles Schmeichlen. |
| 11, Fourthly, he would not fain believe<br>That God should such constraint receive<br>And come to earth in brightness,<br>Until His judgment He should hold,<br>The wicked with the righteous. | 11. Zum vierten wollt nicht Glauben thun,<br>Dass sich Gott sollte zwingen lohn,<br>Auf Erd herab zu kommen,<br>Bis er werd halten sein Gericht,<br>Den Bösen mit den Frommen. |

12. Did several Christian brothers near
(21) Speak then into George Wagner's ear
While still he was yet living,
(He died in fire, a Christian true),
Wilt us a sign be giving.

12. Etlich Christliche Brüder war'n,
(21) Redten Jörg Wagner in sein' Ohr'n,
Weil er noch war beym Leben,
Im Feur sterb als ein frommer Christ,
Wollst uns ein Zeichen geben.

13. He said: This will I gladly do,
(22) Christ, truly God's own Son, as due,
By mouth I'll be confessing;
As long as privilege shall be,
Jesus him be addressing.

13. Er sprach: Das will ich gerne thun,
(22) Christum den wahren Gottes Sohn
Will ich mit'm Mund bekennen,
So lang als mein Vermögen ist,
Will ich ihn Jesum nennen.

14. Two hangmen stood now at his side,
(23) The ring about him they made wide,
George Wagner spake his faith strong,
Around him a great company,
Men, women, an attent throng.

14. Zween Henker stunden bey der Seit,
(23) Den Ring um ihn sie machten weit,
Jörg Wagner sprach den Glauben.
Zugegen stund ein grosse Schaar
Von Männern und von Frauen.

15. George Wagner's gaze did nothing quail,
(24) His lips did never once grow pale,
He spake that many wondered,
T'was in the twenty seventh year,
One thousand and five hundred.

15. Jörg Wagner sah ohn Furcht um sich,
(24) Sein Mund zu keiner Zeit verblich,
Er redt dass manchen wundert.
Geschah im sieben und zwanzigsten Jahr,
Ein tausend und fünf hundert.

16. In February the same year,
(25) The eighth day, openly and clear,
Men on a stake then hung him,
A bag of powder, rather small,
There took his soul quite from him.

16. Im Hornung in demselben Jahr,
(25) Am achten Tag ganz offenbar,
Hing man ihm an sein Kehle
Ein Sack mit Pulver nicht fast klein,
Benahm ihm da sein Seele.

17. Men fastened him to ladder firm
(26) The wood and straw was made to burn,
Now was the laughter dire;
Jesus! Jesus! did he four times
Call loudly from the fire.

17. Man flocht ihn auf ein Leiter hart,
(26) Das Holz und Stroh anzündet ward,
Jetz ward das Lachen theuer.
Jesus, Jesus, zum vierten mahl,
Rief er laut aus dem Feuer.

18. Elias speaks the truth entire
(27) That he in chariot of fire
In paradise did lighten;
So pray we then, the Holy Ghost,
That He may us enlighten.

18. Elias thut die Wahrheit sagen,
(27) Dass er in ein'm feurigen Wagen
Fuhr in das Paradeise:
So bitten wir den Heiligen Geist,
Dass er uns unterweise.

# O THOU ALMIGHTY LORD AND GOD 419

*Thy law is my delight.* Ps. 119:77. *I will delight myself in Thy commandments.* Ps. 119:47. *More to be desired are they than gold.* Ps. 19:10.

From the 16th century Anabaptist *Ausbund*
Hymn No. 8, Hans Hut, died 1527
*O Allmächtiger Herre Gott!*
Tr. John J. Overholt, 1969

ST. MARGARET NEW 8.8.8.8.6.
M.M. 60

Albert Lister Peace, 1885 (1844-1912)
Arr. by Compiler, 1971

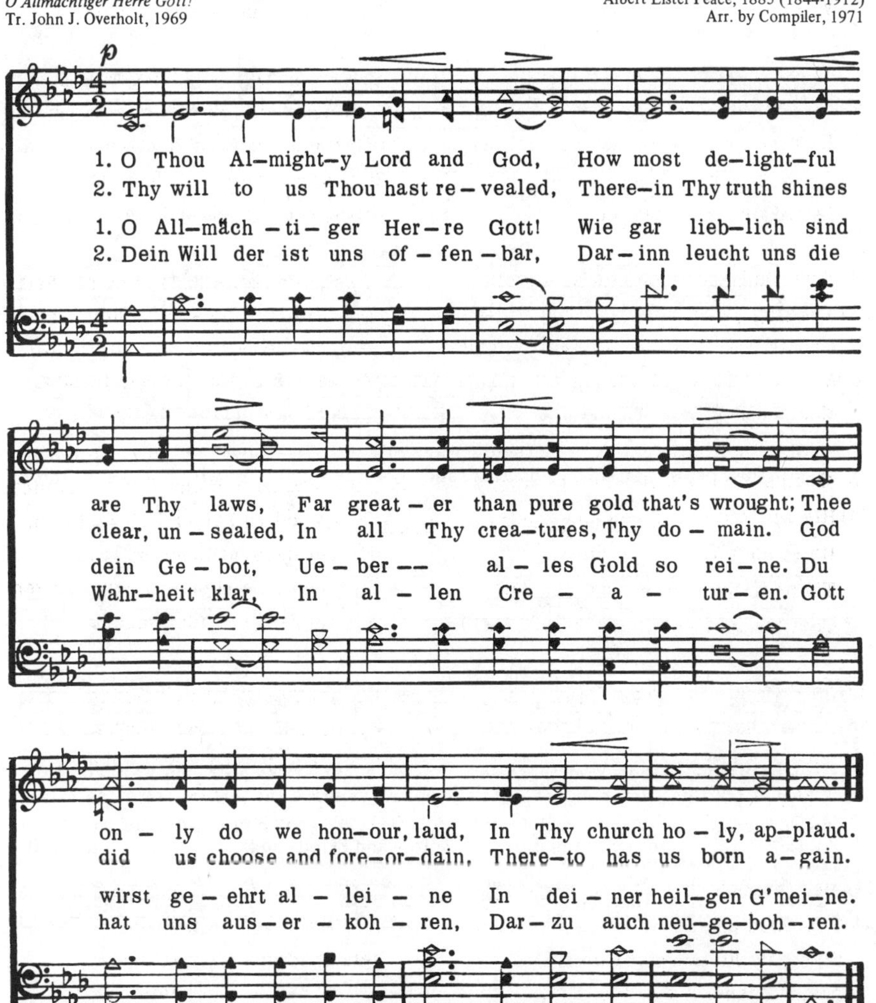
p
1. O Thou Al–might–y Lord and God, How most de–light–ful are Thy laws, Far great – er than pure gold that's wrought; Thee on – ly do we hon–our, laud, In Thy church ho – ly, ap–plaud.
2. Thy will to us Thou hast re – vealed, There–in Thy truth shines clear, un – sealed, In all Thy crea–tures, Thy do – main. God did us choose and fore–or–dain, There–to has us born a – gain.
1. O All–mäch – ti – ger Her – re Gott! Wie gar lieb–lich sind dein Ge – bot, Ue – ber –– al – les Gold so rei – ne. Du wirst ge – ehrt al – lei – ne In dei – ner heil–gen G'mei–ne.
2. Dein Will der ist uns of – fen – bar, Dar – inn leucht uns die Wahr–heit klar, In al – len Cre – a – tur – en. Gott hat uns aus – er – koh – ren, Dar – zu auch neu–ge–boh – ren.

3. The Father honour be, and praise,
(12) Who ever lives, has endless days,
His name shall be forever famed,
Of His Son we shall ne'er be shamed,
Who helps us ever, Amen.

3. Dem Vater sey nun Lob und Ehr,
(12) Der ewig bleibt und immermehr,
Und ewig hält sein'n Namen,
Sein's Sohns wir uns nicht schamen,
Der helf uns ewig, Amen.

# 420 THERE ARE TWO WAYS

*Wide is the gate, and broad is the way, that leadeth to destruction, and many there be which go in thereat . . . narrow is the way, which leadeth unto life, and few there be that find it.* Mt. 7:13-14.

From the 16th century Anabaptist *Ausbund*
Hymn No 125, st. 57–
*Es sind zween Weg in dieser Zeit*
Tr. John J. Overholt, 1970

PARTING HAND L.M.D.
8.8.8.8.D.
M.M. 72

Jeremiah Ingalls, 1764-1828

1. There are two ways in this, our day, One nar – row and the oth – er broad;
2. There–aft – er, there's e – ter – nal rest, There–fore, O man, Thy way pre–pare,
57. Es sind zween Weg in die – ser Zeit, Der ein ist schmal, der an – der weit,
59. Dar – nach hat er e – wi – ge Ruh. Dar–um, O Mensch, schick dich dar–zu,

Who now will go the nar – row way Will be de–spised by all a–broad.
Wilt thou be in God's king–dom blessed E – ter – nal – ly with right–eous there.
Wer jetzt will gahn die schma–le Bahn, Der wird ver–acht von je – der – mann.
Wilt du seyn gleich in Got – tes Reich, Mit al – len From – men e – wig–lich.

This plain–ly God's Word teach–es us, The nar – row en–trance way go in;
Aft – er this time nought shall tran–spire But peace and joy e – ter – nal – ly;
58. Das zeigt uns an des Her – ren Wort: Geht ein durch die – se en – ge Pfort,
60. Da wird nichts seyn nach die – ser Zeit, Dann Fried und Freud in E – wig – keit,

Strait is the gate, who en – ter thus, Must first en–dure great suf – fer–ing.
The right–eous then, this shall a–quire Who God's will hon–or con – stant–ly.
Die Thür ist klein, wer will hin – ein, Der muss vor lei – den gros – se Pein.
Die From–men schon wer–den das hon, Die all – zeit Got – tes Wil–len thun.

3. But he who the broad way shall go,
The stairs to hell, this is the same,
He now is lost, God's wrath shall know,
But blessed is he who's born again.
To him hath God prepared, impearled
A crown eternity shall hold;
It shall not pass away, O world,
Away then, with your gain and gold.

4. O, take the strait and narrow way
That thou the lasting crown obtain,
Which God doth but His church convey
Which He hath cleansed from sin and stain.
Therefore away with all man's gain,
Desire, vain pomp, and arrogance;
Turn sharp away from all known sin,
So thou be known as God's child hence.

5. Nought other can the way become,
Who will eternal suffering flee,
Must righteous be, this is the sum;
Go on your way, nor fancy see.
Press toward the mark till endless day,
For who the prize at last will gain,
All must forsake upon this way
Would he the lasting crown obtain.

---

3. Wer aber geht den breiten Weg,
(61) Dasselbig ist der Höllen Steg,
Der ist verlohrn in Gottes Zorn,
Wohl dem der jetzt ist neugebohrn.
(62) Demselben hat Gott zubereit
Ein Kron, die bleibt in Ewigkeit,
Sie wird nicht welck, darum, o Welt,
Lass fahren alles Gut und Geld.

4. Und mach dich auf die schmale Bahn,
(63) Dass du erlangst die ewig Kron,
Die Gott allein gibt seiner G'mein,
Die er hat g'macht von Sünden rein.
(64) Darum lass fahren alles Gut,
Den Geitz, hoch Pracht und Uebermuth,
Kehr dich behend von aller Sünd,
So wirst du g'zählt vor Gottes Kind.

5. Dann es wird je nicht anders seyn,
(65) Wer meiden will die ewig Pein,
Der werd nur fromm, das ist die Summ,
Mach sich auf d'Bahn, und seh nit um,
(66) Streck sich zum vorgesteckten Ziel.
Dann wer das Kleinod g'winnen will,
Muss alls verlahn, auf dieser Bahn,
Will er erlangen diese Kron.

# 421 JESUS, THE CHRIST, THE SON OF GOD

*... Wait for the promise of the Father, which, saith he, ye have heard of me. For John truly baptized with water; but ye shall be baptized with the Holy Ghost not many days hence.* Acts 1:4-5.

From the 16th century Anabaptist *Ausbund*
Hymn No. 38, Johannes Huss, burnt 1415
*Jesus Christus, Gottes Sohn*
Tr. John J. Overholt, 1969

LOB SEI DEM ALLMÄCHTIGEN
L.M. 8.8.8.8.
M. M. 60

Johann Crüger, 1640 (1598-1662)

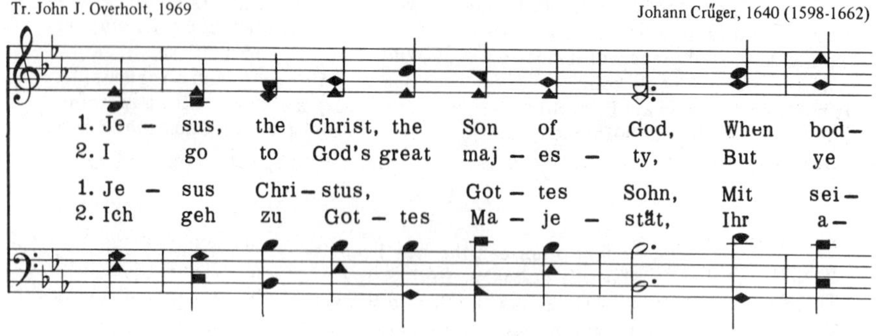
1. Je – sus, the Christ, the Son of God, When bod–
2. I go to God's great maj – es – ty, But ye
1. Je – sus Chri – stus, Got – tes Sohn, Mit sei–
2. Ich geh zu Got – tes Ma – je – stät, Ihr a–

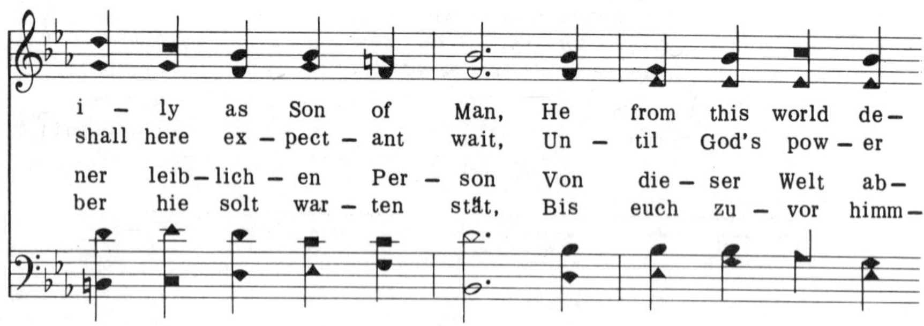
i – ly as Son of Man, He from this world de–
shall here ex – pect – ant wait, Un – til God's pow – er
ner leib – lich – en Per – son Von die – ser Welt ab–
ber hie solt war – ten stät, Bis euch zu – vor himm–

par – ture sought, Thus His dis – ci – ples did com – mand:
from on high You to His knight–hood shall in – state.
schei–den wollt, Und sprach zu sei – nen Jün – gern hold:
li – sche Kraft Be – stä – ti – ge zur Rit – ter – schaft.

3. This the disciples did obey,
Together in a room they stayed,
With one accord, the Christian way,
In earnest prayer to God they prayed.

3. Die Jünger glaubten diesem Wort,
Blieben zusammen an ein'm Ort
Einträchtig nach Christlicher Weiss,
Beten zu Gott mit allem Fleiss.

4. When Pentecost was fully come,
And fifty days from Easter morn,
When Christ to heav'n nine days had gone,
Great things of God to them were borne.

5. That morning at the full ninth hour,
As prayer did in their hearts abound,
The Holy Ghost with mighty power,
Came as a wind with rushing sound.

6. And sat upon each one of them,
And gave them proper minds and meek,
The Holy Scriptures, ground and theme,
With new tongues undefiled to speak.

7. Therefore, together many ran,
Whom the disciples freely taught;
With new tongues great things they began;
Their speech conviction many brought.

8. O brethren, men, what must we do
(11) That we may enter into rest?
We find but sin in us anew;
Through whom can we be loosed and blest?

9. Spake Peter: From your ways repent,
(12) Believe in Jesus, God's own Son;
Confess Him, too, by mouth intent,
Be baptized to His faith anon.

10. As Peter did command did they
(13) Their ways from evil turn, and strife;
Believed, and were baptized straightway,
And walked in godly way of life.

11. O now do grant us, Holy One,
(14) That this, Thy pattern, we upraise;
Thy early church foll'wing hereon,
Thee, Lord and God, may bless and praise.

---

4. Nach Ostern am fünfzigsten Tag,
Den man den Pfingsttag nennen mag,
Neun Tag nach Christi Himmelfahrt,
Gross Ding ihn'n wurden offenbahrt.

5. Des Morgens um die dritte Stund,
Als sie baten aus Herzens Grund
Da kam der Heilig Geist ins Haus,
Wie ein Sturmwind mit grossem Strauss.

6. Sass auf ein jeden unter ihn'n,
Gab allen ein rechtschaffnen Sinn.
Aus zu reden den Grund der Schrift,
Mit neuen Zungen unvergift.

7. Auf diesen Sturm lief viel Volks zu,
Sie die Jünger erregten fruh,
Mit neuen Zungen grosse Ding,
Ihr' Red vielen zu Herzen gieng.

11. O ihr Brüder nun rathet zu,
Wie wir kommen zu rechter Ruh,
Wir finden bey uns nichts dann Sünd,
Saget wer uns davon entbind.

12. Petrus sprach: Bessert euer Thun,
Und glaubt in Christum, Gottes Sohn,
Bekennt ihn auch mit eurem Mund,
Lasst euch taufen auf seinen Bund.

13. Sie thäten wie ihn'n Petrus rieth,
Wandten vom Bösen ihren Tritt,
Glaubten und empfingen den Tauf,
Lieffen ein'n gottseligen Lauff.

14. Ey nun verleih uns, Heilger Geist,
Dass wir uns halten allermeist
Nach dieser ersten Kirchen–Weiss,
Dir Herre Gott zu Lob und Preiss.

# 422 A SAD AND DOLEFUL CARE

*We which live are alway delivered unto death for Jesus' sake, that the life also of Jesus might be made manifest in our mortal flesh.* II Cor. 4:11.

Menno Simons, c. 1550 (1496-1561)
Dutch Anabaptist church leader
*Een truerich droeuich leyt*
Tr. Leonard Verduin, 1955

BENDA NEW (Irregular)
M.M. 69

From the *Philharmonia*, 1875
Arr. John J. Overholt, 1970

Slowly

1. A sad and dole - ful care, This news, dear broth - er, share, Which God hath now for me pre - pared. A chastening He ap - plies, My in - most heart He tries, My flesh in sore af - flict - ion lies. His god - ly wis - dom sure

2. The prop - het has a - verred With clear and clar - ion word That grief is mor - tal man's re - ward; His life ebbs fast a - way, Till death him low doth lay With suff - 'ring, all the wea - ry way. Like to a fad - ing flower

1. Een true - rich droe - uich leyt Broe - ders hoort mijn be - scheyt Heeft my de Hee - re toe - be - reyt Hy went aen my zijn tocht En heeft my hert be - socht Mijn vleesch in swaer el - lende ghe - brocht Sijn God - de - lij - cken raet

2. Het spreect een Pro - pheet Met hel - der cla - re reet Een mensch ghe - boren leeft int ver - driet Sijn le - uen dat gaet voort Gans snel - lijck tot - ter doot En - de wort met veel lijdens ver - stoort Ghe - lijk een bloem

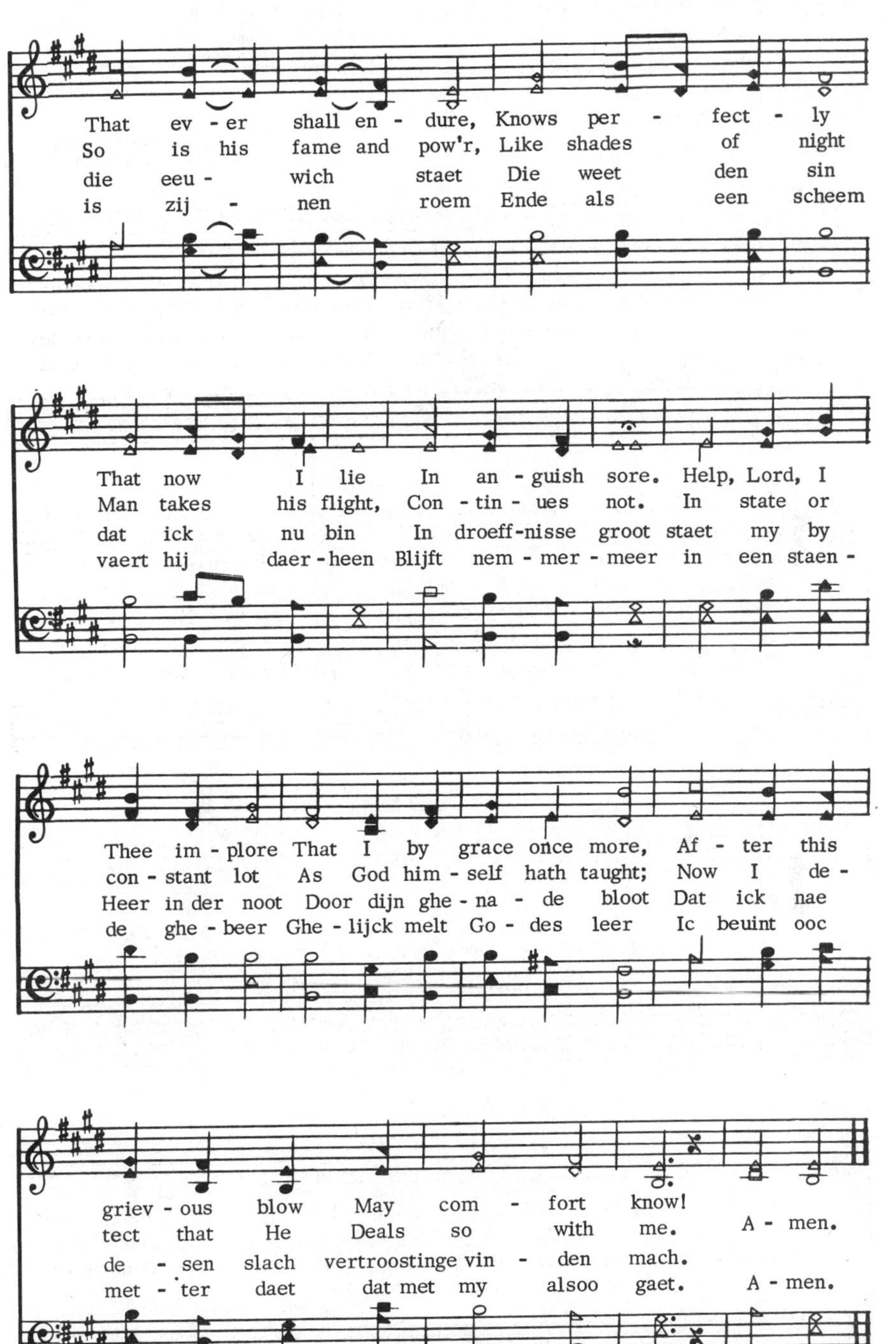
That ev - er shall en - dure, Knows per - fect - ly
So is his fame and pow'r, Like shades of night
die eeu - wich staet Die weet den sin
is zij - nen roem Ende als een scheem
That now I lie In an - guish sore. Help, Lord, I
Man takes his flight, Con - tin - ues not. In state or
dat ick nu bin In droeff-nisse groot staet my by
vaert hij daer - heen Blijft nem - mer - meer in een staen -
Thee im - plore That I by grace once more, Af - ter this
con - stant lot As God him - self hath taught; Now I de -
Heer in der noot Door dijn ghe - na - de bloot Dat ick nae
de ghe - beer Ghe - lijck melt Go - des leer Ic beuint ooc
griev - ous blow May com - fort know!
tect that He Deals so with me. A - men.
de - sen slach vertroostinge vin - den mach.
met - ter daet dat met my alsoo gaet. A - men.

3. The Father's chastenings sore
Most gladly I endure
As Micheas did, the saint of yore.
I by His Word confess
To wretched sinfulness,
The sinful lusts of human flesh;
I, born of Adam's seed, am sinful—born indeed;
Therefore will I right willingly
Chastised stand; Accept all at His hand,
Like Job of storied land,
Till me He to Him takes and blessed makes.

3. Ick wil mijns Vaders slaen
Van herten gheern ontfaen
Ghelijck de vrome Micheas heeft ghedaen
Want ick door dWoort beken
Dat ick een Sondaer ben
En in mijn vleesch met lust behanghen ben
Mijn aert is quaet wt Adams saet
Daerom wil ick goetwillichlick
In smerten staen mijns Heeren straf onfaen
Ghelijck Job heeft ghedaen
Totdat hy my opneemt en zijn genade schenct.

4. Ah, faithful Father, Lord,
My flesh has strength no more,
This earthly house Thou breakest sore.
The vile world hates me quite,
For this Thy witness bright;
Thy cross I bear with grief not light.
And yet—adversity! Thy hand Thou lay'st on me,
And presses so my flesh lays low!
Yet rest I me upon Thy promise free
Which ever sure shall be;
And praise Thy majesty in all eternity!

4. Trouwe Vader Heer
Ick en heb gheen crachten meer
Mijn swacke vleesch breect ghy al te seer
De Werelt haet my gaer
Om dijn ghetuychnis claer
En drage dijn cruys met ancxst ende moeyte swaer
Noch is dijn hant tot my ghesant
Heeft my geraect mijn vleesch te niet gemaect
Nochtans wil hopen ick op dijn beloften rijc
Die zijn ghewisselijck
En dijnen Maiesteyt prijsen in eeuwicheyt.

---

## Accolade to a Champion

**Th. J. van Braght**
**July 27, 1659**

*Klimt op uw' gulden Hoogtt', Voor—vechter van de Bende der heyl'ge Zielen, die God's roode Bloed—Banier navolgde, in't gedrang, in't midden der Ellenden, daer niet dan rook en damp van menschen Offervyer tot door de wolken vloog; noch gingt gy Held haer voor, ja streed, door d' enge poort, ten Ten ruymen Hemel door.*

*Het schriklyk offer—vyer, de glinsterende staken, Den smaed, die Zion leed, kon God's verkoren volk Belet noch hinder doen, noch geensins angstig Maken te dragen Christi naem, als in sen witte wolk: Tot dat een heete vlam haer lyven heeft verslonden; Waer door haer zielen toen by God verkoeling vonden.*

Climb up your golden height, champion of the band of holy souls, who followed God's red banner of blood, in oppression and in the midst of misery, where naught but the smoke and vapor of human burnt sacrifices ascended to the clouds; yet thou, hero, didst go before them, yea, didst fight thy way through the strait gate to the wide heaven.

The dreadful sacrificial fire, the shining stakes, the shame which Zion suffers, could neither disturb nor hinder God's chosen people, nor make them afraid to bear the name of Christ, as in a white cloud: Until a burning flame had consumed their bodies whereby their souls found refreshing with God.

(This tribute by van Braght in *Martyrs Mirror*, p. 6, was paid to Gerardus, who for Jesus' sake went singing before his companions, five other men, two women, and a girl, on the way to burning at the stake, Cologne, A. D. 1163.)

5. Ah, Father, God and Lord,
Incline Thy face once more
In this disease and sickness sore;
Give patience, strength, in grace
The brightness of Thy face,
Mid sorrows that come on apace!
That I may constant be, whate'er Thy way with me;
And, not the last, my soul hold fast!
Yes, Father, kind, preserve in pious mind
Thy sons, who sadness find,
In faith and doctrine whole, so prays my soul!

5. O God Vader en Heer
Dijn aensicht tot my keer
In dese mijnder cranckheyt seer
Gheeft cracht, ende ghedult
En uwe trouwe hult
In mijnen noet, druck, lijden en wederspoet
Dat ick bestae hoet met my gae
En aldermeest in mijnen Gheest
O Vader goet v bedroefde knechten behoet
In een vrome ghemoet
Int geloof en leer gesont bid ick van herten gront.

6. I beg my brethren all,
Who've heard the Master's call
My grief and pain now to recall,
And then, before God's eyes
Lay pleasant sacrifice;
Let pleasing prayer as incense rise;
That I may then again, delivered from this pain,
Behold Thy grace, resume my place,
Serve Christ alway, right well the livelong day,
This is my song I pray
With brethren everywhere, in Word—borne prayer.

6. Ick bid alle broeders mijn
Die inden Heere zijn
Dat sy bedincken mijn droefheyt iammer en pijn
Ende offeren eenen offer soet
Op Godes Outaer goet
Voor haren broeder tot een lieffelijcke lustelijcken rook
Opdat ick mach nae veel beclach
Genade ontfaen weder op Christus acker gaen
En dienen mijn leuen lanc sonder eenich bedwanck
Bid ick met eenen sanck
Mijn Broeders int ghemeyn met Gods woorden reyn.

---

## Invocation to *Martyrs Mirror*

**Th. J. van Braght**

**July 27, 1659**

Pardon me, O my Lord and my God! that I, who am but dust and ashes, approach Thee. Gen. 18:27. ...Thy servant David, a man after Thine own heart, sang, "Precious in the sight of the Lord is the death of his saints." Ps. 116:15.

...Yet that which more than all else caused my tears to flow was the remembrance of the sufferings and the death of Thy martyrs, who altogether innocent, as defenceless lambs, were led to the water, the fire, the sword, or to the wild beasts in the arena, there to suffer and to die for Thy name's sake. However, I experienced no small degree of joy as I contemplated the living confidence they had in Thy grace, and how valiantly they fought their way through the strait gate.

Ah! how often did I wish to have been a partaker with them; my soul went with them, so to speak, into prison; I encouraged them in the tribunal, to bear patiently, without gainsaying or flinching, their sentence of death. It seemed to me as though I accompanied them to the place of execution, scaffold or stake, saying to them in their extremity, Fight valiantly dear brethren and sisters; the crown of life awaits you. I almost fancied that I had died with them; so inseparably was my love bound up with them; for Thy holy name' sake.

...Thou knowest, O my Saviour and Redeemer, the steadfast faith, the unquenchable love, and faithfulness unto death, of those...who gave their precious lives and bodies as a sacrifice to Thee. (Abridged)

(Another champion of Christ, Willem Janss, was burnt alive at Amsterdam, March, 1569, after having made especial effort to be present at the execution of his dear brother Pieter Beckjen, and encouraging him by loudly calling, "Contend valiantly, dear brother!", *Martyrs Mirror*, p. 831.)

# 423 A SAD AND DOLEFUL CARE

*Take, my brethren, the prophets, who have spoken in the name of the Lord, for an example of suffering affliction, and of patience.* Jas. 5:10.

Menno Simons, c 1550 (1496-1561)
Dutch Anabaptist church leader
*Een truerich droeuich leyt*
Tr. Leonard Verduin, 1955

MENNO (Irregular)
M.M. 72

Arr. John J. Overholt, 1970

1. A sad and dole - ful care, This news, dear broth - er, share,
2. The prop - het has a - verred With clear and clar – ion word
1. Een true - rich droe - uich leyt Broe - ders hoort mijn be - scheyt
2. Het spreect een Pro - pheet Met hel - der cla - re reet
Which God hath now for me pre - pared. A chastening
That grief is mor - tal man's re - ward; His life ebbs
Heeft my de Hee - re toe - be - reyt Hy went aen
Een mensch ghe - boren leeft int ver - driet Sijn le - uen
He ap - plies, My in - most heart He tries, My flesh in
fast a - way, Till death him low doth lay With suff - 'ring,
my zijn tocht En heeft my hert be - socht Mijn vleesch in
dat gaet voort Gans snel - lijck tot - ter doot En - de wort
sore af - flict - ion lies. His god - ly wis - dom sure
all the wea - ry way. Like to a fad - ing flower
swaer el - lende ghe - brocht Sijn God - de - lij - cken raet
met veel lijdens ver - stoort Ghe - lijk een bloem

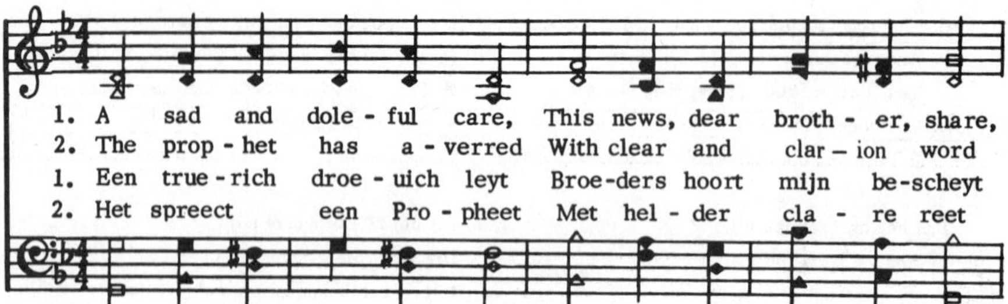

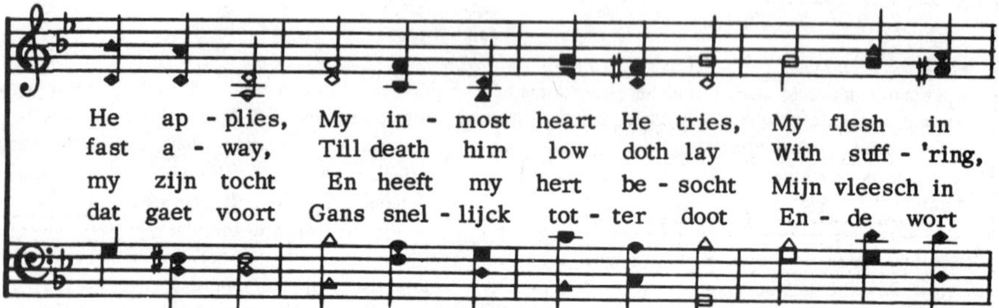

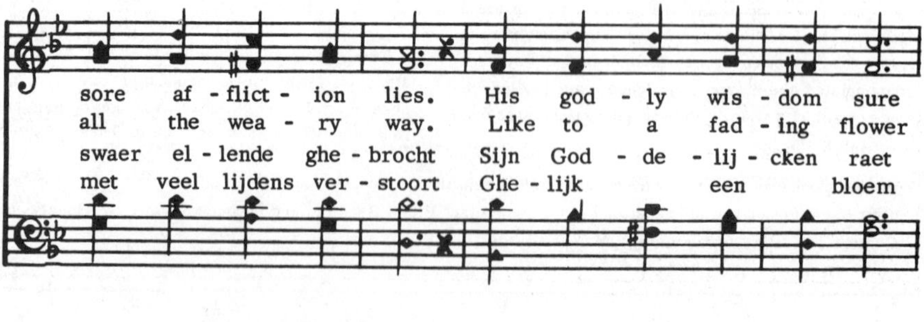

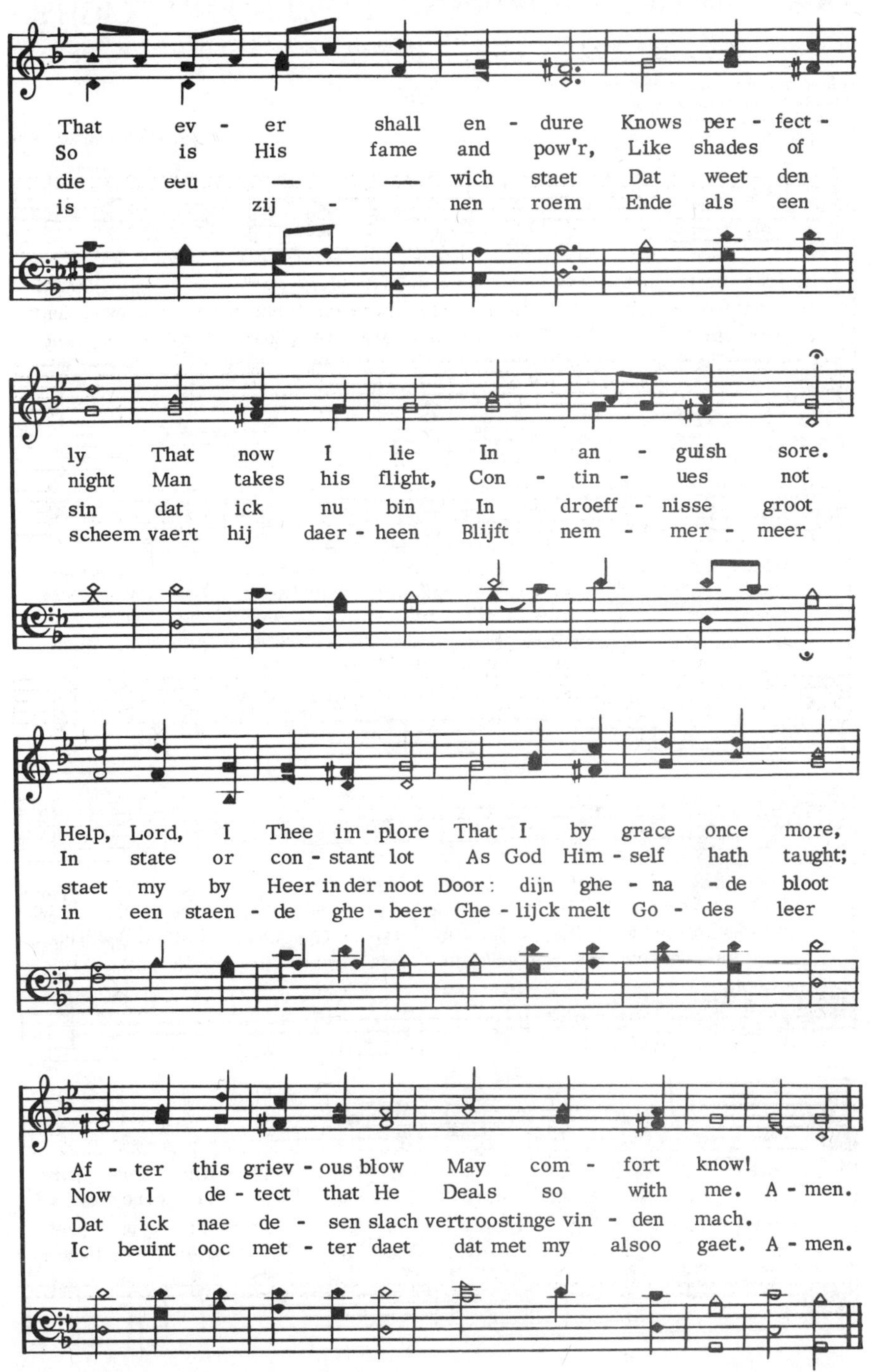
That ever shall endure Knows per-fect-ly That now I lie In an-guish sore.
So is His fame and pow'r, Like shades of night Man takes his flight, Con-tin-ues not
die eeu — — wich staet Dat weet den sin dat ick nu bin In droeff-nisse groot
is zij - nen roem Ende als een scheem vaert hij daer-heen Blijft nem-mer-meer
Help, Lord, I Thee im-plore That I by grace once more,
In state or con-stant lot As God Him-self hath taught;
staet my by Heer in der noot Door: dijn ghe-na-de bloot
in een staen-de ghe-beer Ghe-lijck melt Go-des leer
Af-ter this griev-ous blow May com-fort know!
Now I de-tect that He Deals so with me. A-men.
Dat ick nae de-sen slach vertroostinge vin-den mach.
Ic beuint ooc met-ter daet dat met my alsoo gaet. A-men.

# 424 MY GOD, WHERE SHALL I WEND MY FLIGHT

*My soul is among lions: and I lie even among them that are set on fire, even the sons of men, whose teeth are spears and arrows, and their tongue a sharp sword.* Ps. 57:4.

Menno Simons, c. 1540 (1496-1561)
Dutch Anabaptist church leader
*Mijn God waer sal ic henen gaen*
Tr. Leonard Verduin, 1955
Sts. 8, 11, Altered by Compiler, 1971

EIN TREUER ZEUGE 8.8.8.8.8.8.8.8.
M.M. 63

Arr. John J. Overholt, 1971

1. My God, where shall I wend my flight? Ah, help me on up – on the way; The foe sur–rounds both day and night And fain my soul would rend and slay; Lord God, Thy Spir – it give to me, Then on Thy ways I'll
2. When I in E–gypt still stuck fast, And travel – ed calm broad paths of ease, Then was I famed, a much–sought guest, The world with me was quite at peace; En – meshed was I in Sa – tan's gauze, My life a – bom – i–
1. Mijn God waer sal ic he – nen gaen Wilt my op u – we we – gen stue–ren, De vi – ant coemt nacht en dach om my staen En wil mijn sie – le ver – schue–ren O Herr laet mi v geest ont – faen So blijf ick op u – we
2. Doen ick noch in E – gyp – ten sadt vast Den ruy – men ghinc ick tre – den Doen was ick ghe – sien end een weert gast Van de we–relt was ick doen in vre – den Doen was ick vast in s–duy – uels strick Mijn le – uen was af–

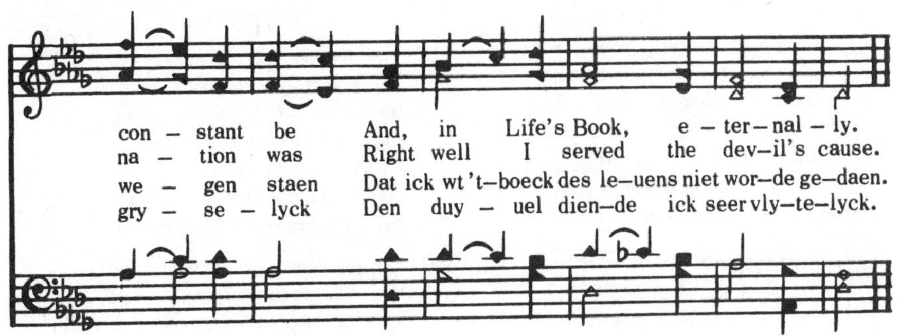
con – stant be And, in Life's Book, e – ter – nal – ly.
na – tion was Right well I served the dev–il's cause.
we – gen staen Dat ick wt 't–boeck des le–uens niet wor–de ge–daen.
gry – se – lyck Den duy – uel dien–de ick seer vly–te–lyck.

3. But when I turned me to the Lord,
And gave the world a farewell look,
Sought help against the evil horde,
The lore of Antichrist forsook;
Then was I mocked and sore defamed,
Since Babel's councils I now disdained;
The righteous man is e'er disclaimed!

3. Doen ick my totten Heer begaf
En my van der werelt ghinck keeren
En liet my helpen wt das boos geslacht
En versaecte Antechrists leeren
Doen wert ick beghect ende seer versmaet
Omdat ick verachte Babels raet
De gerechtige worden altijt gehaet.

4. As one may read of Abel, famed,
Zacharias too—recall it well—
And Daniel too, whom bad men framed
So that he among fierce lions fell;
So were the prophets treated all,
Christ Jesus too—it is good to recall—
Nor were the prophets spared this call.

4. Alsmen oock leest van Abel fijn
Sacharias wiltet niet vergeten
Daniel worde met valschen schijn
Inden cuyl der leeuwen gesmeten
So hebben sy de propheten gedaen
En Christus selue wilt dit verstaen
De Apostolen en syn niet vry ghegaen.

5. I'd rather choose the sorrow sore,
And suffer as of God the child
Than have from Pharaoh all his store,
To revel in for one brief while;
The realm of Pharaoh cannot last,
Christ keeps His kingdom sure and fast;
Around His child His arm He casts.

5. Veel lieuer kies ick ongemack
Al met Gods kinderen te lyden
Dan ick van Pharao ontfang sijn schat
Om een cleyne tijt met hem te verbliden
Pharaos rijck is titelic
Christus rijck duert eewelyc
Hi ontfangt sijn kinder seer blydelyck.

6. In the world, ye saints, you'll be defamed,
Let this be cause for pious glee;
Christ Jesus too was much disdained;
Whereby He wrought to set us free;
He took away of sin the bill
Held by the foe. Now if you will
You too may enter heaven still!

7. If you in fires are tested, tried,
Begin to walk life's narrow way,
Then let God's praise be magnified,
Stand firm on all He has to say;
If you stand strong and constant then,
Confess His Word in the sight of men,
With joy He extends the diadem!

8. Come hither, bride, receive the crown,
A hood* that's wrought of burnished gold;
Put on that white and beauteous ** gown.
Thy years shall nevermore grow old.
From death to life thou didst arise;
All tears shall vanish from thine eyes;
No grief nor sorrow more shall rise!

9. Now standest thou, Zion, in fairest hue,
A crown to thee, of grace, is given;
The name of God and Jerusalem new
Upon thy sides are deeply graven.
Thou wert abused, yes, stripped quite bare,
But now are decked in garment fair;
Art entered to the rest that is there.

10. Then evil men shall,frightened, see
As they behold thy splendor mounted,
That these are they—Where shall we flee?—
Whose life by us was sadly counted
For folly and for ravings wild;
We judged these people were beguiled,
Who live forever, reconciled!

11. He who this hymn for us did write,
And to God's praise sang gladly,
From the old Adam bore despite, ***
Was tempted sore and sadly.
Pray God that love in him may rise,
Let him with Babel ne'er fraternize;
Then the Home awaits him, in the skies.

6. In de werelt wert ghy versmaet
Wilt v daer inne verblyden
Want Christus die wert ooc gehaet
Om ons daer door te beuryden
Hy heeft dat hantschrift wech gedaen
Twelck de viant hadde ontfaen
Wildy ghy muecht int leuen gaen.

7. Als ghy door tvier werdt ondersocht
Den smallen padt begint te treden
Verbreyt als dan des Heeren lof
Blijft vaste op zyne reden
Ist saeck dat ghy volstandlich sijt
Sijn woort al voor de menschen belijdt
Hy geeft v de croon seer blydelyc.

8. Comt hier mijn bruyt ontfangt v croon
Een halsbant root van goude
Trect aen dat cleet seer wit en schoon
V iaren sullen niet verouden
Duer den doot sijt ghy int leuen gegaen
De tranen worden van v oogen gedaen
V en sal geen leedt meer comen aen.

9. Nv staet ghy Syon seer wit en schoon
De croon is v gegeuen
De naem mijns Gods en das nieu Jerusalem
Heb ick op v geschreuen
Ghy waert mismaect en seer ontdaen
Nu hebt ghy het blinckende cleet ontfaen
En sijt tot mijnder rusten ingegaen.

10. Dan sullen de godloose sien
End uwe heerlicheyt aenschouwen,
Dit sijn sy waer sullen wy vlien
Wiens leuen dat wy hebben gehouwen
Voor sotterny en gecheyt
Wy meenden dat sy waren verleyt
Maer nv leuen sy inder eeuwicheyt.

11. Die ons dit Liedeken heeft gestelt
Ter eeren Gods gesongen
Vanden ouden Adam was hy gequelt
Daer toe so seer gedrongen
Bidt God dat de liefde in hem ontfenct
Dat hij hem met Babel niet en vermengt,
Dat hij hem met Babel niet en vermengt.

* halsbant: scarf, collar, hood, cape; ** schoon: beautiful, beauteous; *** ouden Adam ...gequelt: tortured by the old Adam.

# WHEN CHRIST WITH HIS TRUE TEACHING CAME 425

*Precious in the sight of the Lord is the death of His saints.* Ps. 116:15.

From the 16th century Anabaptist *Ausbund*
Hymn No. 7, Michael Sattler, burnt 1527
*Als Christus mit sein'r wahren Lehr*
Tr. John J. Overholt, 1969

WO GOTT ZUM HAUS NICHT GIBT SEIN GUNST
L.M. 8.8.8.8.
M.M. 63

Joseph Klug's *Geistliche Lieder,* 1535

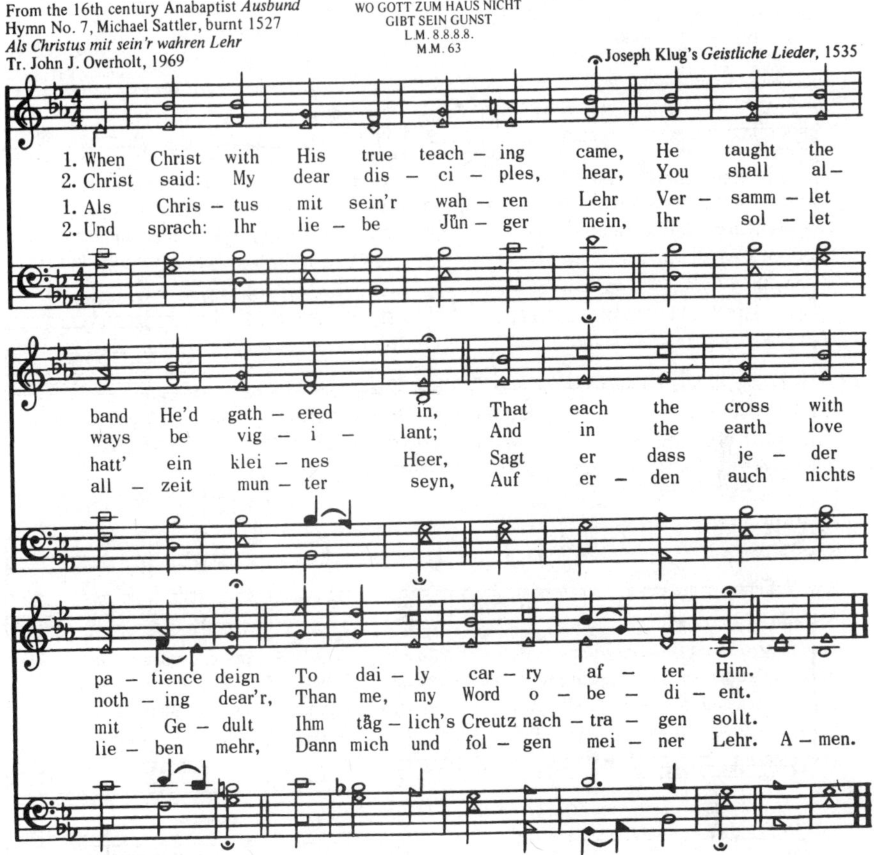
1. When Christ with His true teach – ing came, He taught the band He'd gath – ered in, That each the cross with pa – tience deign To dai – ly car – ry af – ter Him.
2. Christ said: My dear dis – ci – ples, hear, You shall al – ways be vig – i – lant; And in the earth love noth – ing dear'r, Than me, my Word o – be – di – ent.
1. Als Chris – tus mit sein'r wah – ren Lehr Ver – samm – let hatt' ein klei – nes Heer, Sagt er dass je – der mit Ge – dult Ihm täg – lich's Creutz nach – tra – gen sollt.
2. Und sprach: Ihr lie – be Jün – ger mein, Ihr sol – let all – zeit mun – ter seyn, Auf er – den auch nichts lie – ben mehr, Dann mich und fol – gen mei – ner Lehr. A – men.

3. The world upon you will unloose
And cast revilement, insult, too,
Disperse you, saying in excuse,
That Satan dwelling has in you.

4. When men you now revile, disdain,
For my sake persecute and smite,
Be joyful, your reward and gain
At heaven's throne I will requite.

5. Behold me, I, the Son of God,
At all times have been doing good;
Most innocent these ways I trod,
And yet at last they shed my blood.

6. O Christ, Thy people help alway
(12) Who follow faithful after Thee,
That through Thy bitter death, they may
From all their need redeemed be.

7. Praise to Thee, God, in Thy great throne,
(13) And to Thine own beloved Son,
And Holy Spirit, praise, through whom
Be many to Thy kingdom drawn.

3. Die Welt die wird euch stellen nach,
Und anthun manchen Spott und Schmach,
Verjagen und auch sagen frey,
Wie dass der Satan in euch sey.

4. Wann man euch nun lästert und schmächt,
Meinethalben verfolgt und schlägt,
Seyd froh, dann siehe euer Lohn
Ist euch bereit ins Himmels Thron.

5. Seht mich an, Ich bin Gottes Sohn,
Und hab auch allzeit wohl gethan,
Ich bin zwar auch der allerbest,
Noch habens mich getödt zuletzt.

6. O Christe hilf du deinem Volk,
(12) Welch's dir in aller Treu nachfolgt,
Dass es durch deinen bittern Tod
Erlöset werd aus aller Noth.

7. Lob sey dir Gott in deinem Thron,
(13) Darzu auch deinem lieben Sohn:
Auch dem Heiligen Geist zugleich,
Der zieh noch viel zu seinem Reich.

# 426 YOU CHRISTIAN BROTHERS TOGETHER

*For unto us a child is born, unto us a son is given: and the government shall be upon His shoulder: and His name shall be called Wonderful, Counsellor, The mighty God, The everlasting Father, The Prince of Peace.* Is. 9:6.

Dirk Philips, c. 1504-1568
Dutch Anabaptist church leader
*Ghy Christen broeders te samen*
Tr. Doortje Hartemink, 1970
Set to verse, John J. Overholt, 1971

DIRK (SPANISH AIR) 8.6.8.6.9.8.8.
M.M. 58

Traditional Spanish Air
Arr. John J. Overholt, 1971

1. You Chris-tian broth-ers, to-geth-er, Come hear a truth-ful song, Full high-ly praised names, which are Re-lat-ed of God's Son; The Scrip-tures search as the Spir-it leads, So to con-fess and in truth own, That which was from be-gin-ning is He.
2. In the first place, will you no-tice, How Christ is the Word of God, Through whom the Fa-ther worked, as From the be-gin-ning we're taught; When God cre-a-ted the heavens and earth, This Word with God was in con-cord, One with the Fa-ther as One.
1. Ghy Chris-ten broe-ders te sa-men, Wilt aen-hoo-ren een Lie-de-ken recht, Vol hoogh-prij-se-lij-cke na-men, Van den So-ne God's ghe-seght, Aen-schouwt de Schrift al nae den gheest, Dat ghy recht meught be-ken-nen Dat hy van't be-ghin is ghe-weest.
2. In den eer-sten wilt aen-mer-cken, Hoe Chris-tus is dat God-de-jijck woordt, Daer door den Va-der ginck wer-cken, In den be-ghin soo wy heb-ben ghe-hoort, Als Godt He-mel end' Aer-de fon-deer-de reyn. Soo was dit Woordt by hem ver-he-ven, Een met den Va-der ghe-meyn.

3. We own according to Scripture,
He that hath ears let him hear,
That from eternity He is sure;
Who of His birth can speak clear?
He only God's image does assure,
The radiance of His glory,
A reflection of His being, pure.

3. Wy bekennen, nae Schrifts belijden,
Elck een met ooren hoort,
Hy was van eeuwigen tijden,
Wie kan vertellen sijn gheboort?
Hy is Gods even—beeldt alleyn,
Dat schijnsel sijnder heerlijckheyt,
Een spieghel sijns wesens reyn.

4. Out of the mouth of th'Almighty,
Is the Word from eternity,
And the Word with God was in unity,
The Word was God, John did see;
He the great wisdom of God ever is,
Born from th'eternal Father,
To redeem us from death—thus through His.

4. Wt den mont des Alderhooghsten verheven
Is dat Woordt van eeuwigheyt,
End' dat Woordt was Gode beneven,
En God was dat Woordt, so Ioannes seyt
Hy is alleen die Wijsheydt Godes groot,
Gheboren van den Vader,
Om ons te verlossen vander doodt.

5. When God's command man had broken
Through the devil's deceiving word,
So did God's word man betoken,
A promised seed was secured
That us should save from the serpent's hate
And crush his head in pieces,
Therefore do we rejoice and elate.

5. Als de mensch Gods gebodt hadde ghebroken,
Door des listigen duyvels raet,
Soo heeft Godt tot hem ghesproken,
Ende hem belovet een zaet,
Dat ons soude verlossen van svyants nijt
En breken sijn hooft in stucken,
Hierom zijn wy verblijdt.

6. This honorable, promised seed to bring,
Was to God's bride spoken bliss,
To generate from beginning,
Through promises, list to this,
Through generations, as Matthew states,
According to types us promised,
The Son is revealed, he relates.

6. Dit zaedt vol alder eeren,
Werdt Gods Bruydt hier toegheseydt,
Van 't begin te genereren,
Door de beloften, hoort dit bescheydt,
Van geslacht tot geslacht, so Mattheus verklaert,
Nae der beloften in figueren
Is de Sone gheopenbaert.

7. This seed, observe properly with care,
In faith, through the Spirit free,
As a true Isaac, so trustful e'er,
B'fore Abraham was He;
He is the wise Solomon, pertinent,
From the true David descending,
By the promises known, shown assent.

7. Dit zaet, wilt het recht aenschouwen,
Wt den gheloove nae den gheest vry,
Als eenen waren Isaac vol trouwen,
Nochtans voor Abraham was hy:
Hy is die wijse Salomon pertinent
Van den rechten David ghekomen
Nae der beloften bekent.

8. He was also called David,
As a root and trunk secure,
A mighty Lord, called Him David,
E're He to earth came obscure;
All earthly kings of Him a figure were,
For He should eternally reign
With His own scepter pure.

8. Hy werdt oock David gheheeten,
Als een wortel en rechte stam,
David noemde hem een Heer vermeten,
Eer hy op aerden quam:
Alle Koninghen waren van hem een figuer,
Dat hy eeuwelijck soude regneren
Met sijnen Scepter puer.

9. This Rod in Zion was firmly set,
As planted of the Lord well,
High, noble, above all prophets,
The righteous Emmanuel.
He is the Word of true righteousness,
A true and rightful Prince of Peace,
As Isaiah does say and confess.

10. This Son most worthy and honorable,
Who in Godly form was still,
Did there Himself thus abase, humble,
Foll'wing His own Father's will,
He on Himself took a servant's form,
That in example He bid us,
His footsteps to follow, conform.

11. A maiden pure, and highly praised,
God's chosen, reputed high,
As she consented in this, amazed,
Strength through the Spirit found nigh;
Since she God's word believed from heav'n,
A child from her is wondrously born,
And to us truly a Son is giv'n.

12. This Son of immeasurable worth
From heaven, heavenly fair,
He, too, is the other Adam of earth,
Yet earthly minded was ne'er,
For He had from earth surely not come,
This Word from heav'n flesh has taken,
As would indicate John in sum.

13. When He was to the world unsealed,
His work of might then begun,
His Father Him openly revealed
As His belov'd, only Son,
This is the Bread there divided from heav'n,
His flesh is spiritual food for us,
Our debts He has paid and forgiv'n.

14. All that He had from His Father heard,
And He had seen heretofore,
This He Himself shares us in His Word,
Such wonders ne'er were before.
For never had a man God e'er seen,
Save the own Son of the Father,
Blest is He who in Him trusts unseen.

15. The dead brought He back to life again,
The blind caused He tc see,
The sins forgave He, none did retain,
These deeds were wrought graciously;
He is the Door and the straight Way,
No one may come to the Father,
Except through the Son he assay.

9. Dese Roede was in Zyon gheseten,
Als een plantinghe des Heeren wel,
Hoogh edel boven alle Propheten,
Die gherechte Emanuel.
Hy is dat woordt der gherechtigheydt,
Eenen rechten Vorst des vreden,
Als Esaias heeft gheseyt.

10. Desen Soon vol alder eeren,
Die in Godlijcke ghedaente was,
Die ginck hem selven verneeren
Na des Vaders wille te pas,
Die ghedaente eens knechts nam hy aen,
Om ons een exempel te wesen
Sijn voet stappen nae te gaen.

11. Een reyne Maeght ghepresen,
Van Godt voorsien en hoogh gheacht,
Als sy consenteerde in desen,
Ontfinckt sy door des Gheests kracht,
Sy gheloofde Gods woordt, ende ons is
Een kindt uyt haer gheboren,
Ons tot een Soon ghegheven ghewis.

12. Desen Soon hoogh van waerden,
Vanden Hemel hemelsch, soomen bevint,
De ander Adam op aerden,
Nochtans en was hy niet aerdtsch ghesint,
Al vander aerden en was hy niet,
Dat Woordt is vleesch gheworden,
Als ons Ioannes bediedt.

13. Als hy hem op die werelt verklaerde
Heeft hy ghetoont zijn Godlijcke macht,
Sijn Vader hem openbaerde,
Als syn beminden Sone gheacht
Dit is het broot vanden Hemel ghedaelt
Sijn vleesch is ons een spijse
Onse schuldt heeft hy betaelt.

14. Al dat hy van sijnen Vader hoorde
End' wat hy te voren hadde ghesien
Dat selve hy verantwoorde
Noyt sulck wonder en sachmen gheschien,
Daer en had noyt mensch Godt aenschout
Dan die eenighe soon des Vaders
Wel hem die op hem betrout.

15. De dooden gaf hy dat leven,
En de blinden haer ghesicht,
Die sonde mocht hy vergheven,
Dees wercken vielen hem licht,
Hy is de poort en de rechte baen,
Niemant en komt tot den Vader
Hy en moet door den Sone gaen.

16. This Son may in all things teach us,
Since He the Truth is alone,
His lambs inform will He ever thus,
Through His Spirit, Comforter shown;
Will you His yoke carry as He commands,
He of true life is the fountain,
And His mercy He freely commends.

16. Dese Sone mach ons leeren,
Want hy selfs die waerheydt is pleyn
Sijn schaepkens gaet hy informeren,
Door sijnen gheest een vertrooster alleyn,
Wilt draghen zijn last so hy ons ghebiedt,
Hy is een fonteyne des levens,
Sijn gracy gheeft hy om niet.

17. Our many sins has He carried sublime,
Our sorrows, guilt, grief, and pain;
From the beginning of days and of time,
The Lamb thus ever was slain,
For our transgressions He fervently prayed,
While we the enemies of God were,
Sin's price to His Father was paid.

17. Onse zonden heeft hy ghedraghen,
Veel smerten met grooter noot,
Al van 't beghin der daghen
Is dat Lammeken ghedoodt,
Voor ons overtreding heeft hy ghebeen,
Doen wy Gods vyanden waren
Stelde hy sijnen Vader te vreen.

18. This truly is our Saviour,
The Father's own right hand,
In Him there dwelleth in favor
Of God the fullness here spanned;
John Him has named as the one true God
In whom is life eternal;
To some mockery, and some odd.

18. Dit 's onse salighmaecker waerachtigh
Een rechte arm van sijnen Vaer,
In hem soo woont lijfachtigh
Die volle Godheydt eenpaer,
Ioannes noemt hem waerachtigh Godt,
Daer toe dat eeuwigh leven,
Dit is de sommighe een spot.

19. Let us through Christ pray the Father
And gather hence in His name,
He in our midst is together
With those who pray in Spirit, aflame,
Praising His Father in blessedness;
As Thomas did once confess Him,
Clearly, truly we, too, Christ confess.

19. Laet ons den vader door Christum bidden
Ende vergaderen in sijnen naem,
So is hy by ons int midden,
Die hem inden geest aenroepen bequaem,
Tot prijs sijns Vaders altijdt voorwaer,
Soo hem Thomas heeft beleden,
Bekennen wy Christum klaer.

20. This Son so full of all grace and good
To His disciples gave power,
That many miracles they then could
Through His name do the same hour;
To in His name baptize commanded same,
All who in Him were believing,
This His own also do now self–same.

20. Desen sone vol van ghenaden,
Gaf sijn discipulen de macht,
Sy deden veel wonderdaden,
Door sijnen Name gheacht,
Hy bevalse te doopen in sijnen Naem,
Alle die hier aen ghelooven
Die zijn daer oock toe bequaem.

21. All the more that here is written
Of this Son most excellent,
Confess we, too, in addition,
The Old and New Testament;
He God is over all eternally,
In his own letter to the Romans,
Has Paul this explained carefully.

21. Al dat daer meer staet gheschreven
Van desen Soon excellent,
Bekennen wy al beneven,
Dat Oud ende Nieuwe Testament,
Hy is Godt over al in eeuwicheydt
Int neghenste tot den Romeynen
Heeft het Paulus uytgheleyt.

22. This, then, I have not regretted,
Thus to have written this song
For my dear, true fellow–comrades,
This out of love to prolong;
So take the best of this short song,
Should one of Christ all be telling,
My song then should be far too long.

22. Ten heeft my niet verdroten
Al om te dichten dit liedt
Om mijn rechte medeghenoten,
Soo is het uyt liefden gheschiedt
En neemt ten besten dit cort ghesanck,
Soud' ment al van Christo verhalen
Mijn liet viel veel te lanck.

# 427 REJOICE, BE GLAD EXCEEDINGLY

*But when the fulness of the time was come, God sent forth His Son, made of a woman, made under the law, to redeem them that were under the law, that we might receive the adoption of sons.* Gal. 4:4-5.

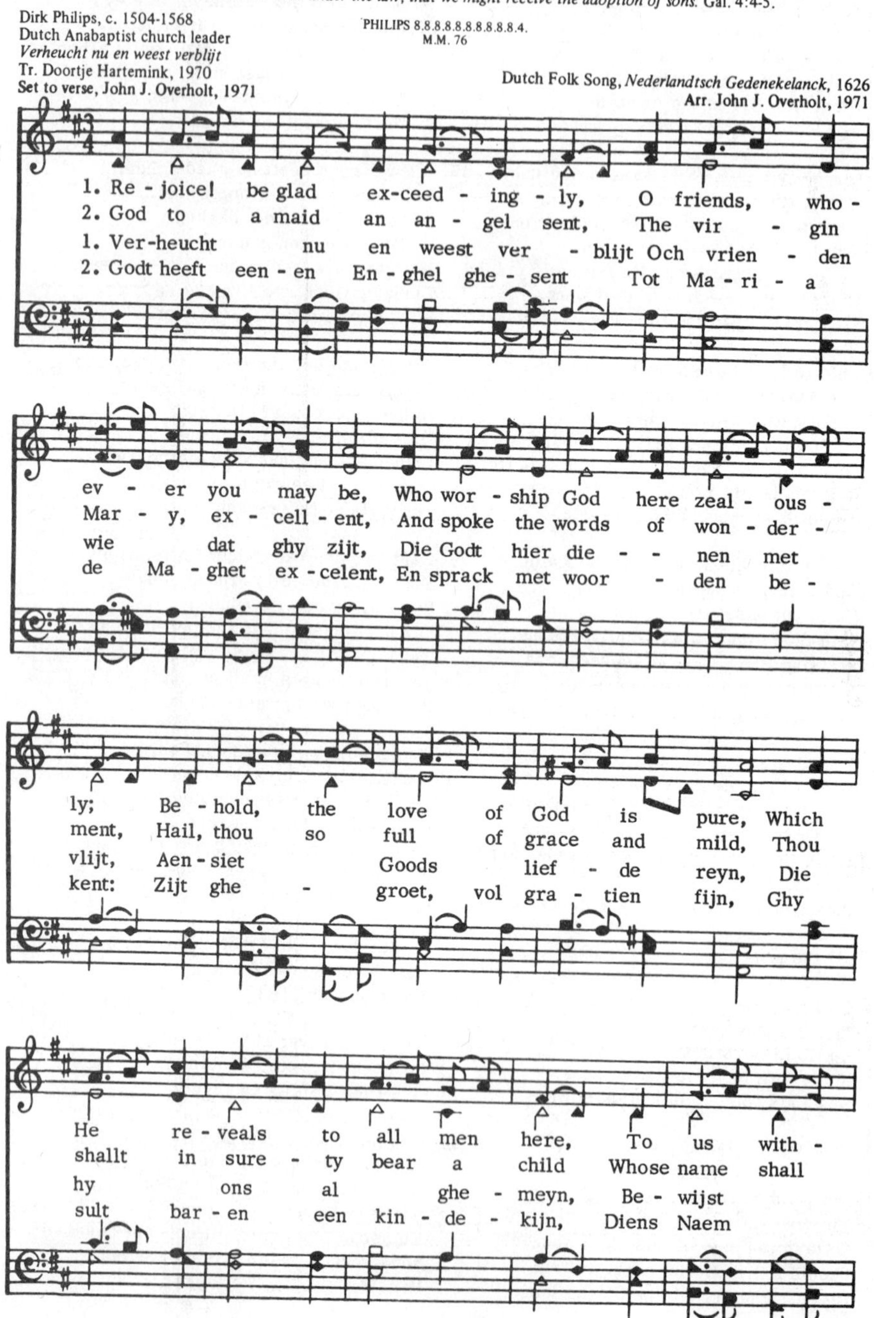
Dirk Philips, c. 1504-1568
Dutch Anabaptist church leader
*Verheucht nu en weest verblijt*
Tr. Doortje Hartemink, 1970
Set to verse, John J. Overholt, 1971
PHILIPS 8.8.8.8.8.8.8.8.8.8.4.
M.M. 76
Dutch Folk Song, *Nederlandtsch Gedenekelanck*, 1626
Arr. John J. Overholt, 1971
1. Re - joice! be glad ex-ceed - ing - ly, O friends, who - ev - er you may be, Who wor - ship God here zeal - ous - ly; Be - hold, the love of God is pure, Which He re - veals to all men here, To us with -
2. God to a maid an an - gel sent, The vir - gin Mar - y, ex - cell - ent, And spoke the words of won - der - ment, Hail, thou so full of grace and mild, Thou shallt in sure - ty bear a child Whose name shall
1. Ver-heucht nu en weest ver - blijt Och vrien - den wie dat ghy zijt, Die Godt hier die - - nen met vlijt, Aen - siet Goods lief - de reyn, Die hy ons al ghe - meyn, Be - wijst
2. Godt heeft een - en En - ghel ghe - sent Tot Ma - ri - a de Ma - ghet ex - celent, En sprack met woor - den be - kent: Zijt ghe - groet, vol gra - tien fijn, Ghy sult bar - en een kin - de - kijn, Diens Naem

in the earth - ly sphere, Be - cause we all through
e'er be Je - sus called; One reads that Ma - ry
in't aerdt - sche pleyn, Want wy doch al, door
sal Ie - sus zijn: Ma - ri - a, men leest
A - dam's fall Were so com - plete - ly lost with -
was a - fraid Of the an - nounce - ment that was
A - dams val, Ghe - heel ver - lo - ren wa -
sy was be - vreest Van de - se nieuw - e ma - -
al; But God in mer - cy great and good Has
made, And said: How will this hap - pen then, See -
ren: Maer Godt door zijn ghe - na - de groot Heeft
re, En sprack: hoe sal dat mo - ghen toe-gaen, Want
pp
saved us through the pre - cious blood; In this new year.
ing that I know not a man,* In this new year.
ons ver - lost, uyt lief - den bloot In de-sen nieuw-en ia-re.
ich be - ken - ne ghe - nen man, In de-sen nieuw-en ia-re.

* Lu. 1:34

3. God's Spirit, holy, from on high,
Shall you o'ershadow, I reply,
And that which born is and is nigh,
Shall be called God's Son, excellent,
He David's throne shall resident,
And Jacob's house rule without end;
Mary , with joy, the message grave
Considered, which the angel gave,
And said: Thy servant is prepared
To do according to thy word,
In this new year.

3. Goods Gheest van boven, seer fijn,
Sal u omschynen, hoort mijn,
Daerom dat van u gheboren sal zijn,
Sal Goods Sone heeten, excelent,
Hy sal Davids zijns Vaders stoele ient,
En Iacobs huys regeren, sonder ent:
Maria, hoort reen, sy was te vreen
Door des Enghels verklaren,
En sprack: hier is u dienstmaecht bereyt,
My geschiede ghelijck als ghy hebt gheseyt,
In desen nieuwen iare.

4. Note fully this, friends one and all,
In Bethlehem, within a stall,
Did she give birth to child so small;
The angels this did gladly say
To shepherds where in fields they lay,
As Scripture clearly does portray,
Rejoicing truly with great joy,
Did openly God praise deploy,
Gladly to Bethlehem they filed,
Where they found mother and small child
In this new year.

4. Aenmerckt doch, vrienden, alghemeen,
Te Bethlehem binnen der steen,
Heeft sy baringhe gheleen,
Soo de Enghelen hebben vertelt,
De Herderkens op het velt,
Soo de Schriftuere vermelt,
Sy waren verblijt met vrolijck iolijt,
Loofden Godt in 't openbare,
En zijn met vreuchden, nae Bethlehem ghetreen,
Daer vonden sy de Moeder met haer Kindeken kleen,
In desen nieuwen iare.

5. The wise men from the East at eve,
This message also did receive,
They through a star did it perceive,
And to Jerusalem were borne,
There diligently to suborn,
Inquiring where Christ should be born;
Which when King Herod heard, in ire
Of this new tiding did enquire;
His council he did there arraign
This news to fully ascertain
In this new year.

5. De Wysen uyt Oosten landt,
Die kreghen oock dit verstant,
Door een Ster die haer werde bekant,
Zy quamen te Ierusalem ghegaen,
En hebben daer neerstich onderstaen,
Waer Christus gheboorte soud' toe gaen,
Herodes dit hoort was seer verstoort
Van dese nieuwe mare,
Hy dede roepen zijn Wyse te gaer,
En ondersocht seer neerstich van haer,
In desen nieuwen iare.

6. They said: In Bethlehem, note well,
The prophet's prophecy doth tell;
Herod the wise men did impel:
Go there and seek, he shrewdly said,
And when you Him have homage paid,
Then bring me word where He is laid,
That I may, too, worship convey,
But he the child would seek to slay;
The wise men left Jerusalem,
The Scripture says, for Bethlehem,
In this new year.

6. Sy spraken, te Bethlehem, hoort mijn,
Nae des Propheten prophecijn,
Herodes riep de Wysen seer fijn,
En sprack, wilt derwaerts gaen,
En als ghy hem hebt ghebeden aen,
Soo willet my oock laten verstaen,
Op dat ick, hoort reen, mach komen aenbeen,
Het Kindt wild' hy beswaren,
De Wyse zijn van Ierusalem ghegaen,
Nae Bethlehem, soo de Schrift doet vermaen,
In desen nieuwen iare.

7. In Bethlehem, the Scriptures say,
The mother and her child, straightway
They found, and did their joy display;
Their treasures sweet opened they there,
And offered joyfully their share
Of gifts: gold, frankincense, and myrrh;
With gladness great and joy profound
In public did praise, God resound,
They worshiped child at mother's arm,
Then joyful homeward did return,
In this new year.

7. Te Bethlehem nae Schrifts belijt,
Daer vonden sy de Moeder subijt,
Met haer Kindt; en waren verblijt,
Sy openden haer schatten soet,
En offerden met blyden moet,
Gout, Wieroock ende Myrrhe seer soet,
Sy waren verheucht met grooter vreucht,
Loofden Godt in 't openbare,
En aenbaden het Kindt by zijn Moeder reen
Doen zijn sy met vreuchden weer om getreen,
In desen nieuwen iare.

8. Note princes, honored friends and dear,
Let us resolve in this new year,
To e're conduct ourselves with fear,
Lest we receive, withal in pain,
The proffered grace of God in vain,
For us He did so much obtain
Through bitter death, great pain; He strove
And suffered much out of pure love;
So bless the Lord with gladdened heart
And from idolatry depart,
In this new year.

8. Oorlof Prince, vrienden eerbaer,
Laet ons dit nieuwe iaer,
Te recht wel nemen waer,
Op dat wy Goods ghenade, merckt aen,
Doch niet te vergheefs en ontfaen,
Want hy heeft seer veel voor ons ghedaen,
Den bitteren doot, met pyne groot,
Leet hy uyt liefden klare,
Dus looft den Heere met alle herten bly,
En doet doch gheen afgodery,
In desen nieuwen iare.

# 428 IN CHRIST IS BROTHERHOOD ALONE

*Love the brotherhood.* I Pet. 2:17. *My brethren are these which hear the Word of God, and do it.* Lk. 8:21.

Wilmer D. Swope, 1971
Alt. John J. Overholt, 1971

DUKE STREET L.M. 8.8.8.8.
M.M. 92

John Hatton, d. 1793

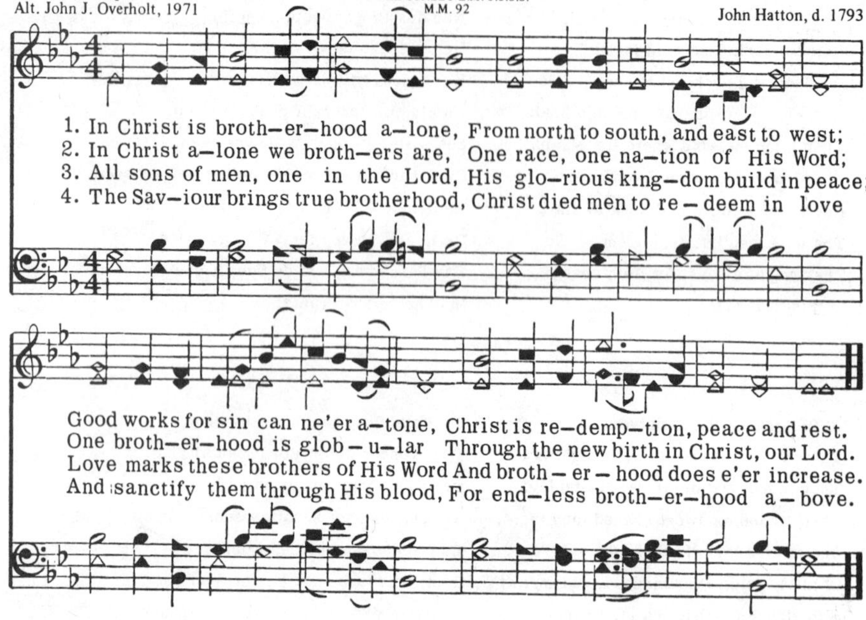
1. In Christ is broth–er–hood a–lone, From north to south, and east to west;
2. In Christ a–lone we broth–ers are, One race, one na–tion of His Word;
3. All sons of men, one in the Lord, His glo–rious king–dom build in peace;
4. The Sav–iour brings true brotherhood, Christ died men to re – deem in love
Good works for sin can ne'er a–tone, Christ is re–demp–tion, peace and rest.
One broth–er–hood is glob – u–lar Through the new birth in Christ, our Lord.
Love marks these brothers of His Word And broth – er – hood does e'er increase.
And sanctify them through His blood, For end–less broth–er–hood a – bove.

# 429 WHEN THY HEART WITH JOY O'ERFLOWING

*But whoso hath this world's good, and seeth his brother have need, and shutteth up his bowels of compassion from him, how dwelleth the love of God in him?* I Jn. 3:17.

Theodore C. Williams, 1891

STEPHANOS 8.5.8.3.
M.M. 72

Henry Williams Baker 1821-1877

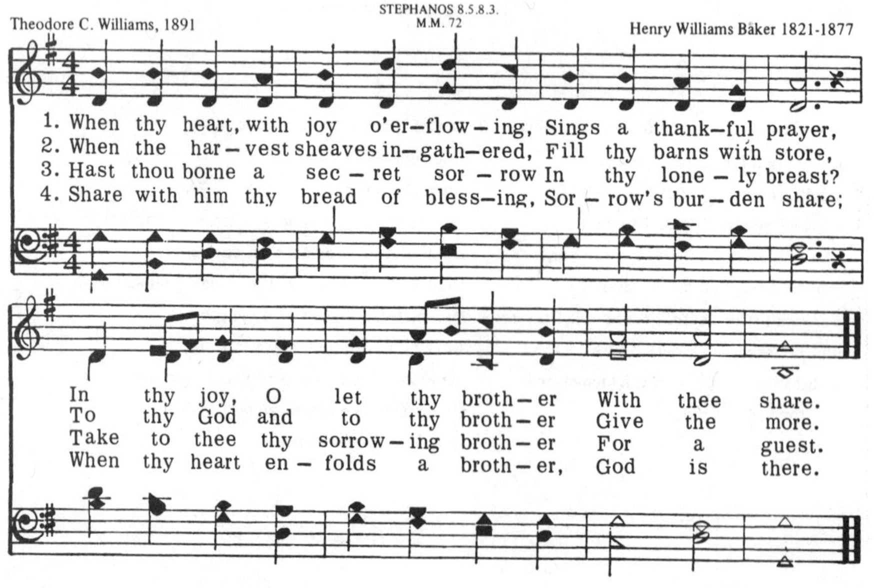
1. When thy heart, with joy o'er–flow–ing, Sings a thank–ful prayer,
2. When the har – vest sheaves in–gath–ered, Fill thy barns with store,
3. Hast thou borne a sec – ret sor – row In thy lone – ly breast?
4. Share with him thy bread of bless–ing, Sor – row's bur – den share;
In thy joy, O let thy broth – er With thee share.
To thy God and to thy broth – er Give the more.
Take to thee thy sorrow – ing broth – er For a guest.
When thy heart en – folds a broth – er, God is there.

# O MAN REDEEMED, FOLD TO THY HEART 430

*And this commandment have we from Him, That he who loveth God love his brother also.* I Jn. 4:21.

John Greenleaf Whittier, 1847 (1807-1892)
Alt. John J. Overholt, 1971
St. 1, Alt. Sanford G. Shetler, 1972
SANDRINGHAM 11.10.11.10.
M.M. 54
Joseph Barnby, 1889 (1838-1896)
1. O man re – deemed, fold to thy heart thy broth – er:
2. For he whom Je – sus loved hath tru – ly spo – ken;
3. Fol – low with rev – erent steps the great ex – am – ple
4. Then shall all shack – les fall: the storm – y clan – gor
Where love pre – vails, the peace of God is there;
Love's great – er ser – vice which He deigns to bless
Of Him whose work was man's e – ter – nal good:
Of wild war mu – sic o'er the earth shall cease;
To wor – ship right – ly and to love each oth – er,
Re – stores the lost, and binds the spir – it bro – ken,
So shall the wide earth seem our Fa – ther's tem – ple,
Love shall tread out the bale – ful fire of an – ger,
Makes life a hymn, each kind – ly deed a prayer.
And feeds the wid – ow and the fa – ther – less.
Each lov – ing life a psalm of grat – i – tude.
And in its ash – es plant the tree of peace. A – men.

# 431 LORD OF THE CHURCH

*Who maketh His . . . ministers a flame of fire.* Heb. 1:7. *Without ceasing I have remembrance of thee in my prayers night and day.* II Tim. 1:3.

BREMEN 8.8.6.8.6.
M.M. 88

Edward Osler, 1836 (1798-1863) | Thomas Hastings, 1836 (1784-1872)

1. Lord of the Church, we humbly pray For those who guide us in Thy way,
2. Help them to preach the truth of God, Re-demp-tion thro' the Saviour's blood;
3. So may they live to Thee a-lone; Then hear the welcome word,—"Well done!"

And speak Thy ho-ly Word: With love di-vine their hearts in-spire,
Nor let the Spir-it cease On all the Church His gifts to show'r;
And take their crown a-bove; En-ter in-to their Mas-ter's joy,

And touch their lips with hallowed fire, And need-ful strength af-ford.
To them a mes-sen-ger of pow'r, To us, of life and peace.
And all e-ter-ni-ty em-ploy In praise, and bliss, and love. A-MEN.

# 432 LET ZION'S WATCHMEN ALL AWAKE

*I have set watchmen upon thy walls, O Jerusalem, which shall never hold their peace day nor night.* Is. 62:6.

DESCEND UPON US C.M. 8.6.8.6.
M.M. 72

Philip Doddridge, 1736 (1702-1751) | S. W. Straub, 1842-1899

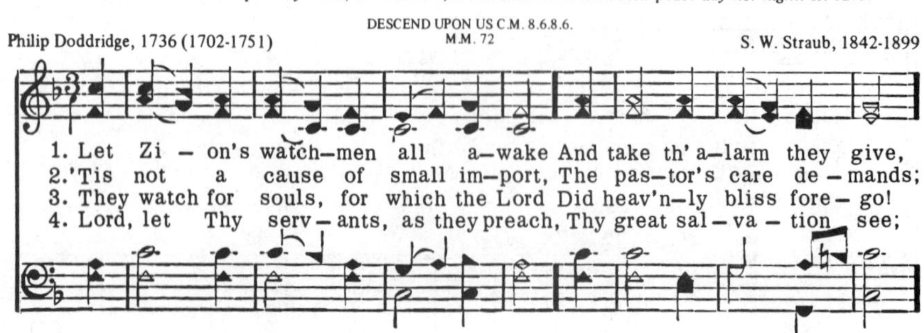
1. Let Zi – on's watch–men all a–wake And take th' a–larm they give,
2. 'Tis not a cause of small im–port, The pas–tor's care de – mands;
3. They watch for souls, for which the Lord Did heav'n–ly bliss fore – go!
4. Lord, let Thy serv – ants, as they preach, Thy great sal – va – tion see;

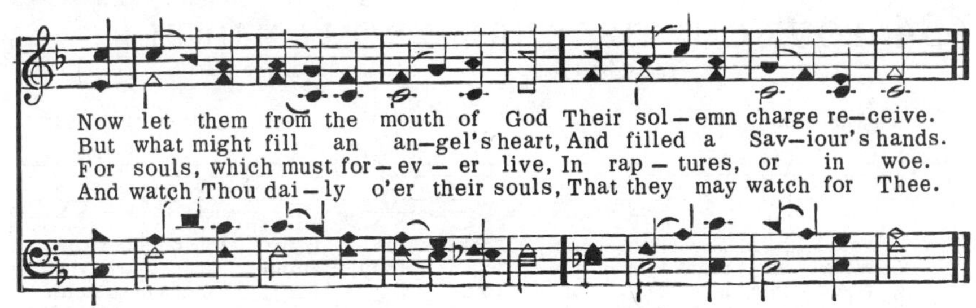
Now let them from the mouth of God Their sol – emn charge re-ceive.
But what might fill an an-gel's heart, And filled a Sav–iour's hands.
For souls, which must for – ev – er live, In rap – tures, or in woe.
And watch Thou dai – ly o'er their souls, That they may watch for Thee.

**THE CHURCH:** RECEIVING OF MEMBERS

# HERE IN THE NAME OF CHRIST 433

*And many . . . hearing believed and were baptized.* Acts 18:8. *And the Lord added to the church daily.* Acts 2:47.

Heinrich von Bruiningk, 1770 (1738-1785)
Arr. Christian Gregor, 1723-1801
Tr. Benjamin La Trobe, 1772 (1725-1786)
Altered by Compiler, 1971

LOB SEI DEM ALLMÄCHTIGEN
L.M. 8.8.8.8.
M.M. 72

Johann Crüger, 1640 (1598-1662)

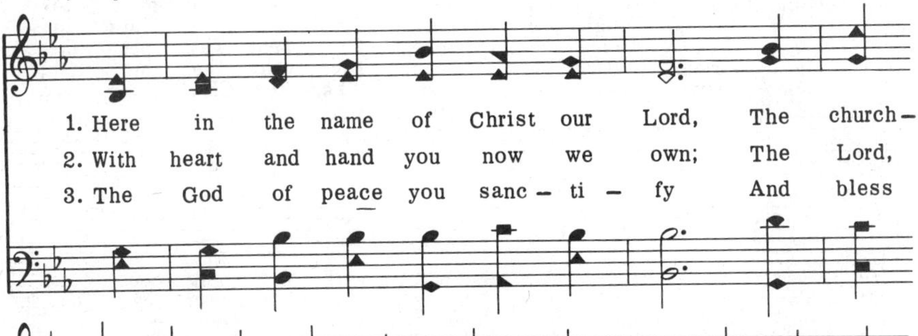

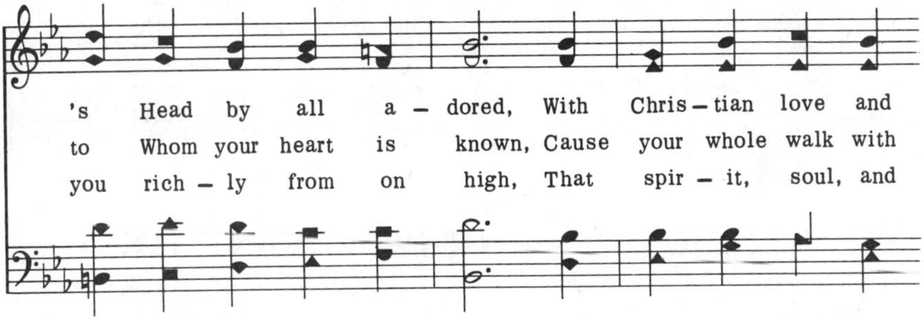

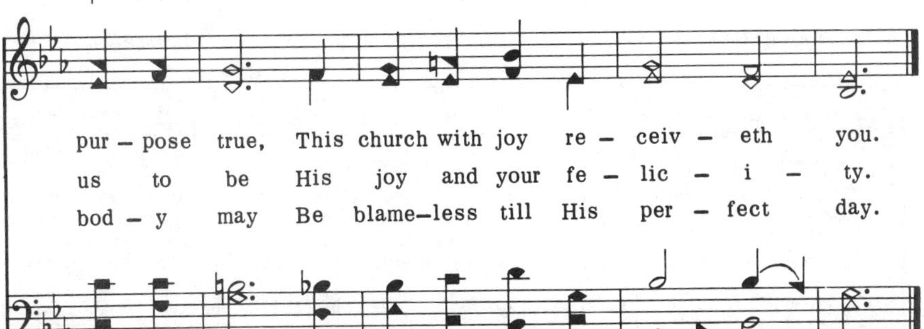

1. Here in the name of Christ our Lord, The church – 's Head by all a – dored, With Chris – tian love and pur – pose true, This church with joy re – ceiv – eth you.

2. With heart and hand you now we own; The Lord, to Whom your heart is known, Cause your whole walk with us to be His joy and your fe – lic – i – ty.

3. The God of peace you sanc – ti – fy And bless you rich – ly from on high, That spir – it, soul, and bod – y may Be blame–less till His per – fect day.

# 434 POUR OUT THY SPIRIT FROM ON HIGH

*Until the Spirit be poured upon us from on high.* Is. 32:15.

HOLLY L.M. 8.8.8.8.
M.M.69

James Montgomery, 1833 (1771-1854) George Hews, 1835 (1806-1873)

1. Pour out Thy Spir - it from on high; Lord, Thine or-
2. With - in Thy tem - ple when they stand To teach the
3. Wis - dom and zeal and faith im - part, Firm - ness with
4. To watch and pray, and nev - er faint; By day and
5. Then, when their work is fin - ished here, In hum - ble

dain - ed serv - ants bless; Grac - es and gifts to
truth as taught by Thee, Sav - iour, like stars in
meek - ness, from a - bove, To bear Thy peo - ple
night strict guard to keep; To warn the sin - ner,
hope their charge re - sign, When the Chief Shep - herd

each sup - ply, And clothe them with Thy right - eous - ness.
Thy right hand The an - gels of the church - es be.
on their heart, And love the souls whom Thou dost love;
cheer the saint, Nour - ish Thy lambs, and feed Thy sheep;
shall ap - pear, O God, may they and we be Thine.

# 435 WITH JOY WE OWN THY SERVANT, LORD

*Remember them which have the rule over you, who have spoken unto you the word of God: whose faith follow.* Heb. 13:7.

DOWNS C.M. 8.6.8.6.
M.M. 58

James Montgomery, 1771-1854 Lowell Mason, 1792-1872

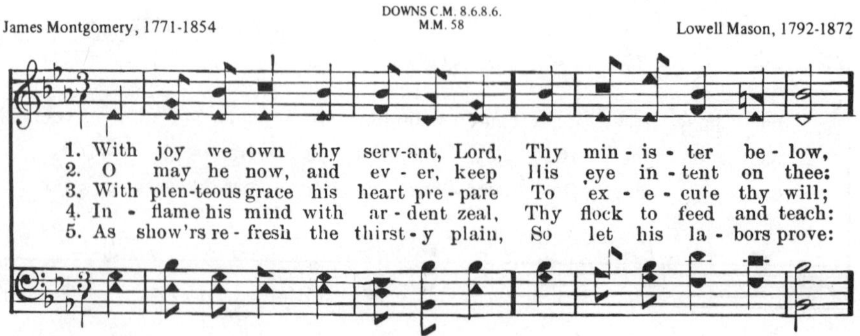
1. With joy we own thy serv-ant, Lord, Thy min - is - ter be - low,
2. O may he now, and ev - er, keep His eye in - tent on thee:
3. With plen-teous grace his heart pre - pare To ex - e - cute thy will;
4. In - flame his mind with ar - dent zeal, Thy flock to feed and teach:
5. As show'rs re - fresh the thirst - y plain, So let his la - bors prove:

Or - dained to spread thy truth a - broad, That all thy name may know.
Do thou, great Shep - herd of the sheep, His bright ex - am - ple be.
And give him pa - tience, love and care, And faith - ful - ness and skill.
And let him live, and let him feel, The truths he's called to preach.
By him ex - tend thy right-eous reign — The reign of truth and love.

## O THOU WHO MAKEST SOULS TO SHINE 436

*Obey them that have the rule over you, and submit yourselves: for they watch for your souls, as they that must give account.* Heb. 13:17. *He gave some, apostles . . . and some, pastors and teachers.* Eph. 4:11.

John Armstrong, 1813-1856 — ERNAN L.M. 8.8.8.8. M.M. 56 — Lowell Mason, 1792-1872

1. O Thou who mak - est souls to shine With light from bright - er worlds a - bove, And drop - pest glis - t'ning dew di - vine On all who seek a Sav - iour's love.

2. Do Thou Thy ben - e - dic - tion give On all who teach, on all who learn, That so Thy Church may ho - lier live, And ev - 'ry lamp more bright - ly burn.

3. Give those that teach pure hearts and wise, Faith, hope, and love, all warmed by prayer: Them-selves first train - ing for the skies, They best will raise their peo - ple there.

4. O bless the shep - herd; bless the sheep; That guide and guid - ed, both be one; One in the faith - ful watch they keep, Un - til this hur - rying life be done.

# 437 GREAT SHEPHERD OF THE CHURCH

*And they prayed, and said, Thou, Lord, which knowest the hearts of all men, show whether of these two Thou hast chosen.* Acts 1:24.

Wilmer D. Swope, 1968
Alt. John J. Overholt, 1969

DORTRECHT L.M.D. 8.8.8.8.D.
M.M. 69

Ludwig van Beethoven, 1770-1827

1. Great Shep-herd of the church on earth, Bless us Thy flock and with us stay;
2. A watch a - bout us safe - ly keep, For hire - ling shep-herds lead a - stray;
3. O Ho - ly Sav–iour, may Thy pow'r, With - in our lives bloom bright and clear,
4. Thy cho - sen ves - sels fill with peace, En - dow with won - drous gifts of grace;
May serv–ants - in the fold be found To guide and feed Thy flock each day;
For wealth and fame Thy gates they leave Un - guard - ed stand, and flee a - way!
In words and deeds, and mis - sion firm; In - dwell our hearts, Thy tem - ple here.
Grant that they blos - som and bear fruit, With tal–ents fill a serv–ant's place;
For shep-herds in the church we need, Who will our hun - gry souls still feed
Lord, give us faith - ful shep - herds true; Give each a shep-herd's heart, to keep
Om - ni - scient God of love, o'er rule, The cast - ing of the lot di - rect;
True shep-herds with God's Word go forth The world to win in Je - sus' name,
With sa - cred man - na from Thy Word; Provide, true Shepherd, and us lead.
And lead the church to life in Christ; In - spire the shep-herds of Thy sheep.
Thy will we seek, do Thou, we pray, Thy serv–ants call and thus se - lect.
With faith - ful hands and hearts of love; Great Shepherd, bless their lives and aim! A - men

# GREAT SHEPHERD OF THE CHURCH 438

*And they gave forth their lots; and the lot fell upon Matthias; and he was numbered with the eleven apostles.* Acts 1:26.

Wilmer D. Swope, 1968
Alt. John J. Overholt, 1969

SWEET HOUR OF PRAYER L.M.D. 8.8.8.8.D.
M.M. 72

William Batchelder Bradbury, 1816-1868

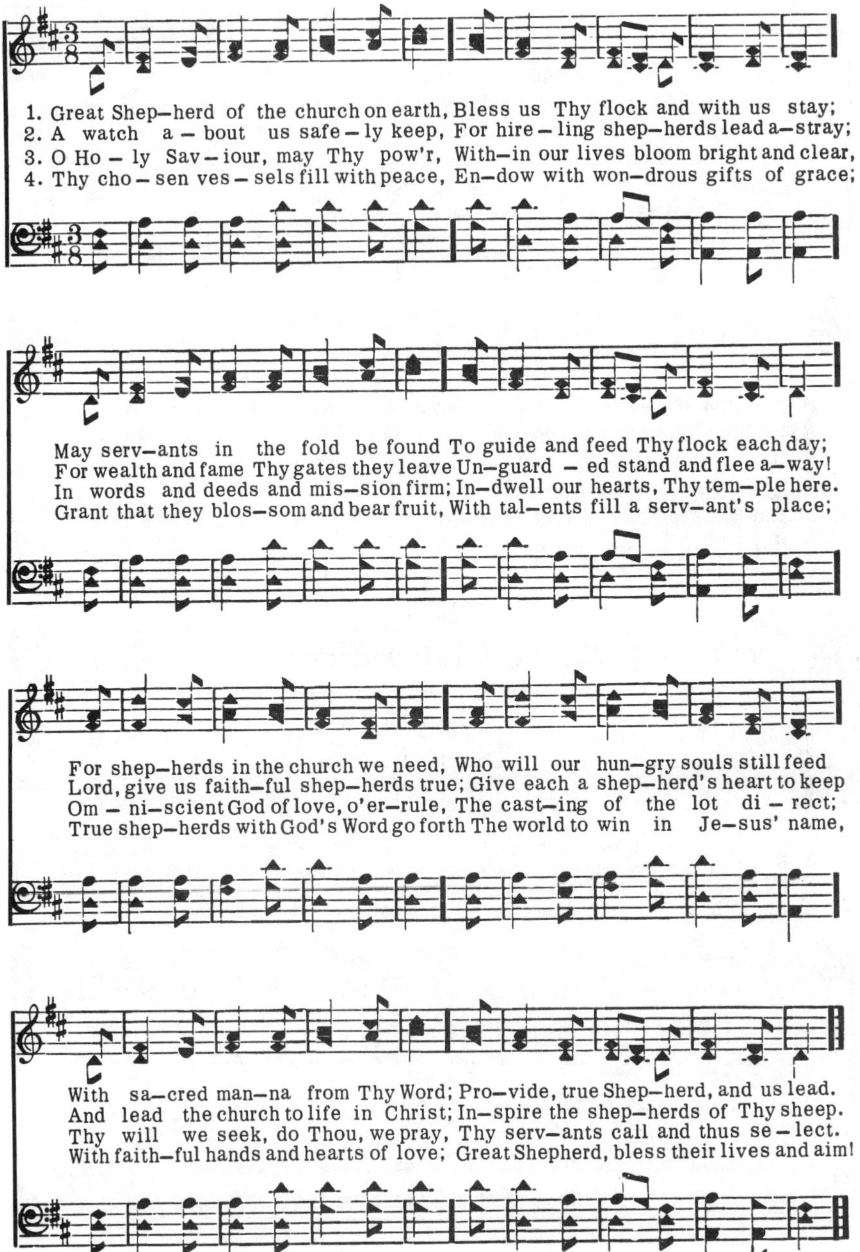

1. Great Shep–herd of the church on earth, Bless us Thy flock and with us stay;
2. A watch a – bout us safe – ly keep, For hire – ling shep–herds lead a–stray;
3. O Ho – ly Sav – iour, may Thy pow'r, With–in our lives bloom bright and clear,
4. Thy cho – sen ves – sels fill with peace, En–dow with won–drous gifts of grace;

May serv–ants in the fold be found To guide and feed Thy flock each day;
For wealth and fame Thy gates they leave Un–guard – ed stand and flee a–way!
In words and deeds and mis–sion firm; In–dwell our hearts, Thy tem–ple here.
Grant that they blos–som and bear fruit, With tal–ents fill a serv–ant's place;

For shep–herds in the church we need, Who will our hun–gry souls still feed
Lord, give us faith–ful shep–herds true; Give each a shep–herd's heart to keep
Om – ni–scient God of love, o'er–rule, The cast–ing of the lot di – rect;
True shep–herds with God's Word go forth The world to win in Je–sus' name,

With sa–cred man–na from Thy Word; Pro–vide, true Shep–herd, and us lead.
And lead the church to life in Christ; In–spire the shep–herds of Thy sheep.
Thy will we seek, do Thou, we pray, Thy serv–ants call and thus se – lect.
With faith–ful hands and hearts of love; Great Shepherd, bless their lives and aim!

# 439 WITNESS YE MEN AND ANGELS

*When thou shalt vow a vow unto the Lord . . . thou shalt not slack to pay it.* Deut. 23:21.

DUNDEE C.M. 8.6.8.6.
M.M. 66

Benjamin Beddome, 1717-1795 | *Scottish Psalter,* 1615

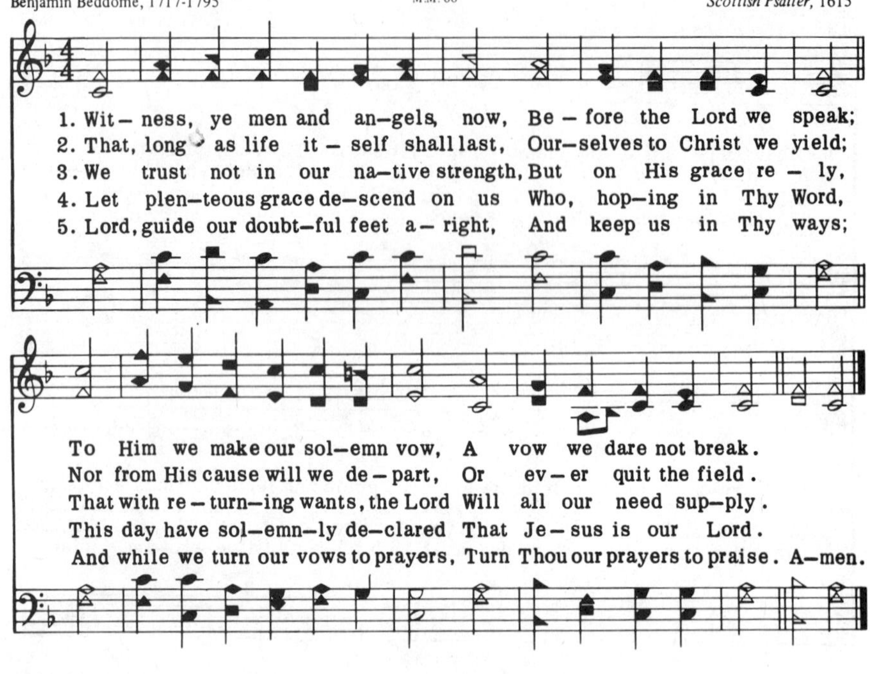
1. Wit– ness, ye men and an–gels, now, Be – fore the Lord we speak;
2. That, long as life it – self shall last, Our–selves to Christ we yield;
3. We trust not in our na–tive strength, But on His grace re – ly,
4. Let plen–teous grace de–scend on us Who, hop–ing in Thy Word,
5. Lord, guide our doubt–ful feet a – right, And keep us in Thy ways;
To Him we make our sol–emn vow, A vow we dare not break.
Nor from His cause will we de – part, Or ev – er quit the field.
That with re – turn–ing wants, the Lord Will all our need sup–ply.
This day have sol–emn–ly de–clared That Je – sus is our Lord.
And while we turn our vows to prayers, Turn Thou our prayers to praise. A–men.

# 440 O LORD, WHILE WE CONFESS

*The answer of a good conscience toward God.* I Pet. 3:21.

MARLOW C.M. 8.6.8.6.
M.M. 60

Mary P. Bowly, 1847 | John Chetham, 1685-1763

1. O Lord, while we con - fess the worth Of this the out - ward seal,
2. Death to the world we here a - vow, Death to each flesh - ly lust;
3. Bap - tized in - to the Fa-ther's name, We'd walk as sons of God;
4. Bap - tized in - to the Ho - ly Ghost, We'd keep His tem - ple pure,
Do Thou the truths here - in set forth, To ev - 'ry heart re - veal.
New - ness of life our call - ing now, A ris - en Lord our trust.
Bap - tized in Christ, we own Thy claim, As ran-somed by Thy blood.
And make Thy grace our on - ly boast, And by Thy strength en - dure.

# WE BLESS THE NAME OF CHRIST, THE LORD 441

*For thus it becometh us to fulfill all righteousness.* Mt. 3:15.

RETREAT L.M. 8.8.8.8.
M.M. 84

Samuel Frederick Coffman, 1926 (1872-1954) Thomas Hastings, 1842 (1784-1872)

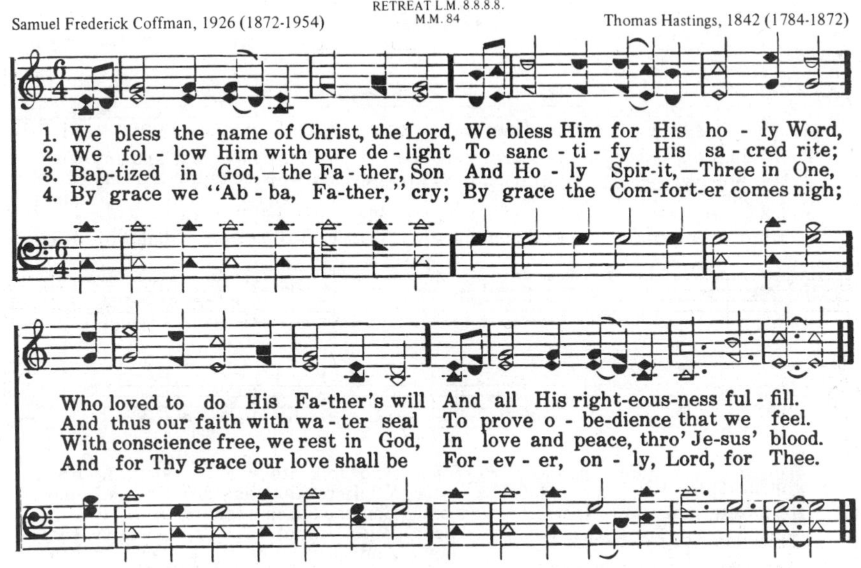
1. We bless the name of Christ, the Lord, We bless Him for His ho - ly Word,
2. We fol - low Him with pure de - light To sanc - ti - fy His sa - cred rite;
3. Bap-tized in God,—the Fa - ther, Son And Ho - ly Spir-it,—Three in One,
4. By grace we "Ab - ba, Fa-ther," cry; By grace the Com-fort-er comes nigh;
Who loved to do His Fa-ther's will And all His right-eous-ness ful - fill.
And thus our faith with wa - ter seal To prove o - be-dience that we feel.
With conscience free, we rest in God, In love and peace, thro' Je-sus' blood.
And for Thy grace our love shall be For - ev - er, on - ly, Lord, for Thee.

# I'M NOT ASHAMED TO OWN MY LORD 442

*Nevertheless I am not ashamed.* II Tim. 1:12.

ARLINGTON C.M. 8.6.8.6.
M.M. 63

Isaac Watts, 1709 (1674-1748) Thomas A. Arne, 1710-1778

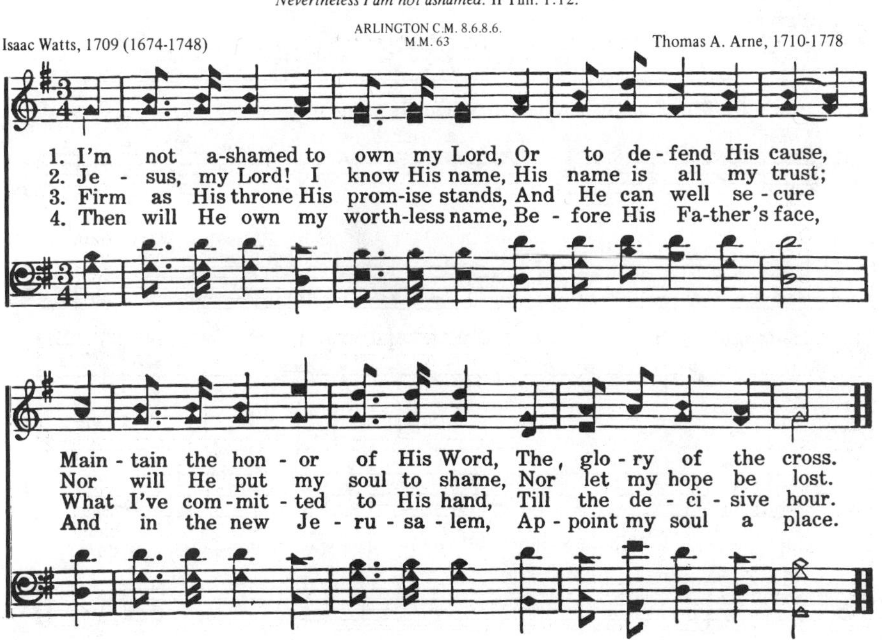
1. I'm not a-shamed to own my Lord, Or to de - fend His cause,
2. Je - sus, my Lord! I know His name, His name is all my trust;
3. Firm as His throne His prom-ise stands, And He can well se - cure
4. Then will He own my worth-less name, Be - fore His Fa-ther's face,
Main - tain the hon - or of His Word, The glo - ry of the cross.
Nor will He put my soul to shame, Nor let my hope be lost.
What I've com - mit - ted to His hand, Till the de - ci - sive hour.
And in the new Je - ru - sa - lem, Ap - point my soul a place.

# 443 O HAPPY DAY

*Thou wilt shew me the path of life: in Thy presence is fulness of joy; at Thy right hand there are pleasures for evermore.* Ps. 16:11.

HAPPY DAY L.M. 8.8.8.8. with Ref.
M.M. 56
Philip Doddridge, 1755 (1702-1751)
From Edward F. Rimbault, 1816-1876
1. O hap - py day that fixed my choice On Thee, my Sav - iour and my God!
2. O hap - py bond that seals my vows To Him who mer - its all my love;
3. 'Tis done, the great trans - ac - tion's done; I am my Lord's and He is mine;
4. Now rest, my long - di - vid - ed heart, Fixed on this bliss - ful cen - ter, rest;
5. High heav'n that heard the sol - emn vow, That vow re - newed shall dai - ly hear,
Well may this glow - ing heart re - joice, And tell its rap - tures all a - broad.
Let cheer - ful an - thems fill His house, While to that sa - cred shrine I move.
He drew me and I fol - lowed on, Charmed to confess the voice di - vine.
Nor ev - er from thy Lord de - part, With Him of ev - 'ry good pos - sessed.
Till in life's lat - est hour I bow, And bless in death a bond so dear.
REFRAIN
Hap - py day, hap - py day, When Je - sus washed my sins a - way;
He taught me how to watch and pray, And live re - joic - ing ev - 'ry day:
Hap - py day, hap - py day, When Je - sus washed my sins a - way.

# HE THAT BELIEVES AND IS BAPTIZED 444

*He that believeth and is baptized shall be saved; but he that believeth not shall be damned.* Mk. 16:16.

Thomas Hansen Kingo, 1689 (1634-1703)
*Enhver som tror og bliver döbt*
Tr. George A. T. Rygh, 1909 (1860-1943)
Johann J. Rambach, 1734 (1693-1735)
*Ich bin getauft auf deinen Namen*
Tr. Catherine Winkworth, 1863 (1829-1878)
Composite arr. John J. Overholt, 1972

NUN FREUT EUCH NEW
8.7.8.7.8.8.7.
M.M. 69

J. Klug's *Geistliche Lieder,* 1535
Arr. John J. Overholt, 1969

*With feeling*

1. He that be–lieves and is bap–tized Shall see the Lord's sal–va–tion;
For he that is by Christ bap–tized, He is a new cre–a–tion.
Through Christ's re–demp–tion he shall stand A–mong the glo–rious
heav'n–ly band Of ev–'ry tribe and na–tion.

2. With one ac–cord, O God, we pray: Grant us Thy Ho–ly Spir–it;
Save us from sin's in–fir–mi–ty Through Je–sus' blood and mer–it.
O grant that through Thy grace this day, Thy grace un–mer–it–
ed, we may E–ter–nal life in–her–it.

3. Bap–tized in–to the tri–une name, Fa–ther, Son, Ho–ly Spir–it,
Through grace a low–ly place we claim In Je–sus' blood and mer–it.
Bap–tized by Christ and dead to sin, Thy Spir–it now shall
live with–in, Since we Thy life in–her–it. A–men.

# 445 HERE, O MY LORD, I SEE THEE FACE TO FACE

*Examine yourselves, whether ye be in the faith; prove your own selves.* II Cor. 13:5. *But let a man examine himself, and so let him eat of that bread, and drink of that cup.* I Cor. 11:28.

PENITENTIA 10.10.10.10.
M.M. 80

Horatius Bonar, 1855 (1808-1889)

Edward Dearle, 1874 (1806-1891)

1. Here, O my Lord, I see Thee face to face;
2. Here would I feed up - on the bread of God,
3. I have no help but Thine, nor do I need
4. Mine is the sin, but Thine the right - eous - ness;
Here would I touch and han - dle things un - seen;
Here drink with Thee the roy - al wine of heav'n;
An - oth - er arm save Thine to lean up - on;
Mine is the guilt, but Thine the cleans - ing blood;
Here grasp with firm - er hand e - ter - nal grace,
Here would I lay a - side each earth - ly load,
It is e - nough, my Lord, e - nough in - deed;
Here is my trust, my ref - uge, and my peace,
And all my wea - ri - ness up - on Thee lean.
Here taste a - fresh the calm of sin for - giv'n.
My strength is in Thy might, Thy might a - lone.
Thy blood, Thy right - eous - ness, O Lord, my God.
A - men.

# THAT DOLEFUL NIGHT BEFORE HIS DEATH 446

*With desire I have desired to eat this passover with you before I suffer.* Lk. 22:15.

Joseph Hart, 1762, (1712-1768) — SOLON C.M. 8.6.8.6. M.M. 69 — Jeremiah Ingalls, 1803 (1764-1828)

1. That dole - ful night be - fore his death, The Lamb, for sin - ners slain,
2. To keep the feast, Lord, we are met, And to re - mem - ber thee;
3. Thy suf -f'rings, Lord, each sa - cred sign To our re - membrance brings;
4. Oh, tune our tongues, and set in frame Each heart that pants for thee,
Did, al - most with his lat - est breath This sol - emn feast or - dain.
Help each poor trem - bler to re - peat, "The Sav - iour died for me."
We eat the bread and drink the wine, But think on no - bler things.
To sing "Ho - san - na to the Lamb, The Lamb that died for me."

# BLEST FEAST OF LOVE 447

*The bread which we break, is it not the communion of the body of Christ?* I Cor. 10:16.

Edward Denny, 1839 (1796-1889)
Refrain, John J. Overholt, 1970 — DUNBAR S.M. 6.6.8.6. M.M. 84 — C. R. Dunbar

1. Blest feast of love di – vine! 'Tis grace that makes us free
2. Thy blood which flowed for sin, In sym – bol here we see,
3. O, if this glimpse of love Be so di – vine – ly sweet,
Ref. In mem – 'ry of Thy love, Thy death, Thy blood out–poured,
To feed up – on this bread and wine, In mem–'ry, Lord, of Thee.
And feel the bless–ed pledge with – in That we are loved by Thee.
What will it be, O Lord, a – bove, Thy gladd'ning smile to meet?
This ser – vice we ob–serve in love, 'Till Thou re – turn, O Lord!

# 448 ACCORDING TO THY GRACIOUS WORD

*This do in remembrance of Me.* Lk. 22:19.

James Montgomery, 1825 (1771-1854)

DALEHURST C.M. 8.6.8.6.
M.M. 63

Arthur Cottman, 1874 (1842-1879)

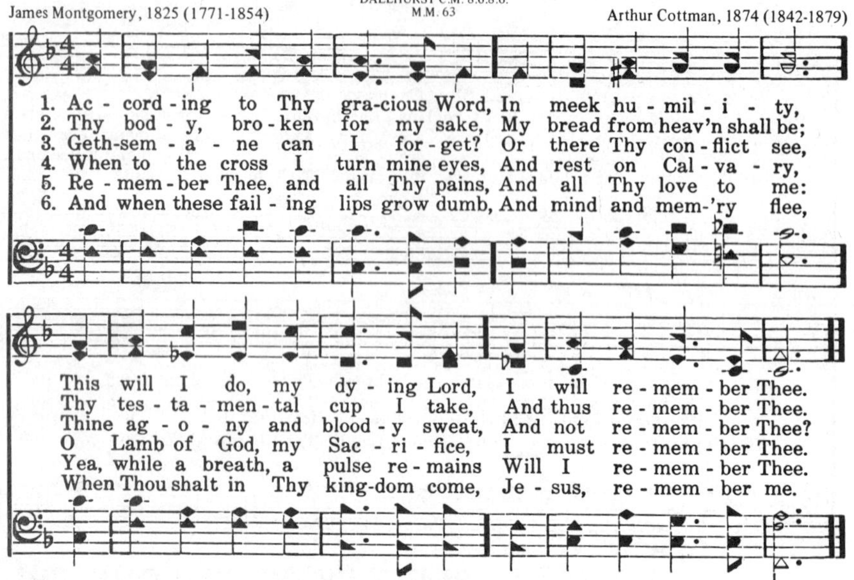
1. Ac - cord - ing to Thy gra-cious Word, In meek hu - mil - i - ty,
2. Thy bod - y, bro - ken for my sake, My bread from heav'n shall be;
3. Geth-sem - a - ne can I for - get? Or there Thy con - flict see,
4. When to the cross I turn mine eyes, And rest on Cal - va - ry,
5. Re - mem - ber Thee, and all Thy pains, And all Thy love to me:
6. And when these fail - ing lips grow dumb, And mind and mem-'ry flee,
This will I do, my dy - ing Lord, I will re - mem - ber Thee.
Thy tes - ta - men - tal cup I take, And thus re - mem - ber Thee.
Thine ag - o - ny and blood - y sweat, And not re - mem - ber Thee?
O Lamb of God, my Sac - ri - fice, I must re - mem - ber Thee.
Yea, while a breath, a pulse re - mains Will I re - mem - ber Thee.
When Thou shalt in Thy king-dom come, Je - sus, re - mem - ber me.

# 449 LORD OF OUR HIGHEST LOVE!

*And as they did eat, Jesus took bread, and blessed, and brake it, and gave it to them, and said, Take, eat: this is my body.* Mk. 14:22.

G. Y. Tickle

FRANCONIA S.M. 6.6.8.6.
M.M. 66

*Harmonischer Liederschatz*, 1738
Arr. William Henry Havergal, 1847 (1793-1870)

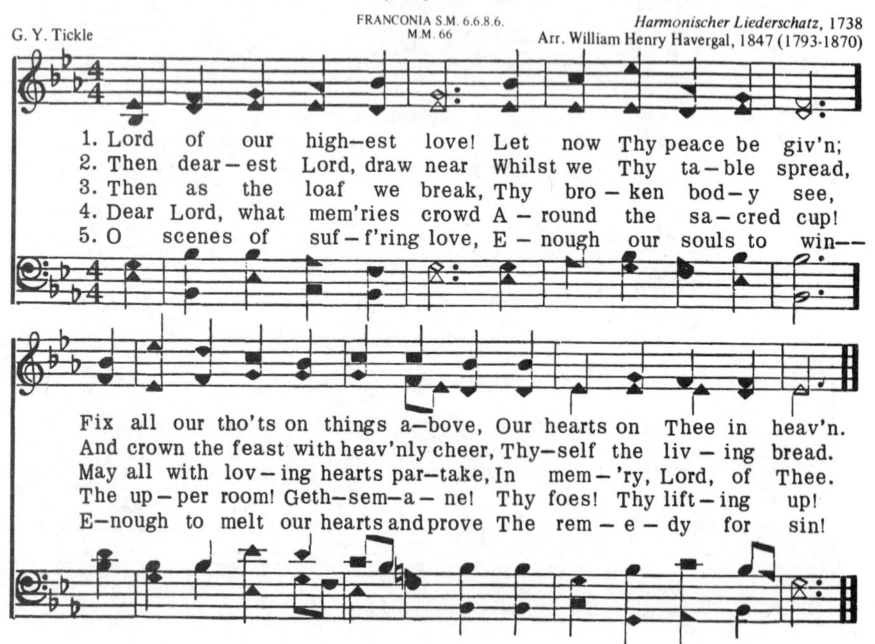
1. Lord of our high–est love! Let now Thy peace be giv'n;
2. Then dear–est Lord, draw near Whilst we Thy ta–ble spread,
3. Then as the loaf we break, Thy bro–ken bod–y see,
4. Dear Lord, what mem'ries crowd A–round the sa–cred cup!
5. O scenes of suf–f'ring love, E–nough our souls to win––
Fix all our tho'ts on things a–bove, Our hearts on Thee in heav'n.
And crown the feast with heav'nly cheer, Thy–self the liv–ing bread.
May all with lov–ing hearts par–take, In mem–'ry, Lord, of Thee.
The up–per room! Geth–sem–a–ne! Thy foes! Thy lift–ing up!
E–nough to melt our hearts and prove The rem–e–dy for sin!

# BREAD OF THE WORLD IN MERCY BROKEN 450

*And He took bread, and gave thanks, and brake it, and gave unto them, saying, This is my body which is given for you.* Lk. 22:19.

Reginald Heber, 1827 (1783–1826)

EUCHARIST 9.8.9.8.
M.M. 72

John Sebastian Bach Hodges, 1830-1915

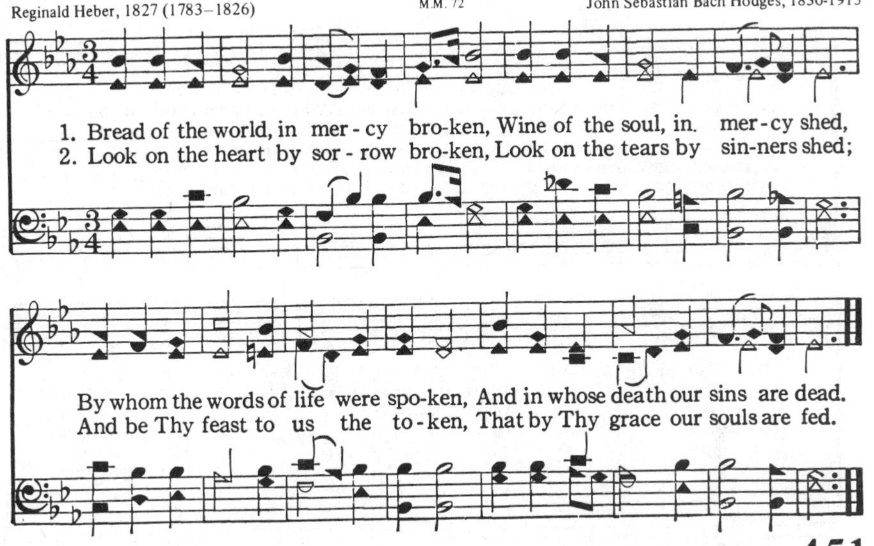
1. Bread of the world, in mer-cy bro-ken, Wine of the soul, in mer-cy shed,
2. Look on the heart by sor-row bro-ken, Look on the tears by sin-ners shed;
By whom the words of life were spo-ken, And in whose death our sins are dead.
And be Thy feast to us the to-ken, That by Thy grace our souls are fed.

# AMIDST US OUR BELOVED STANDS 451

*Worthy is the Lamb.* Rev. 5:12. *For Thou wast slain, and hast redeemed us to God by Thy blood out of every kindred, and tongue, and people, and nation.* Rev. 5:9.

Charles Haddon Spurgeon, 1866 (1834-1892)
Recast, John J. Overholt, 1970

COWPER L.M. 8.8.8.8.
M.M. 58

Lowell Mason, 1792-1872

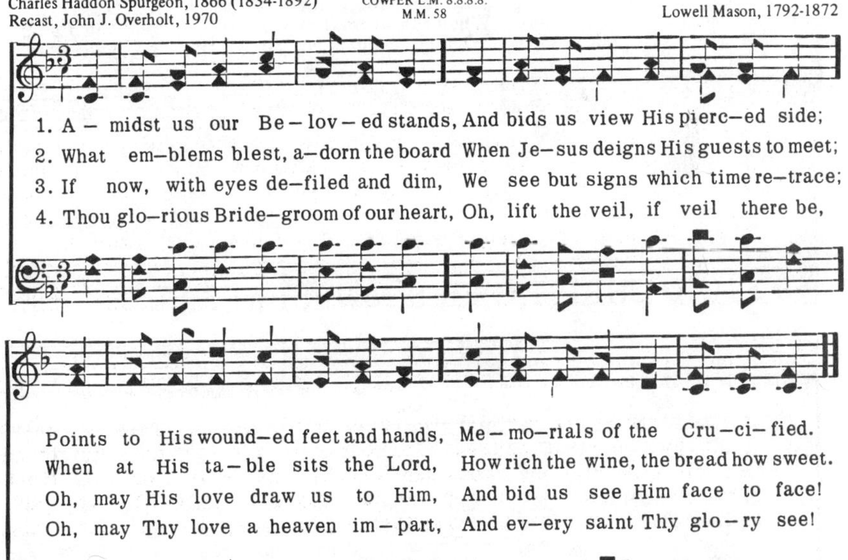
1. A-midst us our Be-lov-ed stands, And bids us view His pierc-ed side;
2. What em-blems blest, a-dorn the board When Je-sus deigns His guests to meet;
3. If now, with eyes de-filed and dim, We see but signs which time re-trace;
4. Thou glo-rious Bride-groom of our heart, Oh, lift the veil, if veil there be,
Points to His wound-ed feet and hands, Me-mo-rials of the Cru-ci-fied.
When at His ta-ble sits the Lord, How rich the wine, the bread how sweet.
Oh, may His love draw us to Him, And bid us see Him face to face!
Oh, may Thy love a heaven im-part, And ev-ery saint Thy glo-ry see!

# 452 SAW YE MY SAVIOUR?

*Saw ye Him whom my soul loveth?* Song. of Sol. 3:3.

Anonymous | ATONEMENT 10.7.7.7.9. M.M. 76 | Anonymous

1. Saw ye my Sav - iour, saw ye my Sav - iour, Saw ye my
2. He was ex - tend - ed, He was ex - tend - ed, Pain - ful - ly
3. Je - sus hung bleed-ing, Je - sus hung bleed - ing Three dread-ful
4. Dark - ness pre - vail - ed, dark - ness pre - vail - ed, Dark - ness pre-

Sav - iour and God? Oh! He died on Cal - va - ry, To a-
nailed to the cross; Here He bowed His head and died, Thus my
hours...... in pain; And the sol - id rocks were rent, Thro' cre-
vailed o'er the land; And the sun re - fused to shine When His

tone for you and me, And to pur - chase our par - don with blood.
Lord was cru - ci - fied, To a - tone for a world that was lost.
a - tion's vast ex - tent, When the Jews cru - ci - fi - ed the Lamb.
Maj - es - ty di - vine Was de - rid - ed, in - sult - ed, and slain.

# 453 DID CHRIST O'ER SINNERS WEEP

*He beheld the city, and wept over it.* Lk. 19:41.

Benjamin Beddome, 1787 (1717-1795) | LOTTIE S.M. 6.6.8.6. M.M. 63 | William Batchelder Bradbury, 1816-1868

1. Did Christ o'er sin - ners weep, And shall our cheeks be dry?
2. The Son of God in tears, The won - d'ring an - gels see;
3. He wept that we might weep, Each sin de - mands a tear;

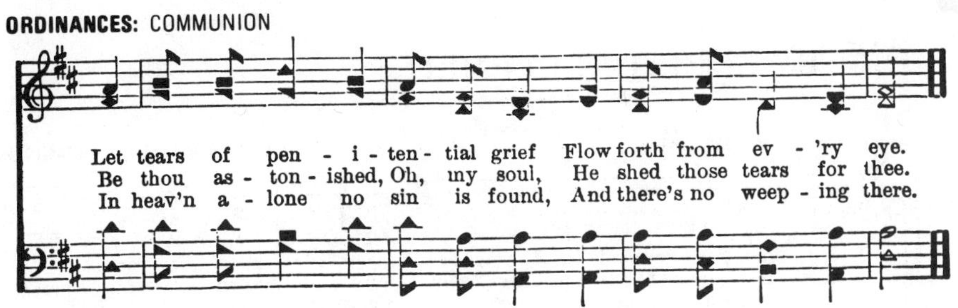
Let tears of pen - i - ten - tial grief Flow forth from ev - 'ry eye.
Be thou as - ton - ished, Oh, my soul, He shed those tears for thee.
In heav'n a - lone no sin is found, And there's no weep - ing there.

# ANOTHER DAY WITH ALL ITS CARES 454

*For even Christ our passover is sacrificed for us.* I Cor. 5:7.

G. Y. Tickle
Alt. by Compiler, 1970

TOULON 10.10.10.10.
M.M. 88

Claude Goudimel, 1508-1572

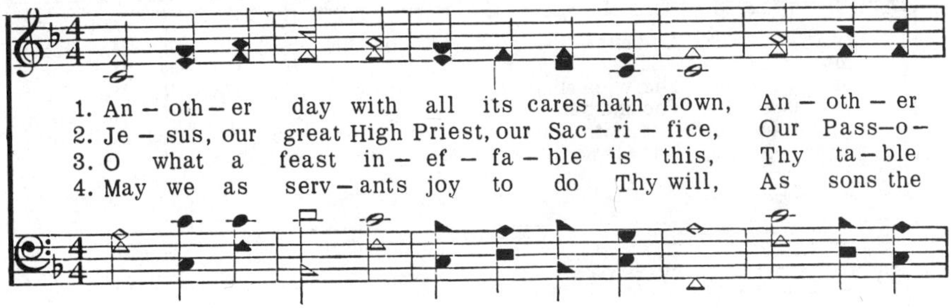

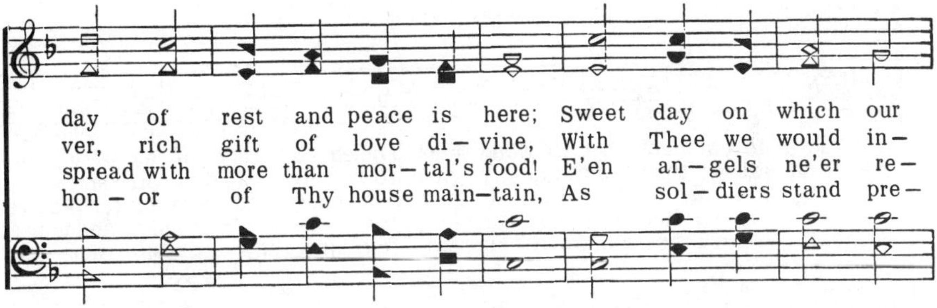

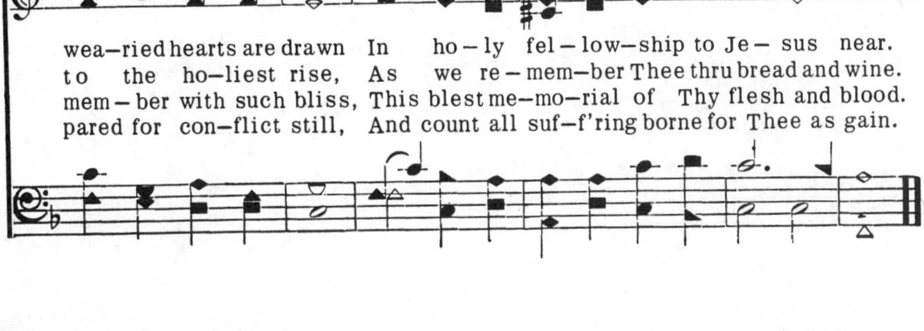

1. An – oth – er day with all its cares hath flown, An – oth – er day of rest and peace is here; Sweet day on which our wea–ried hearts are drawn In ho – ly fel – low–ship to Je – sus near.

2. Je – sus, our great High Priest, our Sac – ri – fice, Our Pass–o–ver, rich gift of love di – vine, With Thee we would in– to the ho–liest rise, As we re – mem–ber Thee thru bread and wine.

3. O what a feast in – ef – fa – ble is this, Thy ta – ble spread with more than mor – tal's food! E'en an – gels ne'er re – mem – ber with such bliss, This blest me–mo–rial of Thy flesh and blood.

4. May we as serv – ants joy to do Thy will, As sons the hon – or of Thy house main–tain, As sol – diers stand pre – pared for con–flict still, And count all suf–f'ring borne for Thee as gain.

# 455 BY CHRIST REDEEMED

*Ye do shew the Lord's death till He come.* I Cor. 11:26.

George L. Rawson, 1857 (1807-1889)

IN MEMORIAM 8.8.8.4.
M.M. 76

Frederick Charles Maker, 1844-1927

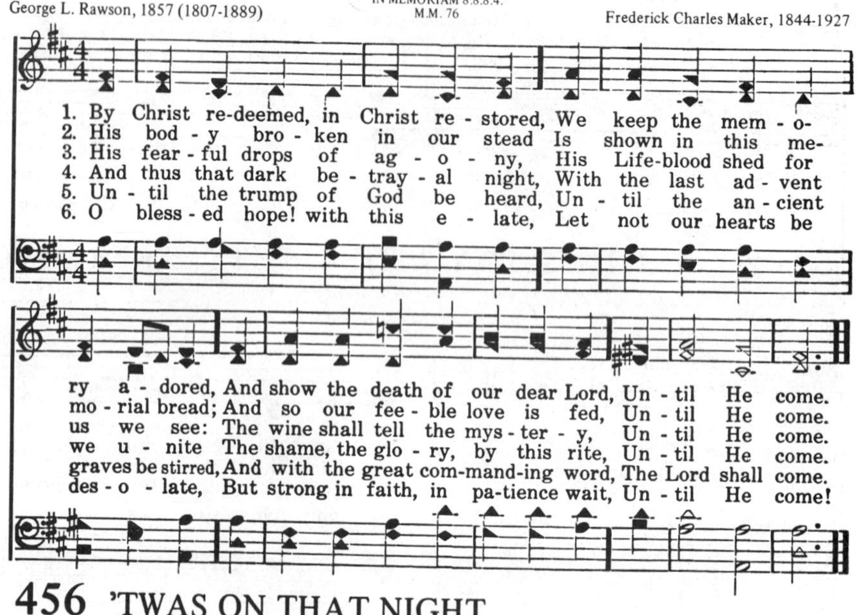
1. By Christ re-deemed, in Christ re - stored, We keep the mem - o-
2. His bod - y bro - ken in our stead Is shown in this me-
3. His fear - ful drops of ag - o - ny, His Life-blood shed for
4. And thus that dark be - tray - al night, With the last ad - vent
5. Un - til the trump of God be heard, Un - til the an - cient
6. O bless - ed hope! with this e - late, Let not our hearts be
ry a - dored, And show the death of our dear Lord, Un - til He come.
mo - rial bread; And so our fee - ble love is fed, Un - til He come.
us we see: The wine shall tell the mys - ter - y, Un - til He come.
we u - nite The shame, the glo - ry, by this rite, Un - til He come.
graves be stirred, And with the great com-mand-ing word, The Lord shall come.
des - o - late, But strong in faith, in pa-tience wait, Un - til He come!

# 456 'TWAS ON THAT NIGHT

*The Lord Jesus the same night in which He was betrayed took bread: And when He had given thanks, He brake it, and said, Take, eat: this is my body which is broken for you.* I Cor. 11:23-24.

*Scottish Paraphrases,* 1781
Alt. by Compiler, 1970

ROCKINGHAM OLD 8.8.8.8.
M.M. 72

Adapted by Edward Miller, 1790 (1735-1807)

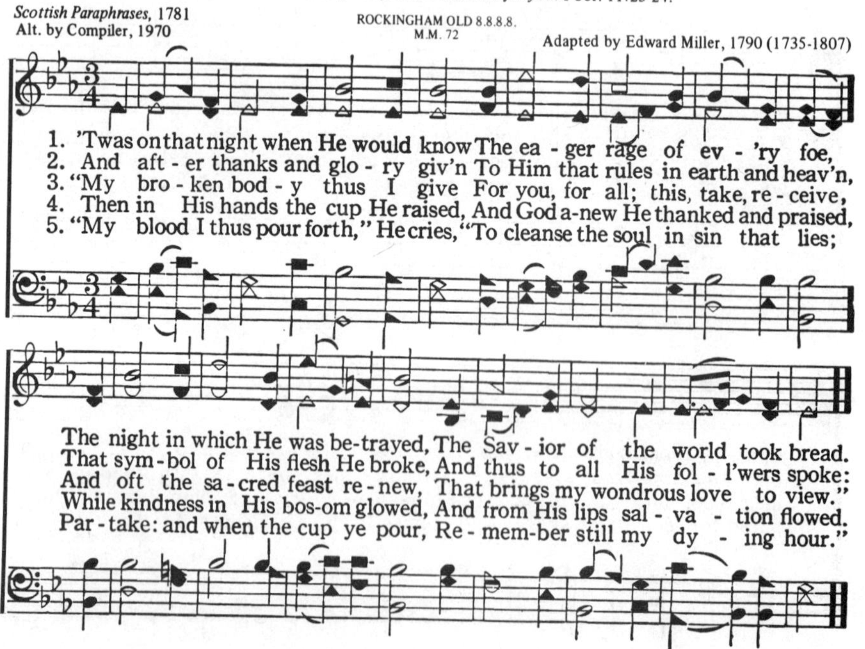
1. 'Twas on that night when He would know The ea - ger rage of ev - 'ry foe,
2. And aft - er thanks and glo - ry giv'n To Him that rules in earth and heav'n,
3. "My bro - ken bod - y thus I give For you, for all; this, take, re - ceive,
4. Then in His hands the cup He raised, And God a-new He thanked and praised,
5. "My blood I thus pour forth," He cries, "To cleanse the soul in sin that lies;
The night in which He was be-trayed, The Sav - ior of the world took bread.
That sym-bol of His flesh He broke, And thus to all His fol - l'wers spoke:
And oft the sa - cred feast re - new, That brings my wondrous love to view."
While kindness in His bos-om glowed, And from His lips sal - va - tion flowed.
Par - take: and when the cup ye pour, Re - mem-ber still my dy - ing hour."

# IN MEMORY OF THE SAVIOR'S LOVE 457

*Hereby perceive we the love of God, because He laid down His life for us: and we ought to lay down our lives for the brethren.* I Jn. 3:16.

Thomas Cotterill, 1805 (1779-1823)
Alt. and St. 2, John J. Overholt, 1970

WINCHESTER OLD C.M. 8.6.8.6.
M.M. 69

T. Este's *Whole Booke of Psalmes*, 1592

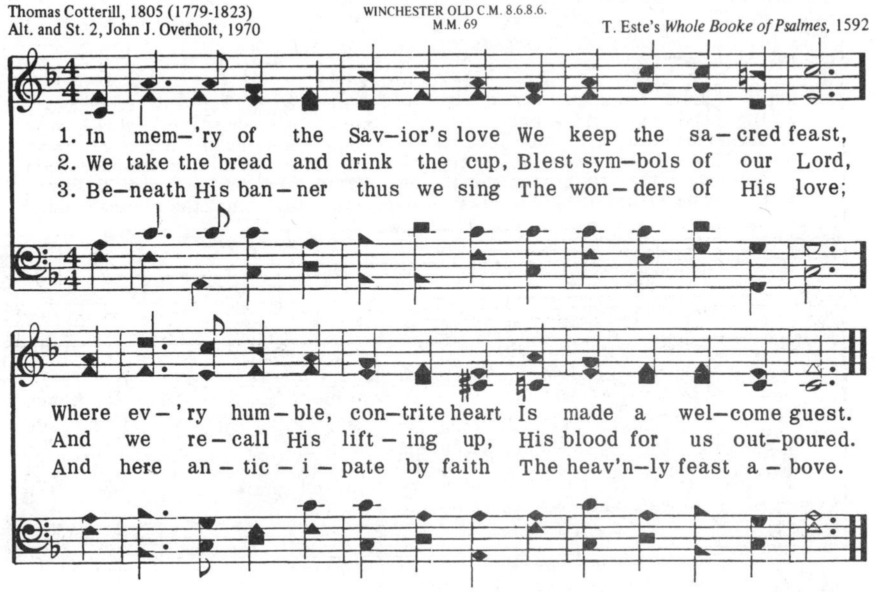
1. In mem–'ry of the Sav–ior's love We keep the sa–cred feast,
2. We take the bread and drink the cup, Blest sym–bols of our Lord,
3. Be–neath His ban–ner thus we sing The won–ders of His love;
Where ev–'ry hum–ble, con–trite heart Is made a wel–come guest.
And we re–call His lift–ing up, His blood for us out–poured.
And here an–tic–i–pate by faith The heav'n–ly feast a–bove.

# O LOVE DIVINE, O MATCHLESS GRACE 458

*Greater love hath no man than this, that a man lay down his life for his friends.* Jn. 15:13. *While we were yet sinners, Christ died for us.* Rom. 5:8.

Edward Turney, 1864 (1817-1872)
Alt. by Compiler, 1970

BYEFIELD C.M. 8.6.8.6.
M.M. 66

Thomas Hastings, 1840 (1784-1872)

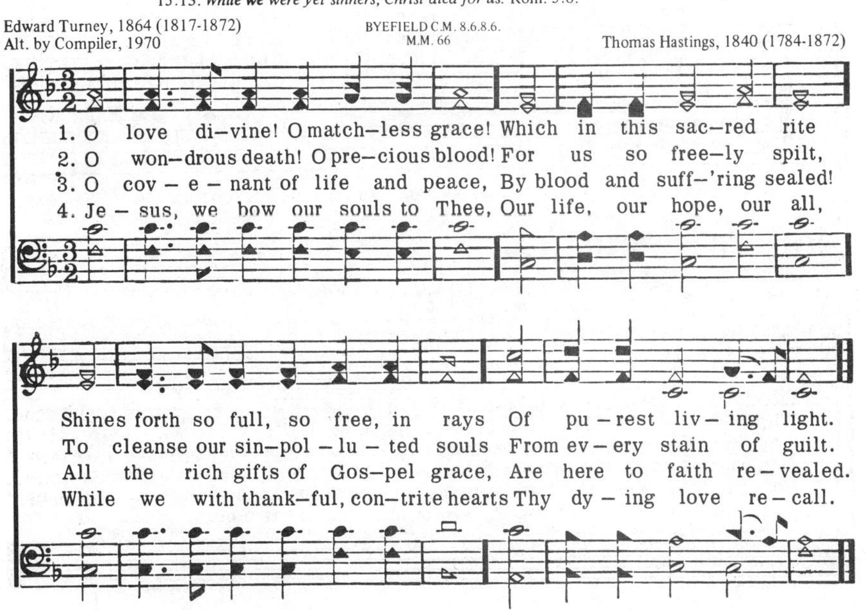
1. O love di–vine! O match–less grace! Which in this sac–red rite
2. O won–drous death! O pre–cious blood! For us so free–ly spilt,
3. O cov–e–nant of life and peace, By blood and suff–'ring sealed!
4. Je–sus, we bow our souls to Thee, Our life, our hope, our all,
Shines forth so full, so free, in rays Of pu–rest liv–ing light.
To cleanse our sin–pol–lu–ted souls From ev–ery stain of guilt.
All the rich gifts of Gos–pel grace, Are here to faith re–vealed.
While we with thank–ful, con–trite hearts Thy dy–ing love re–call.

# 459 HARK! THE VOICE OF LOVE AND MERCY

*It is finished.* Jn. 19:30.

Jonathan Evans, 1784 (1749-1809)
Alt. by Compiler, 1970

MOLUCCA 8.7.8.7.4.4.7.
M.M. 60

Isaac Baker Woodbury, 1819-1854

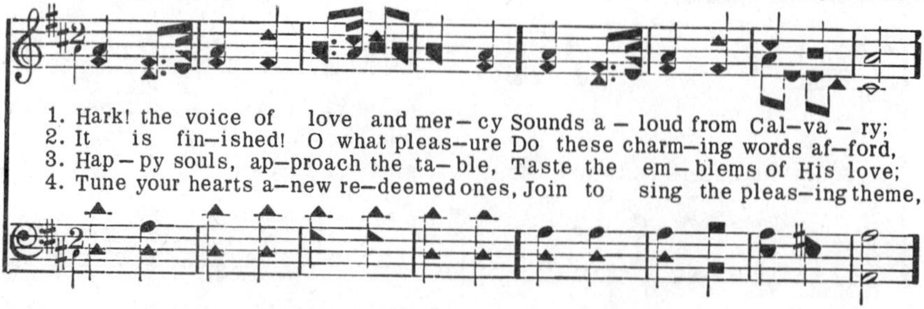

1. Hark! the voice of love and mer – cy Sounds a – loud from Cal – va – ry;
2. It is fin – ished! O what pleas – ure Do these charm – ing words af – ford,
3. Hap – py souls, ap – proach the ta – ble, Taste the em – blems of His love;
4. Tune your hearts a – new re – deemed ones, Join to sing the pleas – ing theme,

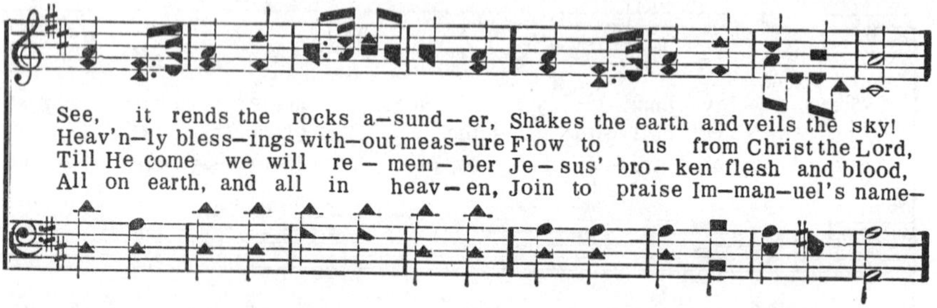

See, it rends the rocks a – sund – er, Shakes the earth and veils the sky!
Heav'n – ly bless – ings with – out meas – ure Flow to us from Christ the Lord,
Till He come we will re – mem – ber Je – sus' bro – ken flesh and blood,
All on earth, and all in heav – en, Join to praise Im – man – uel's name–

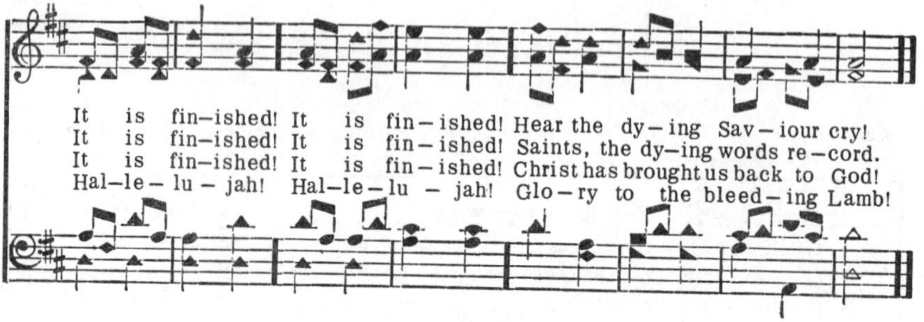

It is fin – ished! It is fin – ished! Hear the dy – ing Sav – iour cry!
It is fin – ished! It is fin – ished! Saints, the dy – ing words re – cord.
It is fin – ished! It is fin – ished! Christ has brought us back to God!
Hal – le – lu – jah! Hal – le – lu – jah! Glo – ry to the bleed – ing Lamb!

# 460 IT IS FINISHED

*I have finished the work which Thou gavest me to do.* Jn. 17:4. *Father into Thy hands I commend My Spirit.* Lk. 23:46.

Stoffard Augustus Brooks, 1832-1915
St. 4, John J. Overholt, 1971

CLARENCE 7.7.7.7.
M.M. 63

Arthur Seymour Sullivan, 1842-1900

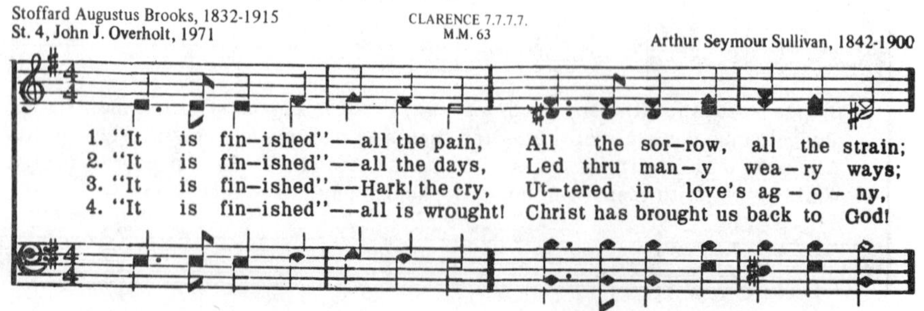
1. "It is fin – ished"—all the pain, All the sor – row, all the strain;
2. "It is fin – ished"—all the days, Led thru man – y wea – ry ways;
3. "It is fin – ished"—Hark! the cry, Ut – tered in love's ag – o – ny,
4. "It is fin – ished"—all is wrought! Christ has brought us back to God!

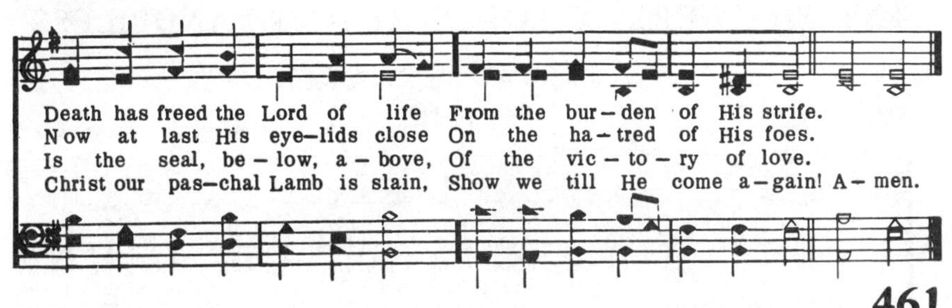
Death has freed the Lord of life From the bur–den of His strife.
Now at last His eye–lids close On the ha–tred of His foes.
Is the seal, be–low, a–bove, Of the vic–to–ry of love.
Christ our pas–chal Lamb is slain, Show we till He come a–gain! A–men.

# 461

## WE NOW SHOW FORTH THE DYING OF OUR LORD

*For as often as ye eat this bread, and drink this cup, ye do shew the Lord's death till He come.* I Cor. 11:26.

Latin hymn, c. 680
Tr. John Mason Neale, 1851 (1818-1866)
Recast, John J. Overholt, 1970

MORECAMBE 10.10.10.10.
M.M. 52

Frederick Cook Atkinson, 1870 (1841-1897)

1. We now show forth the dy–ing of our Lord, Re–mem–ber–
2. Sal–va–tion's giv–er, Christ, the on–ly Son, By His dear
3. He, that His saints in this world rules and shields, To all be–

ing His blood for us out–poured, Saved by His grace through
cross and blood the vic–tory won. Of–fered was He for
liev–ers life e–ter–nal yields, With bound–less grace makes

His a–ton–ing blood, With souls re–newed we ren–der thanks to God.
great–est and for least, Him–self the vic–tim, and Him–self the priest.
them that hun–ger whole, Gives liv–ing waters to the thirst–ing soul. A–men.

# 462 SHEPHERD OF SOULS, REFRESH AND BLESS

*They drank of that spiritual Rock that followed them: and that Rock was Christ.* I Cor. 10:4. *The bread of God is He which . . . giveth life unto the world.* Jn. 6:33.

James Montgomery, 1825 (1771-1854), alt.
St. 5, John J. Overholt, 1970

ST. PETER C.M. 8.6.8.6.
M.M. 66

Alexander Robert Reinagle, 1836 (1799-1877)

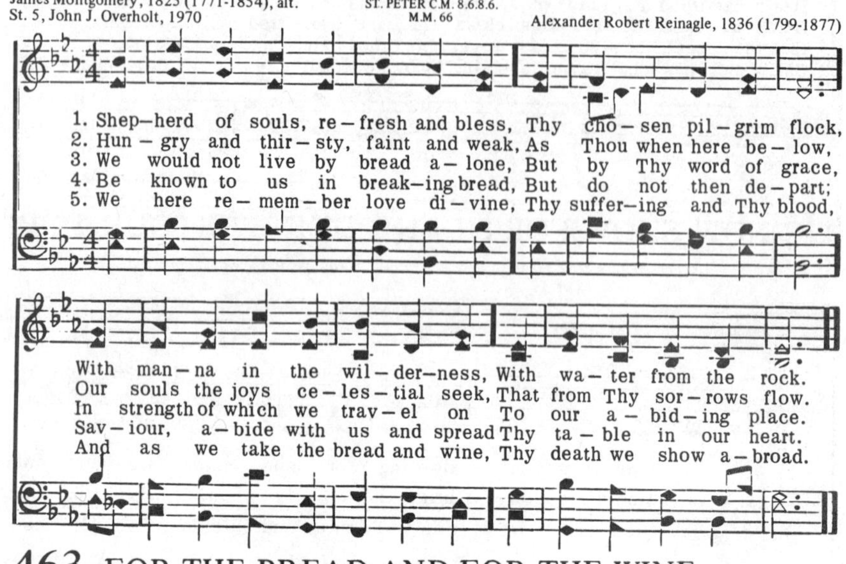
1. Shep–herd of souls, re–fresh and bless, Thy cho–sen pil–grim flock,
2. Hun–gry and thir–sty, faint and weak, As Thou when here be–low,
3. We would not live by bread a–lone, But by Thy word of grace,
4. Be known to us in break–ing bread, But do not then de–part;
5. We here re–mem–ber love di–vine, Thy suffer–ing and Thy blood,
With man–na in the wil–der–ness, With wa–ter from the rock.
Our souls the joys ce–les–tial seek, That from Thy sor–rows flow.
In strength of which we trav–el on To our a–bid–ing place.
Sav–iour, a–bide with us and spread Thy ta–ble in our heart.
And as we take the bread and wine, Thy death we show a–broad.

# 463 FOR THE BREAD AND FOR THE WINE

*Thanks be unto God for His unspeakable gift.* II Cor. 9:15.

Horatius Bonar, 1874 (1808-1889)
Alt. by Compiler, 1970

CAPETOWN 7.7.7.5.
M.M. 66

Frederick Filitz, 1847 (1804-1876)

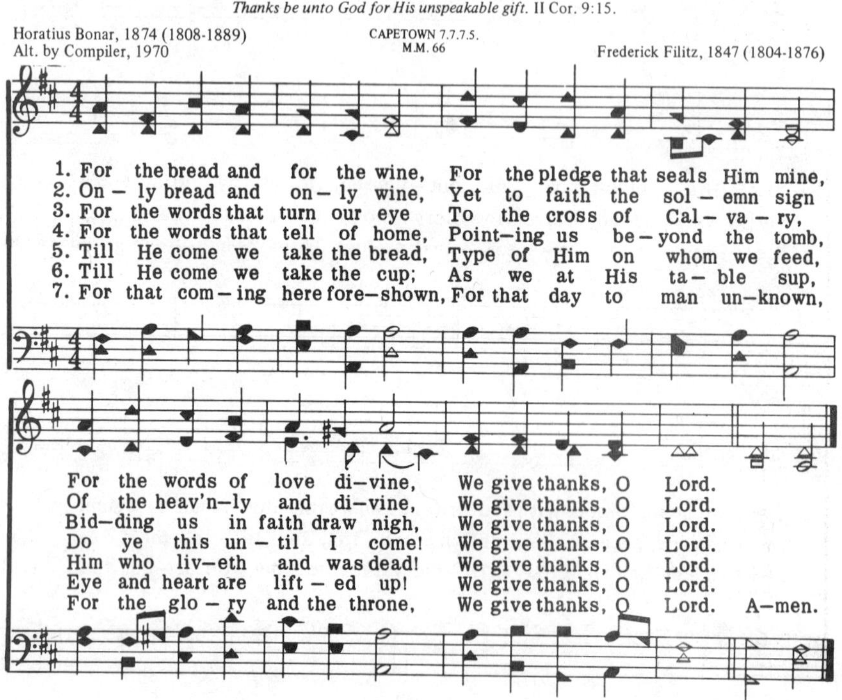
1. For the bread and for the wine, For the pledge that seals Him mine,
2. On–ly bread and on–ly wine, Yet to faith the sol–emn sign
3. For the words that turn our eye To the cross of Cal–va–ry,
4. For the words that tell of home, Point–ing us be–yond the tomb,
5. Till He come we take the bread, Type of Him on whom we feed,
6. Till He come we take the cup; As we at His ta–ble sup,
7. For that com–ing here fore–shown, For that day to man un–known,
For the words of love di–vine, We give thanks, O Lord.
Of the heav'n–ly and di–vine, We give thanks, O Lord.
Bid–ding us in faith draw nigh, We give thanks, O Lord.
Do ye this un–til I come! We give thanks, O Lord.
Him who liv–eth and was dead! We give thanks, O Lord.
Eye and heart are lift–ed up! We give thanks, O Lord.
For the glo–ry and the throne, We give thanks, O Lord. A–men.

## THE SONS OF GOD BELIEVE IT RIGHT 464

*For thus it becometh us to fulfil all righteousness.* Mt. 3:15.

John Winebrenner
Alt. by Compiler, 1970

RETREAT L.M. 8.8.8.8.
M.M. 76

Thomas Hastings, 1842 (1784-1872)

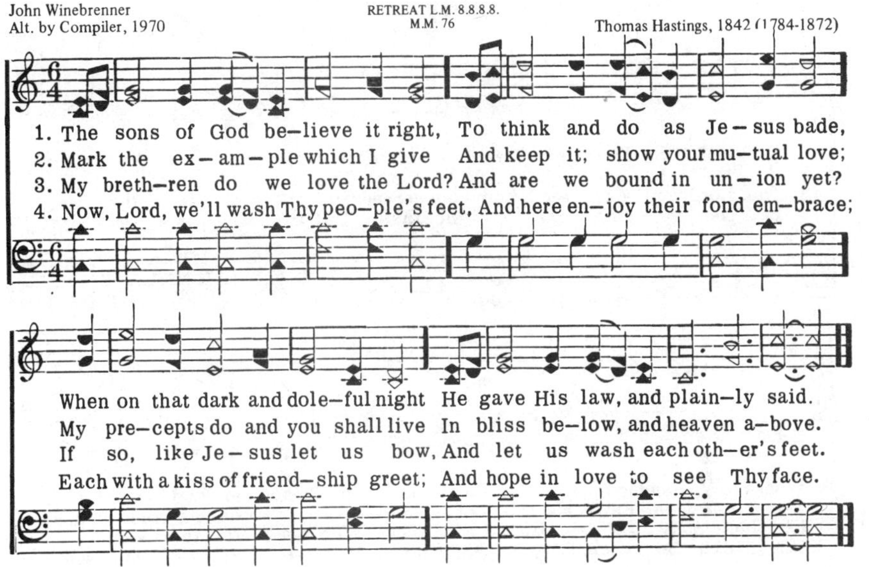
1. The sons of God be–lieve it right, To think and do as Je–sus bade,
2. Mark the ex–am–ple which I give And keep it; show your mu–tual love;
3. My breth–ren do we love the Lord? And are we bound in un–ion yet?
4. Now, Lord, we'll wash Thy peo–ple's feet, And here en–joy their fond em–brace;
When on that dark and dole–ful night He gave His law, and plain–ly said.
My pre–cepts do and you shall live In bliss be–low, and heaven a–bove.
If so, like Je–sus let us bow, And let us wash each oth–er's feet.
Each with a kiss of friend–ship greet; And hope in love to see Thy face.

## CHRIST, IN THE NIGHT HE WAS BETRAYED 465

*I have given you an example, that ye should do as I have done to you.* Jn. 13:15.

Anonymous

HEBRON L.M. 8.8.8.8.
M.M. 60

Lowell Mason, 1830 (1792-1872)

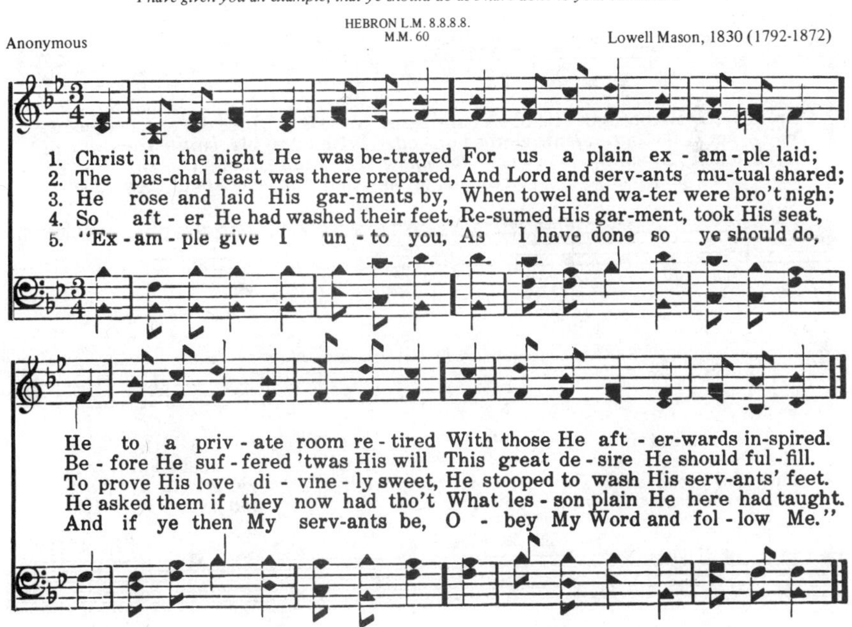
1. Christ in the night He was be-trayed For us a plain ex - am - ple laid;
2. The pas-chal feast was there prepared, And Lord and serv-ants mu-tual shared;
3. He rose and laid His gar-ments by, When towel and wa-ter were bro't nigh;
4. So aft - er He had washed their feet, Re-sumed His gar-ment, took His seat,
5. "Ex - am - ple give I un - to you, As I have done so ye should do,
He to a priv - ate room re - tired With those He aft - er-wards in-spired.
Be - fore He suf - fered 'twas His will This great de - sire He should ful - fill.
To prove His love di - vine - ly sweet, He stooped to wash His serv-ants' feet.
He asked them if they now had tho't What les - son plain He here had taught.
And if ye then My serv-ants be, O - bey My Word and fol - low Me."

# 466 EXTOL THE LOVE OF CHRIST

*He riseth from supper . . . and took a towel, and girded Himself.* Jn. 13:4.

VARINA C.M.D. 8.6.8.6.D.
M.M. 58

Samuel Frederick Coffman, 1925 (1872-1954)

George Frederick Root, 1820-1895

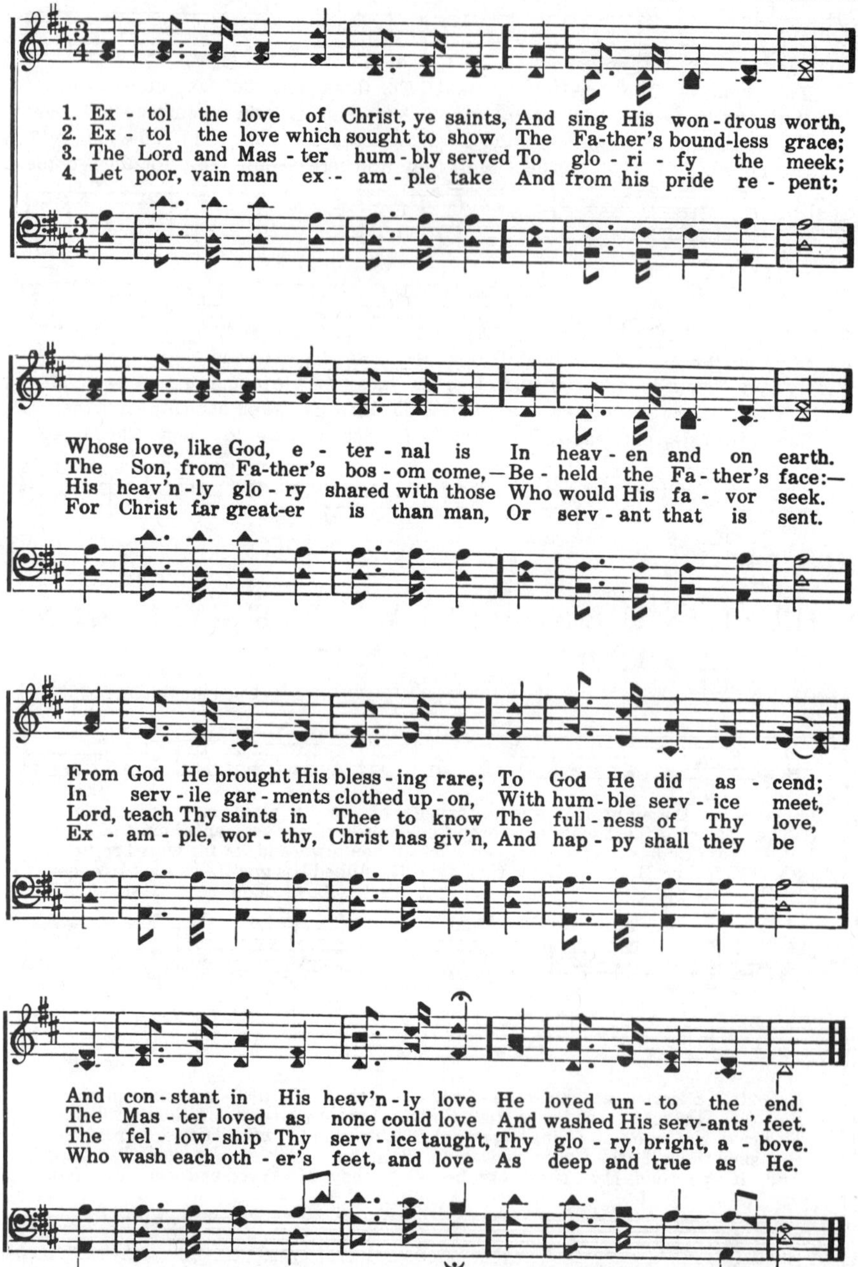

1. Ex - tol the love of Christ, ye saints, And sing His won - drous worth,
2. Ex - tol the love which sought to show The Fa-ther's bound-less grace;
3. The Lord and Mas - ter hum - bly served To glo - ri - fy the meek;
4. Let poor, vain man ex - am - ple take And from his pride re - pent;

Whose love, like God, e - ter - nal is In heav - en and on earth.
The Son, from Fa-ther's bos - om come,—Be - held the Fa - ther's face:—
His heav'n - ly glo - ry shared with those Who would His fa - vor seek.
For Christ far great-er is than man, Or serv - ant that is sent.

From God He brought His bless - ing rare; To God He did as - cend;
In serv - ile gar - ments clothed up - on, With hum - ble serv - ice meet,
Lord, teach Thy saints in Thee to know The full - ness of Thy love,
Ex - am - ple, wor - thy, Christ has giv'n, And hap - py shall they be

And con - stant in His heav'n - ly love He loved un - to the end.
The Mas - ter loved as none could love And washed His serv-ants' feet.
The fel - low - ship Thy serv - ice taught, Thy glo - ry, bright, a - bove.
Who wash each oth - er's feet, and love As deep and true as He.

# EXTOL THE LOVE OF CHRIST 467

*If ye know these things, happy are ye if ye do them.* Jn. 13:17.

Samuel Frederick Coffman, 1925 (1872-1954)
Alt. Wilmer D. Swope, 1969
OLD 44TH C.M.D. 8.6.8.6.D.
M.M. 66
Anglo Genevan Psalter, 1556
1. Ex - tol the love of Christ, ye saints, And sing His won-drous worth,
2. Ex - tol the love which sought to show The Fa - ther's bound-less grace;
3. The Lord and Mas - ter hum - bly served To glo - ri - fy the meek;
4. Let poor, vain man ex - am - ple take And from his pride re - pent;
Whose love, like God, e - ter - nal is in heav - en and on earth.
God's Son, who came in flesh to earth, Be - held the Fa - ther's face:
His heav'n-ly glo - ry shared with those Who would His fa - vor seek.
For Christ far great - er is than man, Or ser - vant that is sent.
From God He brought His bless - ing rare; To God He did as - cend;
In ser - vile gar - ments clothed up - on, With hum - ble ser - vice meet,
Lord, teach Thy saints in Thee to know The full - ness of Thy love,
Ex - am - ple, wor - thy, Christ has giv'n, And hap - py shall they be
And con-stant in His heav'n-ly love He loved un - to the end.
The Mas - ter loved as none could love And washed His ser - vants' feet.
The fel - low - ship Thy ser - vice taught, Thy glo - ry, bright, a - bove.
Who wash each oth - er's feet, and love As deep and true as He. A-men.

# 468 FOREVER HERE MY REST SHALL BE

*If I wash thee not, thou hast no part with me.* Jn. 13:8.

CAPERS NEW C.M. 8.6.8.6.
M.M. 63

Charles Wesley, 1707-1788

Rigdon M. McIntosh, 1836-1899
Arr. John J. Overholt, 1968

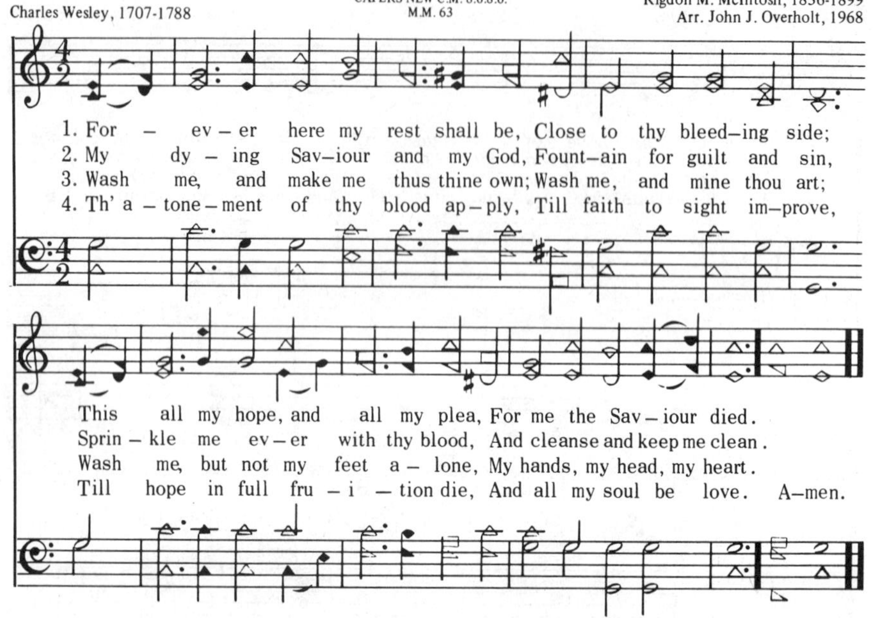
1. For – ev – er here my rest shall be, Close to thy bleed–ing side;
2. My dy – ing Sav–iour and my God, Fount–ain for guilt and sin,
3. Wash me, and make me thus thine own; Wash me, and mine thou art;
4. Th' a – tone – ment of thy blood ap – ply, Till faith to sight im–prove,
This all my hope, and all my plea, For me the Sav – iour died.
Sprin – kle me ev – er with thy blood, And cleanse and keep me clean.
Wash me, but not my feet a – lone, My hands, my head, my heart.
Till hope in full fru – i – tion die, And all my soul be love. A–men.

# 469 BEHOLD, WHERE IN A MORTAL FORM

*Verily, verily, I say unto you, The servant is not greater than His Lord; neither he that is sent greater than he that sent him.* Jn 13:16.

HARTVILLE C.M. 8.6.8.6.
M.M. 63

William Enfield, 1795 (1741-1797)

Marguerite Bixler

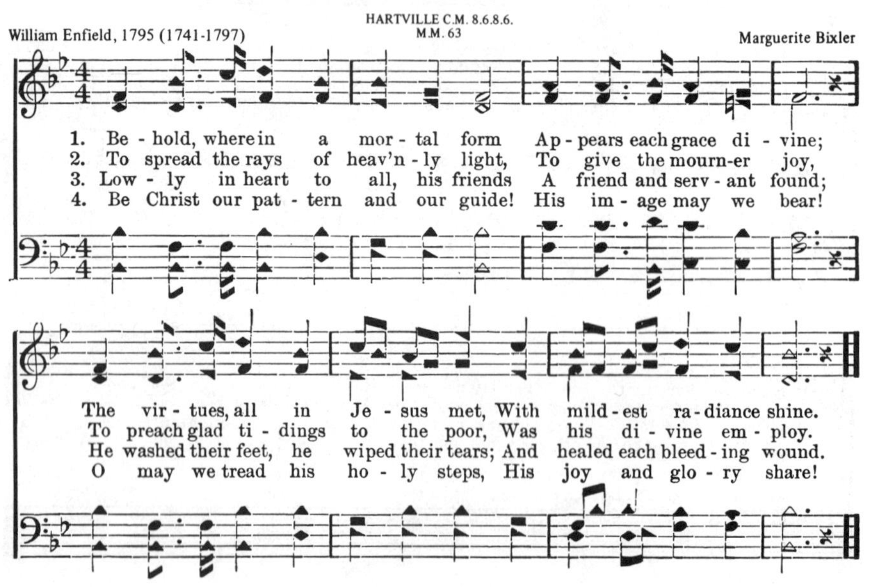
1. Be - hold, where in a mor - tal form Ap - pears each grace di - vine;
2. To spread the rays of heav'n - ly light, To give the mourn - er joy,
3. Low - ly in heart to all, his friends A friend and serv - ant found;
4. Be Christ our pat - tern and our guide! His im - age may we bear!
The vir - tues, all in Je - sus met, With mild - est ra - diance shine.
To preach glad ti - dings to the poor, Was his di - vine em - ploy.
He washed their feet, he wiped their tears; And healed each bleed - ing wound.
O may we tread his ho - ly steps, His joy and glo - ry share!

# WE BOW TO THEE, O LORD 470

*If I then, your Lord and Master, have washed your feet; ye also ought to wash one another's feet.* Jn. 13:14.

GREATFUL SUBMISSION C.M. 8.6.8.6. with Ref.
M.M. 96

Daniel Kauffman, 1865-1944

Abram Bowman Kolb, 1862-1925

1. We bow to thee, O Lord, on high; To thee our hearts in - cline; Sub - mit - ting to thy word, we pray, Thy will be done, not mine.
2. The high - est sta - tion here on earth Is at our Sav-iour's feet; 'Tis there we learn our Mas - ter's will, We find the mer - cy - seat.
3. Our Sav-iour, tho' our Mas - ter, Lord, In true hu - mil - i - ty. By ac - tion taught that we might see The great must ser - vants be.
4. A pat - tern he did kind - ly give To His dis - ci - ples true: He washed their feet, then said to them, "Do as I've done to you."
5. Then af - ter-wards he said to them, "Go forth (I go with you), And teach all na - tions ev - 'ry - thing I've command - ed you to do."
6. Then teach us, Lord, to do thy will, What - ev - er that may be: May thy free grace at - tend us here, And in e - ter - ni - ty.
REFRAIN.
Lord, as this sol - emn rite we keep, With joy we wor - ship thee; May we with hum - ble hearts, O Lord, Thy faith - ful ser - vants be. . . .

# 471 THOU TO WHOM THE SICK AND DYING

*Confess your faults one to another, and pray one for another, that ye may be healed.* Jas. 5:16.

Godfrey Thring, 1871 (1823-1903)
Alt. by Compiler, 1970

JESUS, JESUS, NICHTS ALS JESUS 8.7.8.7.7.7.
M.M. 76

Bonner's *Vollkommenes . . . Choral–Buch*, 1715

1. Thou to whom the sick and dy – ing Ev – er
2. Still the wea – ry, sick and dy – ing Need a
3. May each child of Thine be will – ing, Will – ing
4. So may sick – ness, sin, and sad – ness, To Thy
came, nor came in vain, Still with heal–ing words re – ply – ing
Great Phy – si – cian's care; On Thy high – er help re – ly – ing
both in hand and heart, All the law of love ful – fill – ing,
heal – ing pow – er yield, Till the sick and sad, in glad–ness,
To the wea – ried cry of pain, Hear us, Je – sus,
May they now their bur – den share, For their heal – ing
Ev – er com – fort to im – part; Ev – er bring – ing
Res – cued, ran – som'd, cleansed and healed, One in Thee to-
as we meet Sup–pliants at Thy mer – cy seat.
Thee in – treat, Sup–pliants at Thy mer – cy seat.
of – f'rings meet, Sup–pliants at Thy mer – cy seat.
geth – er meet, Par–don'd at Thy judg–ment seat. A – men.

## WHEN LYING ON THE BED OF PAIN 472

*Is any sick among you? Let him call for the elders of the church; and let them pray over him, anointing him with oil in the name of the Lord.* Jas. 5:14.

GERMANY L.M. 8.8.8.8.
M.M. 88

From a hymn book of the River Brethren, alt. — Ludwig van Beethoven, 1770-1827

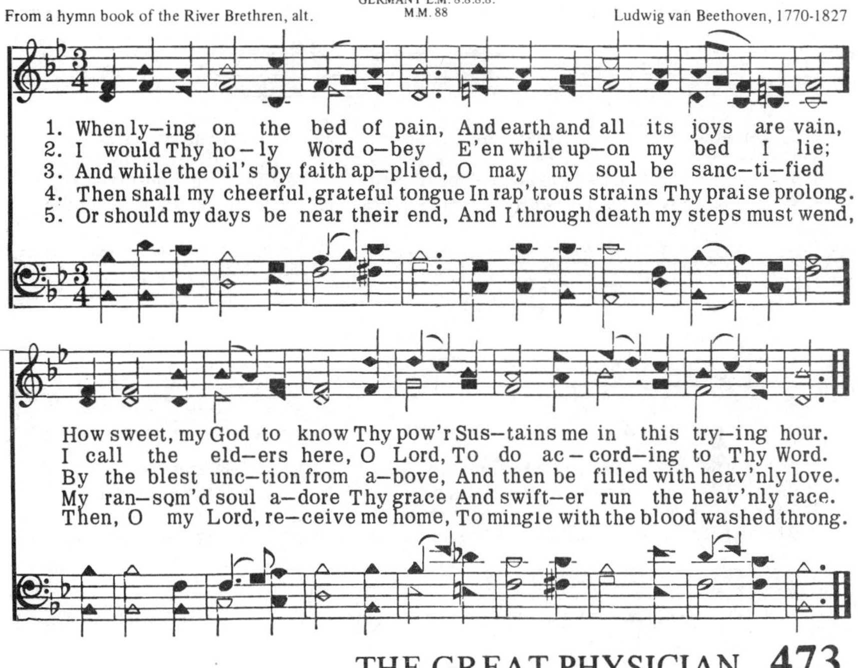
1. When ly–ing on the bed of pain, And earth and all its joys are vain,
2. I would Thy ho–ly Word o–bey E'en while up–on my bed I lie;
3. And while the oil's by faith ap–plied, O may my soul be sanc–ti–fied
4. Then shall my cheerful, grateful tongue In rap'trous strains Thy praise prolong.
5. Or should my days be near their end, And I through death my steps must wend,
How sweet, my God to know Thy pow'r Sus–tains me in this try–ing hour.
I call the eld–ers here, O Lord, To do ac–cord–ing to Thy Word.
By the blest unc–tion from a–bove, And then be filled with heav'nly love.
My ran–som'd soul a–dore Thy grace And swift–er run the heav'nly race.
Then, O my Lord, re–ceive me home, To mingle with the blood washed throng.

## THE GREAT PHYSICIAN 473

*And the prayer of faith shall save the sick, and the Lord shall raise him up.* Jas. 5:15.

THE GREAT PHYSICIAN 8.7.8.7. with Ref.
M.M. 116

William Hunter, 1859 (1811-1877) — John Hart Stockton, 1813-1877

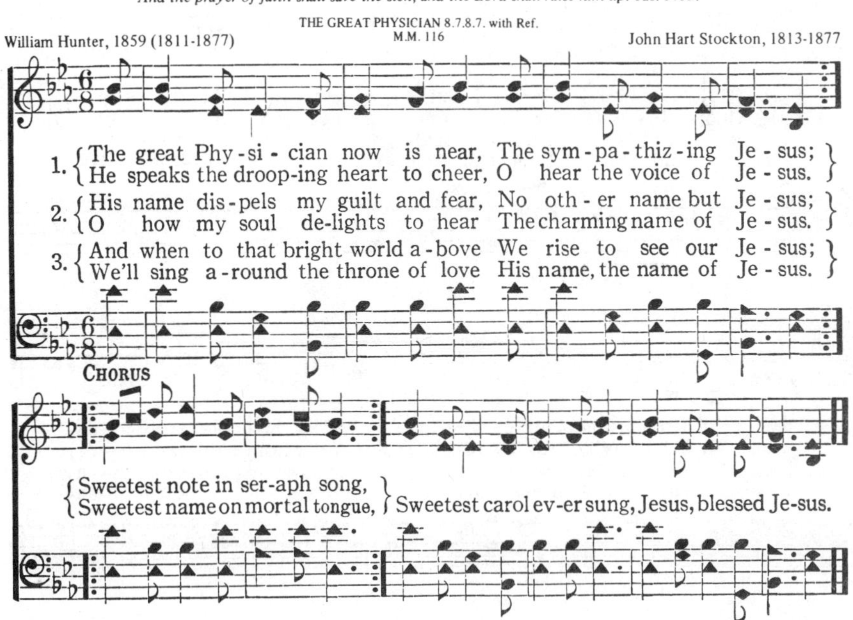
1. The great Phy-si-cian now is near, The sym-pa-thiz-ing Je-sus;
He speaks the droop-ing heart to cheer, O hear the voice of Je-sus.
2. His name dis-pels my guilt and fear, No oth-er name but Je-sus;
O how my soul de-lights to hear The charming name of Je-sus.
3. And when to that bright world a-bove We rise to see our Je-sus;
We'll sing a-round the throne of love His name, the name of Je-sus.
CHORUS
Sweetest note in ser-aph song,
Sweetest name on mortal tongue,
Sweetest carol ev-er sung, Jesus, blessed Je-sus.

# 474 HAVE YOU FOUND THE GREAT PHYSICIAN

*Is there no balm in Gilead; is there no physician there?* Jer. 8:22. *Is any among you afflicted? Let him pray.* Jas. 5:13.

James M. Kirk
Recast, John J. Overholt, 1969
COME YE WANDERERS 8.7.8.7. with Ref.
M.M. 152
Charles Edward Pollock, c. 1902 (b. 1853)
1. Have you found the Great Phy–si–cian, Je–sus Christ of Gal–i–lee? He who bore our sin and sor–row, On the shame–ful, cru–el tree?
2. Con–se–crate your life to Je–sus, Spir–it, soul, and bod–y too; Cleanse your heart from all its sin stains, Je–sus shed his blood for you;
3. Do you doubt God's power to heal you? Take His Word and ask for light, When you seek in deep con–tri–tion, He will guide your heart a–right.
4. Come to Je–sus, wea–ry suf–f'rers, He has more than heal–ing too: Life a–bun–dant, ov–er–flow–ing, He will glad–ly give to you.
Still He heals the sick and suf–f'ring, As He did His earth–ly day; For His Word most plain–ly tells us, He is just the same to–day!
Call God's eld–ers for an–noint–ing you with oil, the Bi–ble way, Then the pray'r of faith can heal you, For our Lord's the same to–day!
If it is His will to heal you, He can heal with–out de–lay; For on earth He glad–ly healed men, And He is the same to–day!
Come and bold–ly claim His prom–ise, Let your sad–ness flee a–way; Je–sus came to bless and com–fort, And He is the same to–day!

# COME ZION'S DAUGHTERS 475

*For if the woman be not covered, let her also be shorn: but if it be a shame for a woman to be shorn or shaven, let her be covered.* I Cor. 11:6.

Wilmer D. Swope, 1970
St. 5, Lawrence Burkhart Brunk, 1970
Alt. John J. Overholt, 1970

PENTECOST L.M. 8.8.8.8.
M.M. 92

William Boyd, 1847-1928

1. Come, Zi – ion's daugh – ters, come, re – joice, Lift heart and
2. What calm di – vine, o – be–di – ence brings, When daugh–ters
3. The power of an – gels shields this sign, When wom – en
4. Come, Zi – on's daugh – ters, wear the veil, Which ev – er

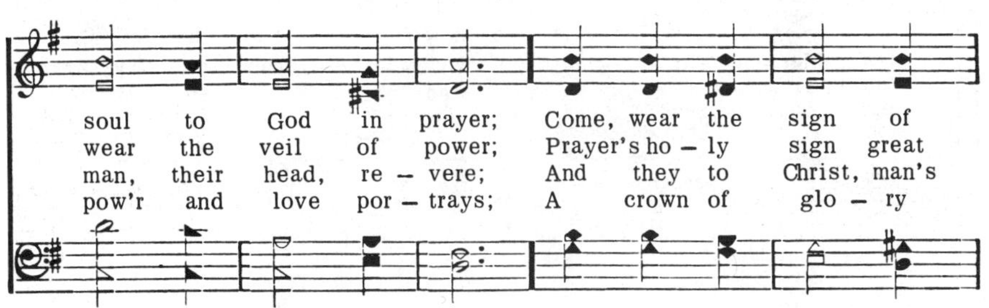
soul to God in prayer; Come, wear the sign of
wear the veil of power; Prayer's ho – ly sign great
man, their head, re – vere; And they to Christ, man's
pow'r and love por – trays; A crown of glo – ry

pil – grim joys, And let God's peace re – place your care.
joy en – rings, When God at – tends prayer's sac – red hour.
head, con – sign The or – der He com – mands them here.
shall not fail To her who thus her Lord o – beys.

5. Come sons, brave soldiers of the cross,
Bow down before our God, the King;
With hearts made pure and heads unveiled,
In prayer and praise, let voices ring!

# 476 GOD HAS ORDAINED

*But I would have you know, that the head of every man is Christ; and the head of the woman is the man; and the head of Christ is God.* I Cor. 11:3.

Margaret Horst, 1964 (b. 1947)

BETHLEHEM NEW C.M.D. 8.6.8.6.D.
M.M. 76

Gottfried Wilhelm Fink, 1842
Arr. by Compiler, 1971

1. God has or–dained that wom – en who Ac – cept His ho – ly plan,
2. God's glo – ry should be man – i–fest– Man does His im – age bear;
3. By heed–ing to God's ho – ly law Each hour of the day,
4. The wom–an who ac – cepts her place In home and church the same,
Shall wear a cov – er – ing to show Sub – mis–sion un – to man.
And thus, to glo – ri – fy his God, Man shall no cov–'ring wear.
The Chris–tian wom–an is pre–pared To proph – e – sy and pray.
Will glad – ly wear the cov – er – ing To glo – ri – fy His name.
At home, in church and ev – 'ry–where Man is to be her head,
The wom–an's glo–ries must be hid, Lest man vain glo – ry know,
For man – y times each day she prays Or speaks to ed – i – fy,
Lord, Thy com–mand is plain and clear– Help each Thy law ful – fill;
And if she will not yield to him, Let her be shorn in – stead.
So wom–en wear a cov–er–ing God's won–drous plan to show.
And do not they who go un–veiled, The Lord's com–mand de–ny?
Thy bless–ing free–ly rest on those Who live with – in Thy will. A–men.

# LORD, WE WOULD NOT DISHONOR THEE 477

*But every woman that prayeth or prophesieth with her head uncovered dishonoureth her head; for that is even all one as if she were shaven.* I Cor. 11:5.

John J. Overholt, 1969 — MAINZER (New) L.M. 8.8.8.8. M.M. 72 — Joseph Mainzer, 1801-1851, Arr. by Compiler

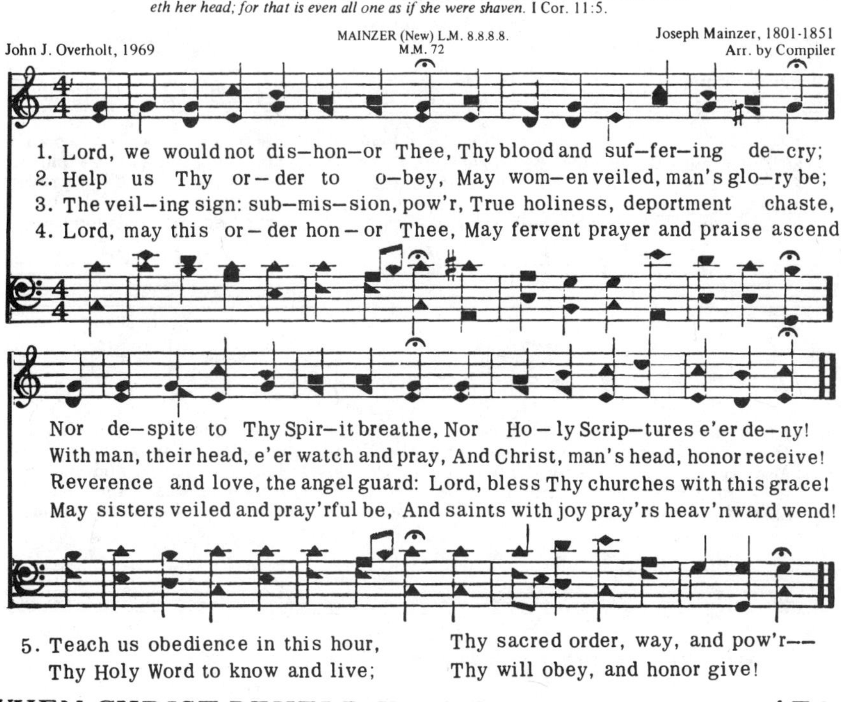
1. Lord, we would not dis–hon–or Thee, Thy blood and suf–fer–ing de–cry;
2. Help us Thy or–der to o–bey, May wom–en veiled, man's glo–ry be;
3. The veil–ing sign: sub–mis–sion, pow'r, True holiness, deportment chaste,
4. Lord, may this or–der hon–or Thee, May fervent prayer and praise ascend;
Nor de–spite to Thy Spir–it breathe, Nor Ho–ly Scrip–tures e'er de–ny!
With man, their head, e'er watch and pray, And Christ, man's head, honor receive!
Reverence and love, the angel guard: Lord, bless Thy churches with this grace!
May sisters veiled and pray'rful be, And saints with joy pray'rs heav'nward wend!

5. Teach us obedience in this hour,
Thy Holy Word to know and live;
Thy sacred order, way, and pow'r—
Thy will obey, and honor give!

# WHEN CHRIST BEHELD IN SIN'S DARK NIGHT 478

*Let her be covered.* I Cor. 11:6. *If any man think himself to be a prophet, or spiritual, let him acknowledge that the things that I write unto you are the commandments of the Lord.* I Cor. 14:37.

Samuel Frederick Coffman, 1911 (1872-1954)
St. 3, John J. Overholt, 1970 — HARTEL L.M. 8.8.8.8. M.M. 56 — Lowell Mason, 1792-1872

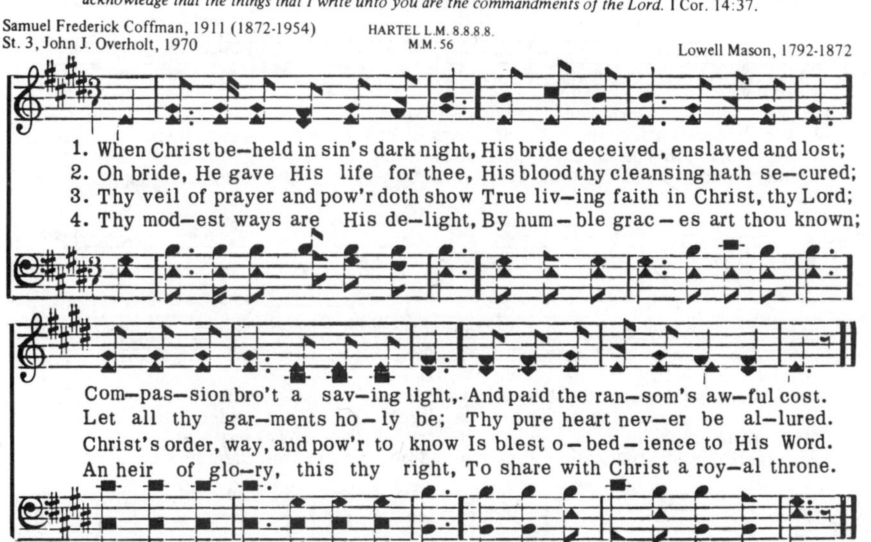
1. When Christ be–held in sin's dark night, His bride deceived, enslaved and lost;
2. Oh bride, He gave His life for thee, His blood thy cleansing hath se–cured;
3. Thy veil of prayer and pow'r doth show True liv–ing faith in Christ, thy Lord;
4. Thy mod–est ways are His de–light, By hum–ble grac–es art thou known;
Com–pas–sion bro't a sav–ing light, And paid the ran–som's aw–ful cost.
Let all thy gar–ments ho–ly be; Thy pure heart nev–er be al–lured.
Christ's order, way, and pow'r to know Is blest o–bed–ience to His Word.
An heir of glo–ry, this thy right, To share with Christ a roy–al throne.

# 479 O GOD OF WISDOM

*What therefore God hath joined together, let not man put asunder.* Mk. 10:9

I DO BELIEVE C.M. 8.6.8.6.
M.M. 54

Menno M. Brubacher, 1926

Early American Melody

1. O God of wis-dom, life and love, Thine is the bless-ed plan
2. These souls be-trothed be-fore Thee stand; Thy bless-ing we im-plore;
3. As they go forth up-on life's way, Sus-tain them by Thy grace;
4. May they with ho-ly lives a-dorn Thy doc-trines, Lord, and be
5. And when Thou, Lord, shalt come a-gain To gath-er home Thine own,
In ho-ly bonds of love to join The twain, cre-a-ted man.
U-nite Thou them in heart and hand, And guide them ev-er-more.
May they Thy ho-ly laws o-bey And live in joy and peace.
A-mid life's sun-shine and its storm True wit-ness-es for Thee.
May they, with du-ty no-bly done, Be blessed be-fore Thy throne.

# 480 WE JOIN TO PRAY

*Marriage is honorable in all, and the bed undefiled: but whoremongers and adulterers God will judge.* Heb. 13:4.

HAND IN HAND C.M. 8.6.8.6.
M.M. 76

William Gaskell, 1837, alt.

Edward D. Naff

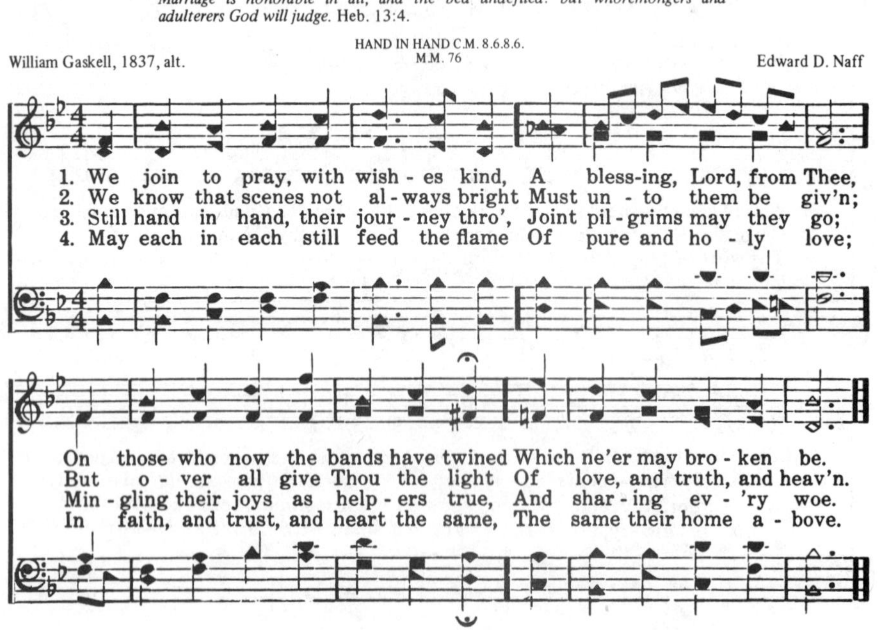
1. We join to pray, with wish-es kind, A bless-ing, Lord, from Thee,
2. We know that scenes not al-ways bright Must un-to them be giv'n;
3. Still hand in hand, their jour-ney thro', Joint pil-grims may they go;
4. May each in each still feed the flame Of pure and ho-ly love;
On those who now the bands have twined Which ne'er may bro-ken be.
But o-ver all give Thou the light Of love, and truth, and heav'n.
Min-gling their joys as help-ers true, And shar-ing ev-'ry woe.
In faith, and trust, and heart the same, The same their home a-bove.

## SINCE JESUS FREELY DID APPEAR 481

*And . . . Jesus was called . . . to the marriage.* Jn. 2:2.

WEDDING GUEST C.M. 8.6.8.6.
M.M. 69

John Berridge, 1785 — Flora H. Good

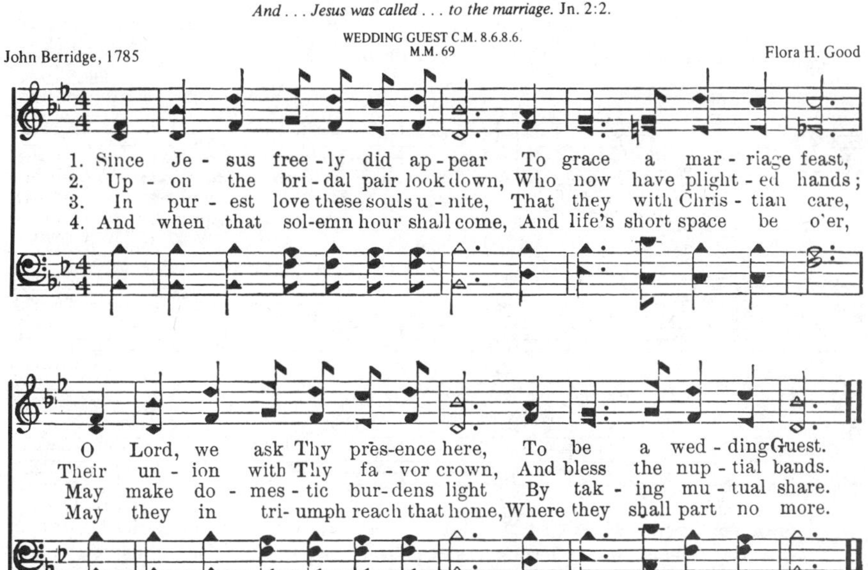
1. Since Je - sus free - ly did ap - pear To grace a mar - riage feast,
2. Up - on the bri - dal pair look down, Who now have plight - ed hands;
3. In pur - est love these souls u - nite, That they with Chris - tian care,
4. And when that sol-emn hour shall come, And life's short space be o'er,
O Lord, we ask Thy pres-ence here, To be a wed - ding Guest.
Their un - ion with Thy fa - vor crown, And bless the nup - tial bands.
May make do - mes - tic bur - dens light By tak - ing mu - tual share.
May they in tri - umph reach that home, Where they shall part no more.

## O LORD DIVINE, WE COME 482

*They two shall be one flesh.* Eph. 5:31.

REMEMBER ME C.M. 8.6.8.6.
M.M. 60

Jacob D. Toews, b. 1903 — Asa Hull, c. 1862

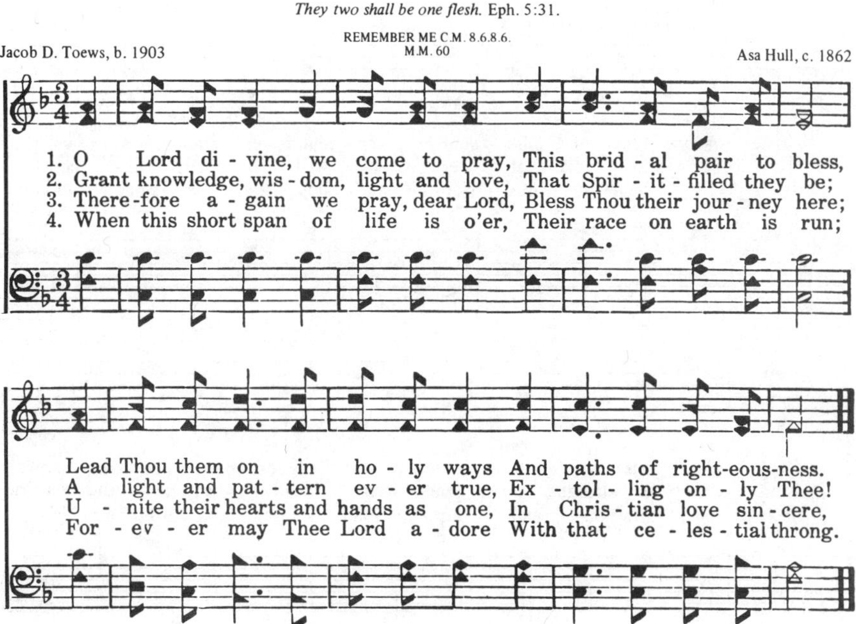
1. O Lord di - vine, we come to pray, This brid - al pair to bless,
2. Grant knowledge, wis - dom, light and love, That Spir - it - filled they be;
3. There-fore a - gain we pray, dear Lord, Bless Thou their jour - ney here;
4. When this short span of life is o'er, Their race on earth is run;
Lead Thou them on in ho - ly ways And paths of right-eous-ness.
A light and pat - tern ev - er true, Ex - tol - ling on - ly Thee!
U - nite their hearts and hands as one, In Chris - tian love sin - cere,
For - ev - er may Thee Lord a - dore With that ce - les - tial throng.

# 483 O LOVE THAT CASTS OUT FEAR

*Perfect love casteth out fear.* I Jn. 4:18.

PART I, ES IST DIR GESAGT MENSCH
6.7.6.7.6.6.6.6.
PART II, O GOTT DU FROMMER GOTT
6.7.6.7.6.6.6.6.
M.M. 63

Johann Sebastian Bach, 1685-1750
Arranged by Compiler, 1967

Horatius Bonar, 1861 (1808-1889)
Clement of Alexandria, 170-220
Composite, Arr. John J. Overholt, 1967

A. Fritsch, 1679
Arr. Johann Sebastian Bach, 1685-1750

1. O love that casts out fear, O love that casts out sin, O stay no more with-out but come and dwell with-in; True sun-light of the soul, sur-round us as we go, So shall our way be safe, our feet no stray-ing know.

2. Thy way, not ours, O Lord, smooth let it be or rough, Lead us by thine own hand, choose thou the path for us; How-ev-er dark it be, it will be still the best; Wind-ing or straight, it leads right on-ward to thy rest.

3. Ev-er be thou our guide, Je-sus, thou Christ of God, Our staff, our stay, and song; lead us where thou hast trod, By thy per-en-nial Word, our Shep-herd and our guide, Make our faith pure and strong, lead where thou dost a-bide.

Part II
Great love of God come in, thou spring of ev - er - last - ing peace,
The king - dom that we seek is thine; so let the ver - y way
So now un - til we die, we lift our hearts to swell the song,
Thou liv - ing wa - ter come! Spring up in us and nev - er cease.
That leads to it be thine, else we must sure - ly go a - stray.
And joy - ful - ly we sing, in love and praise with the glad throng
Love of the liv - ing God! of Fa - ther, and of Son,
Not ours but thine the choice, in things or great or small;
Who to thy church be - long to praise thee far and near,
Love of the Ho - ly Ghost, make thou our hearts as one.
Be thou our guide, our strength, our wis - dom, and our all.
Our liv - ing Lord and King, and love that casts out fear!

# 484 O PERFECT LOVE

*Let every one of you . . . love his wife even as himself; and the wife see that she reverence her husband.* Eph. 5:33.

Dorothy F. Bloomfield, 1883 (1858-1932)
Doxology, St. 4, John Ellerton, 1875 (1826-1893)
SANDRINGHAM 11.10.11.10.
M.M. 50
Joseph Barnby, 1889 (1838-1896)
1 O perfect Love, all human thought transcending,
Lowly we kneel in prayer before Thy throne,
That theirs may be the love which knows no ending,
Whom Thou forevermore dost join in one.
2 O perfect Life, be Thou their full assurance
Of tender charity and steadfast faith,
Of patient hope, and quiet, brave endurance,
With child-like trust that fears nor pain nor death.
3 Grant them the joy which brightens earthly sorrow;
Grant them the peace which calms all earthly strife,
And to life's day the glorious, unknown morrow
That dawns upon eternal love and life.
4 Hear us, O Father, gracious and forgiving,
Through Jesus Christ Thy coeternal Word,
Who, with the Holy Ghost, by all things living
Now and to endless ages art adored. A-men.

**ORDINANCES:** MARRIAGE

## LOOK TO THE GOD OF HEAVEN 485

*Submitting yourselves one to another in the fear of God.* Eph. 5:21.

Joseph E. Martin, 1970
Altered by Compiler, 1970

MAUGANSVILLE 14.14.6.
M.M. 104

Joseph E. Martin, 1970
Har. John J. Overholt, 1970

1. Look to the God of heav'n a-bove for guide-lines ev-'ry day; He gives His Word to be our rule to help in ev-'ry way. To help in ev-'ry way.
2. He hath or-dained that it should be that man be not a-lone; He made a wife for him to love and cher-ish for his own. And cher-ish for his own.
3. He tells man how to love his wife as Christ doth love the church; The wife is to sub-mit her-self as to the Lord a-bove. As to the Lord a-bove.
4. For this cause man shall leave his home and cleave un-to his wife; And twain shall be made one that day for all their wed-ded life. For all their wed-ded life.

**ORDINANCES:** HOLY KISS

## ALL PRAISE TO OUR REDEEMING LORD 486

*Greet all the brethren with an holy kiss.* I Thess. 5:26, Rom. 16:16; I Cor. 16:20; II Cor. 13:12; I Pet. 5:14.

AZMON C.M. 8.6.8.6.
M.M. 58

Charles Wesley, 1707-1788

Carl Gotthelf Glaser, 1784-1829

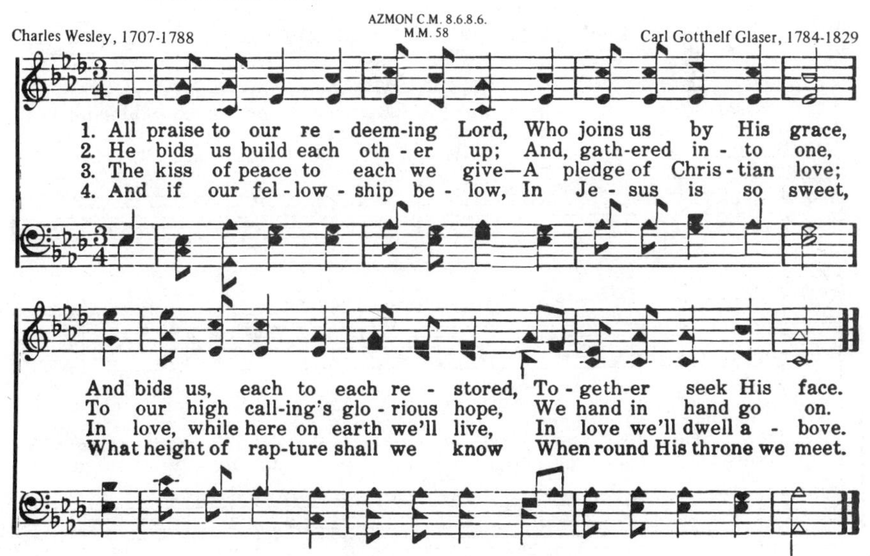
1. All praise to our re - deem-ing Lord, Who joins us by His grace, And bids us, each to each re - stored, To - geth-er seek His face.
2. He bids us build each oth - er up; And, gath-ered in - to one, To our high call-ing's glo - rious hope, We hand in hand go on.
3. The kiss of peace to each we give—A pledge of Chris - tian love; In love, while here on earth we'll live, In love we'll dwell a - bove.
4. And if our fel - low - ship be - low, In Je - sus is so sweet, What height of rap-ture shall we know When round His throne we meet.

No. 464 may also be sung with this section.

# 487 YE CHRISTIAN HERALDS

*Go ye therefore, and teach all nations . . . teaching them to observe all things whatsoever I have commanded you.* Mt. 28:19-20.

Bourne Hall Draper, 1775-1843

MISSIONARY CHANT L.M. 8.8.8.8.
M.M. 58

Charles Heinrich Zeuner, 1795-1857

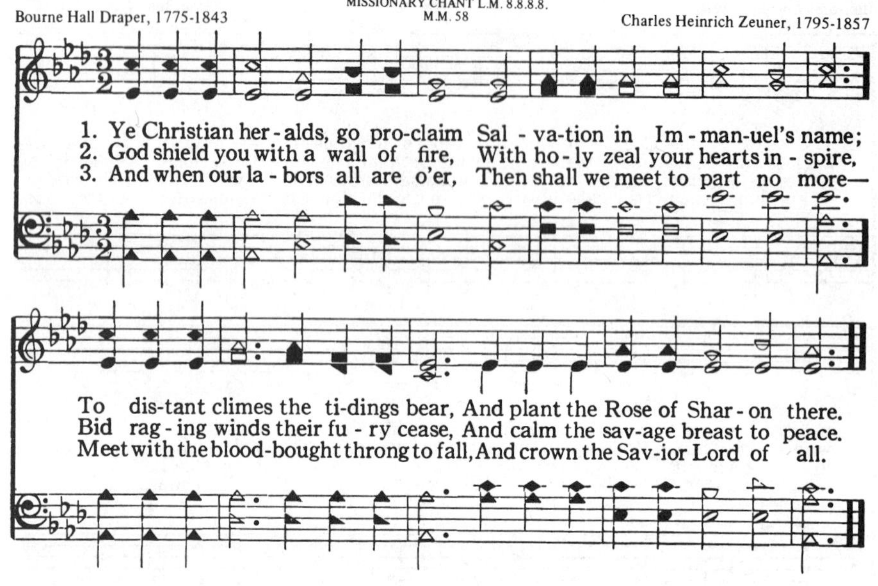

1. Ye Christian her - alds, go pro-claim Sal - va-tion in Im - man-uel's name;
2. God shield you with a wall of fire, With ho - ly zeal your hearts in - spire,
3. And when our la - bors all are o'er, Then shall we meet to part no more—
To dis-tant climes the ti-dings bear, And plant the Rose of Shar - on there.
Bid rag - ing winds their fu - ry cease, And calm the sav-age breast to peace.
Meet with the blood-bought throng to fall, And crown the Sav-ior Lord of all.

# 488 A CHARGE TO KEEP I HAVE

*Go ye into all the world and preach the Gospel to every creature.* Mk. 16:15.

Charles Wesley, 1762 (1708-1788)

FERGUSON S.M. 6.6.8.6.
M.M. 72

George Kingsley, 1843 (1811-1884)

1. A charge to keep I have, A God to glo - ri - fy;
2. To serve the pres - ent age, My call - ing to ful - fill—
3. Arm me with jeal - ous care, As in Thy sight to live;
4. Help me to watch and pray, And on Thy - self re - ly;
A nev - er - dy - ing soul to save, And fit it for the sky.
Oh, may it all my pow'rs en - gage To do my Mas - ter's will.
And, oh, Thy serv - ant, Lord, pre-pare A strict ac-count to give.
As - sured if I my trust be - tray, I shall for - ev - er die.

# TEACH ME THY TRUTH 489

*And He sent them to preach the kingdom of God and to heal the sick.* Lk. 9:2.

GOSHEN C.M. 8.6.8.6.
M.M. 56

Edith Witmer, 1937 (b. 1902) — Walter E. Yoder, 1889-1964

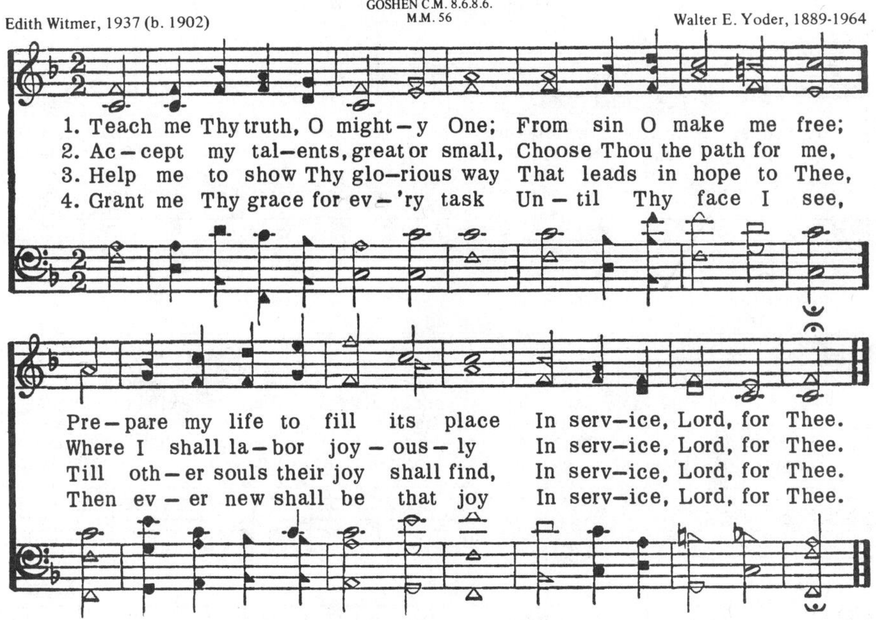
1. Teach me Thy truth, O might-y One; From sin O make me free;
2. Ac-cept my tal-ents, great or small, Choose Thou the path for me,
3. Help me to show Thy glo-rious way That leads in hope to Thee,
4. Grant me Thy grace for ev-'ry task Un-til Thy face I see,
Pre-pare my life to fill its place In serv-ice, Lord, for Thee.
Where I shall la-bor joy-ous-ly In serv-ice, Lord, for Thee.
Till oth-er souls their joy shall find, In serv-ice, Lord, for Thee.
Then ev-er new shall be that joy In serv-ice, Lord, for Thee.

# O STILL IN ACCENTS SWEET 490

*The harvest truly is plenteous, but the laborers are few.* Mt. 9:37.

BELMONT C.M. 8.6.8.6.
M.M. 88

Samuel Longfellow, 1864 (1819-1892) — Arr. from William Gardner, 1812 (1770-1853)

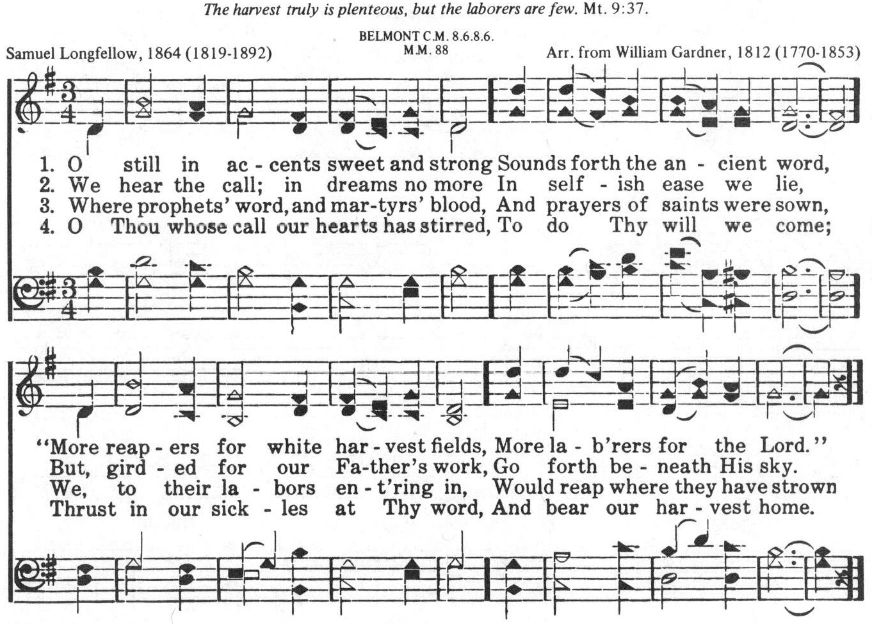
1. O still in ac-cents sweet and strong Sounds forth the an-cient word,
2. We hear the call; in dreams no more In self-ish ease we lie,
3. Where prophets' word, and mar-tyrs' blood, And prayers of saints were sown,
4. O Thou whose call our hearts has stirred, To do Thy will we come;
"More reap-ers for white har-vest fields, More la-b'rers for the Lord."
But, gird-ed for our Fa-ther's work, Go forth be-neath His sky.
We, to their la-bors en-t'ring in, Would reap where they have strown
Thrust in our sick-les at Thy word, And bear our har-vest home.

# 491 ROUSE YE CHRISTIAN WORKERS

*He that winneth souls is wise.* Prov. 11:30.

WINNING SOULS 12.11.12.11. with Ref.
M.M. 63

J. B. Mackay J. B. Mackay

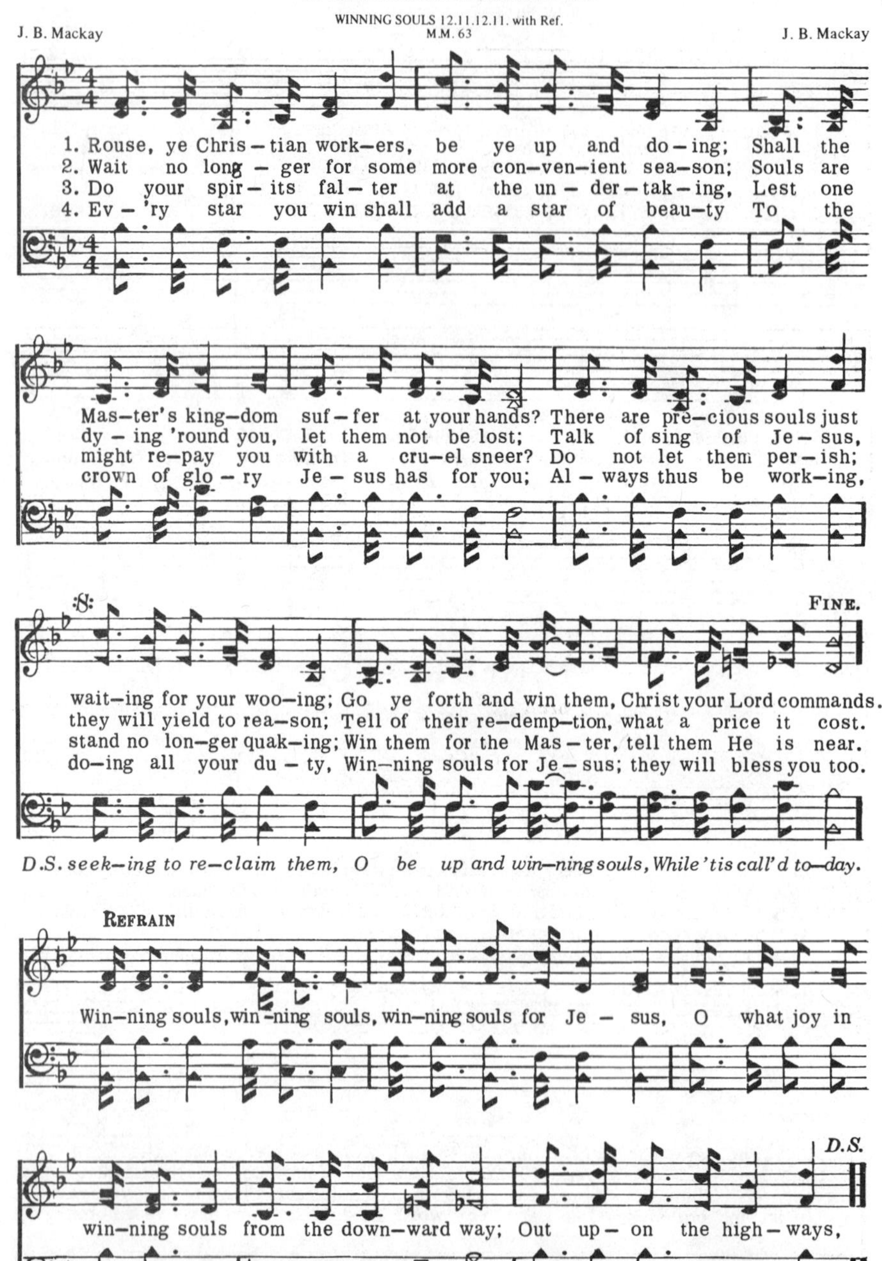

1. Rouse, ye Chris-tian work-ers, be ye up and do-ing; Shall the Mas-ter's king-dom suf-fer at your hands? There are pre-cious souls just wait-ing for your woo-ing; Go ye forth and win them, Christ your Lord commands.
2. Wait no long-ger for some more con-ven-ient sea-son; Souls are dy-ing 'round you, let them not be lost; Talk of sing of Je-sus, they will yield to rea-son; Tell of their re-demp-tion, what a price it cost.
3. Do your spir-its fal-ter at the un-der-tak-ing, Lest one might re-pay you with a cru-el sneer? Do not let them per-ish; stand no lon-ger quak-ing; Win them for the Mas-ter, tell them He is near.
4. Ev-'ry star you win shall add a star of beau-ty To the crown of glo-ry Je-sus has for you; Al-ways thus be work-ing, do-ing all your du-ty, Win-ning souls for Je-sus; they will bless you too.
FINE.
D.S. seek-ing to re-claim them, O be up and win-ning souls, While 'tis call'd to-day.
REFRAIN
Win-ning souls, win-ning souls, win-ning souls for Je-sus, O what joy in win-ning souls from the down-ward way; Out up-on the high-ways,
D.S.

# SOWING IN THE MORNING 492

*He . . . shall . . . come again with rejoicing, bringing his sheaves with him.* Ps. 126:6.

BRINGING IN THE SHEAVES 12.11.12.11. with Ref.
M.M. 66

Knowles Shaw, 1834-1878

George A. Minor, 1845-1904

1. Sow-ing in the morn-ing, sow-ing seeds of kind-ness, Sow-ing in the noon-tide
2. Sow-ing in the sun-shine, sow-ing in the shad-ows, Fear-ing neither clouds nor
3. Go - ing forth with weeping, sow-ing for the Mas - ter, Tho' the loss sus-tained our
and the dew - y eve; Wait-ing for the har - vest, and the time of reap - ing,
winter's chilling breeze; By and by the har - vest, and the la - bor end - ed,
spir - it oft-en grieves; When our weeping's o - ver, He will bid us wel - come,
We shall come, re-joic-ing, bringing in the sheaves.
REFRAIN
Bringing in the sheaves, bringing
in the sheaves, We shall come, rejoicing, bringing in the sheaves; Bringing in the sheaves,
bring-ing in the sheaves, We shall come, re - joic - ing, Bring-ing in the sheaves.

# 493 RESCUE THE PERISHING

*And the Lord said unto the servant, Go out into the highways and hedges, and compel them to come in, that my house may be filled.* Lk. 14:23.

RESCUE THE PERISHING 11.10.11.10. with Ref.
M.M. 60

Fanny J. Crosby, 1820-1915

William Howard Doane, 1832-1915

1. Res - cue the per - ish - ing, Care for the dy - ing, Snatch them in pit - y from sin and the grave; Weep o'er the err - ing one, Lift up the fall - en, Tell them of Je - sus the migh - ty to save.

2. Though they are slighting Him, Still He is wait-ing, Wait - ing the pen - i - tent child to re - ceive; Plead with them ear-nest - ly, Plead with them gen - tly, He will for - give if they on - ly be - lieve.

3. Down in the hu-man heart, Crushed by the tempter, Feel - ings lie bur - ied that grace can re - store; Touched by a lov - ing heart, Wak - ened by kind - ness, Chords that were bro - ken will vi - brate once more.

4. Res - cue the per - ish - ing, Du - ty de-mands it; Strength for thy la - bor the Lord will pro - vide; Back to the nar - row way Pa - tient - ly win them; Tell the poor wan - d'rer a Sav - iour has died.

REFRAIN

Res - cue the per - ish - ing, Care for the dy - ing; Je - sus is mer - ci - ful, Je - sus will save.

# THROW OUT THE LIFELINE 494

*And others save with fear, pulling them out of the fire; hating even the garment spotted by the flesh.* Jude 23.

THROW OUT THE LIFE LINE 10.10.10.11.
M.M. 92

Edward S. Ufford, 1851-1929

Arr. George C. Stebbins, 1846-1945

1. Throw out the Life-Line a - cross the dark wave, There is a broth-er whom
2. Throw out the Life-Line with hand quick and strong: Why do you tar - ry, why
3. Throw out the Life-Line to dan - ger fraught men, Sink - ing in an-guish where
4. Soon will the sea - son of res - cue be o'er, Soon will they drift to e-
some - one should save; Some - bod - y's broth - er! oh, who then will dare To
lin - ger so long? See! he is sink - ing; oh, has - ten to - day— And
you've nev - er been: Winds of temp - ta - tion and bil - lows of woe Will
ter - ni - ty's shore; Haste then, my broth - er, no time for de - lay, But
throw out the Life - Line, his per - il to share?
out with the Life - Boat! a - way, then, a - way!
soon hurl them out where the dark wa - ters flow.
throw out the Life - Line and save them to - day.
CHORUS
Throw out the Life - Line!
Throw out the Life-Line! Some-one is drift - ing a - way;
Throw out the Life - Line! Throw out the Life-Line! Some - one is sink - ing to - day.

# 495 TELL ME THE STORY OF JESUS

*Go and shew John again those things which ye do hear and see.* Mt. 11:4.

TELL ME THE STORY OF JESUS 8.7.8.7.D.
M.M. 63

Fanny J. Crosby, 1820-1915

John R. Sweney, 1837-1899

1. Tell me the sto - ry of Je - sus, Write on my heart ev - 'ry word;
2. Fast-ing a - lone in the des - ert, Tell of the days that are past,
3. Tell of the cross where they nailed Him, Writh-ing in an-guish and pain;

**Ref.** — *Tell me the sto - ry of Je - sus, Write on my heart ev - 'ry word;*

Tell me the sto - ry most pre - cious, Sweet-est that ev - er was heard.
How for our sins He was tempt-ed, Yet was tri - um-phant at last.
Tell of the grave where they laid Him, Tell how He liv - eth a - gain.

FINE.

*Tell me the sto - ry most pre - cious, Sweet-est that ev - er was heard.*

Tell how the an - gels, in cho - rus, Sang as they wel-comed His birth,
Tell of the years of His la - bor, Tell of the sor - row He bore,
Love in that sto - ry so ten - der, Clear-er than ev - er I see:

*D. C. for Refrain*

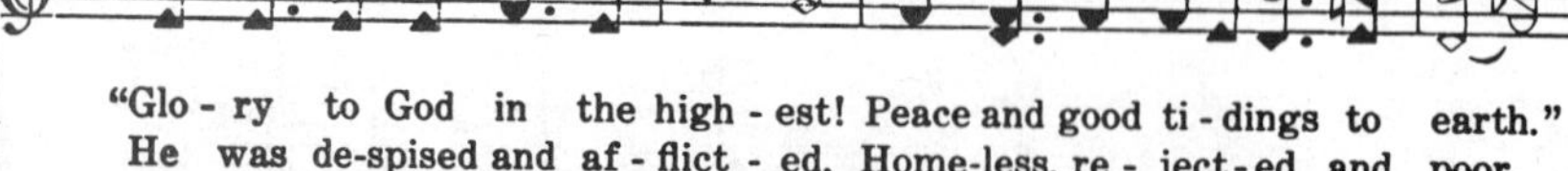

"Glo - ry to God in the high - est! Peace and good ti - dings to earth."
He was de-spised and af - flict - ed, Home-less, re - ject-ed and poor.
Stay, let me weep while you whis - per, Love paid the ran-som for me.

# TELL ME THE OLD, OLD STORY 496

*Sir, we would see Jesus.* Jn. 12:21.

TELL ME THE OLD, OLD STORY 7.6.7.6.D. with Ref.
M.M. 72

Katherine Hankey, 1834-1911

William Howard Doane, 1832-1915

1. Tell me the old, old sto - ry Of un-seen things a - bove, Of Je - sus and His glo - ry, Of Je - sus and His love. Tell me the sto - ry sim - ply, As to a lit - tle child, For I am weak and wea - ry, And help - less and de - filed.
2. Tell me the sto - ry slow - ly, That I may take it in— That won-der-ful re - demp-tion, God's rem - e - dy for sin. Tell me the sto - ry oft - en, For I for - get so soon; The "ear - ly dew" of morn - ing Has passed a - way at noon.
3. Tell me the sto - ry soft - ly, With ear-nest tones and grave; Re - mem-ber, I'm the sin - ner Whom Je - sus came to save. Tell me the sto - ry al - ways, If you would real - ly be, In an - y time of troub - le, A com - fort - er to me.
4. Tell me the same old sto - ry When you have cause to fear That this world's emp - ty glo - ry Is cost - ing me too dear. Yes, and when that world's glo - ry Is dawn-ing on my soul, Tell me the old, old sto - ry: "Christ Je - sus makes thee whole."
CHORUS
Tell me the old, old sto - ry, Tell me the old, old sto - ry, Tell me the old, old sto - ry Of Je - sus and His love.

# 497 CHRIST'S EVERLASTING GOSPEL

*And this Gospel of the kingdom shall be preached in all the world for a witness unto all nations.* Mt. 24:14.

CHRIST'S EVERLASTING GOSPEL 13.13.13.13. with Ref.
M.M. 63

Eliza Edmunds Hewitt, 1851-1920

Louis Le Saint

1. Christ's Ev - er - last - ing Gos - pel is ring - ing out a - gain Its mes - sage
2. Some - times the sky is dark - ened, and storm - y clouds ap - pear, But still, be-
3. The faith where - in is vic - t'ry in Je - sus we pro - claim, Tho' earth - ly

of sal - va - tion, its peace, good - will to men; Tho' sin has hurled its
yond the shad - ows, the light is bright and clear; The God of truth has
thrones may per - ish still lives Em - man - uel's name; Our voi - ces swell with

weap - ons, and e - vil hosts as - sailed, The Gos - pel of Christ Je - sus has
spo - ken; His word will nev - er fail, The Gos - pel of Christ Je - sus shall
tri - umph, above earth's threat'ning gales, The Gos - pel of Christ Je - sus thro'

REFRAIN

ev - er - more pre - vailed:
more and more pre - vail: Our King shall come in glo - ry, His con - qu'ring
ev - 'ry age pre - vails:

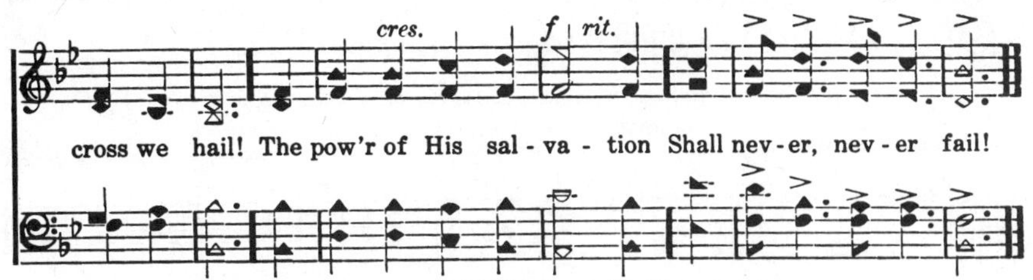
cres.
f rit.
cross we hail! The pow'r of His sal - va - tion Shall nev - er, nev - er fail!

# JESUS SHALL REIGN 498

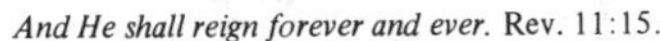
*And He shall reign forever and ever.* Rev. 11:15.

DUKE STREET L.M. 8.8.8.8.
M.M. 56

Isaac Watts, 1719 (1674-1748)

John Hatton, c. 1793 (d. 1793)

1. Je - sus shall reign wher - e'er the sun Does his suc-
2. For Him shall end - less prayer be made, And prais - es
3. Bless - ings a - bound wher - e'er He reigns; The pris - 'ner
4. Let ev - 'ry crea - ture rise and bring Pe - cul - iar

ces - sive jour - neys run; His king - dom stretch from
throng to crown His head; His name, like sweet per-
leaps to lose his chains, The wea - ry find e-
hon - ors to our King, An - gels de - scend with

shore to shore, Till moons shall wax and wane no more.
fume, shall rise With ev - 'ry morn - ing sac - ri - fice;
ter - nal rest, And all the sons of want are blest.
songs a - gain, And earth re - peat the loud A - men.

# 499 O ZION HASTE

*O Jerusalem, that bringest good tidings, lift up thy voice with strength.* Is. 40:9.

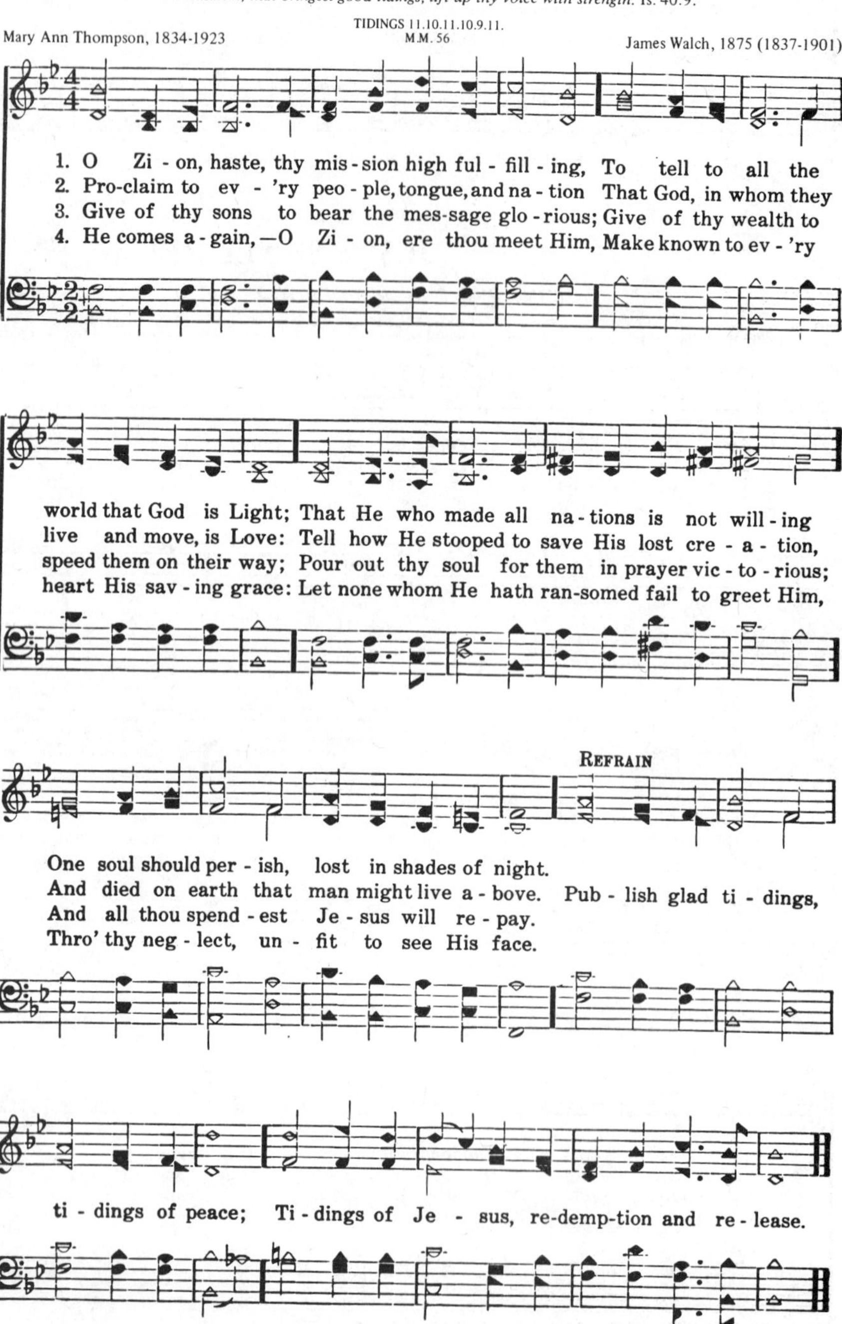
TIDINGS 11.10.11.10.9.11.
M.M. 56
Mary Ann Thompson, 1834-1923
James Walch, 1875 (1837-1901)
1. O Zi - on, haste, thy mis - sion high ful - fill - ing, To tell to all the
2. Pro-claim to ev - 'ry peo - ple, tongue, and na - tion That God, in whom they
3. Give of thy sons to bear the mes-sage glo - rious; Give of thy wealth to
4. He comes a - gain,—O Zi - on, ere thou meet Him, Make known to ev - 'ry
world that God is Light; That He who made all na - tions is not will - ing
live and move, is Love: Tell how He stooped to save His lost cre - a - tion,
speed them on their way; Pour out thy soul for them in prayer vic - to - rious;
heart His sav - ing grace: Let none whom He hath ran-somed fail to greet Him,
Refrain
One soul should per - ish, lost in shades of night.
And died on earth that man might live a - bove. Pub - lish glad ti - dings,
And all thou spend - est Je - sus will re - pay.
Thro' thy neg - lect, un - fit to see His face.
ti - dings of peace; Ti - dings of Je - sus, re-demp-tion and re - lease.

# HERALDS OF CHRIST 500

*Now then we are ambassadors for Christ, as though God did beseech you by us.* II Cor. 5:20.

HERALDS OF CHRIST 10.10.10.10.
M.M. 63
Laura Scherer Copenhaver, 1868-1940
George William Warren, 1828-1902
1. Her - alds of Christ, who bear the King's com - mands,
2. Through des - ert ways, dark fen, and deep mor - ass,
3. Where once the twist - ing trail in dark - ness wound
4. Lord, give us faith and strength the road to build,
Im - mor - tal ti - dings in your mor - tal hands,
Through jun - gles, slug - gish seas, and moun - tain pass,
Let march - ing feet and joy - ous song re - sound,
To see the prom - ise of the day ful - filled,
Pass on and car - ry swift the news ye bring;
Build ye the road, and fal - ter not nor stay;
Where burned the fu - neral pyres, let chil - dren sing,
When war shall be no more and strife shall cease
Make straight, make straight the high - way of the King.
Pre - pare a - cross the earth the King's high - way.
Make straight, make straight the high - way of the King.
Up - on the high - way of the Prince of Peace.
A - men.

# 501 IN THE LAND OF STRANGERS

*And he arose, and came to his father . . . His father saw him . . . and ran, and fell on his neck, and kissed him.* Lk. 15:20.

WELCOME, WANDERER, WELCOME 6.5.6.4. with Ref.
M.M. 92

Horatius Bonar, 1874 (1808-1889)
Refrain added, Ira David Sankey

Ira David Sankey, 1884 (1840-1908)

1 In the land of stran - gers Whith - er thou art gone,
2 From the land of hun - ger, Faint - ing, fam - ished, lone,
3 See the door still o - pen: Thou art still My own;
4 See the well-spread ta - ble, Un - for - got - ten one!
5 Thou art friend - less, hope - less, Hope - less and un - done;

Hear a far voice call - ing, My son, My son!
Come to love and glad - ness, My son, My son!
Eyes of love are on thee, My son, My son!
Here is rest and plen - ty, My son, My son!
Mine is love un - chang - ing, My son, My son!

REFRAIN

Wel - come, wan - d'rer, wel - come, Wel - come back to home;
Thou hast wan - dered far a - way: Come home, come home.

# 502 O WEARY WANDERER

*I will arise and go to my father.* Lk. 15:18.

John Samuel Coffman, 1883 (1848-1899)

REMEMBER ME C.M. 8.6.8.6.
M.M. 60

Asa Hull, b. 1828

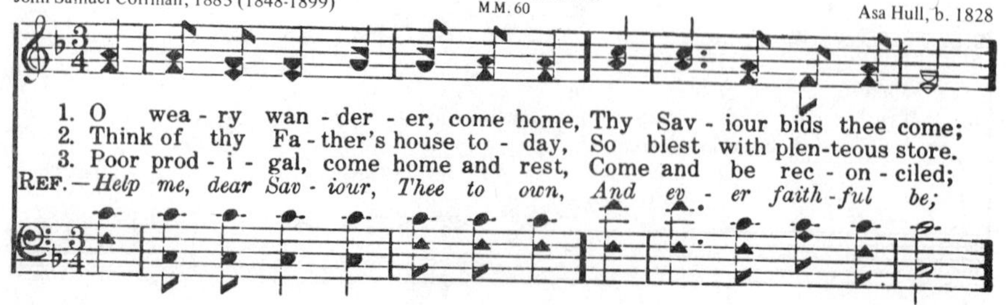
1. O wea - ry wan - der - er, come home, Thy Sav - iour bids thee come;
2. Think of thy Fa - ther's house to - day, So blest with plen-teous store.
3. Poor prod - i - gal, come home and rest, Come and be rec - on - ciled;
REF.—*Help me, dear Sav - iour, Thee to own, And ev - er faith - ful be;*

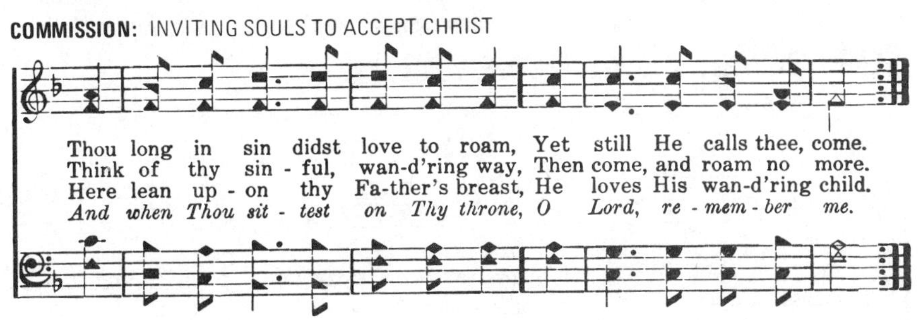
Thou long in sin didst love to roam, Yet still He calls thee, come.
Think of thy sin - ful, wan-d'ring way, Then come, and roam no more.
Here lean up - on thy Fa-ther's breast, He loves His wan-d'ring child.
*And when Thou sit - test on Thy throne, O Lord, re - mem - ber me.*

# GOD LOVED THE WORLD SO THAT HE GAVE 503

*For God so loved the world, that He gave His only begotten Son, that whosoever believeth in Him should not perish, but have everlasting life.* Jn. 3:16.

Anonymous cento, 1791
Tr. August Crull, 1923 (1845-1923)

ST. CRISPIN L.M. 8.8.8.8.
M.M. 100

George J. Elvery, 1862 (1816-1893)

1. God loved the world so that He gave His on - ly
2. Christ Je - sus is the ground of faith, Who was made
3. God would not have the sin - ner die, His Son with
4. Glo - ry to God the Fa - ther, Son, And Ho - ly

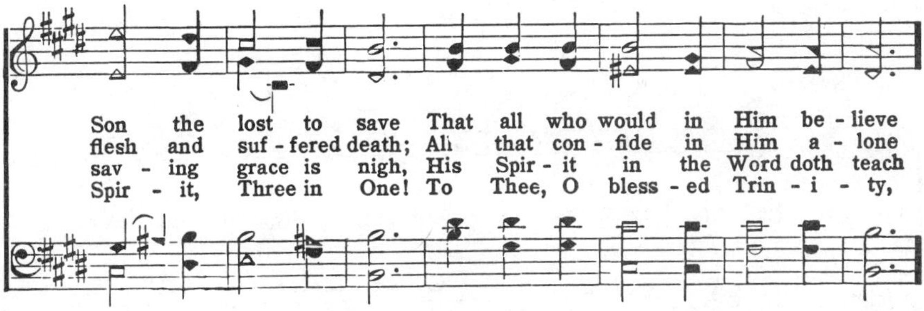

Son the lost to save That all who would in Him be - lieve
flesh and suf - fered death; All that con - fide in Him a - lone
sav - ing grace is nigh, His Spir - it in the Word doth teach
Spir - it, Three in One! To Thee, O bless - ed Trin - i - ty,

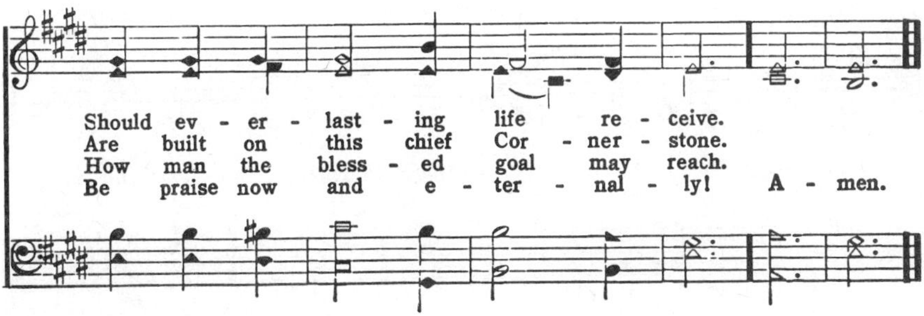

Should ev - er - last - ing life re - ceive.
Are built on this chief Cor - ner - stone.
How man the bless - ed goal may reach.
Be praise now and e - ter - nal - ly! A - men.

# 504 COME, YE WANDERERS

*Come unto Me, all ye that labour and are heavy laden, and I will give you rest.* Mt. 11:28.

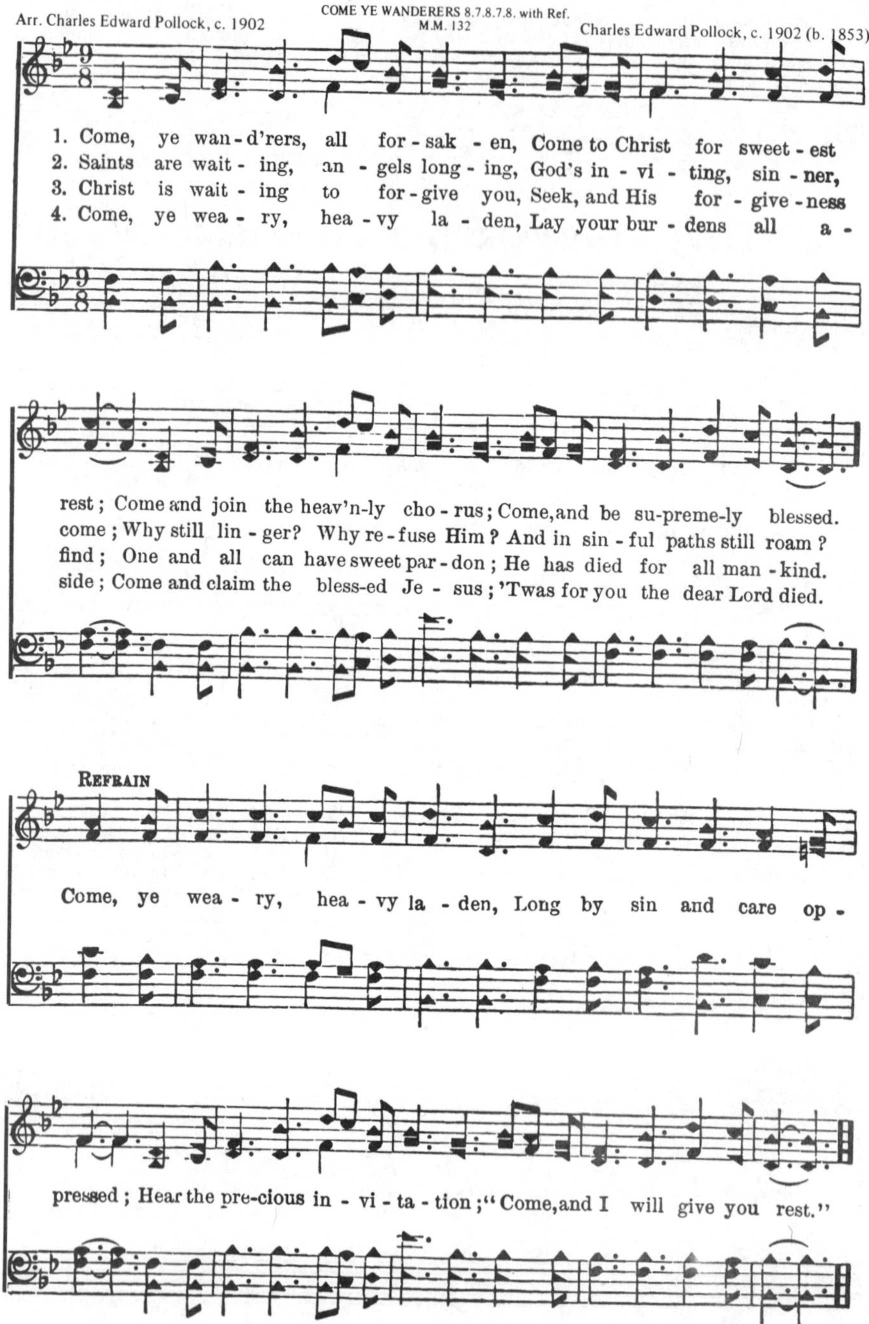
Arr. Charles Edward Pollock, c. 1902
COME YE WANDERERS 8.7.8.7.8. with Ref.
M.M. 132
Charles Edward Pollock, c. 1902 (b. 1853)
1. Come, ye wan-d'rers, all for-sak-en, Come to Christ for sweet-est rest; Come and join the heav'n-ly cho-rus; Come, and be su-preme-ly blessed.
2. Saints are wait-ing, an-gels long-ing, God's in-vi-ting, sin-ner, come; Why still lin-ger? Why re-fuse Him? And in sin-ful paths still roam?
3. Christ is wait-ing to for-give you, Seek, and His for-give-ness find; One and all can have sweet par-don; He has died for all man-kind.
4. Come, ye wea-ry, hea-vy la-den, Lay your bur-dens all a-side; Come and claim the bless-ed Je-sus; 'Twas for you the dear Lord died.
REFRAIN
Come, ye wea-ry, hea-vy la-den, Long by sin and care op-pressed; Hear the pre-cious in-vi-ta-tion; "Come, and I will give you rest."

# COME LOST ONE 505

*Come; for all things are now ready.* Lk. 14:17.

COME LOST ONE 9.8.9.8. with Ref.
M.M. 63

Joseph S. Shoemaker, 1901 (1854-1936) Joseph S. Shoemaker

1. Come, lost one, your Saviour is call - ing, He's pleading with ten - der-est voice;
2. Come with all thy guilt and pol - lu - tion, And call on the name of the Lord;
3. Thy sins tho' they be red like crim-son, Yea, tho' they be man - y and great,
4. The Lord has pro - vid - ed a - bun-dance, Yea, all that ye need is in store;
Come out from your ways of transgression, And has - ten to make Him your choice.
He's read - y to cleanse and to bless you, And save by His life - giv - ing Word.
Shall be blot - ted out by your Sav-iour, If you come to Him ere too late.
Then come and par-take of His boun - ty, And trust Him for grace ev - er - more.
Refrain
Oh, why should you wan-der in dark-ness? Oh, why should you lon-ger de - lay,
When Je - sus is read - y to save you, And keep you from sin ev - 'ry day?

# 506 WHILE JESUS WHISPERS TO YOU

*When Thou saidst, Seek ye my face; my heart said unto Thee, Thy face, Lord, will I seek.* Ps. 27:8.

W. E. Witters, 1878 (b. 1854)
Mrs. C. M. Alexander

COME SINNER COME 7.4.7.4.D.
M.M. 104

Horatio R. Palmer, 1834-1907

1. While Je - sus whis - pers to you, Come, sin - ner, come!
2. Are you too, heav - y - la - den? Come, sin - ner, come!
3. Why will you lon - ger doubt Him? Come, sin - ner, come!
4. Far off you may have wan - dered, Come, sin - ner, come!
5. Oh, hear His ten - der plead - ing, Come, sin - ner, come!
While we are pray - ing for you, Come, sin - ner, come!
Je - sus will bear your bur - den, Come, sin - ner, come!
What will you do with - out Him? Come, sin - ner, come!
God's gifts you may have squan - dered, Come, sin - ner, come!
Come and re - ceive the bless - ing, Come, sin - ner, come!
Now is the time to own Him, Come, sin - ner, come!
Je - sus will not de - ceive you, Come, sin - ner, come!
For you His heart is yearn - ing, Come, sin - ner, come!
Cease now, your heart to hard - en, Come, sin - ner, come!
While Je - sus whis - pers to you, Come, sin - ner, come!
Now is the time to know Him, Come, sin - ner, come!
Je - sus will now re - ceive you, Come, sin - ner, come!
Why not to Him be turn - ing? Come, sin - ner, come!
Je - sus will free - ly par - don, Come, sin - ner, come!
While we are pray - ing for you, Come, sin - ner, come!

# WHO AT MY DOOR IS STANDING 507

*Behold, I stand at the door, and knock.* Rev. 3:20.

KNOCKING AT THE DOOR 7.6.7.6 with Ref.
M.M. 63
May B. C. Slade, 1826-1882
Asa Brooks Everett, 1828-1875
1. Who at my door is stand - ing, Pa - tient - ly draw - ing near,
2. Lone - ly with-out He's stay - ing, Lone - ly with - in am I,
3. All thro' the dark hours drear - y, Knock - ing a - gain is He;
4. Door of my heart, I has - ten! Thee will I o - pen wide,
En - trance with-in de - mand - ing? Whose is the voice I hear?
While I am still de - lay - ing, Will He not pass me by?
Je - sus, art Thou not wea - ry, Wait - ing so long for me?
Tho' He re-buke and chas - ten, He shall with me a - bide.
REFRAIN
Sweet - ly the tones are fall - ing:—"O pen the door for Me!
If thou wilt heed My call - ing, I will a - bide with thee."

# 508 DAYS ARE FILLED WITH SORROW AND CARE

*If we confess our sins, He is faithful and just to forgive us our sins, and to cleanse us from all unrighteousness.* I Jn. 1:9.

BURDENS ARE LIFTED 8.6.9.6. with Ref.
M.M. 112
John M. Moore
John M. Moore
1. Days are filled with sor-row and care, Hearts are lone-ly and drear;
2. Cast your care on Je-sus to-day, Leave your wor-ry and fear,
3. Trou-bled soul, the Saviour can see Ev-'ry heartache and tear.
Bur-dens are lift-ed at Cal-va-ry, Je-sus is ve-ry near.
Bur-dens are lift-ed at Cal-va-ry, Je-sus is ve-ry near.
Bur-dens are lift-ed at Cal-va-ry, Je-sus is ve-ry near.
CHORUS
Bur-dens are lift-ed at Cal-va-ry, Cal-va-ry, Cal-va-ry;
Bur-dens are lift-ed at Cal-va-ry, Je-sus is ve-ry near.

# BEHOLD, BEHOLD, THE WONDROUS LOVE 509

*The Spirit and the Bride say, Come. . . . And whosoever will, let him take the water of life freely.* Rev. 22:17.

Fanny J. Crosby, 1820-1915 | THE WONDROUS LOVE 8.8.8.8. M.M. 84 | Ira David Sankey, 1840-1908

1. Be - hold, be - hold the won - drous love, That ev - er flows from God a -
2. Be - hold a foun - tain in His side, To all the world is o - pened
3. Be - hold Him now ex - alt - ed high A - bove the bright and star - ry
4. Be - hold in Him the Liv - ing Way, That on - ward leads to end - less
bove; Thro' Christ His on - ly Son, who gave His pre - cious blood, our souls to save.
wide; Where all may come, by sin op - prest, And find in Him sweet peace and rest.
sky; Yet through His word He call - eth still, "Come un-to Me," who - ev - er will.
day; Where, saved by grace, the ran-somed throng Lift up the ev - er - last - ing song.
All praise and glo - ry be un - to Je - sus, For He hath pur-chased a full sal -
va-tion; Be - hold how won-drous the pro - cla - ma - tion, "Who-so - ev - er will may come!"

# 510 JESUS CAME TO THE WORLD

*For the Son of Man is come to seek and to save that which was lost.* Lk. 19:10.

Harry Showalter, 1967

JESUS CAME TO THE WORLD 10.9.10.9 with Ref.
M.M. 69

Harry Showalter
Har. John J. Overholt, 1969

1. Je - sus came to the world for the sin - ner; On the cross an a - tone - ment was made For the whole hu - man race which had fall - en, When the first man God's will dis - o - beyed.
2. Je - sus came as the Fa - ther's A - noint - ed To bring peace and good will from a - bove; To es - tab - lish His king - dom of mer - cy, And to share His un - speak - a - ble love.
3. Come to Je - sus the great Me - di - a - tor; Take thy cross and His gos - pel o - bey. He's pre - pared man - y man - sions in glo - ry; He's the life and the truth and the way.
CHORUS
Then fly to His arms for a ref - uge; To the Rock on a storm-toss'd shore. He will shel - ter you un - der His pin - ion, Who for mer - cy and par - don im - plore.

# OH, WEARY SOUL, THE GATE IS NEAR 511

*Thou art not far from the kingdom of God.* Mk. 12:34.

JUST OUTSIDE THE DOOR C.M. 8.6.8.6. with Ref.
M.M. 50

James Rowe, 1865-1933

Bently DeForest Ackley, 1872-1958
Har. for mixed voices, John J. Overholt, 1968

1. Oh, wear - y soul, the gate is near, In sin why still a - bide?
2. For - give - ness Je - sus will im - part- To save your soul He died;
3. The day of life is pass - ing by, Soon night your soul will hide;
4. Come in, be free from chains of sin, Be glad, be sat - is - fied;

Both peace and rest are wait - ing here And you are just out - side.
How can you still of - fend His heart, By stay - ing just out - side?
And then "too late" will be your cry, If you are just out - side!
Be - fore the tem - pest breaks, come in, And leave your past out - side.

Just out - side the door, just out - side the door, Be - hold it stands a - jar!

Just out - side the door, just out - side the door, So near and yet so far!

# 512 HAVE THY AFFECTIONS

*Come now, and let us reason together, saith the Lord: though your sins be as scarlet, they shall be as white as snow; though they be red like crimson, they shall be as wool.* Is. 1:18.

Elisha A. Hoffman, 1839-1929 — IS THY HEART RIGHT WITH GOD 10.6.10.6. with Ref. M.M. 112 — Elisha A. Hoffman

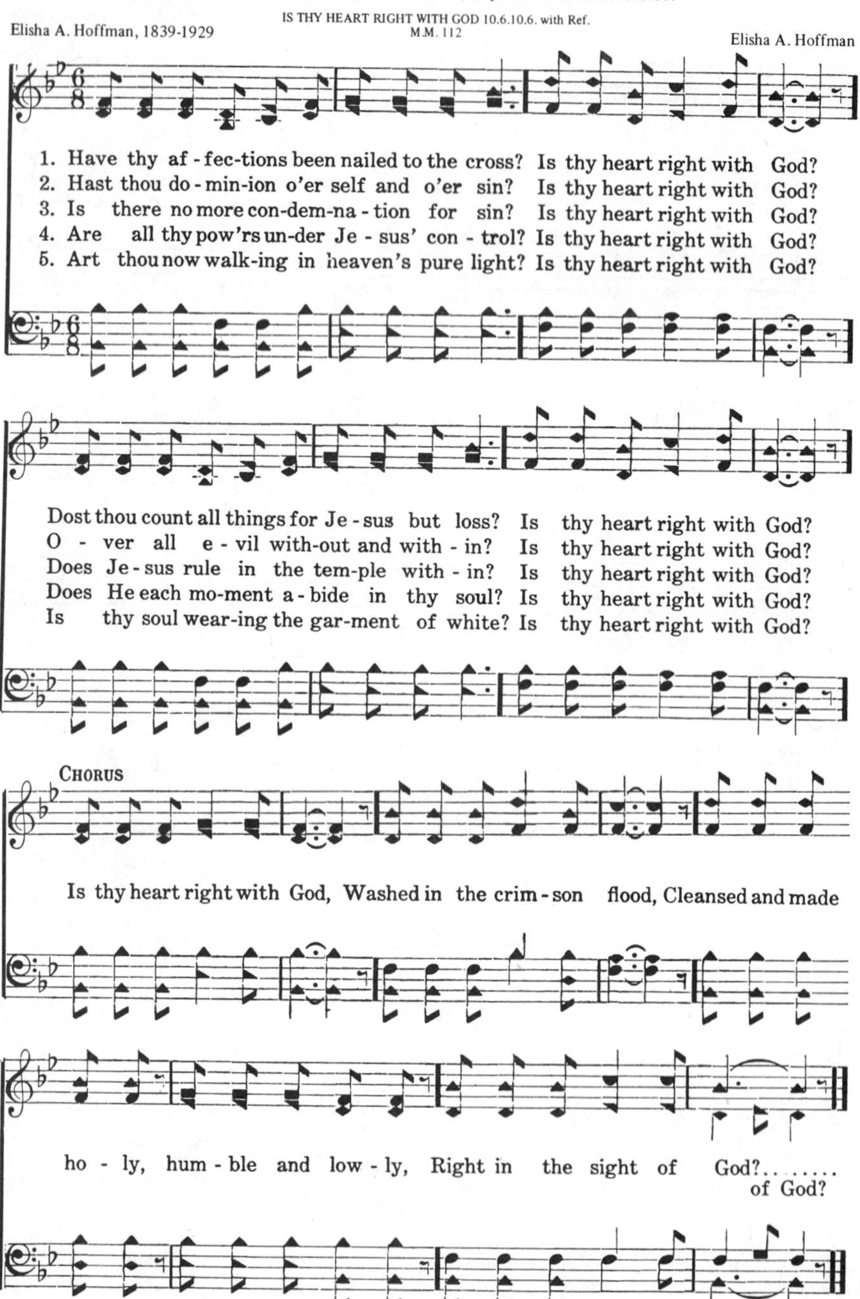
1. Have thy af - fec-tions been nailed to the cross? Is thy heart right with God?
2. Hast thou do - min-ion o'er self and o'er sin? Is thy heart right with God?
3. Is there no more con-dem-na - tion for sin? Is thy heart right with God?
4. Are all thy pow'rs un-der Je - sus' con - trol? Is thy heart right with God?
5. Art thou now walk-ing in heaven's pure light? Is thy heart right with God?
Dost thou count all things for Je - sus but loss? Is thy heart right with God?
O - ver all e - vil with-out and with - in? Is thy heart right with God?
Does Je-sus rule in the tem-ple with - in? Is thy heart right with God?
Does He each mo-ment a - bide in thy soul? Is thy heart right with God?
Is thy soul wear-ing the gar-ment of white? Is thy heart right with God?
CHORUS
Is thy heart right with God, Washed in the crim - son flood, Cleansed and made
ho - ly, hum - ble and low - ly, Right in the sight of God?.......
of God?

# O HAVE YOU NOT HEARD 513

*There is a river, the streams whereof shall make glad the city of God.* Ps. 46:4.

THE BEAUTIFUL RIVER 11.7.11.7. with Ref.
M.M. 92

R. Torrey, Jr. c. 1862, alt. Asa Hull, c. 1862

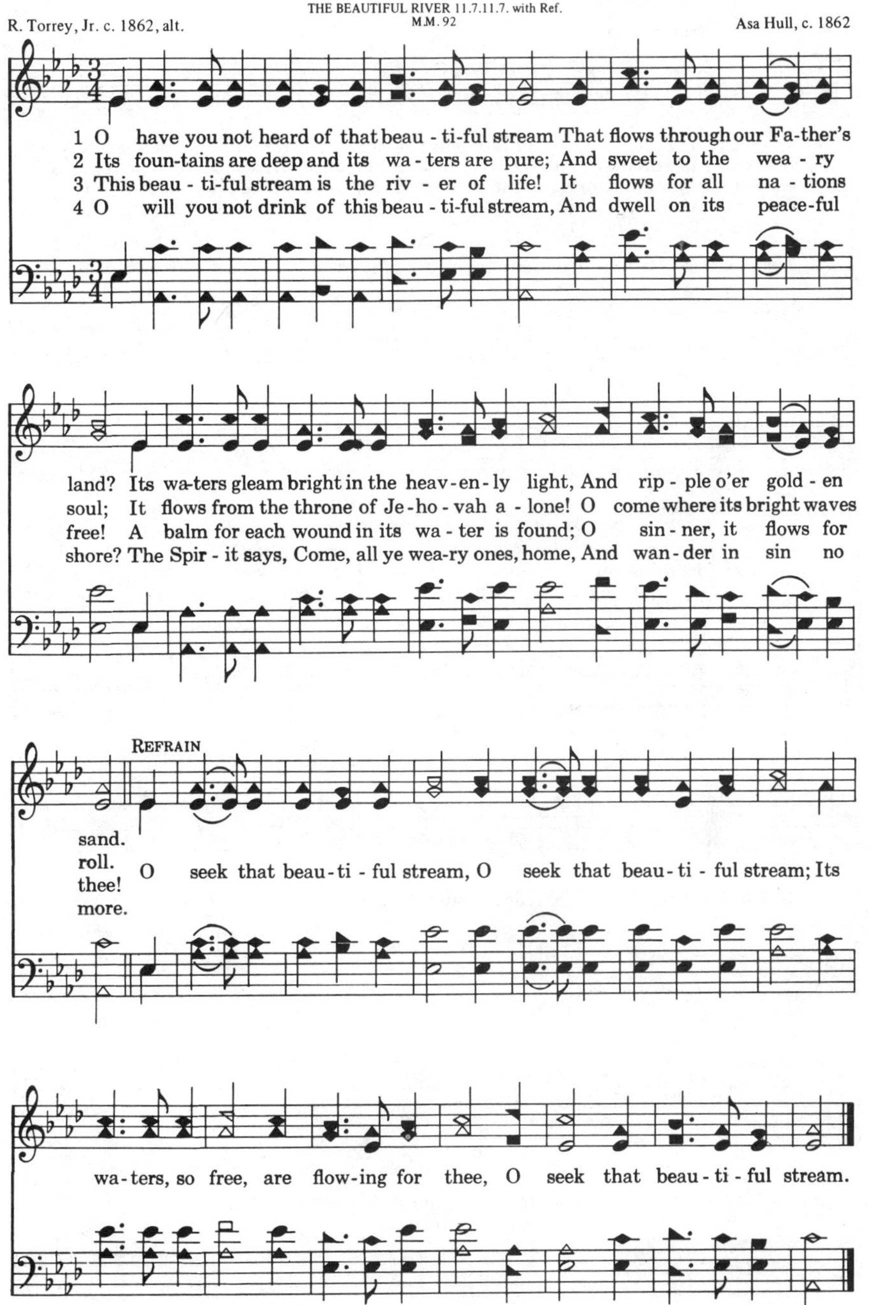

1 O have you not heard of that beau - ti-ful stream That flows through our Fa-ther's
2 Its foun-tains are deep and its wa - ters are pure; And sweet to the wea - ry
3 This beau - ti-ful stream is the riv - er of life! It flows for all na - tions
4 O will you not drink of this beau - ti-ful stream, And dwell on its peace-ful
land? Its wa-ters gleam bright in the heav - en - ly light, And rip - ple o'er gold - en
soul; It flows from the throne of Je - ho - vah a - lone! O come where its bright waves
free! A balm for each wound in its wa - ter is found; O sin - ner, it flows for
shore? The Spir - it says, Come, all ye wea-ry ones, home, And wan - der in sin no
sand.
roll.
thee!
more.
REFRAIN
O seek that beau - ti - ful stream, O seek that beau - ti - ful stream; Its
wa - ters, so free, are flow-ing for thee, O seek that beau - ti - ful stream.

# 514 JESUS IS STANDING IN PILATE'S HALL

*What shall I do then with Jesus which is called Christ?* Mt. 27:22.

STOCKS 9.9.9.7. with Ref.
M.M. 112
Anonymous
M. L. Stocks
1. Je - sus is stand-ing in Pi-late's hall-Friend-less, for-sak-en, be-trayed by all:
2. Je - sus is stand-ing on tri - al still, You can be false to Him if you will,
3. Will you e - vade Him as Pi-late tried? Or will you choose Him, what-e'er be-tide?
4. Will you, like Peter, your Lord de - ny? Or will you scorn from His foes to fly,
5. "Je - sus, I give Thee my heart to - day! Je - sus, I'll fol-low Thee all the way,
Heark-en! what mean-eth the sud - den call! What will you do with Je - sus?
You can be faith-ful thro' good or ill; What will you do with Je - sus?
Vain - ly you strug-gle from Him to hide: What will you do with Je - sus?
Dar - ing for Je - sus to live or die? What will you do with Je - sus?
Glad - ly o - bey - ing Thee!" will you say: "This will I do with Je - sus!"
CHORUS
What will you do with Je - sus? Neu - tral you can - not be;
Some - day your heart will be ask - ing, "What will He do with me?"

# O WHAT WILL YOU DO WITH JESUS? 515

*What shall I do then with Jesus which is called Christ?* Mt. 27:22.

O WHAT WILL YOU DO WITH JESUS 8.6.7.7.7.6.7.6.
M.M. 104

Nathaniel Norton — George Coles Stebbins, 1846-1945

1. O what will you do with Je - sus? The call comes low and sweet;
2. O what will you do with Je - sus? The call comes loud and clear;
3. O think of the King of Glo - ry From heav'n to earth come down,
As ten - der - ly He bids you Your bur - dens lay at His feet;
The sol - emn words are sound - ing In ev - 'ry lis - t'ning ear;
His life so pure and ho - ly, His death, His cross, His crown;
O soul so sad and wea - ry, That sweet voice speaks to thee;
Im - mor - tal life's in the ques - tion, And joy thro' e - ter - ni - ty;
Of His di - vine com - pas - sion, His sac - ri - fice for thee;
Then what will you do with Je - sus? O what shall the an - swer be?
FINE.
D. S.—What will you do with Je - sus? O what shall the an - swer be?
REFRAIN
D. S.
What shall the an - swer be? What shall the an - swer be?

# 516 SHE ONLY TOUCHED THE HEM OF HIS GARMENT

*Thy faith hath made thee whole.* Lk. 8:48.

THE HEM OF HIS GARMENT 10.6.10.6. with Ref.
M.M. 108

George Frederick Root, 1828 (1820-1895) — George Frederick Root

1. She on - ly touched the hem of His gar - ment As to His side she stole, A - mid the crowd that gath - ered a - round Him, And straight-way she was whole.
2. She came in fear and trem - bling be - fore Him, She knew her Lord had come; She felt that from Him vir - tue had healed her, The might - y deed was done.
3. He turned with "Daugh - ter, be of good com - fort, Thy faith hath made thee whole;" And peace that pass - eth all un - der - stand - ing With glad - ness filled her soul.
CHORUS
Oh, touch the hem of His gar - ment! And thou, too, shalt be free;
His sav - ing pow'r this ver - y hour Shall give new life to thee.

# SHALL I COME JUST AS I AM 517

*I am not come to call the righteous, but sinners to repentance.* Mt. 9:13.

COME, JUST AS YOU ARE 7.7.7.7. with Ref.
M.M. 69

Elisha A. Hoffman, 1839-1929 J. Henry Showalter, 1864-1947

1. Shall I come just as I am, Come with all my guilt and sin? If I
2. Shall I come vile as I am, And bend low at Je - sus' feet? Shall I
3. Shall I come with all my fear, Lest my sins have been too great? Shall I
4. Shall I come, tho' far a - way From the lov - ing Shepherd's fold? Will He

Refrain
o - pen wide my heart, Will He en - ter in?
plead His pard'ning grace, And His love en - treat? As you are, just as you are
break thro' all my doubts, To sweet mer-cy's gate?
bless me if I firm To His prom-ise hold?

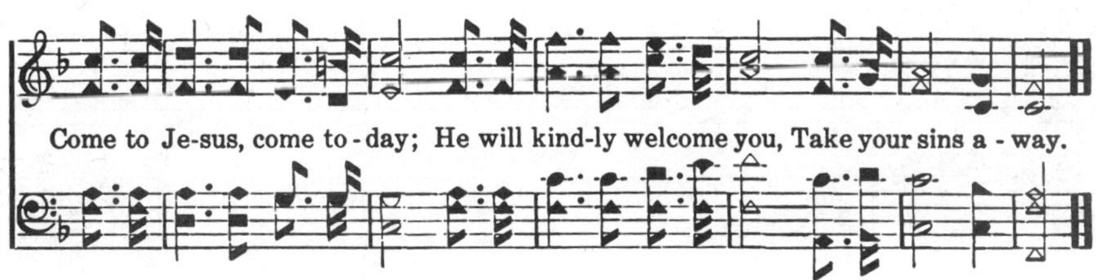
Come to Je-sus, come to - day; He will kind-ly welcome you, Take your sins a - way.

# 518 GOD OUR FATHER, SEND REVIVAL

*Wilt Thou not revive us again: that thy people may rejoice in Thee?* Ps. 85:6.

Adam M. Baer, 1960
Altered by Compiler, 1965
RIPLEY (NEW) 8.7.8.7.D.
M.M. 63
Lowell Mason, 1792-1872
Arr. John J. Overholt, 1965
1. God, our Fa - ther, send re - vi - val To us now in this our day;
2. Ho - ly Sav – iour, bring re - vi - val To the drift - ing church to - day!
3. Lord, re - vive the house of Is - rael Who are blind - ed to the Light;
4. Of't our hearts are filled with sad - ness For the mass - es bound for hell!
Stir Thy peo - ple from their slum - ber To Thy great com-mand o - bey!
Help her now to seek Thy guid - ance To the straight and nar - row way!
May they now see their Mes - si - ah Take their blindness give them sight!
May our souls be stirred to ac - tion And the com - ing judge-ment tell!
Oh, - our Fa – ther, bring re - vi - val, Start the work in me I pray;
Bring a - wak - 'ning to the mil - lions Who are held by Sa - tan's pow'r;
Grant, dear Lord, be - fore Thy com - ing That re - vi - val fires may burn
Help thy ser - vants to be faith - ful To o - bey thy great com - mand,
Help us now to do our du - ty, Bring re - vi - val in our day!
May Thy peo - ple grasp a vi - sion Of the late - ness of the hour!
In the heart of ev - 'ry crea-ture, And to Thee their footsteps turn!
Bring - ing Christ to all the na - tions And throughout this sin - ful land! A-men.

# REVIVE THY WORK, O LORD 519

*O Lord, revive Thy work.* Hab. 3:2.

Albert Midlane, 1858 (1825-1909)

VIGIL S.M. 6.6.8.6.
M.M. 96

Alban's *Tune Book*, 1865

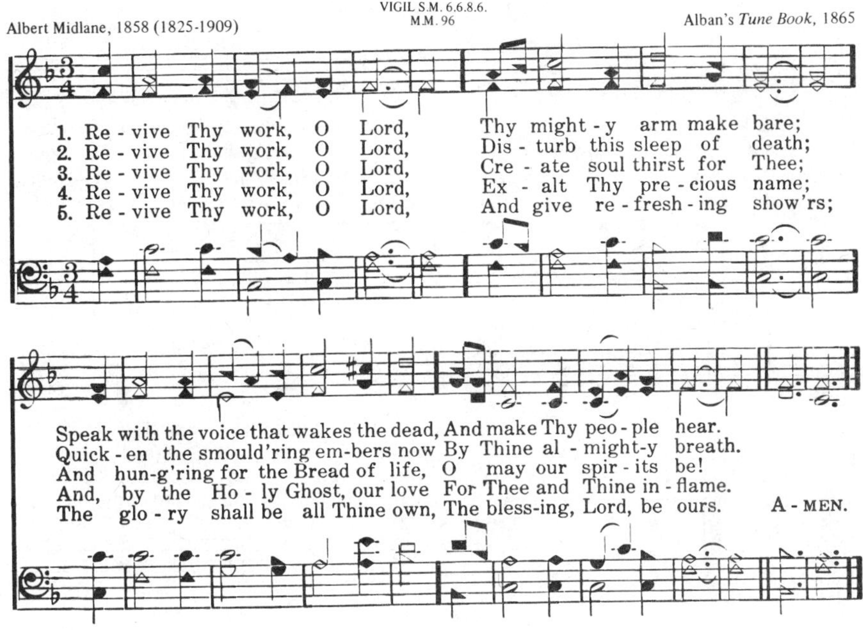

1. Re - vive Thy work, O Lord, Thy might - y arm make bare;
2. Re - vive Thy work, O Lord, Dis - turb this sleep of death;
3. Re - vive Thy work, O Lord, Cre - ate soul thirst for Thee;
4. Re - vive Thy work, O Lord, Ex - alt Thy pre - cious name;
5. Re - vive Thy work, O Lord, And give re - fresh - ing show'rs;
Speak with the voice that wakes the dead, And make Thy peo - ple hear.
Quick - en the smould'ring em-bers now By Thine al - might-y breath.
And hun-g'ring for the Bread of life, O may our spir - its be!
And, by the Ho - ly Ghost, our love For Thee and Thine in - flame.
The glo - ry shall be all Thine own, The bless-ing, Lord, be ours.
A - MEN.

# WE PRAISE THEE O GOD 520

*Turn us again, O God of hosts, and cause Thy face to shine; and we shall be saved.* Ps. 80:7.

William P. Mackay, 1839-1885

REVIVE US AGAIN 11.11. with Ref.
M.M. 84

John J. Husband, 1760-1825

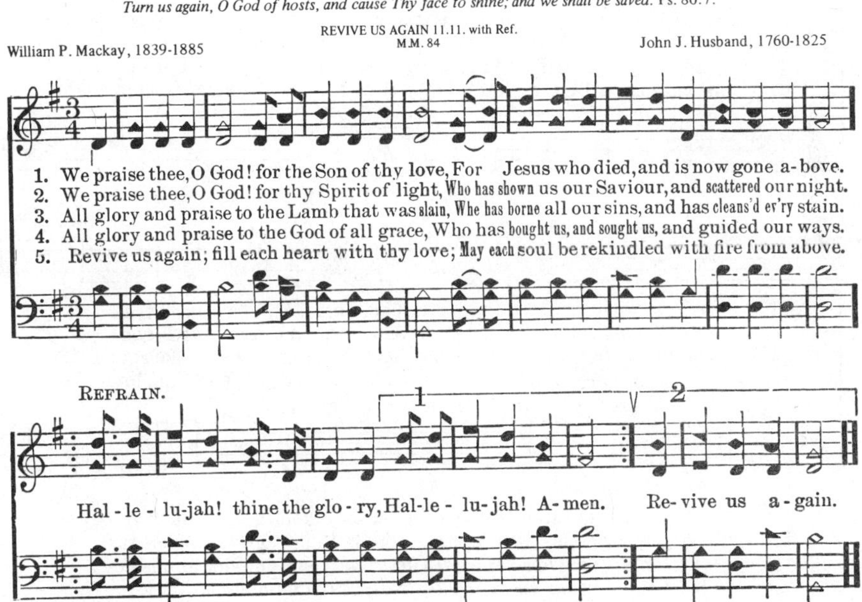

1. We praise thee, O God! for the Son of thy love, For Jesus who died, and is now gone a-bove.
2. We praise thee, O God! for thy Spirit of light, Who has shown us our Saviour, and scattered our night.
3. All glory and praise to the Lamb that was slain, Who has borne all our sins, and has cleans'd ev'ry stain.
4. All glory and praise to the God of all grace, Who has bought us, and sought us, and guided our ways.
5. Revive us again; fill each heart with thy love; May each soul be rekindled with fire from above.
REFRAIN.
Hal - le - lu-jah! thine the glo - ry, Hal - le - lu-jah! A-men. Re- vive us a - gain.
1
2

# 521 ARISE O ZION, RISE AND SHINE

*Arise, shine; for Thy light is come, and the glory of the Lord is risen upon thee.* Is. 60:1.

Lorenzo Dow, 1877-1834, cento
Alt. Wilmer D. Swope

ST. MICHAELS C.M.D. 8.6.8.6.D.
M.M. 80

W. Gawler's *Hymns and Psalms*, 1785

1. A – rise, O Zi – on, rise and shine, Be–hold, thy light is come,
2. Ye her–alds blow your trum–pets loud, The earth shall know her doom,
3. A – rise ye na – tions on the earth, Be–fore the Judge ap – pear,
4. The glo–rious news of Gos–pel grace, To sin – ners then is o'er,
Thy glor–ious con–quer–ing King is near, To take His ex–iles home,
Go, spread the news from pole to pole, Be – hold the Judge is come;
All tongues and lan–gua – ges shall come, Their fi – nal doom to hear;
The trump in Zi – on then is still, And to be heard no more,
His trum–pet sound–ing through the sky, To set poor cap–tives free,
Blow out the sun, burn up the earth, Con–sume the rol–ling flood;
The Lord up – on His daz–zling throne; Ten thou–sand an–gels round;
The watch–men all have left the walls, And with their flocks a – bove,
The day of won–der now is come, The year of Ju – bi – lee.
While ev–'ry star shall dis–ap–pear, Go turn the moon to blood.
The sil – ver trum–pets far and near, Give forth an awe–some sound.
On Ca–naan's hap–py shore they sing, And shout re–deem–ing love. A–men

5. Come all ye brethren in the Lord, Whose hearts are joined in one;
Hold up your heads with courage bold; Your race is almost run,
For Zion's Lord and Saviour King, Shall sin and death destroy,
The morning stars shall jointly sing, And Zion shout for joy.

# SUN OF RIGHTEOUSNESS, ARISE! 522

*Unto you that fear My name shall the Sun of Righteousness arise with healing in His wings.* Mal. 4:2.

Christian David, 1690-1751
Christian Barth, 1799-1862
John Christian Nehring, 1671-1736
*Sonne der Gerechtigkeit*
Composite, Tr. John J. Overholt, 1965

SONNE DER GERECHTIGKEIT 7.9.7.7.4.
M.M. 56

Geistliche Böhmische Brüder, 1566

1. Sun of Right - eous - ness, a - rise! Dis – pel
2. Wake a dead Christ - en - dom from False se-
3. Sal - va - tion do Thou un - fold Es - trange-
4. Doors of na - tions o - pen wide! Naught can
5. Give Thy en - voys pow'r and zeal, Faith's sure
dark – ness from our eyes, In Thy church break
cu - ri - ty's sure tomb! Show Thy pow'r, might-
ment no more be - hold! Man's great Shep - herd,
slow Thy king - dom's tide! Pow'r and craft flee
hope, and love, and weal! May great fruits Thy
forth, that we And the world may then see Thee! Have mer - cy Lord!
ty, un - furled, Ev – ery – where throughout our world! Have mer - cy Lord!
ga - ther in All man - kind from bonds of sin! Have mer - cy Lord!
from Thy might! Send Thy light to dark - est night! Have mer - cy Lord!
grace con - trols Fol - low tears sown for men's souls! Have mer - cy Lord!

6. Let us Thy great glory see
Thy renown, today, that we
In our weakness and our need,
May Christ's soldiers be indeed!
Have mercy, Lord!

7. Pow'r, and praise, glory, honor
To the Highest evermore!
In the Trinity become
We in Him now all in one!
Have mercy, Lord!

# 523 COME NEW-BORN SOULS

*Teaching them to observe all things whatsoever I have commanded you: and, lo, I am with you alway, even unto the end of the world.* Amen. Mt. 28:20.

FEDERAL STREET L.M. 8.8.8.8.
M.M. 60

John J. Overholt, 1970 — Henry Kemble Oliver, 1800-1885

1. Come, new – born souls, love's grace dis – play, Ye who by
2. Come, teach – ers, teach love's won – drous grace, Ye who com –
3. Come, pil – grims to a bet – ter land, Ye who in
4. Lord, help us Thy all things ob – serve, All things re –

blood re – deemed, Christ serve; Come, His com – mand – ments
mis – sioned, preach Christ's Word; Come, he who loves, His
life will Christ o – bey; Come, live and teach your
cord – ed in Thy Word; In love's o – be – dience

all o – bey; This do, and love in deed and word.
Lord o – beys; This teach, and tru – ly love your Lord.
Lord's com – mands; And love, and live in end – less day!
may we serve And ev – er own Thee as our Lord!

# 524 SAVIOUR, TEACH ME DAY BY DAY

*But whoso keepeth His Word, in him verily is the love of God perfected: hereby know we that we are in him.* I Jn. 2:5.

PURITY 7.7.7.7.
M.M. 92

Jane E. Leeson, 1842 (1807-1882) — Anonymous

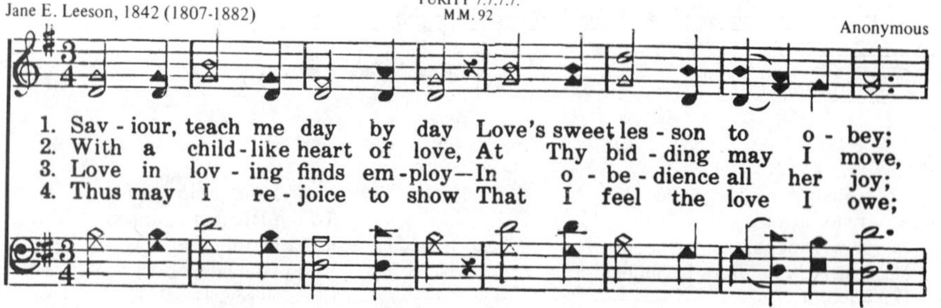
1. Sav - iour, teach me day by day Love's sweet les - son to o - bey;
2. With a child - like heart of love, At Thy bid - ding may I move,
3. Love in lov - ing finds em - ploy—In o - be - dience all her joy;
4. Thus may I re - joice to show That I feel the love I owe;

Sweet - er les - son can - not be: Lov - ing Him who first loved me.
Prompt to serve and fol - low Thee— Lov - ing Him who first loved me.
Ev - er new that joy will be: Lov - ing Him who first loved me.
Sing - ing till Thy face I see, Of His love who first loved me.

# TEACH ME, O LORD 525

*Teach me, O Lord, the way of Thy statutes; and I shall keep it unto the end.* Ps. 119:33.

*Psalter,* 1912 — BISHOP L.M. 8.8.8.8. M.M. 60 — Joseph Perry Holbrook, 1822-1888

1. Teach me, O Lord, Thy way of truth, And from it
2. In Thy com - mand - ments make me walk, For in Thy
3. Turn Thou my eyes from van - i - ty, And cause me
4. Turn Thou a - way re - proach and fear, Thy right - eous

I will not de - part; That I may stead - fast-
law my joy shall be; Give me a heart that
in Thy ways to tread; O let Thy serv - ant
judg - ments I con - fess; To know Thy pre - cepts

ly o - bey, Give me an un - - der - stand - ing heart.
loves Thy will, From dis - con - tent and en - vy free.
prove Thy Word, And thus to god - ly fear be led.
I de - sire, Re - vive me in Thy right - eous - ness.

# 526 SHINE THOU UPON US, LORD

*And, ye fathers, provoke not your children to wrath: but bring them up in the nurture and admonition of the Lord.* Eph. 6:4.

John Ellerton, 1889 (1826-1893) | BROUGHTON 6.6.6.D. M.M. 69 | Thomas Hastings, 1784-1872

1. Shine Thou up - on us, Lord, True Light of men, to - day,
2. Breathe Thou up - on us, Lord, Thy Spir - it's liv - ing flame,
3. Speak Thou for us, O Lord, In all we say of Thee;
4. Live Thou with - in us, Lord; Thy mind and will be ours;
And through the writ - ten Word Thy ver - y Self dis - play;
That so with one ac - cord Our lips may tell Thy name.
Ac - cord - ing to Thy Word Let all our teach - ing be;
Be Thou be - lov'd, a - dored, And served with all our pow'rs,
That so, from hearts which burn With gaz - ing on Thy face,
Give Thou the hear - ing ear, Fix Thou the wan-d'ring thought,
That so Thy lambs may know Their own true Shep-herd's voice,
That so our lives may teach Thy chil - dren what Thou art,
Thy lit - tle ones may learn The won-ders of Thy grace.
That those we teach may hear The great things Thou hast wrought.
Wher - e'er He leads them go, And in His love re - joice.
And plead, by more than speech, For Thee with ev - ery heart. A - men.

# THE CROSS THAT HE GAVE MAY BE HEAVY 527

*Come, take up the cross, and follow me.* Mk. 10:21.

THE CROSS IS NOT GREATER 9.8.9.8. with Ref.
M.M. 66

Ballington Booth, 1855-1940

Ballington Booth

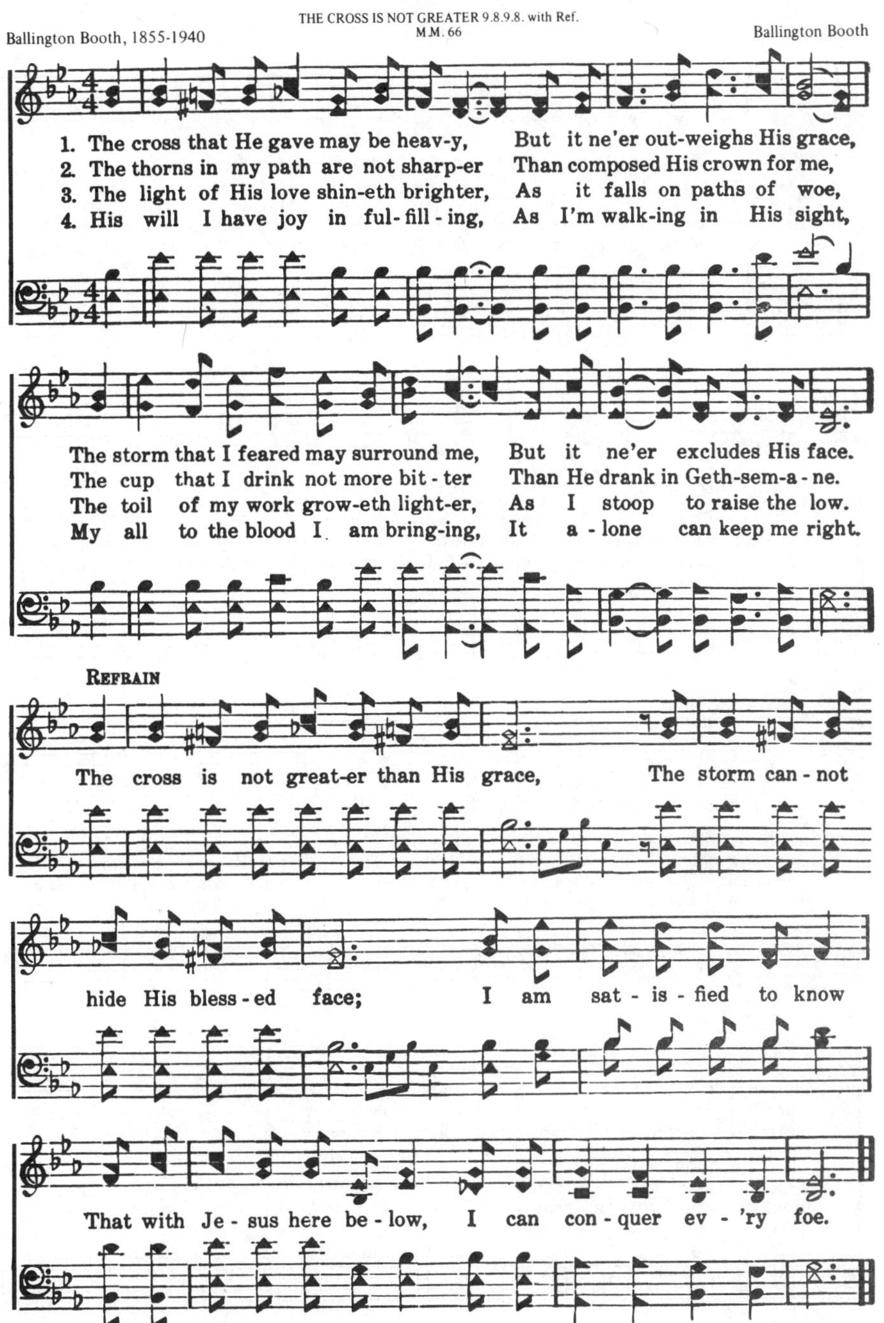
1. The cross that He gave may be heav-y, But it ne'er out-weighs His grace,
2. The thorns in my path are not sharp-er Than composed His crown for me,
3. The light of His love shin-eth brighter, As it falls on paths of woe,
4. His will I have joy in ful-fill-ing, As I'm walk-ing in His sight,
The storm that I feared may surround me, But it ne'er excludes His face.
The cup that I drink not more bit-ter Than He drank in Geth-sem-a-ne.
The toil of my work grow-eth light-er, As I stoop to raise the low.
My all to the blood I am bring-ing, It a-lone can keep me right.
REFRAIN
The cross is not great-er than His grace, The storm can-not hide His bless-ed face; I am sat-is-fied to know That with Je-sus here be-low, I can con-quer ev-'ry foe.

# 528 WHEN TRIALS AND TEMPTATIONS

*If we suffer, we shall also reign with Him.* II Tim. 2:12.

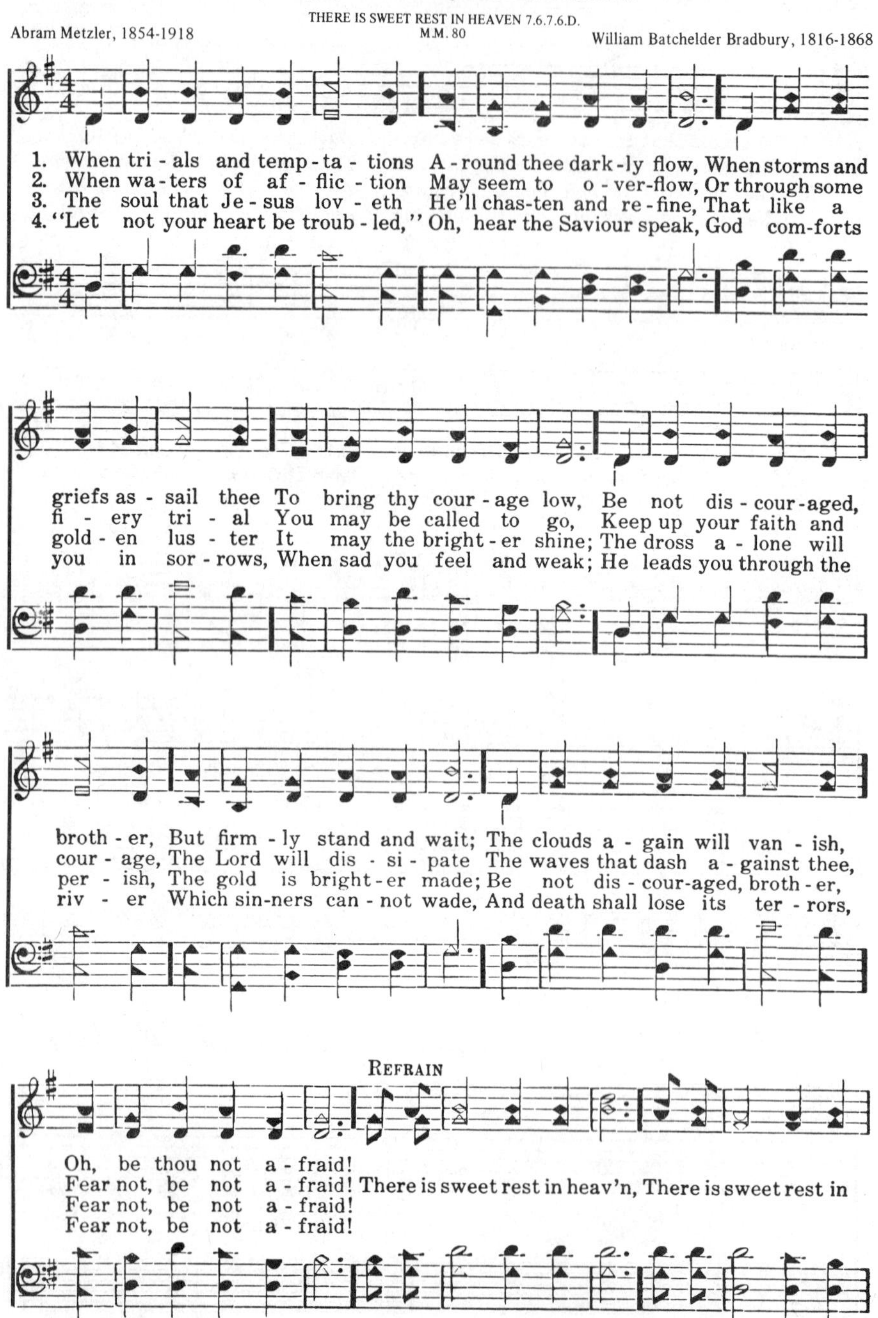
THERE IS SWEET REST IN HEAVEN 7.6.7.6.D.
M.M. 80
Abram Metzler, 1854-1918
William Batchelder Bradbury, 1816-1868
1. When tri - als and temp - ta - tions A - round thee dark - ly flow, When storms and griefs as - sail thee To bring thy cour - age low, Be not dis - cour - aged, broth - er, But firm - ly stand and wait; The clouds a - gain will van - ish, Oh, be thou not a - fraid!
2. When wa - ters of af - flic - tion May seem to o - ver - flow, Or through some fi - ery tri - al You may be called to go, Keep up your faith and cour - age, The Lord will dis - si - pate The waves that dash a - gainst thee, Fear not, be not a - fraid!
3. The soul that Je - sus lov - eth He'll chas - ten and re - fine, That like a gold - en lus - ter It may the bright - er shine; The dross a - lone will per - ish, The gold is bright - er made; Be not dis - cour - aged, broth - er, Fear not, be not a - fraid!
4. "Let not your heart be troub - led," Oh, hear the Saviour speak, God com - forts you in sor - rows, When sad you feel and weak; He leads you through the riv - er Which sin - ners can - not wade, And death shall lose its ter - rors, Fear not, be not a - fraid!
Refrain
There is sweet rest in heav'n, There is sweet rest in

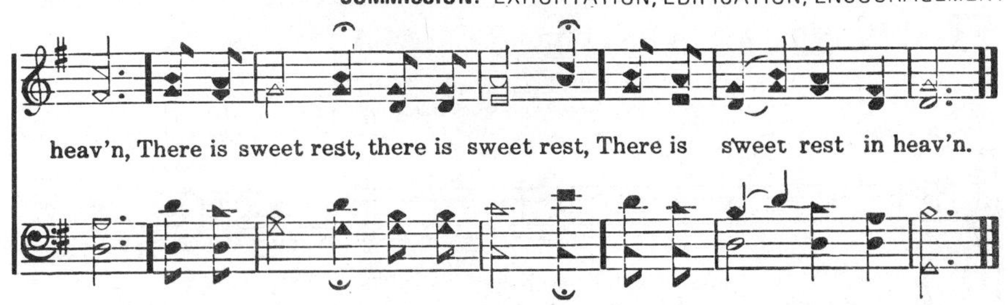
heav'n, There is sweet rest, there is sweet rest, There is sweet rest in heav'n.

# GO TO DARK GETHSEMANE 529

*Though He were a Son, yet learned He obedience by the things which He suffered.* Heb. 5:8.

James Montgomery, 1820 (1771-1854)

AJALON 7.7.7.7.7.7.
M.M. 63

Richard Redhead, 1820-1901

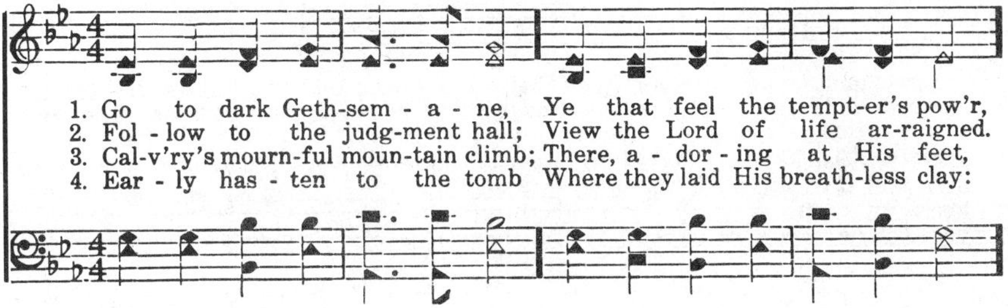

1. Go to dark Geth-sem - a - ne, Ye that feel the tempt-er's pow'r,
2. Fol - low to the judg-ment hall; View the Lord of life ar-raigned.
3. Cal-v'ry's mourn-ful moun-tain climb; There, a - dor - ing at His feet,
4. Ear - ly has - ten to the tomb Where they laid His breath-less clay:

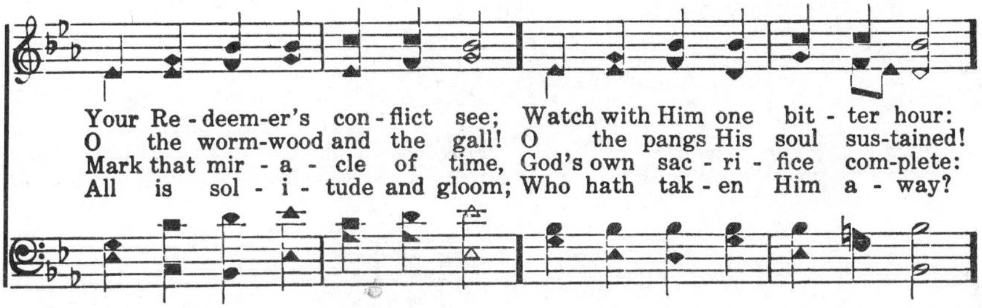

Your Re - deem-er's con - flict see; Watch with Him one bit - ter hour:
O the worm-wood and the gall! O the pangs His soul sus-tained!
Mark that mir - a - cle of time, God's own sac - ri - fice com-plete:
All is sol - i - tude and gloom; Who hath tak - en Him a - way?

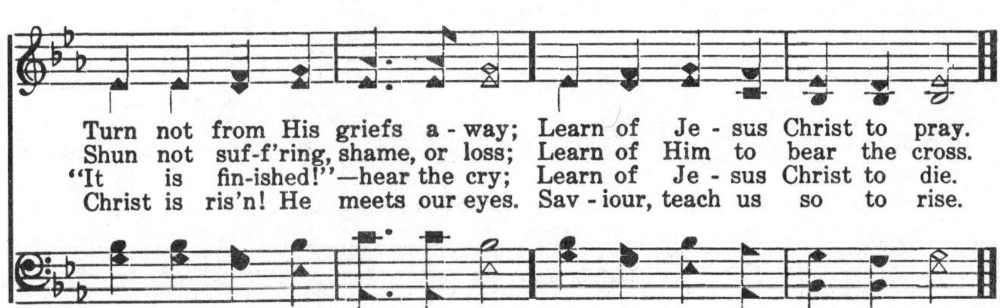

Turn not from His griefs a - way; Learn of Je - sus Christ to pray.
Shun not suf-f'ring, shame, or loss; Learn of Him to bear the cross.
"It is fin-ished!"—hear the cry; Learn of Je - sus Christ to die.
Christ is ris'n! He meets our eyes. Sav - iour, teach us so to rise.

# 530 DOES JESUS CARE

*Who comforteth us in all our tribulation, that we may be able to comfort them which are in any trouble, by the comfort wherewith we ourselves are comforted of God.* II Cor. 1:4.

Frank E. Graeff, 1860-1919
DOES JESUS CARE 9.7.10.8. with Ref.
M.M. 100
J. Lincoln Hall, 1866-1930
1. Does Je - sus care when my heart is pained Too deep - ly for mirth and song; As the bur - dens press, and the cares dis - tress, And the way grows wea - ry and long?
2. Does Je - sus care when my way is dark With a name - less dread and fear? As the day - light fades in - to deep night shades, Does He care e - nough to be near?
3. Does Je - sus care when I've tried and failed To re - sist some temp - ta - tion strong; When for my deep grief I find no re - lief, Tho' my tears flow all the night long?
4. Does Je - sus care when I've said "good-bye" To the dear - est on earth to me, And my sad heart aches till it near - ly breaks— Is it aught to Him? Does He see?
CHORUS
Oh, yes, He cares, I know He cares! His heart is touched with my grief;
ad lib.
When the days are wea - ry, the long nights drear - y,
rit.
I know my Sav - iour cares. (He cares.)

# HE LEADETH ME 531

*For I the Lord thy God will hold thy right hand.* Is. 41:13.

HE LEADETH ME L.M. 8.8.8.8. with Ref.
M.M. 63

Joseph H. Gilmore, 1834-1918 | William Batchelder Bradbury, 1816-1868

1. He lead-eth me: O bless-ed tho't! O words with heav'nly comfort fraught!
2. Sometimes 'mid scenes of deepest gloom, Sometimes where Eden's bow-ers bloom,
3. Lord, I would clasp Thy hand in mine, Nor ev - er mur-mur nor re - pine;
4. And when my task on earth is done, When, by Thy grace, the vic-t'ry's won,
What-e'er I do, wher-e'er I be, Still 'tis God's hand that lead-eth me.
By wa-ters calm—o'er troubled sea,—Still 'tis His hand that lead-eth me.
Con - tent, what-ev - er lot I see, Since 'tis my God that lead-eth me.
E'en death's cold wave I will not flee, Since God thro' Jor - dan lead-eth me.
REFRAIN
He lead - eth me, He lead - eth me; By His own hand He lead-eth me:
His faith-ful fol-l'wer I would be, For by His hand He lead-eth me.

# 532 HAVE YOU HEARD THE SOBBING

*And He saith unto them, Follow me, and I will make you fishers of men.* Mt. 4:19.

A THOUSAND MILLION SOULS ARE DYING 13.8.13.8. with Ref.
M.M. 63

Haldor Lillenas, b. 1855

Haldor Lillenas

1. Have you heard the sob-bing of a thous-and mil-lion souls, Submerged in darkest hea - then night? Vain-ly grop - ing for the way that leads to hope and peace, They plead and wait for Gos - pel light.
2. Have you heard the sob-bing of a thous-and mil-lion souls, By su - per-stitious chains en-slaved? Can you long - er be in - dif-f'rent to their sad es - tate? Thro' Je - sus they can all be saved.
3. Can you hear the sob-bing of a thous-and mil-lion souls, Who seek re-lief of heart in vain? Let them have the bless-ed Gos - pel that can free-dom give, And rend the chains of sin in twain.
Chorus
A thou-sand mil - lion souls are dy - ing, A thou-sand mil - lion souls for whom the Sav - iour died. Can you still de - ny their plea? Can you long - er i - dle be, While a thou-sand mil - lion souls are dy - ing?

# AT HOME AND ABROAD 533

*Whom shall I send, and who will go for us? Then said I, Here am I; send me.* Is. 6:8.

IMMANUEL'S BANNER 10.11.10.11. with Ref.
M.M. 66

Jacob Brubacher Smith, 1870-1951

Amanda Motte

1. At home and a-broad, on life's bat-tle-field, Brave sol-diers are need - ed their ser - vice to yield For Je - sus who died that . all might have life. Come en - ter the bat - tle, be bold in the strife.
2. Our Cap - tain is call - ing for vol - un-teers now, Let all to his mandates sub-mis - sive - ly bow; Not life and not friends let . . an - y hold dear While cries of the need - y break out on your ear.
3. Oh, who then will go in the strength of the Lord, Up-lift - ing his ban - ner, pro-claim - ing his word? Who will help to re-deem dy - ing souls from the grave, In tell - ing of Je - sus the might - y to save?
REFRAIN.
The trum - pet is sounding, we're off to the fray, Im-man - u-el's ban-ner we'll lift up to-day. Then onward, still onward in his name we go, Till all of his crea-tures the Lord's name will know.

# 534 O MIGHT THE SORROWING FACE OF JESUS

*His visage was so marred more than any man.* Is. 52:14. *A man of sorrows, and acquainted with grief.* Is. 53:3.

Christian Gregor, 1723-1801
Johann Jacob Bossert, 1721-1789
Christian Ludwig Braun, 1746-1777, composite
*O drückten Jesu Todesmienen*
Tr. Joseph Overholt, 1968

O DRÜCKTEN JESU TODESMIENEN
9.8.9.8. with Ref.
M.M. 80

Wilhelm Amandus Auberlen, 1798-1874

1. O might the sorr – 'wing face of Je – sus,
O could for sin – ners His re – demp – tion,
In – spire our souls e – ter – nal – ly;
In our hearts strength and pow – er be;

2. One look of faith at Je – sus' suff – 'ring,
The foun – tain pure for joys of the Spir – it,
Gives faint – ing hearts a cour – age bold;
Is His own pre – cious blood which flowed;

REFRAIN

How can we e'er thank our bless–ed Sav – iour;
For our sins flowed His pre – cious blood;
This heals us, poor and need – dy

When His great pow'r our falt'ring heart fac – es,
His love our spir – it does per – vade;
When His rich grace our soul em–

crea – tures, And is e – ter – nal – ly our good.
brac – es, The Spir – it fills us, Christ comes to aid.

3. Lord Jesus, I have seen Thee suffering, I pray Thee, take me as Thine own;
In my heart I will dearly love Thee, Forgive, O leave me not alone.
Thy death has brought us Thy salvation; Thy blood has set our spirits free;
Help us in each remotest nation, To bring Thy Gospel, sea to sea.

# FROM GREENLAND'S ICY MOUNTAINS 535

*Come over into Macedonia and help us.* Acts 16:9.

MISSIONARY HYMN 7.6.7.6.D.
M.M. 84

Reginald Heber, 1819 (1738-1826)

Lowell Mason, 1823 (1792-1872)

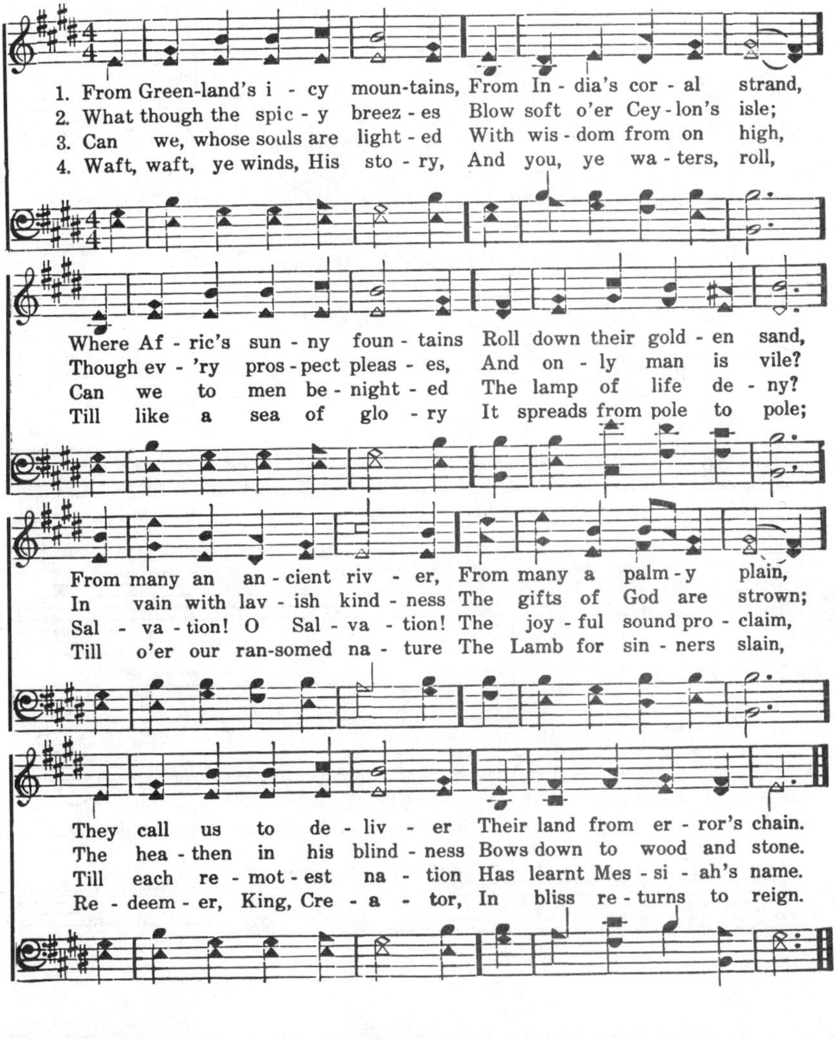

1. From Green-land's i - cy moun-tains, From In - dia's cor - al strand,
2. What though the spic - y breez - es Blow soft o'er Cey - lon's isle;
3. Can we, whose souls are light - ed With wis - dom from on high,
4. Waft, waft, ye winds, His sto - ry, And you, ye wa - ters, roll,

Where Af - ric's sun - ny foun - tains Roll down their gold - en sand,
Though ev - 'ry pros - pect pleas - es, And on - ly man is vile?
Can we to men be - night - ed The lamp of life de - ny?
Till like a sea of glo - ry It spreads from pole to pole;

From many an an - cient riv - er, From many a palm - y plain,
In vain with lav - ish kind - ness The gifts of God are strown;
Sal - va - tion! O Sal - va - tion! The joy - ful sound pro - claim,
Till o'er our ran-somed na - ture The Lamb for sin - ners slain,

They call us to de - liv - er Their land from er - ror's chain.
The hea - then in his blind - ness Bows down to wood and stone.
Till each re - mot - est na - tion Has learnt Mes - si - ah's name.
Re - deem - er, King, Cre - a - tor, In bliss re - turns to reign.

# 536 LORD OF THE LIVING HARVEST

*Pray ye therefore the Lord of the harvest, that He will send forth labourers into His harvest.* Mt. 9:38.

John Samuel Bewley Monsell, 1866 (1811-1875)
Altered by Compiler, 1965

DIEU LUIMEME O MYSTERE
7.6.7.6.7.6.7.6.7.6.
M.M. 88

Mme. Martin Hickel

mf

1. Lord of the liv–ing har–vest, That whit–ens o'er the plain, Where an–gels soon shall gath–er their sheaves of gold–en grain; Ac – cept these hands to la – bor, these hearts to trust and love, And deign with them to has – ten Thy king–dom from a–bove, And deign with them to has–ten Thy kingdom from a–bove.

2. As lab–orers in Thy vine–yard, Send us, O Christ, to be Con–tent to bear the bur–den of wea–ry days for Thee; We ask no oth–er wag–es, when Thou shalt call us home, But to have shared the trav–ail which makes Thy king–dom come, But to have shared the travail which makes Thy kingdom come.

3. Come down, Thou ho–ly Sav–iour! And fill our souls with light, Clothe us in spot–less rain–ment, in lin–en clean and white; Be–side Thy sa–cred al – tar be with us, where we stand, To sanc – ti – fy Thy peo–ple through all this hap–py land, To sanc–ti–fy Thy peo–ple through all this happy land.

p

f

# FAR AND NEAR THE FIELDS 537

*Look on the fields; for they are white already to harvest.* Jn. 4:35.

THE CALL FOR REAPERS 8.7.8.7.D. with Ref.
M.M. 104

J. O. Thompson, 1782-1818

J. B. O. Clemm

*Spirited*

1. Far and near the fields are teem-ing With the waves of rip-ened grain;
2. Send them forth with morn's first beaming, Send them in the noon-tide's glare;
3. O thou, whom thy Lord is send-ing, Gath-er now the sheaves of gold;

Far and near their gold is gleam-ing O'er the sun-ny slope and plain.
When the sun's last rays are gleam-ing; Bid them gath-er ev-'ry-where.
Heav'nward then at eve-ning wend-ing, Thou shalt come with joy un-told.

REFRAIN

Lord of har-vest, send forth reap-ers! Hear us, Lord, to Thee we cry;

Send them now the sheaves to gath-er, Ere the har-vest time pass by.

# 538 SPEED AWAY! SPEED AWAY!

*Preach the Gospel in the regions beyond.* II Cor. 10:16.

W. E. M. Hackleman, b. 1868 | SPEED AWAY (Irregular) M.M. 76 | From Isaac B. Woodbury, 1819-1853 Har. W. E. M. Hackleman, b. 1868

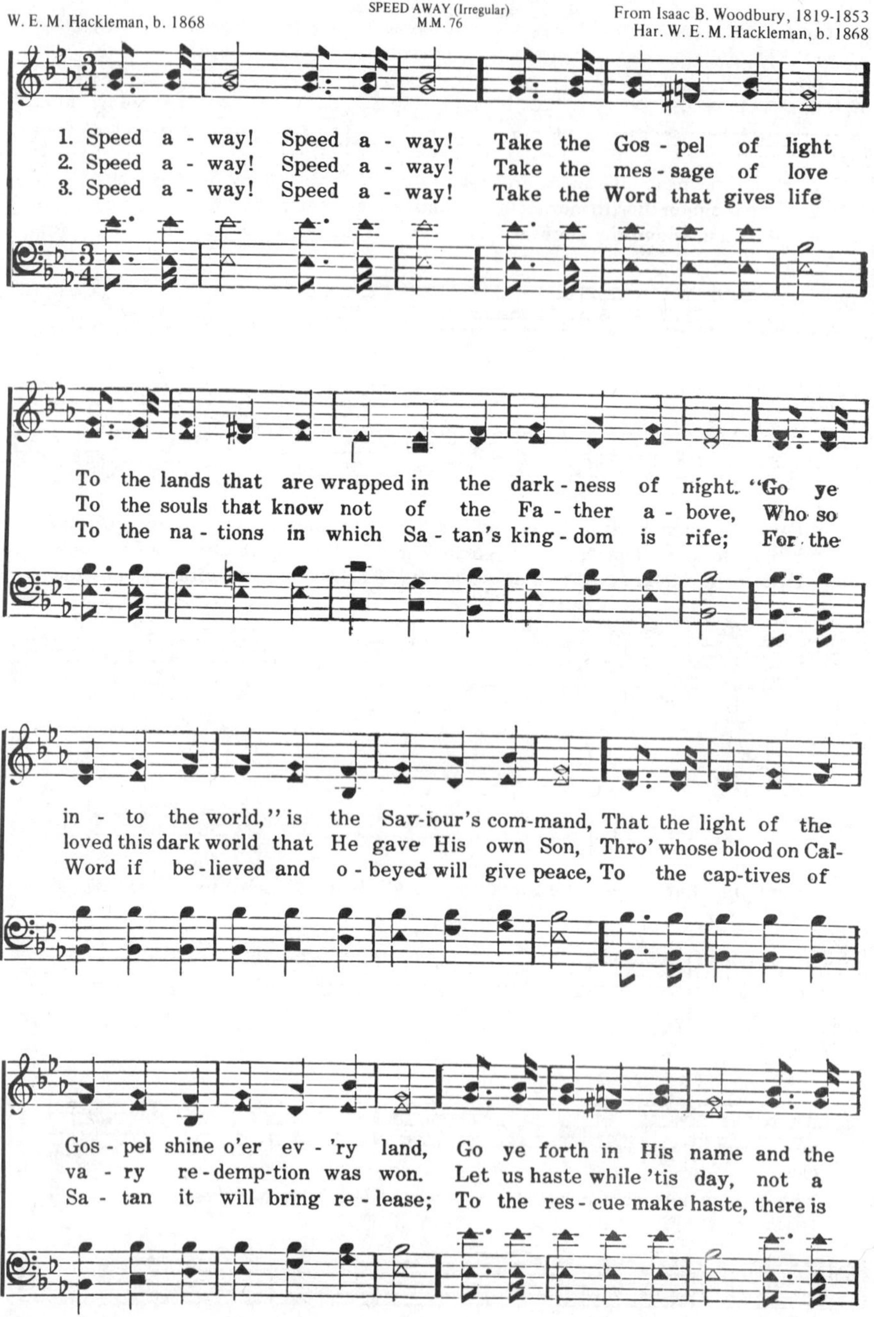
1. Speed a - way! Speed a - way! Take the Gos - pel of light
2. Speed a - way! Speed a - way! Take the mes - sage of love
3. Speed a - way! Speed a - way! Take the Word that gives life
To the lands that are wrapped in the dark - ness of night. "Go ye
To the souls that know not of the Fa - ther a - bove, Who so
To the na - tions in which Sa - tan's king - dom is rife; For the
in - to the world," is the Sav-iour's com-mand, That the light of the
loved this dark world that He gave His own Son, Thro' whose blood on Cal-
Word if be - lieved and o - beyed will give peace, To the cap-tives of
Gos - pel shine o'er ev - 'ry land, Go ye forth in His name and the
va - ry re - demp-tion was won. Let us haste while 'tis day, not a
Sa - tan it will bring re - lease; To the res - cue make haste, there is

rit.
Gos - pel pro - claim, Speed a - way! Speed a - way! Speed a - way!
mo - ment's de - lay, Speed a - way! Speed a - way! Speed a - way!
no time to waste, Speed a - way! Speed a - way! Speed a - way!

# GO LABOR ON 539

*Be ye . . . always abounding in the work of the Lord.* I Cor. 15:58.

WILLIAMS L.M. 8.8.8.8.
M.M. 54

Horatius Bonar, 1843 (1808-1889)

George Kingsley, 1853 (1811-1884)

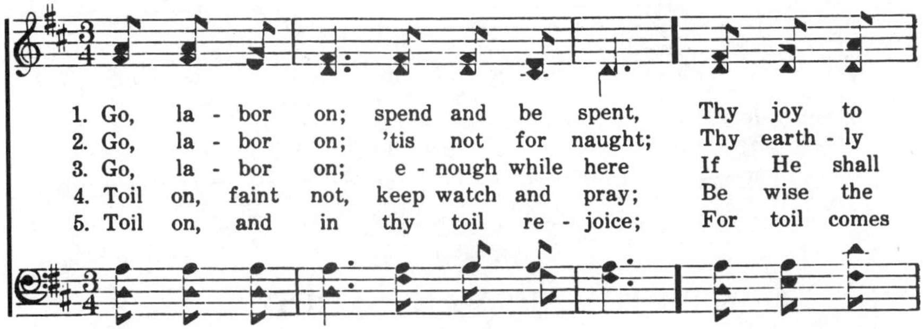

1. Go, la - bor on; spend and be spent, Thy joy to
2. Go, la - bor on; 'tis not for naught; Thy earth - ly
3. Go, la - bor on; e - nough while here If He shall
4. Toil on, faint not, keep watch and pray; Be wise the
5. Toil on, and in thy toil re - joice; For toil comes

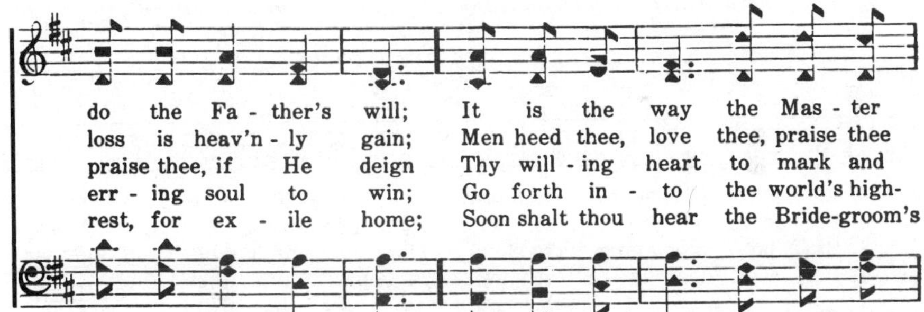

do the Fa - ther's will; It is the way the Mas - ter
loss is heav'n - ly gain; Men heed thee, love thee, praise thee
praise thee, if He deign Thy will - ing heart to mark and
err - ing soul to win; Go forth in - to the world's high-
rest, for ex - ile home; Soon shalt thou hear the Bride-groom's

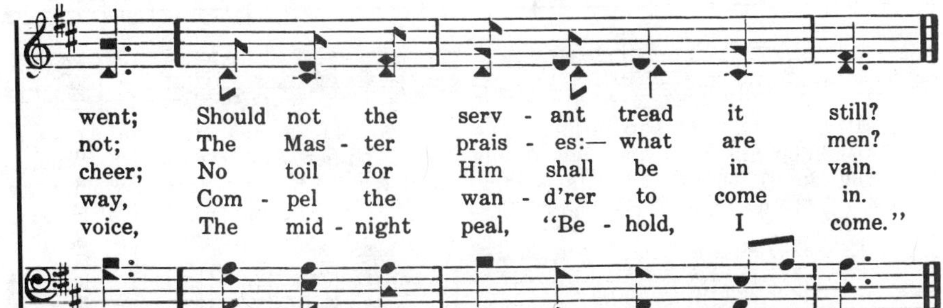

went; Should not the serv - ant tread it still?
not; The Mas - ter prais - es:— what are men?
cheer; No toil for Him shall be in vain.
way, Com - pel the wan - d'rer to come in.
voice, The mid - night peal, "Be - hold, I come."

# 540 FORGET THEM NOT, O CHRIST

*God forbid that I should sin against the Lord in ceasing to pray for you.* I Sam. 12:23.

Margaret Sangster, 1838-1912 — ELSENHAM 8.8. M.M. 76 — J. D. Macey, 1916 (1860-1933)

1 For - get them not, O Christ, who stand
2 In flood, in flame, in dark, in dread,
3 Ex - alt them o - ver ev - ery fear,
4 Thine is the work they strive to do,
5 Be with Thine own, Thy loved, who stand,
Thy van - guard in the dis - tant land.
Sus - tain, we pray, each lift - ed head.
In per - il come Thy - self more near.
Their foes so man - y, they so few.
Christ's van - guard in the storm - swept land. A - men.

# 541 GO WITH THY SERVANT, LORD

*Praying also for us, that God would open unto us a door of utterance, to speak the mystery of Christ.* Col. 4:3.

Anonymous — ALVORD S.M. 6.6.8.6. M.M. 58 — Asa Brooks Everett, 1828-1875

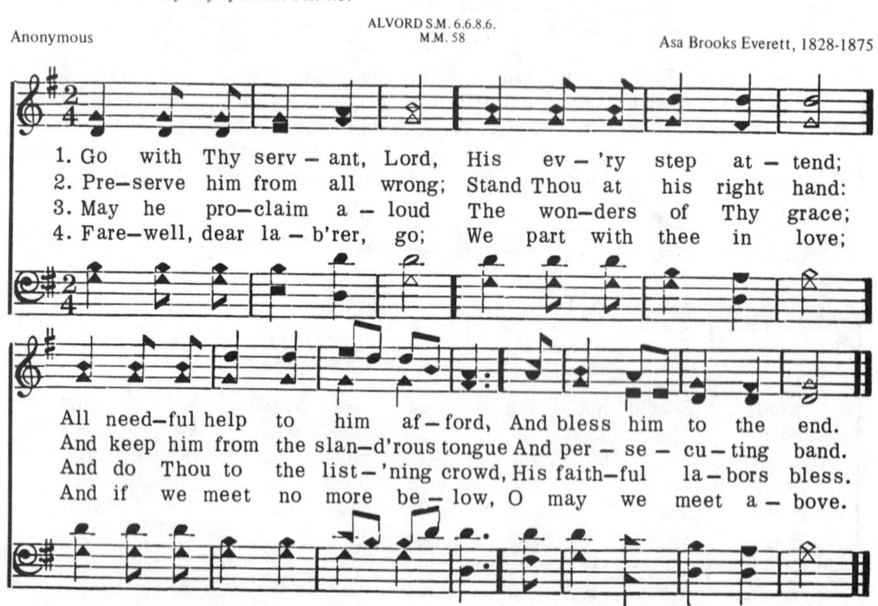
1. Go with Thy serv – ant, Lord, His ev – 'ry step at – tend;
2. Pre–serve him from all wrong; Stand Thou at his right hand:
3. May he pro–claim a – loud The won–ders of Thy grace;
4. Fare–well, dear la – b'rer, go; We part with thee in love;
All need–ful help to him af – ford, And bless him to the end.
And keep him from the slan–d'rous tongue And per – se – cu – ting band.
And do Thou to the list – 'ning crowd, His faith–ful la – bors bless.
And if we meet no more be – low, O may we meet a – bove.

# THE TIME FOR TOIL 542

*He that goeth forth and weepeth, bearing precious seed, shall doubtless come again with rejoicing, bringing his sheaves with him.* Ps. 126:6.

BRINGING HOME OUR SHEAVES 10.10.10.9.6.6.
M.M. 60

Elizabeth Akers | Henry S. Rupp, 1826-1898

1. The time for toil is past, and night has come, The last and sad - dest
2. Few, light, and worth-less—yet their tri-fling weight Thro' all my frame a
3. Full well I know I have more tares than wheat, Bram-bles and flow'rs, dry
4. So do I gath - er hope and strength a-new; For well I know thy

of the har-vest eves; Worn out with la - bor long and wea-ri-some, Droop-ing and
wea - ry ach-ing leaves; For long I strug-gled with my hap-less fate, And staid and
stalks and withered leaves; Wherefore I blush and weep, as at thy feet I kneel down
pa-tient love per-ceives Not what I did, but what I strove to do— And though the

faint, the reapers hasten home, Each laden with his sheaves, Each laden with his sheaves.
toiled till it was dark and late, Yet these are all my sheaves, Yet these are all my sheaves.
rev - er - ent - ly, and re-peat, "Master, behold my sheaves," "Master, behold my sheaves."
full ripe ears be sad-ly few, Thou wilt accept my sheaves, Thou wilt accept my sheaves.

# 543 NOW IS TH'ACCEPTED TIME

*Behold, now is the accepted time.* II Cor. 6:2.

John Dobell, 1806 — DETROIT S.M. 6.6.8.6. M.M. 58 — E. P. Hastings

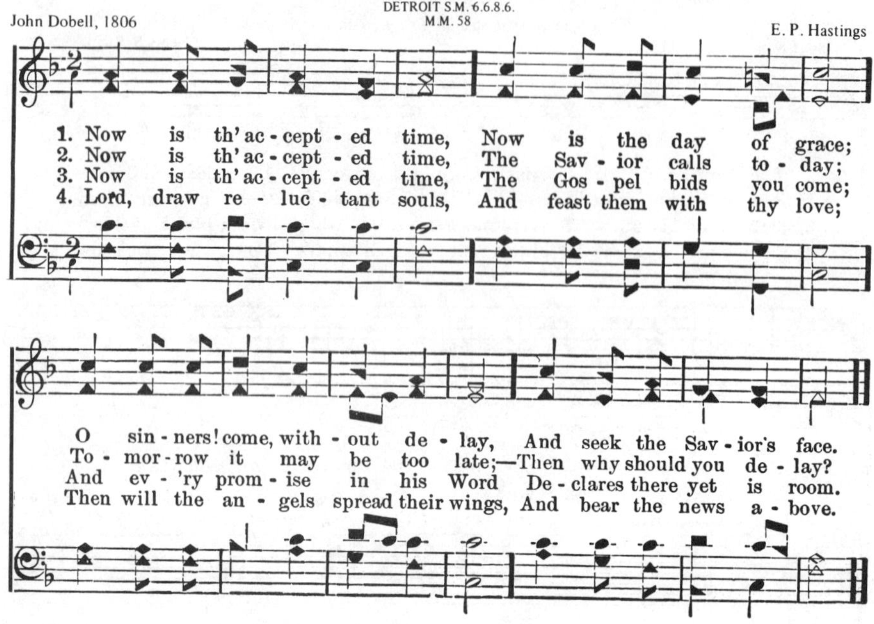
1. Now is th' ac - cept - ed time, Now is the day of grace;
2. Now is th' ac - cept - ed time, The Sav - ior calls to - day;
3. Now is th' ac - cept - ed time, The Gos - pel bids you come;
4. Lord, draw re - luc - tant souls, And feast them with thy love;
O sin - ners! come, with - out de - lay, And seek the Sav - ior's face.
To - mor - row it may be too late;—Then why should you de - lay?
And ev - 'ry prom - ise in his Word De - clares there yet is room.
Then will the an - gels spread their wings, And bear the news a - bove.

# 544 FOR A BLEST TODAY

*While it is said, Today if ye will hear His voice, harden not your hearts, as in the provocation.* Heb. 3:15.

*Gesangbuch mit Noten*
Tr. John J. Overholt, 1970 — WAS MEIN HERZ ERFREUT 5.5.11. M.M. 80 — *Gesangbuch mit Noten*

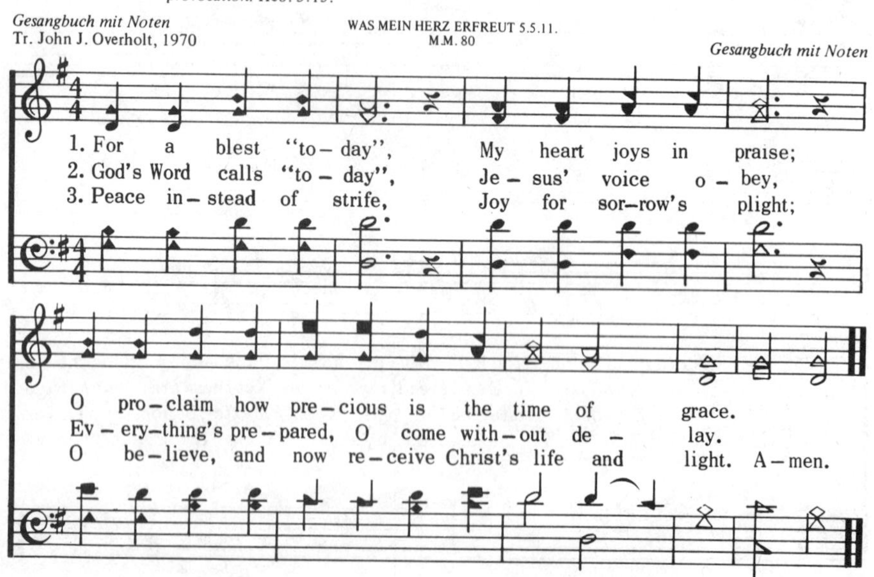
1. For a blest "to – day", My heart joys in praise;
2. God's Word calls "to – day", Je – sus' voice o – bey,
3. Peace in – stead of strife, Joy for sor–row's plight;
O pro – claim how pre – cious is the time of grace.
Ev – ery–thing's pre – pared, O come with – out de – lay.
O be – lieve, and now re – ceive Christ's life and light. A – men.

# COME TO THE SAVIOUR NOW 545

*I give unto them eternal life.* Jn. 10:28.

INVITATION (MAKER) 6.6.6.6.D.
M.M. 76
John M. Wigner, 1871 (1844-1911)
Frederick Charles Maker, 1881 (1844-1927)
1. Come to the Sav - iour now, He gen - tly call - eth thee;
2. Come to the Sav - iour now, Ye who have wan - dered far,
3. Come to the Sav - iour, all, What-e'er your bur - dens be;
In true re - pent - ance bow, Be - fore Him bend the knee:
Re - new your sol - emn vow, For His by right you are;
Hear now His lov - ing call, "Cast all your care on Me."
He wait - eth to be - stow Sal - va - tion, peace, and love,
Come, like poor wan - d'ring sheep Re - turn - ing to His fold;
Come, and for ev - 'ry grief In Je - sus you will find
True joy on earth be - low, A home in heav'n a - bove.
His arm will safe - ly keep, His love will ne'er grow cold.
A sure and safe re - lief, A lov - ing Friend, and kind.

# 546 O JESUS, THOU ART STANDING

*Behold, I stand at the door, and knock.* Rev. 3:20.

William Walsham Howe, 1867 (1823-1897) | ST HILDA 7.6.7.6.D. M.M. 63 | Justin Heinrich Knecht, 1799 (1752-1817)

1. O Je - sus, Thou art stand-ing Out - side the fast-closed door,
2. O Je - sus, Thou art knock-ing; And lo! that hand is scarred,
3. O Je - sus, Thou art plead-ing In ac - cents meek and low,—
In low - ly pa - tience wait - ing To pass the thresh - old o'er:
And thorns Thy brow en - cir - cle, And tears Thy face have marred:
"I died for you, My chil - dren, And will ye treat Me so?"
We bear the name of Chris - tians, His name and sign we bear;
O love that pass - eth knowl - edge, So pa - tient - ly to wait!
O Lord, with shame and sor - row We o - pen now the door;
O shame, thrice shame up - on us, To keep Him stand-ing there!
O sin that hath no e - qual, So fast to bar the gate!
Dear Sav - iour, en - ter, en - ter, And leave us nev - er - more.

# COME, YE SINNERS, POOR AND NEEDY 547

*Come: for all things are now ready.* Lk. 14:17. *Prepare to meet thy God.* Amos 4:12.

Joseph Hart, 1712-1768

GREENVILLE NEW 8.7.D.
M.M. 60

Jean Jaques Rousseau, 1750 (1712-1778)
Arr. John J. Overholt, 1970

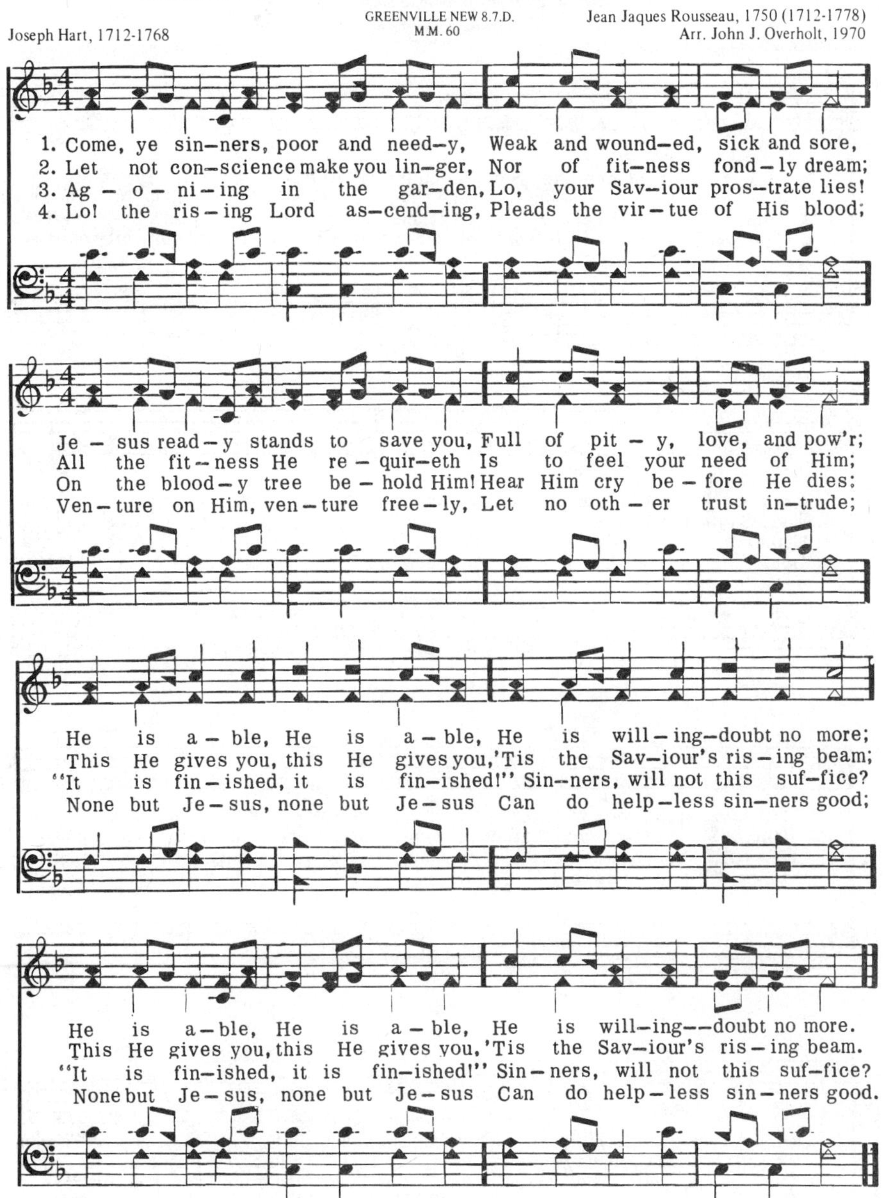
1. Come, ye sin–ners, poor and need–y, Weak and wound–ed, sick and sore,
2. Let not con–science make you lin–ger, Nor of fit–ness fond–ly dream;
3. Ag – o – ni – ing in the gar–den, Lo, your Sav–iour pros–trate lies!
4. Lo! the ris – ing Lord as–cend–ing, Pleads the vir – tue of His blood;
Je – sus read – y stands to save you, Full of pit – y, love, and pow'r;
All the fit – ness He re – quir–eth Is to feel your need of Him;
On the blood – y tree be – hold Him! Hear Him cry be – fore He dies;
Ven – ture on Him, ven – ture free – ly, Let no oth – er trust in–trude;
He is a – ble, He is a – ble, He is will – ing–doubt no more;
This He gives you, this He gives you, 'Tis the Sav–iour's ris – ing beam;
"It is fin – ished, it is fin–ished!" Sin–ners, will not this suf–fice?
None but Je – sus, none but Je – sus Can do help – less sin–ners good;
He is a–ble, He is a – ble, He is will–ing––doubt no more.
This He gives you, this He gives you, 'Tis the Sav–iour's ris – ing beam.
"It is fin–ished, it is fin–ished!" Sin – ners, will not this suf–fice?
None but Je – sus, none but Je – sus Can do help – less sin – ners good.

5. Saints and angels, joined in concert, Chant the praises of the Lamb,
While the blissful seats of heaven Sweetly echo with His name;
Hallelujah! Hallelujah! Sinners here may do the same;
Hallelujah! Hallelujah! Sinners here may do the same.

# 548 'TIS MIDNIGHT, AND THE SAVIOUR CALLS

*All things are ready: come unto the marriage.* Mt. 22:4.

PARTING HAND L.M.D. 8.8.8.8.D.
M.M. 104
C. G. Buerge, 1943 (1863-1948)
Jeremiah Ingals 1863 (1764-1828)
1. 'Tis mid - night and the Sav-iour calls: Come un - to me, both great and small;
2. Ye slum-b'ring na-tions, wake and rise, Lift up your heads, look to the skies;
3. Now is the time, the day of grace, For all the fall - en hu - man race;
4. Then make your bed in torments where God will not hear your bit-ter prayer.
From ev - 'ry kin - dred, na-tion, tongue; Come one, come all, come old and young.
The Sav - iour's in - vi - ta - tion heed, A - wake, a - rise, and make full speed!
Come to the Lord, ac - cept His hand, Or soon you must re - ject-ed stand.
Gnash-ing of teeth will be your doom, No light, no hope— e - ter-nal gloom.
'Tis mid - night and we hear the cry; The Sav - iour now is pass-ing by.
Bring oil in lamps and march a - long, The Lord to meet a hap - py throng;
Oh, will you now the call o - bey, Or will you long - er lin-g'ring stay;
Oh, will you make that aw - ful choice? Or will you hear the Sav-iour's voice?
Oh, will you let Him call in vain, Lie down and fall a-sleep a - gain?
The pre - cious time may soon be o'er, You'll hear the Sav - iour's call no more.
Un - til you hear the trum-pet sound, The dead rise from the quak-ing ground?
Come un - to me while yet I call, For now I will for-give you all.

# LIFE IS THE TIME 549

*Whatsoever thy hand findeth to do, do it with thy might; for there is no work . . . in the grave.* Eccles. 9:10.

Issac Watts, 1709 (1674-1748) — DEVOTION L.M. 8.8.8.8. M.M. 88 — John H. Gower

1. Life is the time to serve the Lord, The time t'in-sure the great re-ward,
2. Life is the hour that God has giv'n To es-cape from hell and fly to heav'n,
3. The liv-ing know that they must die, With-in the earth their dust must lie;
4. Then what my tho'ts de-sign to do, My hands, with all their might pur-sue:
5. There are no acts of par-don passed In the cold grave to which we haste;
And while the lamp holds out to burn, O has-ten, sin-ner, to re-turn!
The day of grace when mor-tals may Se-cure the bless-ings of the day.
Then have no share in all that's done Be-neath the cir-cle of the sun.
Since no de-vice nor work is found, Nor faith nor hope, be-neath the ground.
O may we all re-ceive Thy grace, And see with joy Thy smil-ing face.

# ALMIGHTY MAKER OF MY FRAME 550

*So teach us to number our days that we may apply our hearts unto wisdom.* Ps. 90:12.

Anne Steele, 1760 (1716-1778) — VENN. L.M. 8.8.8.8. M.M. 80 — George Job Elvey, 1816-1893, Arr.

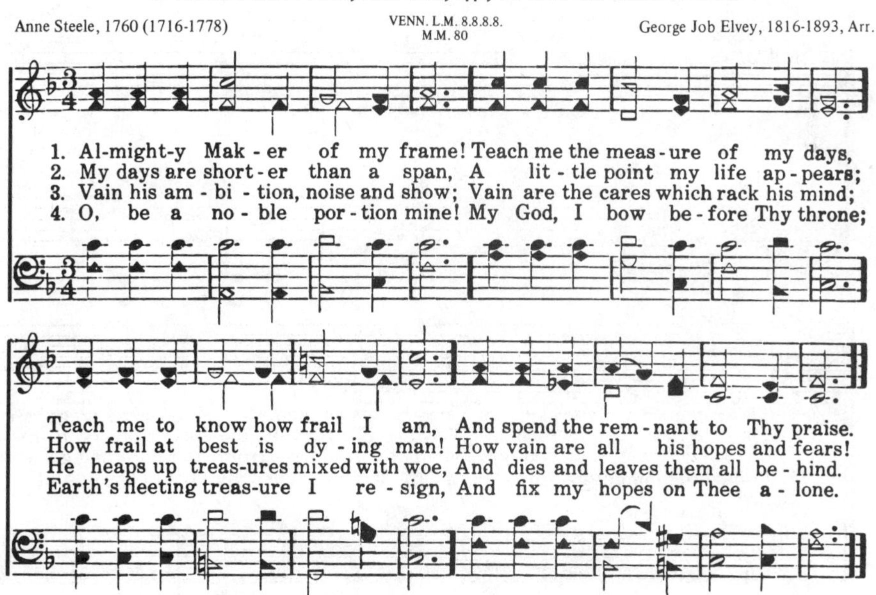

1. Al-might-y Mak-er of my frame! Teach me the meas-ure of my days,
2. My days are short-er than a span, A lit-tle point my life ap-pears;
3. Vain his am-bi-tion, noise and show; Vain are the cares which rack his mind;
4. O, be a no-ble por-tion mine! My God, I bow be-fore Thy throne;
Teach me to know how frail I am, And spend the rem-nant to Thy praise.
How frail at best is dy-ing man! How vain are all his hopes and fears!
He heaps up treas-ures mixed with woe, And dies and leaves them all be-hind.
Earth's fleeting treas-ure I re-sign, And fix my hopes on Thee a-lone.

# 551 WE ARE BUILDING IN SORROW OR JOY

*The fire shall try every man's work of what sort it is.* I Cor. 3:13.

SARGENT 9.8.9.8. with Ref.
M.M. 100

N. B. Sargent — N. B. Sargent

1. We are build-ing in sor-row or joy A tem-ple the world may not see,
2. Ev-'ry tho't that we've ev - er had, Its own lit-tle place has fill'd;
3. Ev-'ry word that so light - ly falls, Giv - ing some heart joy or pain,
4. Are you build-ing for God a - lone? Are you build-ing in faith and love,
Which time can-not mar nor de-stroy: We build for e - ter - ni - ty.
Ev-'ry deed we have done, good or bad, Is a stone in the tem-ple we build.
Will shine in our tem - ple wall, Or ev - er its beau - ty stain.
A tem-ple the Fa - ther will own, In the cit - y of light a - bove?
REFRAIN.
We are build-ing, ev - 'ry day...... A tem- ple the world may not see;
We are build- ing, build - ing ev - 'ry day.
Build - ing, build - ing ev - 'ry day, Building for e - ter - ni - ty!

# WORK FOR THE NIGHT IS COMING 552

*The night cometh, when no man can work.* Jn. 9:4.

WORK FOR THE NIGHT IS COMING 7.6.7.5.D.
M.M. 80

Anna Louisa Coghil, 1868 (1836-1907)

Lowell Mason, 1792-1872

1. Work, for the night is com - ing! Work thro' the morn - ing hours;
Work, while the dew is spar - kling; Work 'mid spring - ing flow'rs;
Work while the day grows bright - er, Un - der the glow - ing sun;
Work, for the night is com - ing, When man's work is done.

2. Work, for the night is com - ing! Work thro' the sun - ny noon;
Fill bright-est hours with la - bor; Rest comes sure and soon.
Give ev - 'ry fly - ing min - ute Some-thing to keep in store;
Work, for the night is com - ing, When man works no more.

3. Work, for the night is com - ing! Un - der the sun - set skies,
While their bright tints are glow - ing, Work, for day - light flies;
Work till the last beam fad - eth, Fad - eth to shine no more;
Work while the night is dark - 'ning, When man's work is o'er.

# 553 A FEW MORE YEARS SHALL ROLL

*When a few years are come, then I shall go the way whence I shall not return.* Job 16:22.

DUNBAR S.M.D. 6.6.8.6.D.
M.M. 112

Horatius Bonar, 1842 (1808-1889)

E. W. Dunbar, b. 1826

1. A few more years shall roll, A few more sea - sons come;
2. A few more suns shall set O'er these dark hills of time,
3. A few more storms shall beat On this wild, rock - y shore;
4. A few more strug - gles here, A few more part - ings o'er,
5. A few more meet - ings here Shall cheer us on our way;
CHO.—*Then, O my Lord, pre - pare My soul for that great day;*
*D. C. for Chorus.*
And we shall lie with them that rest, A - sleep with - in the tomb.
And we shall be where suns are not, A far se - ren - er clime.
And we shall be where tem - pests cease, And sur - ges swell no more.
A few more toils, a few more tears, And we shall weep no more.
And we shall reach the end - less rest, Th' e - ter - nal Sab - bath day.
*O wash me in thy pre - cious blood And take my sins a - way.*

# 554 ONE SWEETLY SOLEMN THOUGHT

*Now they desire a better country, that is, an heavenly.* Heb. 11:16.

DULCE DOMUM S.M. 6.6.8.6.
M.M. 66

Phoebe Carry, 1852 (1824-1871)

Robert Steele Ambrose, 1824-1908

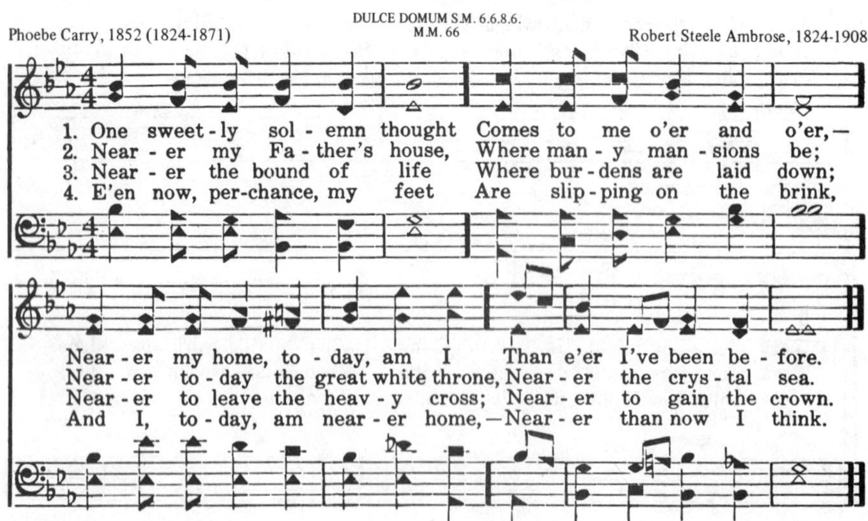
1. One sweet - ly sol - emn thought Comes to me o'er and o'er,—
2. Near - er my Fa - ther's house, Where man - y man - sions be;
3. Near - er the bound of life Where bur - dens are laid down;
4. E'en now, per-chance, my feet Are slip - ping on the brink,
Near - er my home, to - day, am I Than e'er I've been be - fore.
Near - er to - day the great white throne, Near - er the crys - tal sea.
Near - er to leave the heav - y cross; Near - er to gain the crown.
And I, to - day, am near - er home,—Near - er than now I think.

# A FEW MORE YEARS SHALL ROLL 555

*It is appointed unto men once to die.* Heb. 9:27.

THE PILGRIM S.M.D. 6.6.8.6.D.
M.M. 92
Horatius Bonar, 1808-1889
Arranged
1. A few more years shall roll,.... A few more sea - sons come;
2. A few more storms shall beat.... On this wild, rock - y shore;
3. A few more strug - gles here,... A few more part - ings o'er,
4. A few more meet - ings here.... Shall cheer us on our way;
And we shall lie with them that rest, A - sleep with - in the tomb.
And we shall be where tem-pests cease, And surg - es swell no more.
A few more toils, a few more tears, And we shall weep no more.
And we shall reach the end - less rest, Th' e-ter - nal Sab - bath day.
REFRAIN
Then oh, my Lord, pre - pare....... My soul for that great day;.......
Then oh,........ my Lord, pre-pare My soul........ for that great day;
Oh, wash me in Thy pre - cious blood, And take my sins a - way.

# 556 BY COOL SILOAM'S SHADY RILL

*All flesh is as grass, and all the glory of man as the flower of grass. The grass withereth, and the flower thereof falleth away.* I Pet. 1:24.

SILOAM C.M. 8.6.8.6.
M.M. 80

Reginald Heber, 1812 (1783-1826) — Isaac Baker Woodbury, 1850 (1819-1854)

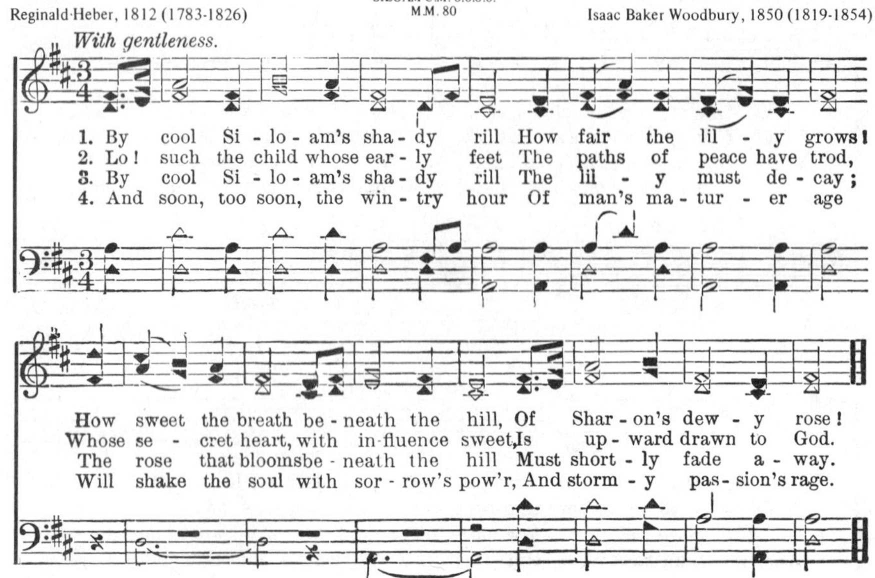
With gentleness.
1. By cool Si - lo - am's sha - dy rill How fair the lil - y grows!
2. Lo! such the child whose ear - ly feet The paths of peace have trod,
3. By cool Si - lo - am's sha - dy rill The lil - y must de - cay;
4. And soon, too soon, the win - try hour Of man's ma - tur - er age
How sweet the breath be - neath the hill, Of Shar - on's dew - y rose!
Whose se - cret heart, with in-fluence sweet, Is up - ward drawn to God.
The rose that blooms be - neath the hill Must short - ly fade a - way.
Will shake the soul with sor - row's pow'r, And storm - y pas - sion's rage.

# 557 THEE WE ADORE, ETERNAL NAME

*Lord, make me to know mine end, and the measure of my days, what it is; that I may know how frail I am.* Ps. 39:4.

NEWCASTLE C.M. 8.6.8.6.
M.M. 72

Isaac Watts, 1709 (1674-1748), alt. — Asa Brooks Everett, 1828-1875

1. Thee we a - dore, e - ter - nal name, And hum - bly own to thee,
2. Our wast - ing lives grow short - er still, As months and days in - crease,
3. The year rolls round, and steals a - way The breath that first it gave;
4. Dan - gers stand thick through all the ground, To push us to the tomb;
5. In - fi - nite joy, or wretch - ed woe, At - tends on ev - 'ry breath;
6. Wa - ken, O Lord, our drow - sy sense, To walk this dan - g'rous road;
How fee - ble is our mor - tal frame, What dy - ing worms are we!
And ev - 'ry beat - ing pulse we tell, Leaves but the num - ber less.
What - e'er we do, what - e'er we be, We're trav - 'ling to the grave.
And fierce dis - eas - es wait a - round, To hur - ry mor - tals home.
And yet how un - con - cerned we go, Up - on the brink of death!
And if our souls are hur - ried hence, May they be found with God.

# SHALL I CRUCIFY MY SAVIOUR 558

*They crucify to themselves the Son of God afresh, and put Him to an open shame.* Heb 6:6.

SHALL I CRUCIFY HIM 8.7.8.7. with Ref.
M.M. 63

Carrie E. Breck, 1855-1934 | Grant Colfax Tullar, 1869-1950

1. Shall I cru–ci–fy my Sav–iour, When for me He bore such loss?
2. Are temp–ta–tions so al–lur–ing? Do earth pleasures so en–thrall?
3. 'Twas my sins that cru–ci–fied Him, Shall they cru–ci–fy Him yet?
4. Oh, the kind–ly hands of Je – sus, Pour–ing bless–ings on all men!

Shall I put to shame my Sav – ior? Can I nail Him to the cross?
That I can–not love my Sav – ior Well e–nough to leave them all?
Black–est day of name–less an–guish, Can my thank–less soul for–get?
Bleed–ing nail–scarred hands of Je–sus! Can I nail them once a–gain?

**Chorus**

Shall I cru–ci–fy my Sav–ior? Cru – ci–fy my Lord a–gain?

Once! oh, once! I cru–ci–fied Him! Shall I cru–ci – fy a–gain?

# 559 IN THE HOUR OF TRIAL

*When He hath tried me, I shall come forth as gold.* Job 23:10.

PENITENCE 6.5.6.5.D.
M.M. 72

James Montgomery, 1834 (1771-1854)

Spencer Lane, 1879 (1843-1903)

1. In the hour of tri - al, Je - sus, plead for me;
2. With its witch - ing pleas - ures Would this vain world charm,
3. If with sore af - flic - tion Thou in love chas - tise,
4. When in dust and ash - es To the grave I sink,
Lest by base de - ni - al I de - part from Thee;
Or its sor - did treas - ures Spread to work me harm,
Pour Thy ben - e - dic - tion On the sac - ri - fice;
While heav'n's glo-ry flash - es O'er the shelv - ing brink,
When Thou seest me wav - er, With a look re - call,......
Bring to my re - mem - brance Sad Geth - sem - a - ne,.......
Then, up - on Thine al - tar Free - ly of - fered up,.......
On Thy truth re - ly - ing Thro' that mor - tal strife,....
Nor for fear or fa - vor Suf - fer me to fall.
Or, in dark - er sem - blance, Cross-crowned Cal - va - ry.
Tho' the flesh may fal - ter, Faith shall drink the cup.
Lord, re - ceive me, dy - ing, To e - ter - nal life.

# WHEN WE IN THE JUDGMENT STAND 560

*For we must all appear before the judgment seat of Christ.* II Cor. 5:10.

Edna Reeder Latta, b. 1839
HOLLINGSIDE 7.7.7.7.D.
M.M. 72
John Bacchus Dykes, 1861 (1823-1876)
1. When we in the judg–ment stand, In that might–y com–pa–ny,
2. When the Lord has gath–ered there, From the land and from the sea,
3. Lord, it is a sol–emn thought, That we must ac–count to Thee.
And the Judge shall ques–tion us, Oh, what shall our an–swer be?
All the fam–i–lies of men, Oh, what shall our an–swer be?
In that great and aw–ful day, What shall our poor an–swer be?
What for ev–'ry tri–fling thought, And each i–dle word we say?
What for all our want of faith, What for all our lack of love?
Oh, pre–pare us, Lord, we pray, In Thy pres–ence there to stand!
What for ev–'ry sin–ful act We may do from day to day?
Can we hope a crown to gain, And a man–sion bright a–bove?
Purge us from each sin–ful blot, Place us, Lord, on Thy right hand! A–men.

# 561 IF I MUST DIE

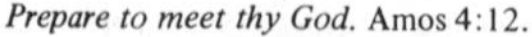

*Prepare to meet thy God.* Amos 4:12.

BYEFIELD C.M. 8.6.8.6.
M.M. 58

Benjamin Beddome, 1794 (1717-1795) — Thomas Hastings, 1840 (1784-1872)

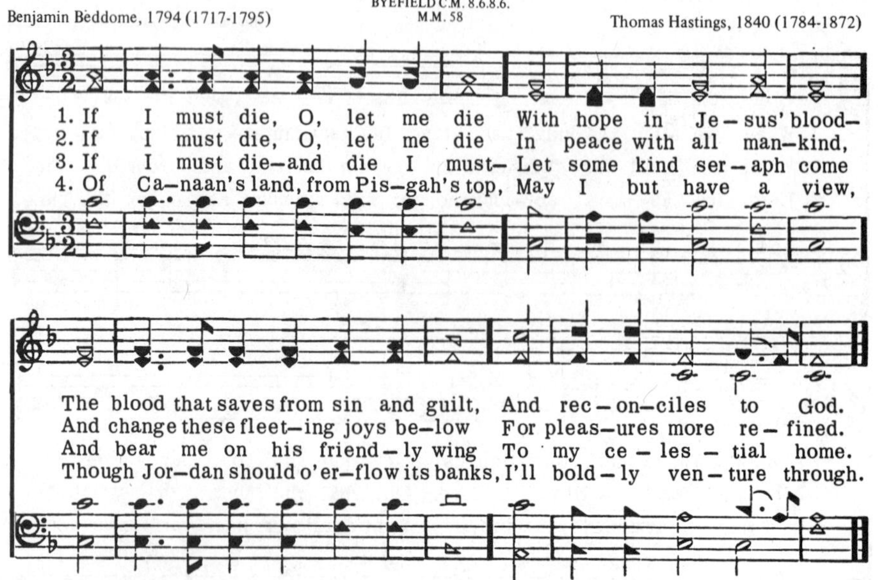
1. If I must die, O, let me die With hope in Je–sus' blood–
2. If I must die, O, let me die In peace with all man–kind,
3. If I must die–and die I must– Let some kind ser–aph come
4. Of Ca–naan's land, from Pis–gah's top, May I but have a view,
The blood that saves from sin and guilt, And rec–on–ciles to God.
And change these fleet–ing joys be–low For pleas–ures more re–fined.
And bear me on his friend–ly wing To my ce–les–tial home.
Though Jor–dan should o'er–flow its banks, I'll bold–ly ven–ture through.

# 562 THAT AWFUL DAY WILL SURELY COME

*It is appointed unto men once to die, but after this the judgment.* Heb. 9:27.

JUDGMENT C.M. 8.6.8.6.
M.M. 80

Isaac Watts, 1674-1748 — Anonymous

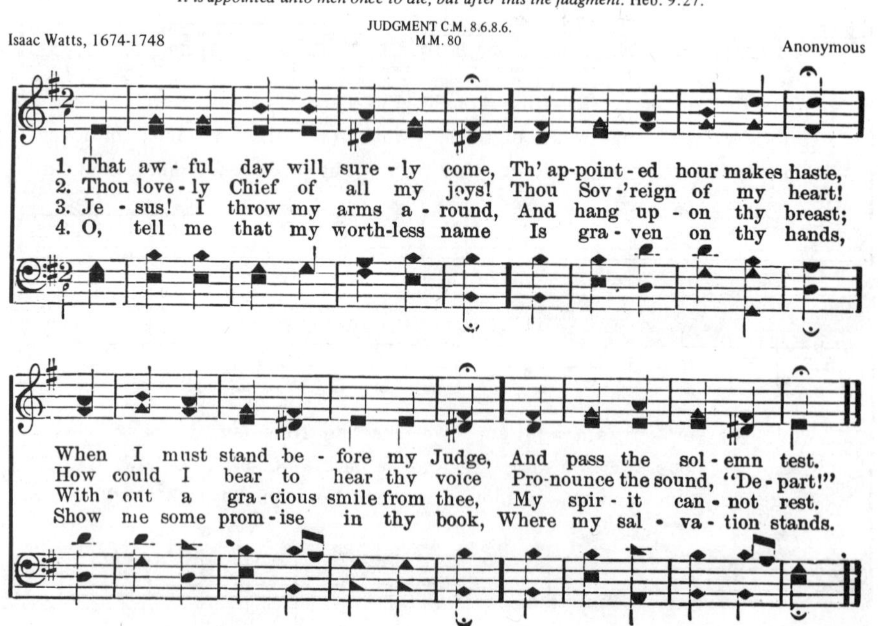
1. That aw-ful day will sure-ly come, Th' ap-point-ed hour makes haste,
2. Thou love-ly Chief of all my joys! Thou Sov-'reign of my heart!
3. Je-sus! I throw my arms a-round, And hang up-on thy breast;
4. O, tell me that my worth-less name Is gra-ven on thy hands,
When I must stand be-fore my Judge, And pass the sol-emn test.
How could I bear to hear thy voice Pro-nounce the sound, "De-part!"
With-out a gra-cious smile from thee, My spir-it can-not rest.
Show me some prom-ise in thy book, Where my sal-va-tion stands.

# O SINNERS, WHAT WILL YOU DO? 563

*Mighty men . . . said to the mountains and rocks, Fall on us, and hide us from the face of Him that sitteth on the throne.* Rev. 6:15, 16.

WHEN THE STARS BEGIN TO FALL
7.7.7.7. with Ref.
M.M. 66

Anonymous
Altered by Compiler, 1963

Arr. E. T. Hildebrand
Arr. John J. Overholt, 1963

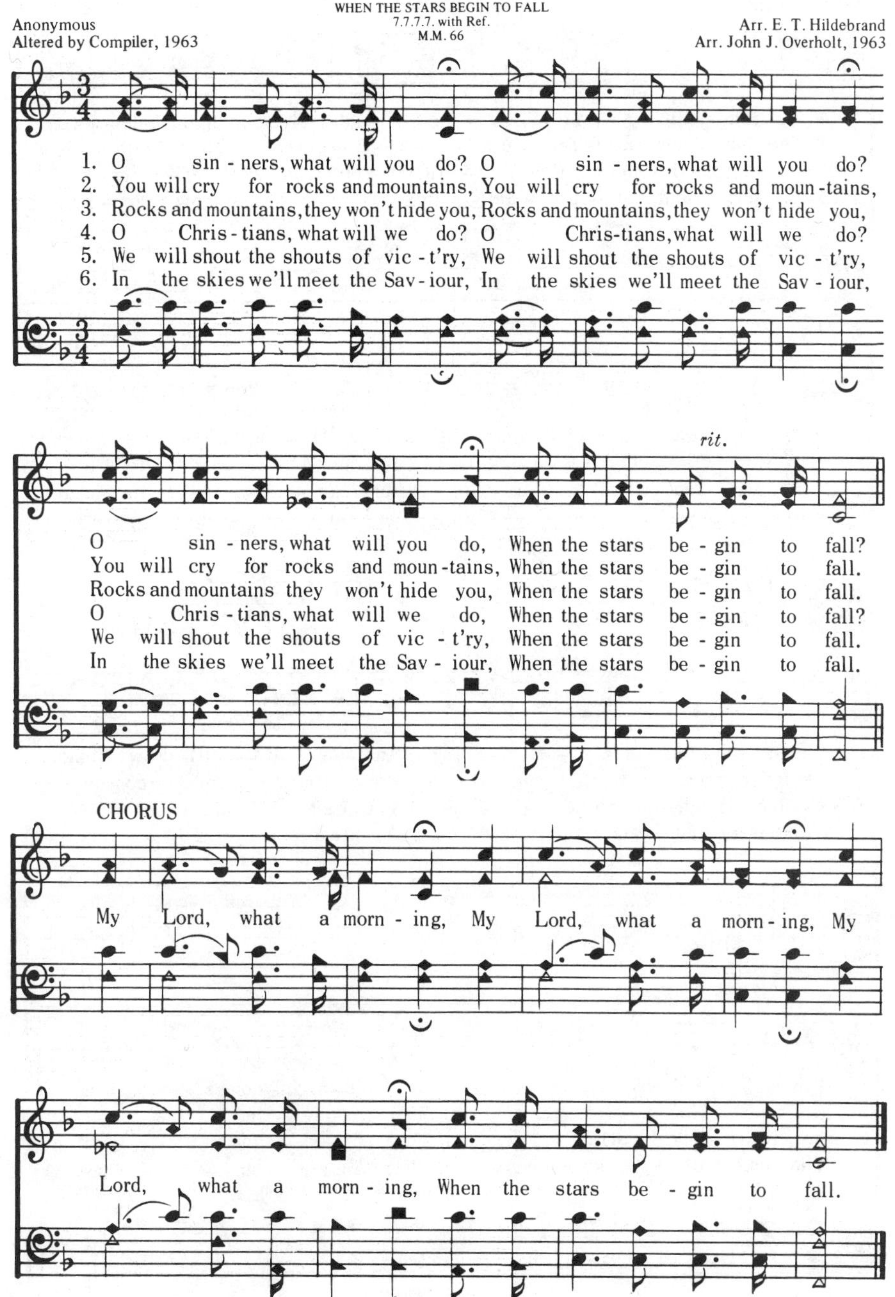
1. O sin - ners, what will you do? O sin - ners, what will you do?
2. You will cry for rocks and mountains, You will cry for rocks and moun - tains,
3. Rocks and mountains, they won't hide you, Rocks and mountains, they won't hide you,
4. O Chris - tians, what will we do? O Chris-tians, what will we do?
5. We will shout the shouts of vic - t'ry, We will shout the shouts of vic - t'ry,
6. In the skies we'll meet the Sav - iour, In the skies we'll meet the Sav - iour,
rit.
O sin - ners, what will you do, When the stars be - gin to fall?
You will cry for rocks and moun - tains, When the stars be - gin to fall.
Rocks and mountains they won't hide you, When the stars be - gin to fall.
O Chris - tians, what will we do, When the stars be - gin to fall?
We will shout the shouts of vic - t'ry, When the stars be - gin to fall.
In the skies we'll meet the Sav - iour, When the stars be - gin to fall.
CHORUS
My Lord, what a morn - ing, My Lord, what a morn - ing, My
Lord, what a morn - ing, When the stars be - gin to fall.

# 564 REJOICE, ALL YE BELIEVERS

*The wise took oil in their vessels with their lamps.* Mt. 25:4.

NEVER ALONE 7.6.7.6.D.
M.M. 100

Laurentius Laurenti, 1700 (1666-1722)

Arr. M. L. McPhail

1. Re-joice, all ye be-liev-ers! And let your lights ap-pear;
2. See that your lamps are burn-ing; Re-plen-ish them with oil;
3. Ye saints, who here in pa-tience Your cross and suf-f'rings bore,
4. Our hope and ex-pec-ta-tion, O Je-sus, now ap-pear;
The eve-ning is ad-vanc-ing, And dark-er night is near.
And wait for your sal-va-tion, The end of earth-ly toil.
Shall live and reign for-ev-er, When sor-row is no more:
A-rise, Thou Sun so longed for, O'er this be-night-ed sphere.
The Bride-groom is a-ris-ing, And soon He will draw nigh;
The watch-ers on the moun-tain Pro-claim the Bride-groom near,
A-round the throne of glo-ry The Lamb ye shall be-hold,
With hearts and hands up-lift-ed, We plead, O Lord, to see
Up! pray, and watch, and wres-tle! At mid-night comes the cry.
Go meet Him as He com-eth, With Al-le-lu-ias clear.
In tri-umph cast be-fore Him Your di-a-dems of gold.
The day of earth's re-demp-tion That brings us un-to Thee.

# WHEN THE TRUMPET SHALL SOUND 565

*For the Lord Himself shall descend from heaven with a shout, with the voice of the archangel, and with the trump of God.* I Thess. 4:16.

IN THE MORNING OF JOY 6.6.6.6.6.6.7.6.
M.M. 72

Mrs. R. A. Evilsizer — Anthony J. Showalter, 1858-1924

1. When the trumpet shall sound, And the dead shall a-rise, And the splendors im-mor-tal Shall en-vel-ope the skies, When the an-gel of death Shall no lon-ger de-stroy, And the dead shall a-wak-en In the morn-ing of joy.
2. When the King shall ap-pear, In His beau-ty on high, And shall summon His chil-dren To the courts of the sky, Shall the cause of the Lord Have been all your em-ploy, That your soul may be spot-less In the morn-ing of joy?
3. O the bliss of that morn When our loved ones we meet, With the songs of the ran-somed We each oth-er shall greet, Sing-ing praise to the Lamb, Thro' e-ter-ni-ty's years, With the past all for-got-ten With its sor-rows and tears.
Refrain
In the morn-ing of joy, In the morn-ing of joy, We'll be gath-ered to glo-ry In the morn-ing of joy; In the morn-ing of joy.
1
2

# 566 THEE WE ADORE, ETERNAL NAME

*All flesh is as grass . . . The grass withereth.* I Pet. 1:24.

Isaac Watts, 1709 (1674-1748) — LIBERTY HALL C.M. 8.6.8.6. M.M. 66 — *Church and Sunday School Hymnal*

1. Thee we a – dore e – ter – nal name, And hum – bly own to Thee,
2. Our wast–ing lives grow short – ter still, As months and days in–crease,
3. Dan–gers stand thick through all the ground, To push us to the tomb;
4. In – fin – nite joy, or wretch – ed woe, At–tends on ev – 'ry breath;
5. Wa – ken, O Lord, our drow – sy sense, To walk this dan – g'rous road;
How fee – ble is our mor – tal frame, What dy – ing worms are we!
And ev – 'ry beat – ing pulse we tell, Leaves but the num–ber less.
And fierce dis – eas – es wait a – round, To hur – ry mor–tals home.
And yet how un – con – cerned we go, Up – on the brink of death!
And if our souls are hur – ried hence, May they be found with God.

# 567 AT EVERY MOTION OF OUR BREATH

*And sware . . . that there should be time no longer.* Rev. 10:6.

James Montgomery, 1825 (1771-1854) — WINDHAM L.M. 8.8.8.8. M.M. 56 — Daniel Read, 1785 (1757-1836)

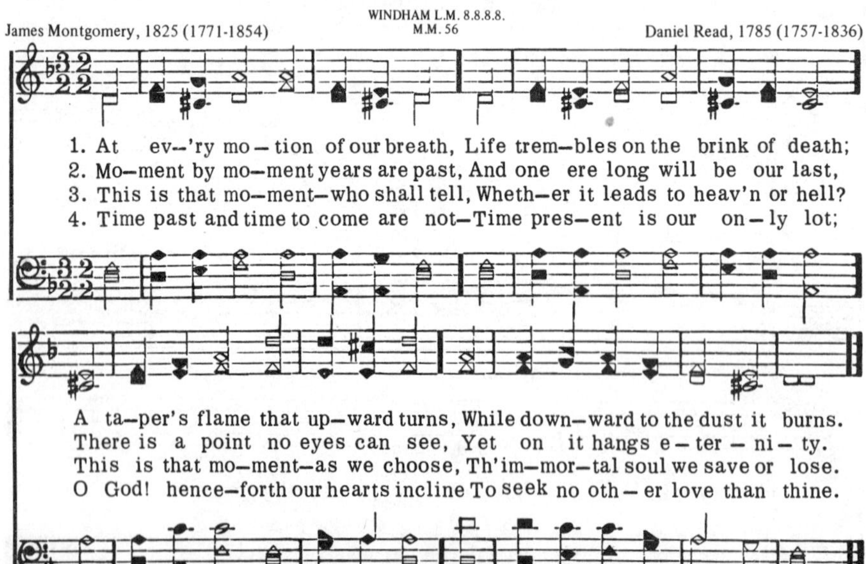
1. At ev–'ry mo – tion of our breath, Life trem–bles on the brink of death;
2. Mo–ment by mo–ment years are past, And one ere long will be our last,
3. This is that mo–ment–who shall tell, Wheth–er it leads to heav'n or hell?
4. Time past and time to come are not–Time pres–ent is our on – ly lot;
A ta–per's flame that up–ward turns, While down–ward to the dust it burns.
There is a point no eyes can see, Yet on it hangs e – ter – ni – ty.
This is that mo–ment–as we choose, Th'im–mor–tal soul we save or lose.
O God! hence–forth our hearts incline To seek no oth – er love than thine.

# YE VIRGIN SOULS, ARISE 568

*Behold, the bridegroom cometh; go ye out to meet Him.* Mt. 25:6.

Charles Wesley, 1749 (1707-1788) | ST. JOHN 6.6.6.6.8.8. M.M. 84 | Arr. William Henry Havergal, 1795-1870 Har. Arr. by compiler, 1965

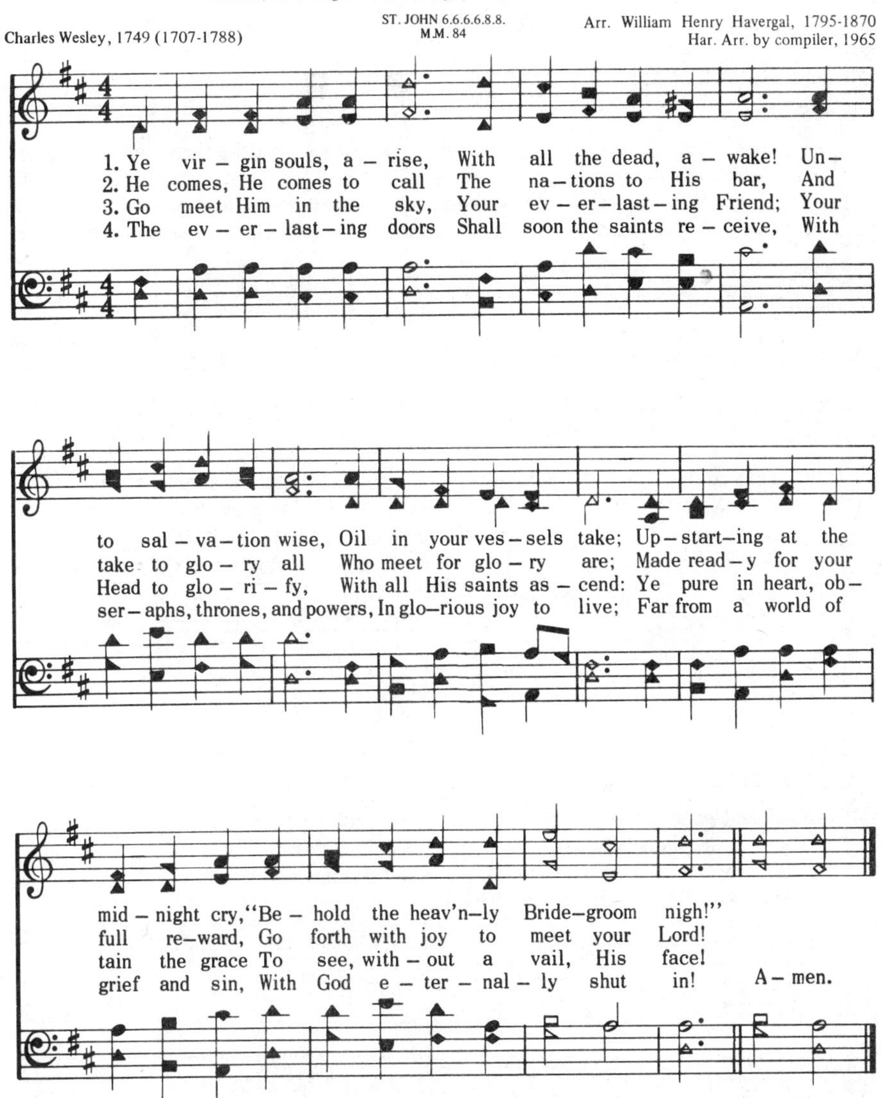

1. Ye vir – gin souls, a – rise, With all the dead, a – wake! Un– to sal – va – tion wise, Oil in your ves – sels take; Up – start–ing at the mid – night cry, "Be – hold the heav'n–ly Bride–groom nigh!"
2. He comes, He comes to call The na – tions to His bar, And take to glo – ry all Who meet for glo – ry are; Made read – y for your full re–ward, Go forth with joy to meet your Lord!
3. Go meet Him in the sky, Your ev – er – last – ing Friend; Your Head to glo – ri – fy, With all His saints as – cend: Ye pure in heart, ob– tain the grace To see, with – out a vail, His face!
4. The ev – er – last – ing doors Shall soon the saints re – ceive, With ser – aphs, thrones, and powers, In glo–rious joy to live; Far from a world of grief and sin, With God e – ter – nal – ly shut in!
A – men.

5. Then let us wait to hear
The trumpet's welcome sound;
To see our Lord appear,
May we be watching found;
And when Thou dost the heavens bow,
Be found––as, Lord, Thou find'st us now!

# I DREAMED THAT THE GREAT JUDGMENT MORNING

*And I saw the dead, small and great, stand before God . . . and the dead were judged . . . according to their works.* Rev. 20:12.

THE GREAT JUDGMENT MORNING 8.8.8.8.9.8.9. with Ref.
M.M. 100

Bert Shadduck — L. L. Pickle

1. I dreamed that the great judg–ment morning Had dawned and the trum–pet had blown;
2. The rich man was there, but his mon–ey Had melt–ed and van–ished a–way;
3. The wid–ow was there with the or–phans, God heard and re–mem–bered their cries;
4. The moral man came to the judg–ment, But his self–right–eous rags would not do;
I dreamed that the na–tions had gath–ered To judg–ment be–fore the white throne;
A pau–per he stood in the judg–ment, His debts were too heav–y to pay;
No sor–row in heav–en for–ev–er, God wiped all the tears from their eyes;
The men who had cru–ci–fied Je–sus Had passed off as mor–tal men, too;
From the throne came a bright shin–ing an–gel, And stood on the land and the sea,
The great man was there, but his greatness, When death came, was left far be–hind!
The gam–bler was there and the drunk–ard, And the man that had sold them the drink,
The soul that had put off sal–va–tion, "Not to–night; I'll get saved by and by,
And swore with his hand raised to heav–en, That time was no long–er to be.
The an–gel that o–pened the rec–ords, Not a trace of his great–ness could find.
With the peo–ple who gave him the li–cense, To–geth–er in hell they did sink.
No time now to think of re–li–gion!" At last they had found time to die.

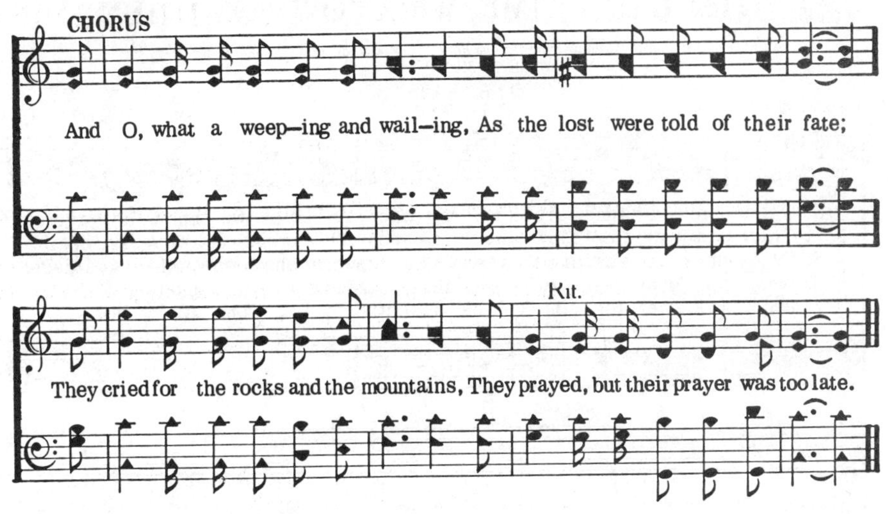
CHORUS
And O, what a weep–ing and wail–ing, As the lost were told of their fate;
Rit.
They cried for the rocks and the mountains, They prayed, but their prayer was too late.

# THE DAY OF WRATH 570

*For the great day of His wrath is come; and who shall be able to stand?* Rev. 6:17.

Thomas of Celano, 13th century
*Dies irae, dies illa*
Tr. Walter Scott, 1771-1832

GERICHT 8.7.8.8.
M.M. 84

John J. Overholt, 1964

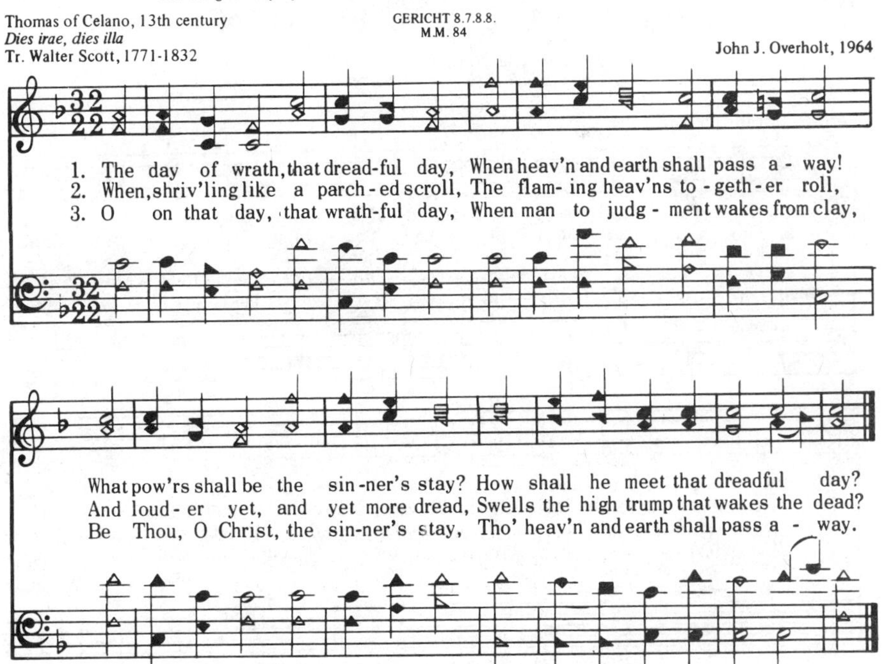
1. The day of wrath, that dread-ful day, When heav'n and earth shall pass a - way!
2. When, shriv'ling like a parch - ed scroll, The flam- ing heav'ns to - geth - er roll,
3. O on that day, that wrath-ful day, When man to judg - ment wakes from clay,
What pow'rs shall be the sin-ner's stay? How shall he meet that dreadful day?
And loud - er yet, and yet more dread, Swells the high trump that wakes the dead?
Be Thou, O Christ, the sin-ner's stay, Tho' heav'n and earth shall pass a - way.

# 571 THERE IS A TIME, WE KNOW NOT WHEN

*And whosoever was not found written in the book of life was cast into the lake of fire.* Rev. 20:17. *How can ye escape the damnation of hell?* Mt. 23:33.

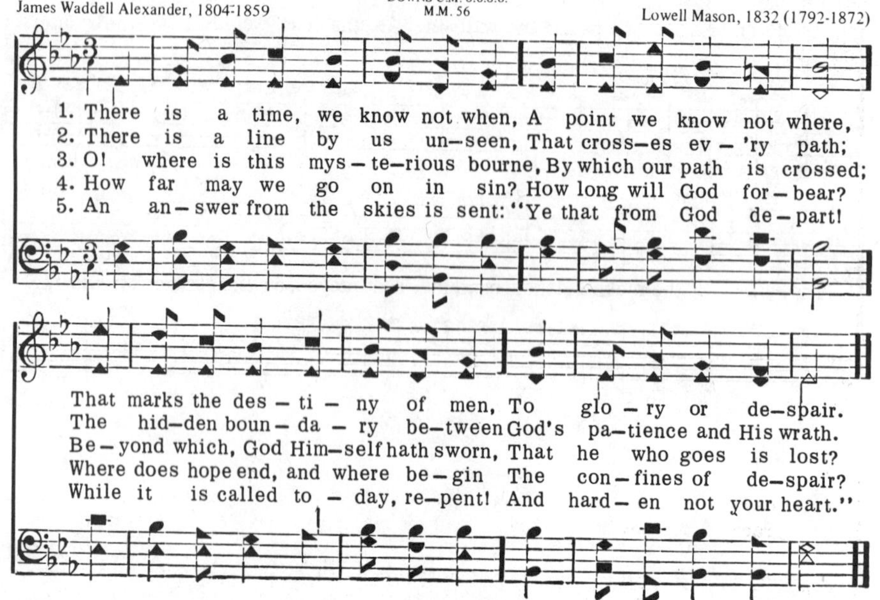
James Waddell Alexander, 1804-1859
DOWNS C.M. 8.6.8.6.
M.M. 56
Lowell Mason, 1832 (1792-1872)
1. There is a time, we know not when, A point we know not where,
2. There is a line by us un–seen, That cross–es ev – 'ry path;
3. O! where is this mys – te–rious bourne, By which our path is crossed;
4. How far may we go on in sin? How long will God for – bear?
5. An an – swer from the skies is sent: "Ye that from God de – part!
That marks the des – ti – ny of men, To glo – ry or de–spair.
The hid–den boun – da – ry be–tween God's pa–tience and His wrath.
Be – yond which, God Him–self hath sworn, That he who goes is lost?
Where does hope end, and where be – gin The con – fines of de–spair?
While it is called to – day, re–pent! And hard – en not your heart."

# 572 O WHERE SHALL REST BE FOUND

*There is no peace, saith my God, to the wicked.* Is. 57:21 *There remaineth therefore a rest to the people of God.* Heb. 4:9.

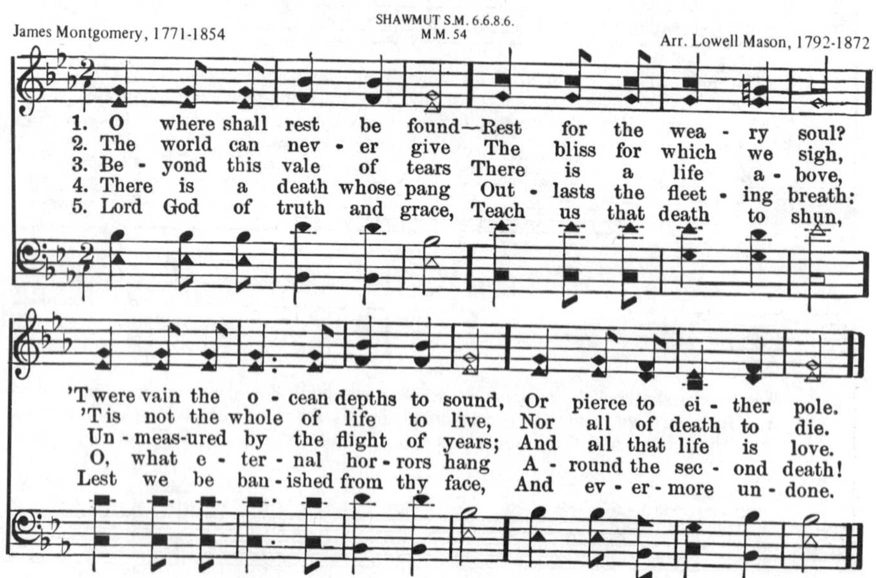
James Montgomery, 1771-1854
SHAWMUT S.M. 6.6.8.6.
M.M. 54
Arr. Lowell Mason, 1792-1872
1. O where shall rest be found—Rest for the wea - ry soul?
2. The world can nev - er give The bliss for which we sigh,
3. Be - yond this vale of tears There is a life a - bove,
4. There is a death whose pang Out - lasts the fleet - ing breath:
5. Lord God of truth and grace, Teach us that death to shun,
'Twere vain the o - cean depths to sound, Or pierce to ei - ther pole.
'Tis not the whole of life to live, Nor all of death to die.
Un - meas-ured by the flight of years; And all that life is love.
O, what e - ter - nal hor - rors hang A - round the sec - ond death!
Lest we be ban - ished from thy face, And ev - er - more un - done.

# WHERE WILL YOU SPEND ETERNITY? 573

*These shall go away into everlasting punishment, but the righteous into life eternal.* Mt. 25:46.

WHERE WILL YOU SPEND ETERNITY? L.M. 8.8.8.8. with Ref.
M.M. 58
Elish A. Hoffman, 1839-1929
John Harrison Tenney, b. 1840
1. Where will you spend e - ter - ni - ty? This ques - tion comes to you and me! Tell me, what shall your an - swer be? Where will you spend e - ter - ni - ty?
2. Man - y are choos - ing Christ to - day, Turn - ing from all their sins a - way; Heav'n shall their hap - py por - tion be; Where will you spend e - ter - ni - ty!
3. Leav - ing the strait and nar - row way, Go - ing the down - ward road to - day, Sad will their fi - nal end - ing be,— Lost through a long e - ter - ni - ty!
4. Re - pent, be - lieve, this ver - y hour, Trust in the Sav - iour's grace and pow'r; Then will your joy - ous an - swer be, Saved through a long e - ter - ni - ty!
REFRAIN
E - ter - ni - ty! e - ter - ni - ty! Where will you spend e - ter - ni - ty?
E - ter - ni - ty! e - ter - ni - ty! Where will you spend e - ter - ni - ty?
E - ter - ni - ty! e - ter - ni - ty! Lost through a long e - ter - ni - ty!
E - ter - ni - ty! e - ter - ni - ty! Saved through a long e - ter - ni - ty!

# 574 MY LATEST SUN IS SINKING FAST

*For I am now ready to be offered, and the time of my departure is at hand.* II Tim. 4:6.

Jefferson Hascall

LAND OF BEULAH C.M. 8.6.8.6. with Ref.
M.M. 100

William Batchelder Bradbury, 1816-1868

1. My lat - est sun is sink - ing fast, My race is near - ly run;
2. I know I'm nearing the ho - ly ranks Of friends and kin - dred dear,
3. I've al - most gained my heav'n-ly home, My spir - it loud - ly sings;
4. O bear my long - ing heart to Him Who bled and died for me;
My strong - est tri - als now are past, My tri - umph is be - gun.
For I brush the dews on Jor - dan's banks, The cross - ing must be near.
Thy ho - ly ones, be - hold, they come! I hear the noise of wings.
Whose blood now cleans - es from all sin, And gives me vic - to - ry.
REFRAIN
O come, an - gel band, Come and a - round me stand; O,
bear me a - way on your snow - y wings To my im - mor - tal home: O,
bear me a - way on your snow - y wings To my im - mor - tal home.

# O THE BLISS OF LOVED ONES RESTING 575

*Blessed are the dead which die in the Lord . . . that they may rest from their labours; and their works do follow them.* Rev. 14:13.

ST. SYLVESTER 8.7.8.7.8.7.
M.M. 58

John Samuel Coffman, 1848-1899

Arr. from John Bacchus Dykes, 1823-1876

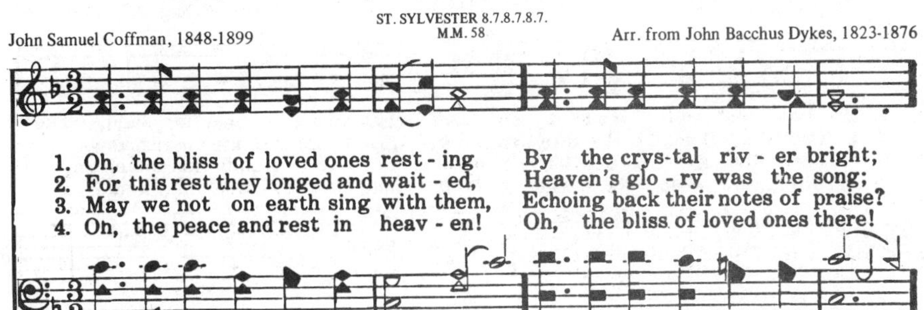

1. Oh, the bliss of loved ones rest - ing By the crys-tal riv - er bright;
2. For this rest they longed and wait - ed, Heaven's glo - ry was the song;
3. May we not on earth sing with them, Echoing back their notes of praise?
4. Oh, the peace and rest in heav - en! Oh, the bliss of loved ones there!

'Neath the shade of trees im - mor - tal, Where no shad-ows dim the light!
Liv - ing faith now bids us hear them Sing-ing with the blood-washed throng;
Yes, but bless - ed hope in - spires us Heav'n's e - ter-nal songs to raise;
Love di - vine now bears us up - ward All their bless-ed - ness to share;

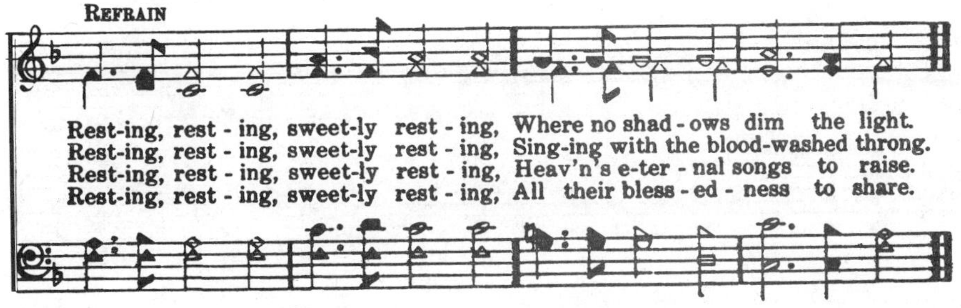

Refrain
Rest-ing, rest - ing, sweet-ly rest - ing, Where no shad - ows dim the light.
Rest-ing, rest - ing, sweet-ly rest - ing, Sing-ing with the blood-washed throng.
Rest-ing, rest - ing, sweet-ly rest - ing, Heav'n's e-ter - nal songs to raise.
Rest-ing, rest - ing, sweet-ly rest - ing, All their bless - ed - ness to share.

# 576 I WILL SING YOU A SONG

*Having a desire to depart, and to be with Christ; which is far better.* Phil. 1:23.

I WILL SING YOU A SONG 12.8.12.9. with Ref.
M.M. 58

Ellen H. Gates, 1835-1920

Charles Edward Pollock, b. 1853

1. I will sing you a song of that beau - ti - ful land, The far a - way home of the soul; Where no storms ev - er beat on that glit - ter - ing strand, While the years of e - ter - ni - ty roll.
2. Oh, that home of the soul in my vis - ions and dreams, Its bright jas - per walls I can see; Till I fan - cy but thin - ly the vale in - ter - venes Be - tween the fair cit - y and me.
3. That un - chang - a - ble home is for you and for me, Where Je - sus of Naz - a - reth stands; The King of all king - doms for - ev - er, is He, And He hold - eth our crowns in His hands.
4. Oh, how sweet it will be in that beau - ti - ful land, So free from all sor - row and pain; With songs on our lips and with harps in our hands To . . meet one an - oth - er a - gain.
REFRAIN
While the years of e - ter - ni - ty roll. While the years of e - ter - ni - ty roll, Where no storms ev - er beat on that glit - ter - ing strand, While the years of e - ter - ni - ty roll.

# I WILL SING YOU A SONG 577

*For we know that if our earthly house of this tabernacle were dissolved, we have a building of God.* II Cor. 5:1.

HOME OF THE SOUL 12.8.12.9.9.
M.M. 66

Ellen H. Gates, 1835-1920

Philip Phillips, 1834-1895

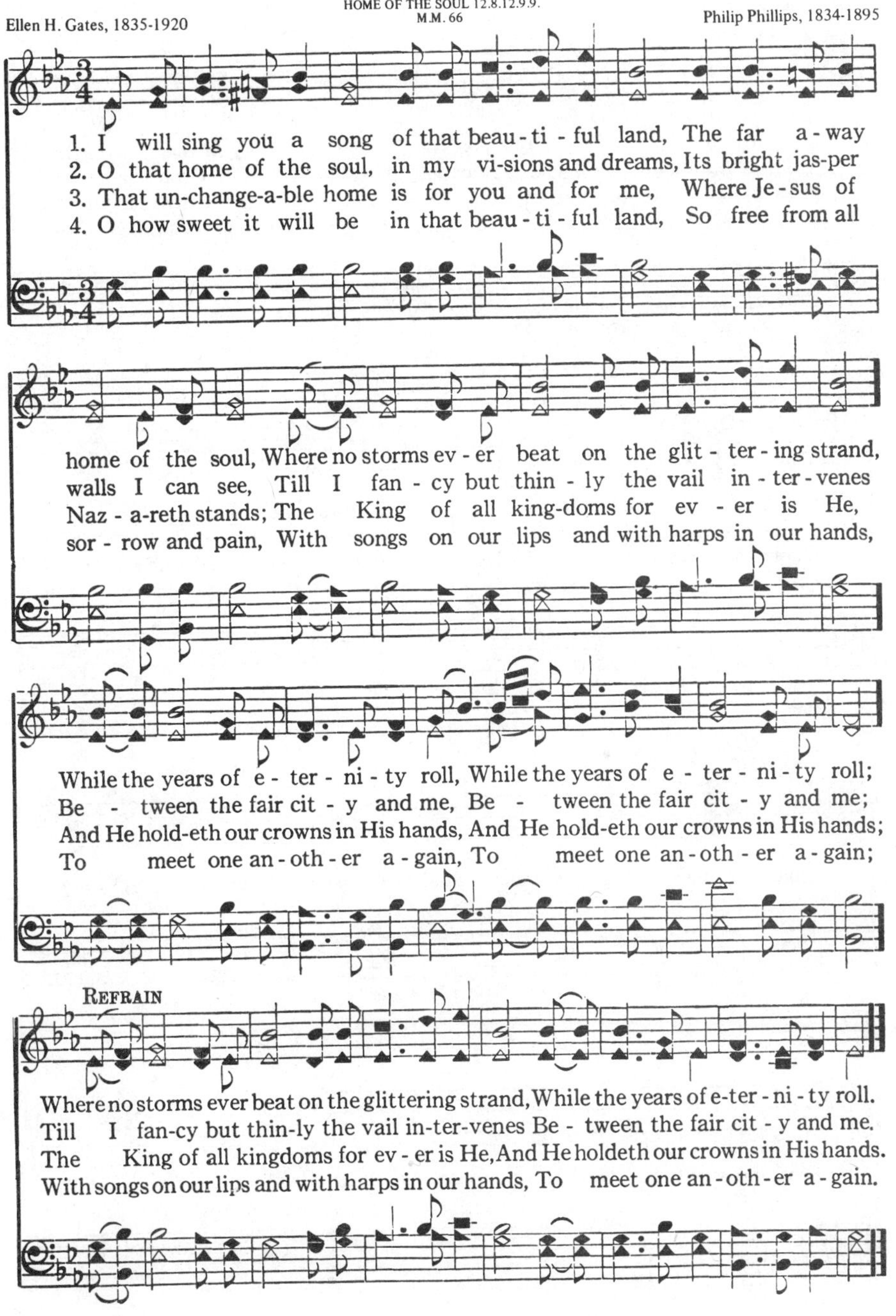
1. I will sing you a song of that beau - ti - ful land, The far a - way
2. O that home of the soul, in my vi-sions and dreams, Its bright jas-per
3. That un-change-a-ble home is for you and for me, Where Je - sus of
4. O how sweet it will be in that beau - ti - ful land, So free from all
home of the soul, Where no storms ev - er beat on the glit - ter - ing strand,
walls I can see, Till I fan - cy but thin - ly the vail in - ter - venes
Naz - a-reth stands; The King of all king-doms for ev - er is He,
sor - row and pain, With songs on our lips and with harps in our hands,
While the years of e - ter - ni - ty roll, While the years of e - ter - ni - ty roll;
Be - tween the fair cit - y and me, Be - tween the fair cit - y and me;
And He hold-eth our crowns in His hands, And He hold-eth our crowns in His hands;
To meet one an - oth - er a - gain, To meet one an - oth - er a - gain;
Refrain
Where no storms ever beat on the glittering strand, While the years of e-ter - ni - ty roll.
Till I fan-cy but thin-ly the vail in-ter-venes Be - tween the fair cit - y and me.
The King of all kingdoms for ev - er is He, And He holdeth our crowns in His hands.
With songs on our lips and with harps in our hands, To meet one an - oth - er a - gain.

# 578 SHALL WE MEET BEYOND THE RIVER

*He shewed me a pure river of water of life, clear as crystal, proceeding out of the throne of God.* Rev. 22:1.

SHALL WE MEET 8.7.8.7. with Ref.
M.M. 56

Horace L. Hastings, 1831-1899

Elihu D. Rice, b. 1827

*Moderato*

1. Shall we meet be-yond the riv-er, Where the sur-ges cease to roll?
Where in all the bright for-ev-er, Sor-row ne'er shall press the soul?

2. Shall we meet in that blest har-bor, When our storm-y voyage is o'er?
Shall we meet and cast the an-chor By the fair ce-les-tial shore?

3. Shall we meet in yon-der cit-y, Where the tow'rs of crys-tal shine,
Where the walls are all of jas-per, Built by work-man-ship di-vine?—

4. Shall we meet with Christ our Saviour, When He comes to claim His own?
Shall we know His bless-ed fa-vor, And sit down up-on His throne?

REFRAIN

Shall we meet, shall we meet, Shall we meet be-yond the riv-er?
Shall we meet be-yond the riv-er, Where the sur-ges cease to roll?

# SHALL WE GATHER AT THE RIVER 579

*On either side of the river, was there the tree of life.* Rev. 22:2.

HANSON PLACE 8.7.8.7. with Ref.
M.M. 69

Robert Lowry, 1826-1899 | Robert Lowry

1. Shall we gath - er at the riv - er Where bright an - gel feet have trod;
2. On the mar - gin of the riv - er, Wash - ing up its sil - ver spray,
3. Ere we reach the shin - ing riv - er, Lay we ev - 'ry bur - den down;
4. Soon we'll gath - er at the riv - er, Soon our pil - grim - age will cease;
With its crys - tal tide for - ev - er Flow - ing by the throne of God?
We will walk and wor - ship ev - er, All the hap - py gold - en day.
Grace our spir - its will de - liv - er, And pro - vide a robe and crown.
Soon our hap - py hearts will quiv - er With the mel - o - dy of peace.
Refrain
Yes, we'll gath - er at the riv - er, The beau - ti - ful, the beau - ti - ful riv - er,—
Gath - er with the saints at the riv - er, That flows by the throne of God.

# 580 OH! WE ARE GOING TO WEAR A CROWN

*The man that endureth temptation . . . **shall receive the crown of life.*** Jas. 1:12. *When the chief Shepherd shall appear, ye shall receive a crown of glory.* I Pet. 5:4.

Anonymous | BELOHNUNG 9.9.9.6. with Ref. M.M. 56 | E. E. Nickerson, Arr. John J. Overholt, 1965

Not too fast
1. Oh! we are go-ing to wear a crown, Oh! we are go-ing to wear a crown,
2. You must be sav'd to wear a crown, You must be sav'd to wear a crown,
3. You must be cleans'd to wear that crown. You must be cleans'd to wear that crown.
4. You must live up-right to wear that crown. You must live up-right to wear that crown.
5. You must fight the fight to wear that crown. You must fight the fight to wear that crown.
6. You must bear the cross to win that crown. You must bear the cross to win that crown.
Oh! we are go-ing to wear a crown, To wear a star-ry crown.
You must be sav'd to wear a crown, To wear a star-ry crown.
You must be cleans'd to wear that crown, To wear a star-ry crown.
You must live up-right to wear that crown, To wear a star-ry crown.
You must fight the fight to wear that crown, To wear a star-ry crown.
You must bear the cross to win that crown, To wear a star-ry crown.
REFRAIN
f
A-way o-ver Jor-dan, With our bless-ed Je-sus
A-way o-ver Jor-dan, To wear a star-ry crown.

# WHEN I SHALL COME TO THE END OF MY WAY 581

*For our conversation (citizenship) is in heaven; from whence also we look for the Saviour, the Lord Jesus Christ.* Phil. 3:20.

William C. Poole, 1875-1949

SUNRISE 10.10.10.8. with Ref.
M.M. 88

Bently DeForest Ackley, 1872-1958
Harmony Arr. for mixed voices, John J. Overholt, 1972

1. When I shall come to the end of my way, When I shall rest at the close of life's day, When "Wel-come home" I shall hear Je - sus say,
2. When in His beau-ty I see the great King, Join with the ran-somed His prais - es to sing, When I shall join them my tri - bute to bring,
3. When life is o - ver and day-light is past, In heav-en's har - bor my an - chor is cast, When I see Je - sus my Sav - ior at last,
O that will be sun-rise for me! For me!
CHORUS
Sun-rise to-mor - row, sun-rise to-mor-row, Sun-rise in glo-ry is wait-ing for me; Sun-rise to-mor-row, sun-rise to-mor - row, Sun-rise with Je - sus for e - ter - ni - ty.

# 582 THERE IS A LAND OF PURE DELIGHT

*When Christ, who is our life, shall appear, then shall ye also appear with Him in glory.* Col. 3:4.

VARINA C.M.D. 8.6.8.6.D.
M.M. 63

Isaac Watts, 1674-1748

George F. Root, 1820-1895

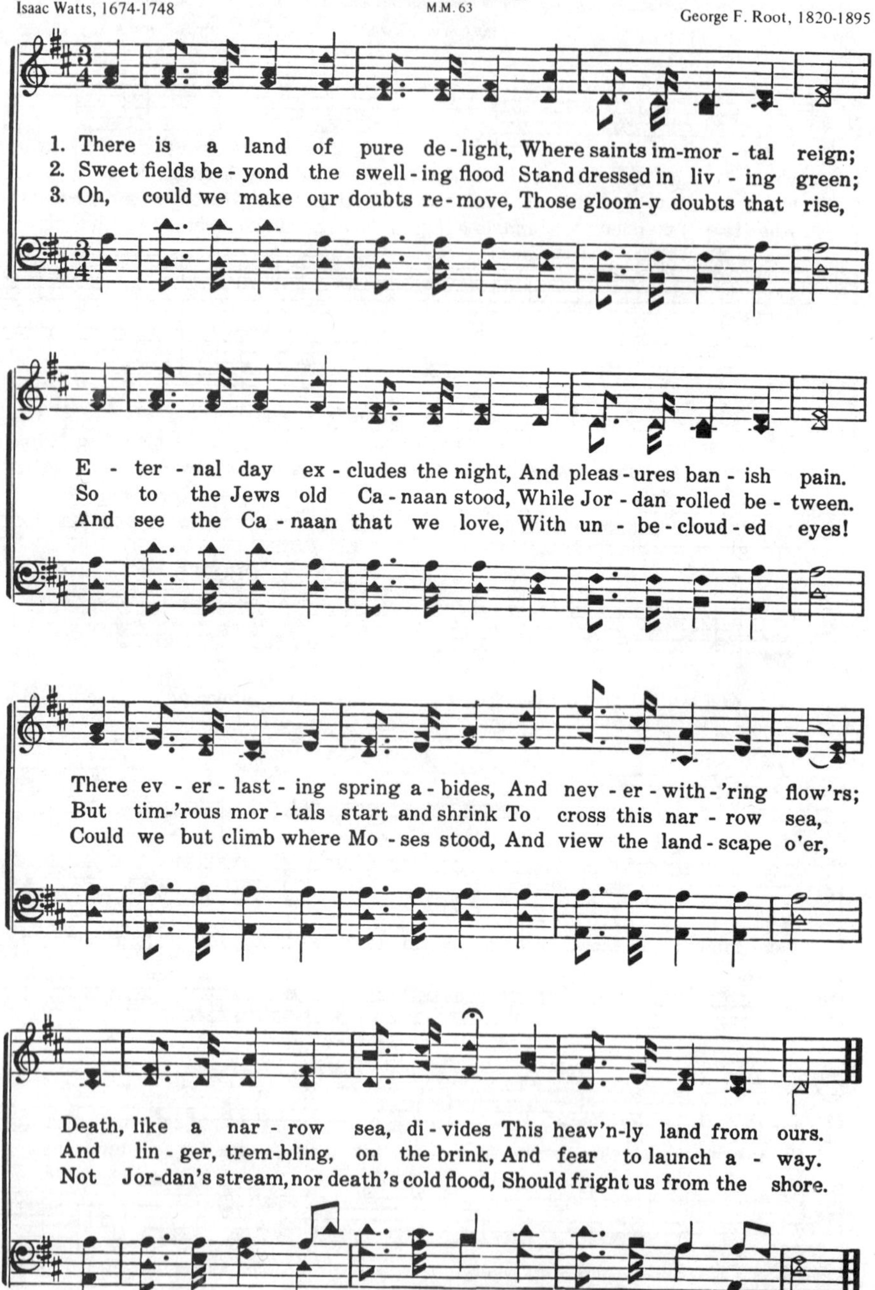
1. There is a land of pure de-light, Where saints im-mor-tal reign;
2. Sweet fields be-yond the swell-ing flood Stand dressed in liv-ing green;
3. Oh, could we make our doubts re-move, Those gloom-y doubts that rise,
E-ter-nal day ex-cludes the night, And pleas-ures ban-ish pain.
So to the Jews old Ca-naan stood, While Jor-dan rolled be-tween.
And see the Ca-naan that we love, With un-be-cloud-ed eyes!
There ev-er-last-ing spring a-bides, And nev-er-with-'ring flow'rs;
But tim-'rous mor-tals start and shrink To cross this nar-row sea,
Could we but climb where Mo-ses stood, And view the land-scape o'er,
Death, like a nar-row sea, di-vides This heav'n-ly land from ours.
And lin-ger, trem-bling, on the brink, And fear to launch a-way.
Not Jor-dan's stream, nor death's cold flood, Should fright us from the shore.

# I HEARD A SOUND OF VOICES 583

*I heard the voice of many . . . around about the throne . . . and the number of them was ten thousand times ten thousand; and thousands of thousands.* Rev. 5:11.

Godfrey Thring, 1886 (1823-1903) — PATMOS 7.6.8.6.D. M.M. 69 — Henry Johnson Storer, 1891 (1860-1935)

1. I heard a sound of voices A-round the great white throne,
With harp-ers harp-ing on their harps To Him that sat there-on:
"Sal-va-tion, glo-ry, hon-or!" I heard the song a-rise,
As thro' the courts of heav'n it rolled In won-drous har-mo-nies.

2. From ev-'ry clime and kin-dred, And na-tions from a-far,
As ser-ried ranks re-turn-ing home In tri-umph from a war,
I heard the saints up-rais-ing, The myr-iad hosts a-mong,
In praise of Him who died and lives, Their one glad tri-umph song.

3. O great and glo-rious vi-sion! The Lamb up-on His throne;
O won-drous sight for man to see! The Sav-iour with His own:
To drink the liv-ing wa-ters And stand up-on the shore,
Where nei-ther sor-row, sin, nor death Shall ev-er en-ter more.

4. And there no sun was need-ed, Nor moon to shine by night,
God's glo-ry did en-light-en all, The Lamb Him-self the light;
And there His serv-ants serve Him, And, life's long bat-tle o'er,
En-throned with Him, their Sav-iour, King, They reign for-ev-er-more.

# 584 O WHAT THE JOY AND THE GLORY MUST BE

*Blessed are they that do His commandments . . . and may enter in through the gates into the city.* Rev. 22:14. *A partaker of the glory that shall be revealed.* I Pt. 5:1.

Pierre Abelard, 1079-1142
*O quanta qualia sunt illa Sabbata*
Tr. John Mason Neale, 1854 (1818-1866), alt.

O QUANTA QUALIA 10.10.10.10.
M.M. 58

*Paris Antiphoner*, 1681
Har. John B. Dykes, 1868 (1823-1876)

1. O what the joy and the glo - ry must be,
Those endless Sab - baths the bless - ed ones see;
Crown for the val - iant, to wear - y ones rest;
God shall be all, and in all ev - er blest.
2. What are the Mon - arch, his court and His throne?
What are the peace and the joy that they own?
O that the blest ones, who in it have share;
All that they feel could as ful - ly de - clare!
3. Tru - ly, Je - ru - sa - lem name we that shore,
Vi - sion of peace, that brings joy ev - er - more;
Wish and ful - fill - ment can sev - ered be ne'er,
Nor the thing prayed for come short of the prayer.
4. There, where no trou - bles dis - trac - tion can bring,
We the sweet an - thems of Si - on shall sing;
While for thy grace, Lord, their voic - es of praise
Thy bless - ed peo - ple e - ter - nal - ly raise.
5. Low be - fore him with our prais - es we fall,
Of whom, and in whom, and through whom are all;
Of whom, the Fa - ther; and in whom, the Son;
Thro' whom, the Spir - it, with them ev - er One.
A - men.

# I AM THINKING TONIGHT OF A FAR AWAY HOME 585

*Earnestly desiring to be clothed upon with our house which is from heaven.* II Cor. 5:2.

MY FAR AWAY HOME 12.8.12.8. with Ref.
M.M. 72
E. T. Hildebrand
E. T. Hildebrand
1. I am think–ing to–night of a far a–way home, Where the an–gels are hap–py in song, And the streets of pure gold, which I long to be–hold, Are trod by the bright an–gel throng.
2. I am think–ing to–night of that heav–en–ly band, And those who are crowned with the blest; 'Tis the host of the Lord who re–ceived the re–ward Which is prom–ised to all who seek rest.
3. I am think–ing to–night of those who have gone To view that great ci–ty a–bove· Oh, may we at length, through Je–sus the Son, Pass in–to that ha–ven of love.
Refrain.
Beau–ti–ful home, land of the blest, Whose glo–ries for–ev–er are bright;
rit.
My soul goes up to the great white throne, Where Je–sus is ev–er the light.

# 586 FAR, FAR BEYOND THE STARRY SKY

*They desire a better country.* Heb. 11:16. *Willing rather to be . . . present with the Lord.* II Cor. 5:8.

Carl Plank, 1801-1825
Tr. Jacob D. Toews, b. 1903

FAR, FAR BEYOND C.M.D. 8.6.8.6.D.
M.M. 76

English Folk Melody

1. Far, far be-yond the star - ry sky There is a bless - ed land,
2. No words of man can ev - er tell The joys so full and free;
3. Its glo-rious gates are o - pen wide To all who trust the Lord;
4. 'Tis but a lit - tle while on earth Where fleet - ing time shall cease;
By faith we see its moun-tains rise As made by God's own hand,
Yet yearn-ings fill my long - ing soul In that fair land to be.
Who con-se-crate their lives to Him— Ac - cept His pre - cious Word.
But ev - er on that bless - ed shore Shall reign e - ter - nal peace.
O hap - py land of fair - est flow'rs! E - ter - nal joys and bliss
Tho' pain and sor - row here my lot, I know they shall de - part,
In si - lent pen - i - ten - tial tears Con-fess their guilt and sin,
The yoke of sin we've cast be-hind, O grasp this truth, my heart!
A - wait the wea - ry wan - der - er, Sweet rest and hap - pi - ness.
For rays of faith and hope, O Lord, Il - lume my long - ing heart.
Peace to the wea - ry wand'ring heart The Lord now gives with - in.
When the re-deemed shall meet a - bove And there shall nev - er part.

# WHEN WE SHALL REACH THE MORE EXCELLENT GLORY

*We shall be like Him; for we shall see Him as He is.* I Jn. 3:2.

W. A. Spencer

WE SHALL BE LIKE HIM 11.7.11.7. with Ref.
M.M. 100

W. A. Spencer

1. When we shall reach the more ex - cel - lent glo - ry, And all our tri - als are past, We shall be - hold Him, O won - der - ful sto - ry! We shall be like Him at last.
2. We shall not wait till the glo - ri - ous dawn - ing Breaks on the vi - sion so fair; Now we may wel - come the heav - en - ly morn - ing, Now we His im - age may bear.
3. More and more like Him: re - peat the blest sto - ry O - ver and o - ver a - gain; Changed by His Spir - it from glo - ry to glo - ry, We shall be sat - is - fied then.
CHORUS
We shall be like Him, We shall be like Him, And in His beau - ty shall shine; We shall be like Him, won - drous - ly like Him, Je - sus, our Sav - ior di - vine.
f
p

# 588 THEY COME FROM THE EAST AND WEST

*A great multitude, which no man could number.* Rev. 7:9. *And they shall come from the east, and from the west, and from the north, and from the south.* Lk. 13:29.

Thomas Harris
St. 5, R. E. Winsett
Alt. John J. Overholt, 1969
SIE KOMMEN VON OST UND WEST
7.7.5.5.7.7.7.7.7.
M.M. 116
Russel De Koven
Har. John J. Overholt, 1969
1. They come from the East and West, They come from the lands a - far,
2. They come to the great high throne, Be - fore it the ran-somed stand;
3. The gates of that ho - ly place, Stand o - pen by night and day;
4. They come from the thorn - y way, From re - gions be - yond the sea;
5. O Je - sus is com - ing soon, The judg - ment will then be - gin!
To feast with the King, to dine as his guests, How blessed these pil - grims are;
No long - er are tears, no sor - row is known, Nor death in that good - ly land.
O look to the Lord who giv - eth more grace, Whose love has prepared the way.
They come from the vale, from moun - tain and dale, O Shepherd of men to thee.
O what if our Lord this mo - ment should come For those who are free from sin!
Be - hold - ing his hal - lowed face, A - glow with a light di - vine;
The Sav - iour has gone be - fore, Pre - par - ing these mansions free
A home in those mansions fair, His hand has re - served for all;
They soar to the mount of God, Be - hold - ing the Bride - groom fair
O then would it bring you joy, Or sor - row and deep des - pair?
Blest par - tak - ers of his grace, and gems in his crown to shine!
Soon we'll meet to part no more through time and e - ter - ni - ty!
For the wed - ding feast pre - pare, o - bey - ing the gra - cious call!
He who trod our earth - ly way will wel - come each pil - grim there!
When the Lord in glo - ry comes we'll meet him up in the air!

# HE'S GONE, THE SPOTLESS SOUL IS GONE 589

*Thousand thousands ministered unto Him, and ten thousand times ten thousand stood before Him.* Dan. 7:10. *The host of heaven worshippeth Thee.* Neh. 9:6. *These are they which came out of great tribulation, and have washed their robes, and made them white in the blood of the Lamb.* Rev. 7:14.

HOSANNA L.M. 8.8.8.8. with Ref.
M.M. 72

Harmonia Sacra, 1847 — Harmonia Sacra, 1847

1. He's gone, the spot-less soul is gone, Tri - umphant to his place a-bove;
The pris-on walls are brok-en down, The an-gels speed his swift re-move;
2. Saved by the mer - its of his Lord, Glo - ry and praise to Christ he gives;
Yet still his mer - ci - ful re-ward Ac-cord - ing to his works re-ceives,
3. Fa - ther, to us vouch-safe the grace Which bro't our friend vic - tor- ious thro';
Let us his shin-ing foot-steps trace; Let us his stead-fast faith pur - sue;

And shout-ing on their wings he flies, And gains his rest in Par - a - dise.
And with the bliss he sowed be - low, His bliss e - ter - nal - ly shall grow.
Fol - low this fol - lower of the Lamb, And con-quer all thro' Je - sus' name.

CHORUS

Ho-san-na! ho - san-na! ho-san-na to the Lamb of God, Glo - ry, glo - ry,
let us sing, Grate-ful hon - ors to our King, Ho - san - na!
ho - - san - na! ho - san - na to the Lamb of God!

# 590 THERE IS A HAPPY LAND

*I go to prepare a place for you.* Jn. 14:2.

THERE IS A HAPPY LAND (Irregular)
M.M. 60

Andrew Young, 1838 (1809-1891)

Melody from India

1. There is a hap-py land, Bright, bright as day; There saints in glo-ry stand, In glad ar-ray: O, how they sweet-ly sing—Wor-thy is the Sav-ior King! Loud let his prais-es ring For ev-er-more.

2. Come to this hap-py land, Come, come a-way; Why will ye doubt-ing stand? Why still de-lay? O, we shall hap-py be! When from sin and sor-row free, Lord, we shall live with thee, Blest ev-er-more.

3. Bright in that hap-py land Beams ev-'ry eye; Kept by a Fa-ther's hand, Love can-not die. O, then to glo-ry run; Be a crown and king-dom won, And bright a-bove the sun, Reign ev-er-more.

# 591 OH! SING TO ME OF HEAV'N

*Rejoice, because your names are written in heaven.* Lk. 10:20b.

THERE'LL BE NO SORROW THERE C.M. 8.6.8.6.
M.M. 92

Mary S. B. Dana, b. 1810

C. R. Dunbar

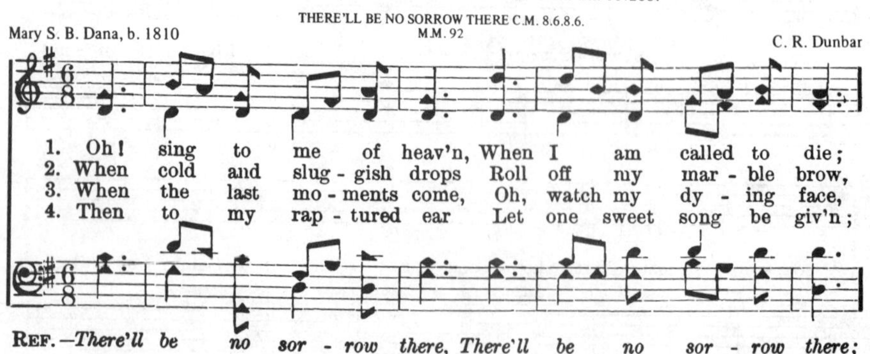
1. Oh! sing to me of heav'n, When I am called to die;
2. When cold and slug-gish drops Roll off my mar-ble brow,
3. When the last mo-ments come, Oh, watch my dy-ing face,
4. Then to my rap-tured ear Let one sweet song be giv'n;
REF.—There'll be no sor-row there, There'll be no sor-row there;

Sing songs of ho - ly ec - sta - sy, To waft my soul on high.
Break forth in songs of joy - ful - ness, Let heav'n be - gin be - low.
To catch the bright ser - aph - ic gleam, Which on each fea - ture plays.
Let mu - sic cheer me last on earth, And greet me first in heav'n.
In heav'n a - bove, where all is love, There'll be no sor - row there.

# THERE'S A CITY OF LIGHT 592

*But ye are come unto mount Sion, and unto the city of the living God.* Heb. 12:22.

THE CITY OF LIGHT 12.9.12.9. with Ref.
M.M. 160

Aldine S. Kieffer, d. 1904 — Aldine S. Kieffer

1. There's a cit - y of light 'mid the stars, we are told, Where they know not a sor - row or care; And the gates are of pearl and the streets are of gold, And the build ing ex - ceed - ing - ly fair;
2. Broth - er dear, nev - er fear, we shall tri - umph at last If we trust in the word He has given; When our tri - als and toils, and our weep - ings are past, We shall meet in that home up in heav'n.
3. Let us walk in the light of the gos - pel di - vine, Let us ev - er keep near to the cross; Let us love, watch, and pray, in our pil - grim - age here, Let us count all things else but as loss.

Fine.

REFRAIN
Let us pray for each oth - er, not faint by the way, In this sad world of sor - row and care.

D.C.

D.C.—*For that home is so bright, and is al - most in sight, And I trust in my heart you'll go there.*

# 593 WELCOME, SWEET DAY OF REST

*I was in the Spirit on the Lord's day.* Rev. 1:10.

SWEET DAY S.M. 6.6.8.6.
M.M. 63

Isaac Watts, 1709 (1674-1748)

B. C. Unseld, 1848-1923

1. Wel - come, sweet day of rest, That saw the Lord a - rise;
2. The King Him - self comes near And feasts His saints to - day;
3. One day a - midst the place Where my dear God hath been,
4. My will - ing soul would stay In such a frame as this,
Wel - come to this re - viv - ing breast, And these re - joic - ing eyes.
Here we may sit and see Him here, And love and praise and pray.
Is sweet - er than ten thou - sand days Of pleas - ur - a - ble sin.
And sit and sing her - self a - way To ev - er - last - ing bliss.

# 594 THIS IS THE DAY THE LORD HATH MADE

*This is the day which the Lord hath made; we will rejoice and be glad in it.* Ps. 118:24.

ARLINGTON C.M. 8.6.8.6.
M.M. 60

Isaac Watts, 1719 (1674-1748)

Thomas Augustine Arne, 1710-1778

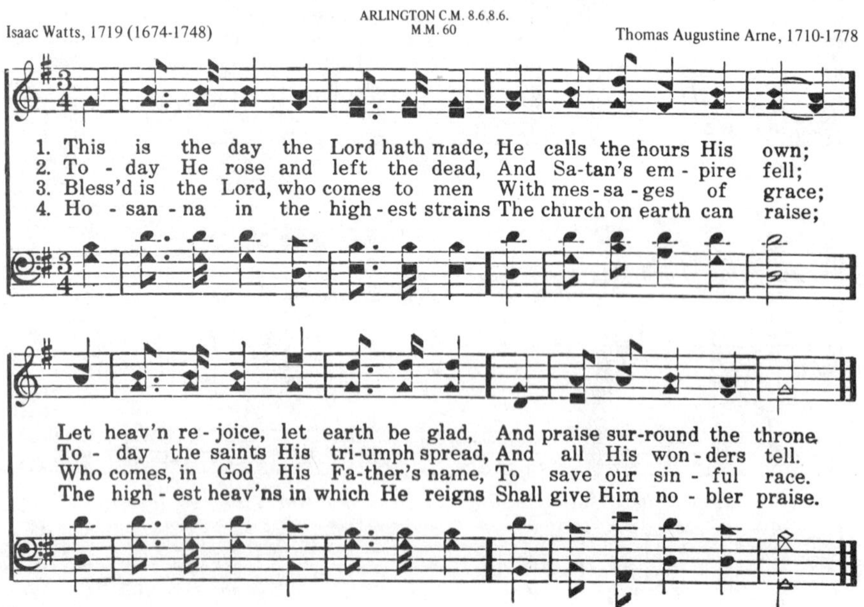
1. This is the day the Lord hath made, He calls the hours His own;
2. To - day He rose and left the dead, And Sa-tan's em - pire fell;
3. Bless'd is the Lord, who comes to men With mes - sa - ges of grace;
4. Ho - san - na in the high - est strains The church on earth can raise;
Let heav'n re - joice, let earth be glad, And praise sur-round the throne.
To - day the saints His tri-umph spread, And all His won - ders tell.
Who comes, in God His Fa-ther's name, To save our sin - ful race.
The high - est heav'ns in which He reigns Shall give Him no - bler praise.

# SAFELY THROUGH ANOTHER WEEK 595

*I was glad when they said unto me, Let us go into the house of the Lord.* Ps. 122:1.

SABBATH 7.7.7.7.D.
M.M. 63
John Newton, 1779 (1725-1807)
Lowell Mason, 1792-1872
1. Safe - ly thro' an - oth - er week God has brought us on our way;
2. While we seek sup-plies of grace, Thro' the blest Re-deem-er's name,
3. Here we come, Thy name to praise: Let us feel Thy pres-ence near;
4. May the Gos - pel's joy - ful sound Con - quer sin - ners, com-fort saints,
Let us each a bless-ing seek, Wait - ing in His courts to - day—
Show Thy rec - on - cil - ing face, Take a - way our sin and shame;
May Thy glo - ry meet our gaze, While we in Thy house ap - pear;
Make the fruits of grace a - bound, Bring re - lief to all com - plaints;
Day of all the week the best, Em - blem of e - ter - nal rest,
From our world - ly care set free, May we rest this day in Thee,
Here af - ford us, Lord, a taste Of our ev - er - last - ing rest,
Thus let all our wor - ship prove, Till we join Thy courts a - bove,
Day of all the week the best, Em - blem of e - ter - nal rest.
From our world - ly care set free, May we rest this day in Thee.
Here af - ford us, Lord, a taste Of our ev - er - last - ing rest.
Thus let all our wor - ship prove, Till we join Thy courts a - bove.

# 596 THIS IS THE DAY OF LIGHT

*Jesus was risen early the first day of the week.* Mk. 16:9.

John Ellerton, 1867 (1826-1893)

ST. JOSEPH S.M. 6.6.8.6.
M.M. 72

S.M.

1. This is the day of light; Let there be light to-day;
2. This is the day of rest; Our fail-ing strength re-new;
3. This is the day of peace; With peace our spir-its fill;
4. This is the day of prayer; Let earth to heav'n draw near;
Rit.
O Day-spring, rise up-on our night, And chase its gloom a-way.
On wea-ry brain and trou-bled breast Shed Thou Thy fresh-'ning dew.
Bid Thou the blasts of dis-cord cease, The waves of strife be still.
Lift up our hearts to seek Thee there, Come down to meet us here.

# 597 WE BLESS THEE FOR THIS SACRED DAY

*The first day of the week.* Jn. 20:19. *Upon the first day of the week, when the disciples came together to break bread, Paul preached.* Acts 20:7.

Caroline Gilman, 1820

BLOOMFIELD CHANT L.M. 8.8.8.8.
M.M. 56

William Batchelder Bradbury, 1816-1868

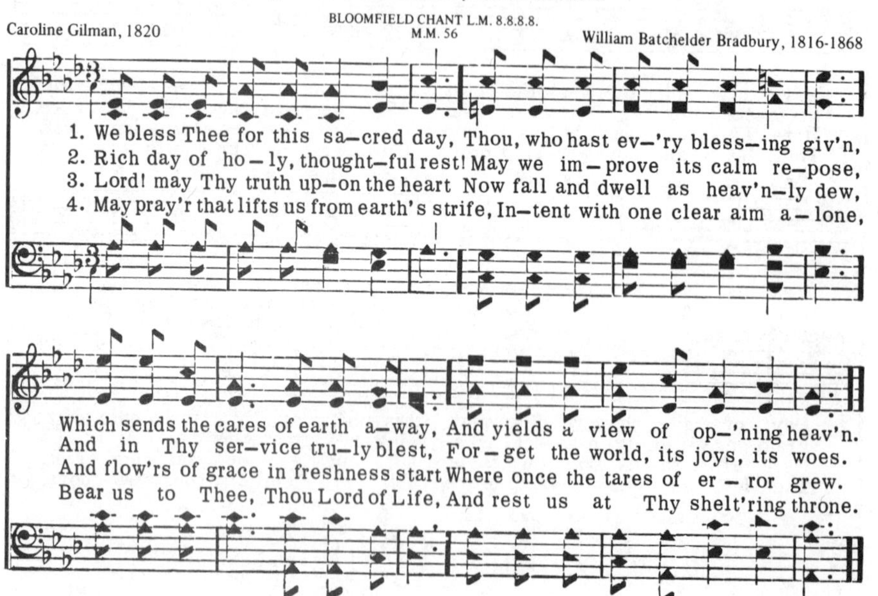
1. We bless Thee for this sa-cred day, Thou, who hast ev-'ry bless-ing giv'n,
2. Rich day of ho-ly, thought-ful rest! May we im-prove its calm re-pose,
3. Lord! may Thy truth up-on the heart Now fall and dwell as heav'n-ly dew,
4. May pray'r that lifts us from earth's strife, In-tent with one clear aim a-lone,
Which sends the cares of earth a-way, And yields a view of op-'ning heav'n.
And in Thy ser-vice tru-ly blest, For-get the world, its joys, its woes.
And flow'rs of grace in freshness start Where once the tares of er-ror grew.
Bear us to Thee, Thou Lord of Life, And rest us at Thy shelt'ring throne.

# PRAISE, LORD, FOR THEE IN ZION WAITS 598

*Praise waiteth for Thee, O God, in Sion. Thou crownest the year with Thy goodness.* Ps. 65:1, 11.

Henry Francis Lyte, 1834 (1793-1847) PARK STREET L.M. 8.8.8.8. M.M. 69 Frederick M. A. Venua, c. 1810 (1788-1872)

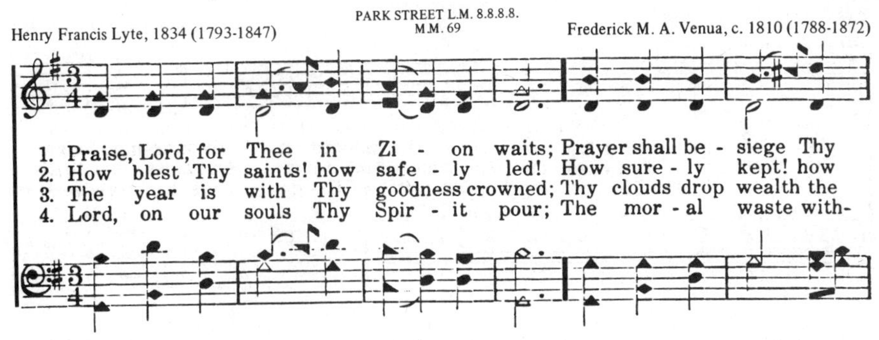
1. Praise, Lord, for Thee in Zi - on waits; Prayer shall be - siege Thy
2. How blest Thy saints! how safe - ly led! How sure - ly kept! how
3. The year is with Thy goodness crowned; Thy clouds drop wealth the
4. Lord, on our souls Thy Spir - it pour; The mor - al waste with-

tem - ple gates; All flesh shall to Thy throne re - pair, And find thro'
rich - ly fed! Sav - iour of all in earth and sea, How hap - py
world a - round; Thro' Thee the des - erts joy - ful sing, And na - ture
in re - store; O let Thy love our spring-tide be, And make us

Christ sal - va - tion there, And find thro' Christ sal - va - tion there.
they who rest in Thee, How hap - py they who rest in Thee.
smiles and owns her King, And na - ture smiles and owns her King.
all bear fruit to Thee, And make us all bear fruit to Thee. A - MEN.

# 599 I THANK THE LORD MY MAKER

*And let them sacrifice the sacrifices of thanksgiving, and declare His works with rejoicing.* Ps. 107:22.

Thomas McKellar, 1812-1899 | WEBB 7.6.7.6.D. M.M. 69 | George J. Webb, 1803-1887

1. I thank the Lord my Mak-er For all His gifts to me; For mak-ing me par-
2. I thank the Lord my Sav-iour Who came for me to die, And bless me with His
3. I thank the Lord for giv - ing The Spir - it of His grace, That I may serve Him

tak - er Of boun-ties rich and free; For fa-ther and for moth-er, Who give me
fa - vor, And fit me for the sky,—That all my sins out-blot-ted, By Je - sus
liv - ing, And dy-ing, reach the place Where Je-sus in His glo - ry I shall for-

clothes and food, For sis - ter and for broth - er, And all the kind and good.
washed a - way, I may be found un-spot - ted When comes the fi - nal day.
ev - er see, And tell the won-drous sto - ry Of all His love for me.

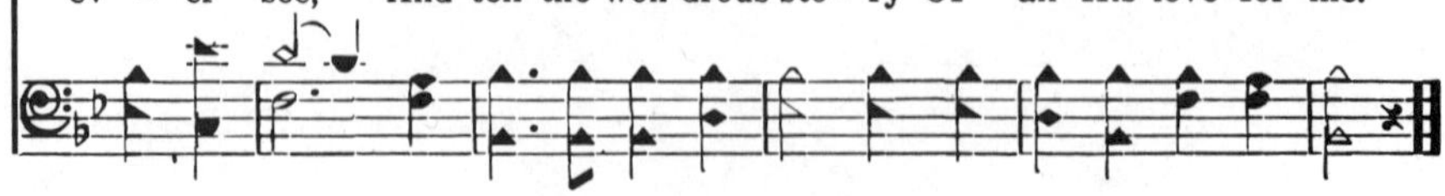

# 600 PRAISE TO GOD, IMMORTAL PRAISE

*When thou hast eaten and art full, then thou shalt bless the Lord thy God.* Deut. 8:10.

Anna L. Barbauld, 1773 (1743-1825) | PRAYER 7.7.7.7. M.M. 58 | Asahel Abbot

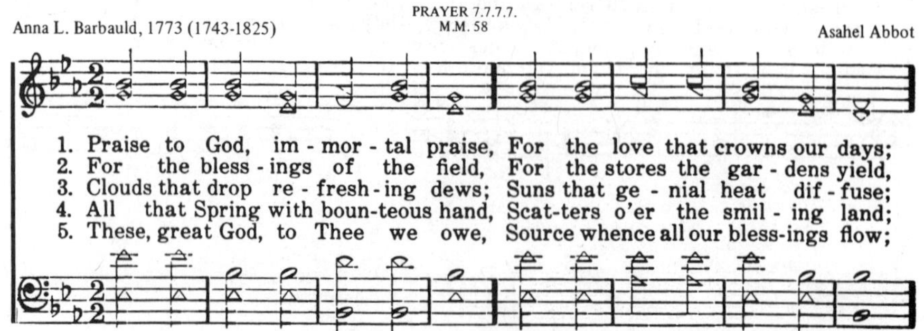
1. Praise to God, im - mor - tal praise, For the love that crowns our days;
2. For the bless - ings of the field, For the stores the gar - dens yield,
3. Clouds that drop re - fresh - ing dews; Suns that ge - nial heat dif - fuse;
4. All that Spring with boun-teous hand, Scat-ters o'er the smil - ing land;
5. These, great God, to Thee we owe, Source whence all our bless-ings flow;

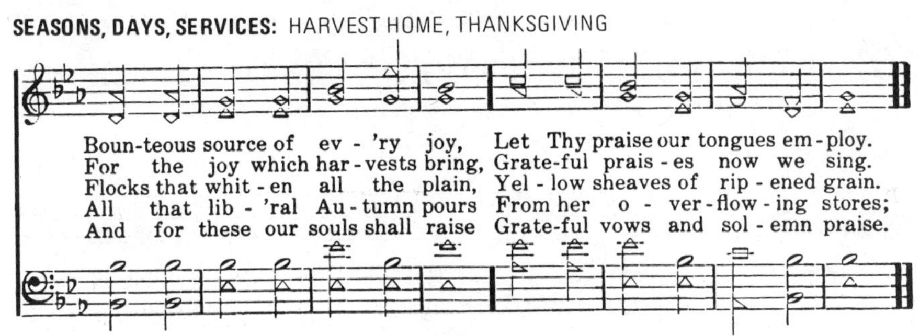
Boun-teous source of ev - 'ry joy, Let Thy praise our tongues em-ploy.
For the joy which har-vests bring, Grate-ful prais-es now we sing.
Flocks that whit-en all the plain, Yel-low sheaves of rip-ened grain.
All that lib-'ral Au-tumn pours From her o-ver-flow-ing stores;
And for these our souls shall raise Grate-ful vows and sol-emn praise.

# ALMIGHTY SOVEREIGN OF THE SKIES 601

*Enter into His gates with thanksgiving, and into His courts with praise.* Ps. 100:4.

BACA L.M. 8.8.8.8.
M.M. 63

Nathan Strong, 1799 (1748-1816)

William Batchelder Bradbury, 1816-1868

1. Al-might-y Sov-'reign of the skies, To thee let songs of glad-ness rise,
2. From thee our choic-est bless-ings flow, Life, health and strength thy hands be-stow;
3. The rich pro-fu-sion na-ture yields, The har-vest wav-ing o'er the fields,
4. At thy com-mand the ver-nal bloom Re-vives the world from win-ter's gloom,

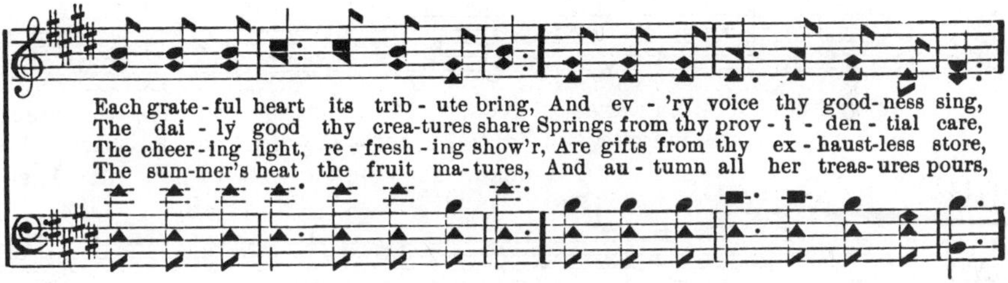

Each grate-ful heart its trib-ute bring, And ev-'ry voice thy good-ness sing,
The dai-ly good thy crea-tures share Springs from thy prov-i-den-tial care,
The cheer-ing light, re-fresh-ing show'r, Are gifts from thy ex-haust-less store,
The sum-mer's heat the fruit ma-tures, And au-tumn all her treas-ures pours,

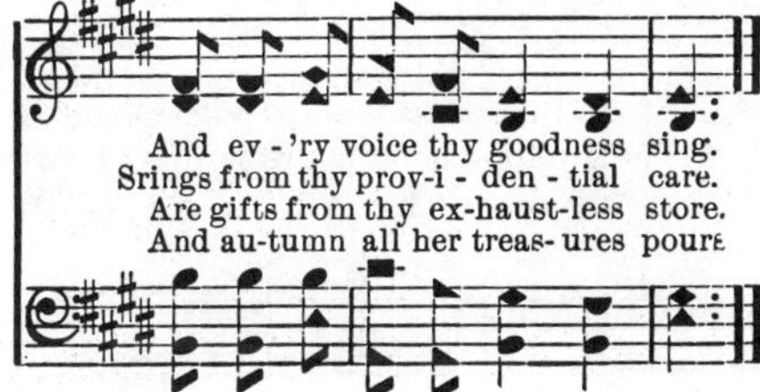
And ev-'ry voice thy goodness sing.
Srings from thy prov-i-den-tial care.
Are gifts from thy ex-haust-less store.
And au-tumn all her treas-ures pours

5 From thee proceed domestic ties,
Connubial bliss, parental joys;
On thy support the nations stand,
Obedient to thy high command.

6 Let every power of heart and tongue,
Unite to swell the grateful song;
While age and youth in chorus join,
And praise the Majesty divine.

# 602 JOIN ALL YE RANSOMED SONS OF GRACE

*Could ye not watch with Me one hour?* Mt. 26:40.

SOLITUDE C.M. 8.6.8.6.
M.M. 54

Charles Wesley, 1742 (1707-1788)

Andrew Johnson Showalter, b. 1858

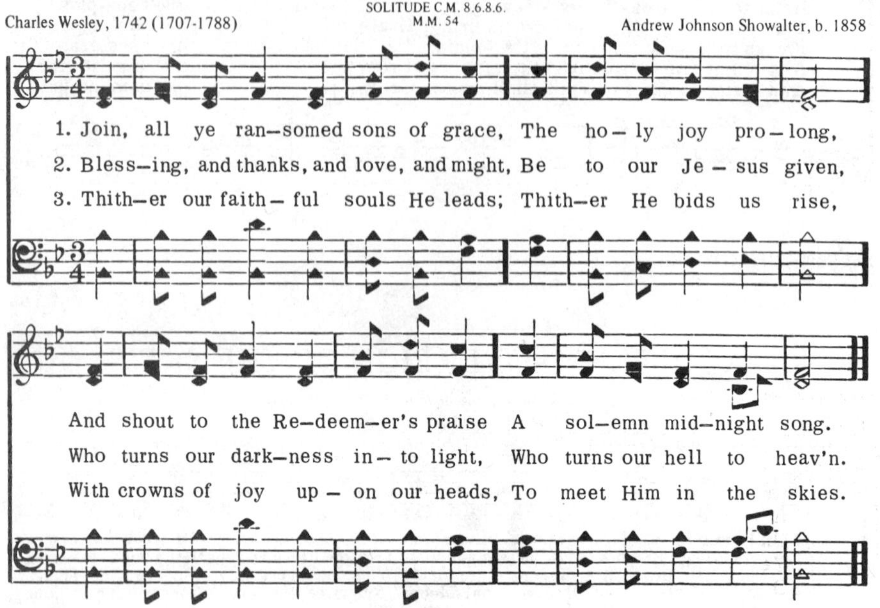
1. Join, all ye ran–somed sons of grace, The ho – ly joy pro – long,
2. Bless–ing, and thanks, and love, and might, Be to our Je – sus given,
3. Thith–er our faith – ful souls He leads; Thith–er He bids us rise,
And shout to the Re–deem–er's praise A sol–emn mid–night song.
Who turns our dark–ness in – to light, Who turns our hell to heav'n.
With crowns of joy up – on our heads, To meet Him in the skies.

# 603 WE WILL NOT CLOSE OUR WAKEFUL EYES

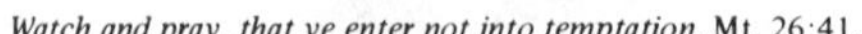

*Watch and pray, that ye enter not into temptation.* Mt. 26:41.

STELLA L.M. 8.8.8.8.
M.M. 76

Charles Wesley, 1707-1788

Old English Air

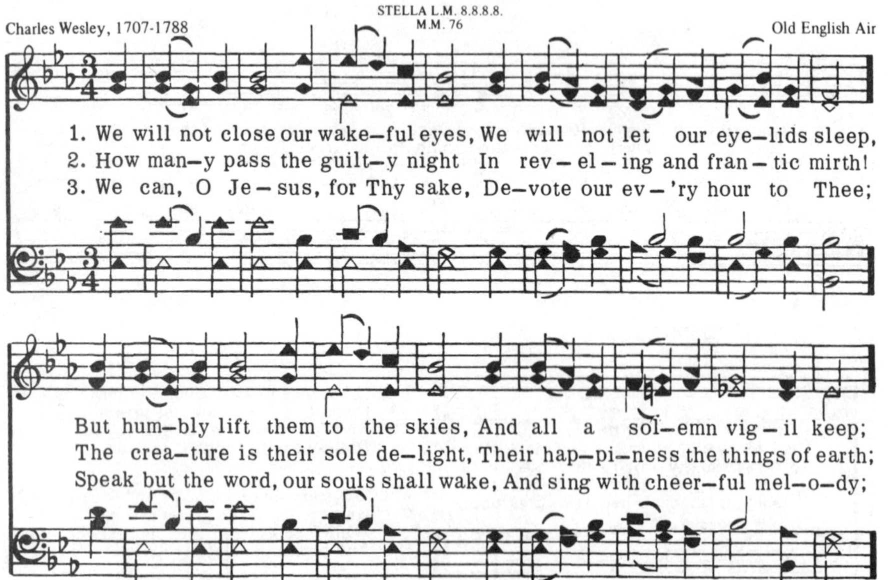
1. We will not close our wake–ful eyes, We will not let our eye–lids sleep,
2. How man–y pass the guilt–y night In rev – el – ing and fran – tic mirth!
3. We can, O Je – sus, for Thy sake, De–vote our ev – 'ry hour to Thee;
But hum–bly lift them to the skies, And all a sol–emn vig – il keep;
The crea–ture is their sole de–light, Their hap–pi–ness the things of earth;
Speak but the word, our souls shall wake, And sing with cheer–ful mel–o–dy;

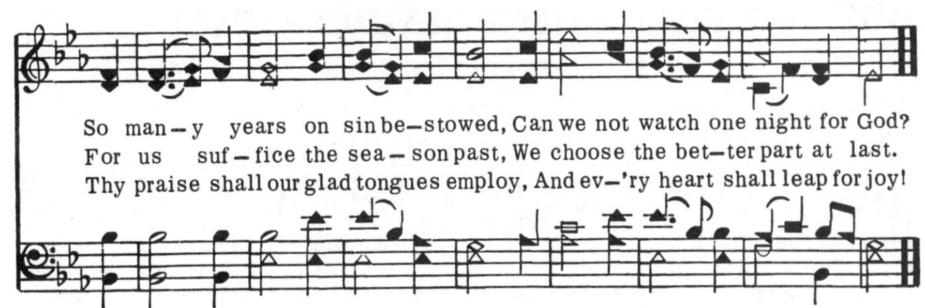
So man-y years on sin be-stowed, Can we not watch one night for God?
For us suf-fice the sea-son past, We choose the bet-ter part at last.
Thy praise shall our glad tongues employ, And ev-'ry heart shall leap for joy!

SEASONS, DAYS, SERVICES: CLOSE OF YEAR

# AWAKE YE SAINTS 604

*Hitherto hath the Lord helped us.* I Sam. 7:12.

ABRIDGE C.M. 8.6.8.6.
M.M. 84

Philip Doddridge, 1702-1751

Isaac Smith, 1735-1800

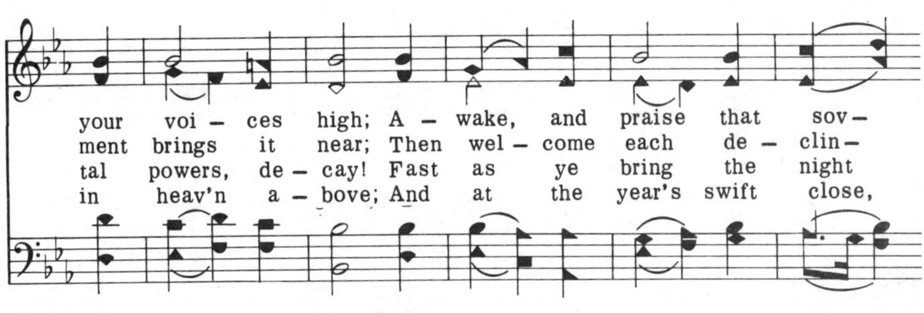

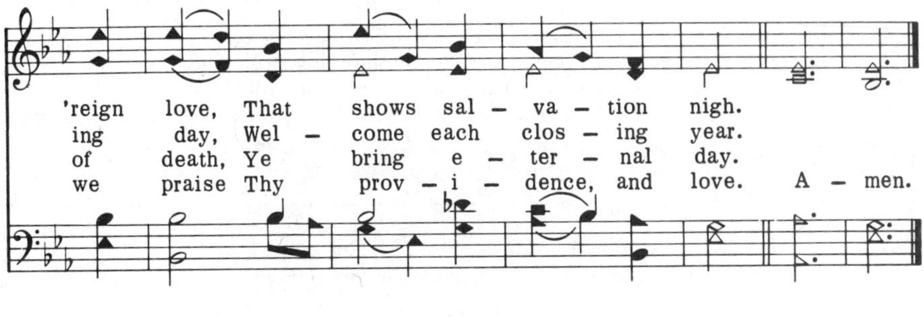

1. A-wake, ye saints, and raise your eyes, And raise your voi-ces high; A-wake, and praise that sov-'reign love, That shows sal-va-tion nigh.
2. On all the wings of time it flies, Each mo-ment brings it near; Then wel-come each de-clin-ing day, Wel-come each clos-ing year.
3. Ye wheels of na-ture, speed your course! Ye mor-tal powers, de-cay! Fast as ye bring the night of death, Ye bring e-ter-nal day.
4. O Fa-ther, here our hearts we raise To Thee in heav'n a-bove; And at the year's swift close, we praise Thy prov-i-dence, and love. A-men.

# 605 THE YEAR IS GONE BEYOND RECALL

*Thou crownest the year with Thy goodness.* Ps. 65:11.

Ancient Anon. Latin Hymn
*Lapsus est annus: redit annus alter*
Tr. Francis Pott, 1832-1909

BEATITUDO C.M. 8.6.8.6.
M.M. 92

John Bacchus Dykes, 1823-1876

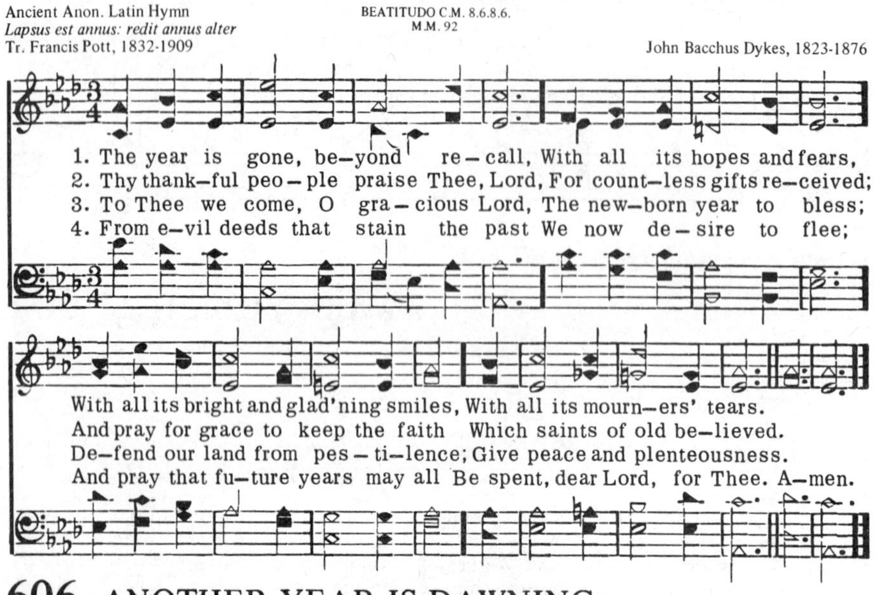
1. The year is gone, be–yond re–call, With all its hopes and fears,
2. Thy thank–ful peo–ple praise Thee, Lord, For count–less gifts re–ceived;
3. To Thee we come, O gra–cious Lord, The new–born year to bless;
4. From e–vil deeds that stain the past We now de–sire to flee;
With all its bright and glad'ning smiles, With all its mourn–ers' tears.
And pray for grace to keep the faith Which saints of old be–lieved.
De–fend our land from pes–ti–lence; Give peace and plenteousness.
And pray that fu–ture years may all Be spent, dear Lord, for Thee. A–men.

# 606 ANOTHER YEAR IS DAWNING

*If Thy presence go not with me, carry us not up hence.* Ex. 33:15.

CHRISTUS DER IST MEIN LEBEN 7.6.7.6.
M.M. 76

Frances Ridley Havergal, 1874 (1836-1879)

Melchior Vulpius, 1609 (1560-1616)

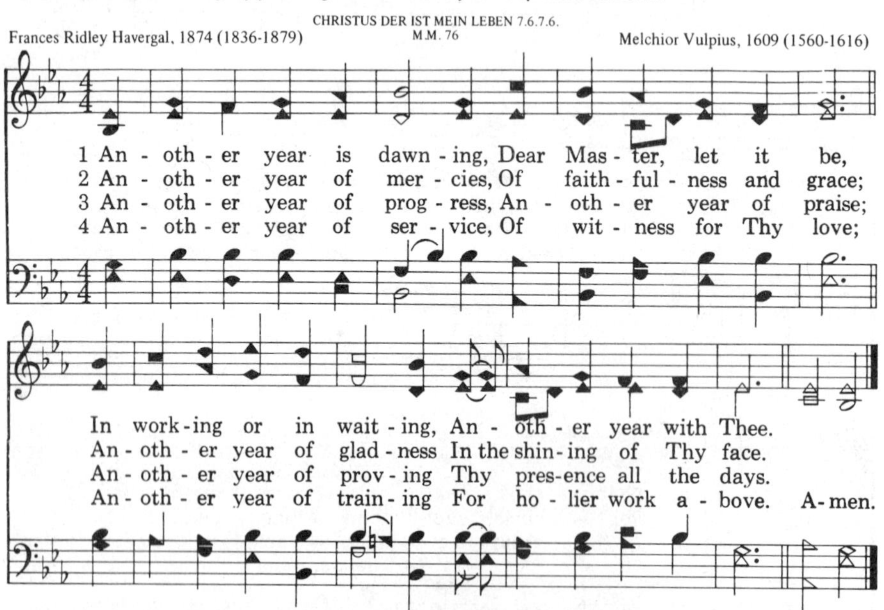
1 An - oth - er year is dawn - ing, Dear Mas - ter, let it be,
2 An - oth - er year of mer - cies, Of faith - ful - ness and grace;
3 An - oth - er year of prog - ress, An - oth - er year of praise;
4 An - oth - er year of ser - vice, Of wit - ness for Thy love;
In work - ing or in wait - ing, An - oth - er year with Thee.
An - oth - er year of glad - ness In the shin - ing of Thy face.
An - oth - er year of prov - ing Thy pres - ence all the days.
An - oth - er year of train - ing For ho - lier work a - bove. A - men.

5 Another year is dawning, Dear Master, let it be,
On earth, or else in heaven, Another year for Thee!

# HOW LONG HATH GOD BESTOWED HIS CARE 607

*If my people . . . shall humble themselves, and pray, and seek My face, and turn from their wicked ways; then will I hear . . . forgive . . . and will heal their land.* II Chron. 7:14.

MELMORE L.M. 8.8.8.8.
M.M. 66

John Newton, 1725-1807

W. Martin

1. How long hath God bestowed his care On this indulged, un-grate-ful land!
How oft in times of dan-ger near, Pre-served us by his sov'reign hand!

2. Here peace and lib-er-ty have dwelt, The glo-rious Gos-pel bright-ly shone;
And oft our mightiest foes have felt That God hath made our cause his own.

3. But, ah! both heav'n and earth have heard Our vile re-qui-tal of his love;
We, whom like chil-dren he has reared, For all his care un-thank-ful prove.

4. See! he up-lifts his chast'ning rod! O, where are now the faith-ful few,
Who trem-ble for the ark of God, And know what Is-rael ought to do?

5. Lord, hear thy peo-ple ev-'ry-where, Who meet this day to weep and pray;
Our sin-ful land in mer-cy spare, In mer-cy turn thy wrath a-way!

# IN GRIEF AND FEAR 608

*I acknowledge my transgressions . . . Purge me with hyssop, and I shall be clean: wash me, and I shall be whiter than snow.* Ps. 51:3, 7.

DUNDEE C.M. 8.6.8.6.
M.M. 58

William Bullock, b. 1798

*Scottish Psalter*

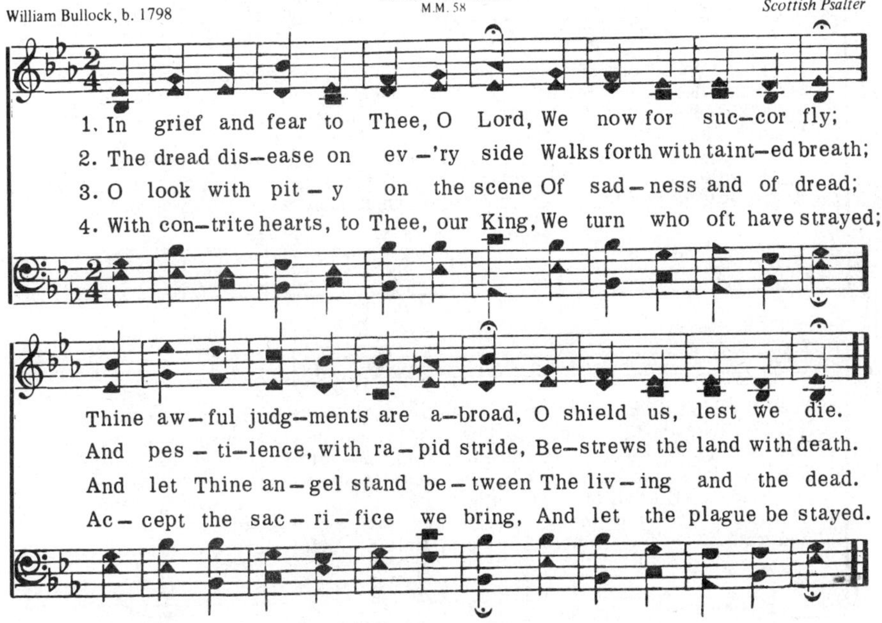
1. In grief and fear to Thee, O Lord, We now for suc-cor fly;
2. The dread dis-ease on ev-'ry side Walks forth with taint-ed breath;
3. O look with pit-y on the scene Of sad-ness and of dread;
4. With con-trite hearts, to Thee, our King, We turn who oft have strayed;
Thine aw-ful judg-ments are a-broad, O shield us, lest we die.
And pes-ti-lence, with ra-pid stride, Be-strews the land with death.
And let Thine an-gel stand be-tween The liv-ing and the dead.
Ac-cept the sac-ri-fice we bring, And let the plague be stayed.

# 609 COME LET OUR SOULS ADORE THE LORD

*I am ashamed and blush to lift up my face . . . for our iniquities are increased over our head, and our trespass is grown up unto the heavens.* Ezra 9:6.

Anne Steele, 1717-1778
Alt. John J. Overholt, 1968

MEDITATION C.M. 8.6.8.6.
M.M. 66

John Henry Gower, 1890 (1855-1922)

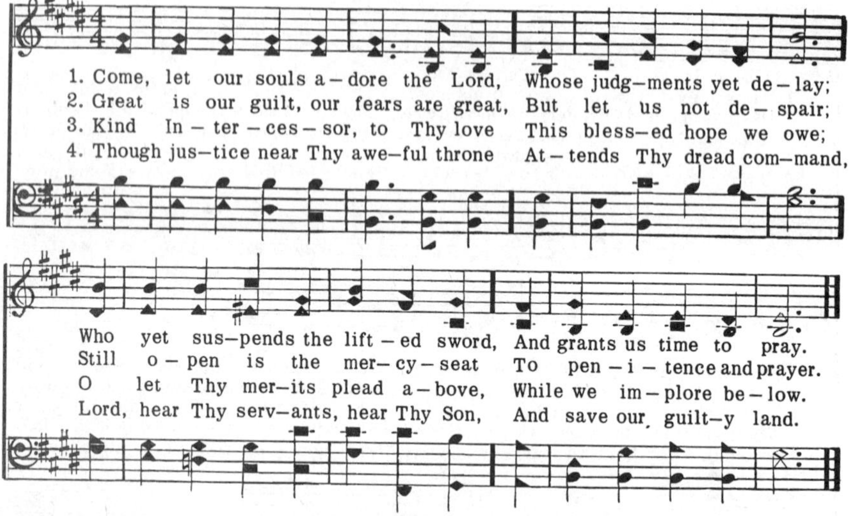

1. Come, let our souls a–dore the Lord, Whose judg–ments yet de–lay;
2. Great is our guilt, our fears are great, But let us not de–spair;
3. Kind In–ter–ces–sor, to Thy love This bless–ed hope we owe;
4. Though jus–tice near Thy awe–ful throne At–tends Thy dread com–mand,

Who yet sus–pends the lift–ed sword, And grants us time to pray.
Still o–pen is the mer–cy–seat To pen–i–tence and prayer.
O let Thy mer–its plead a–bove, While we im–plore be–low.
Lord, hear Thy serv–ants, hear Thy Son, And save our guilt–y land.

# 610 WHEN IN OUR HOUR OF UTMOST NEED

*We have sinned against the Lord our God we and our fathers.* Jer. 3:25.

Paul Eber, 1566 (1511-1569)
*Wenn wir in höchsten Nöthen sein*
Tr. Catherine Winkworth, 1858 (1829-1878)

BERA L.M. 8.8.8.8.
M.M. 52

John Edgar Gould, 1849 (1822-1875)

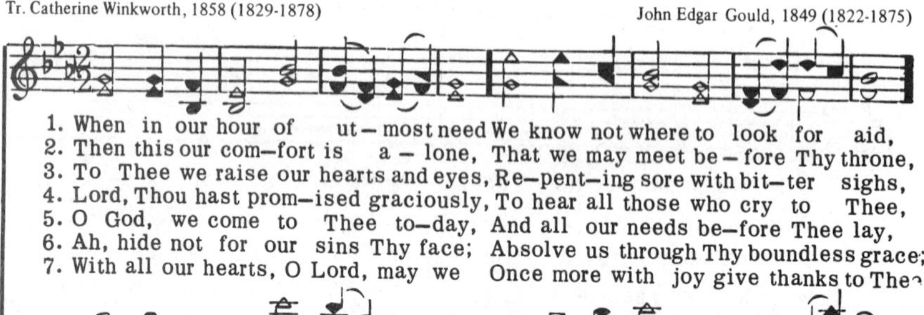
1. When in our hour of ut–most need We know not where to look for aid,
2. Then this our com–fort is a–lone, That we may meet be–fore Thy throne,
3. To Thee we raise our hearts and eyes, Re–pent–ing sore with bit–ter sighs,
4. Lord, Thou hast prom–ised graciously, To hear all those who cry to Thee,
5. O God, we come to Thee to–day, And all our needs be–fore Thee lay,
6. Ah, hide not for our sins Thy face; Absolve us through Thy boundless grace;
7. With all our hearts, O Lord, may we Once more with joy give thanks to Thee.

When days and nights of anxious thought Nor help nor counsel yet have brought.
And cry, O faith–ful God, to Thee For res–cue from our mis–er–y.
And seek Thy par–don for our sin, And res–pite from our griefs within.
Through Him whose name alone is great, Our Sav–iour and our Ad–vo–cate.
For tried, af–flicted, lo, we stand, Per–il and foes on ev–'ry hand.
Be with us in our an–guish still, Free us at last from ev–'ry ill.
And walk o–be–di–ent to Thy Word, And now and ev–er praise the Lord. A–men.

# O GOD OF LOVE, O KING OF PEACE 611

*Pray for the peace of Jerusalem . . . Peace be within thy walls.* Ps. 122:6, 7.

Henry William Baker, 1861 (1821-1877) | HESPERUS L.M. 8.8.8.8. M.M. 76 | Henry William Baker

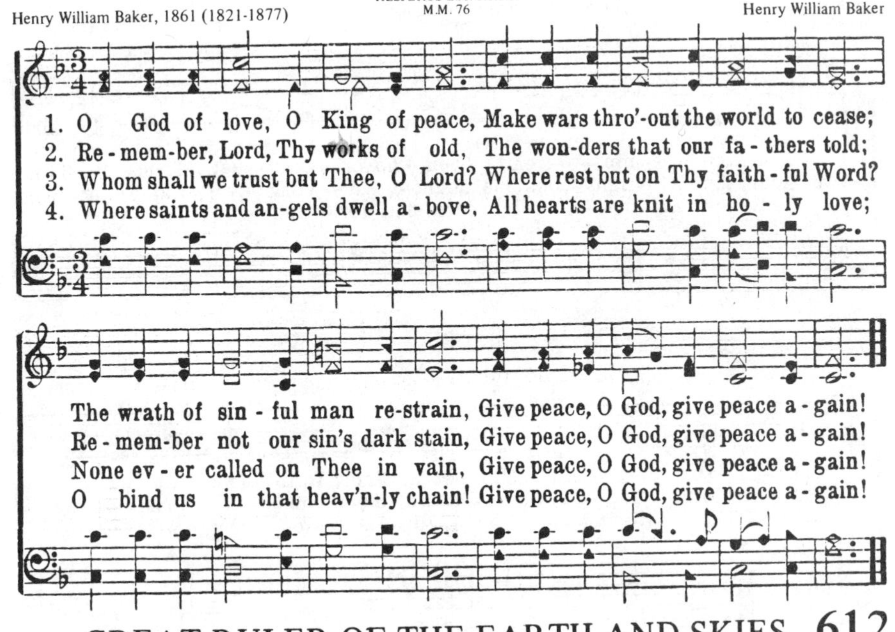

1. O God of love, O King of peace, Make wars thro'-out the world to cease;
2. Re-mem-ber, Lord, Thy works of old, The won-ders that our fa-thers told;
3. Whom shall we trust but Thee, O Lord? Where rest but on Thy faith-ful Word?
4. Where saints and an-gels dwell a-bove, All hearts are knit in ho-ly love;
The wrath of sin-ful man re-strain, Give peace, O God, give peace a-gain!
Re-mem-ber not our sin's dark stain, Give peace, O God, give peace a-gain!
None ev-er called on Thee in vain, Give peace, O God, give peace a-gain!
O bind us in that heav'n-ly chain! Give peace, O God, give peace a-gain!

# GREAT RULER OF THE EARTH AND SKIES 612

*Intercessions . . . be made . . . for all that are in authority; that we may lead a quiet and peaceable life.* I Tim. 2:1-2.

Anne Steele, 1760 (1717-1778)
Altered by Compiler, 1970 | WALTHAM L.M. 8.8.8.8. M.M. 66 | John Baptiste Calkin, 1827-1905

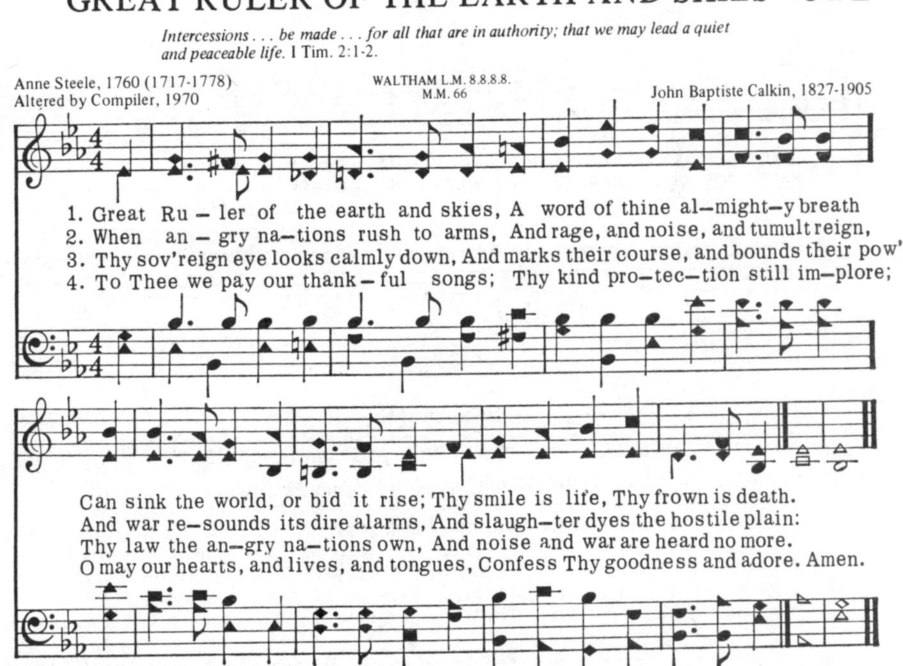

1. Great Ru-ler of the earth and skies, A word of thine al-might-y breath
2. When an-gry na-tions rush to arms, And rage, and noise, and tumult reign,
3. Thy sov'reign eye looks calmly down, And marks their course, and bounds their pow'r,
4. To Thee we pay our thank-ful songs; Thy kind pro-tec-tion still im-plore;
Can sink the world, or bid it rise; Thy smile is life, Thy frown is death.
And war re-sounds its dire alarms, And slaugh-ter dyes the hostile plain:
Thy law the an-gry na-tions own, And noise and war are heard no more.
O may our hearts, and lives, and tongues, Confess Thy goodness and adore. Amen.

# 613 GOD, THE OMNIPOTENT

*Seek the peace of the city . . . and pray unto the Lord for it: for in the peace thereof shall ye have peace.* Jer. 29:7.

Henry Fothergill Chorley, 1842 (1808-1872)
Alt. John Ellerton, 1870 (1826-1893)
Alt. by Compiler, 1971

CONSOLATOR 11.10.11.10.
M.M. 72

Samuel Webbe, 1792 (1740-1816)

1. God, the Om–nip–o–tent! Thou who or–dain–est Thun–der Thy clar–i–on, light–ning Thy sword; Show forth Thy pi–ty high where Thou reign–est; Give to us peace in our time, O Lord.
2. God, the All–right–eous One! might–y A–veng–er, Watch–ing in–vis–i–ble, judg–ing un–heard; Save us in mer–cy, save us from dan–ger; Give to us peace in our time, O Lord.
3. God, the All–mer–ci–ful! earth hath for–sak–en Thy ways all ho–ly, slight–ed Thy Word; Let not Thy wrath in its ter–ror wak–en; Give to us par–don and Thy peace, O Lord.

4. So shall Thy people, with true devotion,
Laud Him who saved from peril and sword,
Shouting in chorus, ocean to ocean,
"Peace to the nations, and praise to the Lord."

# FATHER, WHO ART ALONE 614

*Shew Thy marvellous lovingkindness, O Thou that savest by Thy right hand them which put their trust in Thee.* Ps. 17:7.

LENOX 6.6.6.6.8.8.
M.M. 80

Edith Jones

Lewis Edson, 1782 (1748-1820)

1. Fa – ther, Who art a – lone Our help – er and our stay, Oh, hear us
2. For Thou, our Fa–ther God, Art pres–ent ev–ery–where, And bend–est
3. Oh, com–pass with Thy love The dai–ly path they tread; And may Thy
4. Guard them from ev–ery harm When dan – gers shall as–sail, And teach them
5. We all are travel – lers here A – long life's var–ious road, Meet–ing and

as we plead For loved ones far a–way, And shield with thine almighty hand,
low Thine ear To catch the faintest pray'r, Wait–ing rich bless–ings to be–stow,
light and truth Up–on their hearts be shed, That, one in all things with Thy will,
that Thy pow'r Can nev–er, nev–er fail; We can–not with our loved ones be,
part–ing oft Till we shall mount to God, At home at last with those we love,

And shield with Thine al–might–y hand Our trav–el–ers by sea and land.
Wait–ing rich bless–ings to be–stow On all Thy chil–dren here be – low.
That, one in all things with Thy will, Heav'n's peace and joy their souls may fill.
We can–not with our loved ones be, But trust them, Fa–ther, un– to Thee.
At home at last, with those we love, With–in Thy heav'n–ly home a–bove.

# 615 FOUNDED ON THEE, OUR ONLY LORD

*For other foundation can no man lay than that is laid, which is Jesus Christ.* I Cor. 3:11.

Samuel Francis Smith, 1894 (1808-1895)

MENDON L.M. 8.8.8.8.
M.M. 72

German Air
Arr. Samuel Dyer, 1785-1835

1. Found - ed on Thee, our on - ly Lord, On Thee, the
2. For Thee our wait - ing spir - its yearn, For Thee this
3. Come, with Thy Spir - it and Thy pow'r, The Con - qu'ror,
4. Ac - cept the work our hands have wrought; Ac - cept, O
ev - er - last - ing Rock, Thy Church shall stand as stands Thy
house of praise we rear; To Thee with long - ing hearts we
once the Cru - ci - fied; Our God, our Strength, our King, our
God, this earth - ly shrine; Be Thou our Rock, our Life, our
Word, Nor fear the storm, nor dread the shock.
turn; Come, fix Thy glo - rious pres - ence here.
Tow'r, Here plant Thy throne, and here a - bide.
Thought, And we, as liv - ing tem - ples, Thine. A - MEN.

# 616 THIS NEW BUILT BETHEL NOW IS DONE

*And the king stood by a pillar, and made a covenant before the Lord, to walk after the Lord, and to keep His commandments . . . and all the people stood to the covenant.* II Kings 23:3.

John Winebrenner
St. 4, John Newton, 1725-1807

WINCHESTER OLD C.M. 8.6.8.6.
M.M. 66

*Este's Psalter,* 1592

1. This new–built Beth–el now is done, And here we've met to–day,
2. Here may the pray'r of faith pre–vail, Here may the Gos–pel run;
3. May sin–ners here their sins re–nounce And yield their all to God;
4 With–in these walls let ho–ly peace, And love and con–cord dwell;
5. And when be–fore Thee we ap–pear, In our e–ter–nal home;

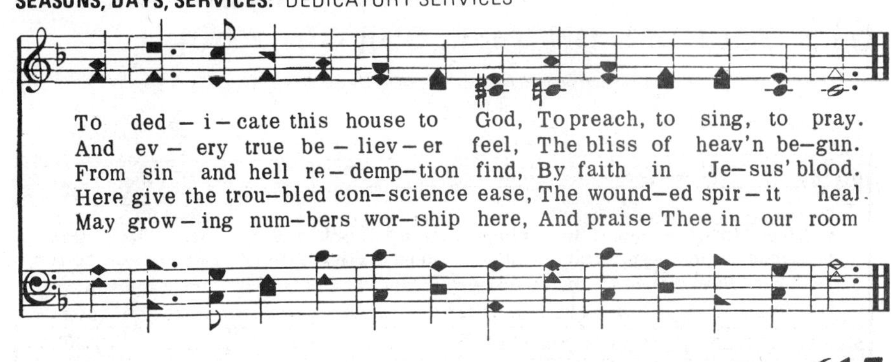
To ded – i – cate this house to God, To preach, to sing, to pray.
And ev – ery true be – liev – er feel, The bliss of heav'n be-gun.
From sin and hell re – demp–tion find, By faith in Je–sus' blood.
Here give the trou–bled con– science ease, The wound–ed spir – it heal.
May grow – ing num–bers wor–ship here, And praise Thee in our room

# IN LOUD EXALTED STRAINS 617

*That Thine eyes may be open toward this house night and day.* I Kings 8:29.

Benjamin Francis, 1734-1799

ST. JOHN 6.6.6.6.8.8.
M.M. 72

William Henry Havergal, 1793-1870
Har. arr. by Compiler, 1965

1. In loud ex – alt – ed strains, The king of glo – ry praise: O'er heav'n and earth He reigns, Thro' ev – er – last – ing days; But Zi – on with His pres – ence blest, Is His de–light, His cho – sen rest.

2. O King of glo – ry, come And with Thy fa – vor crown This tem – ple as Thy home, This peo – ple as Thy own; Be–neath this roof vouch–safe to show How God can dwell with men be – low.

3. Now let Thine ear at – tend Our sup – pli – cat – ing cries; Now let our praise as – cend, Ac – cept – ed, to the skies; Now let Thy Gos–pel's joy – ful sound Spread its ce – les–tial in–fluence 'round.

4. Here may the lis–t'ning throng Im – bibe Thy truth and love; Here Chris–tians join the song Of ser – a – phim a – bove; Till all who hum–bly seek Thy face Re – joice in Thy a – bound – ing grace. A – men.

# 618 BLEST BE THE DEAR UNITING LOVE

*Being taken from you for a short time in presence, not in heart.* I Thess. 2:17.

Charles Wesley, 1707-1788

MARLOW C.M. 8.6.8.6.
M.M. 56

John Chetham, 1685-1763

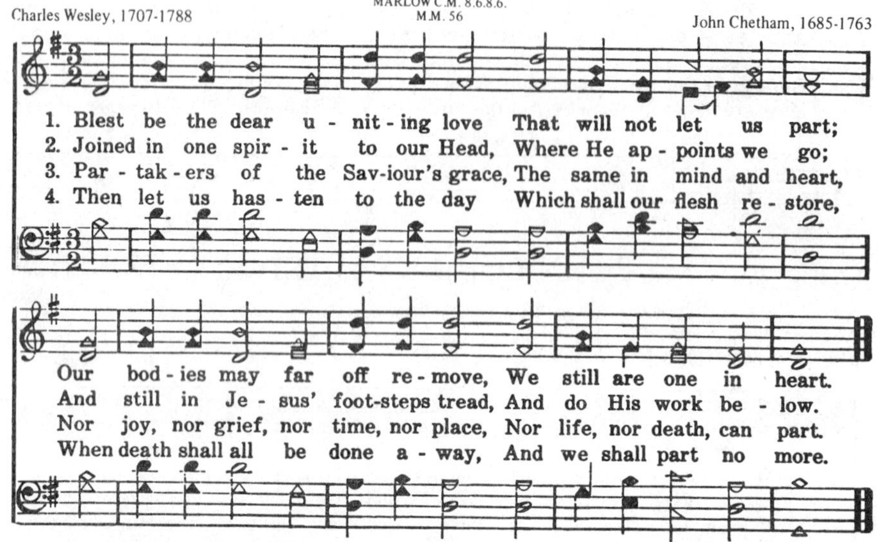
1. Blest be the dear u - nit - ing love That will not let us part;
2. Joined in one spir - it to our Head, Where He ap - points we go;
3. Par - tak - ers of the Saviour's grace, The same in mind and heart,
4. Then let us has - ten to the day Which shall our flesh re - store,
Our bod - ies may far off re - move, We still are one in heart.
And still in Je - sus' foot-steps tread, And do His work be - low.
Nor joy, nor grief, nor time, nor place, Nor life, nor death, can part.
When death shall all be done a - way, And we shall part no more.

# 619 WITH THE SWEET WORD OF PEACE

*The Lord watch between me and thee, when we are absent one from another.* Gen. 31:49.

George Watson, 1867 (1816-1898)

VERBUM PACIS 6.6.8.4.
M.M. 76

William H. Monk, 1823-1889

1. With the sweet word of peace We bid our breth - ren go; Peace
2. With the calm word of prayer We ear - nest - ly com-mend Our
3. With the dear word of love We give our brief fare-well; Our
4. With the strong word of faith We stay our - selves on Thee, That
5. Then the bright word of hope Shall on our part - ing gleam, And
6. Fare-well! in hope and love, In faith, and peace, and prayer; Till
as a riv - er to in-crease, And cease - - less flow.
breth-ren to Thy watch - ful care, E - ter - - - - nal Friend!
love be - low, and Thine a - bove, With them........ shall dwell.
Thou, O Lord, in life and death, Their help........ shalt be;
tell of joys be - yond the scope Of earth - - born dream.
He whose home is ours a - bove, U - nite......... us there. A-MEN.

# MY DEAREST FRIENDS IN BONDS OF LOVE 620

*Finally, brethren farewell. Be perfect, be of good comfort, be of one mind, live in peace; and the God of love and peace shall be with you.* II Cor. 13:11.

PARTING HAND 8.8.8.8.D.
M.M. 104

Anonymous

Jeremiah Ingals, 1805 (1764-1828)

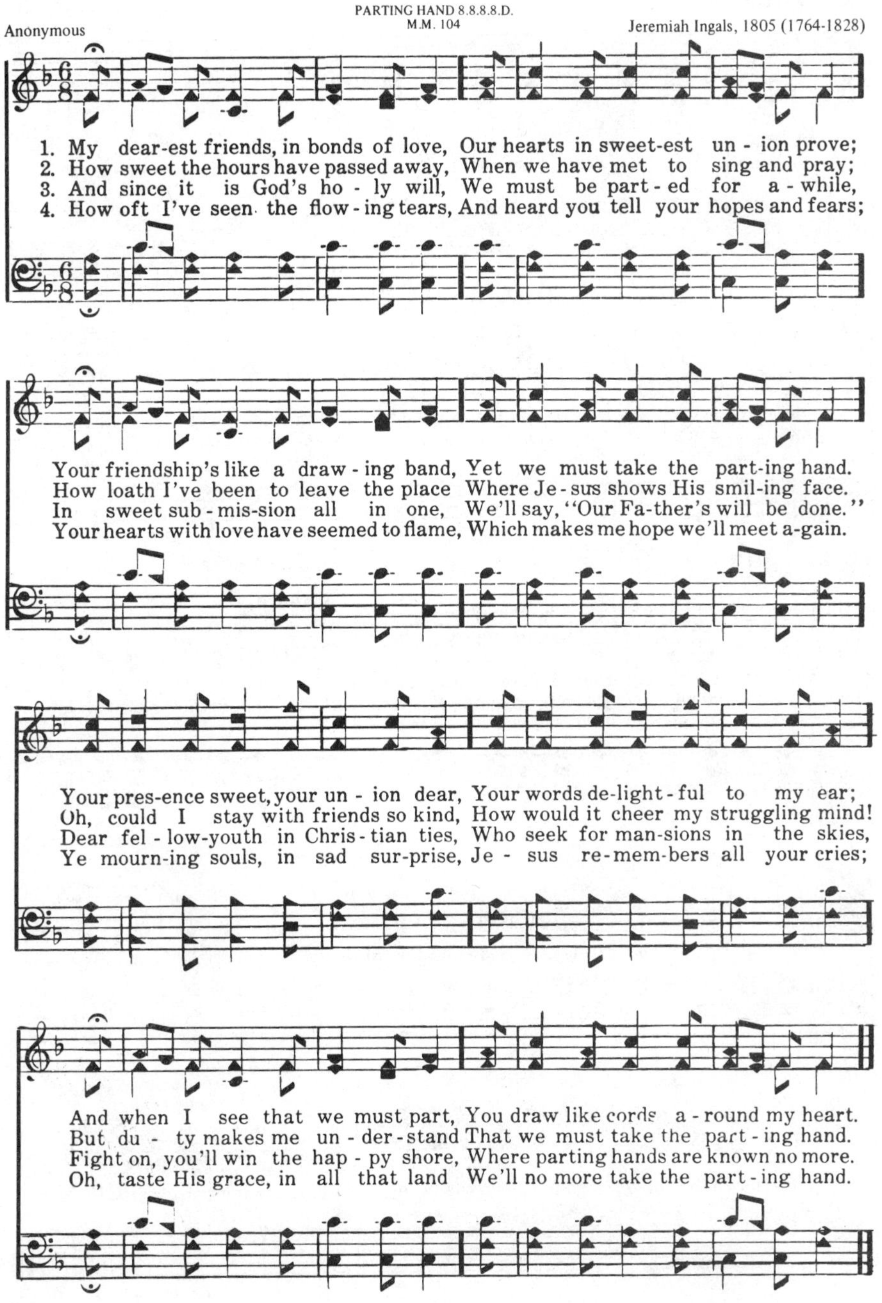
1. My dear-est friends, in bonds of love, Our hearts in sweet-est un - ion prove;
2. How sweet the hours have passed away, When we have met to sing and pray;
3. And since it is God's ho - ly will, We must be part - ed for a - while,
4. How oft I've seen the flow - ing tears, And heard you tell your hopes and fears;
Your friendship's like a draw - ing band, Yet we must take the part-ing hand.
How loath I've been to leave the place Where Je - sus shows His smil-ing face.
In sweet sub - mis-sion all in one, We'll say, "Our Fa-ther's will be done."
Your hearts with love have seemed to flame, Which makes me hope we'll meet a-gain.
Your pres-ence sweet, your un - ion dear, Your words de-light - ful to my ear;
Oh, could I stay with friends so kind, How would it cheer my struggling mind!
Dear fel - low-youth in Chris - tian ties, Who seek for man-sions in the skies,
Ye mourn-ing souls, in sad sur-prise, Je - sus re-mem-bers all your cries;
And when I see that we must part, You draw like cords a - round my heart.
But du - ty makes me un - der - stand That we must take the part - ing hand.
Fight on, you'll win the hap - py shore, Where parting hands are known no more.
Oh, taste His grace, in all that land We'll no more take the part - ing hand.

# 621 WE ARE GOING DOWN THE VALLEY

*Yea, though I walk through the valley of the shadow of death, I will fear no evil.* Ps. 23:4.

Jessie Brown Pounds, 1861-1921
GOING DOWN THE VALLEY 11.11.11.11. with Ref.
M.M. 112
James H. Fillmore, 1849-1936
1. We are go-ing down the val-ley, one by one, With our fa-ces tow'rd the set-ting of the sun; Down the val-ley where the mourn-ful cy-press grows, Where the stream of death in si-lence on-ward flows.
2. We are go-ing down the val-ley, one by one, When the la-bors of the wea-ry day are done; One by one, the cares of earth for-ev-er past, We shall stand up-on the riv-er bank at last.
3. We are go-ing down the val-ley, one by one, Hu-man comrade you or I will there have none; But a ten-der hand will guide us lest we fall, Christ is go-ing down the valley with us all.
Refrain.
We are go-ing down the val-ley, go-ing down the val-ley, Go-ing tow'rd the set-ting of the sun; We are going down the valley, go-ing down the valley, Go-ing down the valley, one by one.
rit.

# LET ME GO WHERE SAINTS ARE GOING 622

*Let me die the death of the righteous, and let my last end be like his!* Num. 23:10.

LET ME GO 8.7.8.7.D.
M.M. 56
Lewis Hartsough, 1828-1919
Lewis Hartsough
1. Let me go where saints are go - ing, To the man - sions of the blest;
2. Let me go where none are wea - ry, Where is raised no wail of woe;
3. Let me go, why should I tar - ry? What has earth to bind me here?
Let me go where my Re - deem-er Has pre- pared his peo - ple rest.
Let me go and bathe my spir - it In the rap - tures an - gels know.
What but cares, and toils, and sor - rows? What but death, and pain, and fear?
I would gain the realms of bright-ness, Where they dwell for - ev - er - more;
Let me go, for bliss e - ter - nal Lures my soul a - way, a - way,
Let me go, for hopes most cher-ished, Blast - ed round me oft - en lie;
I would join the friends that wait me O - ver on the oth - er shore.
And the vic - tor's song tri - um-phant Thrills my heart, — I can - not stay.
Oh! I've gath - ered bright-est flow - ers, But to see them fade and die.

# 623 SILENTLY, SILENTLY, THEY PASS AWAY

*Precious in the sight of the Lord is the death of His saints.* Ps. 116:15.

SILENTLY THEY PASS AWAY 10.10.10.10.8.8.
M.M. 69

Anonymous | C. E. Leslie

p
pp
cres.
dim.
p rit.
1. Si - lent - ly, si - lent - ly, they pass a - way, Si - lent - ly, si - lent - ly, short is their stay; From earth to heav - en they've tak - en their flight, Far from all sor - row and pain and from night, To their Sav - iour who is call - ing, Call - ing, come home, Call-ing, come home.
2. Si - lent - ly, si - lent - ly, sweet is their sleep, Si - lent - ly, si - lent - ly, for them we weep; Oh, how we mourn, and how sad are our hearts, When from the bod - y the spir - it de - parts! But 'tis Je - sus who is call - ing, Call - ing, come home, Call-ing, come home.
3. Si - lent - ly, si - lent - ly, bur - y the dead, Si - lent - ly, si - lent - ly, the soul has fled Up to our heav - en - ly Fa - ther who gave, And through His great lov - ing kind - ness will save. For 'tis Je - sus who is call - ing, Call - ing, come home, Call-ing, come home.
4. Si - lent - ly, si - lent - ly, lay them to rest, Si - lent - ly, si - lent - ly, God thought it best A - loft in heav - en their Sav - iour to meet, And all the sanc - ti - fied an - gels to greet. So, 'tis Je - sus who is call - ing, Call - ing, come home, Call-ing, come home.

## GO TO THY REST, FAIR CHILD 624

*I shall go to him, but he shall not return to me.* II Sam. 12:23.

BURBER S.M. 6.6.8.6.
M.M. 63

Lydia H. Sigourney, 1791-1865

John Harrison Tenney, b. 1840

1. Go to thy rest, fair child! Go to thy dream - less bed,
2. Be - fore thy heart had learned In way - ward - ness to stray;
3. Ere sin had seared the breast, Or sor - row woke the tear;
4. Be - cause thy smile was fair, Thy lip and eye so bright,
5. Shall love, with weak em - brace, Thy up - ward wing de - tain?
While yet so gen - tle, un - de - filed, With bless-ings on thy head.
Be - fore thy feet had ev - er turned The dark and down-ward way;
Rise to thy throne of change-less rest, In yon ce - les - tial sphere!
Be - cause thy lov - ing cra - dle - care Was such a dear de - light;
No! gen - tle spir - it, seek thy place A - mid the cher - ub train.

## SISTER, THOU WAST MILD AND LOVELY 625

*The Spirit shall return unto God Who gave it.* Eccles. 12:7.

MOUNT VERNON 8.7.8.7.
M.M. 60

Samuel F. Smith, 1808-1895

Lowell Mason, 1792-1872

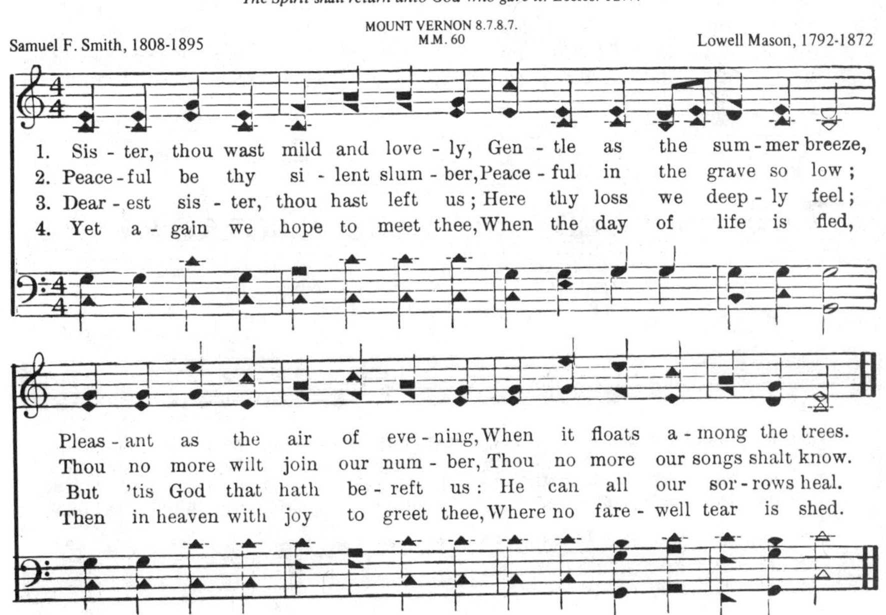
1. Sis - ter, thou wast mild and love - ly, Gen - tle as the sum - mer breeze,
2. Peace - ful be thy si - lent slum - ber, Peace - ful in the grave so low;
3. Dear - est sis - ter, thou hast left us; Here thy loss we deep - ly feel;
4. Yet a - gain we hope to meet thee, When the day of life is fled,
Pleas - ant as the air of eve - ning, When it floats a - mong the trees.
Thou no more wilt join our num - ber, Thou no more our songs shalt know.
But 'tis God that hath be - reft us: He can all our sor - rows heal.
Then in heaven with joy to greet thee, Where no fare - well tear is shed.

# 626 ASLEEP IN JESUS! BLESSED SLEEP

*Blessed are the dead which die in the Lord from henceforth: Yea, saith the Spirit, that they may rest from their labours; and their works do follow them.* Rev. 14:13.

REST L.M. 8.8.8.8.
M.M. 52

Margaret Mackay, 1802-1887

William Batchelder Bradbury, 1816-1868

1. A - sleep in Je - sus! bless - ed sleep, From which none
2. A - sleep in Je - sus! oh, how sweet To be for
3. A - sleep in Je - sus! peace - ful rest! Whose wak - ing
4. A - sleep in Je - sus! oh, for me May such a

ev - er wakes to weep; A calm and un - dis-
such a slum - ber meet! With ho - ly con - fi-
is su - preme - ly blest; No fear, no woe shall
bliss - ful ref - uge be! Se - cure - ly shall my

turbed re - pose, Un - bro - ken by the last of foes.
dence to sing That death has lost its ven - omed sting.
dim that hour Which man - i - fests the Sav - iour's pow'r.
ash - es lie, And wait the sum - mons from on high.

# 627 WHY SHOULD OUR TEARS IN SORROW FLOW

*For we know that if our earthly house of this tabernacle were dissolved, we have a building of God, an house not made with hands, eternal in the heavens.* II Cor. 5:1.

GREEN HILL C.M. 8.6.8.6.
M.M. 63

William Hiley Bathurst, 1796-1877

Albert Lister Peace, 1844-1912

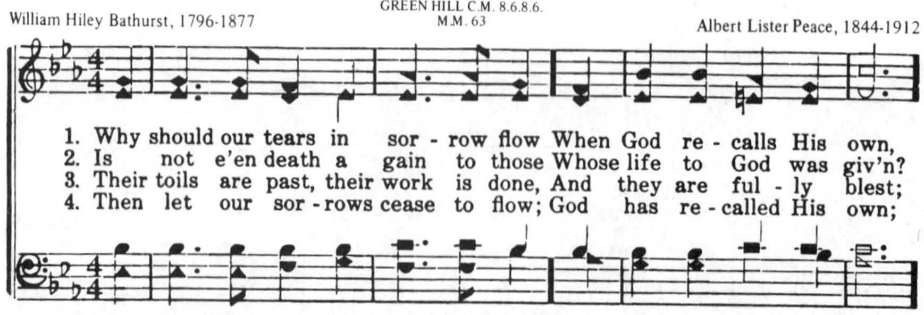
1. Why should our tears in sor - row flow When God re - calls His own,
2. Is not e'en death a gain to those Whose life to God was giv'n?
3. Their toils are past, their work is done, And they are ful - ly blest;
4. Then let our sor - rows cease to flow; God has re - called His own;

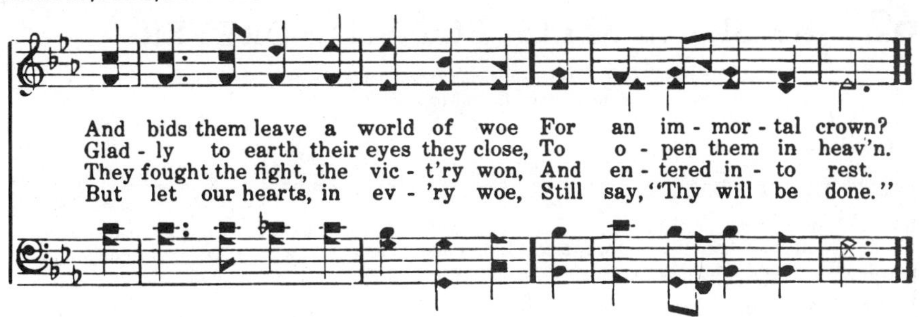
And bids them leave a world of woe For an im - mor - tal crown?
Glad - ly to earth their eyes they close, To o - pen them in heav'n.
They fought the fight, the vic - t'ry won, And en - tered in - to rest.
But let our hearts, in ev - 'ry woe, Still say, "Thy will be done."

## JESUS HAS TAKEN A BEAUTIFUL BUD 628

*The Lord gave, and the Lord hath taken away; blessed be the name of the Lord.* Job. 1:21.

James Rowe, 1865-1933 — GATHERING BUDS 10.7.10.7. with Ref. M.M. 76 — James D. Vaughan, 1864-1941

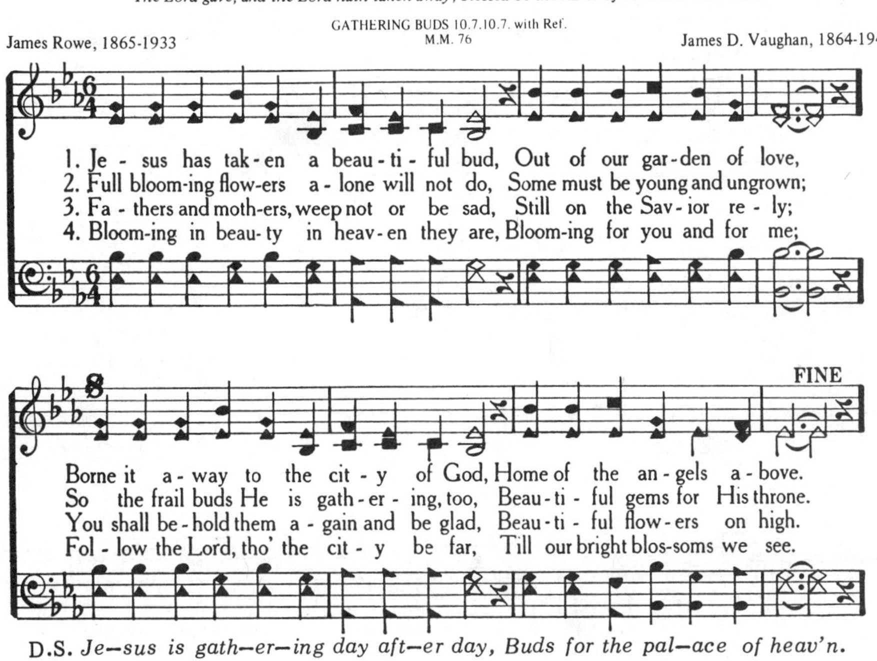
1. Je - sus has tak - en a beau - ti - ful bud, Out of our gar - den of love,
2. Full bloom-ing flow-ers a - lone will not do, Some must be young and ungrown;
3. Fa - thers and moth-ers, weep not or be sad, Still on the Sav - ior re - ly;
4. Bloom-ing in beau - ty in heav - en they are, Bloom-ing for you and for me;
FINE
Borne it a - way to the cit - y of God, Home of the an - gels a - bove.
So the frail buds He is gath - er - ing, too, Beau - ti - ful gems for His throne.
You shall be - hold them a - gain and be glad, Beau - ti - ful flow - ers on high.
Fol - low the Lord, tho' the cit - y be far, Till our bright blos - soms we see.
D.S. Je—sus is gath—er—ing day aft—er day, Buds for the pal—ace of heav'n.

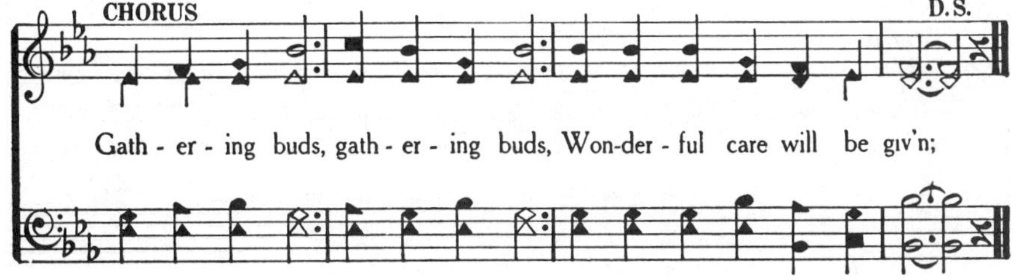
CHORUS
D.S.
Gath - er - ing buds, gath - er - ing buds, Won-der - ful care will be giv'n;

# 629 WE SHALL SLEEP, BUT NOT FOREVER

*I know that he [we] shall rise again in the resurrection at the last day.* Jn. 11:24.

WE SHALL SLEEP BUT NOT FOREVER 8.7.8.7. with Ref.
M.M. 58

Mrs. M. A. Kidder, b. 1825

Silas Jones Vail, 1818-1884

1. We shall sleep, but not for - ev - er, There will be a glo- rious dawn;
2. When we see a pre - cious blos-som That we tend - ed with such care,
3. We shall sleep, but not for - ev - er, In the lone and si - lent grave;
We shall meet to part, no, nev - er, On the res - ur - rec - tion morn.
Rude - ly tak - en from our bo - som, How our ach - ing hearts de - spair!
Bless - ed be the Lord that tak - eth, Bless - ed be the Lord that gave.
From the deep - est caves of o - cean, From the des - ert and the plain,
Round its lit - tle grave we lin - ger, Till the set - ting sun is low,
In the bright e - ter - nal cit - y Death can nev - er, nev - er come!
From the val - ley and the moun-tain, Count - less throngs shall rise a - gain.
Feel - ing all our hopes have per - ished With the flow'r we cher-ished so.
In his own good time he'll call us From our rest, to home, sweet home.
CHORUS.
We shall sleep, but not for - ev - er, There will be a glo-rious dawn;

We shall meet to part, no, nev - er, On the res - ur - rec - tion morn.

# JESUS, WHILE OUR HEARTS ARE BLEEDING 630

*Not My will, but Thine, be done.* Lk. 22:42.

MOUNT VERNON 8.7.8.7.
M.M. 66

Thomas Hastings, 1834 (1784-1872)

Lowell Mason, 1792-1872

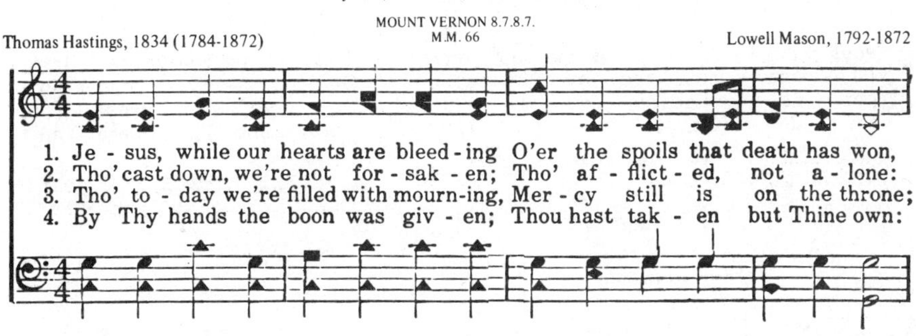
1. Je - sus, while our hearts are bleed - ing O'er the spoils that death has won,
2. Tho' cast down, we're not for - sak - en; Tho' af - flict - ed, not a - lone:
3. Tho' to - day we're filled with mourn-ing, Mer - cy still is on the throne;
4. By Thy hands the boon was giv - en; Thou hast tak - en but Thine own:

We would, at this sol - emn meet - ing, Calm - ly say, "Thy will be done."
Thou didst give, and Thou hast tak - en: Bless - ed Lord, "Thy will be done."
With Thy smiles of love re - turn - ing, We can sing, "Thy will be done."
Lord of earth, and God of heav - en, Ev - er-more, "Thy will be done."

# 631 FATHER OF SPIRITS, WHOSE DIVINE CONTROL

*Today shalt thou be with Me in Paradise.* Lk. 23:43.

Aurelius Clemens Prudentius, 348-413
*Deus ignee fons animarum*
Tr. Percy Dearmer, 1867-1936, alt.
Altered by Compiler, 1971
GENEVA 124 (OLD 124th)
10.10.10.10.10.
M.M. 56
Geneva, 1551
Har. Claude Goudimel, 1565 (1505-1572)
1. Fa – ther of spir – its, whose di – vine con – trol Doth bind the
2. Thou, Mak – er of the bod – y dost or – dain That this thine
3. In that blest re – gion shall this spir – it dwell Where joys su –
4. This pil – grim go – eth by the shin – ing way, That ev – er
soul and bod – y in – to one, Thou shalt re – store this
im – age, mould – ed by Thy will, Our ev – ery hope in
per – nal stand on ev – ery side; For, lo, we trust Thy
to the faith – ful o – pen lies; Lord, keep Thy serv – ant
bod – y now un – done; For once it was the man – sion of a
glo – ry shall ful – fil; So, till the bod – y Thou dost build a –
word, O Cru – ci – fied, When in Thy tri – umph o – ver death and
now in par – a – dise, And bless him in Thy heav'n – ly care, we
soul, Where dwelt a hum – ble pil – grim of Thy Son.
gain, Thou wilt pre – serve the spir – it freed from ill.
hell, The thief for – giv – en took Thee for his guide.
pray, Till Thou shalt bid the bod – y to a – rise.

# BLESSING, HONOUR, THANKS, AND PRAISE 632

*Thanks be to God, which giveth us the victory through our Lord Jesus Christ.* I Cor. 15:57.

Charles Wesley, 1707-1788, alt.
MESSIAH 7.7.7.7.D.
M.M. 66
Arr. from Louis J. F. Herold, 1799-1833
1. Bless–ing, hon–our, thanks, and praise, Pay we gra–cious God to Thee;
2. Hap – py are the faith–ful dead, Bless–ed who in Je – sus die;
3. Ab – sent from our lov – ing Lord We shall not con – tin – ue long;
Thou in Thine a – bun – dant grace Giv – est us the vic – to – ry;
They from all their toils are freed, In God's keep–ing safe – ly lie,
Join we then with one ac – cord In the new, the joy–ful song;
True and faith–ful to Thy Word, Thou hast glo – ri – fied Thy Son;
These the Spir – it hath de–clared Blest, un – ut – ter – a – bly blest,
Bless–ing, hon–our, thanks, and praise, Tri – une God, we pay to Thee,
Je – sus Christ, our ris – en Lord, Has for us the vict'– ry won.
Je – sus is their great re – ward, Je – sus is their end–less rest.
Who in Thine a – bun – dant grace Giv–est us the vic – to – ry!

## HEAR WHAT THE VOICE FROM HEAVEN PROCLAIMS

*And I heard a voice from heaving saying . . . Blessed are the dead which die in the Lord.* Rev. 14:13.

Isaac Watts, 1674-1748 | HARVEY'S CHANT C.M. 8.6.8.6. M.M. 58 | William Batchelder Bradbury, 1816-1878

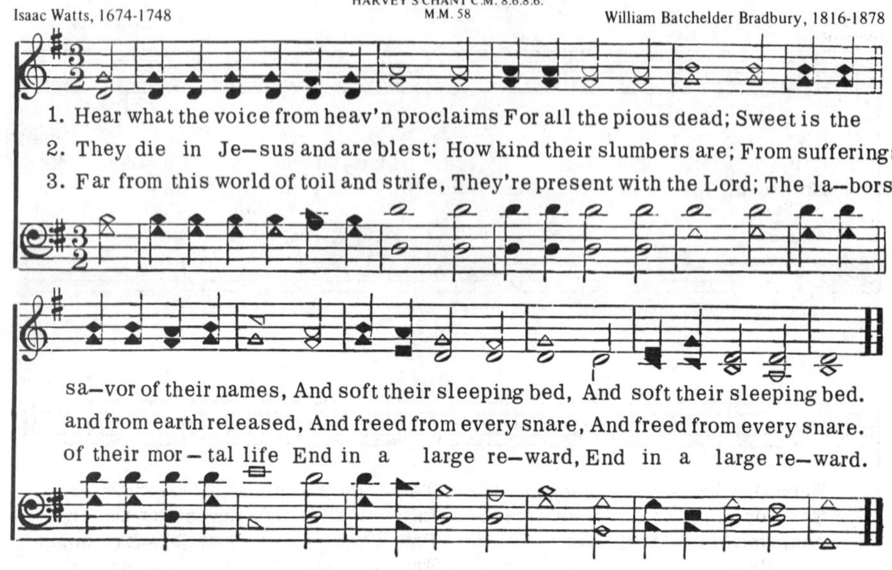
1. Hear what the voice from heav'n proclaims For all the pious dead; Sweet is the sa–vor of their names, And soft their sleeping bed, And soft their sleeping bed.
2. They die in Je–sus and are blest; How kind their slumbers are; From sufferings and from earth released, And freed from every snare, And freed from every snare.
3. Far from this world of toil and strife, They're present with the Lord; The la–bors of their mor – tal life End in a large re–ward, End in a large re–ward.

## 634 O LORD, IN HEAVEN FOREVER FREE

*And I heard as it were the voice of a great multitude, and as the voice of many waters, and as the voice of mighty thunderings, saying, Alleluia: for the Lord God omnipotent reigneth.* Rev. 19:6.

Frederick Lucian Hosmer, 1888 (1840-1929) | VICTORY 8.8.8.4. M.M. 80 | Giovanni Palestrina, 1591 (1525-1594)
Sts. 1-3 alt. John J. Overholt, 1971 | | Adapted William Henry Monk, 1861 (1823-1889)

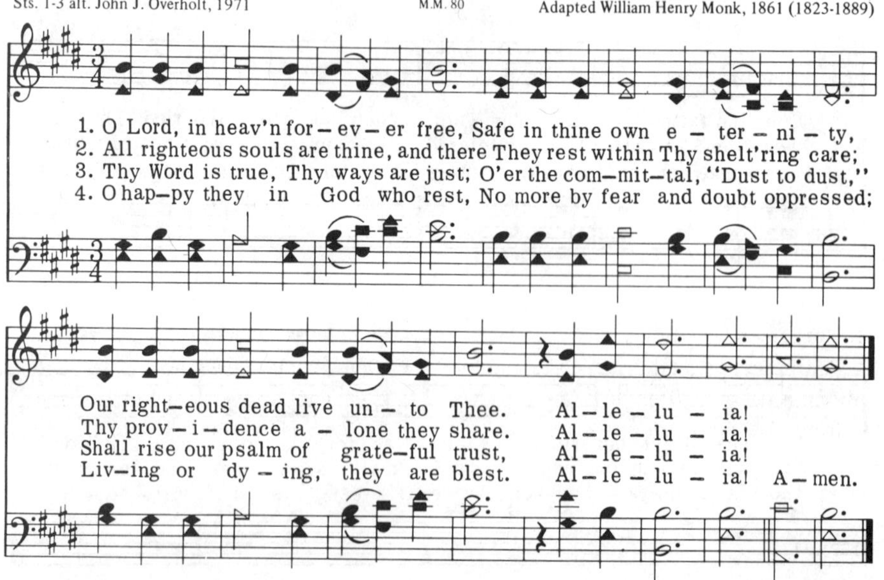
1. O Lord, in heav'n for – ev – er free, Safe in thine own e – ter – ni – ty, Our right–eous dead live un – to Thee. Al – le – lu – ia!
2. All righteous souls are thine, and there They rest within Thy shelt'ring care; Thy prov – i – dence a – lone they share. Al – le – lu – ia!
3. Thy Word is true, Thy ways are just; O'er the com–mit–tal, "Dust to dust," Shall rise our psalm of grate–ful trust, Al – le – lu – ia!
4. O hap–py they in God who rest, No more by fear and doubt oppressed; Liv–ing or dy – ing, they are blest. Al – le – lu – ia! A – men.

# THIS BODY IN THE GRAVE WE LAY 635

*For dust thou art, and unto dust shalt thou return.* Gen. 3:19. *Then shall the dust return to the earth as it was: and the spirit shall return unto God Who gave it.* Eccles. 12:7.

Michael Weisse, 1531 (1480-1534)
*Nun lasst uns den Leib begraben*
Tr. William M. Czamanske, 1938 (b. 1873)

ROSEDALE L.M. 8.8.8.8.
M.M. 66

George Frederick Root, 1820-1895

1. This bod–y in the grave we lay There to a–wait that sol– emn day
2. And so to earth we now en–trust What came from dust and turns to dust
3. The soul for – ev – er lives with God, Who free – ly hath His grace be–stowed
4. All tri – als and all griefs are past, A bless–ed end has come at last.

When God Him–self shall bid it rise To mount tri – um–phant to the skies.
And from the dust shall rise that day In glo – rious tri – umph o'er de – cay.
And through His Son re–deemed it here From ev – ery sin, from ev – ery fear.
Christ's yoke was borne with ready will; Who die – eth thus is liv – ing still.

5. We have no cause to mourn or weep;
Securely shall this body sleep
Till Christ Himself shall death destroy
And raise the blessed dead to joy.

6. For they who with Him suffered here
Shall there be healed from woe and fear;
And when eternal bliss is won,
They'll shine in glory like the sun.

7. Then let us leave this place of rest
And homeward turn, for they are blest
Who heed God's warning and prepare
Lest death should find them unaware.

8. So help us, Jesus, ground of faith;
Thou hast redeemed us by Thy death
From endless death and set us free.
We laud and praise and worship Thee.

# 636 SAFE IN THE ARMS OF JESUS

*And He took them up in His arms . . . and blessed them.* Mk. 10:16.

SAFE IN THE ARMS OF JESUS 7.6.7.6.
M.M. 66
Fanny Jane Crosby, 1820-1915
William Howard Doane, 1832-1915
1. Safe in the arms of Je - sus, Safe on His gen - tle breast,
2. Safe in the arms of Je - sus, Safe from cor - rod - ing care,
3. Je - sus, my heart's dear ref - uge, Je - sus has died for me;
REF.—Safe in the arms of Je - sus, Safe on His gen - tle breast,
rit.
FINE
There by His love o'er - shad - ed, Sweet-ly my soul shall rest.
Safe from the world's temp-ta - tions, Sin can - not harm me there.
Firm on the Rock of A - ges Ev - er my trust shall be.
There by His love o'er - shad - ed, Sweet - ly my soul shall rest.
Hark! 'tis the voice of an - gels, Borne in a song to me,
Free from the blight of sor - row, Free from my doubts and fears;
Here let me wait with pa - tience, Wait till the night is o'er;
D. C.
O - ver the fields of glo - ry, O - ver the jas - per sea......
On - ly a few more tri - als, On - ly a few more tears!....
Wait till I see the morn - ing Break on the gold - en shore....

# WHY DO WE MOURN 637

*For whether we live, we live unto the Lord; and whether we die, we die unto the Lord: whether we live therefore, or die, we are the Lord's.* Rom. 14:8.

INVITATION C.M. 8.6.8.6.
M.M. 69

Isaac Watts, 1674-1748 | William Vincent Wallace, 1814-1865

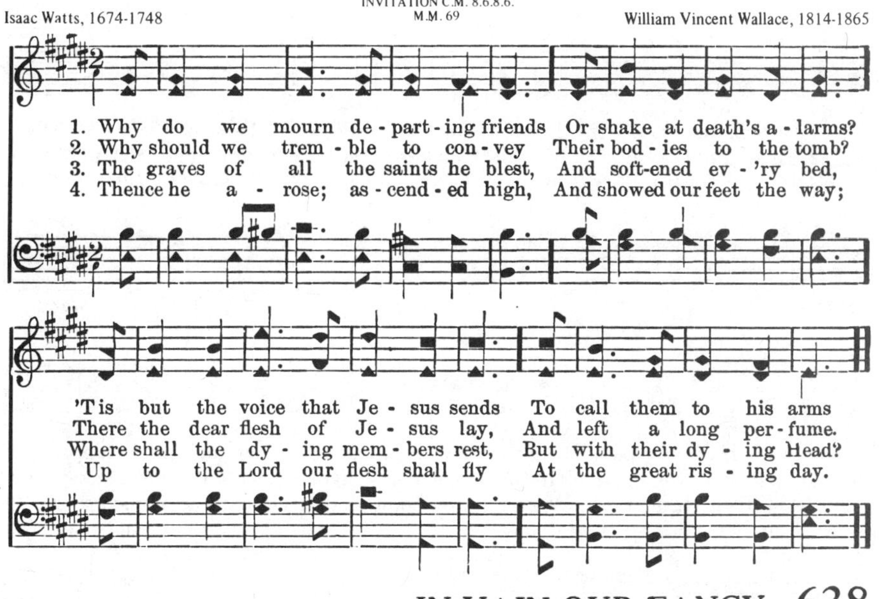
1. Why do we mourn de - part - ing friends Or shake at death's a - larms?
2. Why should we trem - ble to con - vey Their bod - ies to the tomb?
3. The graves of all the saints he blest, And soft-ened ev - 'ry bed,
4. Thence he a - rose; as - cend - ed high, And showed our feet the way;
'Tis but the voice that Je - sus sends To call them to his arms
There the dear flesh of Je - sus lay, And left a long per - fume.
Where shall the dy - ing mem - bers rest, But with their dy - ing Head?
Up to the Lord our flesh shall fly At the great ris - ing day.

# IN VAIN OUR FANCY 638

*Yea, though I walk through the valley of the shadow of death, I will fear no evil: for Thou art with me.* Ps. 23:4.

YORK C.M. 8.6.8.6.
M.M. 66

John Newton, 1725-1807 | *Scottish Psalter*

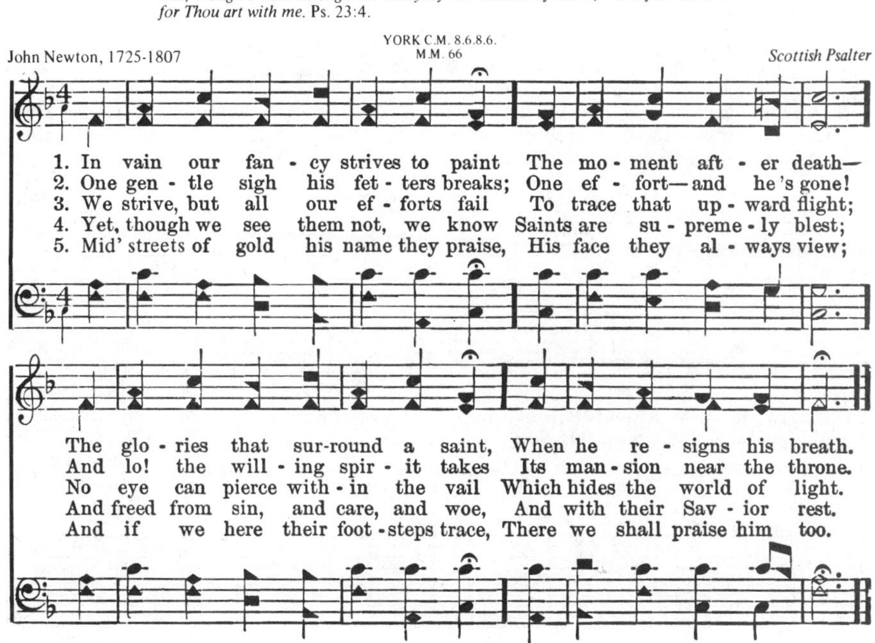
1. In vain our fan - cy strives to paint The mo - ment aft - er death—
2. One gen - tle sigh his fet - ters breaks; One ef - fort—and he 's gone!
3. We strive, but all our ef - forts fail To trace that up - ward flight;
4. Yet, though we see them not, we know Saints are su - preme - ly blest;
5. Mid' streets of gold his name they praise, His face they al - ways view;
The glo - ries that sur-round a saint, When he re - signs his breath.
And lo! the will - ing spir - it takes Its man - sion near the throne.
No eye can pierce with - in the vail Which hides the world of light.
And freed from sin, and care, and woe, And with their Sav - ior rest.
And if we here their foot - steps trace, There we shall praise him too.

# 639 BE STILL, MY SOUL

*Be still, and know that I am God.* Ps. 46:10.

Catherina A.D. von Schlegel, 1752, b. 1697
*Stille, mein Wille*
Tr. Jane Laurie Borthwick, 1855 (1813-1897)

FINDLANDIA 10.10.10.10.10.10.
M.M. 52

From Jean Sibelius, 1899 (1865-1957)

1 Be still, my soul! the Lord is on thy side; Bear pa-tient-ly the cross of grief or pain; Leave to thy God to or-der and pro-vide, In ev-ery change He faith-ful will re-main. Be still, my soul! thy best, thy heav'n-ly Friend Through thorn-y ways leads to a joy-ful end.

2 Be still, my soul! thy God doth un-der-take To guide the fu-ture as He has the past. Thy hope, thy con-fi-dence, let noth-ing shake; All now mys-te-rious shall be bright at last. Be still, my soul! the waves and winds still know His voice who ruled them while He dwelt be-low.

3 Be still, my soul! the hour is has-t'ning on When we shall be for-ev-er with the Lord, When dis-ap-point-ment, grief, and fear are gone, Sor-row for-got, love's pur-est joys re-stored. Be still, my soul! when change and tears are past, All safe and bless-ed we shall meet at last. A-men.

# JESUS, STILL LEAD ON 640

*Whither thou goest, I will go; and where thou lodgest, I will lodge.* Ruth 1:16.

Nicolaus Ludwig von Zinzendorf, 1721 (1700-1760)
*Jesu, geh' voran*
Tr. Jane Laurie Borthwick, 1846 (1813-1897)

SEELENBRÄUTIGAM
5.5.8.8.5.5.
M.M. 63

Adam Drese, 1698 (1620-1701)

1 Je - sus, still lead on, Till our rest be won, And, al - though the way be cheer - less, We will fol - low, calm and fear - less; Guide us by Thy hand To our fa - ther - land.
2 If the way be drear, If the foe be near, Let not faith - less fears o'er-take us, Let not faith and hope for - sake us; For, through ma - ny a woe, To our home we go.
3 When we seek re - lief From a long - felt grief, When op - pressed by new temp-ta - tions, Lord, in - crease and per - fect pa - tience; Show us that bright shore Where we weep no more.
4 Je - sus, still lead on, Till our rest be won; Heav'n-ly lead - er, still di - rect us, Still sup-port, con - sole, pro-tect us, Till we safe - ly stand In our fa - ther - land. A - men.

1
Jesu, geh voran
auf der Lebensbahn,
und wir wollen nicht verweilen,
dir getreulich nachzueilen;
führ uns an der Hand
bis ins Vaterland.

2
Soll's uns hart ergehn,
lass uns feste stehn
und auch in den schwersten Tagen
niemals über Lasten klagen;
denn durch Trübsal hier
geht der Weg zu dir.

3
Rühret eigner Schmerz
irgend unser Herz,
kümmert uns ein fremdes Leiden,
o so gib Geduld zu beiden;
richte unsern Sinn
auf das Ende hin!

4
Ordne unsern Gang,
Jesu, lebenslang.
Führst du uns durch rauhe Wege,
gib uns auch die nötge Pflege;
tu uns nach dem Lauf
deine Türe auf.

# 641 SAY, WHY SHOULD FRIENDSHIP GRIEVE

*Christ . . . hath abolished death, and hath brought life and immortality to light through the gospel.* II Tim. 1:10.

GONE BEFORE L.M. 8.8.8.8.
M.M. 54

Benjamin Clark — J. Henry Showalter, 1864-1947

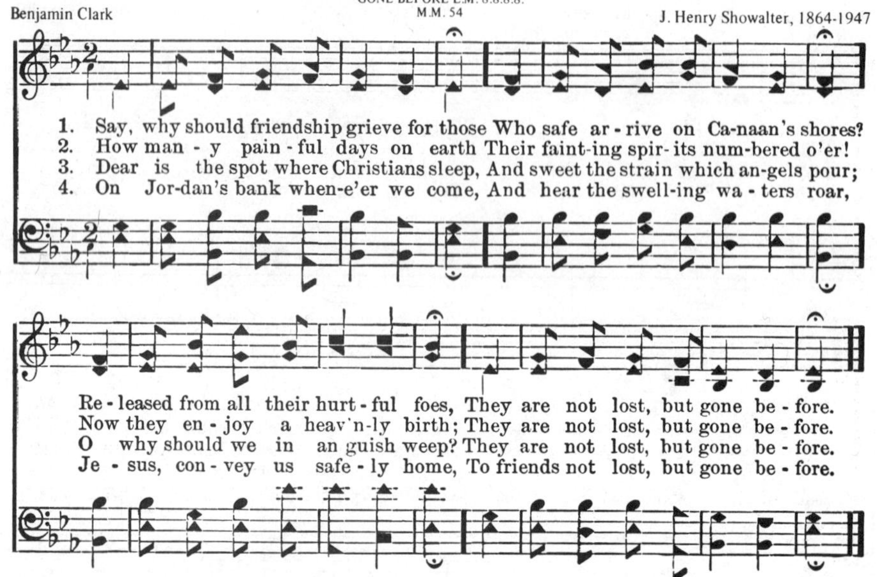
1. Say, why should friendship grieve for those Who safe ar-rive on Ca-naan's shores?
2. How man - y pain - ful days on earth Their faint-ing spir- its num-bered o'er!
3. Dear is the spot where Christians sleep, And sweet the strain which an-gels pour;
4. On Jor-dan's bank when-e'er we come, And hear the swell-ing wa - ters roar,
Re - leased from all their hurt - ful foes, They are not lost, but gone be - fore.
Now they en - joy a heav'n-ly birth; They are not lost, but gone be - fore.
O why should we in an guish weep? They are not lost, but gone be - fore.
Je - sus, con - vey us safe - ly home, To friends not lost, but gone be - fore.

# 642 THERE IS A HOUSE NOT MADE WITH HANDS

*Earnestly desiring to be clothed upon with our house which is from heaven.* II Cor. 5:2.

ST. ANNE C.M. 8.6.8.6.
M.M. 60

Isaac Watts, 1674-1748 — William Croft, 1678-1727

1. There is a house not made with hands, E - ter - nal, and on high,
2. 'Tis he, by his al-might - y grace, That forms thee fit for heav'n:
3. We walk by faith of joys to come, Faith lives up - on his Word;
4. 'Tis pleas - ant to be - lieve thy grace, But we had ra - ther see:
And here my spir - it wait - ing stands, 'Till God shall bid it fly.
And as an ear - nest of the place, Has his own Spir - it giv'n.
But while the bod - y is our home We're ab - sent from the Lord.
We would be ab - sent from the flesh, And pres- ent, Lord, with thee.

# DEATH IS AN ANGEL 643

*When this corruptible shall have put on incorruption, and this mortal shall have put on immortality, then shall be brought to pass the saying . . . Death is swallowed up in victory.* I Cor. 15:54.

BAUMGARDNER 10.10.10.11. with Ref.
M.M. 88

Marvin E. Baumgardner | Marvin E. Baumgardner

1. Death is an an-gel sent down from a-bove, Sent for the buds and the flow-ers we love; Tru-ly 'tis so, for in heav-en's own way Each soul is a flow'r in the Mas-ter's bouquet.
2. Loved ones are pass-ing each day and each hour, Pass-ing a-way "as the life of a flow'r;" But ev-'ry bud and each blos-som some day Will bloom as a flow'r in the Mas-ter's bouquet.
3. Let us be faith-ful till life's work is done, Bloom-ing with love till the reap-er shall come; Then we'll be gath-ered to-geth-er for aye, Trans-plant-ed to bloom in the Mas-ter's bouquet.
REFRAIN
Gath-er-ing flow'rs for the Mas-ter's bouquet, Beau-ti-ful flow'rs that will ne-ver de-cay; Gath-ered by an-gels and car-ried a-way For-ev-er to bloom in the Mas-ter's bouquet.

# 644 AND ARE WE YET ALIVE

*Not forsaking the assembling of ourselves together, as the manner of some is; but exhorting one another: and so much the more, as ye see the day approaching.* Heb. 10:25.

Charles Wesley, 1749 (1707-1788)

DENNIS S.M. 6.6.8.6.
M.M. 72

Johann George Nägeli, 1773-1836
Arr. Lowell Mason, 1792-1872

1. And are we yet a - live, And see each oth - er's face? Glo-
2. Pre - served by pow'r di - vine To full sal - va - tion here, A-
3. What trou - bles have we seen; What con - flicts have we passed; Fight-
4. But out of all, the Lord Hath brought us by His love; And
5. Let us take up the cross Till we the crown ob - tain; And
ry and praise to Je - sus give For His re - deem - ing grace.
gain in Je - sus' praise we join And in His sight ap - pear.
ings with - out and fears with - in Since we as - sem - bled last.
still He doth His help af - ford, And hides our life a - bove.
glad - ly reck - on all things loss, So we may Je - sus gain.

# 645 O GRANT THY SERVANTS, THROUGH THY GRACE

*And from Miletus he sent to Ephesus, and called the elders of the church . . . He said unto them . . . Take heed therefore unto yourselves and to all the flock . . . to feed the church of God, which He hath purchased with His own blood.* Acts 20:17, 18, 28.

John Gambold, 1711-1771

AZMON C.M. 8.6.8.6.
M.M. 56

Johann George Nägeli, 1773-1836
Arr. Lowell Mason, 1792-1872

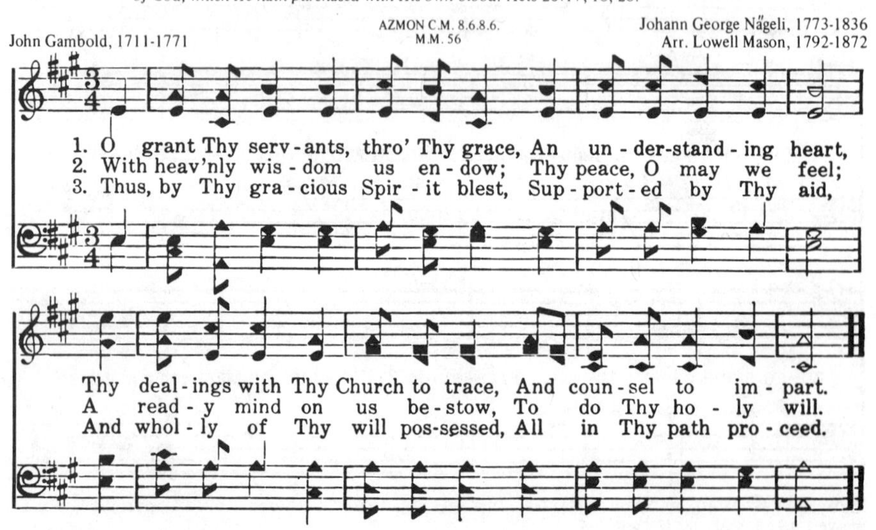
1. O grant Thy serv - ants, thro' Thy grace, An un - der-stand - ing heart,
2. With heav'nly wis - dom us en - dow; Thy peace, O may we feel;
3. Thus, by Thy gra - cious Spir - it blest, Sup - port - ed by Thy aid,
Thy deal - ings with Thy Church to trace, And coun - sel to im - part.
A read - y mind on us be - stow, To do Thy ho - ly will.
And whol - ly of Thy will pos - sessed, All in Thy path pro - ceed.

# LORD OF THE HARVEST 646

*We will give ourselves continually to prayer, and to the ministry of the word.* Acts 6:4. *As they ministered to the Lord, and fasted, the Holy Ghost said, Separate me Barnabas and Saul for the work whereunto I have called them.* Acts. 13:2.

H. J. Bowman
Alt. John J. Overholt, 1970

WILLIAMS L.M. 8.8.8.8.
M.M. 50

George Kingsley, 1853 (1811-1884)

1. Lord of the har – vest, meet this hour, The serv – ants of Thy ho – ly Word; Re – new us with Thy Spir – it's pow'r, While here we wait in one ac – cord.
2. Through all the con – flicts of the year, Mid all the storms and ills we bore, Thy gra – cious help was ev – er near, But still we need Thee more and more.
3. Pre – side Thou o'er our meet – ing here; Give light and wis – dom from a – bove; Di – rect us, keep us, in Thy fear, And bind us close with cords of love.
4. O make us ho – ly men of God, And faith – ful mes – sen – gers of grace, That we may lead to Je – sus' blood The lost and ruin – ed of our race.

# 647 WOULD YOU WIN MEN'S SOULS TO GOD

*He that winneth souls is wise.* Prov. 11:30. *Follow Me, and I will make you fishers of men.* Mt. 4:19. *I am made all things to all men, that I might by all means save some.* I Cor. 9:22.

William Hammond, 1719-1783
Recast, John J. Overholt, 1971

ELTHAM 7.7.7.7.
M.M. 56

Lowell Mason, 1792-1872

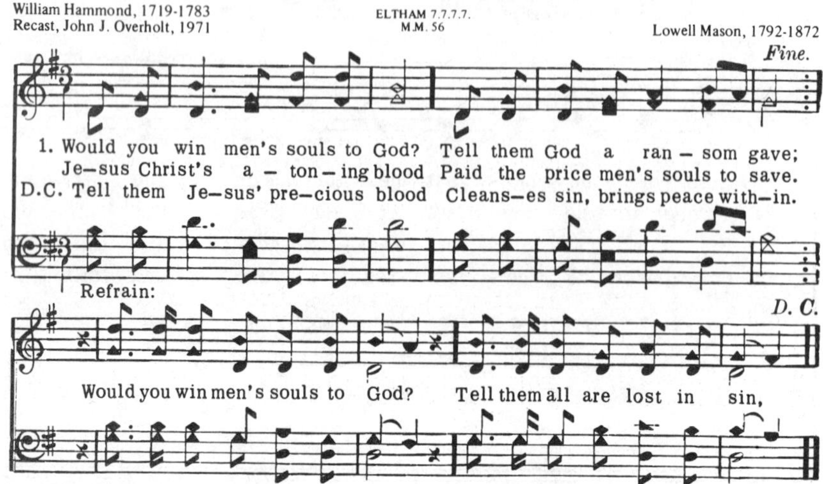
Fine.
1. Would you win men's souls to God? Tell them God a ran – som gave;
Je–sus Christ's a – ton – ing blood Paid the price men's souls to save.
D.C. Tell them Je–sus' pre–cious blood Cleans–es sin, brings peace with–in.
Refrain:
D. C.
Would you win men's souls to God? Tell them all are lost in sin,

2. Would you win men's souls to God?
Tell them men must turn from sin—
Must believe in Jesus' blood—
Must be cleansed and born again.

3. Would you win men's souls to God?
Tell them God in Christ forgives,
Washes clean through Jesus' blood,
Pardon, hope, and new life gives.

# 648 LO, WISDOM CRIETH IN THE STREETS

*Wisdom crieth without; she uttereth her voice in the streets: she crieth in the chief place of concourse . . . in the city . . . saying . . . turn you at my reproof: behold, I will pour out my spirit unto you.* Prov. 1:20, 21, 23.

Daniel S. Warner, 1842-1895
Altered by Compiler, 1971

DOMINUS REGIT ME 8.7.8.7.
M.M. 66

John Bacchus Dykes, 1823-1876

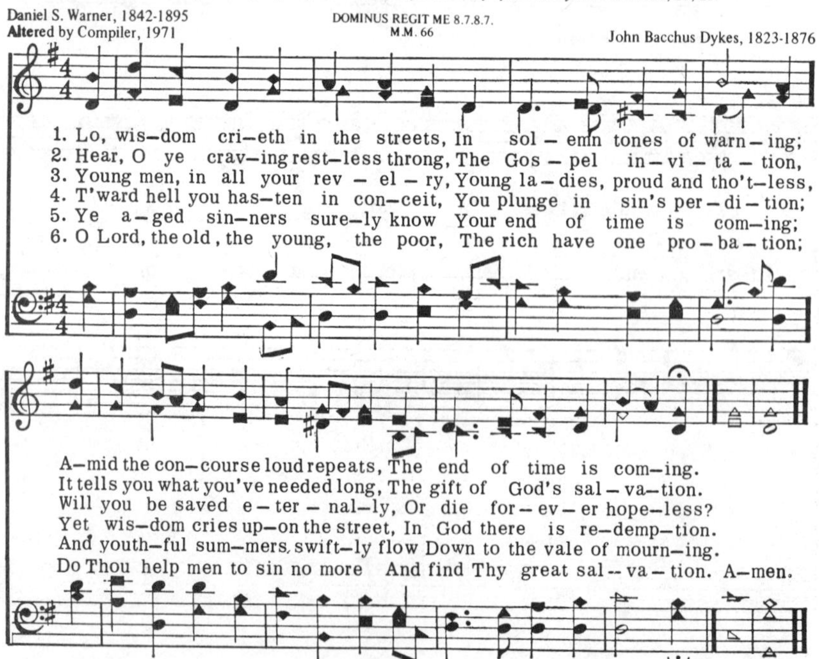
1. Lo, wis–dom cri–eth in the streets, In sol – emn tones of warn – ing;
2. Hear, O ye crav–ing rest–less throng, The Gos – pel in – vi – ta – tion,
3. Young men, in all your rev – el – ry, Young la – dies, proud and tho't–less,
4. T'ward hell you has–ten in con–ceit, You plunge in sin's per – di – tion;
5. Ye a–ged sin–ners sure–ly know Your end of time is com–ing;
6. O Lord, the old, the young, the poor, The rich have one pro – ba – tion;
A–mid the con–course loud repeats, The end of time is com–ing.
It tells you what you've needed long, The gift of God's sal – va – tion.
Will you be saved e – ter – nal–ly, Or die for – ev – er hope–less?
Yet wis–dom cries up–on the street, In God there is re–demp–tion.
And youth–ful sum–mers, swift–ly flow Down to the vale of mourn–ing.
Do Thou help men to sin no more And find Thy great sal – va – tion. A–men.

# STAND UP MY SOUL SHAKE OFF THY FEARS 649

*Therefore, my beloved brethren, be ye stedfast, unmoveable, always abounding in the work of the Lord,* I Cor. 15:58.

Isaac Watts, 1674-1748
Alt. and St. 5, John J. Overholt, 1971

ROTHWELL L.M. 8.8.8.8.
M.M. 88

William Tans'ur, 1706-1783

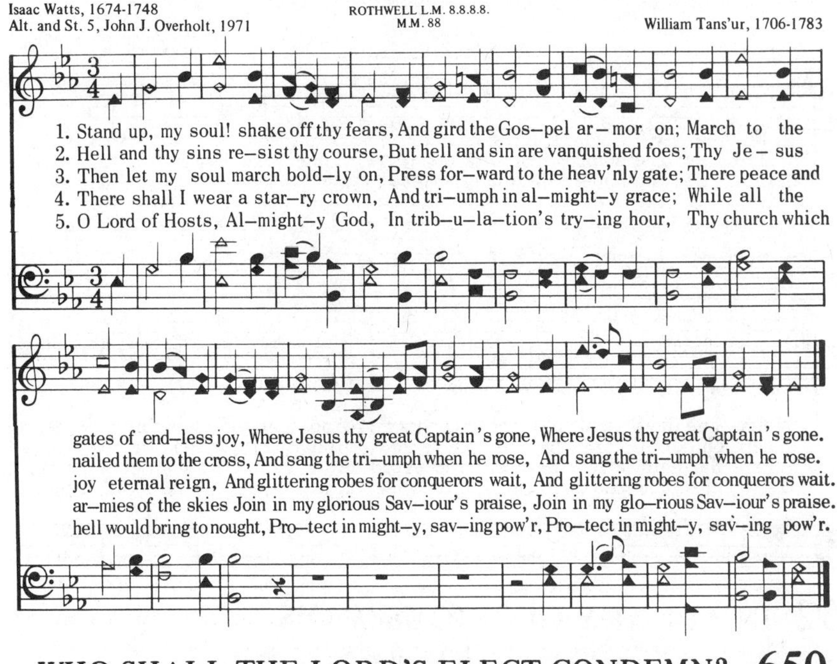
1. Stand up, my soul! shake off thy fears, And gird the Gos–pel ar – mor on; March to the gates of end–less joy, Where Jesus thy great Captain's gone, Where Jesus thy great Captain's gone.
2. Hell and thy sins re–sist thy course, But hell and sin are vanquished foes; Thy Je – sus nailed them to the cross, And sang the tri–umph when he rose, And sang the tri–umph when he rose.
3. Then let my soul march bold–ly on, Press for–ward to the heav'nly gate; There peace and joy eternal reign, And glittering robes for conquerors wait, And glittering robes for conquerors wait.
4. There shall I wear a star–ry crown, And tri–umph in al–might–y grace; While all the ar–mies of the skies Join in my glorious Sav–iour's praise, Join in my glo–rious Sav–iour's praise.
5. O Lord of Hosts, Al–might–y God, In trib–u–la–tion's try–ing hour, Thy church which hell would bring to nought, Pro–tect in might–y, sav–ing pow'r, Pro–tect in might–y, sav–ing pow'r.

# WHO SHALL THE LORD'S ELECT CONDEMN? 650

*Who shall lay anything to the charge of God's elect? It is God that justifieth. Who shall separate us from the love of Christ? . . . in all these things we are more than conquerors.* Rom. 8:33, 35, 37.

Isaac Watts, 1674-1748
Altered by Compiler, 1971

DUNDEE C.M. 8.6.8.6.
M.M. 66

*Scottish Psalter*

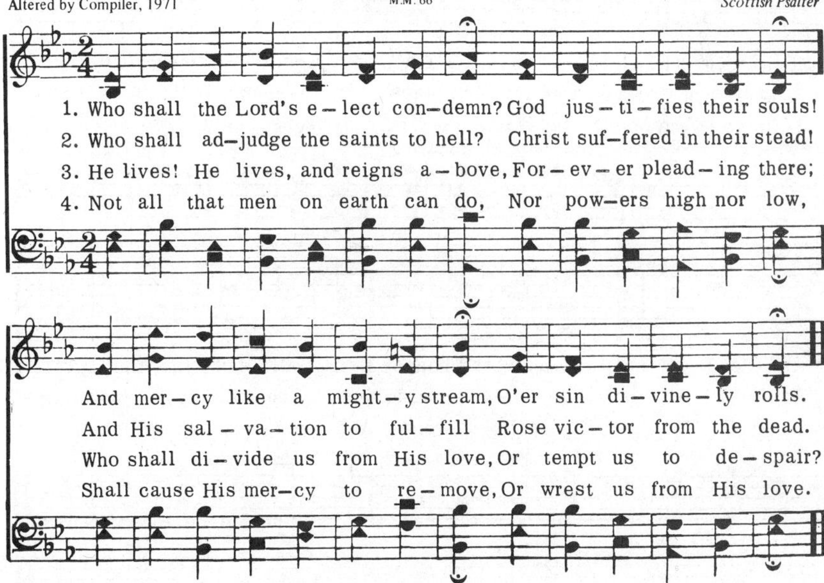
1. Who shall the Lord's e – lect con–demn? God jus – ti – fies their souls! And mer – cy like a might – y stream, O'er sin di – vine – ly rolls.
2. Who shall ad–judge the saints to hell? Christ suf–fered in their stead! And His sal – va – tion to ful – fill Rose vic – tor from the dead.
3. He lives! He lives, and reigns a – bove, For – ev – er plead – ing there; Who shall di – vide us from His love, Or tempt us to de – spair?
4. Not all that men on earth can do, Nor pow–ers high nor low, Shall cause His mer–cy to re – move, Or wrest us from His love.

# 651 HAPPY THE HOME WHEN GOD IS THERE

*Marriage is honourable in all, and the bed undefiled: but whoremongers and adulterers God will judge.* Heb. 13:4. *And Jacob set up a pillar in the place . . . And Jacob called the name of the place where God spake with him, Bethel.* Gen. 35:14, 15.

Henry Ware, 1846 (1794-1843)

EVAN C.M. 8.6.8.6.
M.M. 60

William Henry Havergal, 1793-1870
Arr. Lowell Mason, 1792-1872

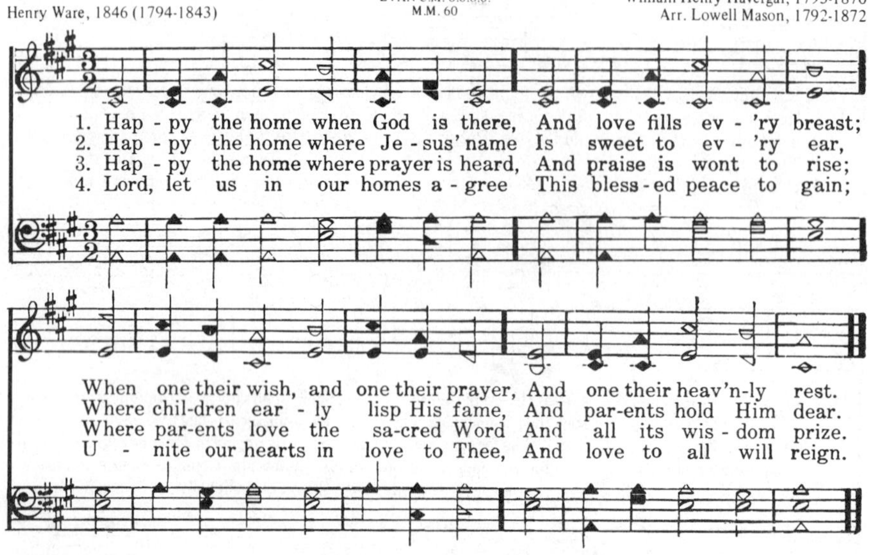
1. Hap - py the home when God is there, And love fills ev - 'ry breast;
2. Hap - py the home where Je - sus' name Is sweet to ev - 'ry ear,
3. Hap - py the home where prayer is heard, And praise is wont to rise;
4. Lord, let us in our homes a - gree This bless - ed peace to gain;
When one their wish, and one their prayer, And one their heav'n-ly rest.
Where chil-dren ear - ly lisp His fame, And par-ents hold Him dear.
Where par-ents love the sa-cred Word And all its wis - dom prize.
U - nite our hearts in love to Thee, And love to all will reign.

# 652 IN ALL THY GLORIOUS WAYS

*As for me and my house, we will serve the Lord.* Josh. 24:15.

John Ryland, 1753-1825
Recast John J. Overholt, 1970

WINGS OF FAITH C.M. 8.6.8.6.
M.M. 58

William Beery, 1852-1956

1. In all Thy glo—rious ways, O God, I would ac—knowl—edge Thee,
2. Wher—e'er I have a dwell—ing place, An al — tar will I raise;
3. Could I my pray'r — ful wish ob—tain, My house—hold, Lord, should be
And seek to keep my heart and house, From all pol — lu — tion free.
And thith — er my ob — la — tions bring, Of hum — ble pray'r and praise.
De — vot — ed to Thy—self a — lone And nur — tured there for Thee.

# LORD, GIVE US CHRISTIAN HOMES 653

*I will therefore that the younger women marry, bear children, guide the house, give none occasion to the adversary to speak reproachfully.* I Tim. 5:14. . . . *Discreet, chaste, keepers at home, good, obedient to their own husbands.* Tit. 2:5.

B. B. McKinney, 1886-1952
Altered by Compiler, 1971

CHRISTIAN HOMES (Irregular)
M.M. 96

B. B. McKinney

1. Lord, give us Chris - tian homes! Homes where the Bi - ble is loved and taught, Homes where the Mas - ter's will is sought, Homes crowned with beau - ty Thy love hath wrought; Lord, give us Chris - tian homes; Lord, give us Chris - tian homes!
2. Lord, give us Chris - tian homes! Homes where the fa - ther is true and strong, Homes that are free from the blight of wrong, Homes that are joy - ous with love and song; Lord, give us Chris - tian homes; Lord, give us Chris - tian homes!
3. Lord, give us Chris - tian homes! Homes where the moth - er, in queen - ly quest, Strives to show oth - ers Thy way is best, Homes where the Lord is an hon - ored guest; Lord, give us Chris - tian homes; Lord, give us Chris - tian homes!
4. Lord, give us Chris - tian homes! Homes where the chil - dren are led to know Christ in His beau - ty Who loves them so, Homes where the al - tar fires burn and glow; Lord, give us Chris - tian homes; Lord, give us Chris - tian homes!
A-MEN.

# 654 O HAPPY HOME WHERE THOU ART LOVED

*Let thy fountain be blessed: and rejoice with the wife of thy youth.* Prov. 5:18.
*Dwell with them according to knowledge, giving honour.* I Pet. 3:7.

Carl Johann Philipp Spitta, 1833 (1801-1859)
*O selig Haus, wo man dich aufgenommen*
Tr. Sarah B. Findlater, 1858 (1823-1911) and others

HAPPY HOME
11.10.11.10.D.
M.M. 56

Gütersloh
Arranged by Compiler, 1972

1. O hap - py home, where Thou art loved the dear - est, Thou lov - ing
2. O hap - py home, whose lit - tle ones are giv - en Ear - ly to
3. O hap - py home, where Thou art not for - got - en When joy is
Friend and Sav - iour of our race, And where a - mong the guests there nev - er
Thee in hum - ble faith and prayer, To Thee, their Friend, who from the heights of
o - ver-flow - ing, full, and free; O hap - py home, where ev - ery wound-ed
com - eth One who can hold such high and hon - ored place!
heav - en Guides them, and guards with more than moth - er's care!
spir - it Is brought, Phy - si - cian, Com - fort - er, to Thee,
O hap - py home, where two in heart u - nit - ed In ho - ly
O hap - py home, where each one serves Thee, low - ly, What - ev - er
Un - til at last, when earth's day's work is end - ed, All meet Thee
faith and bless - ed hope are one; Where joys are shared and love flows un - di -
his ap - point - ed work may be, Till ev - ery com - mon task seems great and
in the bless - ed home a - bove, From whence Thou camest, where Thou hast as -

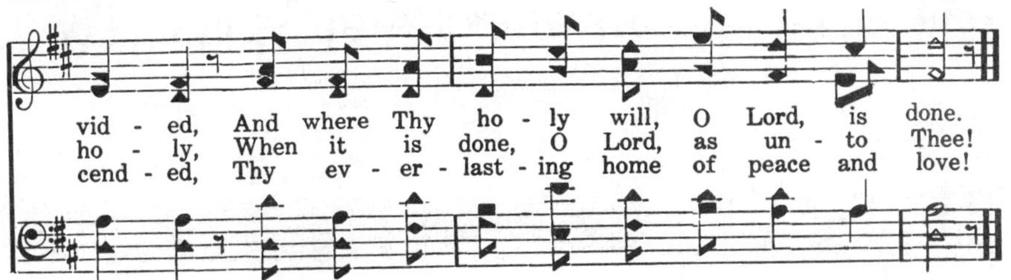
vid - ed, And where Thy ho - ly will, O Lord, is done.
ho - ly, When it is done, O Lord, as un - to Thee!
cend - ed, Thy ev - er - last - ing home of peace and love!

# O HAPPY HOME WHERE THOU ART LOVED 655

*Husbands, love your wives, even as Christ also loved the church, and gave Himself for it.* Eph. 5:25.

Carl Johann Philipp Spitta, 1833 (1801-1859)
*O selig Haus, wo man dich aufgenommen*
Tr. Sarah Borthwick Findlater, 1858 (1823-1911)

VESALIUS 11.10.11.10.
M.M. 88

E. Cooper Perry, b. 1856

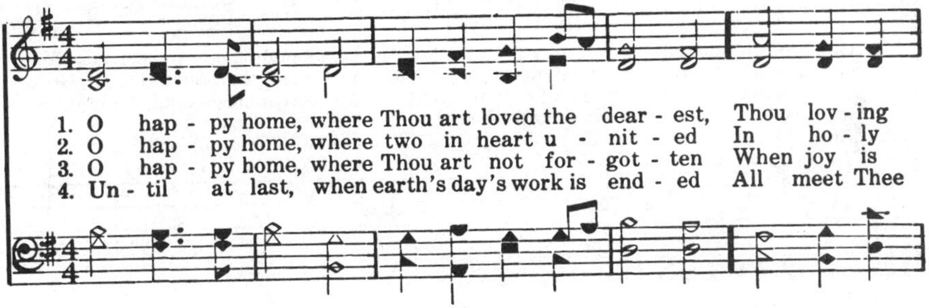

1. O hap - py home, where Thou art loved the dear - est, Thou lov - ing
2. O hap - py home, where two in heart u - nit - ed In ho - ly
3. O hap - py home, where Thou art not for - got - ten When joy is
4. Un - til at last, when earth's day's work is end - ed All meet Thee

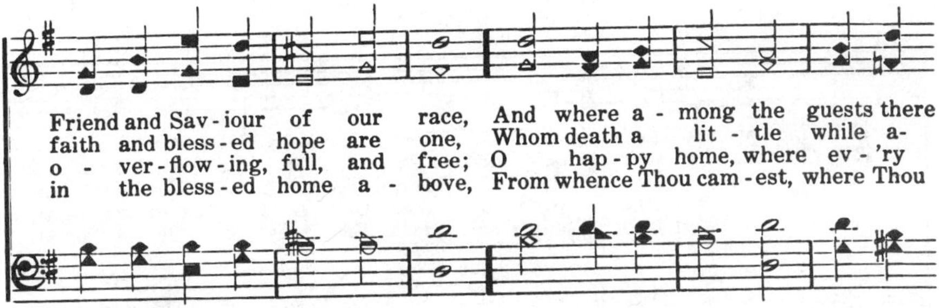

Friend and Sav - iour of our race, And where a - mong the guests there
faith and bless - ed hope are one, Whom death a lit - tle while a-
o - ver - flow - ing, full, and free; O hap - py home, where ev - 'ry
in the bless - ed home a - bove, From whence Thou cam - est, where Thou

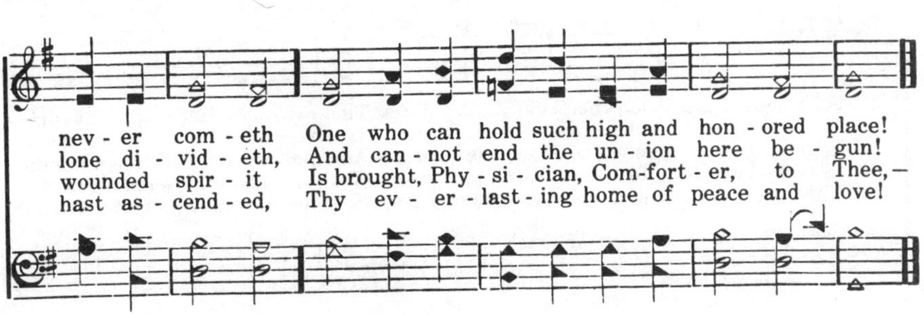

nev - er com - eth One who can hold such high and hon - ored place!
lone di - vid - eth, And can - not end the un - ion here be - gun!
wounded spir - it Is brought, Phy - si - cian, Com - fort - er, to Thee,—
hast as - cend - ed, Thy ev - er - last - ing home of peace and love!

# HOW SHALL THE YOUNG SECURE THEIR HEARTS

*Wherewithal shall a young man cleanse his way? by taking heed thereto according to Thy word.* Ps. 119:9. *Bring them up in the nurture and admonition of the Lord.* Eph. 6:4. *Feed My lambs.* Jn. 21:15.

Isaac Watts, 1719 (1674-1748)

BROWN C.M. 8.6.8.6.
M.M. 76

William Batchelder Bradbury, 1816-1868

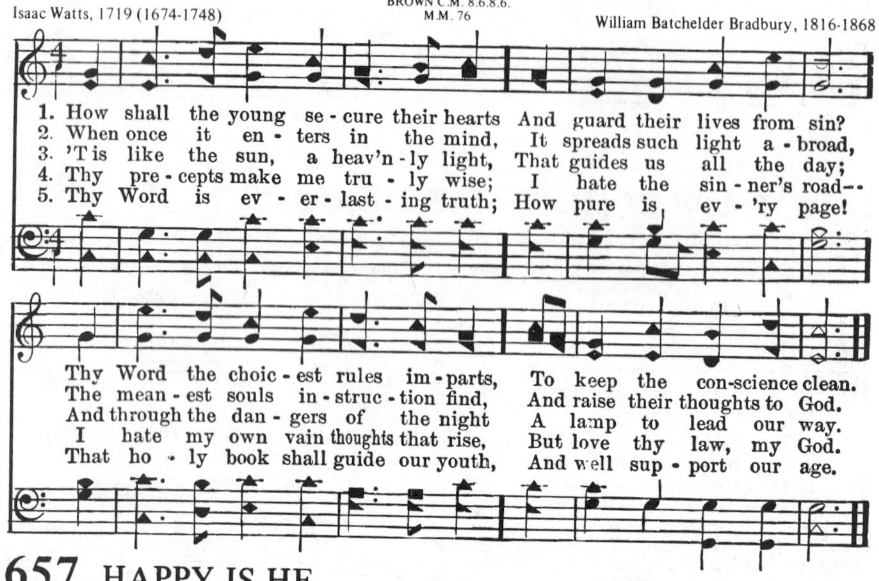
1. How shall the young se-cure their hearts And guard their lives from sin?
2. When once it en-ters in the mind, It spreads such light a-broad,
3. 'Tis like the sun, a heav'n-ly light, That guides us all the day;
4. Thy pre-cepts make me tru-ly wise; I hate the sin-ner's road--
5. Thy Word is ev-er-last-ing truth; How pure is ev-'ry page!
Thy Word the choic-est rules im-parts, To keep the con-science clean.
The mean-est souls in-struc-tion find, And raise their thoughts to God.
And through the dan-gers of the night A lamp to lead our way.
I hate my own vain thoughts that rise, But love thy law, my God.
That ho-ly book shall guide our youth, And well sup-port our age.

# 657 HAPPY IS HE

*Thou shalt teach them diligently unto thy children, and shalt talk of them when thou sittest in thy house, and when thou walkest by the way, and when thou liest down, and when thou risest up.* Deut. 6:7.

Isaac Watts, 1674-1748

HAVEN C.M. 8.6.8.6.
M.M. 58

Thomas Hastings, 1784-1872

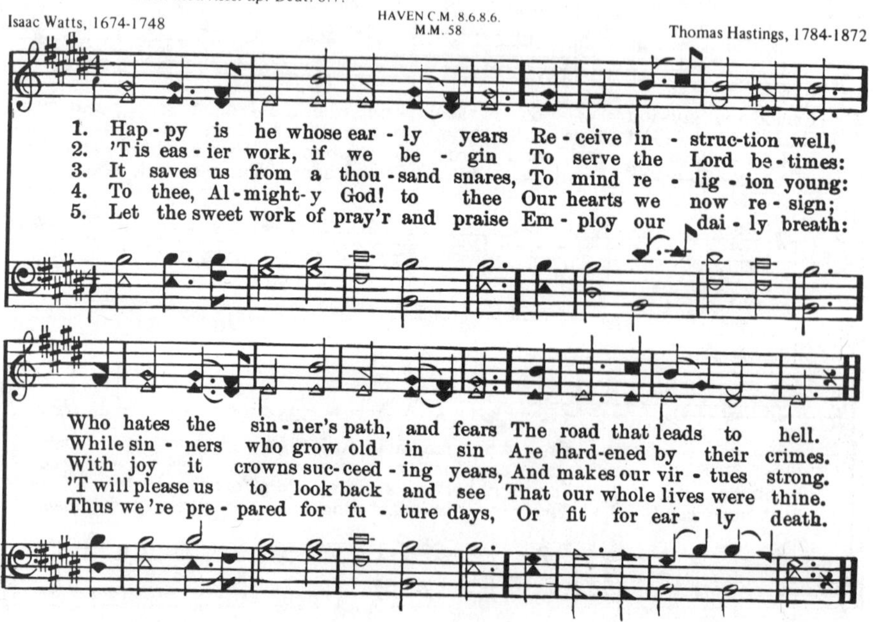
1. Hap-py is he whose ear-ly years Re-ceive in-struc-tion well,
2. 'Tis eas-ier work, if we be-gin To serve the Lord be-times:
3. It saves us from a thou-sand snares, To mind re-lig-ion young:
4. To thee, Al-might-y God! to thee Our hearts we now re-sign;
5. Let the sweet work of pray'r and praise Em-ploy our dai-ly breath:
Who hates the sin-ner's path, and fears The road that leads to hell.
While sin-ners who grow old in sin Are hard-ened by their crimes.
With joy it crowns suc-ceed-ing years, And makes our vir-tues strong.
'T will please us to look back and see That our whole lives were thine.
Thus we're pre-pared for fu-ture days, Or fit for ear-ly death.

# REMEMBER THY CREATOR 658

*Remember now thy Creator in the days of thy youth.* Eccles. 12:1. *Whether therefore ye eat, or drink, or whatsoever ye do, do all to the glory of God.* I Cor. 10:31.

REMEMBER THY CREATOR C.M. 8.6.8.6. with Ref.
M.M. 116

Chorus arr. C. J. Kinne

William Batchelder Bradbury, 1816-1868

1. Re - mem - ber thy Cre - a - tor now, In these thy youth-ful days;
2. Re - mem - ber thy Cre - a - tor now, And seek Him while He's near;
3. Re - mem - ber thy Cre - a - tor now, His will - ing serv - ant be;
4. Al - might - y God, our hearts in - cline Thy heav'n - ly voice to hear;
He will ac - cept thine ear - ly vow, And lis - ten to thy praise.
For e - vil days will come, when thou Shalt find no com - fort near.
Then, when thy head in death shall bow, He will re-mem - ber thee.
Let all our fu - ture days be Thine, De - vot - ed to Thy fear.
CHORUS.
O Thou might - y God, we will re - mem - ber Thee; And
we will de - light in Thy serv - ice now, In these our youth-ful days; Yes,
we will re - mem - ber Thy mer - cies, too, And en - ter Thy courts with praise.

# 659 IF I HAVE WOUNDED ANY SOUL TODAY

*If ye forgive not men their trespasses, neither will your Father forgive your trespasses.* Mt. 6:15.
*Forgive us our debts, as we forgive our debtors.* Mt. 6:12.

C. M. Battersby — AN EVENING PRAYER 10.10.10.4. M.M. 63 — Charles Hutchinson Gabriel, 1856-1932; Har. arr. mixed voices, John J. Overholt, 1972

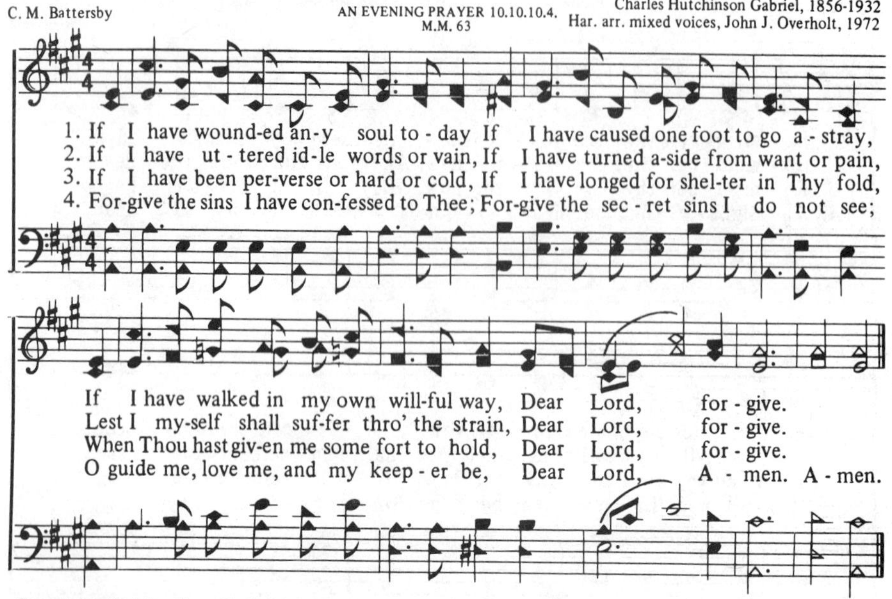
1. If I have wound-ed an-y soul to-day If I have caused one foot to go a-stray,
2. If I have ut-tered id-le words or vain, If I have turned a-side from want or pain,
3. If I have been per-verse or hard or cold, If I have longed for shel-ter in Thy fold,
4. For-give the sins I have con-fessed to Thee; For-give the sec-ret sins I do not see;
If I have walked in my own will-ful way, Dear Lord, for-give.
Lest I my-self shall suf-fer thro' the strain, Dear Lord, for-give.
When Thou hast giv-en me some fort to hold, Dear Lord, for-give.
O guide me, love me, and my keep-er be, Dear Lord, A-men. A-men.

**THE CHRISTIAN HOME:** INTERCESSION FOR YOUTH

# 660 GOD OF MERCY HEAR OUR PRAYER

*Job . . . offered up burnt offerings . . . for Job said, It may be that my sons have sinned.* Job 1:5. *Teach them thy sons, and thy son's sons.* Deut. 4:9.

Thomas Hastings, 1837 (1784-1872) — INNOCENTS 7.7.7.7. M.M. 66 — From a Parish Hymnal

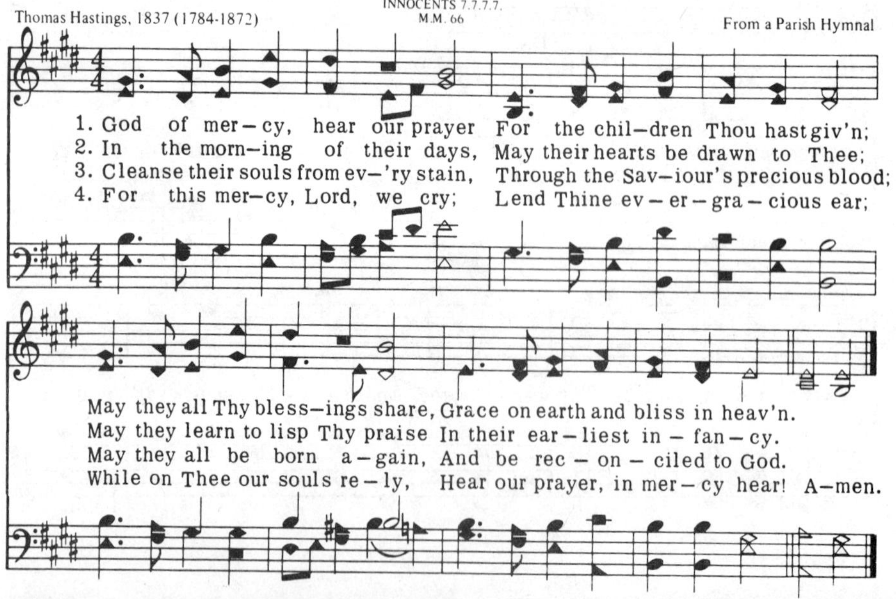
1. God of mer-cy, hear our prayer For the chil-dren Thou hast giv'n;
2. In the morn-ing of their days, May their hearts be drawn to Thee;
3. Cleanse their souls from ev-'ry stain, Through the Sav-iour's precious blood;
4. For this mer-cy, Lord, we cry; Lend Thine ev-er-gra-cious ear;
May they all Thy bless-ings share, Grace on earth and bliss in heav'n.
May they learn to lisp Thy praise In their ear-liest in-fan-cy.
May they all be born a-gain, And be rec-on-ciled to God.
While on Thee our souls re-ly, Hear our prayer, in mer-cy hear! A-men.

# STARTING FORTH ON LIFE'S ROUGH WAY 661

*Train up a child in the way he should go: and when he is old, he will not depart from it.* Prov. 22:6.

William Cullen Bryant
Altered by Compiler, 1971

HOLLINGSIDE 7.7.7.7.D.
M.M. 63

John Bacchus Dykes, 1861 (1823-1876)

1. Start–ing forth on life's rough way, Fa–ther, do Thou guide them;
2. When in pray'r they cry to Thee, Thou wilt ev–er hear them;
3. Un–to Thee we give them up; Lord, wilt Thou re–ceive them;
Oh, we know not what of harm Ev–er may be–tide them;
From the stains of sin and shame Thou wilt swift–ly clear them;
In the world we know must be Sure–ly much to grieve them,
'Neath the shad–ow of Thy wing, Fa–ther, there do hide them;
'Mid the quick–sands and the rocks, Thou wilt safe–ly steer them;
Man–y striv–ing oft and strong Base–ly to de–ceive them;
Wak–ing, sleep–ing, Lord, we pray, Al–ways go be–side them.
In temp–ta–tion, tri–al, grief, Be Thou ev–er near them.
Trust–ful in Thy hands of love Grate–ful–ly we leave them.

# 662 TRYING TO WALK IN THE STEPS

*So likewise, whosoever he be of you that forsaketh not all that he hath, he cannot be My disciple.* Lk. 14:33. *If ye continue in My word, then are ye My disciples indeed.* Jn. 8:31.

STEPPING IN THE LIGHT 11.10.11.10. with Ref.
M.M. 66

Eliza Edmunds Hewitt, 1851-1920

William James Kirkpatrick, 1838-1921

1. Try - ing to walk in the steps of the Sav-iour, Try - ing to fol - low our
2. Press-ing more close - ly to Him who is lead-ing, When we are tempt-ed to
3. Walk-ing in foot - steps of gen - tle for-bear-ance, Foot-steps of faith-ful-ness,
4. Try - ing to walk in the steps of the Sav-iour, Up-ward, still up-ward we'll
Sav - iour and King; Shap - ing our lives by His bless - ed ex - am - ple,
turn from the way; Trust - ing the arm that is strong to de - fend us,
mer - cy and love; Look - ing to Him for the grace free - ly prom - ised,
fol - low our Guide; When we shall see Him, "the King in His beau - ty,"
Hap - py, how hap - py, the songs that we bring.
Hap - py, how hap - py, our prais - es each day.
Hap - py, how hap - py, our jour - ney a - bove!
Hap - py, how hap - py, our place at His side!
REFRAIN
How beau - ti - ful to walk in the steps of the Sav - iour, Step-ping in the light, Step-ping in the light; How beau - ti - ful to walk in the steps of the Sav-iour, Led in paths of light!

## THE BUD WILL SOON BECOME A FLOWER 663

*For I the Lord thy God will hold thy right hand, saying unto thee, Fear not; I will help thee.* Is. 41:13. *Provoke not your children to wrath: but . . . nurture [them].* Eph. 6:4.

SOLITUDE C.M. 8.6.8.6.
M.M. 58

James Very

L. C. Everet, 1818-1867

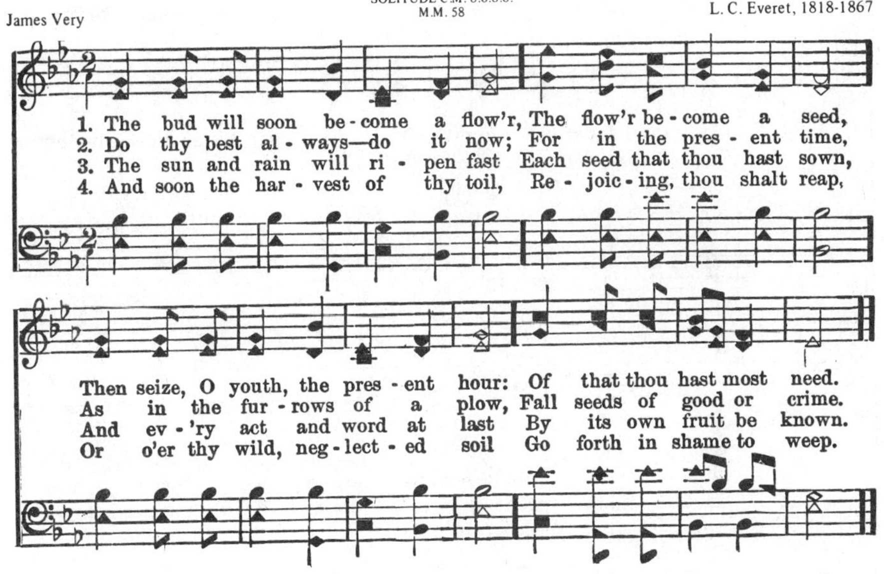
1. The bud will soon be-come a flow'r, The flow'r be-come a seed,
2. Do thy best al-ways—do it now; For in the pres-ent time,
3. The sun and rain will ri-pen fast Each seed that thou hast sown,
4. And soon the har-vest of thy toil, Re-joic-ing, thou shalt reap,
Then seize, O youth, the pres-ent hour: Of that thou hast most need.
As in the fur-rows of a plow, Fall seeds of good or crime.
And ev-'ry act and word at last By its own fruit be known.
Or o'er thy wild, neg-lect-ed soil Go forth in shame to weep.

## LORD OF THE HOME 664

*Can a woman forget her sucking child?* Is. 49:15. *And she sat over against, him and lifted up her voice, and wept.* Gen. 21:16.

BLOOMFIELD CHANT L.M. 8.8.8.8.
M.M. 52

Albert Frederick Bayly, 1947 (b. 1901)

William Batchelder Bradbury, 1816-1868

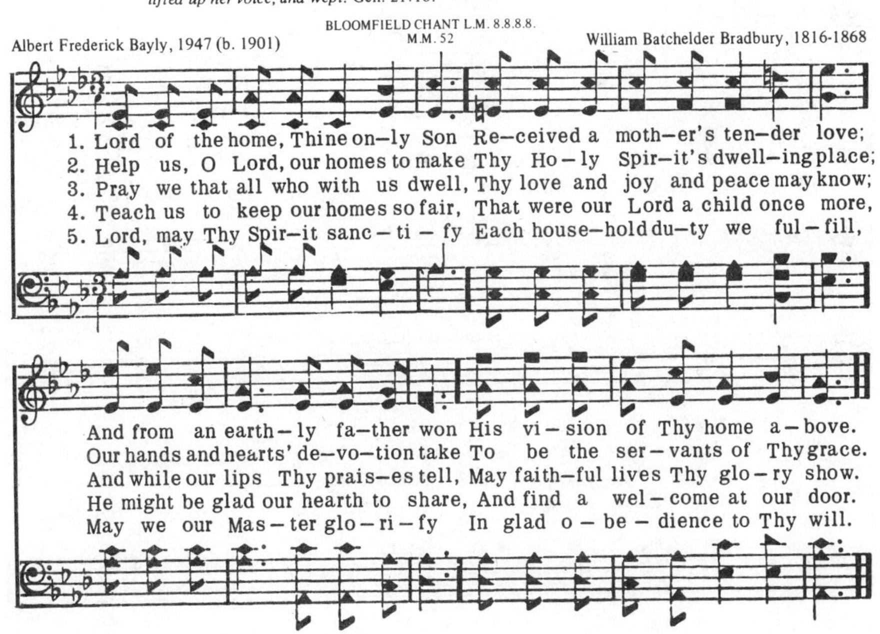
1. Lord of the home, Thine on-ly Son Re-ceived a moth-er's ten-der love;
2. Help us, O Lord, our homes to make Thy Ho-ly Spir-it's dwell-ing place;
3. Pray we that all who with us dwell, Thy love and joy and peace may know;
4. Teach us to keep our homes so fair, That were our Lord a child once more,
5. Lord, may Thy Spir-it sanc-ti-fy Each house-hold du-ty we ful-fill,
And from an earth-ly fa-ther won His vi-sion of Thy home a-bove.
Our hands and hearts' de-vo-tion take To be the ser-vants of Thy grace.
And while our lips Thy prais-es tell, May faith-ful lives Thy glo-ry show.
He might be glad our hearth to share, And find a wel-come at our door.
May we our Mas-ter glo-ri-fy In glad o-be-dience to Thy will.

# 665 O LIFT THY HANDS ON HIGH

*One that ruleth well his own house, having his children in subjection with all gravity.* I Tim. 3:4. *Seek the Lord and His strength, seek His face continually.* I Chron. 16:11. *Praying always.* Eph. 6:18.

Philip Doddridge, 1702-1751
Altered by Compiler

DARWALL 6.6.6.6.8.8.
M.M. 76

John Darwall, 1770 (1731-1789)

1. O lift thy hands on high! O pil – grim, tune thy voice;
2. He gilds thy ra – diant face With beams that can – not fade;
3. In hon – or to His name, Re – flect that sa – cred light;
4. There on His ho – ly hill, A bright – er sun shall rise,
And sing, for Christ is nigh, Tell all the
His all – re – splend – ent grace He pours a –
And loud that grace pro – claim, Which makes thy
And, with His ra – diance fill Those fair – er,
earth thy joys; Re – joice in God, A – rise and shine,
round thy head; All mor – tals here thy bliss shall view,
dark – ness bright; Pur – sue His praise, till sov–'reign love,
pur – er skies; While, round His throne, ten thou – sand times
While rays di – vine stream all a – broad.
With lus – ter new, di – vine – ly crowned.
In worlds a – bove, the glo – ry raise.
Ten thou – sand saints His in – fluence own. A – men.

# O GOD AND FATHER THEE WE BLESS 666

*I will bless the Lord at all times.* Ps. 34:1.

From the 16th century Anabaptist Ausbund
Hymn No. 131, Leonard Clock, c. 1590
*O Gott Vater, wir loben dich*
Tr. John J. Overholt, 1969

MIT FREUDEN ZART
8.7.8.7.8.8.7.
M.M. 52

Adapted from *Geneva 138*,
*Pseaulmes* . . . Lyon, 1547
Bohemian Brethren's *Kirchengeseng*, 1568
Har. John J. Overholt, 1971

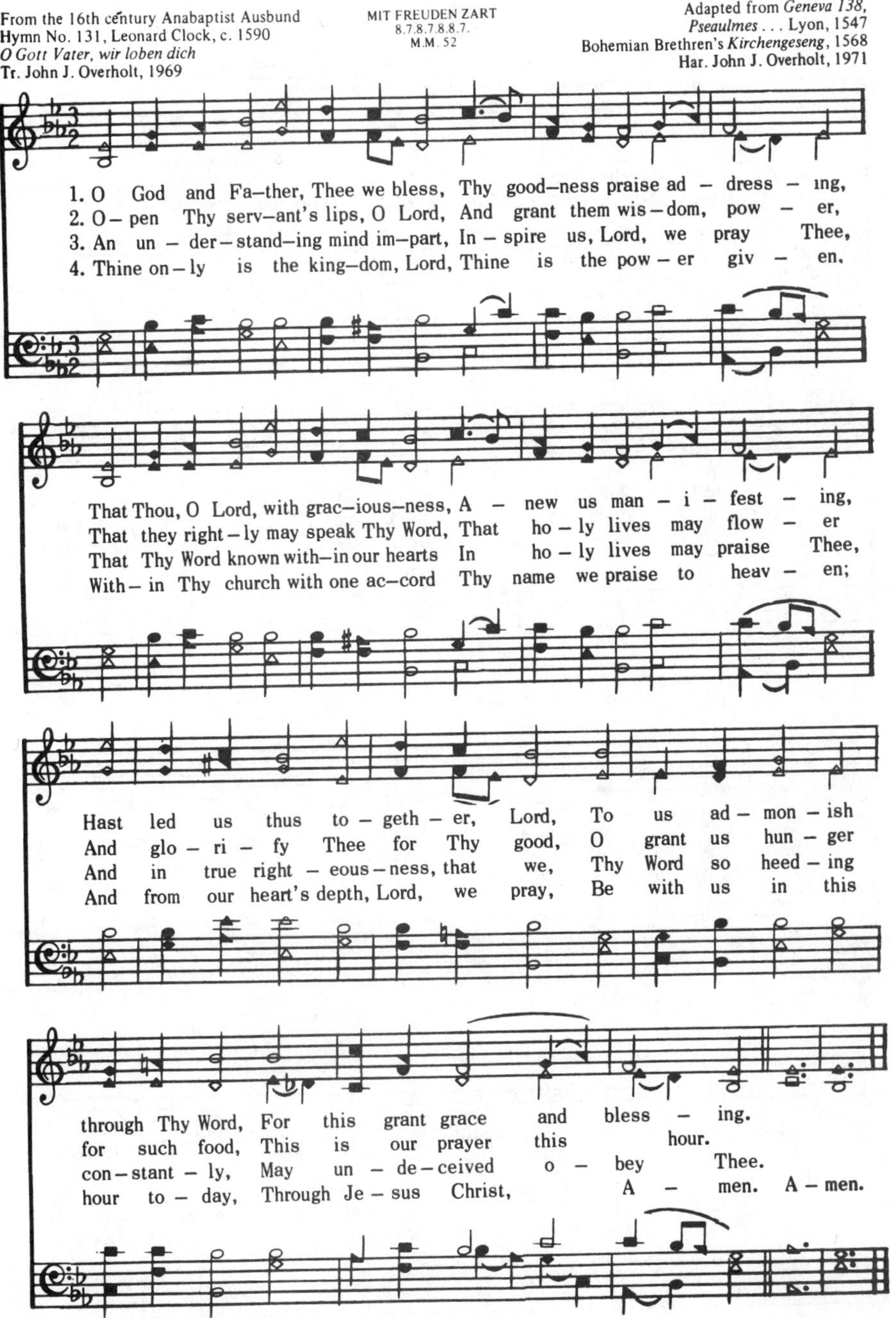
1. O God and Fa–ther, Thee we bless, Thy good–ness praise ad – dress – ing,
2. O – pen Thy serv–ant's lips, O Lord, And grant them wis – dom, pow – er,
3. An un – der – stand–ing mind im–part, In – spire us, Lord, we pray Thee,
4. Thine on – ly is the king–dom, Lord, Thine is the pow – er giv – en,
That Thou, O Lord, with grac–ious–ness, A – new us man – i – fest – ing,
That they right – ly may speak Thy Word, That ho – ly lives may flow – er
That Thy Word known with–in our hearts In ho – ly lives may praise Thee,
With– in Thy church with one ac–cord Thy name we praise to heav – en;
Hast led us thus to – geth – er, Lord, To us ad – mon – ish
And glo – ri – fy Thee for Thy good, O grant us hun – ger
And in true right – eous – ness, that we, Thy Word so heed – ing
And from our heart's depth, Lord, we pray, Be with us in this
through Thy Word, For this grant grace and bless – ing.
for such food, This is our prayer this hour.
con – stant – ly, May un – de – ceived o – bey Thee.
hour to – day, Through Je – sus Christ, A – men. A – men.

# 667 WE PRAISE THEE, O GOD, OUR REDEEMER

*I will . . . yet praise Thee more and more.* Ps. 71:14.

Julia Bulkey Cady Cory, 1902 (b. 1882) | KREMSER 12.11.12.11. M.M. 69 | Dutch Folk Song in *Nederlandtsch Gedenekelanck*, 1626

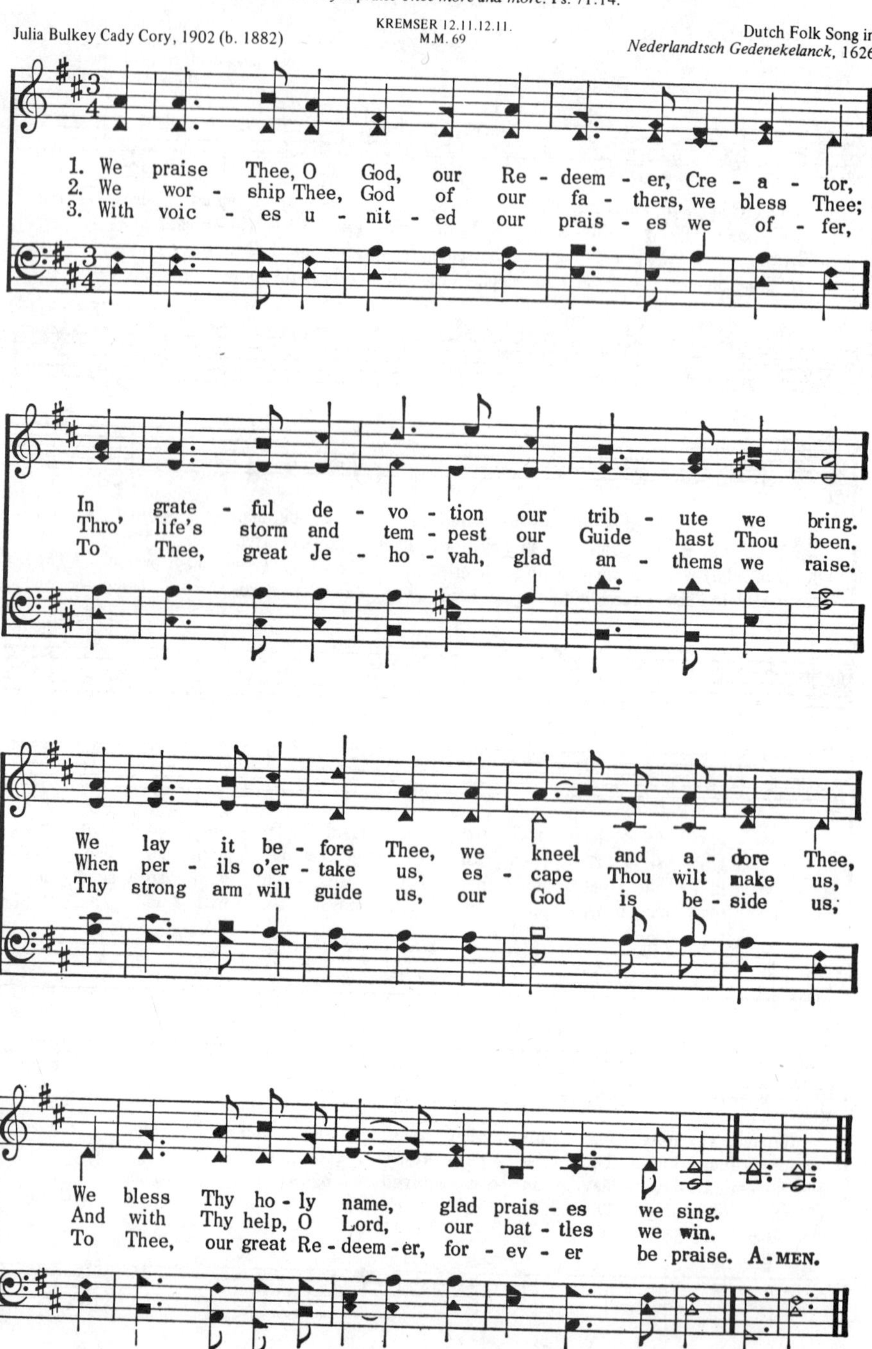
1. We praise Thee, O God, our Re - deem - er, Cre - a - tor,
2. We wor - ship Thee, God of our fa - thers, we bless Thee;
3. With voic - es u - nit - ed our prais - es we of - fer,
In grate - ful de - vo - tion our trib - ute we bring.
Thro' life's storm and tem - pest our Guide hast Thou been.
To Thee, great Je - ho - vah, glad an - thems we raise.
We lay it be - fore Thee, we kneel and a - dore Thee,
When per - ils o'er - take us, es - cape Thou wilt make us,
Thy strong arm will guide us, our God is be - side us,
We bless Thy ho - ly name, glad prais - es we sing.
And with Thy help, O Lord, our bat - tles we win.
To Thee, our great Re - deem - er, for - ev - er be praise. A - MEN.

# OF THE FATHER'S LOVE BEGOTTEN 668

*I am Alpha and Omega, the first and the last.* Rev. 1:11. *His head and His hairs were white like wool, as white as snow; and His eyes were as a flame of fire.* Rev. 1:14.

Aurelius Clemens Prudentius, 348-413
Cordus natus ex Parentis
Tr. Roby Furley Davis
Alt. John J. Overholt, 1971
ZEUCH MICH, ZEUCH MICH (ALL SAINTS)
8.7.8.7.8.7.
M.M. 72
Geistreiches Gesangbuch, Darmstadt, 1968
1. Of the Fa – ther's love be-got – ten, Ere the world from
2. By His word was all cre – a – ted; He com – mand – ed
3. Sing, ye heights of heav'n Christ's prais – es; Ye His blest re –
4. Now let old and young u – nit – ing Sing to Thee har –
cha – os rose, Christ is Al – pha, from that Foun – tain
and 'twas done; Earth and sky and bound – less o – cean,
deemed ones, sing! Where – so – e'er ye be, ye faith – ful,
mon – ious lays, Maid and ma – tron hymn Thy glo – ry,
All that is and hath been flows; Christ O – me – ga
U – ni – verse of three in one, All that sees the
Let your joy – ous an – thems ring, Ev – ery tongue His
In – fant lips their an – them raise, Youth and maid – en
is of all things Yet to come the mys – tic Close.
moon's soft ra – diance, All that breathes be – neath the sun.
name con – fess – ing, Count – less voic – es an – swer – ing.
ev – er sing – ing With pure heart their song of praise. A – men.

# 669 FATHER, IN WHOM WE LIVE

*For in Him we live, and move, and have our being.* Acts. 17:28.

Charles Wesley, 1746 (1707-1788)
Altered by Compiler, 1971

MORNINGTON S.M. 6.6.8.6.
M.M. 63

Garret C. Wellesley, 1760 (1735-1781)

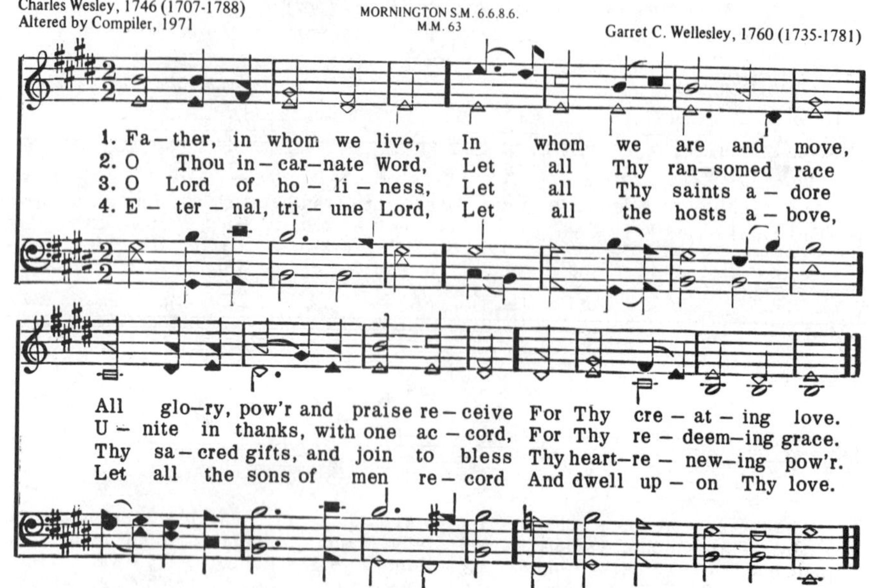
1. Fa – ther, in whom we live, In whom we are and move,
2. O Thou in – car – nate Word, Let all Thy ran – somed race
3. O Lord of ho – li – ness, Let all Thy saints a – dore
4. E – ter – nal, tri – une Lord, Let all the hosts a – bove,
All glo – ry, pow'r and praise re – ceive For Thy cre – at – ing love.
U – nite in thanks, with one ac – cord, For Thy re – deem – ing grace.
Thy sa – cred gifts, and join to bless Thy heart – re – new – ing pow'r.
Let all the sons of men re – cord And dwell up – on Thy love.

# 670 NOW THE BUSY WEEK IS DONE

*Oh how great is Thy goodness, which Thou has laid up for them that fear Thee.* Ps. 31:19.
*This is the day which the Lord hath made; we will rejoice and be glad in it.* Ps. 118:24.

John Samuel Jones
Altered by Compiler, 1971

GUISBOROUGH 7.7.7.7.
M.M. 69

C. T. Bowen, b. 1833

1. Now the bus – y week is done, Now the rest time is be – gun;
2. Soon there comes the first and best Day of wor – ship, light, and rest;
3. All our powers do Thou em – ploy, Be Thy work our chief – est joy;
4. Guide us in the days to come, Till Thy mer – cy call us home,
Now to Thee, O Lord, we pray, Hear our thanks at close of day.
Hal – low, Lord, the com – ing day, When a – gain we praise and pray.
To our hearts be man – i – fest, Lord of la – bour and of rest.
Till Thou call us as Thy guest, Lord, to en – ter in – to rest. A – men.

# TEACH ME TO DO THE THING THAT PLEASETH THEE

*Teach me Thy way, O Lord.* Ps. 27:11. *Teach us what we shall do.* Judg. 13:8. *Lord, teach us to pray.* Lk. 11:1.

John Samuel B. Monsell, 1811-1875
Altered by Compiler, 1971

TOULON 10.10.10.10.
M.M. 54

Claude Goudimel, 1505-1572

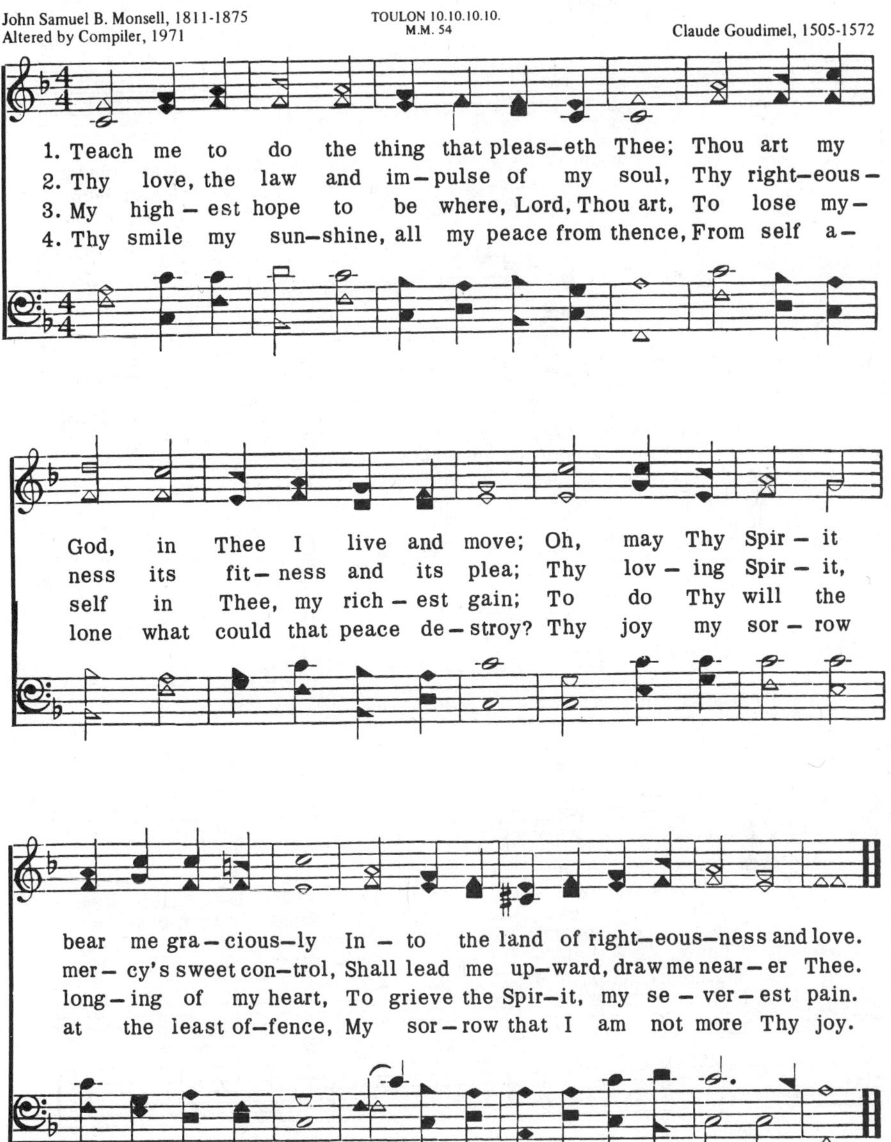
1. Teach me to do the thing that pleas–eth Thee; Thou art my God, in Thee I live and move; Oh, may Thy Spir – it bear me gra – cious–ly In – to the land of right–eous–ness and love.
2. Thy love, the law and im–pulse of my soul, Thy right–eous–ness its fit– ness and its plea; Thy lov – ing Spir – it, mer – cy's sweet con–trol, Shall lead me up–ward, draw me near – er Thee.
3. My high – est hope to be where, Lord, Thou art, To lose my–self in Thee, my rich – est gain; To do Thy will the long – ing of my heart, To grieve the Spir–it, my se – ver – est pain.
4. Thy smile my sun–shine, all my peace from thence, From self a–lone what could that peace de – stroy? Thy joy my sor – row at the least of–fence, My sor – row that I am not more Thy joy.

# 672 CHILDREN OF THE HEAVENLY KING

*Follow Me.* Mt. 4:19. *Follow . . . righteousness.* I Tim. 6:11. *I follow after.* Phil. 3:12. *Master, I will follow Thee.* Mt. 8:19.

John Cennick, 1718-1755

INNOCENTS 7.7.7.7.
M.M. 69

From a Parish Hymnal

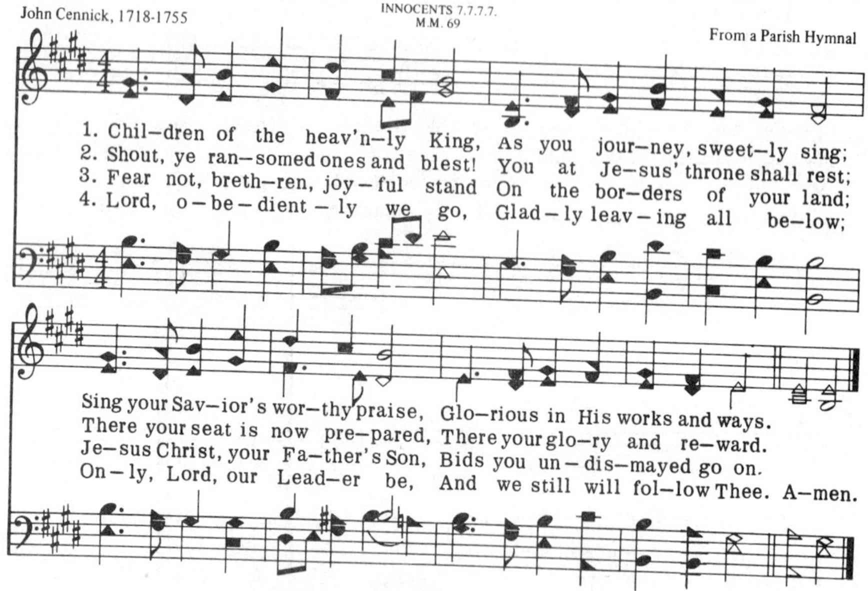
1. Chil–dren of the heav'n–ly King, As you jour–ney, sweet–ly sing;
2. Shout, ye ran–somed ones and blest! You at Je–sus' throne shall rest;
3. Fear not, breth–ren, joy–ful stand On the bor–ders of your land;
4. Lord, o–be–dient–ly we go, Glad–ly leav–ing all be–low;
Sing your Sav–ior's wor–thy praise, Glo–rious in His works and ways.
There your seat is now pre–pared, There your glo–ry and re–ward.
Je–sus Christ, your Fa–ther's Son, Bids you un–dis–mayed go on.
On–ly, Lord, our Lead–er be, And we still will fol–low Thee. A–men.

# 673 FORTH IN THY NAME, O LORD, I GO

*Not with eyeservice, as men-pleasers, but as the servants of Christ, doing the will of God from the heart. With goodwill doing service, as to the Lord, and not to men.* Eph. 6:6, 7.

Charles Wesley, 1749 (1707-1788)

MISSIONARY CHANT L.M. 8.8.8.8.
M.M. 56

Charles Heinrich C. Zeuner, 1832 (1795-1857)

1. Forth in Thy name, O Lord, I go, My dai–ly
2. The task Thy wis–dom hath as–signed, O let me
3. Thee will I set at my right hand, Whose eyes my
4. Give me to bear Thy eas–y yoke, And ev–ery
5. For Thee de–light–ful–ly em–ploy What–e'er Thy
la–bor to pur–sue, Thee, on–ly Thee, re–solved to
cheer–ful–ly ful–fill; In all my works Thy pres–ence
in–most sub–stance see, And la–bor on at Thy com–
mo–ment watch and pray; And e're to things e–ter–nal
boun–teous grace hath giv'n, And run my course with e–ven

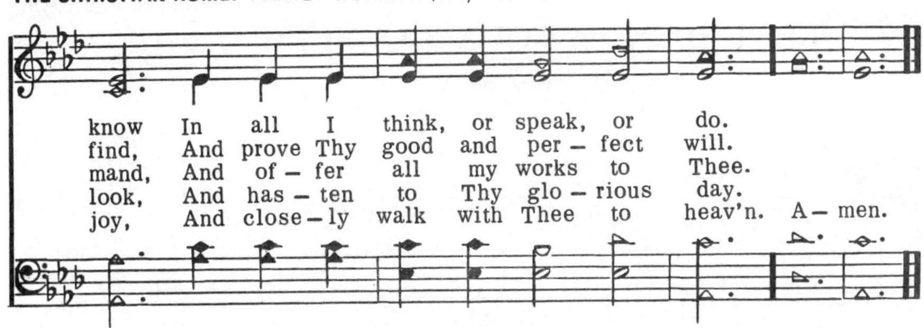
know In all I think, or speak, or do.
find, And prove Thy good and per – fect will.
mand, And of – fer all my works to Thee.
look, And has – ten to Thy glo – rious day.
joy, And close – ly walk with Thee to heav'n. A – men.

**THE CHRISTIAN HOME:** FAMILY WORSHIP (Guarding Against the Power of Sound)

# JESUS, THOU SOURCE OF ALL OUR JOYS 674

*Watch and pray, that ye enter not into temptation.* Mt. 26:41. *Singing with grace in your hearts to the Lord.* Col. 3:16. *Making melody in your heart to the Lord.* Eph. 5:19.

Charles Wesley, 1707-1788
Altered by Compiler, 1971

ARIEL 8.8.6.8.8.6.
M.M. 60

Wolfgang Amadeus Mozart, 1756-1791
Arr. Lowell Mason, 1792-1872

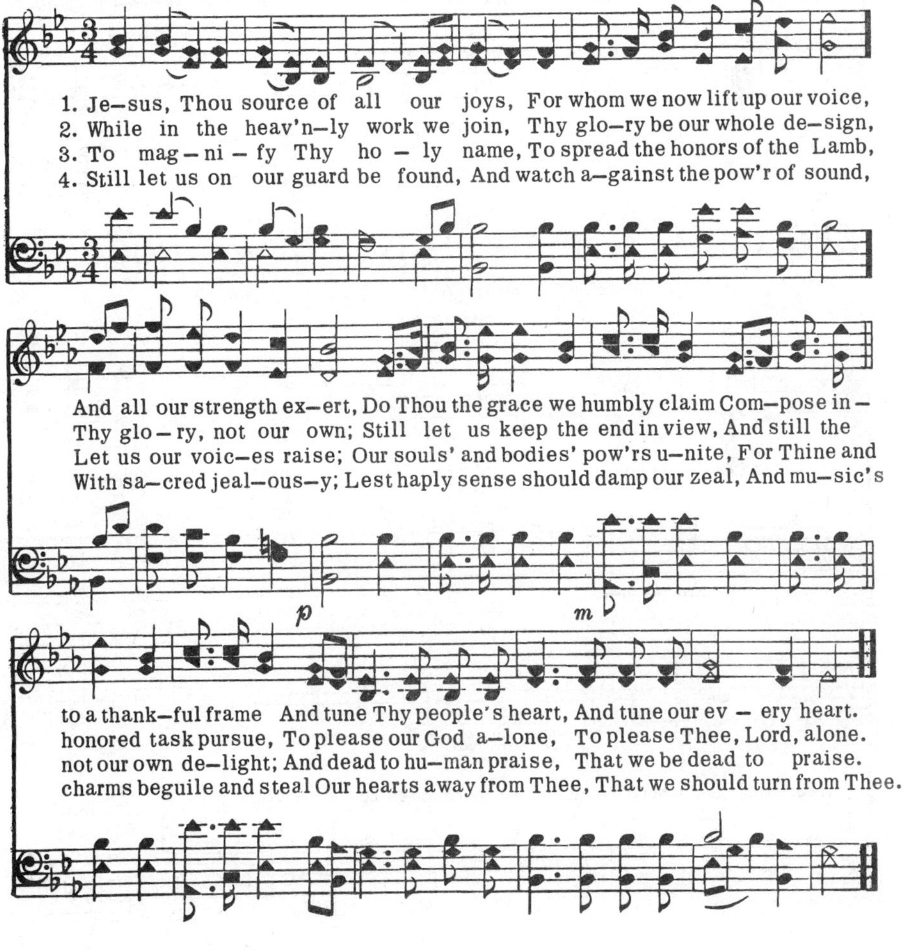

1. Je–sus, Thou source of all our joys, For whom we now lift up our voice,
2. While in the heav'n–ly work we join, Thy glo–ry be our whole de–sign,
3. To mag–ni–fy Thy ho–ly name, To spread the honors of the Lamb,
4. Still let us on our guard be found, And watch a–gainst the pow'r of sound,

And all our strength ex–ert, Do Thou the grace we humbly claim Com–pose in–
Thy glo–ry, not our own; Still let us keep the end in view, And still the
Let us our voic–es raise; Our souls' and bodies' pow'rs u–nite, For Thine and
With sa–cred jeal–ous–y; Lest haply sense should damp our zeal, And mu–sic's

*p* *m*

to a thank–ful frame And tune Thy people's heart, And tune our ev – ery heart.
honored task pursue, To please our God a–lone, To please Thee, Lord, alone.
not our own de–light; And dead to hu–man praise, That we be dead to praise.
charms beguile and steal Our hearts away from Thee, That we should turn from Thee.

# 675 BE PRESENT AT OUR TABLE

*He took bread, and blessed it.* Lk. 24:30.

John Cennick, 1718-1755

OLD HUNDRED L.M. 8.8.8.8.
M.M. 58

*Genevan Psalter,* 1551

Be pres-ent at our ta - ble, Lord, Be here and ev - 'ry-where a-dored,
These mercies bless, and grant that we May feast in Par - a - dise with Thee.

# 676 GREAT GOD, THOU GIVER OF ALL GOOD

*He took bread, and gave thanks to God in presence of them all.* Acts. 27:35.

James Skinner, d. 1881

RETREAT L.M. 8.8.8.8.
M.M. 80

Thomas Hastings, 1842 (1784-1872)

Great God, Thou giv - er of all good, Ac - cept our thanks and bless this food;
Grace, health, and strength to us af-ford, Through Je-sus Christ our ris - en Lord. A-men.

# WE THANK THEE LORD FOR THIS OUR FOOD 677

*He looked up to heaven, and blessed.* Mk. 6:41.

SO LANGE JESUS BLEIBT DER HERR
L.M. 8.8.8.8.
M.M. 56

Anonymous

*Choralbuch der Mennoniten Gemeinden Russlands,* Halbstadt, 1914

We thank Thee, Lord, for this our food, For life, and health, and ev–'ry good; Let man–na to our souls be giv'n, The Bread of Life sent down from heav'n. A – men.

# GOD IS GREAT AND GOD IS GOOD 678

*He took the seven loaves, and gave thanks and brake.* Mk. 8:6.

PRAYER 7.7.7.7.
M.M. 54

Anonymous

Asahel Abbot, c. 1852

God is great, and God is good, And we thank Him for our food;
By His hand we all are fed; Give us Lord, our dai–ly bread.

# 679 BLESSING TO GOD THE FATHER

*Giving thanks always for all things.* Eph. 5:20.

Charles Wesley, 1746 (1707-1788)
Recast, John J. Overholt, 1970

ABIDE WITH ME 10.10.10.10.
M.M. 54

Charles Edward Pollock, b. 1853

1. Bless – ing to God, the Fa–ther ev – er blest, To Christ, the Mas – ter of the hal–lowed feast, Who hath for us a joy–ous ta – ble spread, And from His bounteous hand His crea–tures fed.
2. O, give us all a thank–ful, con–trite heart; Help us from cares and e – vil to de – part Our dai – ly meat, Lord, let it ev – er be, Thy will to do and on – ly fol – low Thee.

# 680 WE PRAISE THEE, LORD OF EARTH AND SKIES

*In everything give thanks.* I Thess. 5:18.

WINGS OF FAITH C.M. 8.6.8.6.
M.M. 63

Brethren-in-Christ Hymnal, 1893

William Beery, 1852-1956

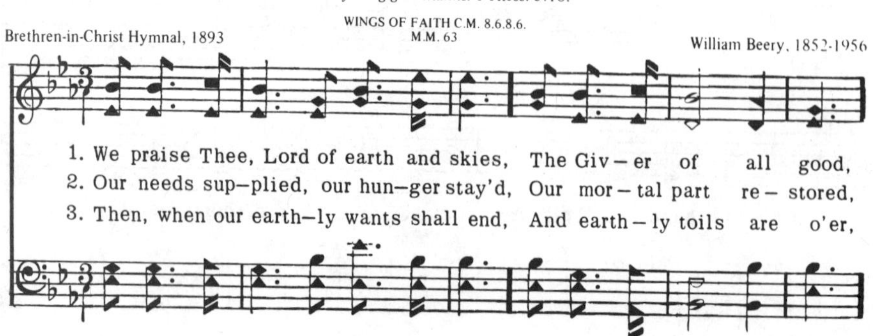
1. We praise Thee, Lord of earth and skies, The Giv – er of all good,
2. Our needs sup–plied, our hun–ger stay'd, Our mor – tal part re – stored,
3. Then, when our earth–ly wants shall end, And earth – ly toils are o'er,

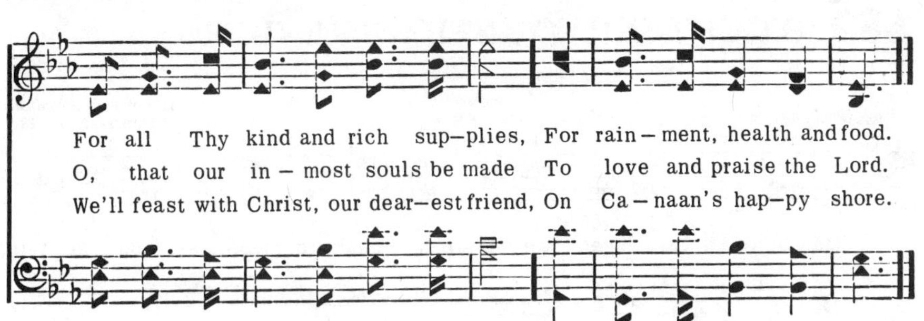
For all Thy kind and rich sup–plies, For rain–ment, health and food.
O, that our in–most souls be made To love and praise the Lord.
We'll feast with Christ, our dear–est friend, On Ca–naan's hap–py shore.

# WE BLESS THE LORD 681

*Intercession, and giving of thanks, be made for all men.* I Tim. 2:1.

RETREAT L.M. 8.8.8.8.
M.M. 80

Isaac Watts, 1719 (1674-1748)

Thomas Hastings, 1784-1872

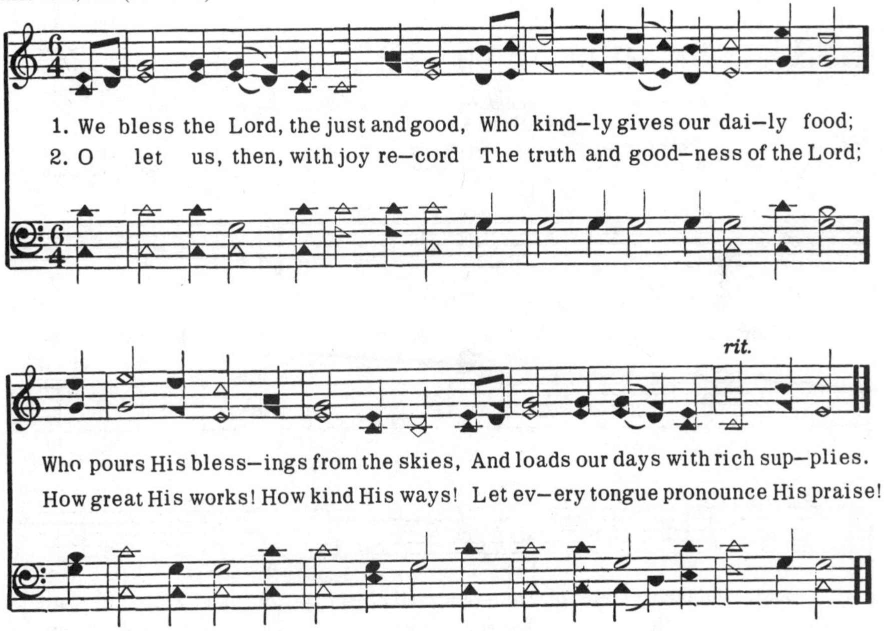

1. We bless the Lord, the just and good, Who kind–ly gives our dai–ly food;
2. O let us, then, with joy re–cord The truth and good–ness of the Lord;

*rit.*

Who pours His bless–ings from the skies, And loads our days with rich sup–plies.
How great His works! How kind His ways! Let ev–ery tongue pronounce His praise!

# 682 O OUR GOD, TO THEE WE RENDER

*The fruit of our lips giving thanks to His name.* Heb. 13:15.

John J. Overholt, 1970

RINGE RECHT 8.7.8.7.
M.M. 66

J. Thommen's *Erbaulicher Musicalischer Christen-Schatz,* 1745

O our God, to Thee we ren–der Thanks for boun–ties Thou hast giv'n;
For Thy mer–cies, faith–ful, ten–der, Thee we praise in earth and heav'n. A–men.

# 683 JESUS' MERCIES NEVER FAIL

*Meats, which God hath created to be received with thanksgiving of them which believe and know the truth.* I Tim. 4:3.

Johann Scheffler, 1657 (1624-1677)
Tr. John Swertner, 1789 (1746-1813)

WAIT MY SOUL 7.7.7.7.
M.M. 66

Lewis Thomas Downs, b. 1827
Arranged by Compiler, 1970

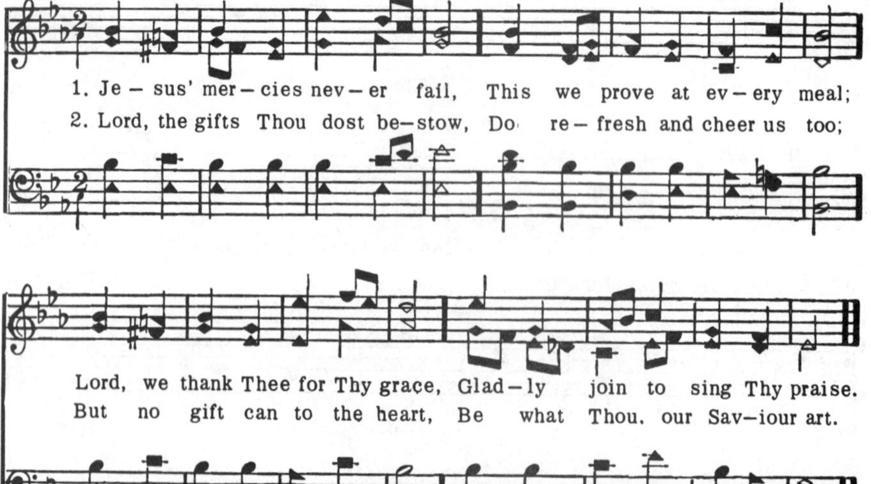
1. Je – sus' mer – cies nev – er fail, This we prove at ev – ery meal;
2. Lord, the gifts Thou dost be – stow, Do re – fresh and cheer us too;
Lord, we thank Thee for Thy grace, Glad – ly join to sing Thy praise.
But no gift can to the heart, Be what Thou, our Sav – iour art.

# LO, GOLDEN LIGHT REKINDLES DAY 684

*In the morning will I direct my prayer unto Thee, and will look up.* Ps. 5:3.

Aurelius Clemens Prudentius, 348-413
*Lux ecce surgit aurea*
Tr. Robert Martin Pope, 1906 (b. 1865)
Altered by Compiler, 1971

WINSCOTT L.M. 8.8.8.8.
M.M. 80

Samuel Sebastian Wesley, 1872 (1810-1876)

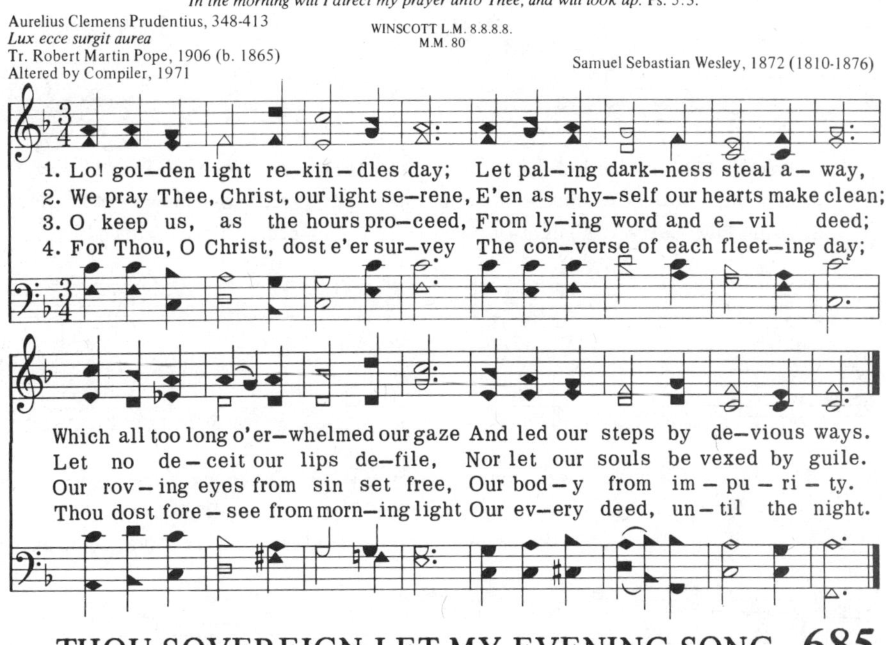
1. Lo! gol–den light re–kin–dles day; Let pal–ing dark–ness steal a– way,
2. We pray Thee, Christ, our light se–rene, E'en as Thy–self our hearts make clean;
3. O keep us, as the hours pro–ceed, From ly–ing word and e–vil deed;
4. For Thou, O Christ, dost e'er sur–vey The con–verse of each fleet–ing day;
Which all too long o'er–whelmed our gaze And led our steps by de–vious ways.
Let no de–ceit our lips de–file, Nor let our souls be vexed by guile.
Our rov–ing eyes from sin set free, Our bod–y from im–pu–ri–ty.
Thou dost fore–see from morn–ing light Our ev–ery deed, un–til the night.

# THOU SOVEREIGN LET MY EVENING SONG 685

*Let my prayer be set forth before Thee as incense; and the lifting up of my hands as the evening sacrifice.* Ps. 141:2.

Anonymous

ST. BERNARD NEW C.M. 8.6.8.6.
M.M. 69

John Richardson, 1816-1879
Arranged by Compiler, 1970

1. Thou sov-'reign, let my eve - ning song Like ho - ly in - cense rise;
2. Thro' all the dan - gers of the day, Thy hand was still my guard,
3. Per - pet - ual bless-ings from a - bove En - com - pass me a - round;
4. Sprinkled a - fresh with pard-'ning blood, I lay me down to rest,
As - sist the of - f'rings of my tongue To reach the loft - y skies.
And still to drive my wants a - way Thy mer - cy stood pre-pared.
But, O, how few re - turns of love Hath my Cre - a - tor found!
As in th' em-bra - ces of my God, Or on my Sav - ior's breast.

## 686 FATHER BLESS OUR SCHOOL TODAY

*He is our help.* Ps. 33:20. *Our help is in the name of the Lord.* Ps. 124:8.

Anonymous
Altered by Compiler, 1970

GOTT SEI DANK 7.7.7.7.
M.M. 72

J. A. Freylinghausen's
*Neues Geistreiches Gesangbuch*

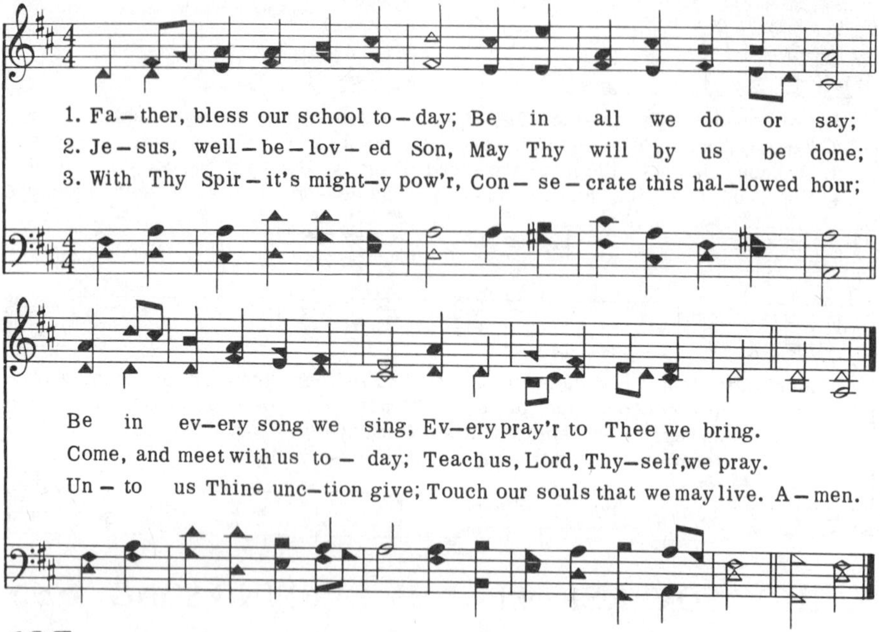

1. Fa – ther, bless our school to – day; Be in all we do or say;
2. Je – sus, well – be – lov – ed Son, May Thy will by us be done;
3. With Thy Spir – it's might–y pow'r, Con– se – crate this hal–lowed hour;

Be in ev–ery song we sing, Ev–ery pray'r to Thee we bring.
Come, and meet with us to – day; Teach us, Lord, Thy–self, we pray.
Un – to us Thine unc–tion give; Touch our souls that we may live. A – men.

## 687 LORD AND SAVIOUR, TRUE AND KIND

*Lord, I will follow Thee.* Lk. 9:57.

Handley C. G. Monk, 1841-1920

FLORA 7.7.7.7.
M.M. 66

Joseph Studebaker

1. Lord and Sav – iour, true and kind, Be the Mas – ter of my mind;
2. Let Thy gra–cious pres – ence rule All I think and speak at school;
3. Here I train for life's swift race; Let me do it in Thy grace;
4. Thou hast made me mind and soul; I for Thee would use the whole;
Bless, and guide, and strength–en still All my powers of thought and will.
Keep me faith – ful, prompt, and keen, At Thy side, my King un – seen.
Here I arm me for life's fight; Let me do it in Thy might.
Thou hast died that I might live; All my powers to Thee I give

# O CHILDREN, WOULD YOU CHERISH 688

*Let the children of Zion be joyful.* Ps. 149:2. *Children that will not lie.* Is. 63:8.
*Children, obey your parents.* Col. 3:20.

Christopher Dock, 1689-1771
*Ach Kinder wollt ihr lieben*
Tr. Samuel Whitaker Pennypacker, 1843-1916
Alt. Wilmer D. Swope, 1970

BLAIRGOURIE (NEW) 7.6.7.6.D.
M.M. 76

John Bacchus Dykes, 1823-1876
Arr. John J. Overholt, 1970

1. O chil - dren would you cher - ish, A wor - thy last - ing love?
The good that does not · per - ish, Is on - ly found a - bove,
Seek God, the lov - ing Sav - iour, With spir - it and with soul,
Then you will find a rap - ture, Your heart can - not con - trol.

2. O Christ, our Lord and Mas - ter, Thou bride - groom of the soul,
Thy Ho - ly Spir - it send us, A liv - ing burn - ing coal,
Our hearts Thy sa - cred dwell - ing, May faith and prac - tice blend,
Give strength and zeal to fol - low, Thy Word un - to the end.

3. The up - ward way to Zi - on, The long and nar - row road,
Is full of toil and bur - den, Our cross a wea - ry load,
Oh, give us love and pa - tience, Thy pre - cious help af - ford,
With - hold not from Thy chil - dren, Thy sweet for - giv - ing word.

4. Praise give to God the Fa - ther, Up - on His high - est throne,
Our lives, our love we of - fer, To Christ His bless - ed son,
And to the Ho - ly Spir - it, In whom we place our trust,
They bring at last to - geth - er, The pi - ous and the just. A - men.

# 689 O COME YE CHILDREN OF MEN MORTAL

*Mark the perfect man, and behold the upright: for the end of that man is peace.* Ps. 37:37.
*... Evildoers ... shall soon be cut down like the grass, and wither as the green herb.* Ps. 37:1, 2.
*The grass withereth, the flower fadeth: but the word of our God shall stand forever.* Is. 40:8.

Christopher Dock, 1689-1771
*Ach kommet her, ihr Menschen Kinder*
Tr. John J. Overholt, 1972

WER NUR DEN LIEBEN GOTT LÄSST WALTEN 9.8.9.8.8.8.
M.M. 96

Georg Neumark, 1641 (1621-1681)

1. O come ye child-dren of men mor-tal, O come and view mor-tal-i-ty, The pride of sin-ners at death's por-tal, And their life's triv-i-al-i-ty; For all, yea all that you sur-vey, The script bears: It shall pass a-way!
2. I lie here on my death-bed, dy-ing, The blight of sin A-dam-ic, heir; My spir-it for no rest is sigh-ing, Which lov-ing hands can me pre-pare, Save in Christ Je-sus' name a-lone, Who, yet in death, my life I own!
1. Ach kom-met her, ihr Men-schen Kin-der, Ach kommt und sieht die Nich-tig-keit, Die Nich-tig-keit der stol-tzen Sün-der, Und ih-res Le-bens Ei-tel-keit; Dann al-les, al-les was ihr seht, Das trägt die Ob-schrift: Es ver-geht!
2. Ich lie-ge hier, im Ster-be-Bet-te, Vom Sün-den Gifft ganz in-fi-ziert, Mein Geist weiss kei-ne Ru-he Stät-te Die mir die lie-be Hand ge-rüst, Als nur dem Na-men Je-su Christ, Der auch im Tod mein Le-ben ist! A-men.

3. My life from time's span soon is parted,
And my brief earthly days are past:
The span of life's short chance is thwarted;
The death–row is my lot at last;
Yet I am glad, Lord Jesus Christ,
That Thou at death's row can'st be prized!

4. Through God's rich grace and mercy given,
The world, long since, I've bid, Good Night!
And in the path of Jesus striven,
A true soul–rest to seek aright;
Yet duty's call I've oft denied,
And much too little zeal applied!

5. O God, through Thy great love transcending,
Make Thou me ready e'en to part:
That I may, when life's day is ending,
In Thy salvation safe depart;
Thy will be mine eternally
A center of great joy with Thee!

3. Mein zeitlich Leben ist verflossen
Und meine Tage sind vorbei:
Die kurze Wahlfahrt ist beschlossen,
Es ist an mir die Todes Reyh;
Doch bin ich froh, Herr Jesu Christ,
Das du auch mit am Reyhen bist.

4. Ich hab durch Gottes reiche Gnade
Die Welt schon längst, gut Nacht gesagt;
Und auf dem schmalen Jesu Pfade,
Nach wahrer Seelen Ruh getracht.
Doch hab ich nicht getan was taugt,
Und viel zu wenig Ernst gebraucht.

5. Ach Gott durch deine Liebes Hände
Mach du mich jetzo noch bereit:
Dass ich an meinem letzden Ende,
In deinem Heyl getrost abscheid;
Dein Will sei mir in Ewigkeit
Ein Centrum der Zufriedenheit.

## MY PEOPLE, GIVE EAR 690

*Give ear, O My people, to My law: incline your ears to the words of My mouth. I will open My mouth in a parable.* Ps. 78:1, 2.

*Psalter*, 1912 — LYONS 10.10.11.11. M.M. 100 — William Croft, 1678-1727

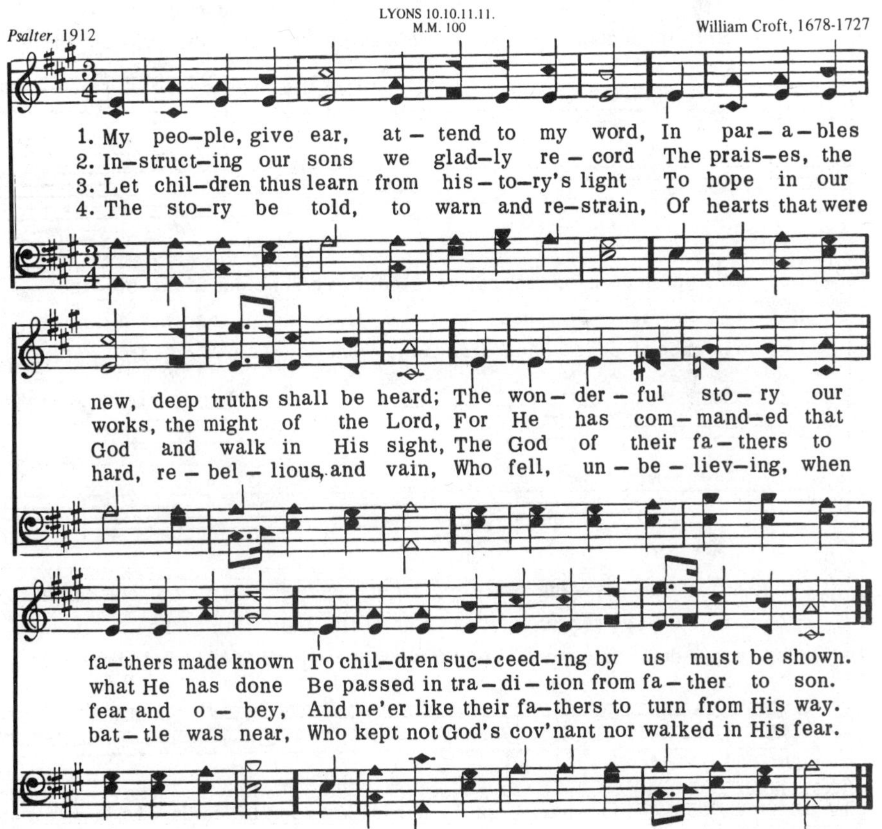
1. My peo–ple, give ear, at – tend to my word, In par – a – bles
2. In–struct–ing our sons we glad–ly re – cord The prais–es, the
3. Let chil–dren thus learn from his – to–ry's light To hope in our
4. The sto–ry be told, to warn and re–strain, Of hearts that were
new, deep truths shall be heard; The won – der – ful sto – ry our
works, the might of the Lord, For He has com – mand–ed that
God and walk in His sight, The God of their fa – thers to
hard, re – bel – lious, and vain, Who fell, un – be – liev–ing, when
fa–thers made known To chil–dren suc–ceed–ing by us must be shown.
what He has done Be passed in tra – di – tion from fa – ther to son.
fear and o – bey, And ne'er like their fa–thers to turn from His way.
bat – tle was near, Who kept not God's cov'nant nor walked in His fear.

# 691 CREATOR OF THE UNIVERSE

*The Lord is nigh unto all them that call upon Him, to all that call upon Him in truth.* Ps. 145:18. *Make me to understand the way of Thy precepts: so shall I talk of Thy wondrous works.* Ps. 119:27.

J. D. Hughes
Altered by Compiler
ALL SAINTS NEW
M.M. 72
Henry Stephen Cutler, 1872 (1824-1902)
1. Cre – a – tor of the u – ni–verse, We lift our minds to Thee,
2. Where minds are dulled with stud – y–ing, When words no life af – ford,
3. Make ev – ery desk an al – tar, Lord, Our learn–ing, too, a prayer,
En – light – en them and lead our thought In Thy own lib – er – ty.
When fields of know–ledge seem too vast, Sus–tain us then, O Lord.
The class–room doors true wor–ship's gates To those who en – ter there.
Let not our search for truth con–cealed, From Thee our souls di–vide;
Let not the love of eas – y ways Leave deep–er truth un–known;
Let sci–ence find in Thee its truth, Tech–nol – o – gy, its goal;
Thou art the liv – ing Lord of truth; Thy Spir – it be our guide.
Teach us that power to learn and grow Is found in Thee a – lone.
Thy wis – dom be our nob–lest thought; Thy light makes knowledge whole.

(Please note: This text may also be sung with the selection, "Faith is the Victory," substituting the words, "Truth is the victory," in the refrain. Arr. John D. Martin. The tune Varina may also be used.)

# GOD, OF TRUTH AND LIGHT CREATOR 692

*Thou art near, O Lord; and all Thy commandments are truth.* Ps. 119:151.

AUSTRIAN HYMN 8.7.8.7.D.
M.M. 66
John J. Overholt, 1972
Franz Joseph Haydn, 1797 (1732-1809)
1. God, of truth and light Cre - a - tor, God most might - y, all - wise, true,
Of our minds il - lu - mi - na - tor, Guide us, lead us now a - new
To the fount of truth and know-ledge, To Thy - self, O God most high!
That we, Thee re-vealed, ac-know-ledge Truth, and Thee may glo - ri - fy!
2. Thou hast cast the bounds of learn - ing And true wis - dom's chart-ed seas;
Know-ledge pass - ing all man's yearn—ing Thou hast grant-ed; Thou didst please
Ab - so - lute and yet un - seal - ed Truth, in-spired, to man im - part
Through Thy ho - ly Word re-veal-ed, Claim - ing, mov-ing, mind and heart!
3. God, all truth and light sus-tain - ing, Cleanse our hearts from fool-ish pride;
Thou, who know-ledge art or - dain - ing, Grant us wis - dom to a - bide
In Thy ho - ly hill, there learn-ing From Thy Spir - it to ac-quire
Truth to sat - is-fy life's yearn-ing, Life in Christ, our sole de-sire! A-men.

## 693 JESUS, FOR THY MERCY'S SAKE

*We are unprofitable servants.* Lk. 17:10. *Teach us of His ways.* Is. 2:3. *Teach us to number our days.* Ps. 90:12.

Jane Crewdson, 1851 (1809-1863)
Altered by Compiler

WAIT MY SOUL UPON THE LORD 7.7.7.7.
M.M. 69

Lewis Thomas Downs, b. 1827
Arranged by Compiler, 1970

1. Je – sus, for Thy mer – cy's sake, Keep me in Thy school of grace;
2. Sweet the les – sons of Thy school, And the low–est place how sweet;
3. Shall the learn – er dare re – bel, Shall the weak dis – ci – ple mourn,
4. Truths which rea – son can–not span, Teach us hum – bly to be–lieve;
5. Give me strength to do Thy will, When Thy pleas – ure is re–vealed;
Though I'm on – ly fit to take, Day by day the low–est place.
When I yield me to Thy rule, When I seat me at Thy feet.
If Thy words seem hard to spell, And Thy thoughts too deep to learn?
Mys – ter – ies too high to scan, Let me qui – et – ly re – cieve.
Give me pa–tience to be still, When Thy know–ledge is con–cealed.

## 694 THE LORD OUR GOD ALONE IS STRONG

*In whom are hid all the treasures of wisdom and knowledge.* Col. 2:3.

Caleb Thomas Winchester, 1871 (1847-1920)
Alt. John J. Overholt, 1970

WINCHESTER NEW L.M. 8.8.8.8.
M.M. 76

George Wittwe's *Handbuch*, 1690

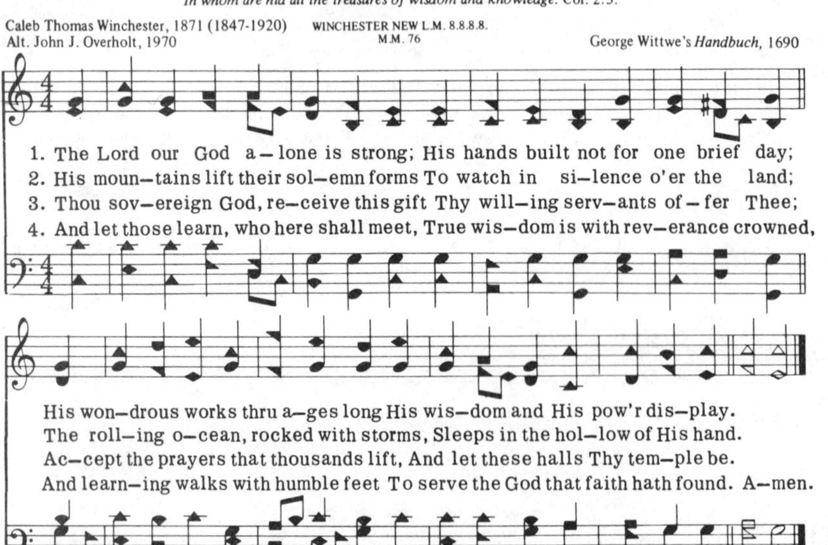
1. The Lord our God a – lone is strong; His hands built not for one brief day;
2. His moun–tains lift their sol–emn forms To watch in si–lence o'er the land;
3. Thou sov–ereign God, re–ceive this gift Thy will–ing serv–ants of – fer Thee;
4. And let those learn, who here shall meet, True wis–dom is with rev–erance crowned,
His won–drous works thru a–ges long His wis–dom and His pow'r dis–play.
The roll–ing o–cean, rocked with storms, Sleeps in the hol–low of His hand.
Ac–cept the prayers that thousands lift, And let these halls Thy tem–ple be.
And learn–ing walks with humble feet To serve the God that faith hath found. A–men.

## LET CHILDREN HEAR THE MIGHTY DEEDS 695

*His wonderful works that He hath done . . . He commanded our fathers, that they should make them known to their children . . . even the children which should be born . . . that they might set their hope in God.* Ps. 78:4-7.

Isaac Watts, 1719 (1674-1748) — GLENLUCE C.M. 8.6.8.6. M.M. 76 — *Scottish Psalter,* 1635

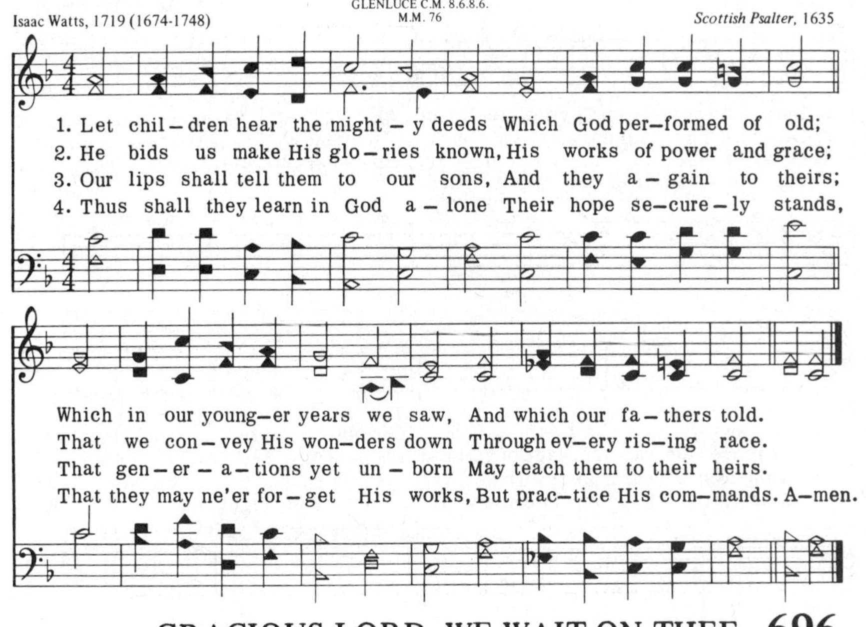
1. Let chil–dren hear the might – y deeds Which God per–formed of old;
2. He bids us make His glo–ries known, His works of power and grace;
3. Our lips shall tell them to our sons, And they a – gain to theirs;
4. Thus shall they learn in God a – lone Their hope se–cure – ly stands,
Which in our young–er years we saw, And which our fa – thers told.
That we con – vey His won–ders down Through ev–ery ris–ing race.
That gen – er – a – tions yet un – born May teach them to their heirs.
That they may ne'er for – get His works, But prac–tice His com–mands. A–men.

## GRACIOUS LORD, WE WAIT ON THEE 696

*I will wait upon thy Lord.* Is. 8:17.

Wilmer D. Swope, 1971
Alt. John J. Overholt, 1971 — EPHRAIM 7.7.7.7. M.M. 52 — Henry J. Leslie, Arranged by Compiler

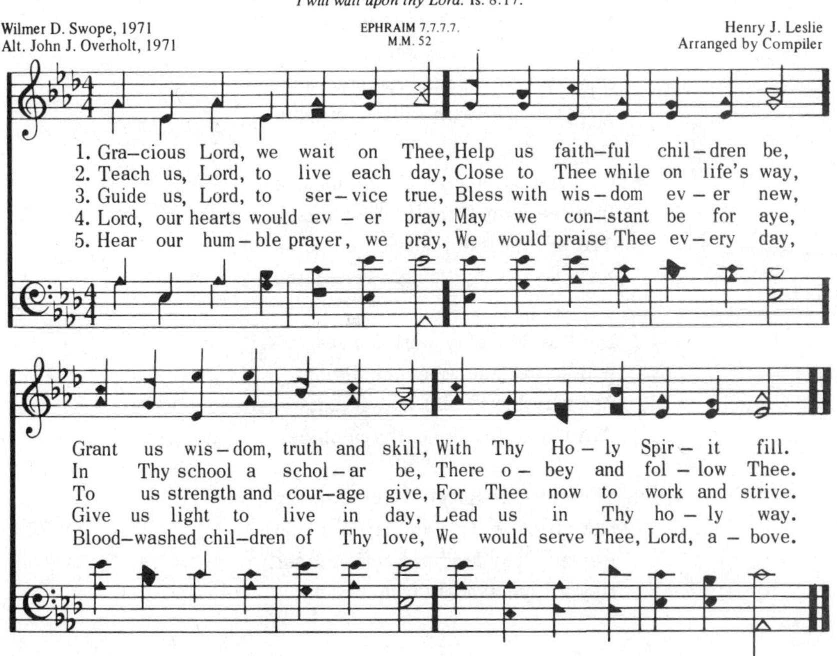
1. Gra–cious Lord, we wait on Thee, Help us faith–ful chil – dren be,
2. Teach us, Lord, to live each day, Close to Thee while on life's way,
3. Guide us, Lord, to ser – vice true, Bless with wis – dom ev – er new,
4. Lord, our hearts would ev – er pray, May we con–stant be for aye,
5. Hear our hum – ble prayer, we pray, We would praise Thee ev – ery day,
Grant us wis – dom, truth and skill, With Thy Ho – ly Spir – it fill.
In Thy school a schol – ar be, There o – bey and fol – low Thee.
To us strength and cour–age give, For Thee now to work and strive.
Give us light to live in day, Lead us in Thy ho – ly way.
Blood–washed chil–dren of Thy love, We would serve Thee, Lord, a – bove.

# 697 LORD, THOU HAST BEEN THY CHILDREN'S GOD

*I am God, and there is none else.* Is. 45:22. *I am God, there is none like Me.* Is. 46:9.

Anne Steele, 1760 (1716-1778) | LEESVILLE NEW L.M. 8.8.8.8. M.M. 56 | E. T. Hildebrand, Arranged by Compiler, 1971

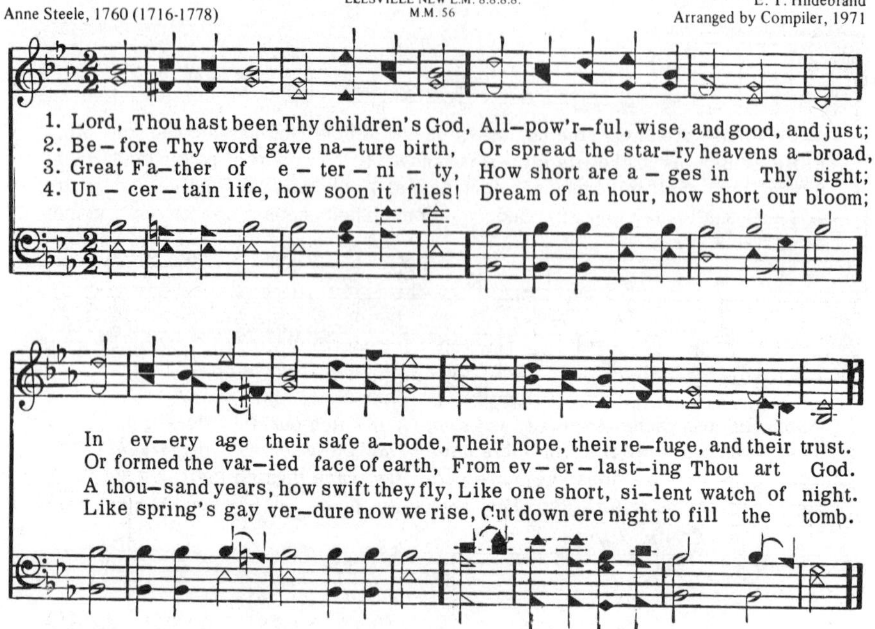
1. Lord, Thou hast been Thy children's God, All–pow'r–ful, wise, and good, and just;
2. Be – fore Thy word gave na–ture birth, Or spread the star–ry heavens a–broad,
3. Great Fa–ther of e – ter – ni – ty, How short are a – ges in Thy sight;
4. Un – cer – tain life, how soon it flies! Dream of an hour, how short our bloom;
In ev–ery age their safe a–bode, Their hope, their re–fuge, and their trust.
Or formed the var–ied face of earth, From ev – er – last–ing Thou art God.
A thou–sand years, how swift they fly, Like one short, si–lent watch of night.
Like spring's gay ver–dure now we rise, Cut down ere night to fill the tomb.

5. Teach us to count our shortening days,
And with true diligence, apply
Our heart to wisdom's sacred ways,
That we may learn to live and die.

6. O, make our sacred pleasures rise,
In sweet proportion to our pains,
Till ere the sad remembrance dies,
Not one uneasy thought complains.

7. Let Thy almighty work appear
With power and evidence divine,
And may the bliss Thy servants share,
Continued to their children shine.

8. Thy glorious image, fair imprest,
Let all our hearts and lives declare;
Beneath Thy kind protection blest,
May all our labours own Thy care.

# O TEACHER, REDEEMER, AND SAVIOUR 698

*Thou art a teacher come from God.* Jn. 3:2. *Teach me Thy paths.* Ps. 25:4.

PARADISE MENNONITE SCHOOL 9.6.9.7.
M.M. 112

John D. Martin, 1971

Marvin Charles Martin, 1969 (b. 1953)
Har. arr. by Compiler, 1971

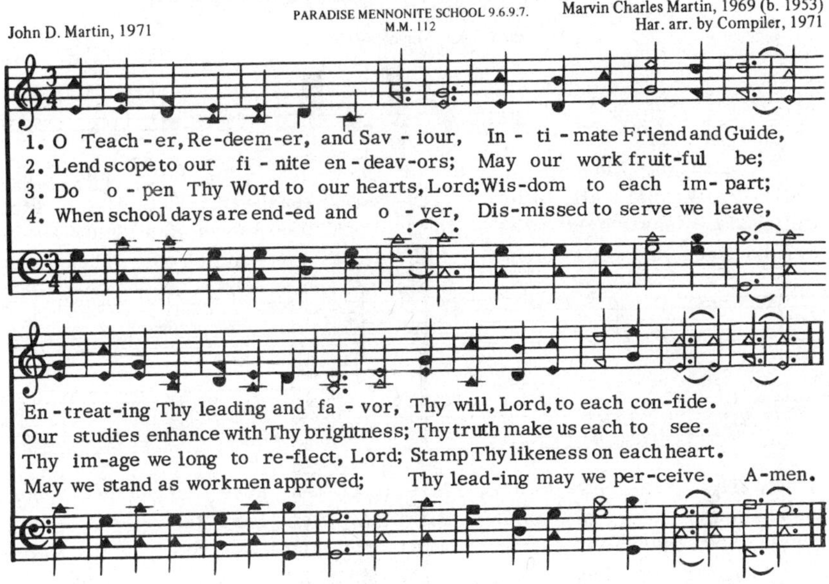
1. O Teach-er, Re-deem-er, and Sav - iour, In - ti - mate Friend and Guide,
2. Lend scope to our fi - nite en-deav-ors; May our work fruit-ful be;
3. Do o - pen Thy Word to our hearts, Lord; Wis-dom to each im - part;
4. When school days are end-ed and o - ver, Dis-missed to serve we leave,
En - treat-ing Thy leading and fa - vor, Thy will, Lord, to each con-fide.
Our studies enhance with Thy brightness; Thy truth make us each to see.
Thy im-age we long to re-flect, Lord; Stamp Thy likeness on each heart.
May we stand as workmen approved; Thy lead-ing may we per-ceive. A-men.

# AS THE SUN DOTH DAILY RISE 699

*The Lord God is a sun and shield.* Ps. 84:11. *He maketh His sun to rise.* Mt. 5:45.
*Teach Transgressor Thy ways.* Ps. 51:13.

INNOCENTS 7.7.7.7.
M.M. 66

Anon.

From a Parish hymnal

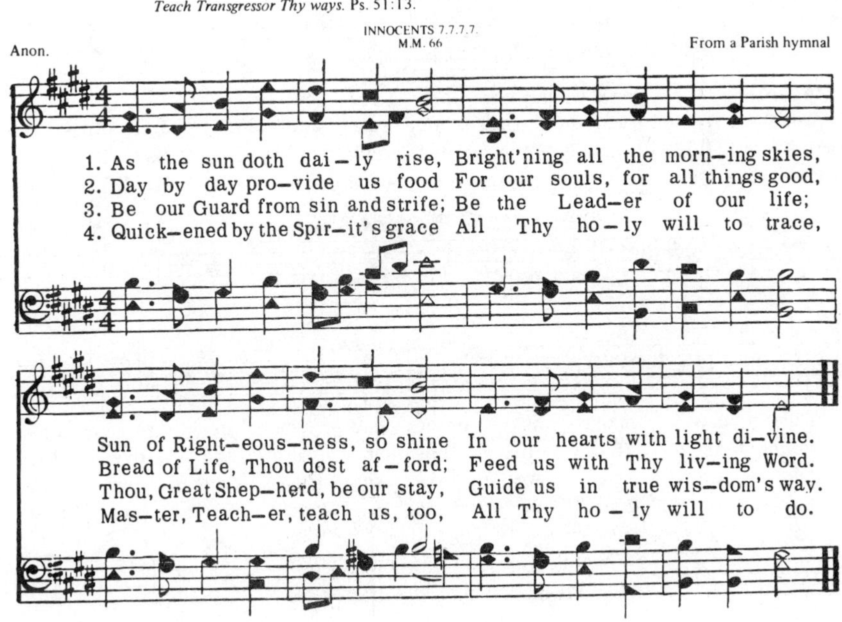
1. As the sun doth dai-ly rise, Bright'ning all the morn-ing skies,
2. Day by day pro-vide us food For our souls, for all things good,
3. Be our Guard from sin and strife; Be the Lead-er of our life;
4. Quick-ened by the Spir-it's grace All Thy ho-ly will to trace,
Sun of Right-eous-ness, so shine In our hearts with light di-vine.
Bread of Life, Thou dost af-ford; Feed us with Thy liv-ing Word.
Thou, Great Shep-herd, be our stay, Guide us in true wis-dom's way.
Mas-ter, Teach-er, teach us, too, All Thy ho-ly will to do.

# 700 O LORD OF HOSTS, ALL HEAVEN POSSESSING

*The Lord of hosts is with us; the God of Jacob is our refuge. Selah.* Ps. 46:7. *Thy truth reacheth unto the clouds.* Ps. 108:4. *Thy law is the truth.* Ps. 119:142.

Edward Hayes Plumptre, 1864 (1821-1891)
Altered by Compiler, 1971

MIR IST ERBARMUNG 9.8.9.8.8.8.
M.M. 84

Johann Gottfried Schicht (1753-1823)
*Allgemeines Choral-Buch . . .*, 1819

1. O Lord of hosts, all heaven pos – sess – ing, Be – hold us
2. Il – lu – mine all, dis – ci – ples, teach – ers, Thy Word's deep
3. May faith now light the lamp of sci – ence, And knowl – edge
4. Bind Thou our life in full – est un – ion To Thee and
from Thy sap – phire throne. In faith and hope – ful – ness con –
won – ders to un – fold; With rev – erent hand let wis – dom's
pass from truth to truth, And wis – dom, in its full re –
saints from sin set free; Up – hold us in that blest com –
fess – ing Thy Son, whom we as Lord now own; For Thou in
preach – ers Bring forth their treas – ures, new and old; Let old – est,
li – ance, Now claim the hearts and minds of youth; So ho – lier,
mun – ion Of all Thy saints on earth with Thee; Keep Thou our
Christ hast made us Thine, And on us all Thy
young – est, find in Thee Of truth and love the
wis – er, may we grow, As time's swift cur – rents
souls, or there, or here, In might – iest love, that

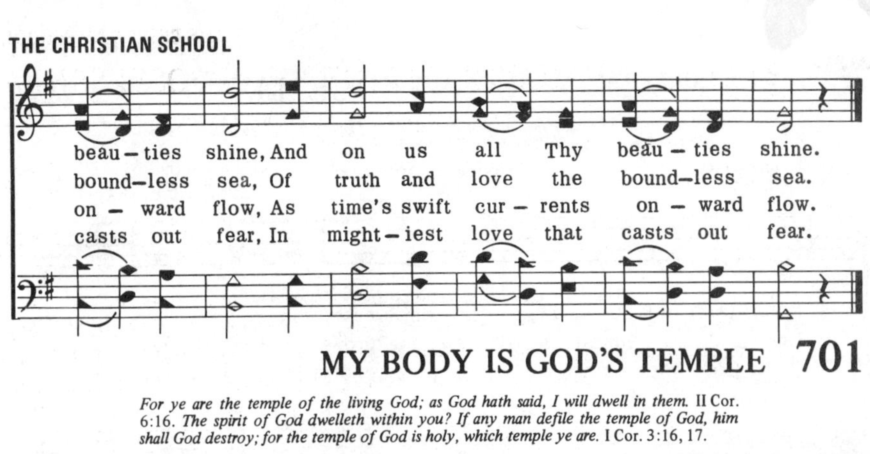
beau – ties shine, And on us all Thy beau – ties shine.
bound–less sea, Of truth and love the bound–less sea.
on – ward flow, As time's swift cur – rents on – ward flow.
casts out fear, In might – iest love that casts out fear.

# MY BODY IS GOD'S TEMPLE 701

*For ye are the temple of the living God; as God hath said, I will dwell in them.* II Cor. 6:16. *The spirit of God dwelleth within you? If any man defile the temple of God, him shall God destroy; for the temple of God is holy, which temple ye are.* I Cor. 3:16, 17.

GOD'S TEMPLE 7.6.7.6.D.
M.M. 84

Elizabeth A. Showalter, c. 1945 (b. 1907)

George Frederick Root, 1820-1895
Arr. Walter E. Yoder, 1889-1964
Har. arr. John J. Overholt, 1972

1. My bod - y is God's tem - ple; I'm build - ing ev - 'ry day,
2. My mind shall be God's work - shop; That ev - 'ry thought and word
3. My soul is God's pos - ses - sion, Kept by Him ev - 'ry hour,

In home and church and school - room, By stud - ies, work, and play.
And deed be kind and no - ble, And hon - or Christ, my Lord.
For - giv - en, cleansed, and quick - en'd, By His re - deem - ing pow'r.

I know if I build wise - ly, Re - fus - ing all that's wrong,
I know if I think tru - ly, Test - ing the things I do,
I know that if I trust Him, Walk close-ly by His side,

My tem - ple will grow love - ly, For God both pure and strong.
My mind will grow more like His, My deeds more like His, too.
My soul will have com - mun - ion With God what - e'er be - tide.

# 702 FOUNTAIN OF KNOWLEDGE, LIVING BREATH

*If any of you lack wisdom, let him ask of God, that giveth to all men liberally, and upbraideth not; and it shall be given him.* Jas. 1:5.

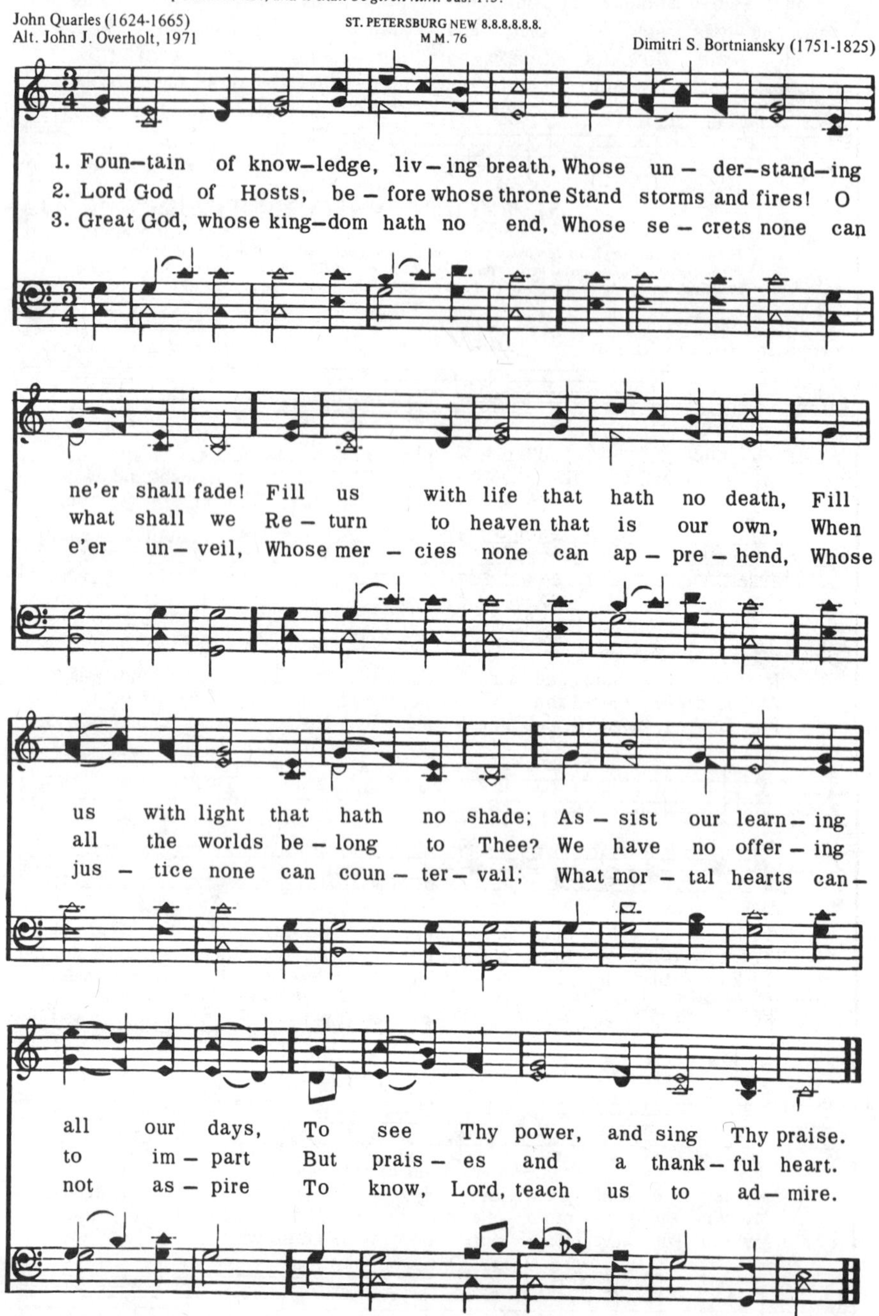
John Quarles (1624-1665)
Alt. John J. Overholt, 1971
ST. PETERSBURG NEW 8.8.8.8.8.8.
M.M. 76
Dimitri S. Bortniansky (1751-1825)
1. Foun–tain of know–ledge, liv–ing breath, Whose un – der-stand–ing ne'er shall fade! Fill us with life that hath no death, Fill us with light that hath no shade; As – sist our learn– ing all our days, To see Thy power, and sing Thy praise.
2. Lord God of Hosts, be – fore whose throne Stand storms and fires! O what shall we Re – turn to heaven that is our own, When all the worlds be – long to Thee? We have no offer – ing to im – part But prais – es and a thank – ful heart.
3. Great God, whose king–dom hath no end, Whose se – crets none can e'er un – veil, Whose mer – cies none can ap – pre – hend, Whose jus – tice none can coun – ter – vail; What mor – tal hearts can – not as – pire To know, Lord, teach us to ad – mire.

# O MASTER TEACHER, TEACH US NOW 703

*A wise man will hear, and will increase learning; and a man of understanding shall attain unto wise counsels.* Prov. 1:5.

Carlton C. Buck, 1959
St. 5, Louis Fitzgerald Benson, 1894 (1855-1930)

ABRIDGE C.M. 8.6.8.6.
M.M. 84

Isaac Smith (1735-1800)

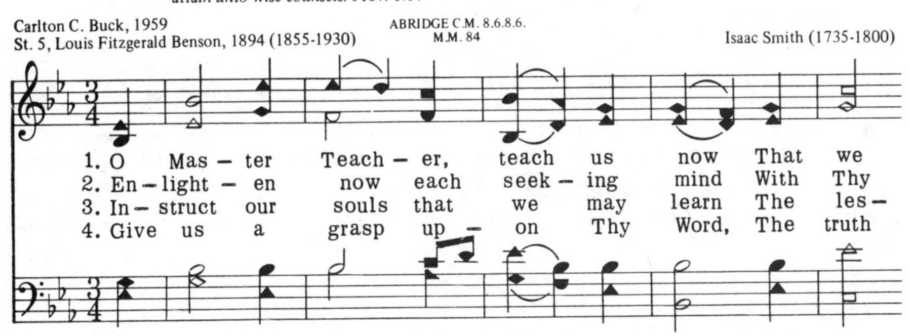
1. O Mas – ter Teach – er, teach us now That we
2. En – light – en now each seek – ing mind With Thy
3. In – struct our souls that we may learn The les –
4. Give us a grasp up – on Thy Word, The truth

in turn may teach; Re – veal Thy truth and teach
great mind of love; That in our seek – ing we
sons of the heart; That taught by Thee, we may
that comes from Thee; Help men to teach till all

us how The hearts of men to reach.
may find The wis – dom from a – bove.
in turn Thy sav – ing truth im – part.
have heard, And ev – ery mind is free. A – men.

5. Thy life the bond of fellowship,
Thy love the law that rules,
Thy name, proclaimed by every lip,
The Master of our schools.

# 704 MAY THE GRACE OF CHRIST OUR SAVIOUR

*The grace of our Lord Jesus Christ be with you all. Amen.* II Thess. 3:18.

John Newton, 1779 (1725-1807)

RINGE RECHT 8.7.8.7.
M.M. 66

J. Thommen's *Erbaulicher Musicalischer Shatz,* 1745

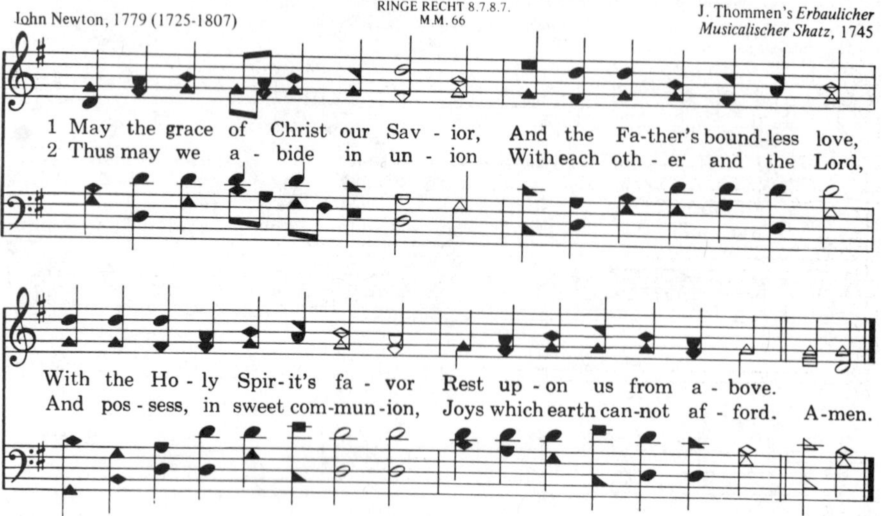
1 May the grace of Christ our Sav - ior, And the Fa-ther's bound-less love,
2 Thus may we a - bide in un - ion With each oth - er and the Lord,
With the Ho - ly Spir-it's fa - vor Rest up - on us from a - bove.
And pos - sess, in sweet com-mun-ion, Joys which earth can-not af - ford. A-men.

# 705 MAY THE GRACE OF OUR LORD, JESUS CHRIST

*The grace of the Lord Jesus Christ, and the love of God, and the communion of the Holy Ghost, be with you all. Amen.* II Cor. 13:14.

GREGOR DOXOLOGY 9.8.10.10.
M.M. 69

Christian Gregor (1723-1801)

Ἡ χά - ρις τοῦ κυ-ρί-ου Ἰη-σοῦ Χρι-στοῦ καὶ ἡ ἀ-
Gra-tia Do-mi-ni nos-tri Je - su Chri - sti, et
Que la gra - ce de no-tre Sei - gneur Je-sus Christ, et l'a -
May the grace of our Lord, Je - sus Christ, and the
Die Gna - de un-sers Herrn Je - su Chri - sti, und die

γά - πη τοῦ θε - οῦ καὶ ἡ κοι - νω - νί - α τοῦ ἁ-
cha - ri - tas Pa - tris, et com - mu - ni - ca - ti - o
mour de Dieu le Pe - re, et la com - mu - ni - on
love of God the Fa - ther and the com - mu - nion
Lie - be Got - tes und die Ge - mein - schaft des

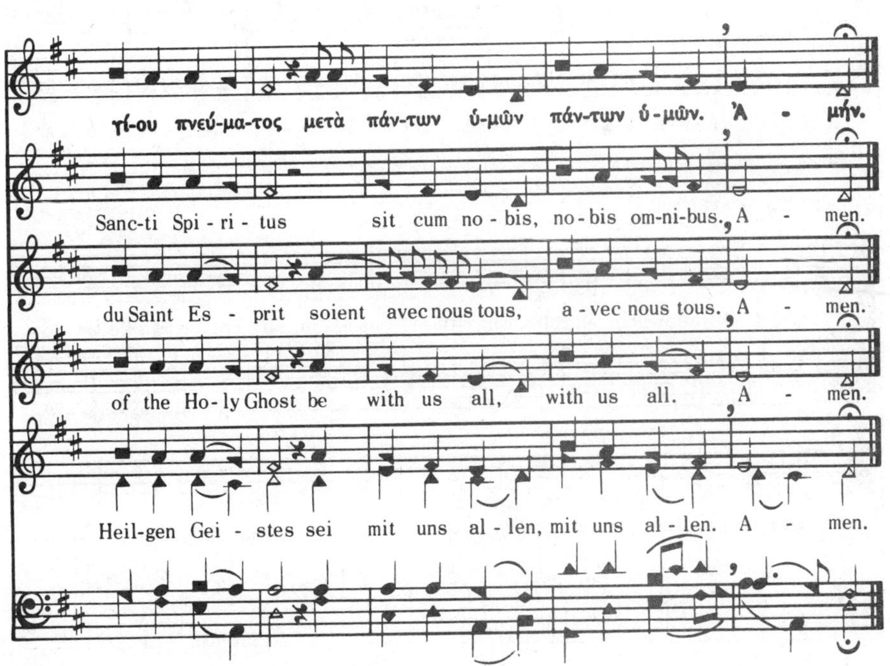
γί-ου πνεύ-μα-τος μετὰ πάν-των ὑ-μῶν πάν-των ὑ-μῶν. Ἀ - μήν.
Sanc-ti Spi - ri - tus sit cum no - bis, no - bis om-ni-bus. A - men.
du Saint Es - prit soient avec nous tous, a - vec nous tous. A - men.
of the Ho - ly Ghost be with us all, with us all. A - men.
Heil-gen Gei - stes sei mit uns al - len, mit uns al - len. A - men.

# 706 BLEST BE THE TIE THAT BINDS

*The Lord watch between me and thee, when we are absent from one another.* Gen. 31:49.

John Fawcett, 1772 (1739-1817)

DENNIS S.M. 6.6.8.6.
M.M. 72

Johann Georg Nägeli, 1832 (1773-1836)
Arr. Lowell Mason, 1845 (1792-1872)

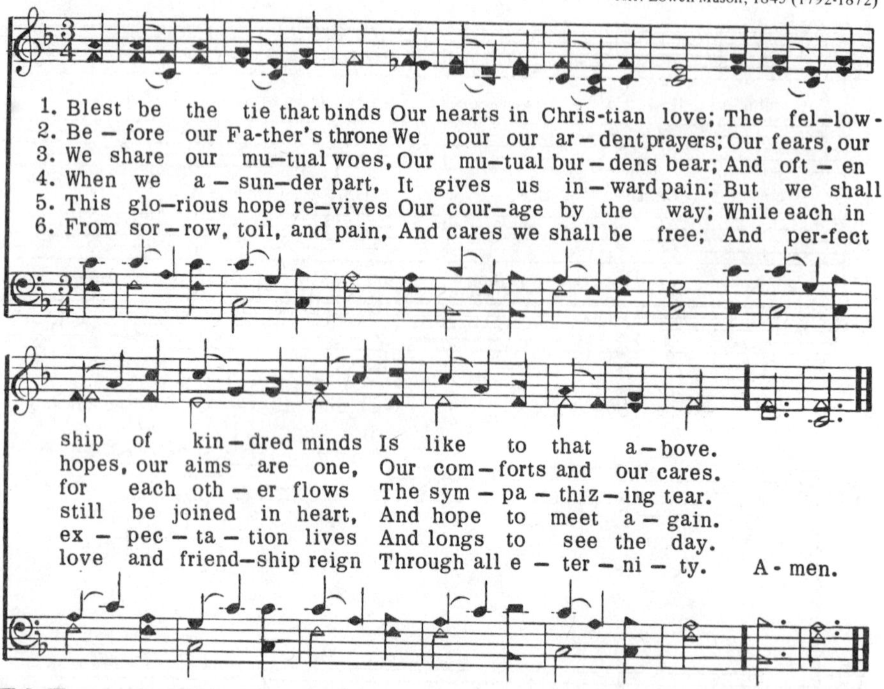

1. Blest be the tie that binds Our hearts in Chris-tian love; The fel–low-ship of kin–dred minds Is like to that a–bove.
2. Be–fore our Fa-ther's throne We pour our ar–dent prayers; Our fears, our hopes, our aims are one, Our com–forts and our cares.
3. We share our mu–tual woes, Our mu–tual bur–dens bear; And oft–en for each oth–er flows The sym–pa–thiz–ing tear.
4. When we a–sun–der part, It gives us in–ward pain; But we shall still be joined in heart, And hope to meet a–gain.
5. This glo–rious hope re–vives Our cour–age by the way; While each in ex–pec–ta–tion lives And longs to see the day.
6. From sor–row, toil, and pain, And cares we shall be free; And per-fect love and friend–ship reign Through all e–ter–ni–ty.

A-men.

# 707 PRAISE GOD FROM WHOM ALL BLESSINGS FLOW

*Now the God of peace, that brought again from the dead our Lord Jesus, that great shepherd of the sheep, through the blood of the everlasting covenant, Make you perfect in every good work to do His will, working in you that which is wellpleasing in His sight, through Jesus Christ; to whom be glory for ever and ever. Amen.* Heb. 13:20, 21.

Thomas Ken, 1695 (1637-1710)

OLD HUNDRED L.M. 8.8.8.8.
M.M. 63

Guillaume Franc, 1543 (1520-1570)
*Genevan Psalter*, 1551

Praise God from whom all bless-ings flow, Praise Him all creatures here be-low,
Praise Him a-bove, ye heav'n-ly host, Praise Fa-ther, Son, and Ho-ly Ghost.

# PRAISE GOD FROM WHOM ALL BLESSINGS FLOW

*Now unto Him that is able to keep you from falling, and to present you faultless before the presence of his glory with exceeding joy, To the only wise God our Saviour, be glory and majesty, dominion and power, both now and ever. Amen.* Jude 24, 25.

SILOAM DOXOLOGY L.M. 8.8.8.8.
M.M. 69

Thomas Ken, 1695 (1637-1710)

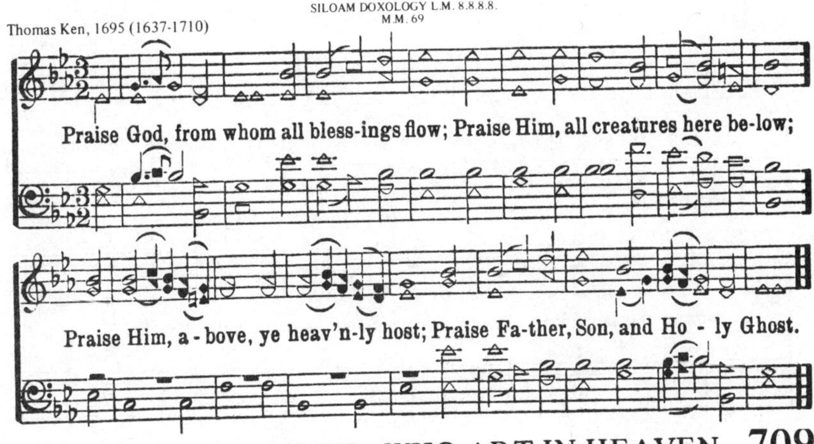
Praise God, from whom all bless-ings flow; Praise Him, all creatures here be-low;
Praise Him, a-bove, ye heav'n-ly host; Praise Fa-ther, Son, and Ho - ly Ghost.

# OUR FATHER, WHO ART IN HEAVEN 709

*After this manner therefore pray ye: Our Father which art in heaven, Hallowed be Thy name.* Mt. 6:9.

PALMER DOXOLOGY (Irregular)
M.M. 76

Matthew 6:9-13

Horatio Richard Palmer (1834-1907)

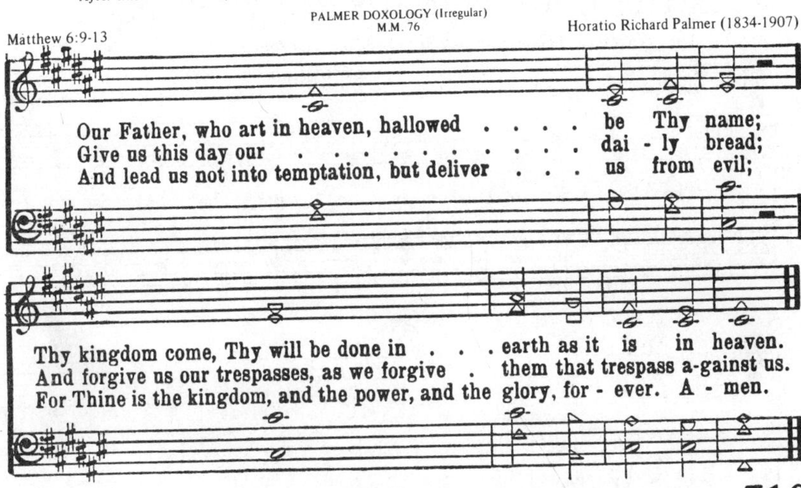
Our Father, who art in heaven, hallowed . . . . be Thy name;
Give us this day our . . . . . . . . . . . . dai - ly bread;
And lead us not into temptation, but deliver . . . us from evil;
Thy kingdom come, Thy will be done in . . . earth as it is in heaven.
And forgive us our trespasses, as we forgive . them that trespass a-gainst us.
For Thine is the kingdom, and the power, and the glory, for - ever. A - men.

# GLORY BE TO THE FATHER 710

*Give unto the Lord the glory due unto His name: bring an offering, and come before Him: worship the Lord in the beauty of holiness.* I Chron. 16:29.

GLORIA PATRI (Scottish) Irregular
M.M. 66

Anon.

Old Scottish Chant

Glo - ry be to the Fa-ther, and to the Son, and to the Ho - ly Ghost;
As it was in the be-gin-ning, is now, and ev-er shall be, world with-out end. A - men.

# 711 GLORY BE TO THE FATHER

*Now unto the King eternal, immortal, invisible, the only wise God, be honour and glory for ever and ever. Amen.* I Tim. 1:17.

Anon.

GLORIA PATRI (Greatorex) 7.10.8.7.4.
M.M. 76

From Henry W. Greatorex's Collection, 1851 (1811-1858)

Glo - ry be to the Fa-ther, and to the Son, and to the Ho - ly Ghost; As it
was in the beginning, is now, and ever shall be, world without end. A - men, A - men.

# 712 THE LORD IS IN HIS HOLY TEMPLE

*But the Lord is in His holy temple: let all the earth keep silence before Him.* Hab. 2:20.

Hab. 2:20
Anon.

THE LORD IS IN HIS HOLY TEMPLE (Root) 9.9.7.10.9.
M.M. 69

George Frederick Root, 1820-1895

The Lord is in His ho - ly tem - ple, The Lord is in His ho - ly
tem - ple, Let all the earth keep si - lence, Let all the earth keep
si - lence be - fore Him, Keep si-lence, keep si - lence be - fore Him. A-men.

# SEND OUT THY LIGHT AND THY TRUTH 713

*O send out Thy light and Thy truth: let them lead me; let them bring me unto Thy holy hill, and to Thy tabernacles.* Ps. 43:3.

LUX FIAT 11.10.11.10.10.10.
M.M. 80

Charles F. Gounod (1818-1893)

Send out Thy light and Thy truth, let them lead me; O, let them
bring me to Thy ho - - ly hill. Send out Thy light and Thy
truth, let them lead me; O, let them bring me to Thy ho - ly
hill. O, let them lead me, O, let them lead me;
O, let them bring me to Thy ho - ly hill. A - MEN.

# 714 NOW THE HOUR OF WORSHIP O'ER

*Therefore, my beloved brethren, be ye stedfast, unmoveable, always abounding in the work of the Lord, forasmuch as ye know that your labour is not in vain in the Lord.* I Cor. 15:58.

Hartman Schenck, 1680 (1634-1681)
*Nun Gott Lob es ist vollbracht*
Tr. Sts. 1, 2 Composite
St. 3, Oskar Kaiser, 1938

NUN GOTT LOB 7.8.7.8.8.8
M.M. 54

Traditional Amish Melody
As sung by the compiler's mother,
Hannah Wagler Overholt, 1876-1965
Har. John J. Overholt, 1966, 1972

1. Now, the hour of wor – ship o'er, Teach – ing, hear – ing, pray – ing, sing – ing, Let us glad – ly God a – dore, For His Word our prais – es bring – ing; For the rich re – past He gave us Bless the Lord, who deigned to save us.
2. Now, God's bless – ing cheers our heart, By His grace to us ex – tend – ed. Let us joy – ful – ly de – part; Be our souls to God com – mend – ed. May His Spir – it ev – er guide us And with all good gifts pro – vide us.
3. Bless our go – ing out we pray, Bless our en – trance in like meas – ure; Bless our bread, O Lord, each day, Bless our toil, our rest, our pleas–ure; Bless us when we reach death's por – tal, Bless us here with life im – mor – tal. A–men.

# O JESUS FRIEND UNFAILING 715

*There is a friend that sticketh closer than a brother.* Prov. 18:24.

Samuel C. H. Küster, 1829 (1762-1838)
*O Jesu, Freund der Seelen*
Tr. H. K. Burlingham, 1842-1901

MISSIONARY HYMN 7.6.7.6.D.
M.M. 69

Lowell Mason, 1823 (1792-1872)

1. O Je–sus, Friend un–fail–ing, How dear Thou art to me!
2. Nought, nought I count as pleas–ure, Com–pared, O Lord, with Thee;
3. O world–ly pomp and glo–ry, Your charms are spread in vain!
4. For ev–'ry trib–u–la–tion, For ev–'ry sore dis–tress,
Are cares or fears as–sail–ing? I find my strength in Thee.
Thy sor–row with–out meas–ure, Earned peace and joy for me.
I've heard a sweet–er sto–ry, I've found a tru–er gain.
In Christ I have sal–va–tion, Sure help and qui–et rest.
Why should my feet grow wea–ry Of this, my pil–grim way?
I love to own, Lord Je–sus, Thy claims o'er me di–vine;
Where Christ a place pre–par–eth, There is my loved a–bode;
No fear of foes pre–vail–ing! I tri–umph, Lord, in Thee:
Rough tho' the path and drear–y, It ends in per–fect day.
Bought with Thy blood most pre–cious, Whose can I be but Thine?
There shall I gaze on Je–sus, There shall I dwell with God.
O Je–sus, Friend un–fail–ing, How dear Thou art to me!

# 716 ON OUR WAY REJOICING

*He went on his way rejoicing.* Acts 8:39. *Alway rejoicing.* II Cor. 6:10.

John Samuel Bewley Monsell, 1863 (1811-1875)
Alt. by Compiler, 1970
PRINCETHORPE 6.5.6.5.D.
M.M. 72
William Pitts (1829-1903)
1. On our way re – joic–ing, As we home–ward move, Heark–en to our
2. If with hon–est–heart – ed Love for God and man, Day by day Thou
3. On our way re – joic–ing Glad–ly let us go; Je – sus is our
prais–es, O Thou God of love! Is there grief or sad – ness? Thine it
find us Do–ing what we can, Thou who giv'st the seed–time Wilt give
Lead–er, He has quelled the foe. He with – in, our safe – ty; He with–
can – not be; Is our sky be – cloud–ed? Clouds are not from Thee.
sure in–crease, Crown the head with bless–ings, Fill the heart with peace.
in, our joy; Who if we be faith – ful, Can our hope de–stroy?

4. Unto God the Father, Joyful songs we sing;
Unto God the Saviour, Thankful hearts we bring;
Unto the great Godhead, Bow we and adore,
On our way rejoicing Ever, evermore.

# FOLLOW THE PATH OF JESUS 717

*Teach me Thy way, O Lord, and lead me in a plain path.* Ps. 27:11. *Follow His steps.* I Pet. 2:21.

Christopher Ruby Blackall, 1871, alt.

BOUND BROOK 7.6.7.5.D.
M.M. 80

From *Hymns And Tunes*, 1890

1. Fol - low the path of Je - sus, Walk where His foot - steps lead;
2. Cling to the hand of Je - sus, All through the day and night;
3. Take up the cross of Je - sus, Shar - ing the shame He bore;
Keep in His beam - ing pres - ence, Ev - 'ry coun - sel heed;
Dark though the way and drear - y, He will guide you right.
Self and the world de - ny - ing, Love the Sav - iour more;
Watch, while the hours are fly - ing, Read - y some good to do;
Live for the good of oth - ers, Help - less, op-pressed and wrong;
Tell all the world of Je - sus, Think of their gloom and loss,
Quick, while His voice is call - ing, Yield o - be - dience true!
Lift them from depths of sor - row, In His strength be strong!
Tell of His great sal - va - tion, Glo - ry in His cross.

# LIVE IN ME LORD JESUS 718

*I am crucified with Christ: nevertheless I live; yet not I, but Christ liveth in me: and the life which I now live in the flesh I live by the faith of the Son of God, who loved me, and gave Himself for me.* Gal. 2:20.

Anonymous
3rd St. John J. Overholt, 1968
LIVE IN ME 9.9.7.7.9.
M.M. 66
Anonymous
Har. John J. Overholt, 1968
1. Live in me, Lord Je - sus, live in me; Live in me, Lord Je - sus,
2. Work through me, Lord Je - sus, work through me; Work through me, Lord Je - sus,
3. Come for me, Lord Je - sus, come for me; Come for me, Lord Je - sus,
live in me; There's a work that must be done, There's a
work through me; There's a work that must be done, There's a
come for me, When the work shall all be done, And the
vic- t'ry to be won, Ev - ery hour, by thy power, live in me!
vic- t'ry to be won, Ev - ery hour, by thy power, work through me!
vic- to - ry is won, In that hour, of thy power, come for me!

# 719 LET'S TALK ABOUT JESUS

*For we cannot but speak the things which we have seen and heard.* Acts 4:20.

Herbert Buffum BUFFAM 6.6.6.6.6.6.6.9. M.M. 96 Herbert Buffum

Let's talk a - bout Je - sus, The King of
Kings is He, The Lord of Lords su - preme,
Through all e - ter - ni - ty. The great I
AM, the Way, The Truth, the Life, the Door.
Let's talk a - bout Je - sus More and more.

## JESUS IS THE SWEETEST NAME 720

*His name shall be called Wonderful, Counsellor, The Mighty God, The everlasting Father, The Prince of Peace.* Is. 9:6.

JESUS IS THE SWEETEST NAME (Irregular)
M.M. 63

Lela Long
Arr. John J. Overholt, 1971

Je - sus is the sweet - est name I know, And He's just the
same as His ho - ly name, That's the rea - son why I
love Him so, Yes, Je - sus is the sweet - est name I know.

## IT IS TRULY WONDERFUL 721

*To Him who alone doeth great wonders: for His mercy endureth forever.* Ps. 136:4.

IT IS TRULY WONDERFUL (Irregular)
M.M. 66

B. E. Warren

B. E. Warren

It is tru - ly won - der-ful What the Lord has done! It is
tru - ly won - der - ful! It is tru - ly won - der - ful! It is
tru - ly won - der-ful What the Lord has done! Glo - ry to His name.

# 722 JESUS IS A WONDERFUL SAVIOUR

*This is indeed the Christ, the Saviour of the world.* Jn. 4:42.

David Morken
Dora Deanie Nauman

MORKEN-NAUMAN (Irregular)
M.M. 84

Arr. David Morken and Dora Deanie Nauman
Arr. for mixed voices, John J. Overholt, 1969

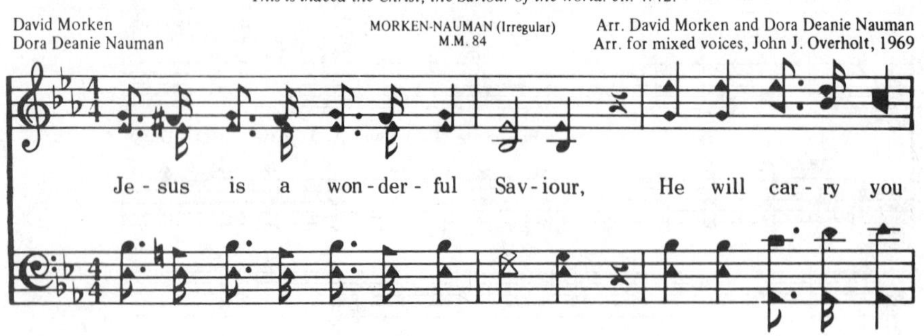
Je - sus is a won - der - ful Sav - iour, He will car - ry you

thru; Je - sus is a won - der - ful Sav - iour, He will

car - ry you thru; Je - sus is a won - der - ful Sav - iour,

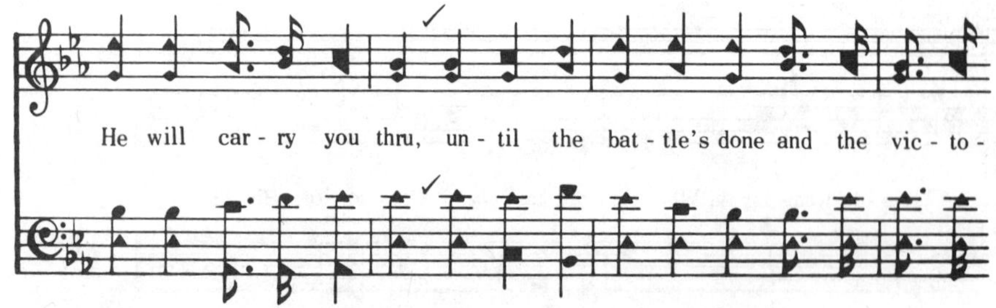
He will car - ry you thru, un - til the bat - tle's done and the vic - to -

ry is won my Lord will car - ry you thru; O my pre - cious
broth - er when the world's on fire, You'll need my Je - sus
to be your Sav - iour; He'll hide you ev - er in the Rock of
A - ges, In the Rock of A - ges just cleft for you.

# 723 WE ARE CONQUERORS THROUGH CHRIST

*We are more than conquerors through Him that loved us.* Rom. 8:37.

Ruth Buxton
Willard Buxton
BUXTON (Irregular)
M.M. 88
Ruth Buxton
Willard Buxton
We are con - quer - ors through Christ, (our Sav - iour) Con - quer - ors through
We are con - quer - ors through Christ, (our Sav - iour) Con - quer - ors through
Christ; (our lead - er) Striv - ing to o - bey His Word, Trust - ing Him each
Christ; (our lead - er) He has prom-ised us His pow'r For each day and
day. We are yield - ing all to Him, (to Him) Wait - ing now on
hour. We are more than con - quer-ors, (thru Him) Through His might - y
Him, (on Him) Christ the vic - tor wins the bat - tle, Let Him have His way.
love, (His love) In all things we claim His prom-ise, Con-quer-ors through Christ.

# LORD, LAY SOME SOUL UPON MY HEART 724

*Knowing therefore the terror of the Lord, we persuade men.* II Cor. 5:11.

MY PRAYER (Irregular) C.M. 8.6.8.6.
M.M. 100

Ira David Sankey, 1840-1908
Arr. David H. Johnson

Lord, lay some soul up-on my heart, And love that soul thro' me;
And may I no - bly do my part To win that soul for Thee.

*Refrain:* To win that soul for Thee, To win that soul for Thee;
And may I nobly do my part To win that soul for Thee.

# LEAD ME TO SOME SOUL TODAY 725

*Then the Spirit said unto Philip, Go near, and join thyself to this chariot. Then Philip opened his mouth . . . and preached unto him Jesus.* Acts 8:29, 35.

LEAD ME TO SOME SOUL TODAY (Irregular)
M.M. 66

Will H. Houghton

Wendell P. Loveless

Lead me to some soul to - day, O teach me, Lord, just what to say; Friends of mine are
lost in sin, And can-not find their way. Few there are who seem to care, And few there
are who pray;
who pray;
Melt my heart and fill my life, Give me one soul to - day.

# 726 EVERYBODY OUGHT TO KNOW

*Neither is there salvation in any other: for there is none other name under heaven given among men, whereby we must be saved.* Acts 4:12.

Anon.
Arr. John J. Overholt

HE'S THE LILY OF THE VALLEY (Irregular)
M.M. 63

Arr. John J. Overholt, 1968

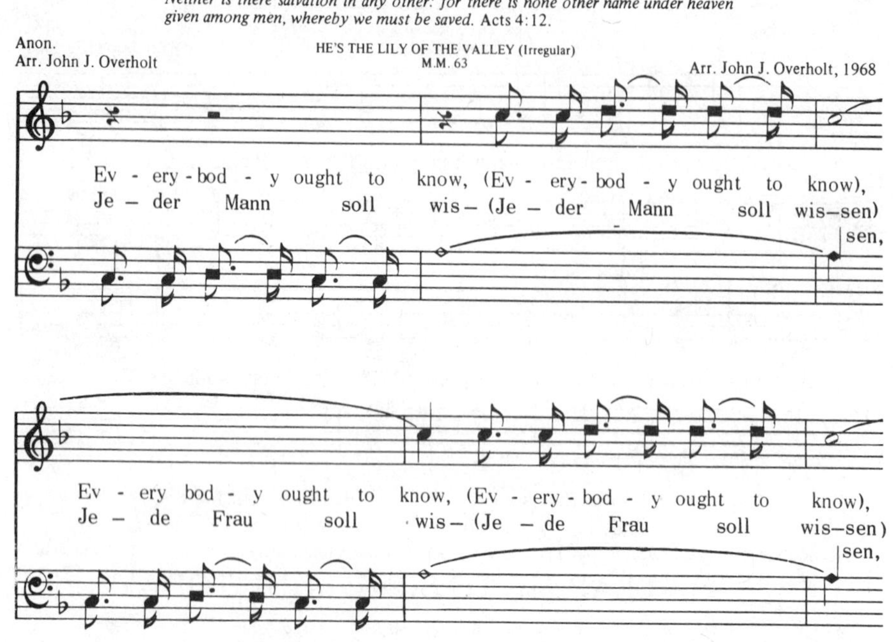

Ev - ery - bod - y ought to know, (Ev - ery - bod - y ought to know),
Je – der Mann soll wis – (Je – der Mann soll wis–sen)
sen,
Ev - ery bod - y ought to know, (Ev - ery - bod - y ought to know),
Je – de Frau soll wis – (Je – de Frau soll wis–sen)
sen,

Ev - ery bod - y ought to know, (Ev - ery-bod-y ought to know) Who Je - sus is!
Je – des Kind soll wis – (Je – des Kind soll wis–sen) Wer Je - sus ist!
sen,

He's the Li – ly of the Val – ley,
Er, die Lil – ie in dem Thal – e,
He's the Li - ly of the Val - ley He's the Bright
Er, die Lil - ie in dem Thal - e Er, der hel –

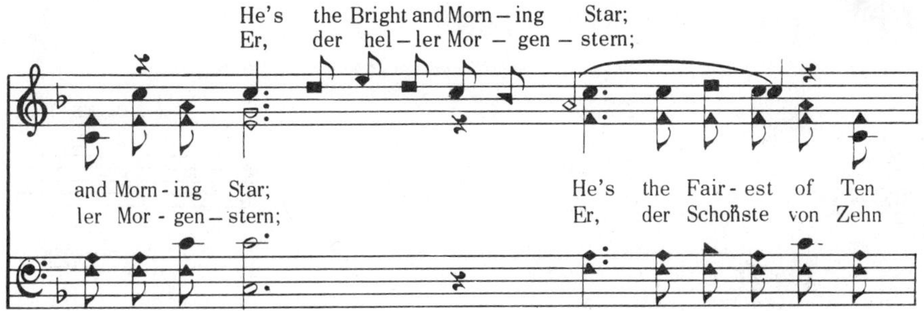
He's the Bright and Morn – ing Star;
Er, der hel – ler Mor – gen – stern;
and Morn - ing Star;
ler Mor - gen – stern;
He's the Fair - est of Ten
Er, der Schönste von Zehn

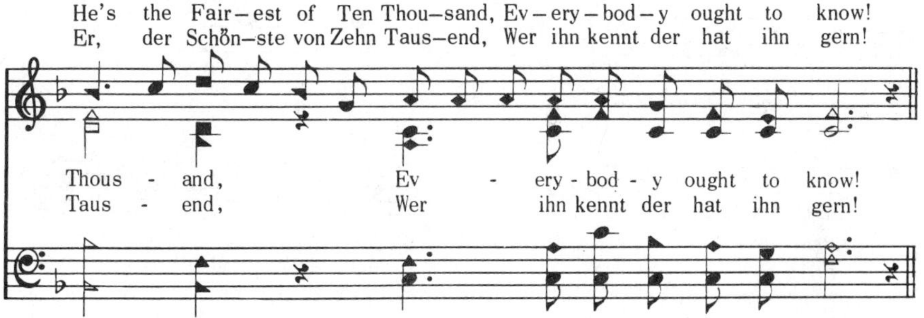
He's the Fair – est of Ten Thou–sand, Ev – ery – bod – y ought to know!
Er, der Schön–ste von Zehn Taus–end, Wer ihn kennt der hat ihn gern!
Thous - and, Ev - ery - bod - y ought to know!
Taus - end, Wer ihn kennt der hat ihn gern!

# LORD, GIVE ME STRENGTH 727

*I can do all things through Christ which strengtheneth me.* Phil 4:13.

CONESTOGA 7.8.8.8.
M.M. 92

Clarence Y. Fretz, 1929

Clarence Y. Fretz, 1929
Har. arr. John Henry Miller, 1971
Har. arr. Clarence Y. Fretz, 1971

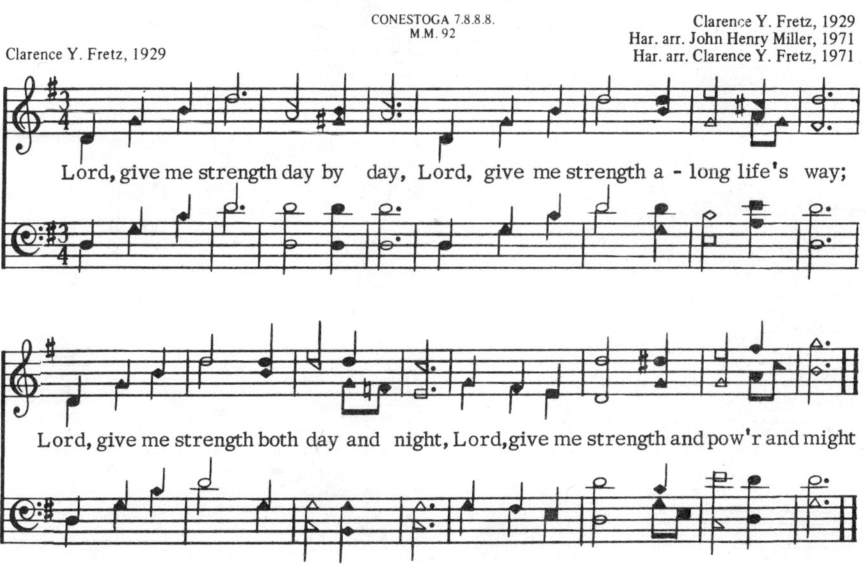
Lord, give me strength day by day, Lord, give me strength a - long life's way;
Lord, give me strength both day and night, Lord, give me strength and pow'r and might

# 728 I HAD SO MANY SINS

*Who His own self bare our sins in His own body on the tree.* I Pet. 2:24.

Anon.
Arr. by Compiler, 1969
ALL THE WAY TO CALVARY 13.6.6.13. with Ref.
M.M. 72
Arr. John J. Overholt, 1969
1. I had so man - y sins and he took them all a - way, He took them all a - way, He took them all a - way; I has so man - y sins and he took them all a - way,
2. I had so man - y doubts and he took them all a - way, He took them all a - way; He took them all a - way; I had so man - y doubts and he took them all a - way,
3. I was a guilt - y sin - ner and he washed me white as snow, He washed me white as snow He washed me white as snow, I was a guilt - y sin-ner, and he washed me white as snow,
4. My heart sings hal - le - lu - jah, for he gave a song to me, He gave a song to me, He gave a song to me, My heart sings hal-le-lu-jah, for he gave a song to me
And now he sets me free. All the way to Cal - va - ry he went for me, He went for me, He went for me;

All the way to Cal - va - ry he went for me and now he sets me free!

# I HAVE DECIDED TO FOLLOW JESUS 729

*Master, I will follow Thee whithersoever Thou goest.* Mt. 8:19.

I HAVE DECIDED 10.9.10.8.
M.M. 63

Anon.

Har. Dorothea Hart

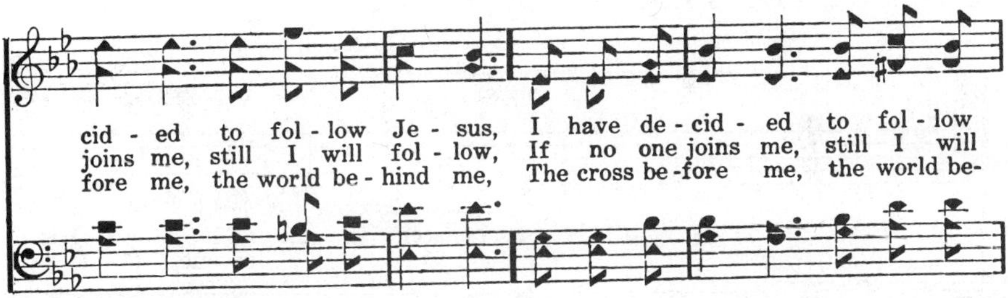

1. I have de - cid - ed to fol - low Je - sus, I have de - cid - ed to fol - low Je - sus, I have de - cid - ed to fol - low Je - sus, No turn - ing back, no turn - ing back.
2. If no one joins me, still I will fol - low, If no one joins me, still I will fol - low, If no one joins me, still I will fol - low, No turn - ing back, no turn - ing back.
3. The cross be - fore me, the world be - hind me, The cross be - fore me, the world be - hind me, The cross be - fore me, the world be - hind me, No turn - ing back, no turn - ing back.

# 730 TAKE A CLOSER LOOK AT CALVARY

*But God forbid that I should glory save in the cross of our Lord Jesus Christ, by Whom the world is crucified unto me, and I unto the world.* Gal. 6:14.

John D. Martin, 1965

DILLER 9.9.9.9.
M.M. 66

John D. Martin
Har. arr. by Compiler, 1971

Take a clos-er look at Cal-va - ry, There the Lord would sweetly say to thee;
By your faith ac-cept my par-don free, I have shed my life-blood; trust in me.

# 731 LET THE BEAUTY OF JESUS

*That the life also of Jesus might be made manifest in our body.* II Cor. 4:10.

Anon.

THE BEAUTY OF JESUS 13.11.11.11.
M.M. 120

Arr. E. Edwin Young (b. 1895)

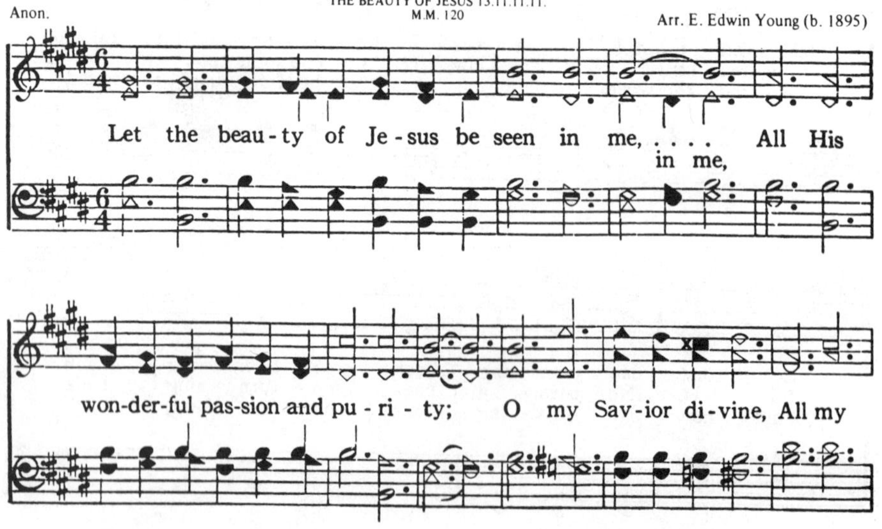
Let the beau-ty of Je-sus be seen in me, . . . . All His
in me,
won-der-ful pas-sion and pu - ri - ty; O my Sav-ior di-vine, All my

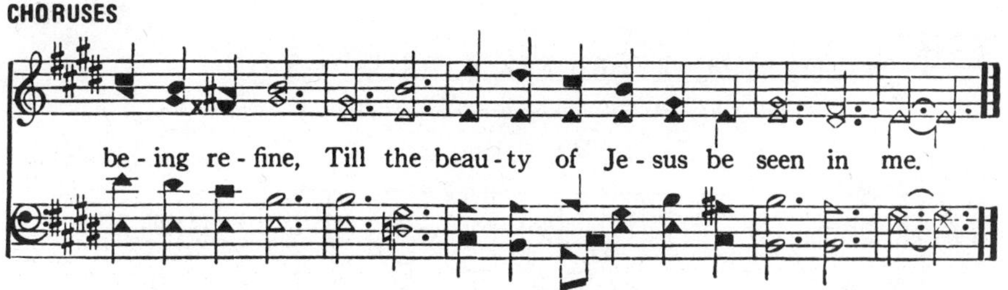


# EVERYTHING'S ALRIGHT 732

*In Thy presence is fullness of joy; at Thy right hand there are pleasures for evermore.* Ps. 16:11.

Anon.
Arr. by Compiler, 1969

IN MY FATHER'S HOUSE 10.5.5.10.5.
M.M. 72

Anon.
Arr. John J. Overholt, 1969

1. Ev - ery - thing's al - right in my Fa - ther's house, In my Fa - ther's house, In my Fa - ther's house; Ev - ery - thing's al - right in my Fa - ther's house, there is joy, joy, joy!
2. There will be no sin in my Fa - ther's house, In my Fa - ther's house, In my Fa - ther's house; There will be no sin in my Fa - ther's house, there is joy, joy, joy!
3. I want to go there to my Fa - ther's house, To my Fa - ther's house, To my Fa - ther's house; I want to go there to my Fa - ther's house, there is joy, joy, joy!
4. Come and go with me to my Fa - ther's house, To my Fa - ther's house, To my Fa - ther's house; Come and go with me to my Fa - ther's house, there is joy, joy, joy!
5. Je - sus will be there in my Fa - ther's house, In my Fa - ther's house, In my Fa - ther's house; Je - sus will be there in my Fa - ther's house, there is joy, joy, joy!

# 733 MY DESIRE, TO BE LIKE JESUS

*And every man that hath this hope in him purifieth himself, even as he is pure.* I Jn. 3:3.

MY DESIRE 8.7.5.5.8.
M.M. 58

Lillian Plankenhorn — Lillian Plankenhorn

My de-sire, to be like Je-sus; My de-sire,
to be like Him. His Spir-it fill me, His love o'er-
rit.
whelm me — In deed and word, to be like Him.

# 734 LORD JESUS, I LOVE THEE

*Jesus Christ . . . is Lord of all.* Acts 10:36. *Made unto us wisdom, and righteousness [justification].* I Cor. 1:30. *He is our peace.* Eph. 2:14. *Christ in you, the hope of glory.* Col. 1:27. *That if thou shalt confess with thy mouth the Lord Jesus, and shalt believe in thine heart that God hath raised Him from the dead, thou shalt be saved.* Rom. 10:9.

BEETHOVEN 6.6.6.6.
M.M. 108

John J. Overholt, 1972 — Ludwig van Beethoven, 1770-1827; Arr. John Henry Miller, 1965 (b. 1939)

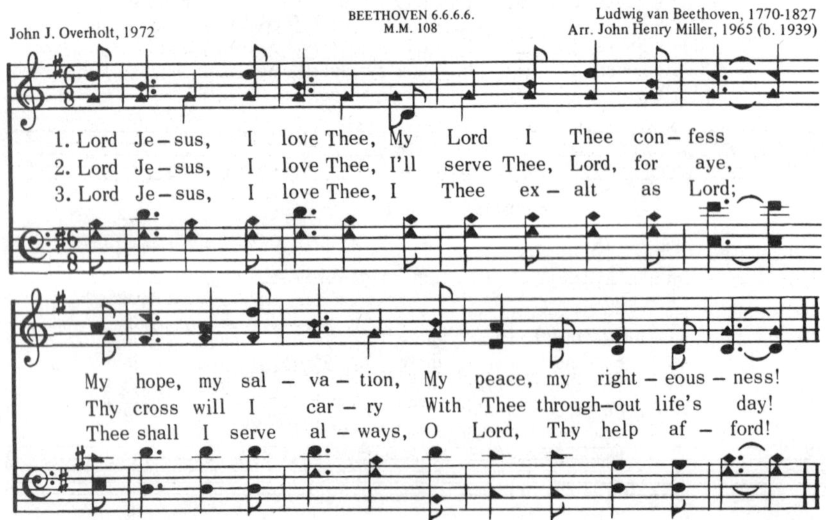

1. Lord Je-sus, I love Thee, My Lord I Thee con-fess
2. Lord Je-sus, I love Thee, I'll serve Thee, Lord, for aye,
3. Lord Je-sus, I love Thee, I Thee ex-alt as Lord;
My hope, my sal-va-tion, My peace, my right-eous-ness!
Thy cross will I car-ry With Thee through-out life's day!
Thee shall I serve al-ways, O Lord, Thy help af-ford!

# HALLELUJAH, HALLELUJAH, HALLELUJAH 735

*Behold, the bridegroom cometh; go ye out to meet Him.* Mt. 25:6.

Anon.
Arr. John J. Overholt, 1970

HALLELUJAH, HALLELUJAH
M.M. 66

Anon.
Arr. John J. Overholt

* 1. Hal – le – lu – jah, hal – le – lu – jah, hal – le – lu – jah, Hal – le – lu – jah,
2. Lord Je – sus, with Thy Ho – ly Spir – it fill us, Lord Je – sus,
3. Be watch – ful, be watch–ful, ye His peo – ple, Be watch–ful,
hal – le – lu – jah, hal – le – lu – jah; Hal – le – lu – jah, hal – le – lu – jah, hal–le–
with Thy Ho–ly Spir – it fill us; Dear Je – sus, with Thy Ho – ly Spir–it
Be watch–ful, ye His peo–ple; Be watch–ful, be watch–ful ye His
lu – jah, He is com – ing soon, Our Bride–groom's com–ing soon.
fill us, Thou art com – ing soon, Our Bride–groom, com–ing soon.
peo – ple, He is com – ing soon, Our Bride–groom's com–ing soon.

* First stanza can also be sung as refrain

1. Hallelujah, hallelujah, hallelujah,
Hallelujah, hallelujah, hallelujah,
Hallelujah, hallelujah, hallelujah,
Den der Bräutigam, der Bräutigam, der kommt!

2. Lieber Jesus, erfüll uns mit dem Geist,
Lieber Jesus, erfüll uns mit dem Geist,
Lieber Jesus, erfüll uns mit dem Heiligen Geist,
Den der Bräutigam, der Bräutigam, der kommt!

3. Seid wachsam, seid wachsam, alle Frommen,
Seid wachsam, seid wachsam, alle Frommen,
Seid wachsam, seid wachsam, alle Frommen,
Den der Bräutigam, der Bräutigam, der kommt!

# HEAVENLY FATHER, HEAR THY CHILDREN 736

*They shall call His name Emmanuel, which being interpreted is, God with us.* Mt. 1:23.

C.B.A. VESPER HYMN NEW 8.7.8.7. with Ref. M.M. 72

Dimitri S. Bortniansky, 1751-1825
Arr. Vera Sommers Overholt, 1968

1. Heav'n-ly Fa - ther, hear Thy child-ren, As we come to Thee in prayer.
2. Keep our hearts and minds from e - vil, Help us walk in Je - sus' way.
Help us al - ways to re - mem - ber God is with us ev - 'ry-where.
Make us lov - ing, kind, and truth - ful, Keep us safe - ly night and day.
CHORUS:
God is with us! God is with us! God is with us ev - 'ry-where.

# 737 O COME, ALL YE CHILDREN

*For unto you is born this day in the city of David a Saviour, which is Christ the Lord.* Lk. 2:11.

Christian V. Schmidt, 1768-1854
*Ihr Kindelein kommet*
Tr. Anon.
Alt. by Compiler, 1968

IHR KINDERLEIN KOMMET 11.11.11.11.
M.M. 96

Johann Abraham Peter Schulz, 1747-1800

*Simply*

1. O come, all ye children, O come, one and all,
To Bethlehem haste, to the manger so small,
God's Son for salvation is sent you this night
To be your Redeemer, your Joy and Delight.

2. He's born in a stable for you and for me,
Draw near by the bright gleaming starlight to see,
In swaddling clothes lying, so meek and so mild,
And purer than angels, the heavenly Child.

3. See Mary and Joseph with lovebeaming eyes
Are gazing upon the rude bed where he lies,
The shepherds are kneeling, with hearts full of love,
While angels chant loud Alleluias above.

4. Kneel down and adore Him with shepherds today,
Lift up holy hands now, and praise Him as they;
Rejoice that a Savior from sin you can boast,
And join in the song of the heavenly host.

5. Dear Saviour and Lord, what are gifts to bestow
By which our affection and gladness to show?
No riches and treasures of value can be,
But hearts that believe are accepted with thee.

6. Our hearts, then, to thee we will offer today,
We offer them gladly, accept them, we pray,
And make them so spotless and pure that we may
Abide in thy presence in heaven for aye.

Amen.

# TELL ME THE STORIES OF JESUS 738

*And they brought young children to Him, that He should touch them.* Mk. 10:13.

STORIES OF JESUS 8.4.8.4.5.4.5.4.
M.M. 126

William H. Parker, 1904 (1845-1929) | Frederic A. Challinor (b. 1866)

1. Tell me the sto - ries of Je - sus I love to hear; Things I would
2. First let me hear how the chil - dren Stood round His knee; And I shall
3. In - to the cit - y I'd fol - low The chil - dren's band, Wav - ing a
4. Tell me, in ac - cents of won - der, How rolled the sea, Toss - ing the
ask Him to tell me If He were here; Scenes by the way - side,
fan - cy His bless - ing Rest - ing on me: Words full of kind - ness,
branch of the palm - tree High in my hand; One of His her - alds,
boat in a tem - pest On Gal - i - lee! And how the Mas - ter,
Tales of the sea, Sto - ries of Je - sus, Tell them to me.
Deeds full of grace, All in the love - light Of Je - sus' face.
Yes, I would sing Loud - est ho - san - nas! Je - sus is King!
Read - y and kind, Chid - ed the bil - lows, And hushed the wind. A-men.

5. Tell how the sparrow that twitters
 On yonder tree,
And the sweet meadow-side lily
 May speak to me–
Give me their message,
 For I would hear
How Jesus taught us
 Our Father's care.

6. Show me that scene in the garden,
 Of bitter pain;
And of the cross where my Saviour
 For me was slain–
Sad ones or bright ones,
 So that they be
Stories of Jesus,
 Tell them to me.

# 739 JESUS CALLS THE CHILDREN

*Suffer the little children to come unto Me, and forbid them not: for of such is the kingdom of God.* Mk. 10:14.

JESUS LOVES THE LITTLE CHILDREN 7.7.11.7.7.11.
M.M. 58
C. H. Woolston
George F. Root (1820-1895)
1. Je - sus calls the chil - dren dear, "Come to me and nev - er fear,
2. Je - sus is the Shep - herd true, And He'll al - ways stand by you,
3. I am com - ing, Lord, to Thee, And Thy sol - dier I will be,
For I love the lit - tle chil - dren of the world. I will take you
For He loves the lit - tle chil - dren of the world. He's a Sav - iour
For He loves the lit - tle chil - dren of the world. And His cross I'll
by the hand, Lead you to the bet - ter land, For I love the lit - tle
great and strong, And He'll shield you from the wrong, For He loves the lit - tle
al - ways bear, And for Him I'll do and dare, For He loves the lit - tle
chil - dren of the world."
REFRAIN:
Je - sus loves the lit - tle chil - dren All the
lit - tle chil - dren, All the
chil - dren of the world;
chil - dren of the world;
Red and yel - low, black and white, They are

pre-cious in His sight, Je - sus loves the lit - tle chil - dren of the world.

# LORD A LITTLE BAND AND LOWLY 740

*Those that seek Me early shall find Me.* Prov. 8:17.

CHILDREN'S SONG OF PRAISE 7.7.8.7. with Ref.
M.M. 56

Martha Evans Shelly

Arr. J. Henry Showalter, 1864-1947

1. Lord, a lit - tle band, and low - ly, We are come to sing to Thee;
2. Fill our hearts with tho'ts of Je - sus, And of heav'n, where He has gone;
3. For we know the Lord of glo - ry Al - ways sees what chil-dren do,
4. Let our sins be all for - giv - en; Make us fear what-e'er is wrong;

Thou art great, and high, and ho - ly— Oh, how sol - emn we should be!
And let noth - ing ev - er please us He would grieve to look up - on.
And is writ - ing now the sto - ry Of our thoughts and ac - tions, too.
Lead us on our way to heav - en, There to sing a no - bler song.

FINE.

*D.S. Press-ing on, in the line of du - ty, We shall meet to part no more.*

REFRAIN.

Far a - way, in the realms of beau - ty, Far-ther on, to the gold-en shore,

*D.S.*

# 741 COME AND DINE, THE MASTER CALLETH

*All things are ready: come unto the marriage.* Mt. 22:4. *A feast is made for laughter.* Eccles. 10:19. *When thou makest a feast, call the poor, the maimed, the lame, the blind: and thou shalt be blessed.* Lk. 14:13, 14.

Nathan Jonathan Overholt, 1972 (b. 1966) — COME AND DINE 8.8.8.3. M.M. 60 — Nathan Jonathan Overholt; Har. John J. Overholt, 1972

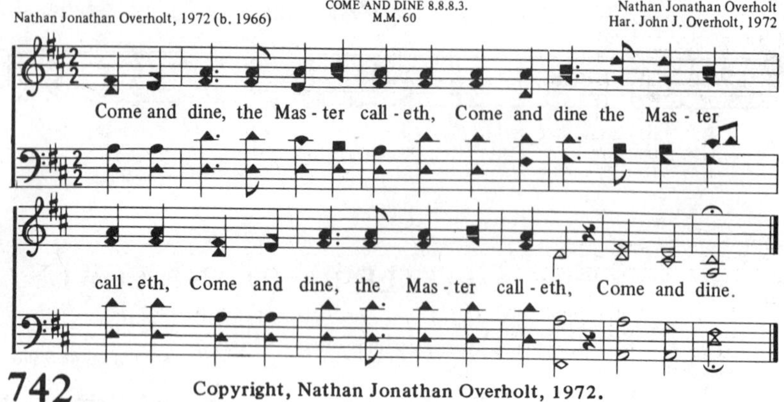
Come and dine, the Mas - ter call - eth, Come and dine the Mas - ter
call - eth, Come and dine, the Mas - ter call - eth, Come and dine.

# 742 SWEETLY LORD HAVE WE HEARD THEE CALLING

*Lord, I will follow Thee whithersoever Thou goest.* Lk. 9:57.

Mary Bridges Canedy Slade, 1826-1882 — FOOTPRINTS OF JESUS 9.4.9.4. with Ref. M.M. 72 — Asa Brooks Everett, 1828-1875

1. Sweet - ly, Lord, have we heard Thee call - ing, Come, fol - low me!
And we see where Thy foot-prints fall - ing Lead us to Thee.

2. Tho' they lead o'er the cold, dark moun-tains, Seek - ing His sheep;
Or a - long by Si - lo - am's foun-tains, Help - ing the weak:

3. If they lead thro' the tem - ple ho - ly, Preach-ing the word;
Or in homes of the poor and low - ly, Serv - ing the Lord.

4. By and by, thro' the shin - ing por - tals, Turn - ing our feet,
We shall walk, with the glad im - mor - tals, Heav'n's gold-en street.

REFRAIN:
Foot - prints of Je - sus, that make the path - way glow;
We will fol - low the steps of Je - sus, wher - e'er they go.

# I WILL TRUST AND NOT BE AFRAID 743

*Behold, God is my salvation; I will trust, and not be afraid.* Is. 12:2.

I WILL TRUST 8.8.7.7.
M.M. 69

Elva Yoder, 1969 — Elva Yoder, 1969 (b. 1903)

1. I will trust and not be a - fraid, I will trust and not be a - fraid;
2. God will care for me ev - 'ry day, He will care for me ev - 'ry day;
3. I will thank and praise Him al - way, I, will thank and praise Him al - way;
3
3
I will trust and nev - er fear, I will trust for God is near.
He will keep me all of the way, God is near at work or play.
Read His Word and trust and o - bey, He will hear me when I pray.

# JESUS LOVES ME 744

*And He took them up in His arms, put His hands upon them, and blessed them.* Mk. 10:16.

JESUS LOVES ME 7.7.7.7. with Ref.
M.M. 96

Anna Bartlet Warner, 1859 (1821-1915) — William Batchelder Bradbury, 1816-1868

1. Je - sus loves me! this I know, For the Bi - ble tells me so;
2. Je - sus loves me! He who died, Heav-en's gate to o - pen wide;
3. Je - sus loves me! loves me still, Tho' I'm ver - y weak and ill;
4. Je - sus loves the chil-dren dear, Chil - dren far a - way or near;
5. Je - sus, take this heart of mine, Make it pure and whol - ly Thine;

Lit - tle ones to Him be - long; They are weak but He is strong.
He will wash a - way my sin, Let His lit - tle child come in.
From His shin - ing throne on high, Comes to watch me where I lie.
They are safe when in His care, Ev - 'ry day and ev - 'ry - where.
Thou hast bled and died for me; I will hence-forth live for Thee.

REFRAIN:

Yes, Je-sus loves me; Yes, Je-sus loves me; Yes, Je-sus loves me; The Bible tells me so.

## 745 LITTLE CHILDREN PRAISE THE LORD

*Children: Let them praise the name of the Lord: for His name alone is excellent; His glory is above the earth and heaven.* Ps. 148:12, 13.

Charles Edward Pollock (c. 1902) | PRAISE THE LORD 7.6.7.4. M.M. 104 | Charles Edward Pollock

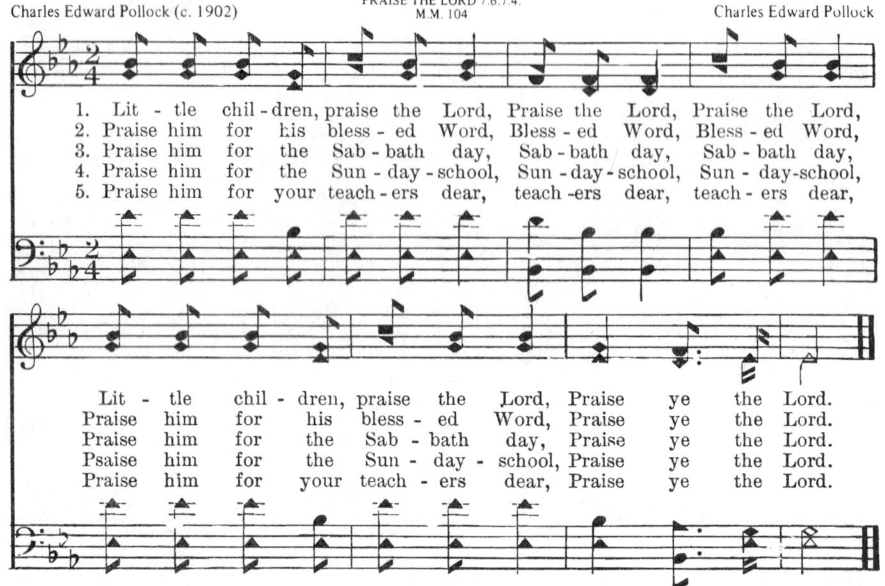

1. Lit - tle chil - dren, praise the Lord, Praise the Lord, Praise the Lord,
2. Praise him for his bless - ed Word, Bless - ed Word, Bless - ed Word,
3. Praise him for the Sab - bath day, Sab - bath day, Sab - bath day,
4. Praise him for the Sun - day - school, Sun - day - school, Sun - day-school,
5. Praise him for your teach - ers dear, teach -ers dear, teach - ers dear,
Lit - tle chil - dren, praise the Lord, Praise ye the Lord.
Praise him for his bless - ed Word, Praise ye the Lord.
Praise him for the Sab - bath day, Praise ye the Lord.
Psaise him for the Sun - day - school, Praise ye the Lord.
Praise him for your teach - ers dear, Praise ye the Lord.

## 746 GOD HAS MADE THE EARTH SO BRIGHT

*Praise ye the Lord . . . Which made heaven, and earth, the sea, and all that therein is: which keepeth truth forever.* Ps. 146:1, 6.

Elva Yoder, 1969 | PRAYER 7.7.7.7. M.M. 63 | Asahel Abbot (c. 1852)

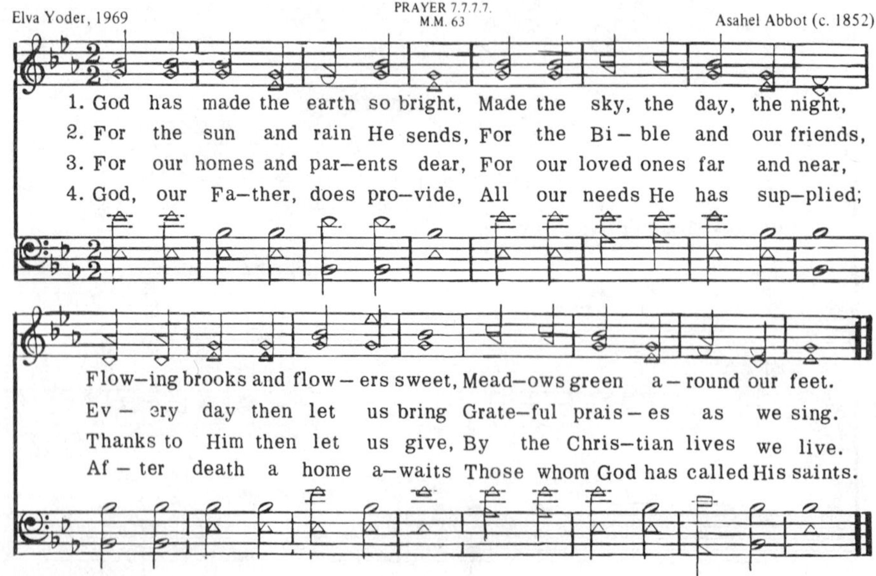

1. God has made the earth so bright, Made the sky, the day, the night,
2. For the sun and rain He sends, For the Bi – ble and our friends,
3. For our homes and par – ents dear, For our loved ones far and near,
4. God, our Fa – ther, does pro – vide, All our needs He has sup – plied;
Flow – ing brooks and flow – ers sweet, Mead – ows green a – round our feet.
Ev – ery day then let us bring Grate – ful prais – es as we sing.
Thanks to Him then let us give, By the Chris – tian lives we live.
Af – ter death a home a – waits Those whom God has called His saints.

## WHEN HE COMETH 747

*And they shall be Mine, saith the Lord of hosts, in that day when I make up My jewels.* Mal. 3:17.

JEWELS 8.6.8.5.
M.M. 72

William Orcutt Cushing, 1823-1902

George Frederick Root, 1820-1895

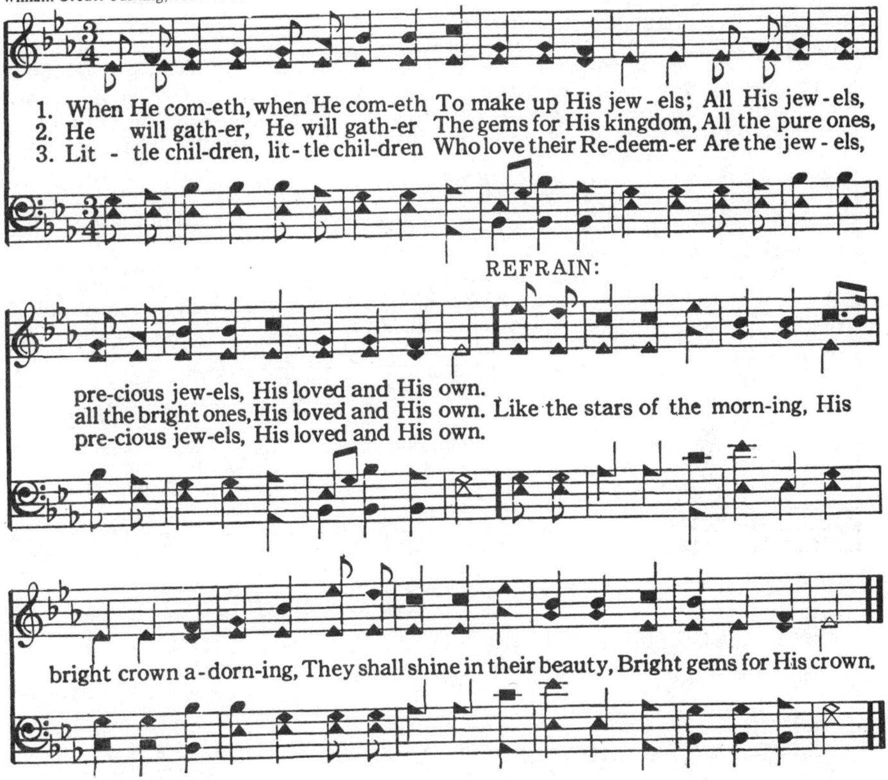

1. When He com-eth, when He com-eth To make up His jew - els; All His jew - els, pre-cious jew-els, His loved and His own.
2. He will gath-er, He will gath-er The gems for His kingdom, All the pure ones, all the bright ones, His loved and His own.
3. Lit - tle chil-dren, lit-tle chil-dren Who love their Re-deem-er Are the jew - els, pre-cious jew-els, His loved and His own.

REFRAIN:
Like the stars of the morn-ing, His bright crown a-dorn-ing, They shall shine in their beauty, Bright gems for His crown.

## LOVE HIM, LOVE HIM 748

*God is love.* I Jn. 4:8.

LOVE HIM 9.9.
M.M. 76

Arr.

Anon.

1
2
1. Love Him, love Him, all ye little chil-dren: God is Love, God is Love; God is Love.
2. Praise Him, praise Him, all ye little chil-dren: God is Love, God is Love; God is Love.

# 749 TWO LITTLE HANDS

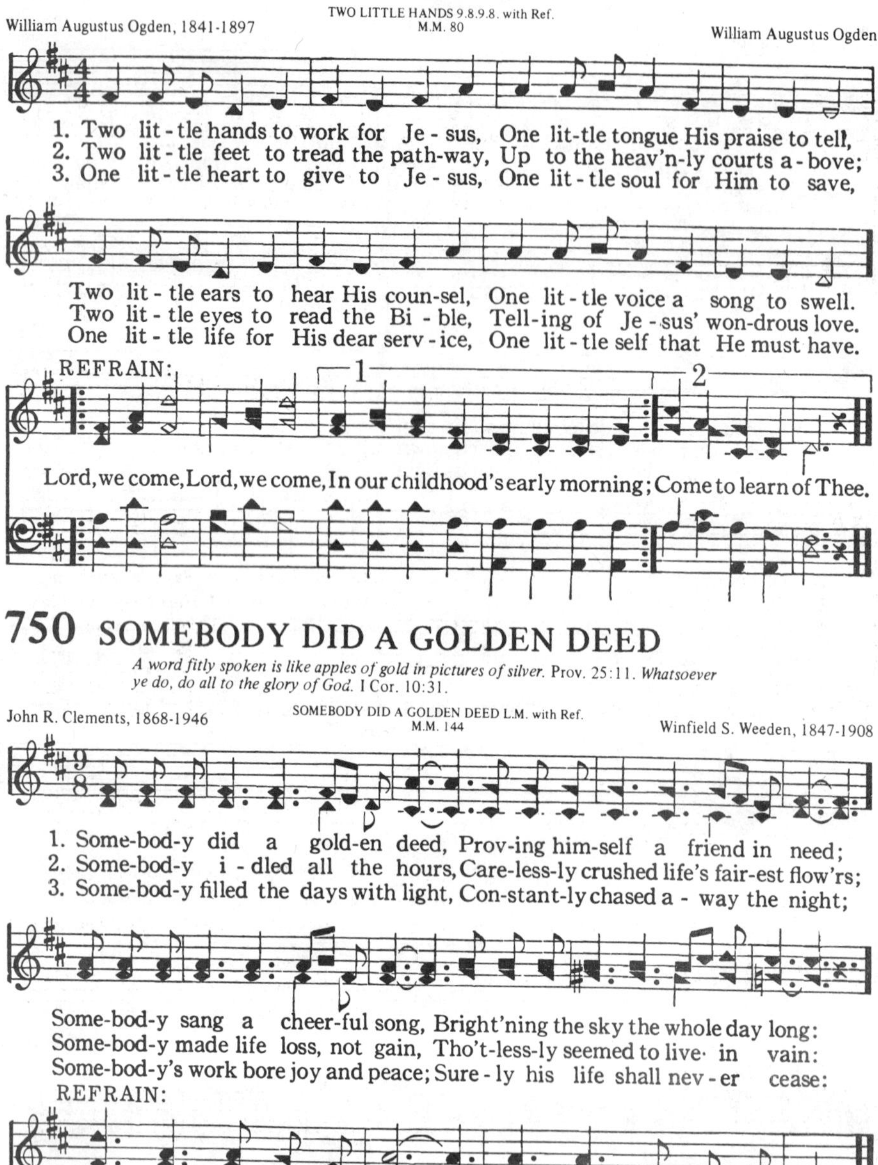

*O God, Thou art my God; early will I seek Thee.* Ps. 63:1.

William Augustus Ogden, 1841-1897 — TWO LITTLE HANDS 9.8.9.8. with Ref. M.M. 80 — William Augustus Ogden

1. Two lit-tle hands to work for Je-sus, One lit-tle tongue His praise to tell,
Two lit-tle ears to hear His coun-sel, One lit-tle voice a song to swell.

2. Two lit-tle feet to tread the path-way, Up to the heav'n-ly courts a-bove;
Two lit-tle eyes to read the Bi-ble, Tell-ing of Je-sus' won-drous love.

3. One lit-tle heart to give to Je-sus, One lit-tle soul for Him to save,
One lit-tle life for His dear serv-ice, One lit-tle self that He must have.

REFRAIN:
Lord, we come, Lord, we come, In our childhood's early morning; Come to learn of Thee.

# 750 SOMEBODY DID A GOLDEN DEED

*A word fitly spoken is like apples of gold in pictures of silver.* Prov. 25:11. *Whatsoever ye do, do all to the glory of God.* I Cor. 10:31.

John R. Clements, 1868-1946 — SOMEBODY DID A GOLDEN DEED L.M. with Ref. M.M. 144 — Winfield S. Weeden, 1847-1908

1. Some-bod-y did a gold-en deed, Prov-ing him-self a friend in need;
Some-bod-y sang a cheer-ful song, Bright'ning the sky the whole day long:

2. Some-bod-y i-dled all the hours, Care-less-ly crushed life's fair-est flow'rs;
Some-bod-y made life loss, not gain, Tho't-less-ly seemed to live in vain:

3. Some-bod-y filled the days with light, Con-stant-ly chased a-way the night;
Some-bod-y's work bore joy and peace; Sure-ly his life shall nev-er cease:

REFRAIN:
Was that some-bod-y you? . . Was that some-bod-y you?

## JESUS CAN NEVER FAIL 751

*The Lord . . . will not fail thee.* Deut. 31:6.

Anon.
Words, Music Arranged by Compiler, 1971
JESUS CAN NEVER FAIL 12.9.
M.M. 63
Anon.
1. Je - sus can nev - er fail, nev - er fail, nev - er fail, Je - sus can nev - er fail, No, never fail.
2. Je - sus can sat - is - fy, sat - is - fy, sat - is - fy, Je - sus can sat - is - fy, Yes, sat–is–fy.

## JESUS LOVES A LITTLE CHILD 752

*Lo, children are an heritage of the Lord.* Ps. 127:3.

Anon.

LET THEM COME TO ME 7.7.6.5.7.7.7.5.
M.M. 132

E. T. Hildebrand

1. Je - sus loves a lit - tle child, Smil-ing in its child - ish glee; Says of such in
2. In the bless-ed Sun-day school, They are taught to fear the Lord; Here they find his
3. When life's toilsome work is done, When the stormy strife is o'er, Then a - round his

accents mild, "Let them come to me." Let them come, forbid them not, They will sing a -
ho - ly way, Learn to love his word. Armed with this they may go forth, Triumph o - ver
shining throne, On the bliss- ful shore, Shall his hap - py children meet, Sing and shout, their

round the throne; Mil - lions now are sing - ing there, Mil - lions more may come.
ev - 'ry foe, Spread-ing joy o'er all the earth, Sooth - ing hu - man woe.
suf-f'rings o'er, Cast their crowns at Je - sus' feet, Praise him ev - er - more.

# 753 I THINK WHEN I READ THAT SWEET STORY

*Forbid them not.* Mk. 10:14.

Mrs. Jemima Thompson Luke, 1813-1906

DAVENANT 11.8.12.9.11.8.12.9.
M.M. 80

Old English Melody

1. I think when I read that sweet sto - ry of old, When
2. Yet still to His foot - stool in pray'r I may go, And
Je - sus was here a - mong men, How He called lit - tle chil - dren as
ask for a share in His love; And if I now earn - est - ly
lambs to His fold, I should like to have been with them then.
seek Him be - low, I shall see Him and hear Him a - bove.
I wish that His hands had been placed on my head, His
In that beau - ti - ful place He has gone to pre - pare For
arms had been thrown a - round me, And that I might have seen His kind
all who are washed and for - giv'n; And ma - ny dear chil - dren are

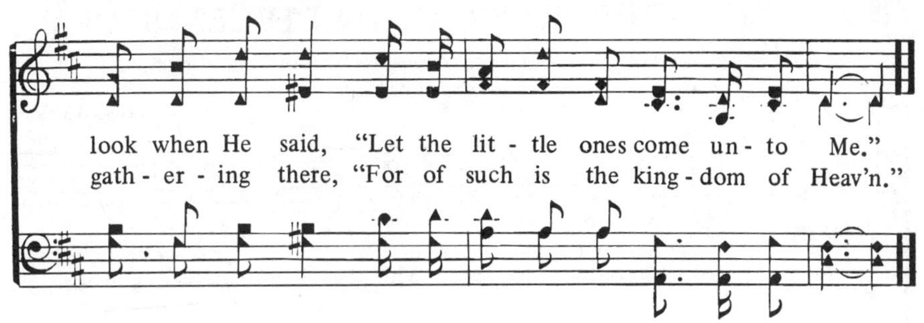
look when He said, "Let the lit - tle ones come un - to Me."
gath - er - ing there, "For of such is the king - dom of Heav'n."

# I WASHED MY HANDS THIS MORNING 754

*See then that ye walk circumspectly, not as fools, but as wise.* Eph. 5:15.

ROSECRANS 7.6.7.6.
M.M. 63

Mrs. L. M. Boteman

J. H. Rosecrans

1. I washed my hands this morn - ing, O ver - y clean and white,
2. I told my ears to lis - ten Quite close-ly all day through
3. My eyes are set to watch them A - bout their work or play,

And lent them both to Je - sus, To work for Him till night.
For an - y act of kind - ness Such lit - tle hands can do.
To keep them out of mis - chief, For Je - sus' sake all day.

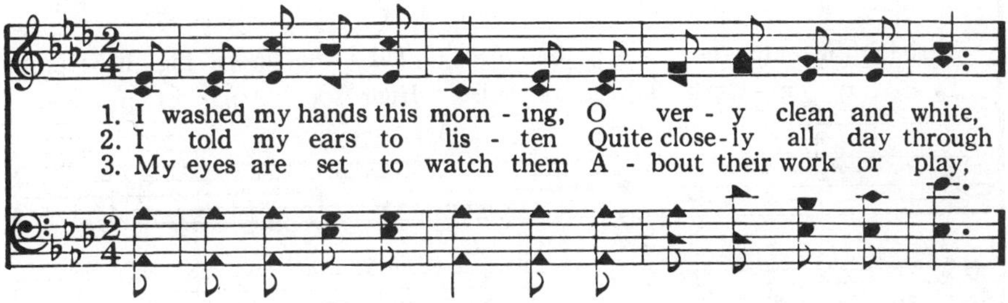

REFRAIN

Little feet, be careful Where you take me to; Anything for Je-sus, On-ly let me do.

# 755 LITTLE CHILDREN CAN YOU TELL?

*The name of the Lord is a strong tower: the righteous runneth into it, and is safe.* Prov. 18:10.

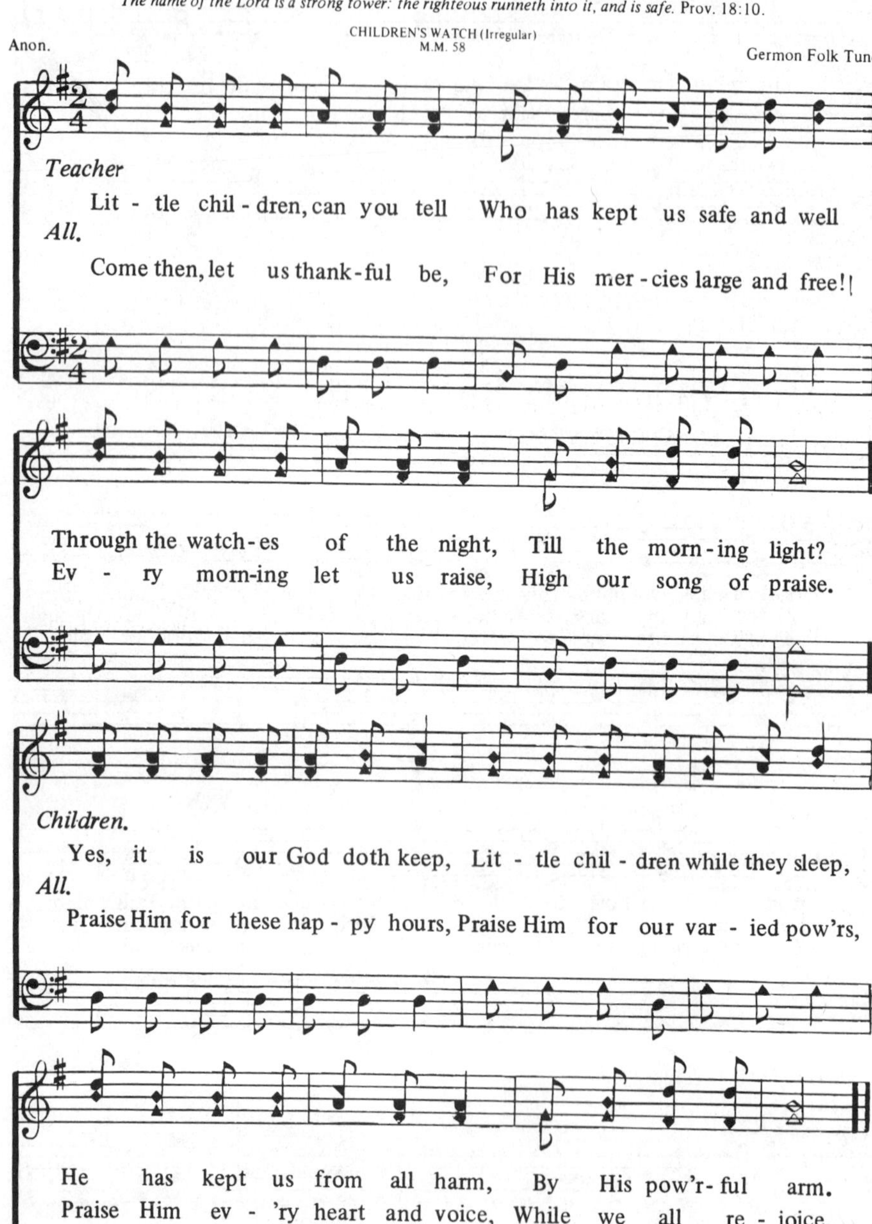
Anon.
CHILDREN'S WATCH (Irregular)
M.M. 58
Germon Folk Tune
Teacher
Lit - tle chil - dren, can you tell Who has kept us safe and well
All.
Come then, let us thank - ful be, For His mer - cies large and free!
Through the watch - es of the night, Till the morn - ing light?
Ev - ry morn-ing let us raise, High our song of praise.
Children.
Yes, it is our God doth keep, Lit - tle chil - dren while they sleep,
All.
Praise Him for these hap - py hours, Praise Him for our var - ied pow'rs,
He has kept us from all harm, By His pow'r - ful arm.
Praise Him ev - 'ry heart and voice, While we all re - joice.

# FATHER IN MY LIFE'S YOUNG MORNING 756

*Blessed are the undefiled in the way, who walk in the law of the Lord.* Ps. 119:1.

GORTON 8.7.8.7.D.
M.M. 76

Thomas MacKellar, 1812-1899 — Christian H. Brunk, 1845-1891

1. Fa - ther! in my life's young morning, May thy word di - rect my way;
2. Fa - ther! gen - tle is thy teach-ing; Be a doc - ile spir - it mine;
3. Fa - ther! let me nev - er cov - et Things of van - i - ty and pride;

Let me heed each gra - cious warn-ing, Lest my feet should go a - stray;
Ev - 'ry day thy grace be - seech -ing, Let thy lov - ing kind - ness shine
Teach me truth, and may I love it Bet - ter than all else be - side.

Make me will - ing, make me will - ing, All its pre - cepts to o - bey;
Al - ways on me, al - ways on me, And my heart be whol - ly thine.
Bless - ed Bi - ble! bless - ed Bi - ble! May it be my heavenward guide.

Let me heed each gra - cious warn -ing, Lest my feet should go a - stray.
Ev - 'ry day thy grace be - seech -ing, Let thy lov - ing - kind- ness shine.
Teach me truth, and may I love it Bet - ter than all else be - side.

# BE HAPPY, BE JOYFUL 757

*Rejoice in the Lord alway: and again I say, Rejoice.* Phil. 4:4.

BE HAPPY, BE JOYFUL 6.7.6.4.
M.M. 76

Nathan Jonathan Overholt, 1971 (b. 1966) — Nathan Jonathan Overholt, 1971

Be hap - py, be joy - ful! Come all ye lit - tle
chil - dren; Be hap - py, be joy - ful! A - men, A - men.

# 758 I AM SO GLAD THAT OUR FATHER

*Thy testimonies have I taken as an heritage for ever: for they are the rejoicing of my heart.* Ps. 119:111.

I AM SO GLAD 10.10.10.10. with Ref.
M.M. 116

Philip Paul Bliss, 1838-1876 | Philip Paul Bliss

1. I am so glad that our Fa - ther in heav'n Tells of his love in the
2. Tho' I for - get him and wan - der a - way, Still he doth love me wher-
3. Oh, if there's on - ly one song I can sing, When in his beau - ty I
Book he has giv'n, Won - der - ful things in the Bi - ble I see;
ev - er I stray; Back to his dear lov - ing arms would I flee,
see the Great King, This shall my song in e - ter - ni - ty be:
This is the dear - est, that Je - sus loves me.
When I re - mem - ber, that Je - sus loves me.
"Oh, what a won - der that Je - sus loves me."
REFRAIN:
I am so glad that
Je - sus loves me, Je - sus loves me, Je - sus loves me,
I am so glad that Je - sus loves me, Je - sus loves e - ven me.

## CAN YOU COUNT THE STARS 759

*He stretcheth out the north over the empty place, and hangeth the earth upon nothing.* Job 26:7. *He telleth the number of the stars; He calleth them all by their names.* Ps. 147:4.

Johann Hey
Tr. E.L.J.

STERNENZAHL 8.7.8.7.8.8.7.7.
M.M. 66

German Folk Tune

1. Can you count the stars of eve-ning That are shin-ing in the sky?
Can you count the clouds that dai-ly O-ver all the world go by?
2. Can you count the birds that war-ble In the sun-shine all the day?
Can you count the lit-tle fish-es That in spar-kling wa-ters play?
3. Can you count the man-y chil-dren In their lit-tle beds at night,
Who with-out a thought of sor-row Rise a-gain at morn-ing light?
God the Lord, who doth not slum-ber, Keep-eth all the bound-less num-ber:
God the Lord their num-ber know-eth, For each one His care He show-eth:
God the Lord, who dwells in heav-en, Lov-ing care to each has giv-en:
But He car-eth more for thee, But He car-eth more for thee.
Shall He not re-mem-ber thee? Shall He not re-mem-ber thee?
He has not for-got-ten thee, He has not for-got-ten thee.

## FATHER, WE THANK THEE 760

*Now therefore, our God, we thank Thee, and praise Thy glorious name.* I Chron. 29:13.

Rebecca J. Weston

HURSLY L.M. 8.8.8.8.
M.M. 76

Peter Ritter, 1792 (1760-1846)
Arr. William H. Monk, 1823-1899

1. Father, we thank Thee for the night, And for the pleasant morning light,
2. Help us to do the things we should, To be to oth-ers kind and good;
For rest and food, and lov-ing care, And all that makes the day so fair.
In all our work, and all our play, To love Thee bet-ter ev-'ry day.

# 761 DONA NOBIS PACEM (Grant to Us Peace)

*Now the Lord of peace Himself give you peace always by all means. The Lord be with you all.* II Thess. 3:16.

Anon.
English text, John J. Overholt, 1971

GRANT TO US PEACE (Irregular)
M.M. 69

Anon.

Part I
Do - na no - bis pa - cem pa - cem
Grant us Thy peace, Grant us peace.
Do - na no - bis pa - cem.
Grant us Thy peace, Grant us Thy peace.

Part II
Do - na no - bis pa - cem
Grant us, Grant us Thy peace,
Do - na no - bis pa - cem.
Grant us, Thy peace, Grant us Thy peace.

Part III
Do - na no - bis pa - cem
Grant us, Grant us Thy peace,
Do - na no - bis pa - cem.
Grant us, Thy peace, Grant us Thy peace.

# 762 A IS FOR ANYONE

*For precept must be upon precept, precept upon precept; line upon line, line upon line; here a little, and there a little.* Is. 28:10.

Anonymous
Adapted by Elizabeth Gingerich
Altered by Compiler, 1969

A. B. C. Song
M.M. 66

Anon.
Arr. John J. Overholt, 1969

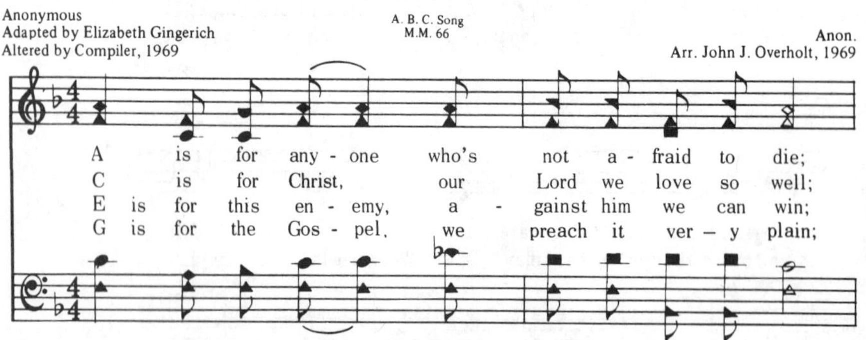
A is for any - one who's not a - fraid to die;
C is for Christ, our Lord we love so well;
E is for this en - emy, a - gainst him we can win;
G is for the Gos - pel, we preach it ver - y plain;

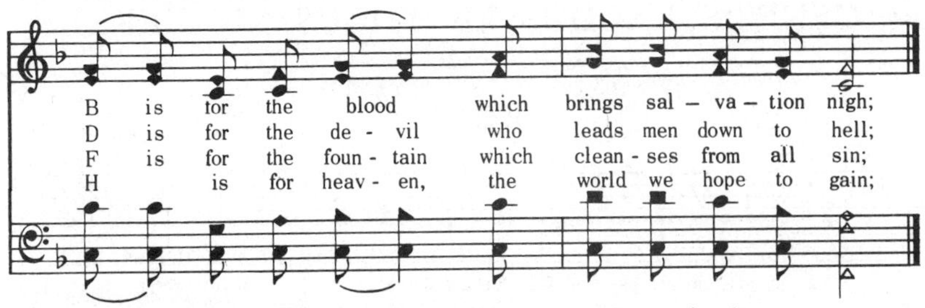
B is for the blood which brings sal – va – tion nigh;
D is for the de - vil who leads men down to hell;
F is for the foun - tain which clean - ses from all sin;
H is for heav - en, the world we hope to gain;

I is for the ignorant, which many folk do seem; J is for Jesus, who did our souls redeem;
K is for the kingdom through grace is ours to gain; L is for the Lamb of God who was for sinners slain;
M is for the many who find they are too late; N is for the narrow way that leads to heaven's gate;
O is like eternity, for it has no end; P is for the promise which God did to us send;
Q is for the queer folks who say there is no hell; R is for the right folks, the truth they always tell;
S is for salvation that lifts us from sin's strife; T is for the trumpet that brings the dead to life;
U is for unity within the Christian band; V is for victory, the saints in Christ will stand;
W is for the world which we must all forsake; X is for the crossroad where we our choice must make;
Y is for you; for pardon Christ entreat; Z is for the *zero hour* when God will judgment mete!

# I WILL MAKE YOU FISHERS OF MEN 763

*And He saith unto them, Follow Me, and I will make you fishers of men.* Mt. 4:19.

FISHERS OF MEN 8.8.8.5.10.8.5.
M.M. 76

Anon. Anon.

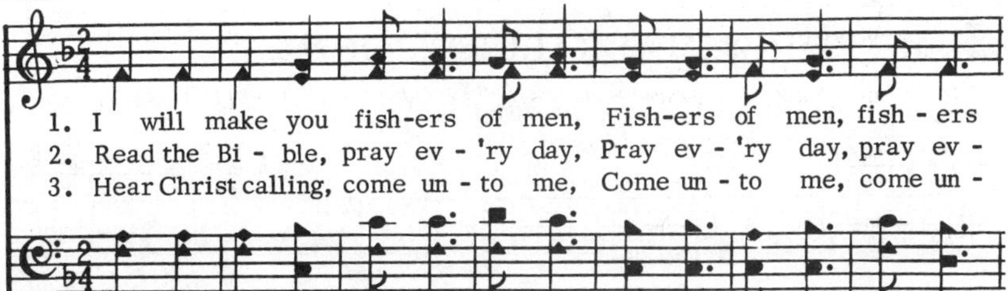

1. I will make you fish-ers of men, Fish-ers of men, fish - ers
2. Read the Bi - ble, pray ev - 'ry day, Pray ev - 'ry day, pray ev -
3. Hear Christ calling, come un - to me, Come un - to me, come un -

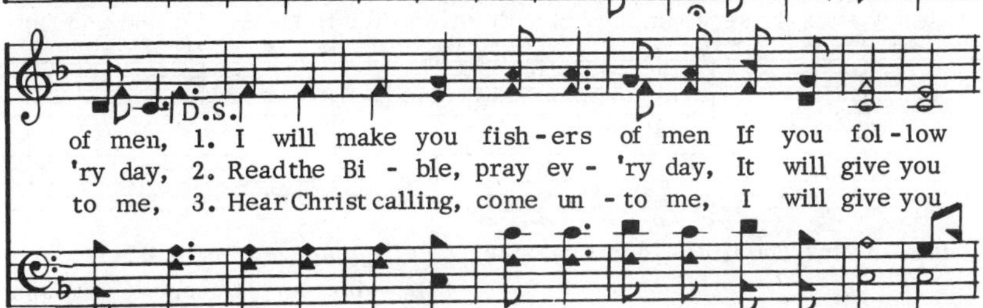

of men, 1. I will make you fish - ers of men If you fol - low
'ry day, 2. Read the Bi - ble, pray ev - 'ry day, It will give you
to me, 3. Hear Christ calling, come un - to me, I will give you

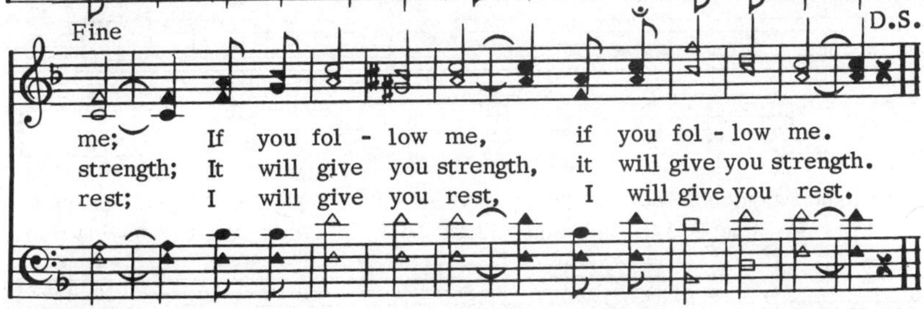

Fine D.S.

me; If you fol - low me, if you fol - low me.
strength; It will give you strength, it will give you strength.
rest; I will give you rest, I will give you rest.

# 764 GENESIS, EXODUS, LEVITICUS, NUMBERS

*All scripture is given by inspiration of God, an; is profitable for doctrine, for reproof, for correction, for instruction in righteousness.* II Tim. 3:16.

Books of the Old Testament — NETTLETON 8.7.8.7.D. M.M. 60 — Asahel Nettleton, 1783-1844

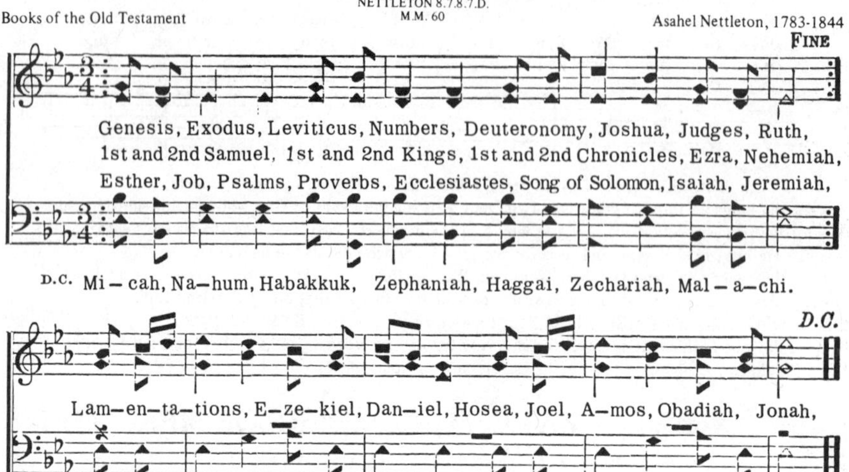
FINE
Genesis, Exodus, Leviticus, Numbers, Deuteronomy, Joshua, Judges, Ruth,
1st and 2nd Samuel, 1st and 2nd Kings, 1st and 2nd Chronicles, Ezra, Nehemiah,
Esther, Job, Psalms, Proverbs, Ecclesiastes, Song of Solomon, Isaiah, Jeremiah,
D.C. Mi – cah, Na – hum, Habakkuk, Zephaniah, Haggai, Zechariah, Mal – a – chi.
D.C.
Lam – en – ta – tions, E – ze – kiel, Dan – iel, Hosea, Joel, A – mos, Obadiah, Jonah,

# 765 MATTHEW, MARK, LUKE, JOHN

*For the prophecy came not in old time by the will of man: but holy men of God spake as they were moved by the Holy Ghost.* II Pet. 1:21.

Books of the New Testmant — NEAR THE CROSS 7.6.7.6. M.M. 132 — William Howard Doane, 1831-1915

Matthew, Mark, Luke, John, the Acts, Epistle to the Romans, 1st and 2nd Cor –
inth – i – ans, Galatians, and Ephesians, Philippians, Colossians, 1st and
He – brews, James, 1st and
2nd Thessalonians, 1st and 2nd Tim – o – thy, Ti – tus, and Phi – le – mon,
2nd Pe – ter, 1st and 2nd and 3rd John, Jude, and Rev – e – la – tion.

# THERE WERE TWELVE DISCIPLES 766

*And when He had called unto Him His twelve disciples, He gave them power against unclean spirits, to cast them out, and to heal all manner of sickness and all manner of disease.* Mt. 10:1.

BRINGING IN THE SHEAVES 12.4.12.11. with Ref.
M.M. 66

Anon. George A. Minor, 1845-1904

There were twelve disciples Je–sus called to help Him, Si–mon Pe–ter, An–drew.
James, his broth–er John; Philip, Thomas, Matthew, James the son of Al–phaeus,
Si–mon, Thad–daeus, Ju–das, and Bar–thol–o–mew.
CHORUS
Je–sus calls us too,
Je–sus calls us too; We are His dis–ci–ples, I am one and you;
Je–sus calls us too, Je–sus calls us too; We are His disciples, We His work must do.

**BEGINNING OF WORSHIP**

## THE LORD IS IN HIS HOLY TEMPLE 767

*And the temple of God was opened in heaven, and there was seen in His temple the ark of His testament: and there were lightnings, and voices, and thunderings, and an earthquake, and great hail.* Rev. 11:19.

Hab. 2:20
Anon.
THE LORD IS IN HIS HOLY TEMPLE (Kirkpatrick) 9.10.6.6.
M.M. 76
William James Kirkpatrick, 1838-1921
The Lord is in His ho - ly tem-ple: Let all the earth keep si-lence be-
Softly
fore Him; Keep si - lence, keep si - lence, Keep si - lence be - fore Him.

## BE SILENT, BE SILENT 768

*Be silent, O all flesh, before the Lord.* Zech. 2:13.

TREAD SOFTLY 6.5.6.5.D.
M.M. 80

Fanny J. Crosby, 1820-1915 — William Howard Doane, 1832-1915

*Gently*

1. Be si - lent, be si - lent, A whis - per is heard, Be si - lent, and lis - ten, Oh, treas - ure each word.
2. Be si - lent, be si - lent, For ho - ly this place, This al - tar that ech - oes The mes - sage of grace.
3. Be si - lent, be si - lent, Breathe humbly our prayer, A fore - taste of E - den This mo - ment we share.
4. Be si - lent, be si - lent, His mer - cy re - cord; Be si - lent, be si - lent, And wait on the Lord.

REFRAIN

Tread soft - ly, tread soft - ly, The Mas - ter is here; Tread soft - ly, tread soft - ly, He bids us draw near.
Tread soft-ly here, tread softly here, Tread softly here, tread softly here,

*p* *p* *rit.*

# 769 COME WE THAT LOVE THE LORD

*O come, let us sing unto the Lord: let us make a joyful noise to the Rock of our salvation.* Ps. 95:1.

Isaac Watts, 1709 (1674-1748)
Ref. Robert Lowry, 1826-1899
MARCHING TO ZION 6.6.8.8.6.6. with Ref.
M.M. 108
Robert Lowry
1. Come, we that love the Lord, And let our joys be known,
2. Let those re - fuse to sing Who nev - er knew our God;
3. The hill of Zi - on yields A thou - sand sa - cred sweets
4. Then let our songs a - bound, And ev - 'ry tear be dry;
Join in a song with sweet ac - cord, Join in a song with sweet ac- cord,
But chil - dren of the heav'n-ly King, But chil-dren of the heav'n-ly King,
Be - fore we reach the heav'n-ly fields, Be - fore we reach the heav'n-ly fields,
We're marching thro' Im-manuel's ground, We're march-ing thro' Im-man-uel's ground,
And thus sur - round the throne, And thus sur-round the throne.
May speak their joys a - broad, May speak their joys a - broad.
Or walk the gold - en streets, Or walk the gold - en streets.
To fair - er worlds on high, To fair - er worlds on high.
And thus sur-round the throne, And thus sur - round the throne.
REFRAIN:
We're march - ing to Zi - on, Beau - ti- ful, beau - ti - ful Zi - on;
We're march-ing on to Zi - on,
We're march-ing up-ward to Zi - on, The beau - ti - ful cit - y of God.
Zi - on, Zi - on,

# COME YE THAT LOVE THE LORD 770

*Let us come before His presence with thanksgiving, and make a joyful noise unto Him with psalms.* Ps. 95:2.

SPURGEON 6.6.8.8.6.6.6.
M.M. 60
Isaac Watts, 1709 (1674-1748)
Old English Hymn Tune
Arr. John J. Overholt, 1970
1. Come ye that love the Lord, And let your joys be known;
2. Let those re - fuse to sing, Who nev - er knew our God;
3. This awe - ful God is ours, Our Fa - ther and our love;
4. Then let our songs a - bound, And ev - 'ry tear be dry;
Join in a song with sweet ac - cord
(Join) in a song with sweet ac - cord
But chil - dren of the heav'n - ly King,
(But) chil - dren of the heav'n - ly King,
He will send down His heav'n - ly pow'rs,
(He) will send down His heav'n - ly pow'rs
We're march - ing through Im - man - uel's ground,
(We're) march - ing through Im - man - uel's ground,
(Join) in a song with sweet ac - cord While ye sur - round the throne,
(But) chil - dren of the heav'n - ly King, Shall speak their joys a - broad,
(He) will send down His heav'n - ly pow'rs To car - ry us a - bove,
(We're) march - ing through Im - man - uel's ground To fair - er worlds on High,
While ye sur - round the throne, While ye sur - round the throne.
Shall speak their joys a - broad, Shall speak their joys a - broad.
To car - ry us a - bove, To car - ry us a - bove.
To fair - er worlds on high, To fair - er worlds on high. A - men.

# 771 O LORD MY GOD! (How Great Thou Art)

*The earth is the Lord's, and the fulness thereof; the world, and they that dwell therein.* Ps. 24:1.

Carl Boberg, 1859-1940
*O store Gud*
Tr. Stuart K. Hine, 1899-
O STORE GUD 11.10.11.10. with Ref.
M.M. 58
Swedish Folk Melody
Arr. Manna Music Inc.
*Slowly*
1. O Lord my God! When I in awe-some won-der Con-sid-er all the worlds Thy hands have made,— I see the stars, I hear the roll-ing thun-der, Thy pow'r through-out the un-i-verse dis-played,—
2. When through the woods and for-est glades I wan-der And hear the birds sing sweet-ly in the trees;— When I look down from loft-y moun-tain gran-deur And hear the brook and feel the gen-tle breeze;—
3. And when I think that God, His Son not spar-ing, Sent Him to die, I scarce can take it in;— That on the cross, my bur-den glad-ly bear-ing, He bled and died to take a-way my sin;—
4. When Christ shall come with shout of ac-cla-ma-tion And take me home, what joy shall fill my heart!— Then I shall bow in hum-ble ad-o-ra-tion And there pro-claim, my God, how great Thou art!—
REFRAIN
Then sings my soul, my Sav-ior God to Thee;— How great Thou art, how great Thou art!— Then sings my soul, my Sav-ior God to Thee;— How great Thou art,— how great Thou art!—

**GOD:** CREATION OF

# THE HEAVENS ARE TELLING 772

*The heavens declare the glory of God; and the firmament sheweth His handiwork.* Ps. 19:1. *But will God indeed dwell on the earth? behold, the heaven and heaven of heavens cannot contain Thee.* I Kings 8:27.

THE HEAVENS ARE TELLING (Irregular) M.M. 96

Joseph Addison, 1672-1719 — Franz Joseph Haydn, 1732-1809

f
The heav-ens are tell - ing the glo - ry of God, The won-der of His
work dis-plays the firm - a - ment. In all the lands re -
In all the
sounds the word, Nev-er un-per-ceiv - ed, ev - er un-der-stood,
lands re-sounds the word,
ev - er, ev - er, ev - er un - der - stood. The heav-ens are
tell - ing the glo - ry of God, The won - der of His
The
work, The won-der of His work dis-plays the firm - a - ment.
won - ders of His work, His work

# 773 HALLELUJAH, PRAISE JEHOVAH

*Both young men, and maidens; old men, and children: Let them praise the name of the Lord: for His name alone is excellent; His glory is above the earth and heaven.* Ps. 148:12, 13.

HALLELUJAH PRAISE JEHOVAH 8.7.8.7.D. with Ref.
M.M. 72
Psalm 148
William James Kirkpatrick, 1838-1921
1. Hal - le - lu - jah, praise Je - ho - vah! From the heav-ens praise His name;
2. Let them prais - es give Je - ho - vah! They were made at His com-mand;
3. All ye fruit - ful trees and ce - dars, All ye hills and moun-tains high,
Praise Je - ho - vah in the high - est; All His an - gels praise pro-claim.
Them for ev - er He es - tab - lished: His de - cree shall ev - er stand.
Creep-ing things and beasts and cat - tle, Birds that in the heav - ens fly,
All His hosts to - geth - er praise Him, Sun and moon and stars on high;
From the earth, O praise Je - ho - vah, All ye floods, ye drag - ons all,
Kings of earth, and all ye peo - ple, Princ-es great, earth's judg-es all;
Praise Him, O ye heav'n of heav - ens, And ye floods a - bove the sky.
Fire and hail and snow and va - pors, Storm-y winds that hear Him call.
Praise His name, young men and maid - ens, A - ged men, and chil-dren small.
REFRAIN:
Let them prais - - es give Je - ho - vah, For His name a - lone is high,
Let them prais-es

pp
p
ff
And His glo - - ry is ex-alt-ed, And His glo - - ry is ex-alt-ed,
And His glo-ry
And His glo-ry
And His glo - - ry is ex-alt-ed Far a-bove the earth and sky.
And His glo-ry

# IN THANKS WE LIFT OUR HEARTS TO THEE 774

*O come, let us worship and bow down: let us kneel before the Lord our maker.* Ps. 95:6. *I will give Thee thanks in the great congregation: I will praise Thee among much people.* Ps. 35:18.

GREENCASTLE C.M. 8.6.8.6.
M.M. 60

John D. Martin, 1965

John D. Martin
Har. John J. Overholt, 1971

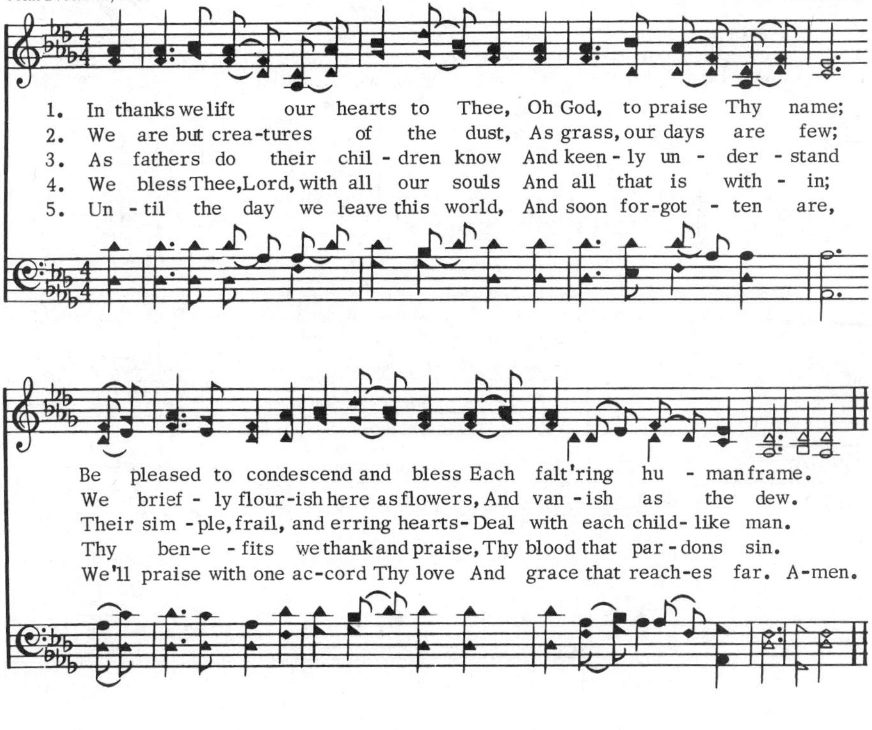

1. In thanks we lift our hearts to Thee, Oh God, to praise Thy name;
Be pleased to condescend and bless Each falt'ring hu-man frame.

2. We are but crea-tures of the dust, As grass, our days are few;
We brief-ly flour-ish here as flowers, And van-ish as the dew.

3. As fathers do their chil-dren know And keen-ly un-der-stand
Their sim-ple, frail, and erring hearts- Deal with each child-like man.

4. We bless Thee, Lord, with all our souls And all that is with-in;
Thy ben-e-fits we thank and praise, Thy blood that par-dons sin.

5. Un-til the day we leave this world, And soon for-got-ten are,
We'll praise with one ac-cord Thy love And grace that reach-es far. A-men.

# 775 PRAISE HIM! PRAISE HIM!

*Make His praise glorious.* Ps. 66:2. *Let us offer the sacrifice of praise . . . continually.* Heb. 13:15.
*Seven times a day do I praise Thee.* Ps. 119:164. *O Lord . . . Thou art my praise.* Jer. 17:14.

ALLEN (Irregular) with Ref.
M.M. 126
Fanny Jane Crosby, 1820-1915
Chester G. Allen, 1869 (1812-1877)
1. Praise Him! praise Him! Je-sus, our blessed Redeemer! Sing, O Earth, His won-der-ful love pro-claim! Hail Him! hail Him! high-est archangels in glo - ry; Strength and hon - or give to His ho - ly name! Like a shepherd, Je-sus will guard His child-ren; In His arms He carries them all day long:
2. Praise Him! praise Him! Je-sus, our blessed Redeemer! For our sins He suffered and bled and died; He our Rock, our hope of e-ter-nal sal-va-tion, Hail Him! hail Him! Je - sus the cru - ci - fied: Sound His prais-es! Je-sus who bore our sor-rows, Love unbounded, wonderful, deep, and strong:
3. Praise Him! praise Him! Je-sus, our blessed Redeemer! Heav'n-ly por - tals loud with ho-san-nas ring! Je - sus, Sav - iour, reigneth for-ev-er and ev - er; Crown Him! crown Him! prophet and priest and king! Christ is com-ing, o-ver the world vic - to-rious, Pow'r and glo-ry un-to the Lord be - long:
Refrain
Praise Him! praise Him! tell of His ex-cel-lent great-ness; Praise Him! praise Him! ev-er in joy - ful song!

**GOD:** PRAISE OF

## GLORY BE TO GOD ON HIGH 776

*Glory to God in the highest, and on earth peace, good will toward men.* Lk. 2:14.

GLORIA 7.9.
M.M. 58

Luke 2:14 — Charles Zeuner, 1795-1857

Glory be to God on high: and on earth peace, good will toward men.

**GOD:** POWER, PROVIDENCE OF

## A MIGHTY FORTRESS IS OUR GOD 777

*God is our refuge and strength, a very present help in trouble.* Ps. 46:1. *The Lord thy God is among you, a mighty God and terrible.* Deut. 7:21.

EIN FESTE BURG (Irregular)
M.M. 63

Martin Luther, 1529 (1483-1546) — Martin Luther

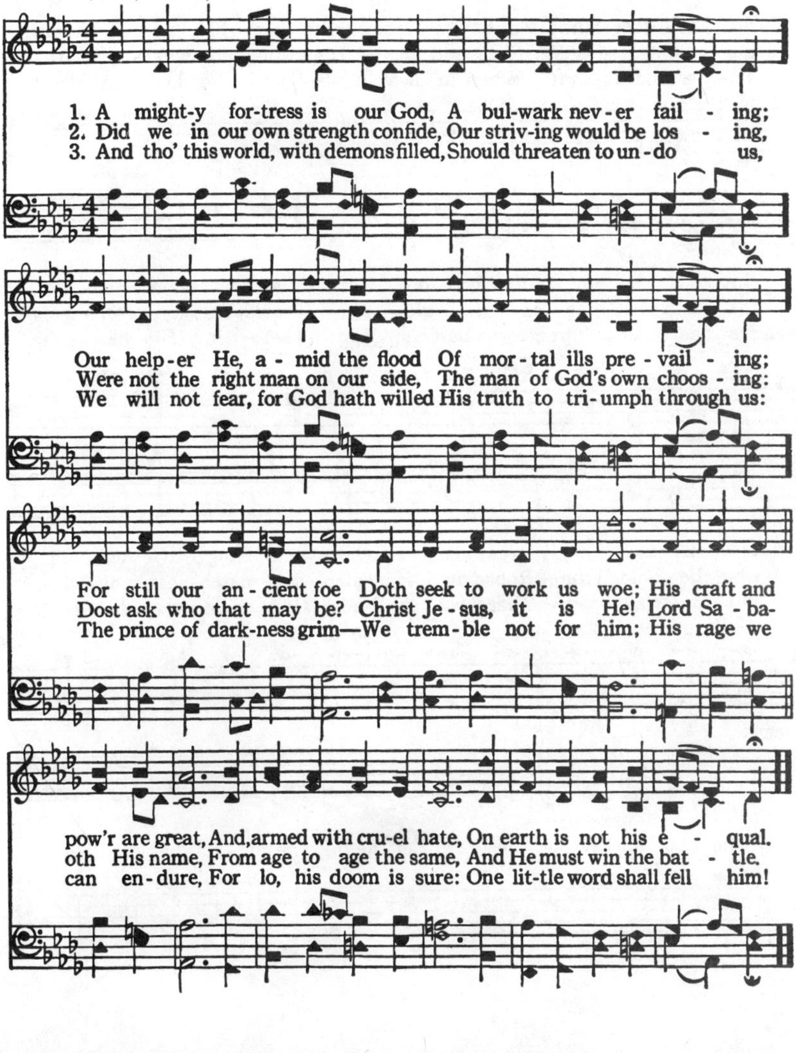

1. A mighty fortress is our God, A bulwark never failing;
Our helper He, amid the flood Of mortal ills prevailing;
For still our ancient foe Doth seek to work us woe; His craft and pow'r are great, And, armed with cruel hate, On earth is not his equal.

2. Did we in our own strength confide, Our striving would be losing,
Were not the right man on our side, The man of God's own choosing:
Dost ask who that may be? Christ Jesus, it is He! Lord Sabaoth His name, From age to age the same, And He must win the battle.

3. And tho' this world, with demons filled, Should threaten to undo us,
We will not fear, for God hath willed His truth to triumph through us:
The prince of darkness grim—We tremble not for him; His rage we can endure, For lo, his doom is sure: One little word shall fell him!

# 778 HOLY, HOLY, HOLY IS THE LORD

*Holy, holy, holy, is the Lord of hosts.* Is. 6:3.

HOLY IS THE LORD 9.10.9.9.10.9. with Ref.
M.M. 66
Fanny J. Crosby, 1820-1915
William Batchelder Bradbury, 1816-1868
1. Ho - ly, ho - ly, ho - ly is the Lord! Sing, O ye peo - ple,
2. Praise Him, praise Him, shout a - loud for joy! Watch-man of Zi - on,
3. King E - ter - nal, bless - ed be His name! So may His chil - dren
glad - ly a - dore Him; Let the moun-tains trem - ble at His Word,
her - ald the sto - ry; Sin and death His king - dom shall de - stroy,
glad - ly a - dore Him; When in heav'n we join the hap - py strain,
Let the hills be joy - ful be - fore Him; Might - y in wis - dom,
All the earth shall sing of His glo - ry; Praise Him, ye an - gels,
When we cast our bright crowns be-fore Him; There in His like - ness,
bound - less in mer - cy, Great is Je - ho - vah, King o - ver all.
ye who be - hold Him Robed in His splen - dor, match - less, di - vine.
joy - ful a - wak - ing, There we shall see Him, there we shall sing.
CHORUS
Ho - ly, ho - ly, ho - ly is the Lord, Let the hills be joy - ful be - fore Him.

# THE LOVE OF GOD 779

*Behold, what manner of love the Father hath bestowed upon us, that we should be called the sons of God.* I Jn. 3:1. *Herein is love . . . that He loved us, and sent His Son to be the propitiation for our sins.* I Jn. 4:10.

LOVE OF GOD 8.8.8.8.8.6.8.6. with Ref. M.M. 60

F. M. Lehman, 1917

F. M. Lehman
Arranged by Claudia Lehman Mays

1. The love of God is great-er far Than tongue or pen can ev - er tell;
2. When hoar - y time shall pass a - way, And earth-ly thrones and kingdoms fall;
3. Could we with ink the o - cean fill, And were the skies of parchment made;
It goes be-yond the high - est star, And reach-es to the low - est hell.
When men who here re - fuse to pray, On rocks and hills and mountains call;
Were ev - 'ry stalk on earth a quill, And ev - 'ry man a scribe by trade;
The guilt - y pair, bowed down with care, God gave His Son to win;
God's love, so sure, shall still en - dure, All meas - ure - less and strong;
To write the love of God a - bove Would drain the o - cean dry;
His err - ing child He rec - on - ciled, And par-doned from his sin,
Re - deem - ing grace to Ad - am's race— The saints' and an - gels' song.
Nor could the scroll con - tain the whole, Tho' stretched from sky to sky.
REFRAIN:
1
2
Oh, love of God, how rich and pure! How meas-ure-less and strong!
It shall for - ev - er - more en - dure- The saints' and an - (Omit) gels' song.

# 780 SINCE THE LOVE OF GOD HAS SHED

*But God commendeth His love toward us, in that, while we were yet sinners, Christ died for us.* Rom. 5:8.

Lawrence Highfield

THE LOVE OF GOD (Beazley) 7.7.6.7.7.6. with Ref.
M.M. 66

Samuel W. Beazley, 1873-1944

1. Since the love of God has shed Price-less bless-ings on my head, I have made it my own; I will hide it in my heart, That it nev-er may de-part, It shall rule there a-lone . . . . . . . . . . .
2. Since the Son of God came down With His love our lives to crown, He with us would re - main; Great - er love there could not be, Je - sus died for you and me, In our hearts He would reign . . . . . . . . . . .
3. He who gave His love to me, That I might from sin be free, Bids me share it to - day; "As I loved you," He has said, "You must serve men in my stead, As you go on your way." . . . . . . . . . .
4. While His love burns true and bright, We are walking in the light, He has shown us the road; We His glo - ry must re-flect, Lest our dim-ness and neg-lect Keep some soul from its God. . . . . . . . . . .
(1.) I have made it my own,
It shall rule there a - lone.
REFRAIN:
The love of God . . . . . . . . . . . . . . with-in the
The love of God . . . . . . . . . . .

heart, . . . . . . . . . . . . . Will kind-li - ness . . . . . . . . . . . . and warmth im-
. . . . . with-in the heart, . . . . . . . . . . . . . Will kind-li-ness . . . . . . . . . . .
part, . . . . . . . . . The soul will grow like Je - sus in His ten-der mer-cy,
. . . . and warmth impart, ,
If the heart is made His dwell - ing place: The love of
If the heart is made His dwell-ing place:
God . . . . . . . . . . . . glows like a flame, . . . . . . . . . . . . Thro' end-less
The love of God . . . . . . . . . . . . . . . glows like a flame, . . . . . . . . .
years . . . . . . . . . . . . . . . . it is the same, . . . . . . . . . . The love of
. . . . . Thro' end-less years . . . . . . . . . . . . . . . it is the same,
God will nev - er fail nor lose its glo - ry Till we see Him face to face.

# 781 JOY TO THE WORLD

*For unto you is born this day in the city of David a Saviour, which is Christ the Lord.* Lk. 2:11. *And she shall bring forth a Son, and thou shalt call His name Jesus: for He shall save His people from their sins.* Mt. 1:21.

Isaac Watts, 1719 (1674-1748) | ANTIOCH C.M. 8.6.8.6. M.M. 62 | George Friederich Handel, 1685-1759 Arr. by Lowell Mason, 1830 (1792-1872)

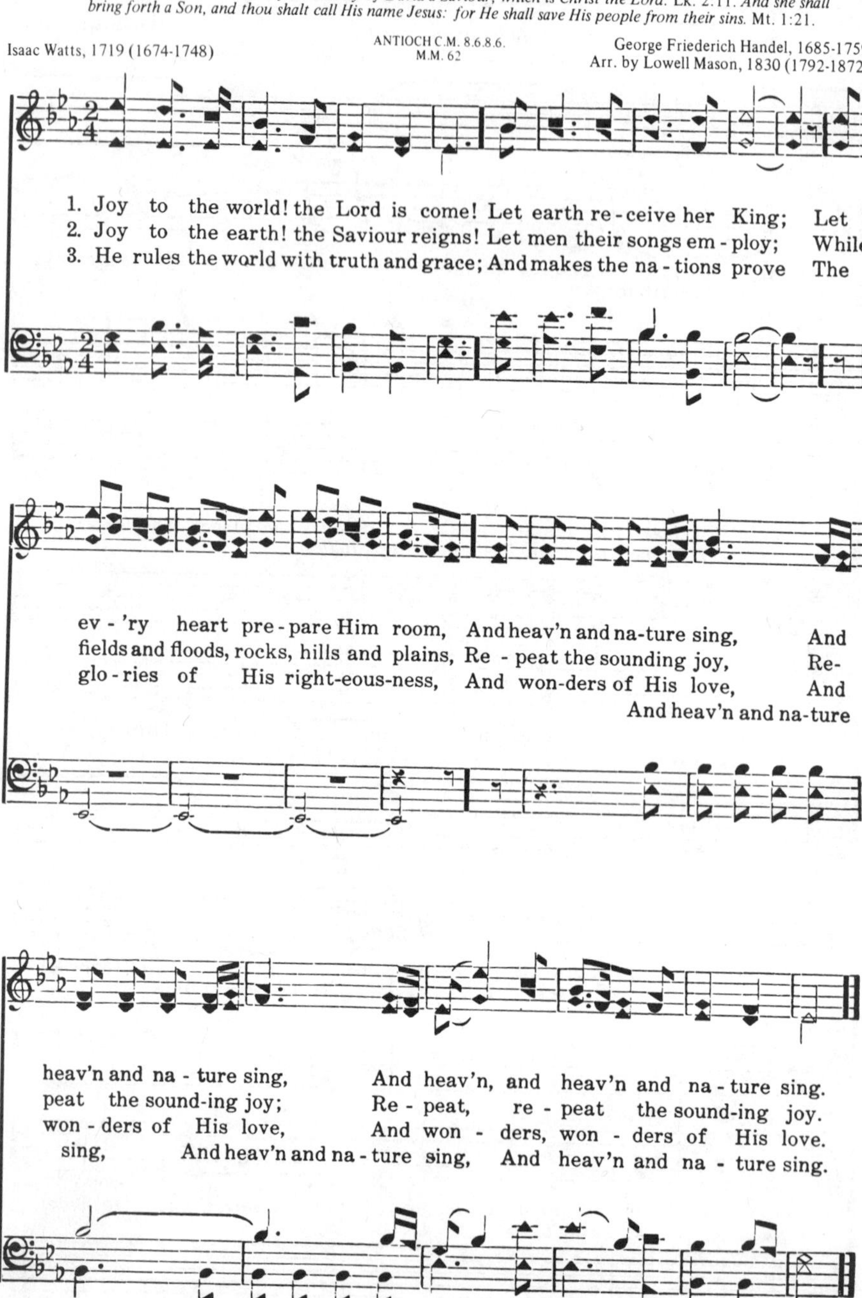
1. Joy to the world! the Lord is come! Let earth re-ceive her King; Let ev-'ry heart pre-pare Him room, And heav'n and na-ture sing, And heav'n and na-ture sing, And heav'n, and heav'n and na-ture sing.
2. Joy to the earth! the Saviour reigns! Let men their songs em-ploy; While fields and floods, rocks, hills and plains, Re-peat the sounding joy, Re-peat the sound-ing joy; Re-peat, re-peat the sound-ing joy.
3. He rules the world with truth and grace; And makes the na-tions prove The glo-ries of His right-eous-ness, And won-ders of His love, And won-ders of His love, And won-ders, won-ders of His love.
And heav'n and na-ture sing, And heav'n and na-ture sing, And heav'n and na-ture sing.

# FEAR NOT, FEAR NOT, O YE SHEPHERDS 782

*And the angel said unto them, Fear not: for, behold, I bring you good tidings of great joy, which shall be to all people. Glory to God in the highest, and on earth peace, good will toward men.* Lk. 2:10, 14.

ANGELS' HYMN 8.7.8.7. with Ref.
M.M. 80
John W. Wayland
John David Brunk, 1872-1926
1. Fear not, fear not, O ye shep - herds, Rath - er give ye
2. For in yon - der town of Da - vid— Seek ye there with
3. This the sign by which to know Him, Seek ye, then, be
thanks and sing, For to you and to all peo - ple Ti - dings
one ac - cord—There is born to you a Sav - iour Which is
not a - fraid—Ye shall find a Babe in Beth-l'hem, In a
of great joy I bring.
e - ven Christ the Lord.
low - ly man - ger laid.
REFRAIN:
"Glo - ry in the high - est!
"Glo - ry, glo - ry in the high - est!
Praise in - crease, let praise in-crease!
Un - to God let praise in - crease!
Glo - ry,
glo - ry in the high - est! Un - to men good - will and peace."

# 783 SILENTLY O'ER BETHLEHEM

*And suddenly there was with the angel a multitude of the heavenly host praising God.* Lk. 2:13.

SILENTLY O'ER BETHLEHEM 7.6.7.6. with Ref.
M.M. 104

John W. Wayland — John David Brunk, 1872-1926

1. Si - lent-ly o'er Beth-le - hem Come zeph - yrs from the sea; Gen - tly, like a per - fumed breath, Or some sweet mys-ter - y.
2. Si - lent-ly o'er Beth-le - hem The heav - ens smile a - bove; All the shin - ing stars beam down Like watch - ing eyes of love.
3. Si - lent-ly o'er Beth-le - hem, From wait - ing courts on high, An - gel choirs with tun - ed lyres In read - i - ness draw nigh.
4. Si - lent-ly o'er Beth-le - hem From heav - en un - de - filed, Meek - ly now doth en - ter in The Spir - it of a Child.
1. Si - lent-ly, si - lent-ly o'er Beth-le-hem, Si - lent-ly come zeph-yrs from the sea, the sea; Gen-tly, like perfumed, perfumed breath; Gen - tly, like perfumed, perfumed breath, Or mys-ter-y, sweet mys-ter - y.
2. Si - lent-ly, si - lent-ly o'er Beth-le-hem, Si - lent-ly the heav-ens smile a - bove, a-bove; And all the shin - ing stars beam down, And all the shin - ing stars beam down, Like watching eyes, like eyes of love.
3. Si - lent-ly, si - lent-ly o'er Beth-le-hem, Si - lent-ly, from wait-ing courts on high, on high, Bright angel choirs with tun - ed lyres, Bright an-gel choirs with tun - ed lyres, In read-i - ness from heav'n draw nigh.
4. Si - lent-ly, si - lent-ly o'er Beth-le-hem, Si - lent-ly from heav-en, pure and un - de-filed, All meek-ly now doth en - ter in, All meek-ly now doth en - ter in, The Spir-it of the ho - ly Child.

p REFRAIN:
1. Si - lent - ly, si - lent - ly, Zeph - yrs from the sea;
2. Si - lent - ly, si - lent - ly, Smile ye heav'ns a - bove;
3. Si - lent - ly, si - lent - ly, Wait ye courts on high;
4. Si - lent - ly, si - lent - ly, Meek and un - de - filed;
pp
rit. e dim.
Si - lent - ly, si - lent - ly, O sweet mys - ter - y.
Si - lent - ly, si - lent - ly, Watch, O eyes of love!
Si - lent - ly, si - lent - ly, Come ye an - gels nigh.
Si - lent - ly, si - lent - ly, Come, O heav'n - ly Child!

# ANGEL HOSTS WERE HEARD ON HIGH 784

*Behold, a virgin shall be with child, and shall bring forth a son, and they shall call His name Emmanuel, which being interpreted is, God with us.* Mt. 1:23.

French Carol
Alt. Earl Marlatt, b. 1892
Alt. John J. Overholt, 1972

GLORIA 7.7.7.7. with Ref.
M.M. 80

French Carol

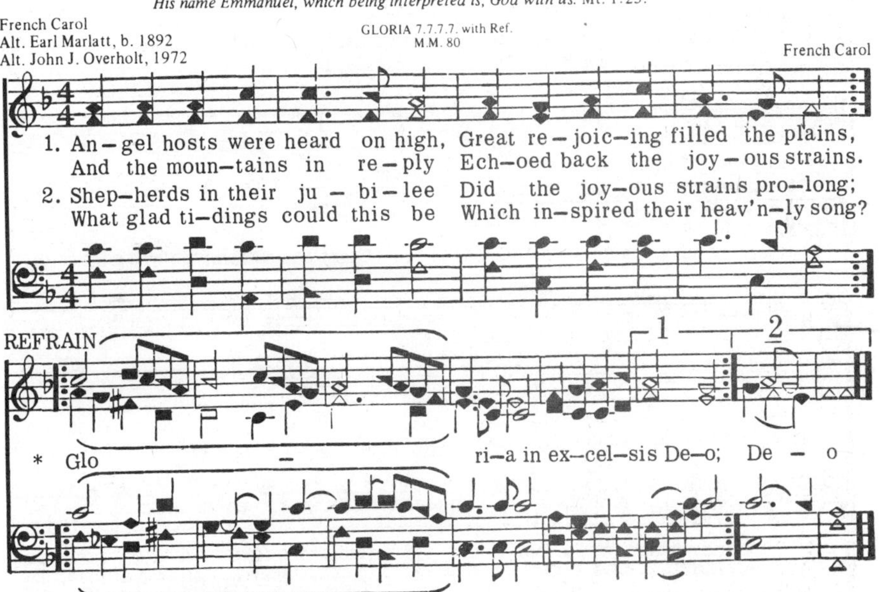
1. An–gel hosts were heard on high, Great re–joic–ing filled the plains,
And the moun–tains in re–ply Ech–oed back the joy–ous strains.
2. Shep–herds in their ju – bi – lee Did the joy–ous strains pro–long;
What glad ti–dings could this be Which in–spired their heav'n–ly song?
REFRAIN
1
2
* Glo – ri–a in ex–cel–sis De–o; De – o

3. Come to Christ, the Lord, and see
Him whose birth the angels hailed;
Come, adore on bended knee,
Him whose blood o'er sin prevailed.

4. See Him, once in manger laid,
Whom the hosts of angels praised;
See Him who our ransom paid,
Christ, our King, to glory raised.

* *Glory to God in the highest.* Lu. 2:14

# 785 HALLELUJAH FOR THE BLOOD

*For if the blood of bulls and of goats, and the ashes of an heifer sprinkling the unclean, sanctifieth to the purifying of the flesh: How much more shall the blood of Christ.* Heb. 9:13 14.

HALLELUJAH FOR THE BLOOD 7.7.6.6.7.7.6.6. with Ref.
M.M. 72

Mrs. Charles H. Morris, 1862-1929
Mrs. Charles H. Morris
1. Hal - le-lu-jah for the blood, for the sin-cleansing fountain, For the Lamb has been slain,
2. Hal - le-lu-jah for the blood; sing for joy all ye nations, And rejoice that the work
3. Hal - le-lu-jah for the blood, hal - le - lu-jah for - ev-er, We shall sing it a - new
and the ransom price paid; Fully cancelled was the debt, when on Cal-va-ry's mountain
of re-demp-tion is done; Here is pardon free for all, and a per-fect sal - va - tion
in the kingdom of God, Where the anthems of delight shall be si-lent, no, nev - er,
All the sins of this world up-on Je-sus were laid.
Thro' the sin-cleansing blood of the Crucified One.
Ev - er-more hal-le-lu-jah for Christ and the blood.
p REFRAIN:
There was no arm to save, there was
cres.
no eye to pit-y, Un-til Je-sus our Savior from Glory came down; He was mighty to
mf
save, he was strong to deliver, He has bro't us salvation, a robe and a crown. Hal-le-lu-jah,
f
hal-le-lu-jah, sing the triumphant strain: Hallelujah, for the blood and the Lamb that was slain.

# O, NOW I SEE THE CRIMSON WAVE 786

*Unto Him that loved us, and washed us from our sins in His own blood.* Rev. 1:5.

THE CLEANSING WAVE C.M. 8.6.8.6 with Ref.
M.M. 60

Phoebe Palmer — Mrs. Joseph Fairfield Knapp, 1839-1908

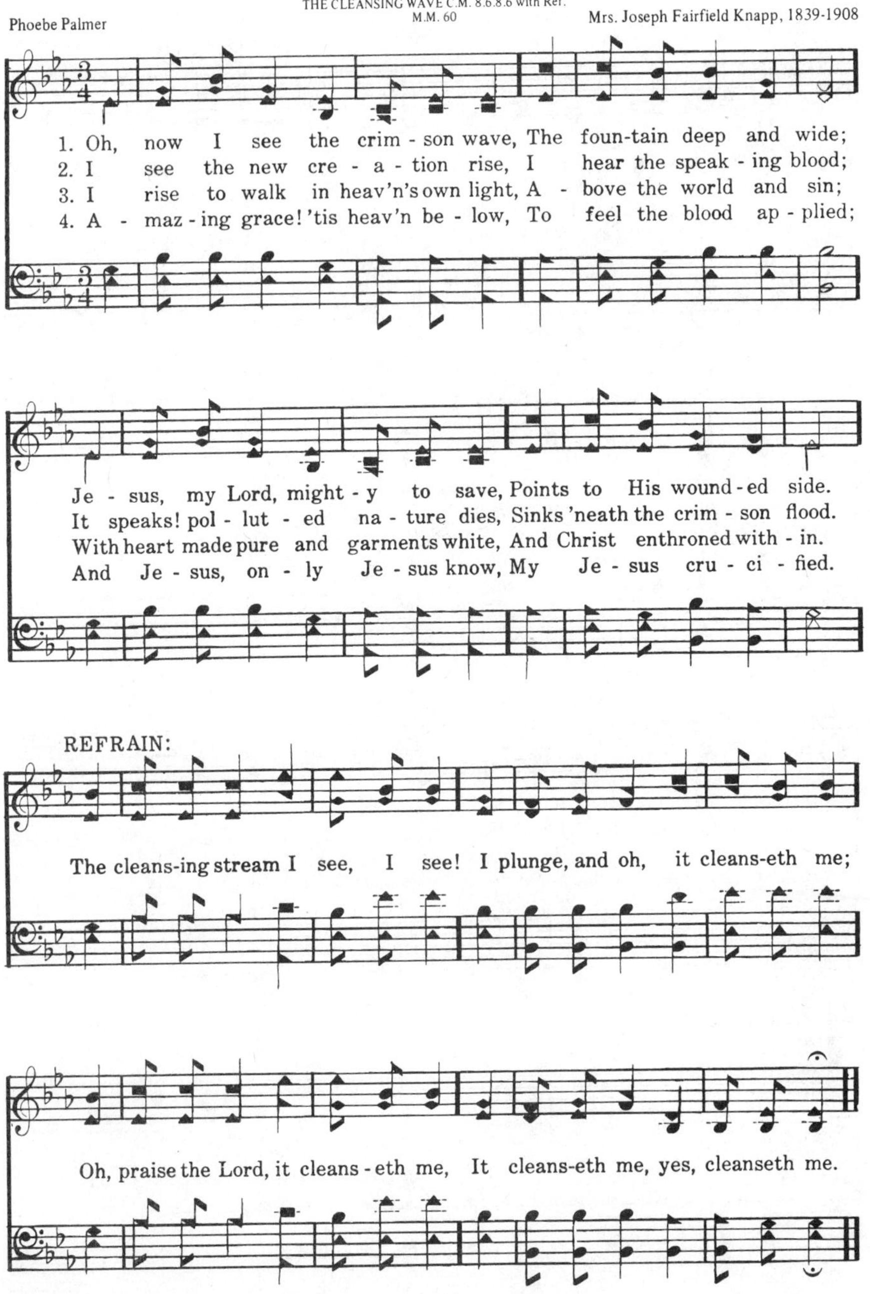
1. Oh, now I see the crim - son wave, The foun-tain deep and wide;
2. I see the new cre - a - tion rise, I hear the speak - ing blood;
3. I rise to walk in heav'n's own light, A - bove the world and sin;
4. A - maz - ing grace! 'tis heav'n be - low, To feel the blood ap - plied;
Je - sus, my Lord, might - y to save, Points to His wound - ed side.
It speaks! pol - lut - ed na - ture dies, Sinks 'neath the crim - son flood.
With heart made pure and garments white, And Christ enthroned with - in.
And Je - sus, on - ly Je - sus know, My Je - sus cru - ci - fied.
REFRAIN:
The cleans-ing stream I see, I see! I plunge, and oh, it cleans-eth me;
Oh, praise the Lord, it cleans - eth me, It cleans-eth me, yes, cleanseth me.

# 787 ONCE IN SIN'S DARKEST NIGHT

*And to Jesus the mediator of the new covenant, and to the blood of sprinkling, that speaketh better things than than of Abel.* Heb. 12:24.

Nellie Edwards

STOREY NEW 12.8.12.9. with Ref.
M.M. 63

Ran C. Storey
Arr. John J. Overholt, 1968

1. Once in sin's dark - est night I was wand'-ring a - lone, A
2. From the bur - den I car - ried now I am set free, For
3. I can ne'er un - der - stand why He sought ev - en me, Why
4. Now He comes to my heart and re - moves ev - 'ry care, He
strang - er to mer - cy I stood; But the Sav - ior came nigh When He
Je - sus has lift - ed my load; O the love and the grace I re-
His life-blood on Cal -v'ry flowed; But suf - fi - cient for me, Since He
bears all my cum - ber - ing load; In a path - way re - plete With His
heard my faint cry, And He put my sins un - der the blood.
ceived in its place When He put my sins un - der the blood.
died on the tree, He has put my sins un - der the blood.
love are my feet, Since He put my sins un - der the blood.
REFRAIN:
They are cov -ered by the blood, they are cov-ered by the blood, My

sins are all cov - ered by the blood My in–
pre - cious blood
iq – ui - ties so vast, Have been blot - ted out at
last, My sins are all cov - ered by the blood.
pre - cious blood

# NOT ALL THE BLOOD OF BEASTS 788

*For this is My blood of the new testament, which is shed for many for the remission of sins.* Mt. 26:28.

BOYLSTON S.M. 6.6.8.6.
M.M. 58

Isaac Watts, 1674-1748

Lowell Mason, 1792-1872

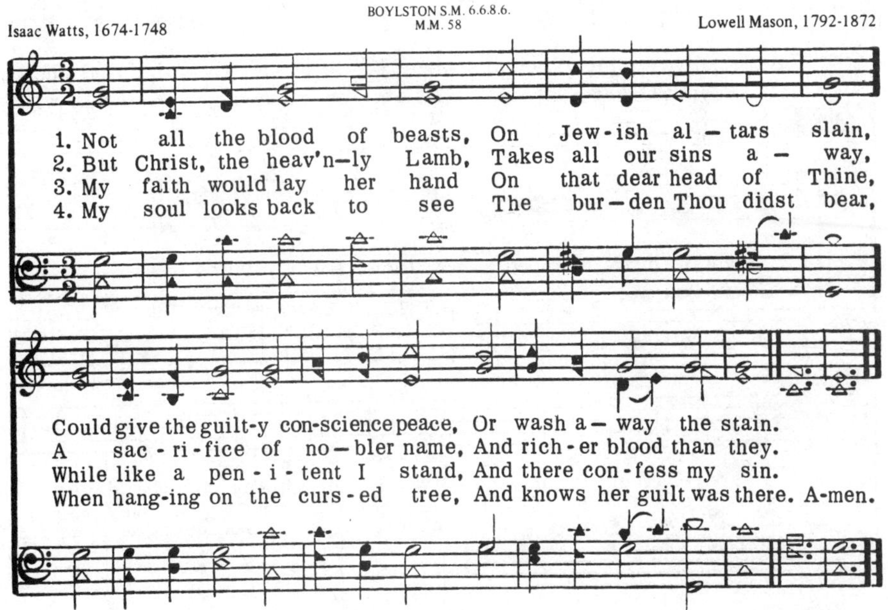
1. Not all the blood of beasts, On Jew-ish al – tars slain,
2. But Christ, the heav'n–ly Lamb, Takes all our sins a – way,
3. My faith would lay her hand On that dear head of Thine,
4. My soul looks back to see The bur – den Thou didst bear,
Could give the guilt-y con-science peace, Or wash a – way the stain.
A sac - ri - fice of no – bler name, And rich - er blood than they.
While like a pen - i - tent I stand, And there con - fess my sin.
When hang-ing on the curs - ed tree, And knows her guilt was there. A-men.

# 789 ALAS! AND DID MY SAVIOUR BLEED?

*In Whom we have redemption through His blood, the forgiveness of sins, according to the riches of His grace.* Eph. 1:7.

Isaac Watts, 1674-1748 AT THE CROSS C.M. 8.6.8.6. with Ref. M.M. 69 Ralph E. Hudson, 1843-1901

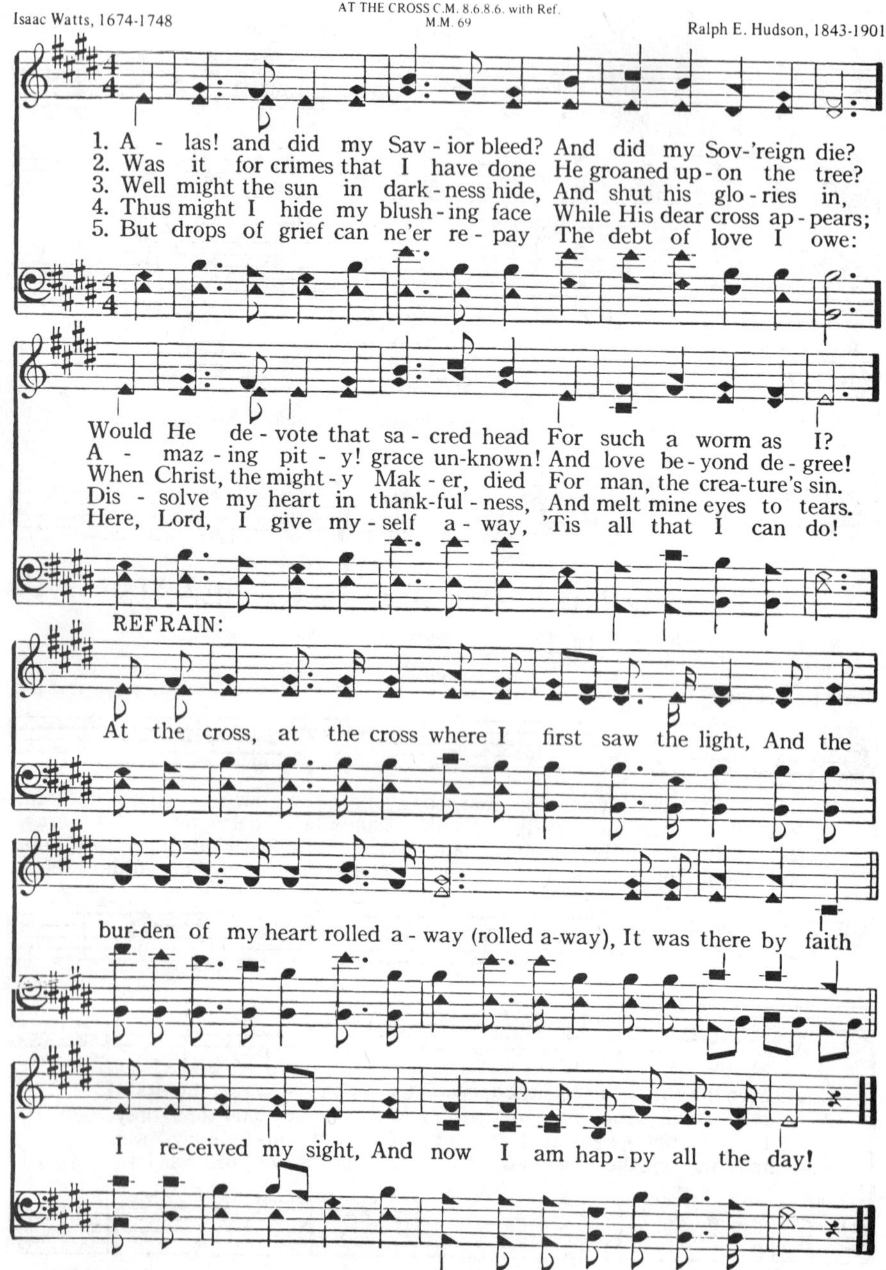
1. A - las! and did my Sav - ior bleed? And did my Sov-'reign die?
2. Was it for crimes that I have done He groaned up - on the tree?
3. Well might the sun in dark - ness hide, And shut his glo - ries in,
4. Thus might I hide my blush - ing face While His dear cross ap - pears;
5. But drops of grief can ne'er re - pay The debt of love I owe:
Would He de - vote that sa - cred head For such a worm as I?
A - maz - ing pit - y! grace un - known! And love be - yond de - gree!
When Christ, the might - y Mak - er, died For man, the crea - ture's sin.
Dis - solve my heart in thank - ful - ness, And melt mine eyes to tears.
Here, Lord, I give my - self a - way, 'Tis all that I can do!
REFRAIN:
At the cross, at the cross where I first saw the light, And the
bur - den of my heart rolled a - way (rolled a - way), It was there by faith
I re - ceived my sight, And now I am hap - py all the day!

## ALAS! AND DID MY SAVIOUR BLEED 790

*In Whom we have redemption through His blood, even the forgiveness of sins.* Col. 1:14.

O HOW I LOVE JESUS C.M. 8.6.8.6 with Ref.
M.M. 112

Isaac Watts, 1674-1748 | Anon.

1. A - las! and did my Sav-ior bleed? And did my Sov-'reign die? Would He de-vote that sa-cred head For such a worm as I?

CHORUS

O how I love Je - sus, O how I love Je - sus, O how I love Je - sus, Be-cause He first loved me.

## ALAS! AND DID MY SAVIOUR BLEED 791

*Much more then, being now justified by His blood, we shall be saved from wrath through Him.* Rom. 5:9.

HULL C.M. 8.6.8.6
M.M. 63

Isaac Watts, 1674-1748 | Asa Hull, b. 1828

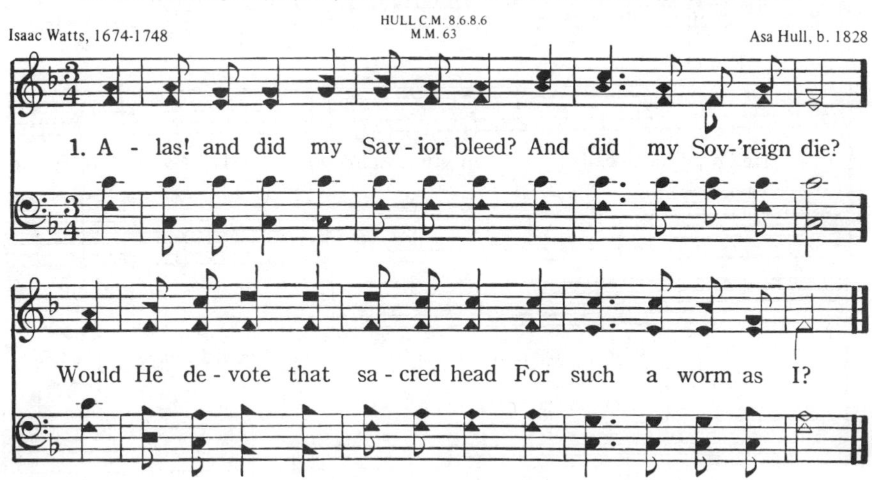
1. A - las! and did my Sav - ior bleed? And did my Sov-'reign die?
Would He de - vote that sa - cred head For such a worm as I?

# 792 THEY BOUND THE HANDS OF JESUS

*Thinkest thou that I cannot now pray to my Father, and He shall presently give me more than twelve legions of angels?* Mt. 26:53.

Ray Overholt

TEN THOUSAND ANGELS 8.7.8.7.6.9. with Ref.
M.M. 56

Ray Overholt

*Slowly with feeling*

1. They bound the hands of Je-sus in the gar-den where He prayed; They led Him thro the streets in shame. They spat up-on the Sav-iour so pure and free from sin; They said, "Cru-ci-fy Him, He's to blame."
2. Up-on His pre-cious head they placed a crown of thorns; They laughed and said, "Behold the King." They struck Him and they cursed Him and mocked His ho-ly name. All a-lone He suf-fered ev-'ry-thing.
3. When they nailed Him to the Cross, His moth-er stood nearby; He said, "Wo-man, be-hold thy son!" He cried, "I thirst for wa-ter," but they gave Him none to drink. Then the sin-ful work of man was done.
4. To the howl-ing mob He yield-ed; He did not for mer-cy cry. The Cross of shame He took a-lone. And when He cried, "It's fin-ished," He gave Him-self to die; Sal-va-tion's wondrous plan was done.

REFRAIN:

He could have called ten thou-sand an-gels To de-stroy the world and set Him free. He could have called,
the world

rall.
ten thou-sand an - gels, But He died a - lone, for you and me.
a-lone

# DOWN AT THE CROSS 793

*Forasmuch as ye know that ye were not redeemed with corruptible things, as silver and gold, from your vain conversation received by tradition from your fathers; But with the precious blood of Christ, as a lamb without blemish and without spot.* I Pet. 1: 18, 19.

Elisha A. Hoffman, 1839-1929

GLORY TO HIS NAME 9.9.9.5. with Ref.
M.M. 66

John H. Stockton, 1813-1877

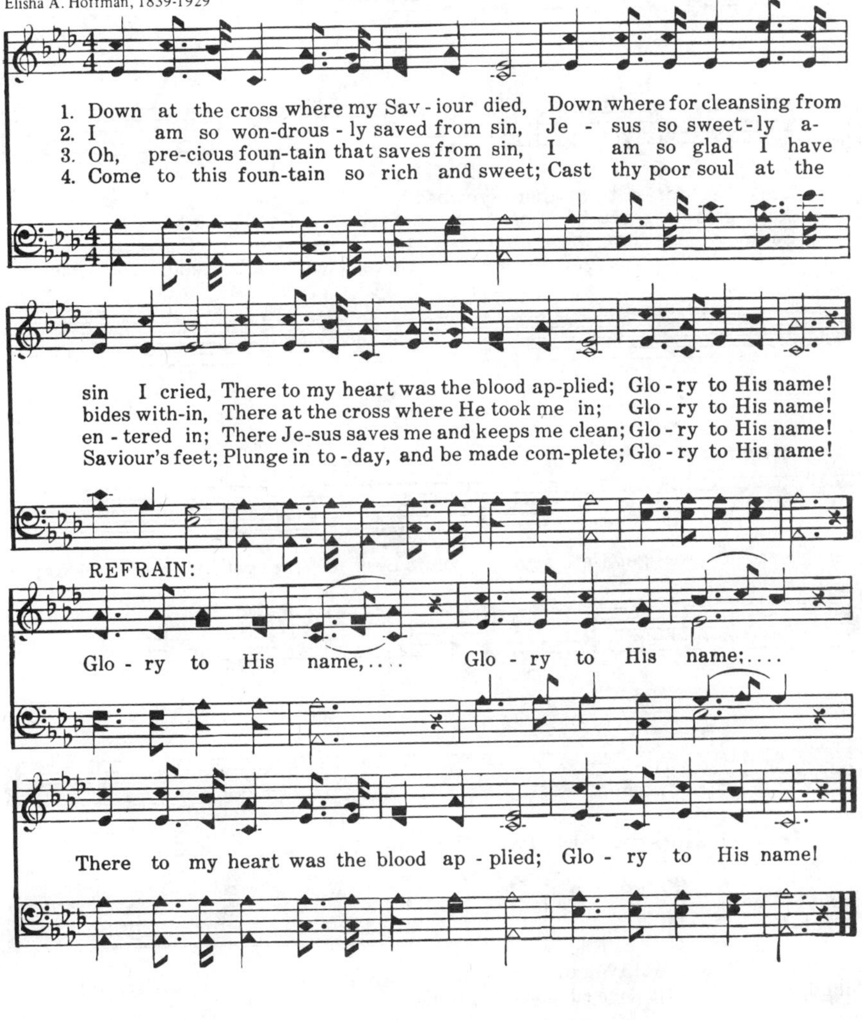

1. Down at the cross where my Sav - iour died, Down where for cleansing from sin I cried, There to my heart was the blood ap-plied; Glo - ry to His name!
2. I am so won-drous - ly saved from sin, Je - sus so sweet-ly a- bides with-in, There at the cross where He took me in; Glo - ry to His name!
3. Oh, pre-cious foun-tain that saves from sin, I am so glad I have en - tered in; There Je-sus saves me and keeps me clean; Glo - ry to His name!
4. Come to this foun-tain so rich and sweet; Cast thy poor soul at the Saviour's feet; Plunge in to - day, and be made com-plete; Glo - ry to His name!

REFRAIN:

Glo - ry to His name,.... Glo - ry to His name;.... There to my heart was the blood ap - plied; Glo - ry to His name!

# 794 KING OF MY LIFE, I CROWN THEE NOW

*And when they were come to the place, which is called Calvary, there they crucified Him, and the malefactors, one on the right hand, and the other on the left.* Lk. 23:33.

Jennie Evelyn Hussey, 1874-

LEAD ME TO CALVARY C.M. 8.6.8.6. with Ref.
M.M. 69

William J. Kirkpatrick, 1838-1921

1. King of my life I crown Thee now, Thine shall the glo - ry be;
2. Show me the tomb where Thou wast laid, Ten - der - ly mourned and wept;
3. Let me like Ma-ry, through the gloom, Come with a gift to Thee;
4. May I be will - ing, Lord, to bear Dai - ly my cross for Thee;

Lest I for - get Thy thorn-crowned brow, Lead me to Cal - va - ry.
An - gels in robes of light ar - rayed Guard-ed Thee whilst Thou slept.
Show to me now the emp - ty tomb, Lead me to Cal - va - ry.
E - ven Thy cup of grief to share, Thou hast borne all for me.

REFRAIN:

Lest I for - get Geth-sem - a - ne; Lest I for - get Thine ag - o - ny;

Lest I for - get Thy love for me, Lead me to Cal - va - ry.

# WONDERFUL REDEMPTION 795

*But now in Christ Jesus ye who sometimes were far off are made nigh by the blood of Christ.* Eph. 2:13.

Anon. German
Tr. John J. Overholt, 1968

WUNDERBARE LIEBE 9.6.6. with Ref.
M.M. 69

Arr. John J. Overholt, 1968

1. Won - der - ful re - demp - tion full and free
2. Will you spurn His mer - cy, grace, and love?
3. Soon the day is com - ing, when a lone.

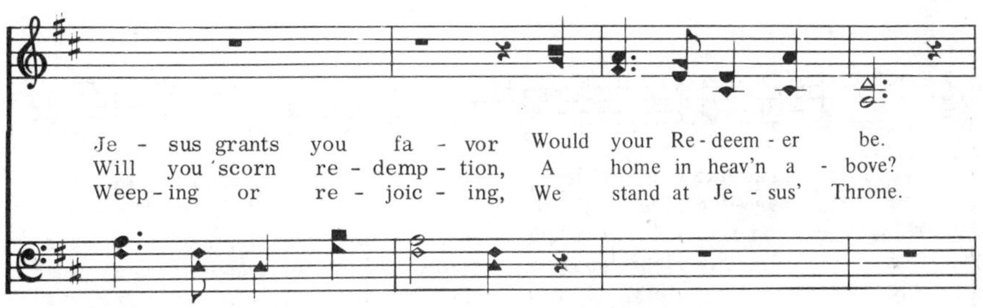
Je - sus grants you fa - vor Would your Re - deem - er be.
Will you ′scorn re - demp - tion, A home in heav'n a - bove?
Weep - ing or re - joic - ing, We stand at Je - sus' Throne.

REFRAIN:

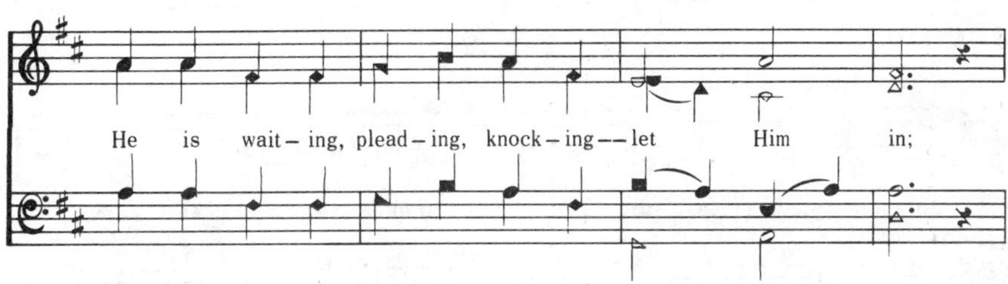
He is wait – ing, plead – ing, knock – ing –– let Him in;

Je – sus –– wait – ing, plead – ing, knock – ing –– let Him in.

# 796 WHAT CAN WASH AWAY MY SIN?

*And, having made peace through the blood of His cross, by Him to reconcile all things unto Himself; by Him, I say, whether they be things in earth, or things in heaven.* Col. 1:20.

Robert Lowry, 1826-1899

NOTHING BUT THE BLOOD 7.8.7.8. with Ref.
M.M. 76

Robert Lowry

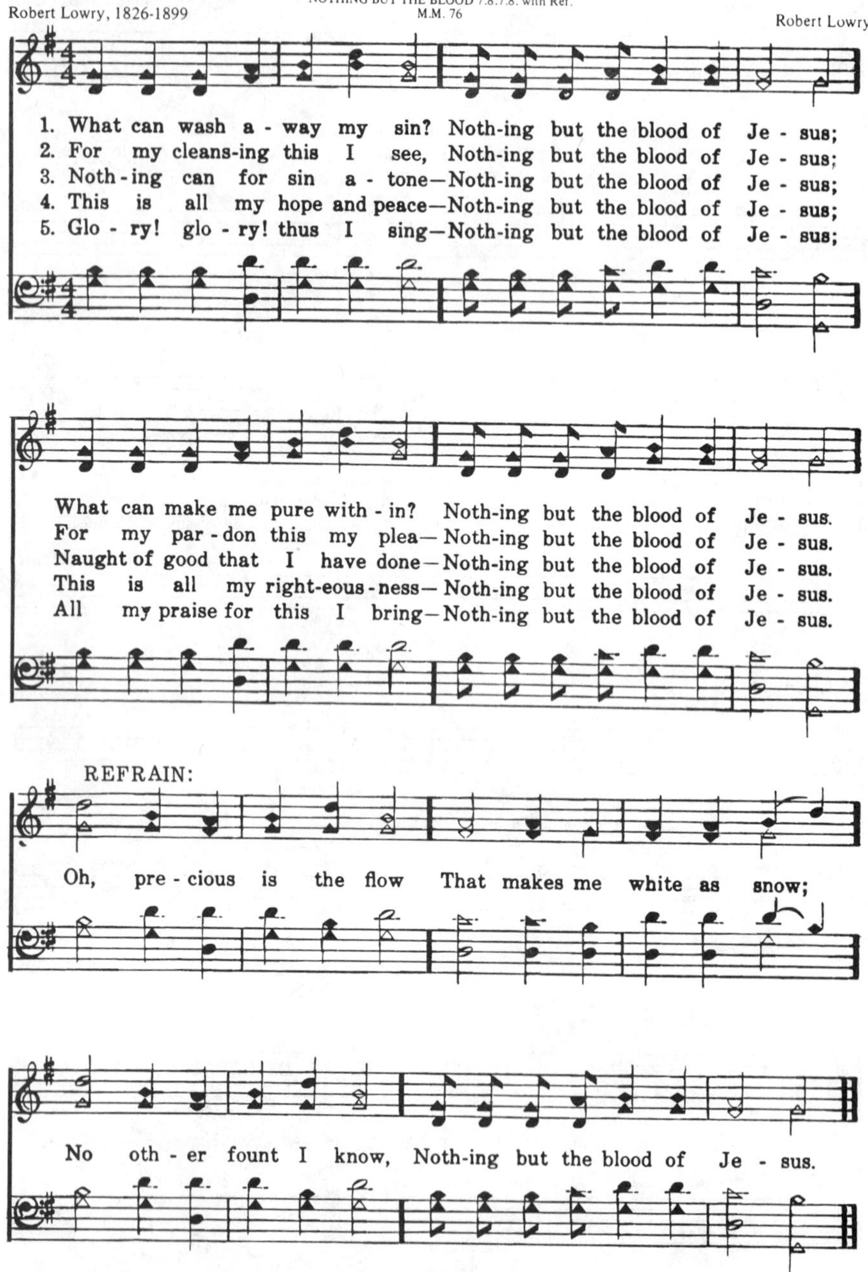
1. What can wash a - way my sin? Noth-ing but the blood of Je - sus;
2. For my cleans-ing this I see, Noth-ing but the blood of Je - sus;
3. Noth - ing can for sin a - tone—Noth-ing but the blood of Je - sus;
4. This is all my hope and peace—Noth-ing but the blood of Je - sus;
5. Glo - ry! glo - ry! thus I sing—Noth-ing but the blood of Je - sus;
What can make me pure with - in? Noth-ing but the blood of Je - sus.
For my par - don this my plea—Noth-ing but the blood of Je - sus.
Naught of good that I have done—Noth-ing but the blood of Je - sus.
This is all my right-eous - ness—Noth-ing but the blood of Je - sus.
All my praise for this I bring—Noth-ing but the blood of Je - sus.
REFRAIN:
Oh, pre - cious is the flow That makes me white as snow;
No oth - er fount I know, Noth-ing but the blood of Je - sus.

# WOULD YOU BE FREE FROM YOUR BURDEN OF SIN

*But if we walk in the light, as He is in the light, we have fellowship one with another, and the blood of Jesus Christ His Son cleanseth us from all sin.* I Jn. 1:7.

THERE IS POWER IN THE BLOOD 10.9.10.8. with Ref.
M.M. 76
Lewis E. Jones, 1865-1936
Lewis E. Jones
1. Would you be free from your bur - den of sin? There's pow'r in the blood,
2. Would you be free from your pas - sion and pride? There's pow'r in the blood,
3. Would you be whit - er, much whit - er than snow? There's pow'r in the blood,
4. Would you do serv - ice for Je - sus your King? There's pow'r in the blood,
pow'r in the blood; Would you o'er e - vil a vic - to - ry win?
pow'r in the blood; Come for a cleans - ing to Cal - va - ry's tide,
pow'r in the blood; Sin - stains are lost in its life - giv - ing flow,
pow'r in the blood; Would you live dai - ly, His prais - es to sing?
REFRAIN:
There's won - der - ful pow'r in the blood. There is pow'r, pow'r,
there is pow'r,
won-der-work - ing pow'r In the blood of the Lamb; There is
In the blood of the Lamb;
pow'r, pow'r, won-der-work-ing pow'r In the pre-cious blood of the Lamb.
there is pow'r,

# 798 CHRIST, OUR REDEEMER, DIED ON THE CROSS

*And the blood shall be to you for a token upon the houses where ye are: and when I see the blood, I will pass over you, and the plague shall not be upon you to destroy you.* Ex. 12:13.

BLOOD OF THE LAMB 9.9.8.9. with Ref.
M.M. 66

John Foote — J. Henry Showalter, 1864-1947

1. Christ, our Re-deem-er, died on the cross, Died for the sin-ner, paid all his due;
2. Chief-est of sin-ners Je-sus can save, As he has prom-ised, so will he do;
3. Judg-ment is com-ing, all will be there Who have re-ject-ed, who have re-fused:
4. Oh, what compas-sion! oh, boundless love! Je-sus hath pow-er, Je-sus is true:
All who re-ceive him need nev-er fear, For he will pass, will pass o-ver you.
O, sin-ner, hear him, trust in his word, Then he will pass, will pass o-ver you.
O, sin-ner, hast-en, let Je-sus in, Then God will pass, will pass o-ver you.
All who be-lieve are safe from the storm, Oh, he will pass, will pass o-ver you.
REFRAIN:
When I see the blood, I will pass o-ver you;
Yes, when I see the blood, I will pass o-ver you;
When I see the blood, I will pass, I will pass o-ver you.
Yes, when I see the blood of the Lamb, I will pass, I will pass o-ver you.

# WHAT A WONDERFUL, WONDERFUL SAVIOUR 799

*Who His own self bare our sins in His own body on the tree, that we, being dead to sins, should live unto righteousness: by Whose stripes ye were healed.* I Pet. 2:24.

HE WAS NAILED TO THE CROSS 10.8.9.8. with Ref.
M.M. 104:66

F. A. Graves
Arr. John J. Overholt, 1965

F. A. Graves

1. What a won-der-ful, won-der-ful Sav-iour, Who would die on the cross for me! Free-ly shed-ding His pre-cious life-blood, That the sin-ner might be made free.
2. Thus He left His heav-en-ly glo-ry To ac-com-plish His Fa-ther's plan; He was born of the vir-gin Ma-ry, Took up-on Him the form of man.
3. He was wound-ed for our trans-gres-sions, And He car-ried our sor-rows, too; He's the heal-er for sin and sick-ness, This He came to the world to do.
4. So He gave His life for oth-ers In re-deem-ing this world from sin, And He's gone to pre-pare a man-sion, That at last we may en-ter in.
REFRAIN:
He was nailed to the cross for me, He was nailed to the cross for me;
He was nailed to the cross, He was nailed to the cross,
On the cross cru-ci-fied, for me He died, He was nailed to the cross for me.

# 800 WONDERFUL SAVIOUR, REDEEMER

*Of this man's seed hath God according to His promise raised unto Israel a Saviour, Jesus.* Acts 13:23.

WONDERFUL SAVIOUR 8.5.8.5. with Ref.
M.M. 112

Wellington K. Jacobs, 1902 (b. 1876) — W. K. Jacobs

1. Won - der - ful Sav - iour, Re - deem - er, Thou in ten - d'rest love
2. Thou hast in great - est com - pas - sion Died our souls to save:
3. O - pen my heart e'er to hear Thee, Quick to hear Thy voice;
Watch-est o'er ev - 'ry be - liev - er, From Thy throne a - bove.
Pur - chased for us our re - demp - tion, Hope be - yond the grave.
Fill Thou my soul with Thy prais - es, Let my heart re - joice.
REFRAIN:
Won - der - ful Sav - iour! Mer - ci - ful Sav - - iour!
Je - sus, won-der-ful Sav - iour! Je - sus, mer-ci - ful Sav-iour!
My hope and Re - deem - er, Who shed His blood for me.
Who shed His blood for me. (for me.)

# I SAW ONE HANGING ON A TREE 801

*For Christ also hath once suffered for sins, the just for the unjust, that he might bring us to God.* I Pet. 3:18.

John Newton, 1725-1807

HE DIED FOR ME C.M. 8.6.8.6. with Ref.
M.M. 100

Edwin Othello Excell, 1851-1921

1. I saw one hang-ing on a tree, In ag - o - ny and blood;
2. Sure, nev-er, till my lat - est breath, Can I for-get that look:
3. My con-science felt and owned the guilt, And plunged me in de - spair;
4. A - las! I knew not what I did,—But now my tears are vain:
5. A sec - ond look He gave, which said, "I free - ly all for - give:
He fixed His lan - guid eyes on me, As near His cross I stood.
It seemed to charge me with His death, Tho' not a word He spoke.
I saw my sins His blood had spilt And helped to nail Him there.
Where shall my trembling soul be hid? For I the Lord have slain.
This blood is for thy ran-som shed, I die that thou may'st live."
CHORUS.
Oh can it be, up-on a tree The Sav - ior died for me? My
soul is thrilled, My heart is filled, To think He died for me! A - men.

# 802 CHRIST WHO LEFT HIS HOME IN GLORY

*Now is Christ risen from the dead, and become the firstfruits of them that slept.* I Cor. 15:20.

CHRIST IS RISEN 8.7.8.7. with Ref.
M.M. 69

Abram Bowman Kolb, 1896 (1862-1925)

Abram B. Kolb

1. Christ who left His home in glo - ry, And up - on the cross was slain,
2. While the world in peace was sleep-ing, Ear - ly on that Eas - ter day,
3. Christ, our lov - ing Me - di - a - tor, Now with God for you and me
Now is ris'n! Oh, tell the sto - ry That the Sav - iour lives a - gain.
Came the faith - ful wom-en, weep - ing, But the stone was rolled a - way.
In - ter-cedes, and our Cre - a - tor Hears and an - swers ev - 'ry plea.
REFRAIN
Hail Him! Hail Him! Tell the sto - - ry;
Hail to the King, the mighty Redeemer! Hail Him who robbed the grave of its pow'r!
Hail! all hail!... .... Je - sus lives for - ev - er - more.
Tell ev - 'ry na - tion, all is well,

# THE STRIFE IS O'ER 803

*Alleluia: for the Lord God omnipotent reigneth.* Rev. 19:6. *I am He that liveth, and was dead; and, behold, I am alive for evermore, Amen; and have the keys of hell and of death.* Rev. 1:18.

Latin XVII Cent.
Tr. Francis Pott, 1859 (1832-1909)

VICTORY 8.8.8.4.
M.M. 88

Palestrina, 1591 (1525-1594)
Adapt. William H. Monk, 1823-1889
Alleluias by William H. Monk

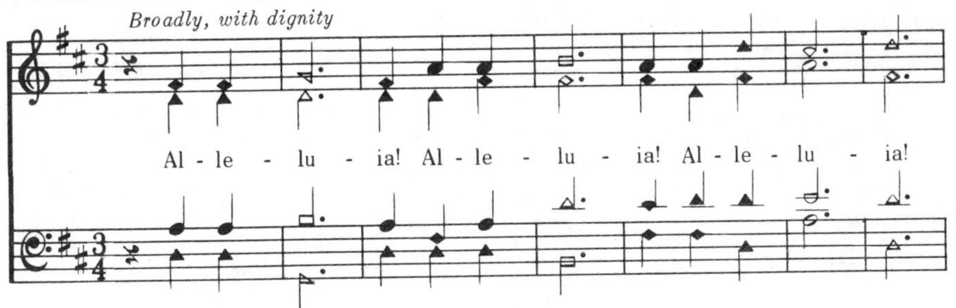
Broadly, with dignity
Al - le - lu - ia! Al - le - lu - ia! Al - le - lu - ia!

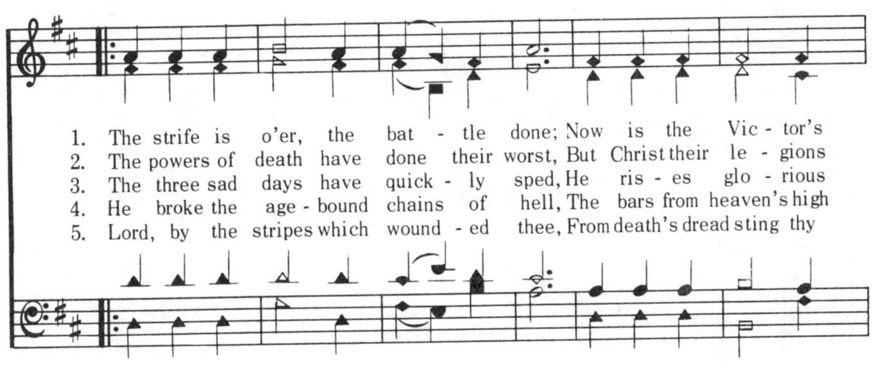
1. The strife is o'er, the bat - tle done; Now is the Vic - tor's
2. The powers of death have done their worst, But Christ their le - gions
3. The three sad days have quick - ly sped, He ris - es glo - rious
4. He broke the age - bound chains of hell, The bars from heaven's high
5. Lord, by the stripes which wound - ed thee, From death's dread sting thy

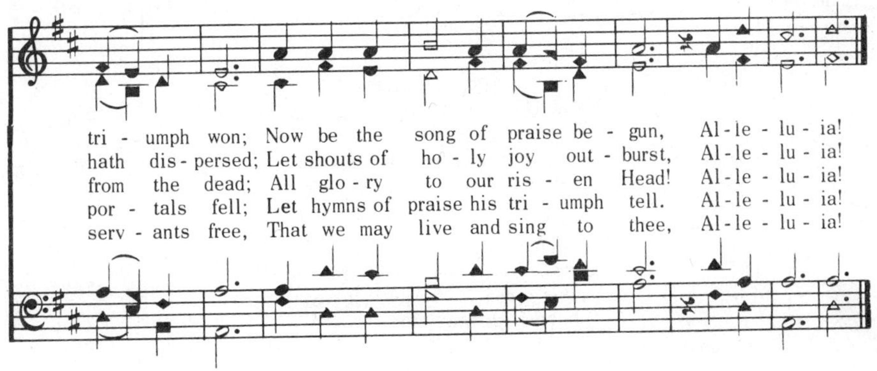
tri - umph won; Now be the song of praise be - gun, Al - le - lu - ia!
hath dis - persed; Let shouts of ho - ly joy out - burst, Al - le - lu - ia!
from the dead; All glo - ry to our ris - en Head! Al - le - lu - ia!
por - tals fell; Let hymns of praise his tri - umph tell. Al - le - lu - ia!
serv - ants free, That we may live and sing to thee, Al - le - lu - ia!

# 804 CHRIST THE LORD IS RISEN AGAIN

*The Lord is risen indeed.* Lk. 24:34. *Who was delivered for our offenses, and was raised again for our justification.* Rom. 4:25.

Michael Weisse, 1531 (c. 1480-1534)
*Christus ist erstanden*
Tr. Catherine Winkworth, 1858

STRAF MICH NICHT IN DEINEM ZORN
7.7.7.7. with Ref.
M.M. 76

*Hundert . . . geistliche Arien,*
*Dresden,* 1694
Arranged by Compiler, 1971

1 Christ the Lord is risen a - gain! Christ hath bro - ken ev - ery chain!
2 He who gave for us His life, Who for us en - dured the strife,
3 He who bore all pain and loss Com - fort - less up - on the cross,
4 He who slum - ber'd in the grave, Is ex - alt - ed now to save;
Hark, the an - gels shout for joy, Chant - ing ev - er - more on high,
Is our Pas - chal Lamb to - day! We too sing for joy, and say:
Lives in glo - ry now on high, Pleads for us and hears our cry:
Now through Chris - ten - dom it rings That the Lamb is King of kings!
Refrain
Christ the Lord, Christ the Lord, Christ the Lord is ris - en! Al - le - lu - ia!

5 Now He bids us tell abroad,
How the lost may be restored,
How the penitent forgiven,
How we too may enter heav'n.
(Refrain)

6 Thou our Paschal Lamb indeed,
Christ, today Thy people feed;
Take our sins and guilt away,
That we all may sing for aye,
(Refrain)

# AWAKE, AWAKE, O EARTH! 805

*While they beheld, He was taken up; and a cloud received Him out of their sight.* Acts 1:9.

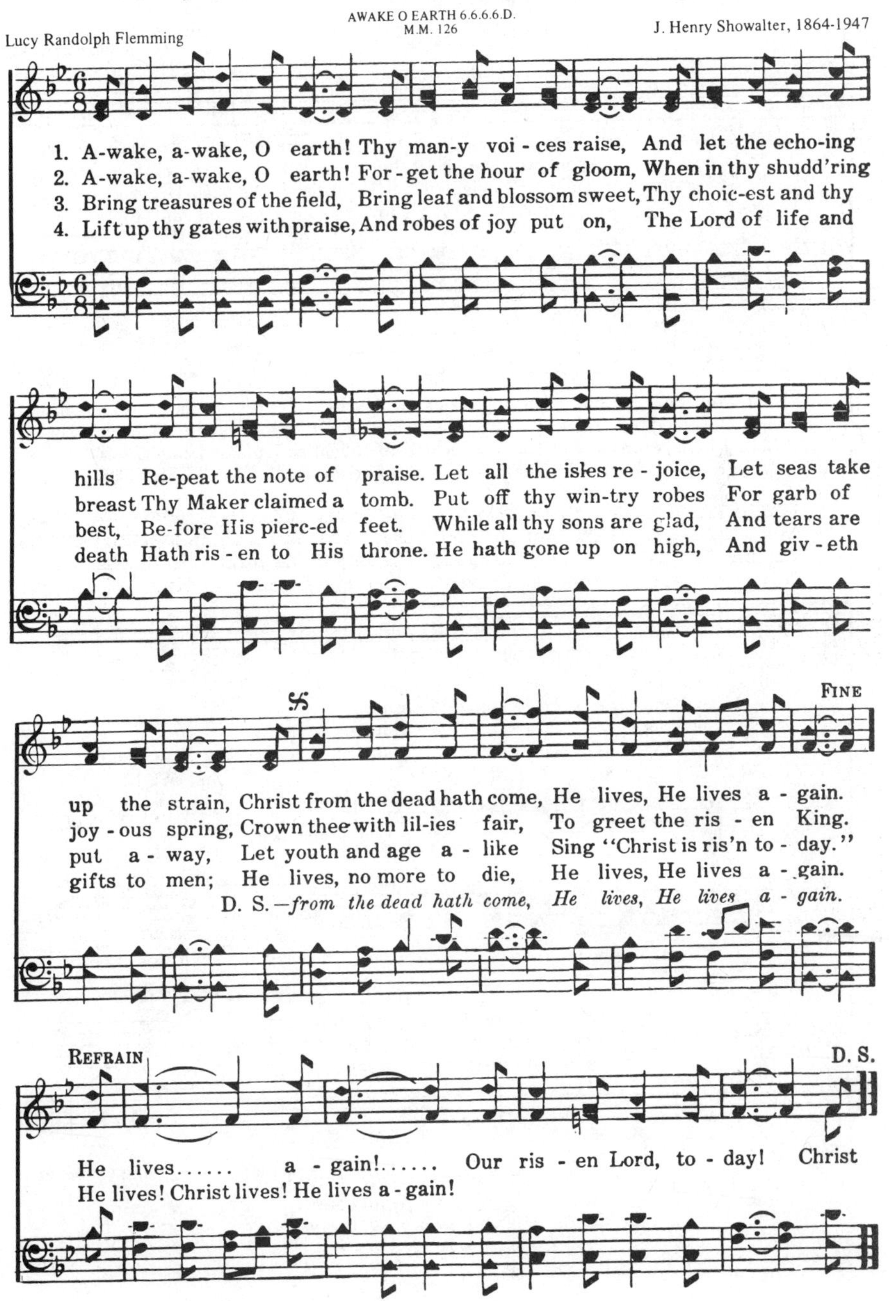
AWAKE O EARTH 6.6.6.6.D.
M.M. 126
Lucy Randolph Flemming
J. Henry Showalter, 1864-1947
1. A-wake, a-wake, O earth! Thy man-y voi - ces raise, And let the echo-ing
2. A-wake, a-wake, O earth! For-get the hour of gloom, When in thy shudd'ring
3. Bring treasures of the field, Bring leaf and blossom sweet, Thy choic-est and thy
4. Lift up thy gates with praise, And robes of joy put on, The Lord of life and
hills Re-peat the note of praise. Let all the isles re - joice, Let seas take
breast Thy Maker claimed a tomb. Put off thy win-try robes For garb of
best, Be-fore His pierc-ed feet. While all thy sons are glad, And tears are
death Hath ris - en to His throne. He hath gone up on high, And giv - eth
FINE
up the strain, Christ from the dead hath come, He lives, He lives a - gain.
joy - ous spring, Crown thee with lil-ies fair, To greet the ris - en King.
put a - way, Let youth and age a - like Sing "Christ is ris'n to - day."
gifts to men; He lives, no more to die, He lives, He lives a - gain.
D. S.—from the dead hath come, He lives, He lives a - gain.
REFRAIN
D. S.
He lives...... a - gain!...... Our ris - en Lord, to - day! Christ
He lives! Christ lives! He lives a - gain!

# 806 OUR SAVIOUR WILL COME

*This same Jesus, which is taken up from you into heaven, shall so come in like manner as ye have seen Him go into heaven.* Acts 1:11.

George Dunn

HE'S COMING AGAIN 11.11.11.8. with Ref.
M.M. 72

Austin Hazelwood

1. Our Sav-iour will come once more up - on this earth, Ex - alt - ed on high and
2. He's com-ing a - gain with an - gels shin-ing bright, In glo - ry so fair from
3. He's com-ing a - gain to judge the quick and dead, The wick- ed shall flee be-
4. He's com-ing a - gain, we do not know the hour, He told us to watch and
not of low - ly birth; He'll gath - er with Him all those who love His name,
out the land of light; Tri - umph - ant in pow'r, to earth He will de - scend,
fore His face in dread; The righteous will shout and praise His ho - ly name,
pray to Him for pow'r; That, come when He may, He'll find us read - y then,
He's com - ing, yes, com - ing a - gain.
He's com - ing, yes, com - ing a - gain.
He's com - ing, yes, com - ing a - gain.
And wait - ing His com - ing a - gain.
REFRAIN
He's com - ing, I have so oft - en heard, He's com - ing, 'tis writ - ten in His word; He's com - ing, we'll sing the glad re - frain, He's com-ing, yes, com-ing a - gain.
He's com - ing a - gain, He's com - ing a - gain, com - ing a - gain,

# REJOICE, ALL YE BELIEVERS 807

*The wise took oil in their vessels with their lamps.* Mt. 25:4.

Laurentius Laurenti, 1700

GREENLAND 7.6.7.6.D.
M.M. 88

Arr. from Johann Michael Haydn, 1737-1806

1. Re - joice, all ye be - liev - ers! And let your lights ap - pear;
2. See that your lamps are burn - ing; Re - plen - ish them with oil;
3. Ye saints, who here in pa - tience Your cross and suf-f'rings bore,
4. Our hope and ex - pec - ta - tion, O Je - sus, now ap - pear;
The eve - ning is ad - vanc - ing, And dark - er night is near.
And wait for your sal - va - tion, The end of earth - ly toil.
Shall live and reign for - ev - er, When sor - row is no more:
A - rise, Thou Sun so longed for, O'er this be - night - ed sphere.
The Bride-groom is a - ris - ing, And soon He will draw nigh;
The watch - ers on the moun - tain Pro - claim the Bride-groom near,
A - round the throne of glo - ry The Lamb ye shall be - hold,
With hearts and hands up - lift - ed, We plead, O Lord, to see
Up! pray, and watch, and wres - tle! At mid - night comes the cry.
Go meet Him as He com - eth, With Al - le - lu - ias clear.
In tri - umph cast be - fore Him Your di - a - dems of gold.
The day of earth's re - demp - tion That brings us un - to Thee.

# 808 BEHOLD WHAT MANNER OF MAN IS THIS

*What manner of man is this, that even the winds and the sea obey Him!* Mt. 8:27. *His head and His hairs were white like wool, as white as snow; and His eyes were as a flame of fire.* Rev. 1:14. *I am Alpha and Omega, the beginning and the ending.* Rev. 1:8.

HE'S THE LORD OF GLORY 9.7.8.6.9.7.9.7. with Ref.
M.M. 60
Phyllis C. Spiers
Phyllis C. Spiers
1. Be - hold what man - ner of man is this, who stands be - tween God and man? His eyes are as a flame of fire, His fan is in His hand. John saw Him in the sev - en church - es, As the Sun in bril - lian - cy.
2. Be - hold what man - ner of man is this, who sits upon His heav'n - ly throne? He rules and reigns from heav'n a - bove, His be - loved and His own. He's the Li - on of the tribe of Jud - ah, The root of David is He.
3. Be - hold what man - ner of man is this, who spake to the woman at the well? Ever - last - ing life I'll give to Thee, Far richer than man can tell. And who - so - e'er shall drink of this well, Shall live on e - ter - nal - ly.
4. Be - hold what man - ner of man is this, who speaks to the maimed and halt? He says, Thy sins be for - giv - en Thee, Take up thy bed and walk. He stands as the might-
y Sav - iour now, And He cries, Look un - to Me.

Be - hold what man-ner of man is this? What man-ner of man is He?
Be - hold what man-ner of man is this? What man-ner of man is He?
Be - hold what man-ner of man is this? What man-ner of man is He?
Be - hold what man-ner of man is this? What man-ner of man is He?
CHORUS
He's the Lord of Glo - ry, He is the great I Am;
He's the Al - pha and O - me - ga, the be - gin - ning and the end.
His name is Won - der - ful, The Prince of Peace is He.
The Ev - er - last - ing Fa - ther through-out e - ter - ni - ty.

# 809 ALL HAIL THE POWER

*Worthy is the Lamb that was slain to receive power, and riches, and wisdom, and strength, and honour, and glory, and blessing.* Rev. 5:12.

Edward Perronet, 1726-1792
Alt. and Cho. John J. Overholt, 1967
BALTZELL C.M.D. 8.6.8.6.D.
M.M. 66
W. Isaiah Baltzell, 1832-1893
Arr. John J. Overholt, 1962
1. All hail the pow'r of Je - sus' name! Let an - gels pros - trate fall;
2. Ye cho - sen seed of Is - rael's race, Ye ran-somed from the fall,
3. Let ev - ery kin - dred, ev - ery tribe, On this ter - res - trial ball,
Bring forth the roy - al di - a - dem, And crown him Lord of all.
Hail him who saves you by his grace, And crown him Lord of all.
To him all maj - es - ty a - scribe, And crown him Lord of all.
Crown him ye morn - ing stars of light, Which 'round this earth - ly ball;
Ye Gen-tile sin - ners ne'er for - get The worm-wood and the gall;
O that with yon - der sa - cred throng We at his feet may fall!
Now hail the strength of Je - sus' might, And crown him Lord of all.
Go, spread your tro - phies at his feet, And crown him Lord of all.
We'll join the ev - er - last - ing song, And crown him Lord of all.

CHORUS

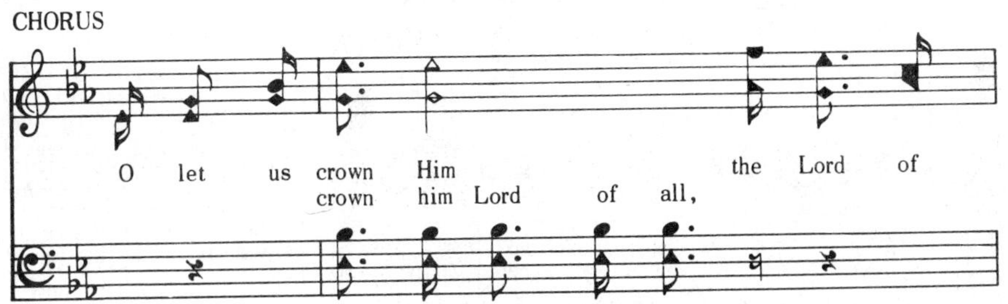
O let us crown Him the Lord of
crown him Lord of all,

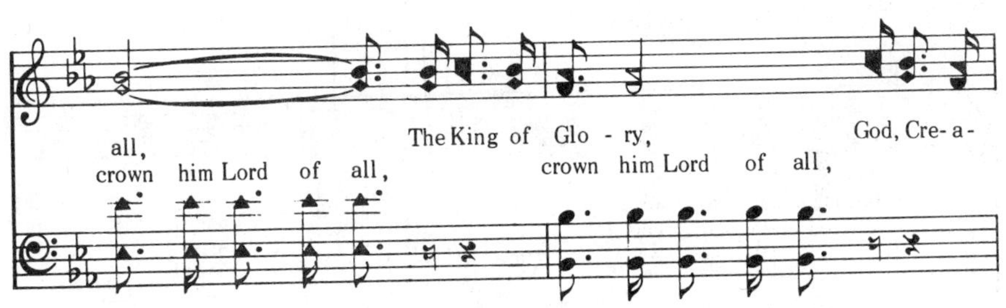
all, The King of Glo - ry, God, Cre- a -
crown him Lord of all, crown him Lord of all,

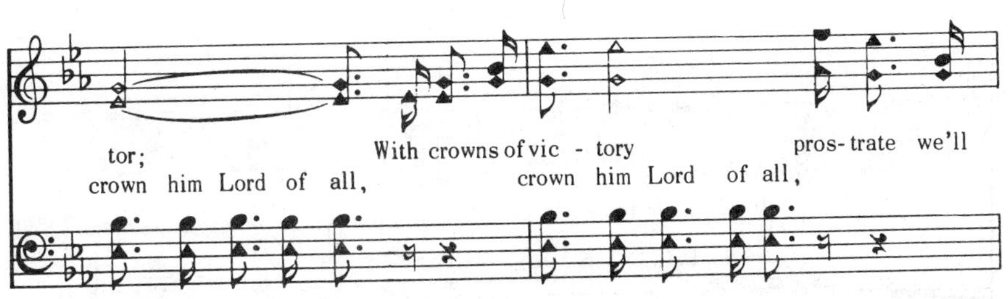
tor; With crowns of vic - tory pros- trate we'll
crown him Lord of all, crown him Lord of all,

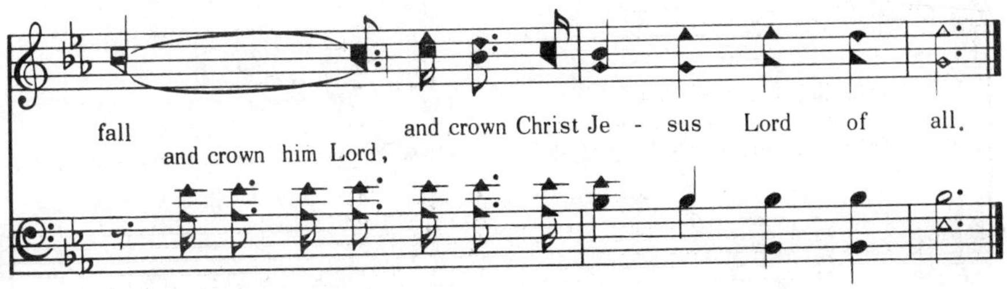
fall and crown Christ Je - sus Lord of all.
and crown him Lord,

# 810 O FOR A THOUSAND TONGUES TO SING

*My tongue shall sing aloud of Thy righteousness.* Ps. 51:14. *Blessed be the name of the Lord.* Job. 1:21.

Charles Wesley, 1707-1788

BLESSED NAME 8.8.8.8. with Ref.
M.M. 72

Ralph E. Hudson, 1843-1901

1. O for a thou-sand tongues to sing, Bless-ed be the name of the Lord!
2. Je-sus, the name that calms my fears, Bless-ed be the name of the Lord!
3. He breaks the power of can-celed sin, Bless-ed be the name of the Lord!
The glo-ries of my God and King, Bless-ed be the name of the Lord!
'Tis mu-sic in the sin-ner's ears, Bless-ed be the name of the Lord!
His blood can make the foul-est clean, Bless-ed be the name of the Lord!
Refrain
Bless-ed be the name, Bless-ed be the name, Bless-ed be the name of the Lord!
Bless-ed be the name, Bless-ed be the name, Bless-ed be the name of the Lord.

# WHEN I SAW THE CLEANSING FOUNTAIN 811

*I will sing unto the Lord as long as I live: I will sing praise to my God while I have my being.* Ps. 104:33.

I WILL PRAISE HIM 8.7.8.7 with Ref.
M.M. 69

Mrs. M. J. Harris — Mrs. M. J. Harris

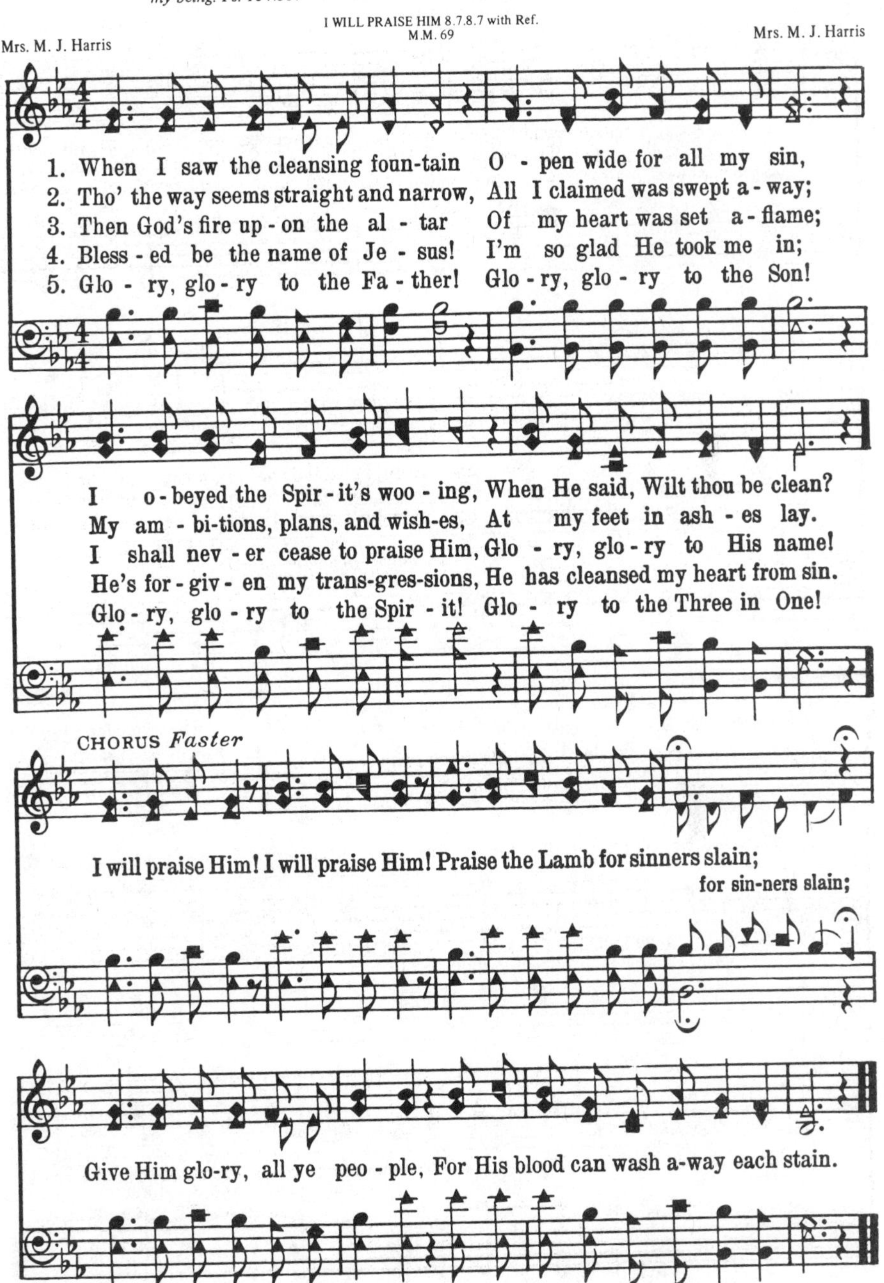
1. When I saw the cleansing foun-tain O - pen wide for all my sin,
2. Tho' the way seems straight and narrow, All I claimed was swept a - way;
3. Then God's fire up - on the al - tar Of my heart was set a - flame;
4. Bless - ed be the name of Je - sus! I'm so glad He took me in;
5. Glo - ry, glo - ry to the Fa - ther! Glo - ry, glo - ry to the Son!
I o - beyed the Spir - it's woo - ing, When He said, Wilt thou be clean?
My am - bi-tions, plans, and wish-es, At my feet in ash - es lay.
I shall nev - er cease to praise Him, Glo - ry, glo - ry to His name!
He's for - giv - en my trans-gres-sions, He has cleansed my heart from sin.
Glo - ry, glo - ry to the Spir - it! Glo - ry to the Three in One!
CHORUS Faster
I will praise Him! I will praise Him! Praise the Lamb for sinners slain;
for sin-ners slain;
Give Him glo-ry, all ye peo - ple, For His blood can wash a-way each stain.

# O, THE GREAT LOVE THE DEAR SAVIOUR HAS SHOWN

*Unto Him that loved us, and washed us from our sins in His own blood.* Rev. 1:5.

I. N. McHose, Alt.

O SUCH WONDERFUL LOVE 10.8.10.8. with Ref.
M.M. 104

I. N. McHose

1. Oh, the great love the dear Sav - iour has shown To shame - ful - ly
2. Pal - a - ces, man - sions and inns had no room For Christ, who so
3. Man of great sor - rows and home - less was he, But yet my Re -
die on the tree, Leav - ing his scep - tre and beau - ti - ful throne
joy - ful - ly came Down from yon hea - ven our path to il - lume,
deem - er and Friend, Pour - ing in in - fi - nite streams up - on me
To res - cue a sin - ner like me!
And save us from sin and from shame.
A love that can nev - er - more end.
REFRAIN.
Oh, . . . . . . such
Oh, such won - der - ful,
won - der - ful love! Oh, . . . such won - der - ful love! Je - sus, my
Oh, such won - der - ful
Sav - iour, left scep - tre and throne, To res - cue a sin - ner like me.

# JESUS WEPT, THOSE TEARS ARE OVER 813

*Jesus wept. Then said the Jews, Behold how He loved him!* Jn. 11:35, 36.

WEEPING ONE OF BETHANY
8.7.8.7. with Ref.
M.M. 76

John Ross MacDuff, 1859 (1818-1895)
Arr. J. Calvin Bushey

J. Calvin Bushey

1. Je - sus wept! those tears are o - ver, But His love is still the same;... Kins - man, Friend, and Eld - er Broth - er, Is His ev - er - last - ing name.
2. Je - sus wept! and still in glo - ry He must mark the mourn-er's tear;.... Lov - ing still to trace the sto - ry Of the hearts He strength-ened here.
3. Je - sus wept! that tear of sor - row If a leg - a- cy of love,.... Yes - ter - day, to - day, to - mor - row, He the same doth ev - er prove.
Refrain
p
Weep - ing One, weep - ing One,
Weep-ing One, weep-ing One,
Sav - iour, who can love like Thee?
p
Weep - ing One, weep - ing One,
Weep-ing One, weep-ing One,
Weep - ing One of Beth - an - y.

# TENDER LOVE OF JESUS, SO LOVELY AND SO PURE

*And to know the love of Christ, which passeth knowledge, that ye might be filled with all the fulness of God.* Eph. 3:19. *For the love of Christ constraineth us.* II Cor. 5:14.

TENDER LOVE OF JESUS
12.12.12.12. with Ref.
M.M. 66

Ruth Emswiler, 1970

Ruth Emswiler and Martha Miller, 1970
Arr. John J. Overholt, 1970

1. Ten-der love of Je-sus, so love-ly and so pure; Flow-ing thru this ves-sel,
2. Thru the pass-ing a - ges flowed down this love di-vine, Light-ing men and an-gels,
to strength-en, fill and cure All the doubt and tur-moil that's caused by sin and shame;
and caus-ing them to shine, With a heav'n-ly ra-diance, His glo - ry from a - bove,
Mak - ing me a wit - ness to His most Ho - ly name.
Sun - shine of the Spir - it, the ho - ly light of love.
Yes, love, Christ's love,
The ho - ly pres - ence, the liv - ing flame,

Pure love,
The Spir - it's wit - ness
great love;
that lauds His name;

With joy my heart is sing - ing, the things of life grow dim,

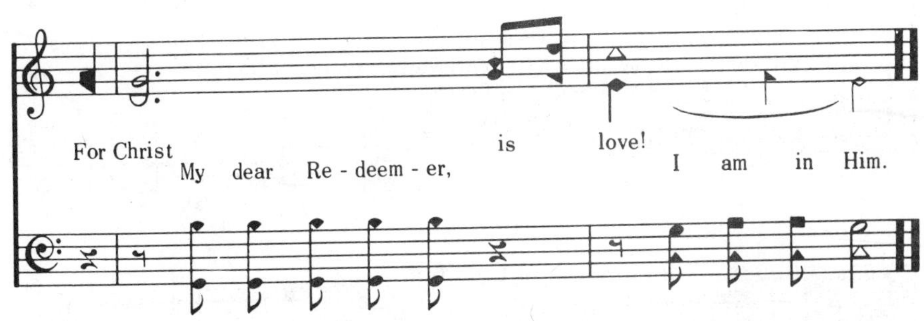
For Christ
My dear Re - deem - er,
is love!
I am in Him.

# 815 CLING TO THE BIBLE

*Great peace have they which love Thy law: and nothing shall offend them. I rejoice at Thy word, as one that findeth great spoil. Thou art near, O Lord; and all Thy commandments are truth. Thy word is a lamp unto my feet, and a light.* Ps. 119:165, 162, 151, 105.

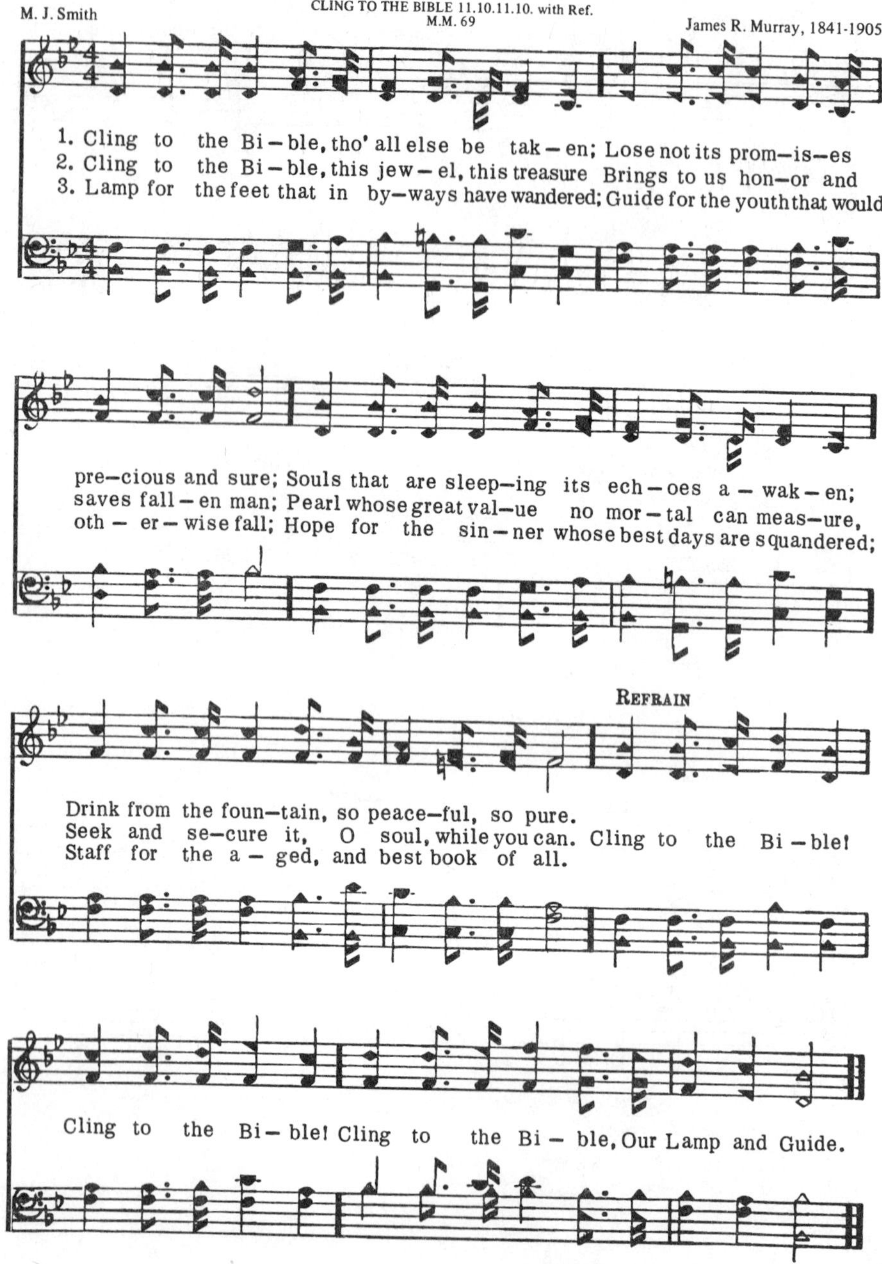
M. J. Smith
CLING TO THE BIBLE 11.10.11.10. with Ref.
M.M. 69
James R. Murray, 1841-1905
1. Cling to the Bi-ble, tho' all else be tak-en; Lose not its prom-is-es pre-cious and sure; Souls that are sleep-ing its ech-oes a-wak-en; Drink from the foun-tain, so peace-ful, so pure.
2. Cling to the Bi-ble, this jew-el, this treasure Brings to us hon-or and saves fall-en man; Pearl whose great val-ue no mor-tal can meas-ure, Seek and se-cure it, O soul, while you can.
3. Lamp for the feet that in by-ways have wandered; Guide for the youth that would oth-er-wise fall; Hope for the sin-ner whose best days are squandered; Staff for the a-ged, and best book of all.
REFRAIN
Cling to the Bi-ble! Cling to the Bi-ble! Cling to the Bi-ble, Our Lamp and Guide.

# SING THEM OVER AGAIN TO ME 816

*Search the scriptures; for in them ye think ye have eternal life: and they are they which testify of Me.* Jn. 5:39.

WONDERFUL WORDS OF LIFE 8.6.8.6.6.6.8.6.8.6.
M.M. 126

Philip P. Bliss, 1838-1876

Philip P. Bliss

1. Sing them o - ver a - gain to me, Won-der - ful words of Life;
2. Christ, the bless-ed One, gives to all Won-der - ful words of Life;
3. Sweet -ly ech - o the gos - pel call, Won-der - ful words of Life;
Let me more of their beau - ty see, Won-der - ful words of Life;
Sin - ner, list to the lov - ing call, Won-der - ful words of Life;
Of - fer par - don and peace to all, Won-der - ful words of Life;
Words of life and beau - ty, Teach me faith and du - ty;
All so free - ly giv - en, Woo - ing us to heav - en;
Je - sus, on - ly Sav - iour, Sanc - ti - fy for - ev - er.
Beau - ti - ful words, won - der - ful words, Won - der - ful words of Life;....
Beau - ti - ful words, won - der - ful words, Won-der - ful words of Life...

# 817 MARVELOUS GRACE OF OUR LOVING LORD

*For by grace are ye saved through faith; and that not of yourselves: it is the gift of God.* Eph. 2:8.

MARVELOUS GRACE 9.9.9.9. with Ref.
M.M. 84

Julia Harriette Johnston, c. 1910 (1849-1919)

Daniel Brink Towner, 1910 (1850-1919)

1 Mar - vel- ous grace of our lov - ing Lord, Grace that ex - ceeds our sin and our guilt, Yon - der on Cal - va - ry's mount out - poured, There where the blood of the Lamb was spilt.
2 Sin and de - spair like the sea waves cold, Threat-en the soul with in - fi - nite loss; Grace that is great - er, yes, grace un - told, Points to the re - fuge, the might - y cross.
3 Dark is the stain that we can - not hide, What can a - vail to wash it a - way? Look! there is flow - ing a crim - son tide; Whit - er than snow you may be to - day.
4 Mar - vel-ous, in - fi - nite, match - less grace, Free - ly be - stowed on all who be - lieve; You that are long - ing to see His face, Will you this mo - ment His grace re - ceive?
REFRAIN
Grace, grace, God's grace, Grace that will par - don and cleanse with - in; Grace, grace, God's grace, Grace that is great - er than all our sin.
Mar - vel-ous grace, in - fi-nite grace, Mar - vel-ous grace, in - fi-nite grace,

# THROUGH NIGHT AND DAY THY GLORY 818

*I will arise and go to my father.* Lk. 15:18. *As for me and my house, we will serve the Lord.* Josh. 24:15.

Jonathan Paul, (1853-1931)
*Es schaut bei Nacht und Tage*
Tr. John J. Overholt, 1965

ES SCHAUT BEI NACHT UND TAGE 7.6.7.6. with Ref.
M.M. 63

Fr. Eckhardt

1. Through night and day Thy glo – ry, In grace be – nign I see,
2. The joys of earth – ly pleas–ure, I saw as foam im – pair;
3. How of – ten would I mur – mur, By Sa – tan's pow'r o'er–thrown;
4. Now night and day Thy glo – ry Con – tin–u–ing in my heart,

And I am made to que – ry, Can I de – part from Thee?
They ne'er could be my treas – ure, For I Thy cross must bear!
Now firm I hold, and firm – er, Him, Who did sin a – tone!
Con–strains me with the sto – ry, How won – drous great Thou art!

CHORUS

My God, I have de – cid – ed E – ter – nal – ly for Thee! With – out Thy peace pro – vid – ed, and Thee, I can – not be!

## 819 NOW I COME, MY LORD AND SAVIOUR

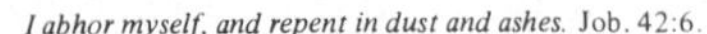

*I abhor myself, and repent in dust and ashes.* Job. 42:6.

HALLMAN 8.7.8.7.
M.M. 58

B. E. Warren — U. E. Hallman

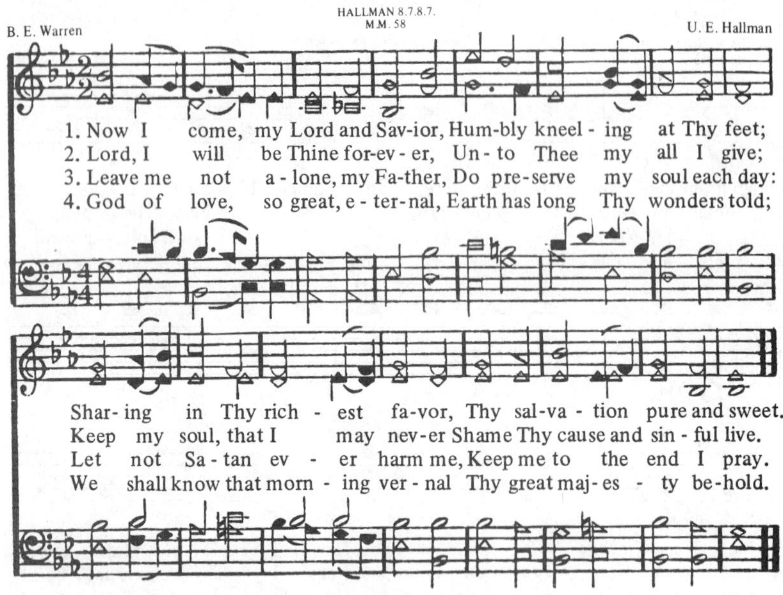
1. Now I come, my Lord and Sav-ior, Hum-bly kneel - ing at Thy feet;
2. Lord, I will be Thine for-ev - er, Un - to Thee my all I give;
3. Leave me not a - lone, my Fa-ther, Do pre-serve my soul each day:
4. God of love, so great, e - ter-nal, Earth has long Thy wonders told;
Shar- ing in Thy rich - est fa-vor, Thy sal-va - tion pure and sweet.
Keep my soul, that I may nev-er Shame Thy cause and sin - ful live.
Let not Sa - tan ev - er harm me, Keep me to the end I pray.
We shall know that morn - ing ver - nal Thy great maj- es - ty be-hold.

## 820 JUST AS I AM

*Lord, to whom shall we go? Thou hast the words of eternal life.* Jn. 6:68. *Thou art the Christ, the Son of the living God.* Mt. 16:16.

SO WIE ICH BIN 8.8.8.6.
M.M. 54

Charlotte Elliott, c. 1834 (1789-1871) — *Deutsches Lieder und Melodienbuch,* 1895

1. Just as I am, with-out one plea, But that Thy blood was shed for me,
2. Just as I am, and wait - ing not To rid my soul of one dark blot,
3. Just as I am, though tossed a - bout With many a con - flict, many a doubt,
4. Just as I am, poor, wretched, blind, Sight, rich-es, heal - ing of the mind,
5. Just as I am, Thou wilt re-ceive, Wilt welcome, par-don, cleanse, re - lieve;
6. Just as I am, Thy love un-known Hath brok-en ev - 'ry bar - rier down;
And that Thou bid'st me come to Thee, O Lamb of God, I come! I come!
To Thee whose blood can cleanse each spot, O Lamb of God, I come! I come!
Fight-ings and fears with - in, with - out, O Lamb of God, I come! I come!
Yea, all I need in Thee to find, O Lamb of God, I come! I come!
Be - cause Thy prom-ise I be - lieve, O Lamb of God, I come! I come!
Now, to be Thine, yea, Thine a - lone, O Lamb of God, I come! I come!

## STAND BEFORE THE LORD WITH JOY 821

*Rejoice in the Lord alway: and again I say, Rejoice.* Phil. 4:4.

HERRNHUT 7.7.7.7.
M.M. 72

*Jesus komm doch selbst zu mir*
Herrnhut, c. 1735; J. Thommen, 1745
C. Gregor *Choralbuch,* 1784

Wilmer D. Swope, 1970

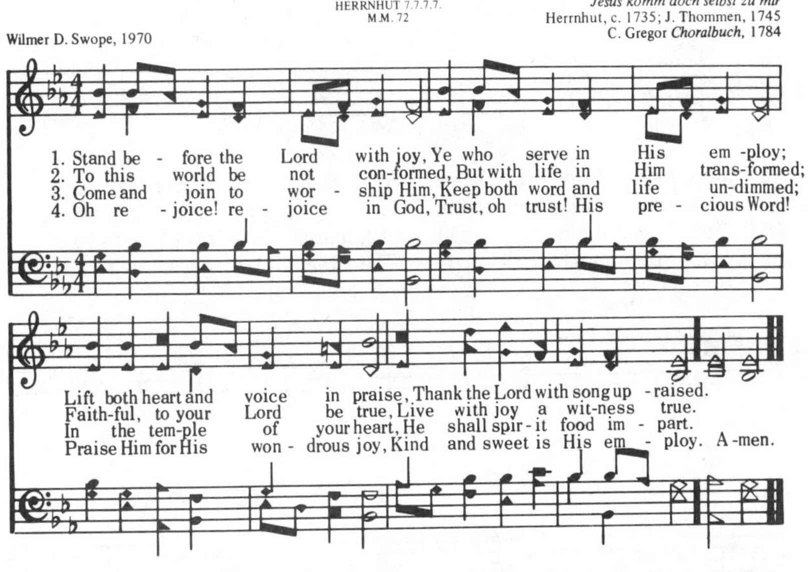
1. Stand be - fore the Lord with joy, Ye who serve in His em -ploy;
2. To this world be not con-formed, But with life in Him trans-formed;
3. Come and join to wor - ship Him, Keep both word and life un-dimmed;
4. Oh re - joice! re - joice in God, Trust, oh trust! His pre - cious Word!
Lift both heart and voice in praise, Thank the Lord with song up - raised.
Faith-ful, to your Lord be true, Live with joy a wit-ness true.
In the tem-ple of your heart, He shall spir - it food im - part.
Praise Him for His won - drous joy, Kind and sweet is His em - ploy. A -men.

## WALKING IN SUNLIGHT 822

*As sorrowful, yet alway rejoicing.* II Cor. 6:10.

WALKING IN SUNLIGHT 10.9.10.9.
M.M. 144

H. J. Zelley, 1859-1942

G. H. Cook (20th Century)

1. Walk-ing in sun-light all of my jour-ney, O-ver the mountains, thro' the deep vale;
2. Shad-ows around me, shadows above me, Nev-er conceal my Savior and Guide;
3. In the bright sun-light, ev-er re - joic - ing, Pressing my way to mansions above;
FINE
Je - sus has said, "I'll nev-er forsake thee," Promise divine that never can fail.
He is the light, in Him is no dark-ness, Ev-er I'm walking close to His side.
Singing His prais-es, glad-ly I'm walk-ing, Walking in sunlight, sunlight of love.
D.S.—Hal - le - lu - jah! I am re - joic - ing, Singing His prais-es, Je - sus is mine!
CHORUS
Heav-en-ly sun-light, heav-en-ly sun-light, Flooding my soul with glory di - vine;
D. S.

# 823 REJOICE, YE PURE IN HEART

*I will be glad and rejoice in Thee: I will sing praise to Thy name, O Thou most High.* Ps. 9:2.

Edward H. Plumtre, 1821-1891 — MARION 6.6.8.6. with Ref. M.M. 72 — Arthur H. Messiter, 1834-1916

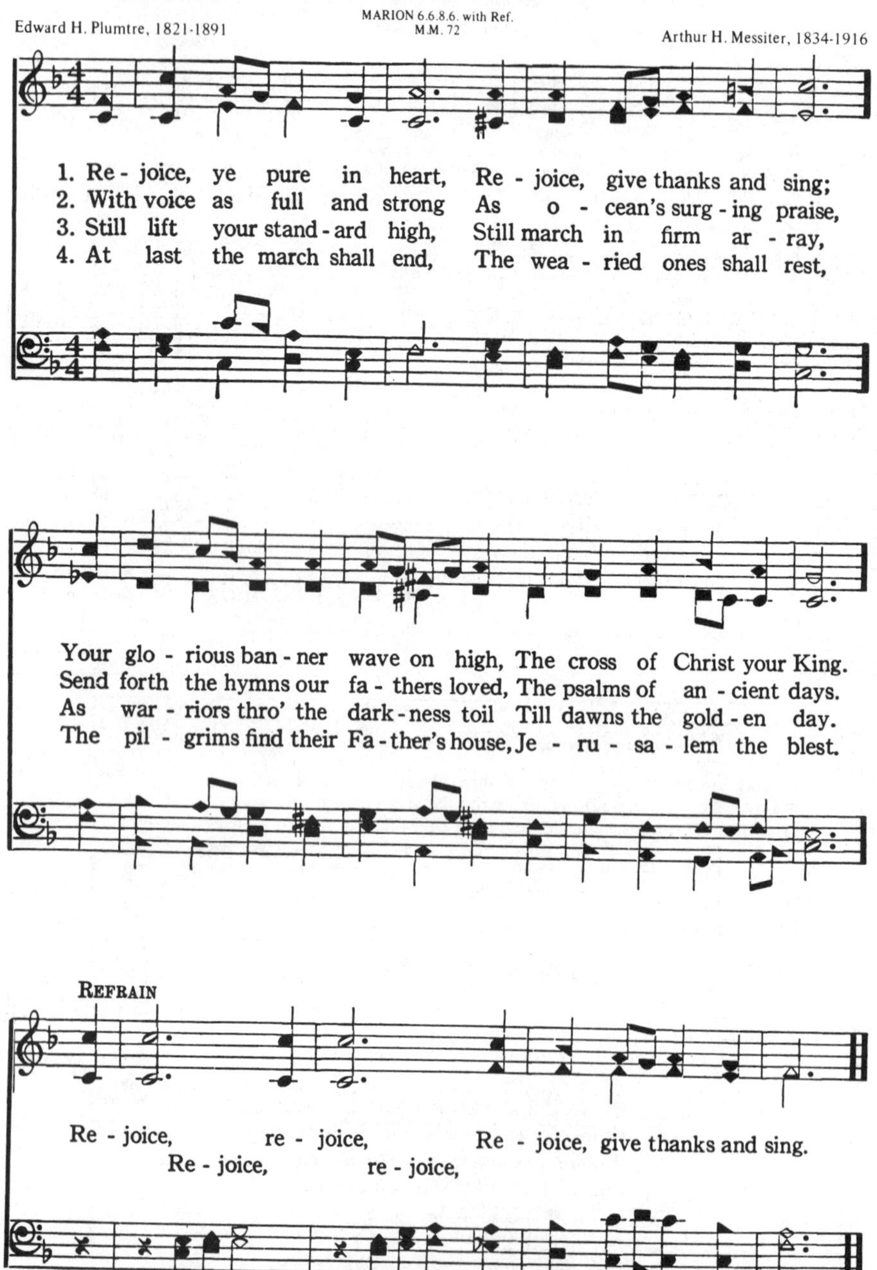
1. Re - joice, ye pure in heart, Re - joice, give thanks and sing;
2. With voice as full and strong As o - cean's surg - ing praise,
3. Still lift your stand - ard high, Still march in firm ar - ray,
4. At last the march shall end, The wea - ried ones shall rest,
Your glo - rious ban - ner wave on high, The cross of Christ your King.
Send forth the hymns our fa - thers loved, The psalms of an - cient days.
As war - riors thro' the dark - ness toil Till dawns the gold - en day.
The pil - grims find their Fa - ther's house, Je - ru - sa - lem the blest.
REFRAIN
Re - joice, re - joice, Re - joice, give thanks and sing.
Re - joice, re - joice,

# GIVE TO OUR GOD IMMORTAL PRAISE 824

*By Him therefore let us offer the sacrifice of praise to God continually, that is, the fruit of our lips giving thanks to His name.* Heb. 13:15.

Based on Psalm 136
Isaac Watts, 1719 (1674-1748)

WARRINGTON L.M. 8.8.8.8.
M.M. 88

Ralph Harrison, 1784 (1748-1810)

1 Give to our God im - mor - tal praise; Mer - cy and truth are all His ways: Won - ders of grace to God be - long; Re - peat His mer - cies in your song.
2 Give to the Lord of lords re - nown; The King of kings with glo - ry crown; His mer - cies ev - er shall en - dure, When lords and kings are known no more.
3 He built the earth, He spread the sky, And fixed the star - ry lights on high: Won - ders of grace to God be - long; Re - peat His mer - cies in your song.
4 He fills the sun with morn - ing light; He bids the moon di - rect the night: His mer - cies ev - er shall en - dure, When suns and moons shall shine no more. A - men.

5 He sent His Son with power to save
From guilt, and darkness, and the grave:
Wonders of grace to God belong;
Repeat His mercies in your song.

6 Through this vain world He guides our feet,
And leads us to His heav'nly seat:
His mercies ever shall endure,
When this vain world shall be no more.

# 825 EACH STEP I TAKE

*The steps of a good man are ordered by the Lord.* Ps. 37:23.

William Elmo Mercer, (b. 1932)

EACH STEP I TAKE 11.10.11.9. with Ref.
M.M. 58

William Elmo Mercer

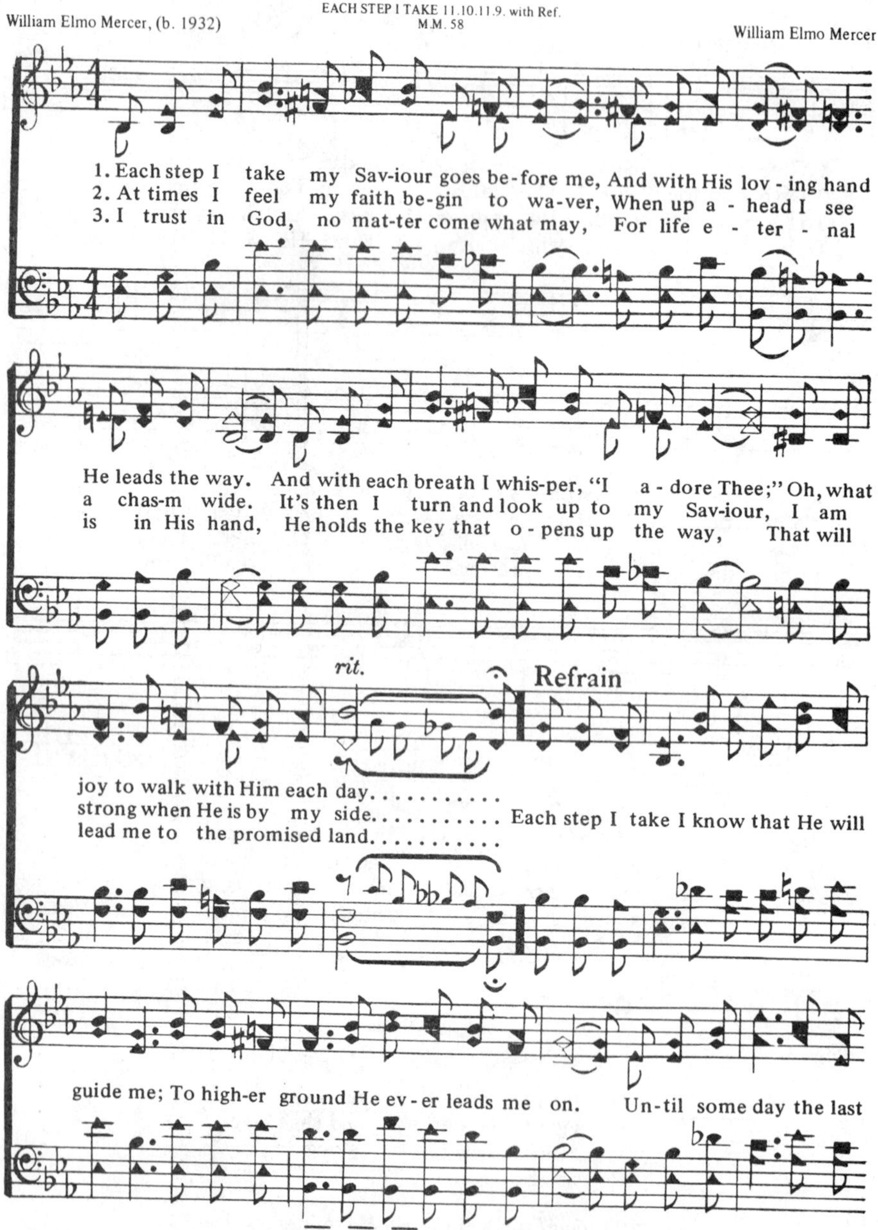
1. Each step I take my Sav-iour goes be-fore me, And with His lov - ing hand
2. At times I feel my faith be-gin to wa-ver, When up a - head I see
3. I trust in God, no mat-ter come what may, For life e - ter - nal
He leads the way. And with each breath I whis-per, "I a - dore Thee;" Oh, what
a chas-m wide. It's then I turn and look up to my Sav-iour, I am
is in His hand, He holds the key that o - pens up the way, That will
rit.
Refrain
joy to walk with Him each day...........
strong when He is by my side...........
lead me to the promised land...........
Each step I take I know that He will
guide me; To high-er ground He ev - er leads me on. Un-til some day the last

rit.
step will be tak - en, Each step I take just leads me clos - er home.

CHRISTIAN LIFE: FELLOWSHIP, DISCIPLESHIP

## WHAT A FELLOWSHIP, WHAT A JOY DIVINE 826

*The eternal God is thy refuge, and underneath are the everlasting arms.* Deut. 33:27.

LEANING ON THE EVERLASTING ARMS 10.9.10.9. with Ref.
M.M. 72

Elisha A. Hoffman, 1839-1929

Anthony J. Showalter, 1858-1924

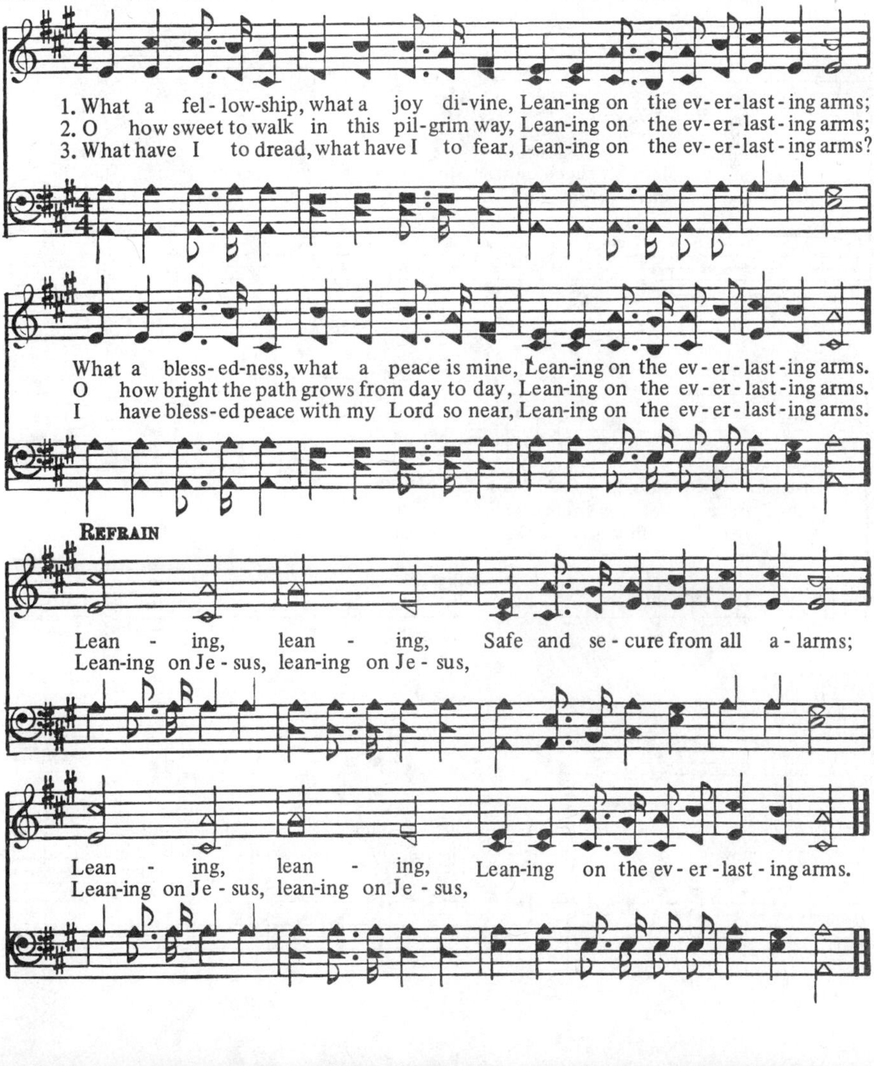

1. What a fel - low-ship, what a joy di-vine, Lean-ing on the ev-er-last-ing arms;
2. O how sweet to walk in this pil-grim way, Lean-ing on the ev-er-last-ing arms;
3. What have I to dread, what have I to fear, Lean-ing on the ev-er-last-ing arms?

What a bless-ed-ness, what a peace is mine, Lean-ing on the ev-er-last-ing arms.
O how bright the path grows from day to day, Lean-ing on the ev-er-last-ing arms.
I have bless-ed peace with my Lord so near, Lean-ing on the ev-er-last-ing arms.

REFRAIN

Lean - ing, lean - ing, Safe and se - cure from all a - larms;
Lean-ing on Je - sus, lean-ing on Je - sus,

Lean - ing, lean - ing, Lean-ing on the ev - er - last - ing arms.
Lean-ing on Je - sus, lean-ing on Je - sus,

# 827 MY SHEEP KNOW MY VOICE

*My sheep hear My voice, and I know them, and they follow Me.* Jn. 10:27.

1st Stanza, Cho., Herbert Buffum
MY SHEEP KNOW MY VOICE
M.M. 100
Herbert Buffum
Arr. I. G. Martin
1. My sheep know my voice, And the path that I take, They fol - low where-ever I go; My sheep know my voice And come at my call, But a stranger's voice do they not know.
2. My sheep know my voice, And the pas - tures of green, Where I lead them so oft - en to feed; My sheep know my voice And the cool sparkling stream Where beside its still wa - ters I lead.
3. My sheep know my voice, And the val - ley of death Thro' which I shall lead them some day; But no dan - ger nor harm Can touch one of them, For I will be with them al - way.
CHORUS
My sheep know my voice. day by day, My sheep know my voice day by day, They a - bide in the fold, They go not a-stray,
My sheep know my voice, And day by day, They a - bide in the fold

And go not a - stray, They love me be,
A - bide in the fold, They go not a - stray, They love me be - cause I

cause I have made them my choice, And they
made them my choice, They love me be- cause I made them my choice, They

fol - low my call, For my sheep know my voice.
fol - low my call, They fol - low my call, my sheep know my voice.

# 828 I SHALL NOT WANT

*The Lord is my Shepherd; I shall not want.* Ps. 23:1.

I SHALL NOT WANT L.M. 8.8.8.8. with Ref.
M.M. 58

Mrs. C. H. Morris, 1862-1929

Mrs. C. H. Morris
Harmony Arr. for mixed voices, John J. Overholt, 1972

1. I shall not want while Je-sus leads, Nor hun-ger while my soul He feeds;
My Guide for ev-er-more is He, His rod and staff they com-fort me.

2. E'en tho' I pass thro' death's dark vale, My rod of com-fort shall not fail;
The val-ley's shade shall not a-larm, I shall not want or suf-fer harm.

3. I shall not want for joy, for lo, My cup with grace shall o-ver-flow;
My soul by pow'r di-vine re-stored, Love's oil up-on my head out-poured.

4. My song thro' life shall ev-er be, Good-ness and mer-cy fol-low me,
And in God's house for-ev-er-more, I'll dwell on Can-aan's hap-py shore.

CHORUS

I shall not want, I shall not want, The Lord my Shep-herd is,
In pas-tures green He feed-eth me, By wa-ters still He lead-eth me,
I shall not want, I shall not want: The Lord my Shep-herd is.

# SWEET ARE THE PROMISES 829

*For this God is our God for ever and ever: He will be our guide even unto death.* Ps. 48:14.

WHERE HE LEADS I'LL FOLLOW 6.4.12.6.4.12.
M.M. 66
William A. Ogden, 1841-1897
William A. Ogden
1. Sweet are the prom-is-es, Kind is the word, Dear-er far than an - y mes-sage man ev - er heard; Pure was the mind of Christ, Sin - less I see; He the great ex- am - ple is, and pat - tern for me.
2. Sweet is the ten-der love Je-sus hath shown, Sweeter far than an - y love that mortals have known; Kind to the err-ing one, Faith-ful is He; He the great ex- am - ple is, and pat - tern for me.
3. List to His loving words, "Come un - to Me!" Wea-ry, heav-y - la-den, there is sweet rest for thee; Trust in His prom-is-es, Faithful and sure; Lean up - on the Sav-iour, and thy soul is se-cure.
CHORUS
Where..... ........ He leads I'll fol - - - low, Fol - - - - low all the way;
Where He leads I'll fol - low, Where He leads I'll fol-low, Fol-low all the way, yes, fol - low all the way;
Where....... He leads I'll fol - - low, Fol-low Je-sus ev - 'ry day.
Where He leads I'll follow, Where He leads I'll follow,

# 830 WHERE HE MAY LEAD ME I WILL GO

*He leadeth me in the paths of righteousness.* Ps. 23:3.

I REMEMBER CALVARY L.M. 8.8.8.8. with Ref.
M.M. 56

W. C. Martin (19th Century) James M. Black, 1856-1938

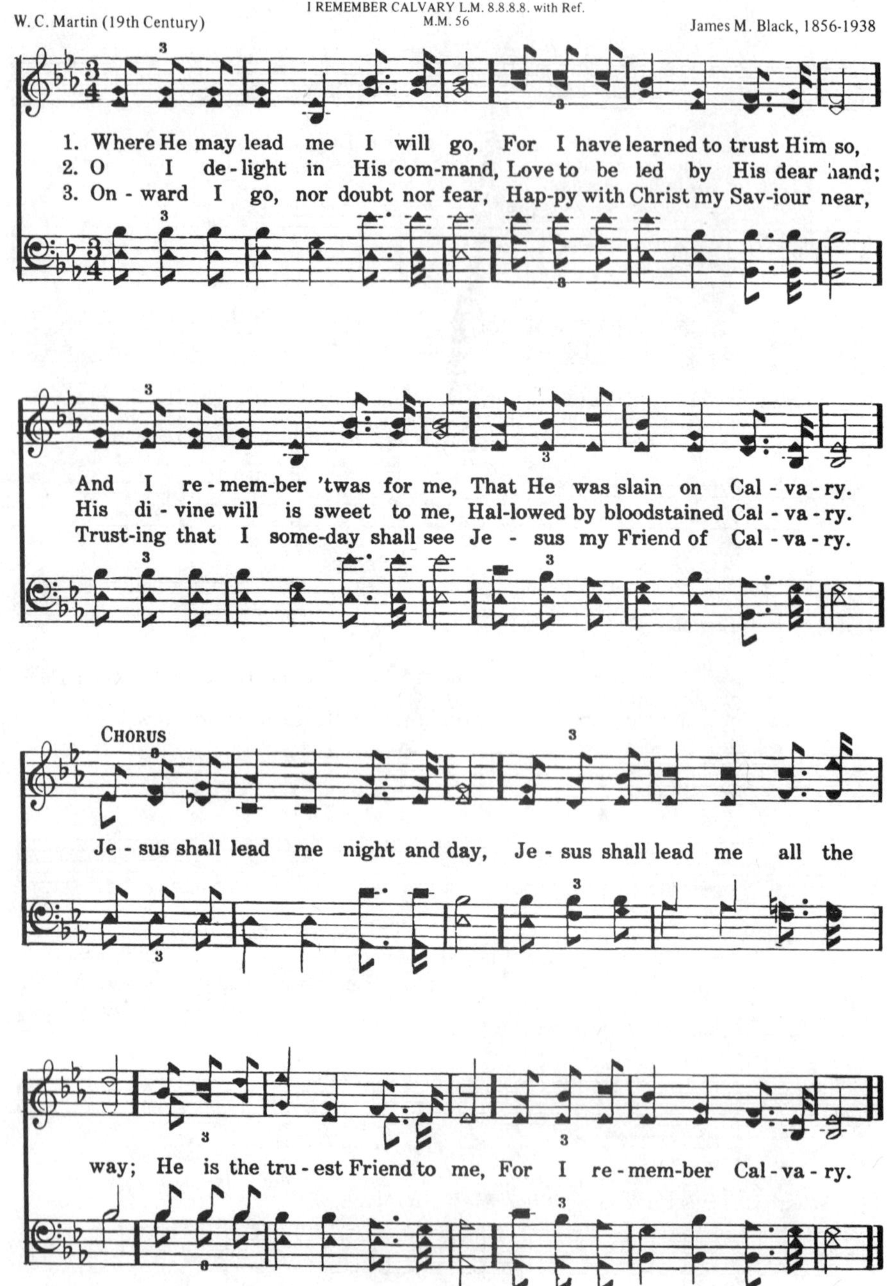
1. Where He may lead me I will go, For I have learned to trust Him so,
2. O I de-light in His com-mand, Love to be led by His dear hand;
3. On-ward I go, nor doubt nor fear, Hap-py with Christ my Sav-iour near,
And I re-mem-ber 'twas for me, That He was slain on Cal-va-ry.
His di-vine will is sweet to me, Hal-lowed by bloodstained Cal-va-ry.
Trust-ing that I some-day shall see Je-sus my Friend of Cal-va-ry.
CHORUS
Je-sus shall lead me night and day, Je-sus shall lead me all the
way; He is the tru-est Friend to me, For I re-mem-ber Cal-va-ry.

# I WOULD NOT HAVE MY WAY 831

*Not My will, but Thine, be done.* Lk. 22:42.

I WOULD NOT HAVE MY WAY 10.10.10.10. with Ref.
M.M. 58

Mrs. W. H. Olinger

Andrew L. Byers, 1869-1952

1. I would not have my way, dear Lord, but Thine; I would not walk alone, for I might fall: Thou knowest what is best, so lead me on; I'll listen, Lord, I'll hear Thy faintest call.

2. I would not have my way, dear Lord, but Thine; E'en tho' the road be rough I will not fear: E'en tho' the sun refuse sometimes to shine, I'll walk by faith and know that Thou art near,

3. I would not have my way, dear Lord, but Thine; I do not ask for beds with flow'rs entwined: Thy way might be some mountain-side to climb, Some wand'ring sheep or some lost lamb to find.

**Refrain**

I would not have my way, dear Lord, but Thine; O keep me for Thyself and Thine alone: When shadows fall and darkest night has come, I'll trust in Thee to guide me safely home.

# 832 I KNOW THAT MY REDEEMER LIVETH

*I know that my Redeemer liveth; and that He shall stand at the latter day upon the earth.* Job 19:25.
*And hereby we do know that we know Him, if we keep His commandments.* I Jn. 2:3.

I KNOW THAT MY REDEEMER LIVETH 9.8.9.8. with Ref.
M.M. 63

Jessie Brown Pounds, 1893 (1861-1921)

James H. Filmore, 1893 (1849-1936)

1. I know that my Re-deem-er liv - eth, And on the earth...... a-gain shall stand;
2. I know His promise nev-er fail - eth, The word He speaks,.... it can-not die;
3. I know my mansion He pre-par - eth, That where He is........ there I may be;
I know e - ter - nal life He giv - eth, That grace and pow'r........ are in His hand.
That cru - el death my flesh as - sail - eth, Yet I shall see .......... Him by and by.
O won-drous tho't, for me He car - eth, And He at last......... will come for me.
CHORUS
I know, I know......... that Je - sus liv - eth, And on the earth........... a-gain shall stand;
I know, I know,
And on the earth
I know, I know...... that life He giv-eth, That grace and pow'r...... are in His hand.
I know, I know
That grace and pow'r

# I KNOW THAT MY REDEEMER LIVES 833

*As for our Redeemer, the Lord of hosts is His name, the Holy One of Israel.* Is. 47:4. *If God be for us, who can be against us . . . Who shall separate us from the love of Christ?* Rom. 8:31, 35.

MY REDEEMER LIVES 8.8.8.8.
M.M. 69

Arr. M. G. Prescott — Arr. M. G. Prescott

1. I know that my Re-deem-er lives, That he's pre-pared a home for me, And crowns of vic-to-ry he gives To those who would his chil-dren be.
2. I'm trust-ing Je-sus Christ for all,.... I know his blood a-tones for me, I'm list-'ning for the gen-tle call To say, "The Mas-ter wait-eth thee."
3. And now, be-wil-dered at the thought, I stand and won-der at his love, How he from heav'n to earth was brought To die, that I might live a-bove.
4. I know that soon my Lord will come, I know he will not tar-ry long, I know he soon will call me home To sing with joy the heav'n-ly song.
Fine.
CHORUS.
Then ask me not to min-gle on A-mid the gay and thought-less throng,
D. C.—For I am on-ly wait-ing here,.... To hear the sum-mons, "Child, come home;" For I am on-ly wait-ing here, To hear the sum-mons, "Child, come home."
D. C.

# 834 IN THE RIFTED ROCK I'M RESTING

*Neither is there any rock like our God.* I Sam. 2:2. *My God is the rock of my refuge.* Ps. 94:22.

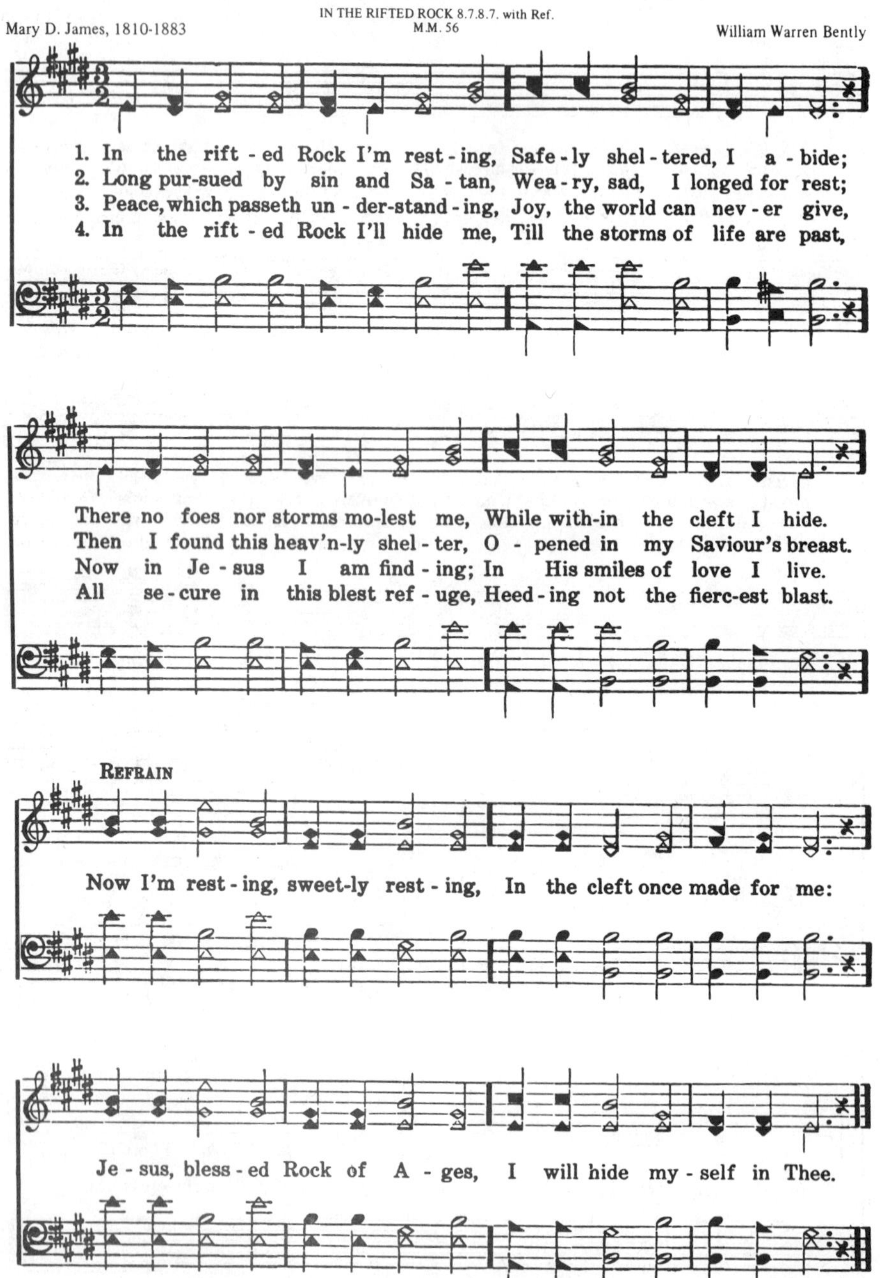
IN THE RIFTED ROCK 8.7.8.7. with Ref.
M.M. 56
Mary D. James, 1810-1883
William Warren Bently
1. In the rift - ed Rock I'm rest - ing, Safe - ly shel - tered, I a - bide;
2. Long pur-sued by sin and Sa - tan, Wea - ry, sad, I longed for rest;
3. Peace, which passeth un - der-stand - ing, Joy, the world can nev - er give,
4. In the rift - ed Rock I'll hide me, Till the storms of life are past,
There no foes nor storms mo-lest me, While with-in the cleft I hide.
Then I found this heav'n-ly shel - ter, O - pened in my Saviour's breast.
Now in Je - sus I am find - ing; In His smiles of love I live.
All se - cure in this blest ref - uge, Heed - ing not the fierc-est blast.
Refrain
Now I'm rest - ing, sweet-ly rest - ing, In the cleft once made for me:
Je - sus, bless - ed Rock of A - ges, I will hide my - self in Thee.

# WHEN PEACE LIKE A RIVER 835

*Is it well with thee? . . . And she answered, It is well.* II Kings 4:26.

IT IS WELL 11.8.11.9. with Ref.
M.M. 66
Horatio G. Spafford, 1873 (1828-1888)
Philip Paul Bliss, 1876 (1838-1876)
1 When peace, like a river, attendeth my way, When sorrows like sea billows roll; Whatever my lot, Thou hast taught me to say, It is well, it is well with my soul.
2 Though Satan should buffet, though trials should come, Let this blest assurance control, That Christ hath regarded my helpless estate, And hath shed His own blood for my soul.
3 My sin! O the bliss of this glorious thought, My sin! not in part, but the whole, Is nailed to His cross and I bear it no more, Praise the Lord, praise the Lord, O my soul!
4 And, Lord, haste the day when the faith shall be sight, The clouds be rolled back as a scroll, The trump shall resound and the Lord shall descend, "Even so," it is well with my soul.
REFRAIN
It is well with my soul, It is well, it is well with my soul.
It is well with my soul,

# 836 JESUS, ROSE OF SHARON

*I am the rose of Sharon, and the lily of the valleys.* Song of Sol. 2:1.

JESUS, ROSE OF SHARON 11.11.11.11. with ref.
M.M. 66

Ida A. Guirey — Charles H. Gabriel (1856-1932)

1. Je - sus, Rose of Shar - on, bloom with - in my heart; Beau - ties of Thy
2. Je - sus, Rose of Shar - on, sweet - er far to see Than the fair - est
3. Je - sus, Rose of Shar - on, balm for ev - 'ry ill, May Thy ten - der
4. Je - sus, Rose of Shar - on, bloom for - ev - er - more; Be Thy glo - ry
truth and ho - li - ness im - part, That wher - e'er I go my life may
flow'rs of earth could ev - er be, Fill my life com - plete - ly, add - ing
mer - cy's heal - ing pow'r dis - til For af - flic - ted souls of wea - ry,
seen on earth from shore to shore, Till the na - tions own Thy sov' - reign -
shed a - broad Fra - grance of the knowledge of the love of God.
more each day Of Thy grace di - vine and pu - ri - ty, I pray.
bur - dened men, Giv - ing need - y mor - tals health and hope a - gain.
ty com - plete, Lay their hon - ors down and wor - ship at Thy feet.
REFRAIN
Je - sus, . . . . . Rose of Shar - on, . . . . .
Bless - ed Je - sus, Rose of Shar - on,
Bloom in ra - diance and in love with - in my heart.

# LORD, I AM FONDLY, EARNESTLY LONGING 837

*With joy shall ye draw water out of the wells of salvation.* Is. 12:3.

OPEN THE WELLS OF SALVATION 10.9.10.9. with Ref.
M.M. 116

Elisha A. Hoffman c. 1902 (1839-1929) — Charles Edward Pollock, c. 1902 (b. 1853)

*Earnestly.*
1. Lord, I am fond - ly, ear - nest - ly long - ing In - to thy ho - ly like-ness to grow; Thirsting for more and deep-er com-mun-ion, Yearning thy love more ful - ly to know.
2. Dead to the world would I be, O Fa - ther! Dead un - to sin, a - live un - to thee; Cru - ci - fy all the earth-ly with - in me, Emptied of sin and self may I be.
3. I would be thine, and serve thee for - ev - er, Filled with thy spir - it, lost in thy love; Come to my heart, Lord, come with annointing, Showers of grace send down from a - bove.
REFRAIN.
O - pen the wells of grace and sal - va - tion, Pour the rich streams deep in - to my heart; Cleanse and re - fine my tho't and af - fec-tion, Seal me and make me pure as thou art.
O - pen the wells of grace and sal - va - tion, Pour the rich streams deep in - to my heart;
Cleanse and re-fine my tho't and af - fec - tion, Seal me and make me pure as thou art.

# 838 LIFT ME UP ABOVE THE SHADOWS

*I will extol Thee, O Lord; for Thou hast lifted me up.* Ps. 30:1. *The shadows of the evening are stretched out.* Jer. 6:4.

Herbert Buffum
3rd v. Robert Emmett Winsett
LIFT ME UP ABOVE THE SHADOWS
M.M. 63
Robert Emmett Winsett, 1876-1952
1. Lift me up a-bove the shad-ows,Plant my feet on high - er ground,Lift me
2. Lift me up a-bove the shad-ows,For the storms are rag - ing high, Lift me
3. Lift me up a-bove the shad-ows,Out of sor-row in - to joy; Lift me
4. Lift us up a-bove the shad-ows,When to earth You come a - gain, Let us
up a-bove the clouds,Lord,Where the pure sun-shine is found.Lift me up a -
up, my bless-ed Sav-ior,Let me to Thy bos-om fly;There no e - vil
up a - bove my grief,Lord,Give me gold for my al - loy;Then,when death must
be in the as-sem-bly,As Thy Bride to ev - er reign;In Thy king-dom,
bove my weak-ness, lift me up in - to Thy strength,Lift me up a - bove the
thing can touch me, o - ver on the shin - ing side, Lift me up a - bove the
claim my spir - it and the storms of life are past, Lift me up a - bove the
full of glo - ry, with our friends we'll ev - er be, Lift us up a - bove the
CHORUS
shad-ows,Till I stand with Thee at length.Lift me up a-
shad-ows,Let me ev - er-more a - bide.
shad-ows,Till in heav'n I stand at last.
shad-ows,There to dwell e - ter - nal - ly. Lift me up a - bove the shad-ows,
bove the shad-ows, Lift me up and
lift me up a - bove the shad-ows, Lift me up and let me stand;

let me stand on the moun - - - - - tain tops of
lift me up and let me stand on the moun-tain tops of glo - ry, on the
glo - ry, Let me dwell in Beu-lah land.
moun-tain tops of glo-ry, Let me dwell in Beu-lah land, O let me dwell in Beulah land.

# WHEN I BEHOLD THE RISEN LORD 839

*Mary Magdalene came and told the disciples that she had seen the Lord . . . Then were the disciples glad, when they saw the Lord.* Jn. 20:18, 20.

Brownie May Burkholder, 1966 (b. 1912)
Alt. by Compiler, 1972

ROCKINGHAM OLD L.M. 8.8.8.8.
M.M. 88

A. Williams, 1780
Adapted Edward Miller, 1790 (1731-1807)
Harmony arr. by Compiler, 1965

1. When I behold the risen Lord,
He rose that resurrection day,
All praise to Him, blest be His name,
Lo, all my sins are washed away.

2. And when I see the souls of men,
In Satan's grip on ev'ry side,
Oh, move me by Thy Spirit Lord,
Help me to show them Thou hast died.

3. Oh may I serve them day by day,
In prayer and supplication be,
Raising their names to Thee on high,
In lowly, loving service free.

4. All those I meet along life's way,
Lord, help me serve as unto Thee,
Blest by Thy Spirit, hear my plea,
May they be ever drawn to Thee.

5. Oh, fill me with Thy Spirit, Lord, Fill Thou my heart with love divine
That souls may see Thee, Lord, in me, The praise, the glory be all Thine!

# 840 WHEN STORMS OF LIFE

*He . . . continued all night in prayer.* Lk. 6:12. *He went up into a mountain apart to pray: and when the evening was come, He was there alone.* Mt. 14:23.

ALONE WITH GOD 9.8.9.8. with Ref.
M.M. 60
Johnson Oatman Jr., 1856-1926
William J. Kirkpatrick, 1838-1921
1. When storms of life are round me beat - ing, When rough the path that I have trod,
2. What tho' the clouds have gathered o'er me? What tho' I've passed beneath the rod?
3. 'Tis there I find new strength for du - ty, As o'er the sands of time I plod,
4. And when I see the mo-ment near - ing When I shall sleep be-neath the sod,
With - in my clos-et door re-treat - ing, I love to be a - lone with God.
God's perfect will there lies be - fore me, When I am thus a - lone with God.
I see the King in all His beau - ty, While resting there a - lone with God.
When time with me is dis - ap - pear - ing, I want to be a - lone with God.
REFRAIN
A - lone with God, . . . . . . the world for - bid - den, A - lone with
A - lone with God,
God, . . . . . O blest re - treat! A - lone with God, . . . .
A - lone with God,
A-lone with God,
and in Him hid - den, To hold with Him . . . . . com-mun - ion sweet.
To hold with Him
rit.

# I HAVE A SONG I LOVE TO SING 841

*And they sung a new song . . . Thou was slain, and hast redeemed us . . . by Thy blood.* Rev. 5:9. *And they sing the song of Moses . . . and the song of the Lamb.* Rev. 15:3. *I will sing unto the Lord, for He hath triumphed gloriously.* Ex. 15:1.

Edwin Othello Excell, 1851-1921

REDEEMED C.M. 8.6.8.6. with Ref.
M.M. 76

E. O. Excell

1. I have a song I love to sing, Since I have been re - deemed,
2. I have a Christ that sat - is - fies, Since I have been re - deemed;
3. I have a wit - ness bright and clear, Since I have been re - deemed,
4. I have a home pre-pared for me, Since I have been re - deemed,
Of my Re - deem - er, Sav - iour, King, Since I have been re-deemed.
To do His will my high - est prize, Since I have been re-deemed.
Dis - pel - ling ev - ery doubt and fear, Since I have been re-deemed.
Where I shall dwell e - ter - nal - ly, Since I have been re-deemed.
CHORUS
Since I . . . . . have been re-deemed, Since I have been re-
Since I have been re-deemed, Since I have been re-deemed,
deemed, I will glo - ry in His name; Since I . . . . . have been re-
Since I have been re-deemed, Since
deemed, I will glo - ry in my Sav - iour's name.
I have been re - deemed.

# 842 MY FAITH HAS FOUND A RESTING PLACE

*My heart is fixed, O God, my heart is fixed: I will sing and give praise.* Ps. 57:7. *Be ye steadfast, unmoveable.* I Cor. 15:58. *Our epistle written in our hearts, known and read of all men.* II Cor. 3:2.

Lidie H. Edmunds
Alt. by Compiler, 1972

LANDAS C.M. 8.6.8.6. with Ref.
M.M. 63

Norwegian Folk Melody
Arr. by William James Kirkpatrick, 1839-1921

1. My faith has found a rest-ing place, In Je - sus' blood and creed;
2. E - nough for me that Je - sus saves, This ends my fear and doubt;
3. My heart is lean - ing on the Word, The writ - ten Word of God,
4. My great Phy - si - cian heals the sick, The lost He came to save;
I trust the Ev - er - liv - ing One, His wounds for me shall plead.
A need - y soul I come to Him, He'll nev - er cast me out.
Sal - va - tion by my Sav - iour's name, Sal - va - tion thro' His blood.
For me His pre - cious blood He shed, For me His life He gave.
REFRAIN
I need no oth - er ar - gu - ment, I need no oth - er plea,
It is e - nough that Je - sus died, And that He died for me.

# ALL MY LIFE LONG I HAD PANTED 843

*I found Him Whom my soul loveth.* Song of Sol. 3:4. *We have found the Messias, which is, being interpreted, the Christ.* Jn. 1:41.

SATISFIED 8.7.8.7. with Ref.
M.M. 76

Clara Tear Williams, 1858-1937

Ralph E. Hudson, 1843-1901

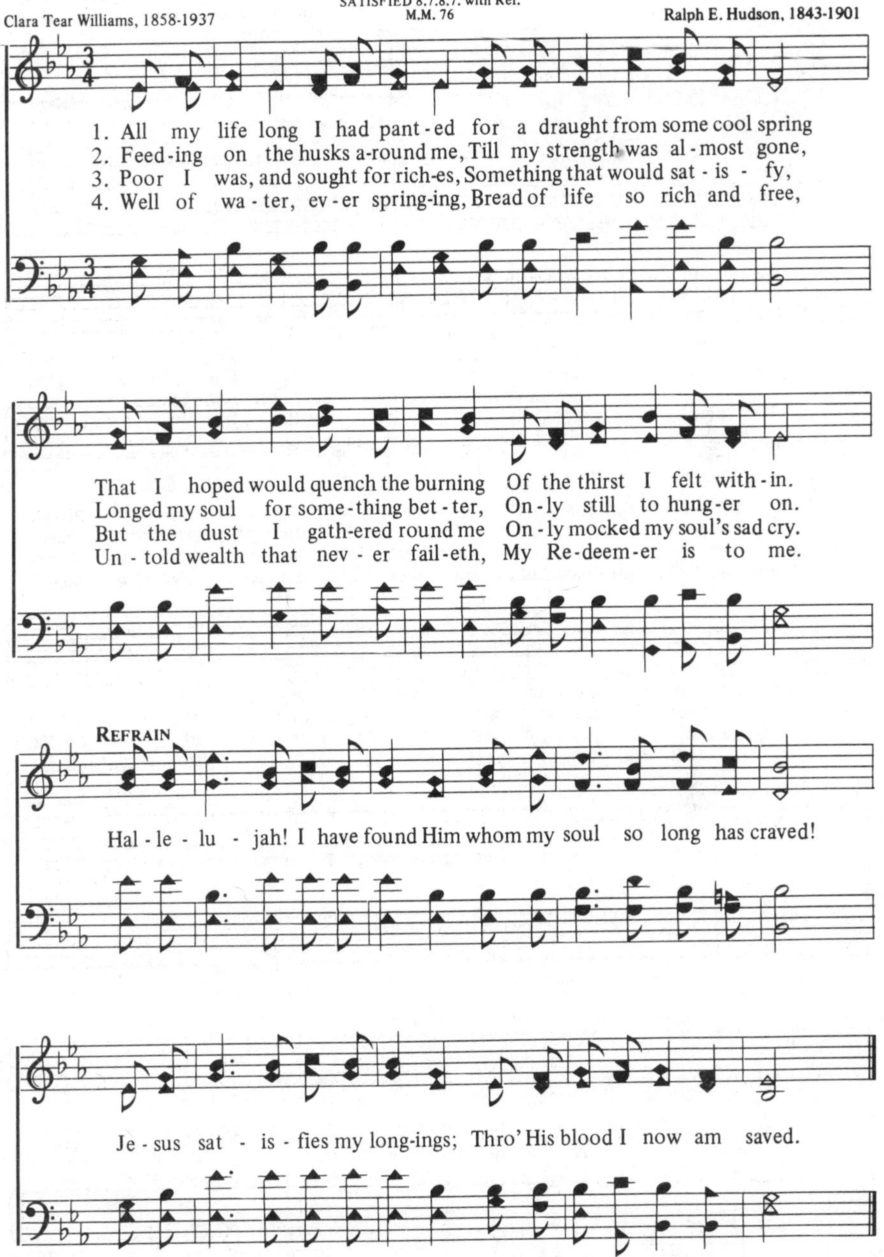
1. All my life long I had pant-ed for a draught from some cool spring
2. Feed-ing on the husks a-round me, Till my strength was al-most gone,
3. Poor I was, and sought for rich-es, Something that would sat-is-fy,
4. Well of wa-ter, ev-er spring-ing, Bread of life so rich and free,
That I hoped would quench the burning Of the thirst I felt with-in.
Longed my soul for some-thing bet-ter, On-ly still to hung-er on.
But the dust I gath-ered round me On-ly mocked my soul's sad cry.
Un-told wealth that nev-er fail-eth, My Re-deem-er is to me.
REFRAIN
Hal-le-lu-jah! I have found Him whom my soul so long has craved!
Je-sus sat-is-fies my long-ings; Thro' His blood I now am saved.

# 844 STAND UP, STAND UP FOR JESUS

*Stand fast in the faith, quit you like men, be strong.* I Cor. 16:13.

WEBB 7.6.7.6.D.
M.M. 76

George Duffield, Jr., 1858 (1818-1888) George James Webb, 1830 (1803-1887)

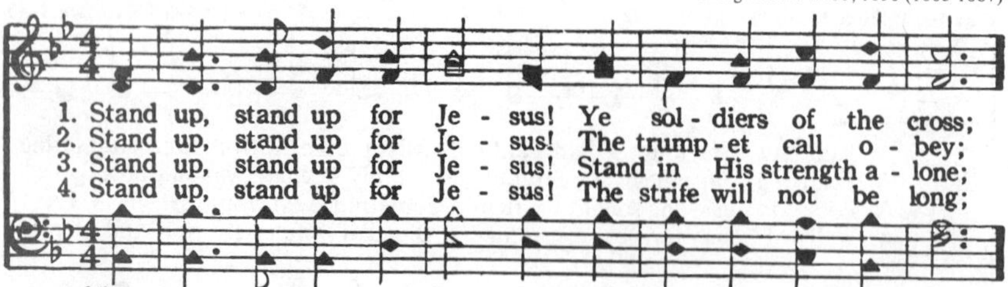

1. Stand up, stand up for Je - sus! Ye sol - diers of the cross;
2. Stand up, stand up for Je - sus! The trump - et call o - bey;
3. Stand up, stand up for Je - sus! Stand in His strength a - lone;
4. Stand up, stand up for Je - sus! The strife will not be long;

Lift high His roy - al ban - ner, It must not suf - fer loss;
Forth to the might - y con - flict In this His glo - rious day;
The arm of flesh will fail you, Ye dare not trust your own;
This day the noise of bat - tle, The next the vic - tor's song;

FINE

*D.S.*—Till ev - 'ry foe is van-quished, And Christ is Lord in - deed.
*D.S.*—Let cour - age rise with dan - ger, And strength to strength op - pose.
*D.S.*—Where du - ty calls, or dan - ger, Be nev - er want - ing there.
*D.S.*—He with the King of Glo - ry Shall reign e - ter - nal - ly.

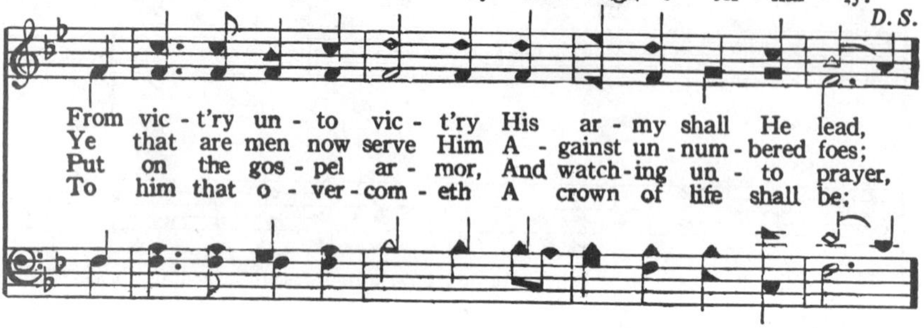

D. S.

From vic - t'ry un - to vic - t'ry His ar - my shall He lead,
Ye that are men now serve Him A - gainst un - num - bered foes;
Put on the gos - pel ar - mor, And watch - ing un - to prayer,
To him that o - ver - com - eth A crown of life shall be;

# 845 LEAD ON, O KING ETERNAL

*For Thy name's sake lead me.* Ps. 31:3. *Lead me . . . in Thy righteousness.* Ps. 5:8. *Lead me in Thy truth.* Ps. 25:5. *So fight I, not as one that beateth the air.* I Cor. 9:26.

LANCASHIRE 7.6.7.6.D.
M.M. 72

Ernest Warburton Shurtleff, 1862-1917 Henry Smart, 1813-1879

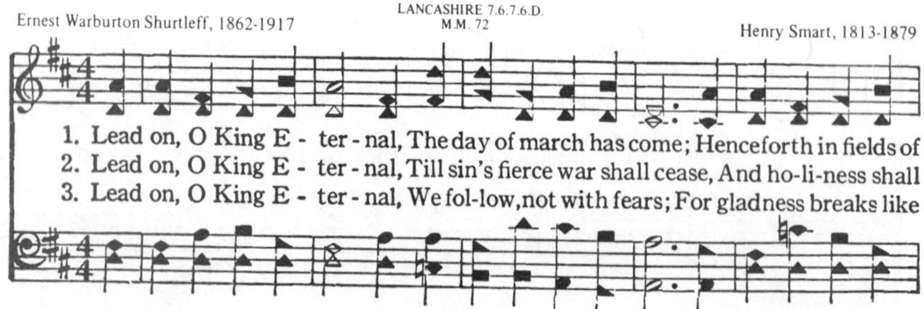
1. Lead on, O King E - ter - nal, The day of march has come; Henceforth in fields of
2. Lead on, O King E - ter - nal, Till sin's fierce war shall cease, And ho-li-ness shall
3. Lead on, O King E - ter - nal, We fol-low, not with fears; For gladness breaks like

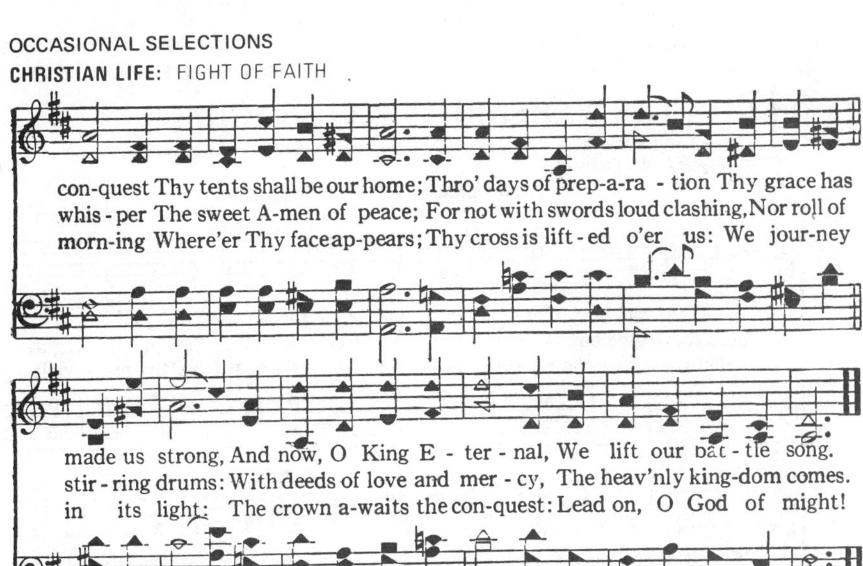
con-quest Thy tents shall be our home; Thro' days of prep-a-ra - tion Thy grace has
whis - per The sweet A-men of peace; For not with swords loud clashing, Nor roll of
morn-ing Where'er Thy face ap-pears; Thy cross is lift - ed o'er us: We jour-ney
made us strong, And now, O King E - ter - nal, We lift our bat - tle song.
stir - ring drums: With deeds of love and mer - cy, The heav'nly king-dom comes.
in its light: The crown a-waits the con-quest: Lead on, O God of might!

## HO, MY COMRADES 846

*Occupy till I come.* Lk. 19:13. *Stewards of the manifold grace of God.* I Pet. 4:10. *Resist stedfast in the faith.* I Pet. 5:9.

HOLD THE FORT 8.5.8.5. with Ref.
M.M. 66

Philip Paul Bliss, 1838-1876 | Philip Paul Bliss

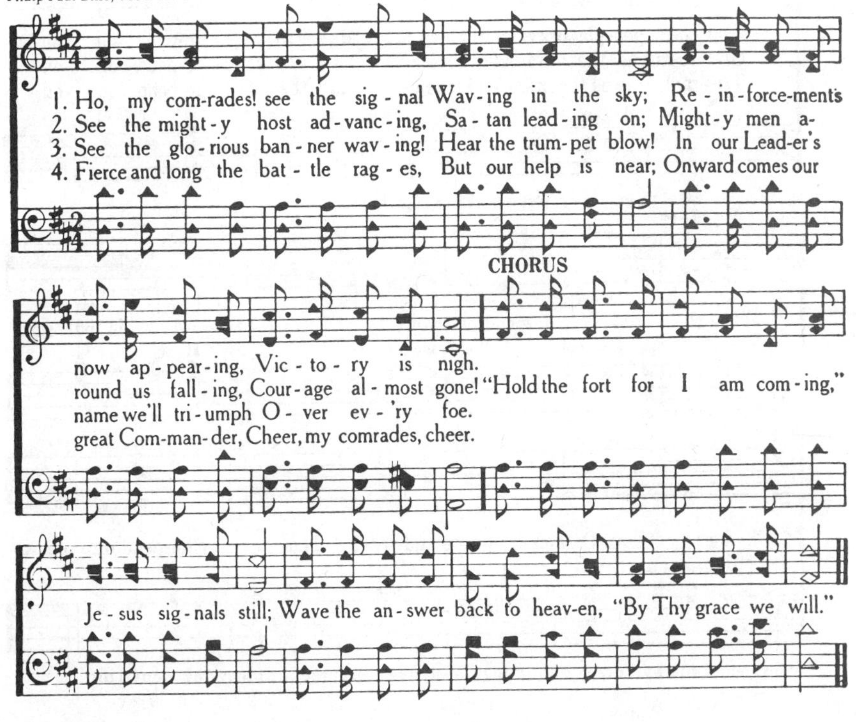

1. Ho, my com-rades! see the sig - nal Wav-ing in the sky; Re - in-force-ments now ap - pear-ing, Vic - to - ry is nigh.
2. See the might - y host ad - vanc - ing, Sa - tan lead - ing on; Might - y men a- round us fall - ing, Cour - age al - most gone!
3. See the glo - rious ban - ner wav - ing! Hear the trum - pet blow! In our Lead-er's name we'll tri - umph O - ver ev - 'ry foe.
4. Fierce and long the bat - tle rag - es, But our help is near; Onward comes our great Com-man - der, Cheer, my comrades, cheer.

CHORUS

"Hold the fort for I am com - ing," Je - sus sig - nals still; Wave the an - swer back to heav-en, "By Thy grace we will."

# 847 IN THE WARFARE THAT IS RAGING

*Resist the devil, and he will flee from you.* Jas. 4:7. *Who then is willing to consecrate his service this day unto the Lord?* I Chron. 29:5.

MAY GOD DEPEND ON YOU? 8.7.8.7.7.7. with Ref.
M.M. 69

W. C. Martin

Ira B. Wilson, 1880-1950

1. In the war-fare that is rag - ing For the truth and for the right,
2. See, they come on sa - ble pin - ions, Come in strong, Sa-tan - ic might,—
3. From His throne the Fa - ther sees us; An - gels help us to pre - vail;
When the con-flict, fierce, is rag - ing With the pow - ers of the night,
Pow - ers come, and dark do - min - ions, From the re - gions of the night;
And our lead - er true is Je - sus, And we shall not, can - not fail:
God needs peo-ple brave and true: May He then de-pend on you?
God re-quires the brave and true: May He then de-pend on you?
Tri-umph crowns the brave and true,— May the Lord de-pend on you?
(1) peo - ple brave and true:
REFRAIN.
May the Lord de-pend on you? Loy - al - ty is but His
May the Lord de - pend on you? Loy - al - ty is
due; Say, O spir-it, brave and true, That He may de-pend on you.
but His due;

# ENCAMPED ALONG THE HILLS OF LIGHT 848

*This is the victory that overcometh the world, even our faith.* I Jn. 5:4.

FAITH IS THE VICTORY C.M.D. 8.6.8.6.D. with Ref.
M.M. 152

John H. Yates, 1837-1900

Ira D. Sankey, 1840-1908

1. En-camped a - long the hills of light, Ye Chris-tian sol - diers, rise, And
2. His ban - ner o - ver us is love, Our sword the Word of God; We
3. To him that o - ver-comes the foe, White rai-ment shall be given; Be-
press the bat - tle ere the night Shall veil the glowing skies. A-gainst the foe in
tread the road the saints a-bove With shouts of triumph trod. By faith they, like a
fore the an - gels he shall know His name confessed in heaven. Then onward from the
vales be-low Let all our strength be hurled; Faith is the vic - to - ry, we know,
whirlwind's breath,Swept on o'er ev - ery field; The faith by which they conquered Death
hills of light, Our hearts with love a-flame, We'll vanquish all the hosts of night,
That o - ver-comes the world.
Is still our shin - ing shield.
In Je-sus' conquering name.
CHORUS
Faith is the vic - to - ry! Faith is the
Faith is the vic - to - ry! Faith is the
vic - to - ry! Oh, glo - ri - ous vic - to - ry, That o - ver-comes the world.
vic - to - ry!

# 849 AM I A SOLDIER OF THE CROSS

*Thou therefore endure hardness, as a good soldier of Jesus Christ.* II Tim. 2:3.

BATTLE HYMN C.M. 8.6.8.6. with Ref.
M.M. 96
Isaac Watts, 1647-1748
Arr. William M. Blake
1. Am I a sol-dier of the cross, A fol-l'wer of the Lamb?
And shall I fear to own his cause, Or blush to speak his name?
2. Must I be car-ried to the skies On flow-'ry beds of ease,
While oth-ers fought to win the prize, And sail'd thro' blood-y seas?
3. Are there no foes for me to face? Must I not stem the flood?
Is this vile world a friend to grace To help me on to God?
4. Sure I must fight if I would reign; In-crease my cour-age, Lord,
I'll bear the toil, en-dure the pain, Sup-port-ed by thy word.
REFRAIN.
And when the bat-tle's o-ver we shall wear a crown! Yes, we shall wear a crown! Yes, we shall wear a crown! And when the bat-tle's o-ver we shall wear a crown In the new Je-ru-sa-lem. Wear a crown, wear a crown, Wear a bright and shining crown.
Wear a crown, wear a crown,
FINE.
D S.

# AM I A SOLDIER OF THE CROSS 850

*No man that warreth entangleth himself with the affairs of this life; that he may please Him who hath chosen Him to be a soldier.* II Tim. 2:4.

WE WILL STAND THE STORM 8.8.8.6. with Ref.
M.M. 69

Isaac Watts, 1647-1748 Anon.

1. Am I a sol-dier of the cross, Am I a sol-dier of the cross, Am I a sol-dier of the cross, A follow-er of the Lamb?
And shall I fear to own His cause, And shall I fear to own His cause, And shall I fear to own His cause, Or blush to speak His name?
2. Are there no foes for me to face, Are there no foes for me to face, Are there no foes for me to face, Must I not stem the flood?
Is this vile world a friend to grace, Is this vile world a friend to grace, Is this vile world a friend to grace, To help me on to God?
3. Sure I must fight if I would reign, Sure I must fight if I would reign, Sure I must fight if I would reign; In-crease my courage, Lord!
I'll bear the toil, en-dure the pain, I'll bear the toil, en-dure the pain, I'll bear the toil, en-dure the pain, Sup-port-ed by Thy word.
CHORUS
We will stand the storm, We will an-chor by and by, by and by;
the storm, 'twill not be long,
We will stand the storm, We will an-chor by and by.
the storm, 'twill not be long, by and by.

# 851 A FULL SURRENDER I HAVE MADE

*I beseech you therefore, brethren, by the mercies of God, that ye present your bodies a living sacrifice, holy, acceptable unto God, which is your reasonable service.* Rom. 12:1.

A FULL SURRENDER 8.7.8.7. with Ref.
M.M. 63

Johnson Oatman, Jr., 1856-1926

George H. Hugg, 1848-1907

1. A full sur-ren-der I have made, I've giv - en all to Je - sus;
2. My hands, my feet, my head, my heart, I've giv - en all to Je - sus;
3. My loss or gain, my hopes and fears, I've giv - en all to Je - sus;
4. My mon - ey, la - bors, bur - dens, cares, I've giv - en all to Je - sus;
5. My life, my love, my fam - i - ly, I've giv - en all to Je - sus;
My all is on the al - tar laid, I've giv - en all to Je - sus.
I've not re - tained a sin - gle part, I've giv - en all to Je - sus.
My health and strength, my grief and tears, I've giv - en all to Je - sus.
My voice, my pen, my songs, my prayers, I've giv - en all to Je - sus.
For time, and for e - ter - ni - ty, I've giv - en all to Je - sus.
REFRAIN.
I've sur - ren-dered all, surrendered all, I've sur - ren-dered all; surrendered all;
Ev - 'ry - thing is on the al - tar, I've sur - ren-dered all. . . . .
sur-ren-dered all.

# MY SAVIOUR NEEDS HELPERS 852

*I will go in the strength of the Lord God: I will make mention of Thy righteousness.* Ps. 71:16.

I'LL GO WHERE HE SENDETH ME 10.7.10.7. with Ref.
M.M. 112

James Rowe, 1865-1933

W. C. Tinsley

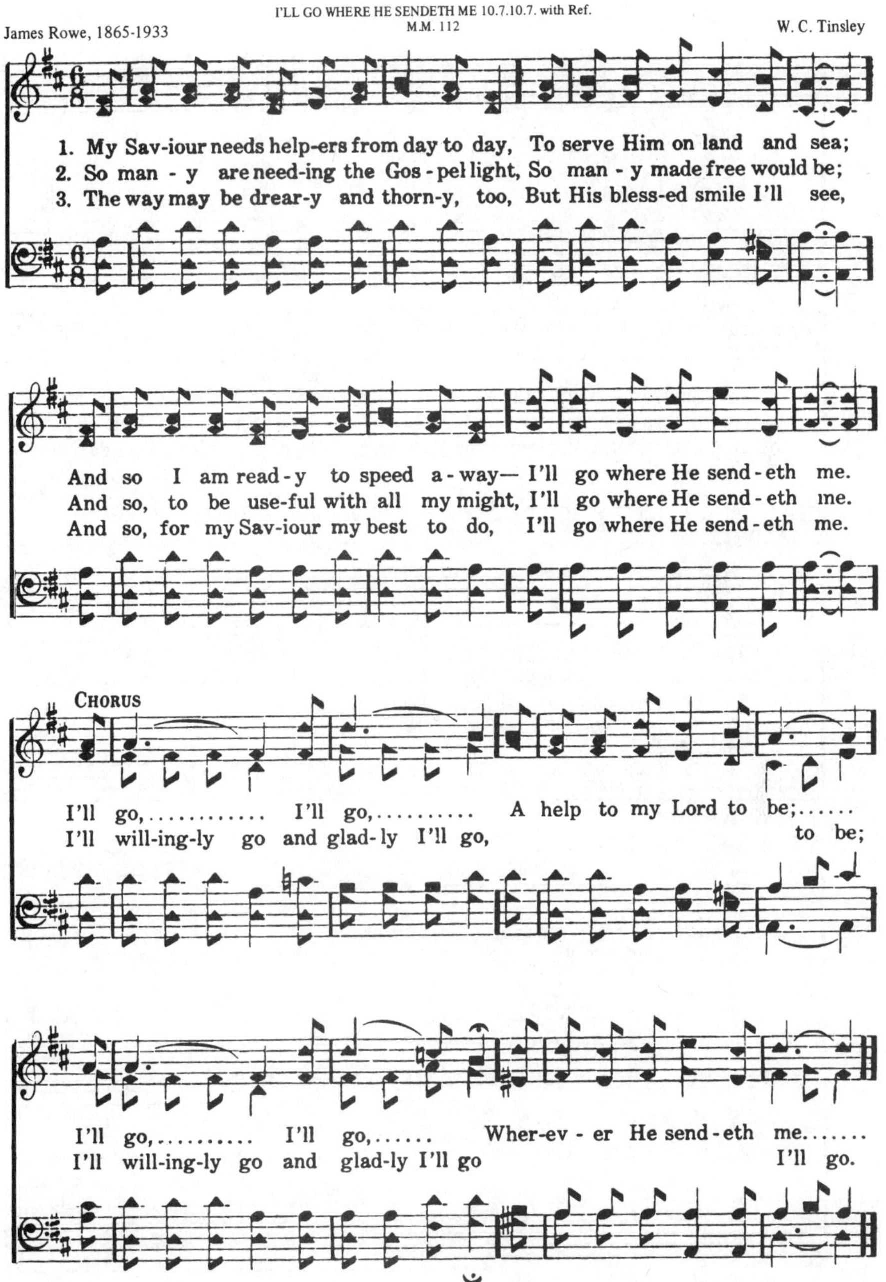
1. My Sav-iour needs help-ers from day to day, To serve Him on land and sea;
2. So man - y are need-ing the Gos - pel light, So man - y made free would be;
3. The way may be drear-y and thorn-y, too, But His bless-ed smile I'll see,
And so I am read-y to speed a-way— I'll go where He send-eth me.
And so, to be use-ful with all my might, I'll go where He send-eth me.
And so, for my Sav-iour my best to do, I'll go where He send-eth me.
CHORUS
I'll go,............ I'll go,.......... A help to my Lord to be;......
I'll will-ing-ly go and glad-ly I'll go, to be;
I'll go,......... I'll go,...... Wher-ev - er He send-eth me.......
I'll will-ing-ly go and glad-ly I'll go I'll go.

# 853 NOW THAT HARVEST TIME IS HERE

*Also I heard the voice of the Lord, saying, Whom shall I send, and who will go for us? Then said I, Here am I; send me.* Is. 6:8.

HERE AM I, SEND ME 7.7.9.7.7.9. with Ref.
M.M. 63

Lida Shivers Leech, 1873-1962 — Lida Shivers Leech

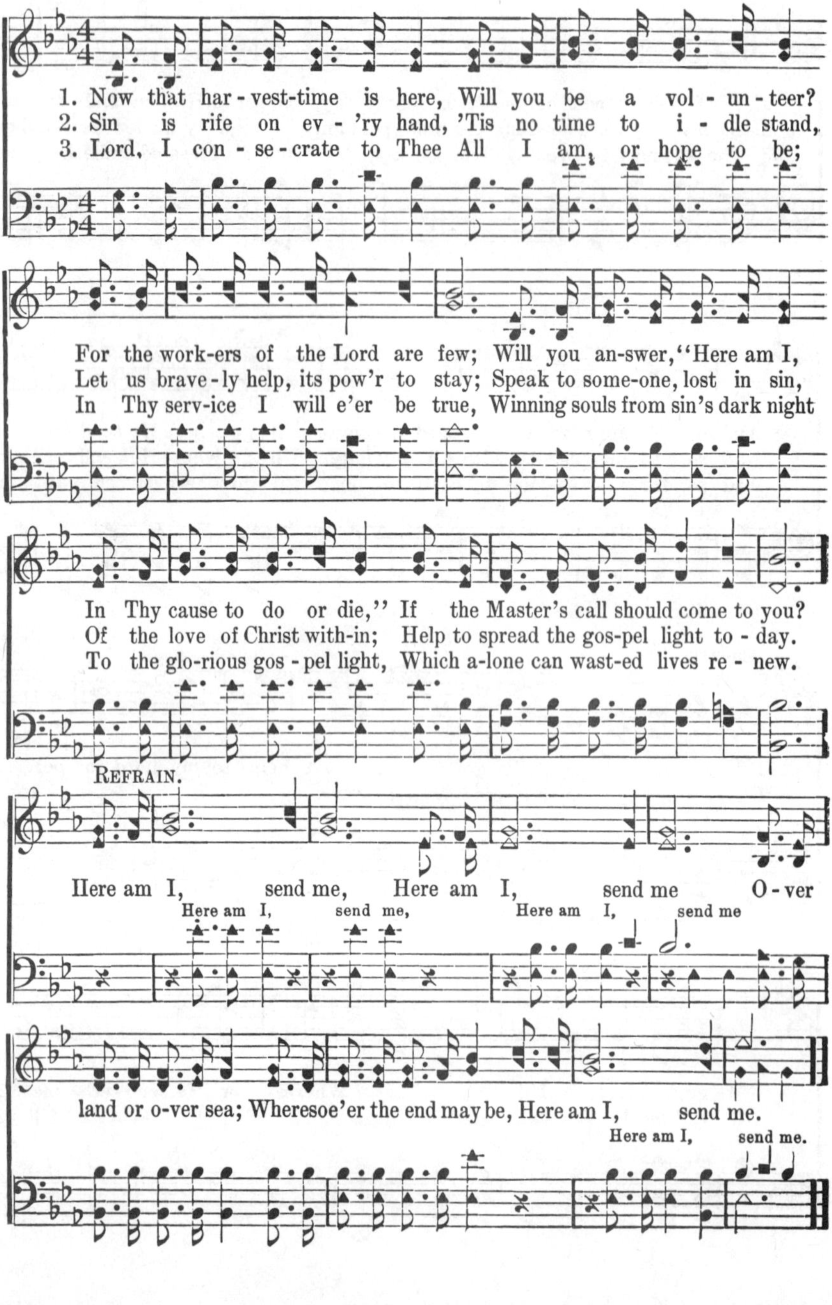

1. Now that harvest-time is here, Will you be a volunteer? For the workers of the Lord are few; Will you answer, "Here am I, In Thy cause to do or die," If the Master's call should come to you?

2. Sin is rife on ev'ry hand, 'Tis no time to idle stand, Let us bravely help, its pow'r to stay; Speak to someone, lost in sin, Of the love of Christ within; Help to spread the gospel light today.

3. Lord, I consecrate to Thee All I am, or hope to be; In Thy service I will e'er be true, Winning souls from sin's dark night To the glorious gospel light, Which alone can wasted lives renew.

REFRAIN.

Here am I, (Here am I,) send me, (send me,) Here am I, (Here am I,) send me (send me) Over land or over sea; Wheresoe'er the end may be, Here am I, (Here am I,) send me. (send me.)

# THERE IS MUCH TO DO 854

*Thou shalt go to all that I shall send Thee, and whatsoever I command thee thou shall speak.* Jer. 1:7.

LORD, SEND ME 11.11.6.5.11. with Ref.
M.M. 63
M. W. Spencer
M. W. Spencer
1. There is much to do, there's work on ev'ry hand, Hark! the cry for help comes ring-ing thru the land; Je-sus calls for reap-ers, I must ac-tive be, What wilt Thou, O Mas-ter? here am I, send me.
2. There's the plaintive cry of mourning souls distressed, And the sigh of hearts who seek but find no rest; These should have my love and ten-der sym-pa-thy, Read-y at Thy bid-ding, here am I, send me.
3. There are hung'ring souls who cry aloud for bread, With the bread of life they're long-ing to be fed; Shall they starve and fam-ish while a feast is free? I must be more faith-ful, here am I, send me.
4. There are souls who linger on the brink of woe, Lord, I must not, can not bear to let them go: Let me go and tell them, broth-er, turn and flee, Mas-ter, I would save them, here am I, send me.
Chorus
Here am I, Lord, send me, Here am I, Read-y at Thy bid-ding, Lord, send me.
Here am I, send me, Lord, send me, Here am I, send me, Lord, send me, Here am I, send me, Lord, send me, me,

# 855 TREASURES HERE WILL SOON DECAY

*Keep that which is committed to thy trust.* I Tim. 6:20. *Set your affections on things above, not on things on the earth . . . seek those things which are above.* Col. 3:2, 1.

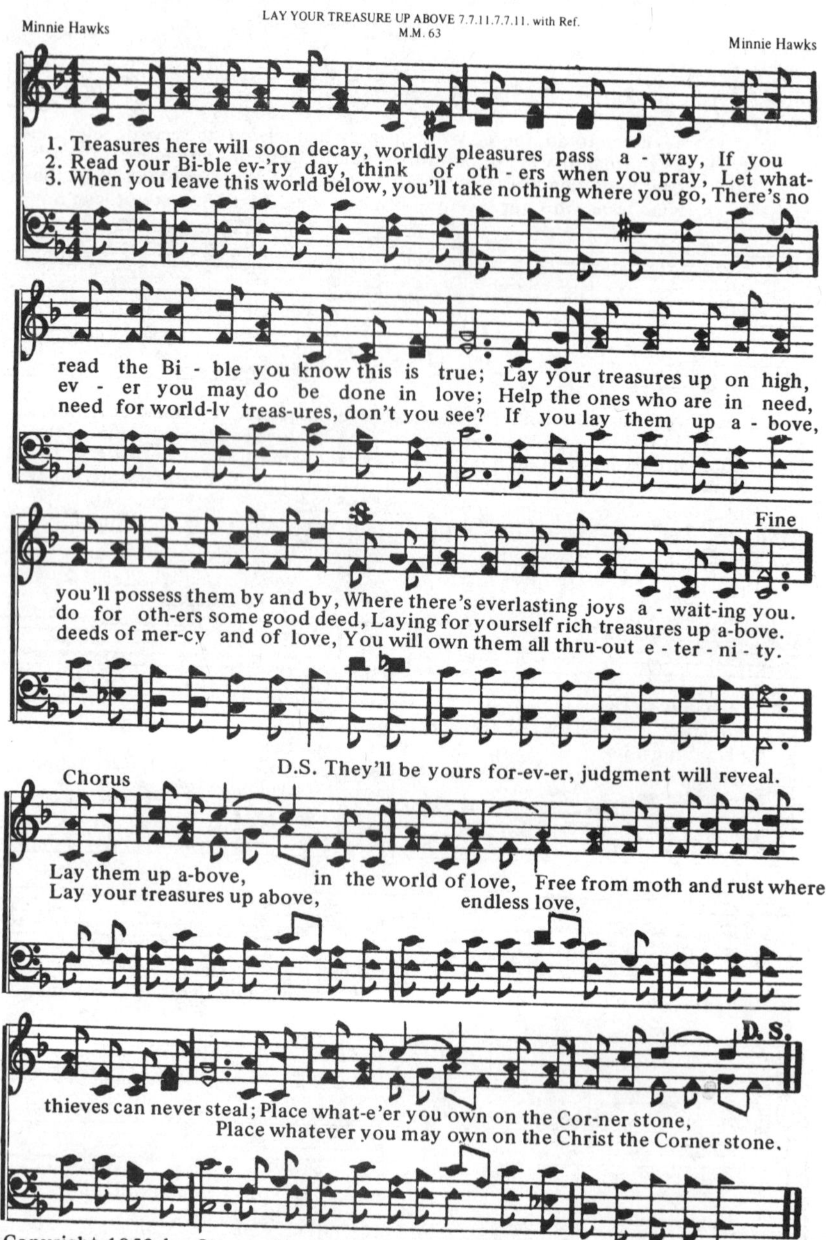
Minnie Hawks
LAY YOUR TREASURE UP ABOVE 7.7.11.7.7.11. with Ref.
M.M. 63
Minnie Hawks
1. Treasures here will soon decay, worldly pleasures pass a - way, If you read the Bi - ble you know this is true; Lay your treasures up on high, you'll possess them by and by, Where there's everlasting joys a - wait-ing you.
2. Read your Bi-ble ev-'ry day, think of oth - ers when you pray, Let what-ev - er you may do be done in love; Help the ones who are in need, do for oth-ers some good deed, Laying for yourself rich treasures up a-bove.
3. When you leave this world below, you'll take nothing where you go, There's no need for world-ly treas-ures, don't you see? If you lay them up a - bove, deeds of mer-cy and of love, You will own them all thru-out e - ter - ni - ty.
Fine
D.S. They'll be yours for-ev-er, judgment will reveal.
Chorus
Lay them up a-bove, in the world of love, Free from moth and rust where thieves can never steal; Place what-e'er you own on the Cor-ner stone,
Lay your treasures up above, endless love,
Place whatever you may own on the Christ the Corner stone.
D.S.

# MUST I GO AND EMPTY-HANDED 856

*Every one of us shall give account of himself to God.* Rom. 14:12. *Every man's work shall be made manifest.* I Cor. 3:13. *Not a forgetful hearer, but a doer of the work, this man shall be blessed in his deed.* Jas. 1:25.

MUST I GO AND EMPTY-HANDED 8.7.8.7. with Ref.
M.M. 96
Charles C. Luther, 1847-1924
George C. Stebbins, 1846-1945
1. "Must I go, and emp - ty-hand - ed," Thus my dear Re-deem - er meet?
2. Not at death I shrink nor fal - ter, For my Sav - iour saves me now,
3. O the years in sin - ning wast - ed, Could I but re - call them now,
4, O ye saints, a-rouse, be ear - nest, Up and work while yet 'tis day;
Not one day of serv - ice give Him, Lay no tro - phy at His feet?
But to meet Him emp-ty - hand - ed, Thought of that now clouds my brow.
I would give them to my Sav - iour, To His will I'd glad - ly bow.
Ere the night of death o'er-take thee, Strive for souls while still you may.
CHORUS
"Must I go and emp - ty-hand - ed?" Must I meet my Sav - iour so?
Not one soul with which to greet Him: Must I 'emp - ty-hand - ed go?

# 857 GOD OF THE FERTILE FIELDS

*The place whereon thou standest is holy ground.* Ex. 3:5. *The earth is the Lord's, and the fulness thereof; the world, and they that dwell therein.* Ps. 24:1. *Replenish the earth, and subdue it.* Gen. 1:28.

Georgia Harkness, 1953 (b. 1891)

KIRBY BEDON 6.6.4.6.6.6.4.
M.M. 69

Edward Bunnet, 1834-1923

1. God of the fer–tile fields, Lord of the earth that yields
2. We would Thy stew–ards be, Hold–ing in trust from Thee
3. As grows the hid – den seed To fruit that serves men's need,
4. God of the coun – try side, Dear to our Lord who died

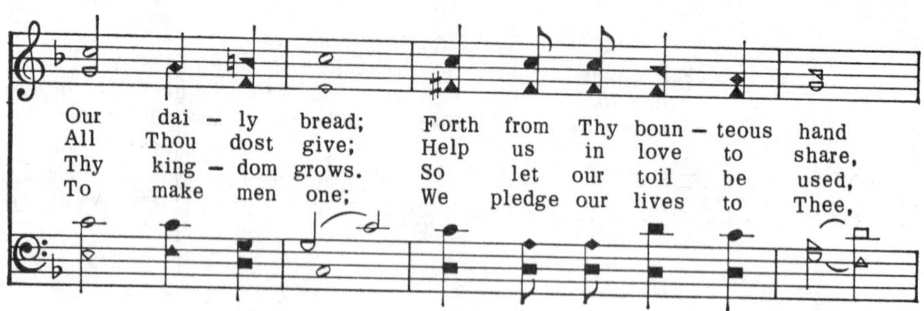
Our dai – ly bread; Forth from Thy boun – teous hand
All Thou dost give; Help us in love to share,
Thy king – dom grows. So let our toil be used,
To make men one; We pledge our lives to Thee,

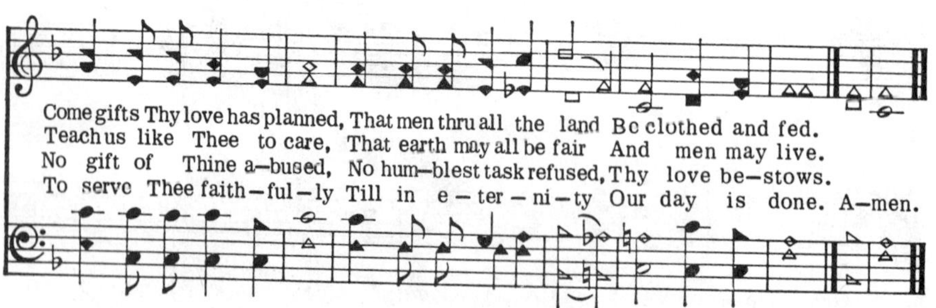
Come gifts Thy love has planned, That men thru all the land Be clothed and fed.
Teach us like Thee to care, That earth may all be fair And men may live.
No gift of Thine a–bused, No hum–blest task refused, Thy love be–stows.
To serve Thee faith–ful–ly Till in e – ter – ni – ty Our day is done. A–men.

# CHILDREN OF FRIENDSHIP AND LOVE 858

*A friend loveth at all times, and a brother is born for adversity.* Prov. 17:17. *Ye are my friends, if ye do whatsoever I command you.* Jn. 15:14.

Frederick Rapp (ne Reichert), 1775-1834
St. 1 Tr. Anon; Ed. John S. Duss Alt.

FREUT EUCH IHR KINDER
11.11. with Ref.
M.M. 66

F. Rapp
Arr. Richard D. Wetzel

1. Chil - dren of friend-ship and love lift your voic-es, Sing the sweet
2. Joy - ful - ly sound - ing di - vine friend-ship's praises, Join the great
1. Freut euch ihr Kin - der der Freund-schaft und Lie - be, Fei - ert dem
2. Fey - ert ihr Gu - ten im frö - lich - en Krei - se, Sing - et der
bond that up - lifts and re - joic - es;
hymn the an - gel - ic host rais - es.
sanf - ten Ver - ein - i - gungs - Trie - be;
himm - lisch - en Freund-schaft zum Prei - se;
REFRAIN:
In grate - ful hom - age to heav - en - ly love, Lift your glad hearts to yon heav-en a - bove, Lift your glad hearts to yon heav - en a - bove.
Weiht ihr ein Lob - lied im hö - her - en Chor: Schwingt euch ihr Her - zen zum Him-mel empor, Schwingt euch ihr Her -zen zum Him-mel em-por.

# 859 THE LOVE OF JESUS

*I count all things but loss for the excellency of the knowledge of Christ Jesus my Lord.* Phil. 3:8. *And to know the love of Christ, which passeth knowledge.* Eph. 3:19.

THE LOVE OF GOD 10.9.10.9. with Ref.
M.M. 60

Orvin S. Davis, b. 1902 — Orvin S. Davis

1. The love of Je - sus to me is great-er, Than an - y - thing else I've ev - er known; It reach-es deep-er, than an - y sin-stain, It reach-es high-er than heav-en's throne.
2. It brought the Sav-ior from heav-en's glo - ry, To give His life for a world of sin; Tho' God of heav-en, He con-de-scend-ed, To prove to you that He is your friend.
3. It giv-eth com-fort to those in sor - row, It bring-eth peace to a trou-bled soul; The love of Je - sus goes in the by-ways, To seek the sin - sick and make them whole.
Refrain
The love of God ...................... is more to me ..................... than all the world ............ could ev - er be; ....................
The love of God, is more to me, Than all this world could ev-er be;
It reach - es down from the throne of glo-ry, And sets the vil-est sin - ner free.

# LEAD ME SAFELY ON 860

*Let us go on unto perfection.* Heb. 6:1. *Lead me in a plain path.* Ps. 27:11.

LEAD ME SAFELY ON 10.10.10.10.
M.M. 69

J. H. Leslie — Charles Edward Pollock (c. 1902)

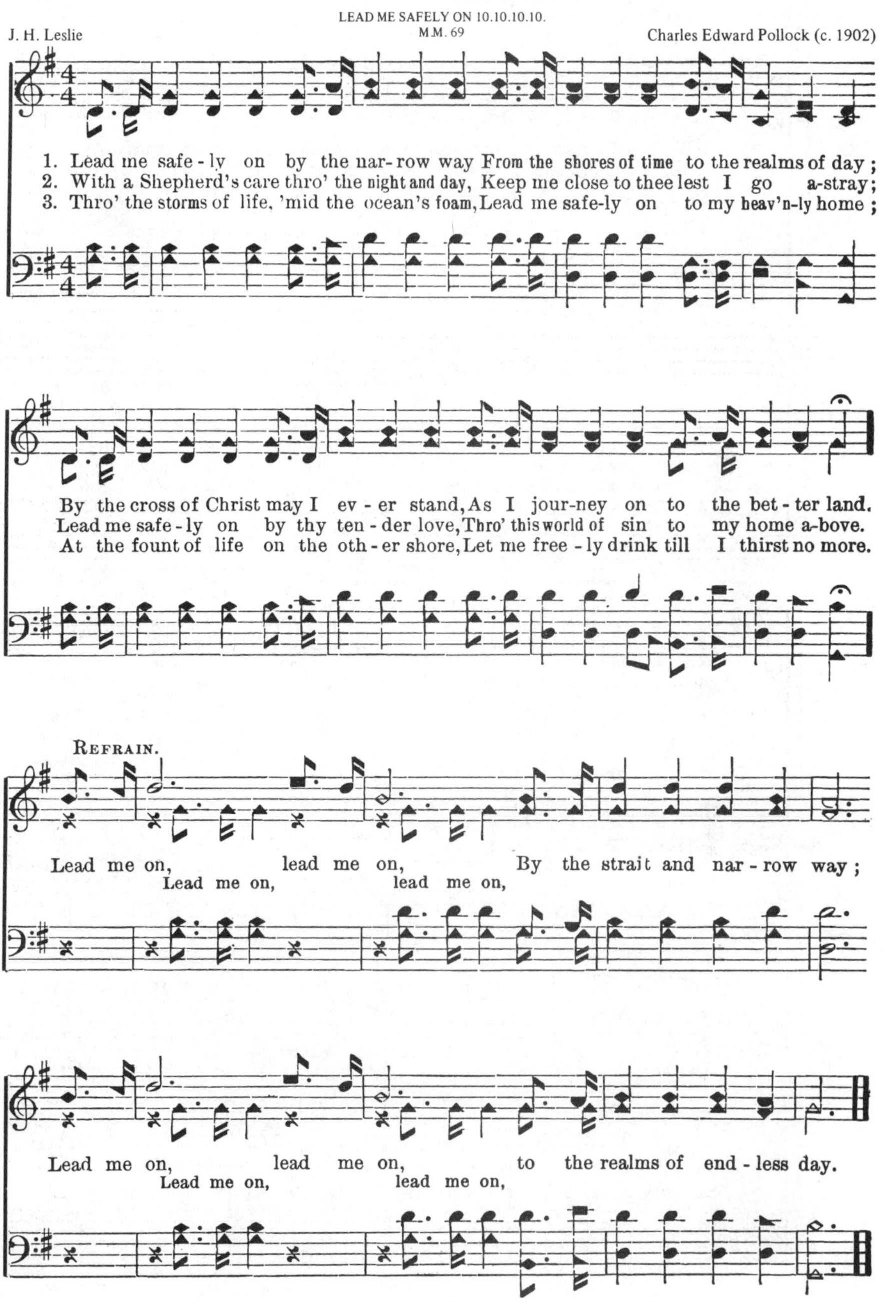
1. Lead me safe - ly on by the nar - row way From the shores of time to the realms of day;
2. With a Shepherd's care thro' the night and day, Keep me close to thee lest I go a-stray;
3. Thro' the storms of life, 'mid the ocean's foam, Lead me safe-ly on to my heav'n-ly home;
By the cross of Christ may I ev - er stand, As I jour-ney on to the bet - ter land.
Lead me safe - ly on by thy ten - der love, Thro' this world of sin to my home a-bove.
At the fount of life on the oth - er shore, Let me free - ly drink till I thirst no more.
REFRAIN.
Lead me on, lead me on, By the strait and nar - row way;
Lead me on, lead me on,
Lead me on, lead me on, to the realms of end - less day.
Lead me on, lead me on,

# 861 MY HEART WAS DISTRESSED

*He brought me up also out of an horrible pit, out of the miry clay, and set my feet upon a rock and established my goings. And He hath put a new song in my mouth, even praise unto our God.* Ps. 40:2, 3.

Rev. H. J. Zelley, 1859-1942
Cho. by H. L. G.

HE BROUGHT ME OUT 11.11.11.11. with Ref.
M.M 76

Henry L. Gilmour, 1837-1920

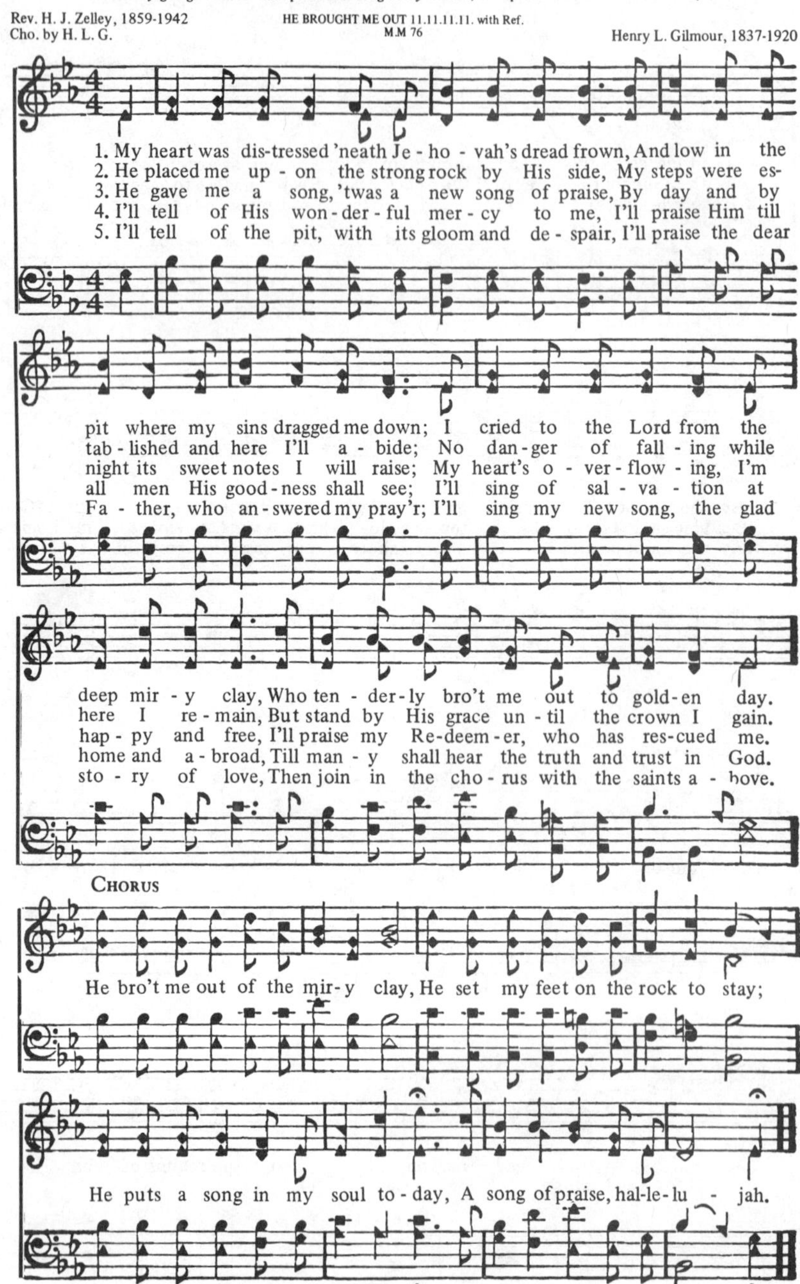
1. My heart was dis-tressed 'neath Je - ho - vah's dread frown, And low in the
2. He placed me up - on the strong rock by His side, My steps were es-
3. He gave me a song, 'twas a new song of praise, By day and by
4. I'll tell of His won-der-ful mer - cy to me, I'll praise Him till
5. I'll tell of the pit, with its gloom and de - spair, I'll praise the dear
pit where my sins dragged me down; I cried to the Lord from the
tab - lished and here I'll a - bide; No dan - ger of fall - ing while
night its sweet notes I will raise; My heart's o - ver - flow - ing, I'm
all men His good - ness shall see; I'll sing of sal - va - tion at
Fa - ther, who an - swered my pray'r; I'll sing my new song, the glad
deep mir - y clay, Who ten - der - ly bro't me out to gold - en day.
here I re - main, But stand by His grace un - til the crown I gain.
hap - py and free, I'll praise my Re - deem - er, who has res - cued me.
home and a - broad, Till man - y shall hear the truth and trust in God.
sto - ry of love, Then join in the cho - rus with the saints a - bove.
CHORUS
He bro't me out of the mir - y clay, He set my feet on the rock to stay;
He puts a song in my soul to - day, A song of praise, hal - le - lu - jah.

# THERE ARE TWO COMMANDS RECORDED 862

*Jesus said unto him, Thou shalt love the Lord thy God with all thy heart, and with all thy soul, and with all thy mind. This is the first and great commandment. And the second is like unto it, Thou shalt love thy neighbor as thyself.* Mt. 22:37-39.

TWO COMMANDS 12.11.12.11. with Ref.
M.M. 63

Harry Showalter, 1966

Harry Showalter, b., 1889
Har. John J. Overholt, 1970

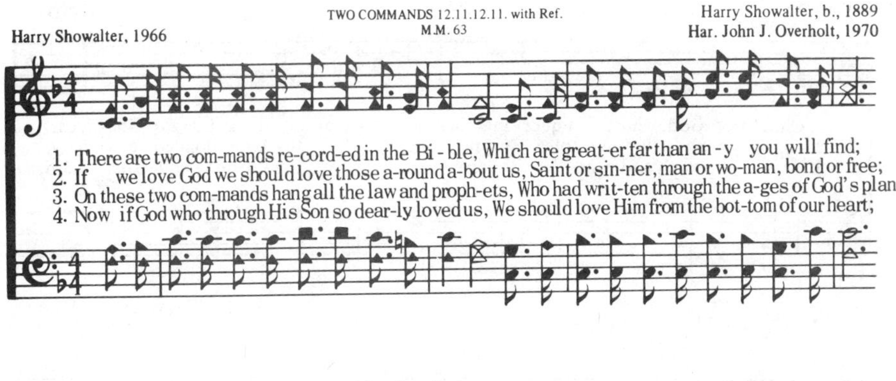
1. There are two com-mands re-cord-ed in the Bi - ble, Which are great-er far than an - y you will find;
2. If we love God we should love those a-round a-bout us, Saint or sin-ner, man or wo-man, bond or free;
3. On these two com-mands hang all the law and proph-ets, Who had writ-ten through the a-ges of God's plan;
4. Now if God who through His Son so dear-ly loved us, We should love Him from the bot-tom of our heart;

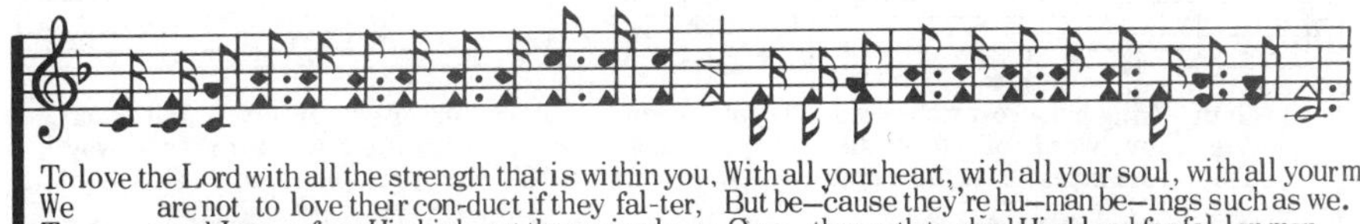
To love the Lord with all the strength that is within you, With all your heart, with all your soul, with all your mind.
We are not to love their con-duct if they fal-ter, But be-cause they're hu-man be-ings such as we.
To send Je-sus from His high-est throne in glo-ry, On the earth to shed His blood for fal-len man.
Heed - ing all the pre-cious pre-cepts He has giv-en, And from none of His ex-am - ples e'er de-part.

CHORUS

Love the Lord, ye His cre - a - tion, Un - to Him all hon - or give;

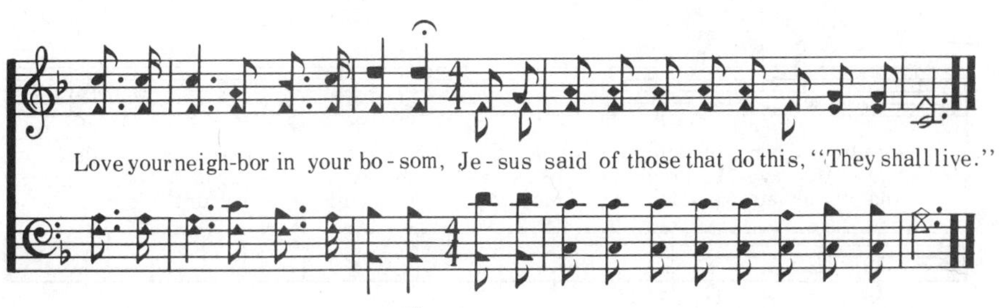
Love your neigh-bor in your bo - som, Je - sus said of those that do this, "They shall live."

# 863

## CHURCH OF GOD WHOSE CONQUERING BANNERS

*Awake, awake, stand up, O Jerusalem.* Is. 51:17. *Awake thou that sleepest, and arise from the dead, and Christ shall give thee light.* Eph. 5:14.

CHURCH OF GOD AWAKE 8.7.8.7.D.
M.M. 72

Mrs. Emily Bugbee

T. C. O'Kane

1. Church of God, whose con-quer-ing ban-ners, Float a - long the glo-rious years,
2. In your cost-ly tem-ples pray - ing, "Let thy king-dom come, we pray."
3. Shake the earth and rend the heav - en, Wake thy sleep-ing chil-dren, Lord,

Gath - 'ring har - vest rich and gold - en, Sown in pov - er - ty and tears,
Are but words of i - dle mean - ing If with these we turn a - way.
Till the meas - ure full and e - ven Has been ren-dered at Thy word.

On - ward press, the cross is bend-ing Far to - ward the morn-ing skies,
Bound-less wealth to you is giv - en From His hand who owns it all,
Then from out her chrism of sor - row Shall the earth re-deemed a - rise,

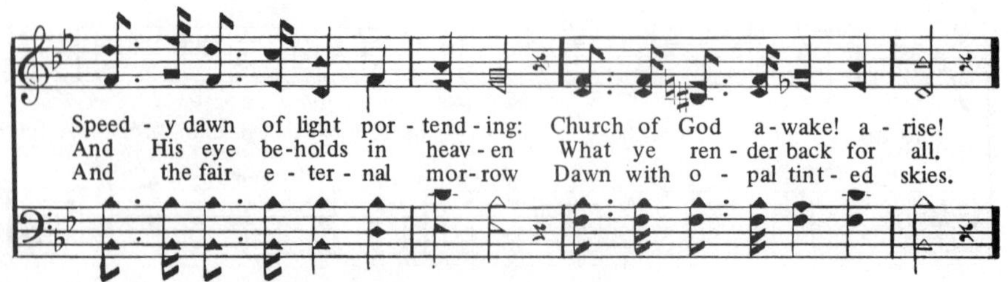
Speed - y dawn of light por - tend - ing: Church of God a - wake! a - rise!
And His eye be-holds in heav - en What ye ren - der back for all.
And the fair e - ter - nal mor - row Dawn with o - pal tint - ed skies.

REFRAIN.
Church of God, .......... a - wake! a - rise! Christ, your Head .......... and Mas - ter,
Church of God, a - wake! a - rise! Christ, your Head and
cries, Send the gos - pel's joy-ful sound Un - to earth's re - mot - est bound.
Mas-ter cries, Oh, send the gos - pel's joy-ful sound

## THERE IS A GREEN HILL FAR AWAY 864

*Christ also suffered for us, leaving us an example, that ye should follow His steps.* I Pet. 2:21.
*Looking unto Jesus the author and finisher of our faith.* Heb. 12:2.

Cecil Frances Alexander, 1848 (1818-1895) | MEDITATION C.M. 8.6.8.6. M.M. 76 | John Henry Gower, 1890 (1855-1922)

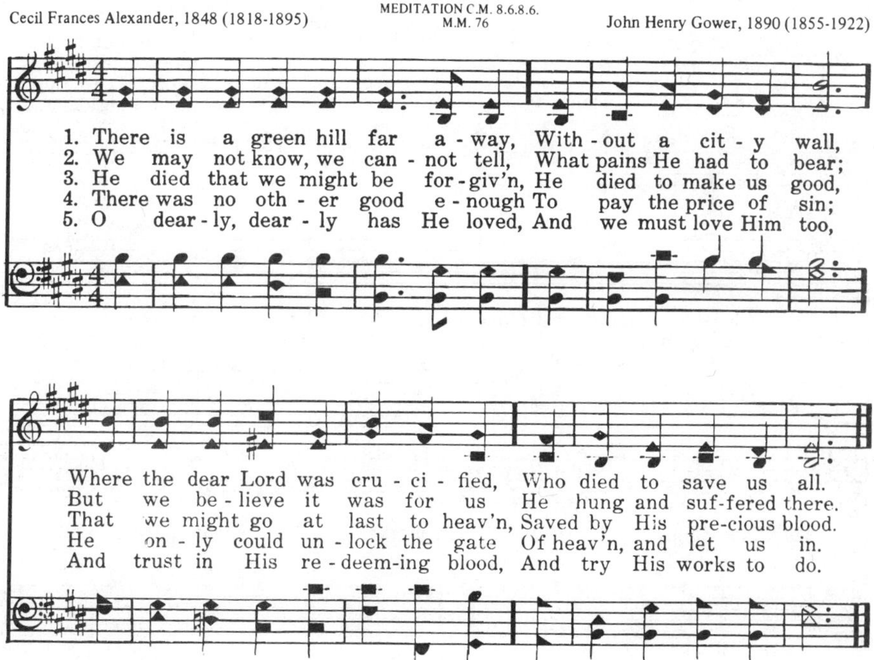

1. There is a green hill far a - way, With - out a cit - y wall,
Where the dear Lord was cru - ci - fied, Who died to save us all.

2. We may not know, we can - not tell, What pains He had to bear;
But we be - lieve it was for us He hung and suf-fered there.

3. He died that we might be for - giv'n, He died to make us good,
That we might go at last to heav'n, Saved by His pre-cious blood.

4. There was no oth - er good e - nough To pay the price of sin;
He on - ly could un - lock the gate Of heav'n, and let us in.

5. O dear - ly, dear - ly has He loved, And we must love Him too,
And trust in His re - deem-ing blood, And try His works to do.

# 865 FOR CHRIST AND THE CHURCH

*Now it is high time to awake out of sleep.* Rom. 13:11. *Therefore let us not sleep, as do others; but let us watch and be sober.* 1 Thess. 5:6.

FOR CHRIST AND THE CHURCH 10.12.11.11. with Ref.
M.M. 66

Eliza E. Hewitt, 1851-1920 — William J. Kirkpatrick, 1838-1921

1. "For Christ and the Church" let our voi - ces ring, Let us hon - or the
2. "For Christ and the Church" be our ear - nest prayer, Let us fol - low His
3. "For Christ and the Church" will-ing of-f'rings make, Time and tal - ents and
4. "For Christ and the Church" let us cast a - side, By His con - quer-ing
name of our own bless - ed King; Let us work with a will in the
ban - ner the cross dai - ly bear; Let us yield, whol - ly yield, to the
gold for the dear Mas-ter's sake; We will ren - der the best we can
grace, chains of self, fear, and pride; May our lives be en-riched by an
strength of youth, And loy - al - ly stand for the king - dom of truth.
Spir - it's pow'r, And faith - ful - ly serve Him in life's bright-est hour.
bring to Him, The heart's wealth of love, that will nev - er grow dim.
aim so grand; Then hap - py the call to the Sav - iour's right hand.
REFRAIN
For Christ, our dear Re-deem - er, For Christ, who died to save;
For Christ, For Christ,
For the Church . . His blood hath purchased; Lord, make us pure and brave.
For the Church

## RISE UP, O MEN OF GOD 866

*Rise up, let us go.* Mk. 14:42. *Go out into the highways and hedges, and compel them to come in, that my house may be filled.* Lk. 14:23.

FESTAL SONG S.M. 6.6.8.6.
M.M. 72

William Pierson Merril, 1867-1954 — William Henry Walter, 1825-1893

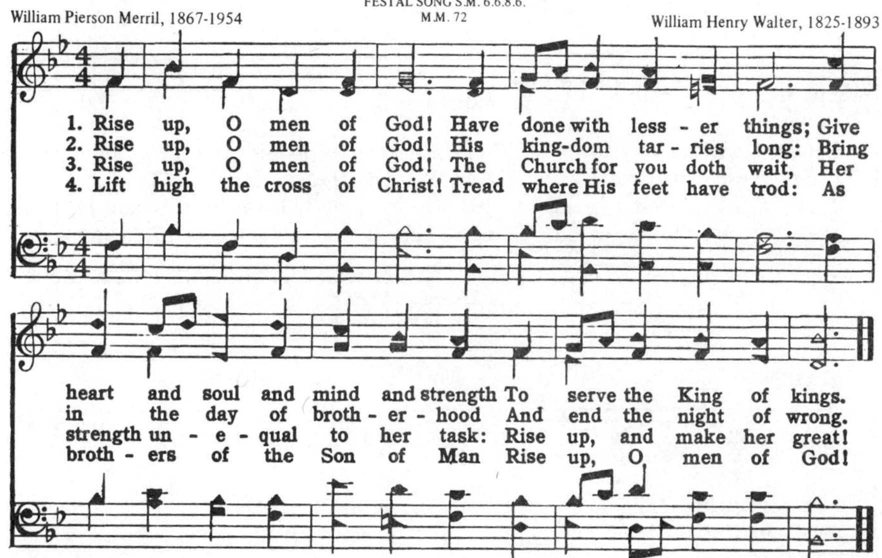
1. Rise up, O men of God! Have done with less - er things; Give
2. Rise up, O men of God! His king-dom tar - ries long: Bring
3. Rise up, O men of God! The Church for you doth wait, Her
4. Lift high the cross of Christ! Tread where His feet have trod: As
heart and soul and mind and strength To serve the King of kings.
in the day of broth - er - hood And end the night of wrong.
strength un - e - qual to her task: Rise up, and make her great!
broth - ers of the Son of Man Rise up, O men of God!

## O WHERE ARE KINGS AND EMPIRES NOW 867

*A thousand years in Thy sight are but as yesterday.* Ps. 90:4. *Upon this rock I will build My church.* Mt. 16:18. *Revive Thy work in true midst of the years.* Hab. 3:2.

ST. ANNE C.M. 8.6.8.6.
M.M. 63

Arthur Cleveland Coxe, 1839 (1818-1896) — William Croft, 1708 (1678-1727)

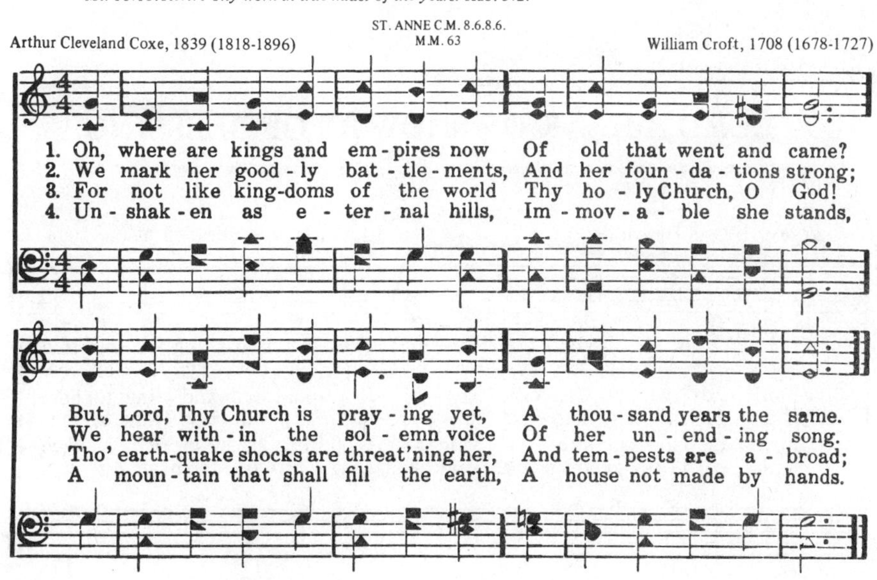
1. Oh, where are kings and em - pires now Of old that went and came?
2. We mark her good - ly bat - tle - ments, And her foun - da - tions strong;
3. For not like king-doms of the world Thy ho - ly Church, O God!
4. Un - shak - en as e - ter - nal hills, Im - mov - a - ble she stands,
But, Lord, Thy Church is pray - ing yet, A thou - sand years the same.
We hear with - in the sol - emn voice Of her un - end - ing song.
Tho' earth-quake shocks are threat'ning her, And tem - pests are a - broad;
A moun - tain that shall fill the earth, A house not made by hands.

# 868 DEAR LORD AND FATHER OF MANKIND

*As soon as Zion travailed, she brought forth her children.* Is. 66:8. *Turn us again, O God of hosts, and cause Thy face to shine; and we shall be saved.* Ps. 80:7.

John Greenleaf Whittier, 1807-1892 | REST 8.6.8.8.6. M.M. 63 | Frederic Charles Maker, 1844-1927

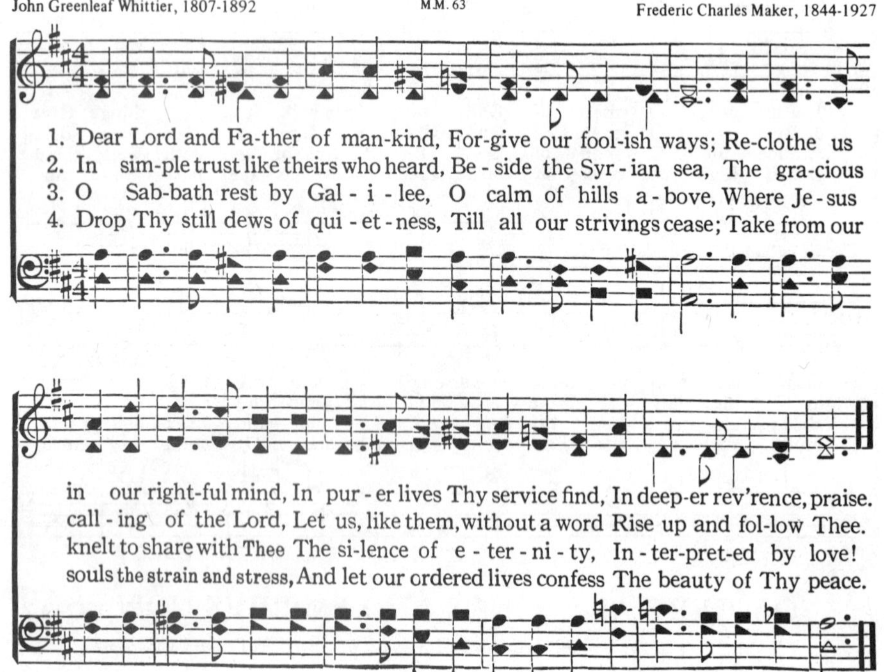
1. Dear Lord and Fa-ther of man-kind, For-give our fool-ish ways; Re-clothe us
2. In sim-ple trust like theirs who heard, Be - side the Syr - ian sea, The gra-cious
3. O Sab-bath rest by Gal - i - lee, O calm of hills a - bove, Where Je - sus
4. Drop Thy still dews of qui - et - ness, Till all our strivings cease; Take from our
in our right-ful mind, In pur - er lives Thy service find, In deep-er rev'rence, praise.
call - ing of the Lord, Let us, like them, without a word Rise up and fol-low Thee.
knelt to share with Thee The si-lence of e - ter - ni - ty, In - ter-pret-ed by love!
souls the strain and stress, And let our ordered lives confess The beauty of Thy peace.

# 869 LORD, I HEAR OF SHOW'RS OF BLESSING

*They that wait upon the Lord shall renew their strength.* Is. 40:31. *Be ye transformed by the renewing of your mind.* Rom. 12:2.

Elizabeth Codner, 1858 Alt. (1824-1919) | EVEN ME 8.7.8.7.6.7. M.M. 92 | William B. Bradbury, 1816-1868

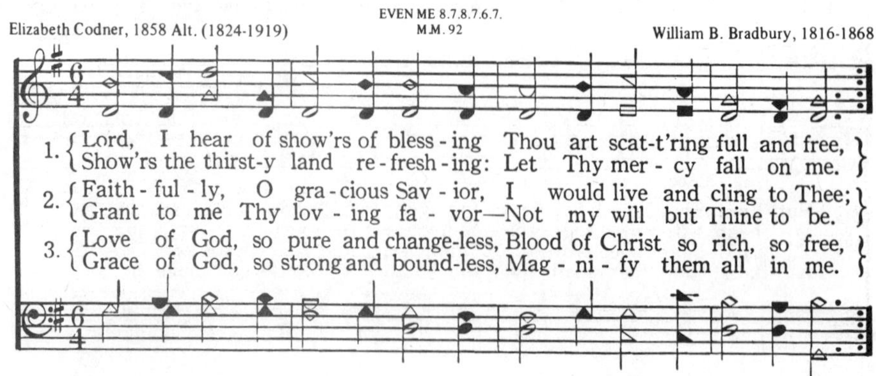
1. Lord, I hear of show'rs of bless - ing Thou art scat-t'ring full and free,
Show'rs the thirst-y land re - fresh - ing: Let Thy mer - cy fall on me.
2. Faith - ful - ly, O gra - cious Sav - ior, I would live and cling to Thee;
Grant to me Thy lov - ing fa - vor—Not my will but Thine to be.
3. Love of God, so pure and change-less, Blood of Christ so rich, so free,
Grace of God, so strong and bound-less, Mag - ni - fy them all in me.

REFRAIN
p
E - ven me, E - ven me, Let Thy mer - cy fall on me.

# 870

## LORD JESUS, I LONG TO BE PERFECTLY WHOLE

*Thy faith hath made thee whole; go in peace.* Mk. 5:34. *Though your sins be as scarlet, they shall be as white as snow.* Is. 1:18.

WHITER THAN SNOW 11.11.11.11. with Ref.
M.M. 72

James Nicholson, 1872 (c. 1828-1876) | William G. Fischer, 1872 (1835-1912)

1. Lord Je-sus, I long to be per-fect-ly whole; I want Thee for-ev-er to live in my soul; Break down ev-'ry i-dol, cast out ev-'ry foe: Now wash me, and I shall be whit-er than snow.
2. Lord Je-sus, look down from Thy throne in the skies, And help me to make a com-plete sac-ri-fice; I give up my-self and what-ev-er I know:
3. Lord Je-sus, Thou see-est I pa-tient-ly wait; Come now, and within me a new heart cre-ate; To those who have sought Thee, Thou never saidst No:

CHORUS

Whit-er than snow, yes, whit-er than snow; Now wash me, and I shall be whit-er than snow.

# 871 IF YE THEN WITH CHRIST BE RISEN

*If ye then be risen with Christ, seek those things which are above, where Christ sitteth on the right hand of God.* Col. 3:1.

IF YE THEN BE RISEN 8.5.8.5.8.7.8.7. with Ref.
M.M. 69
Grant Colfax Tullar, 1926 (1869-1950)
I. H. Meredith, 1926 (1872-1962)
1 If ye then with Christ be ris - en, Seek those things a - bove; Let His glo - ry shine a - round thee, Show-ing forth His love. Once up - on the cross He suf - fered, Gave His life a ran - som free, Yet the grave could not re - tain Him, And He lives e - ter - nal - ly.
2 If ye then with Christ be ris - en, And the vic - t'ry won, Let your thoughts on Him be cen - tered Till the race is run; Let no anx - ious thought per - plex thee, Or temp - ta - tion still dis - may, Think when - e'er the clouds sur - round thee, Soon shall dawn a bright - er day.
3 If ye then with Christ be ris - en, Let thy soul re - joice; Let con - tin - ual praise be sound - ing, With glad heart and voice. He who died to be your Sav - ior Rose a - gain to be your King; If ye then with Him be ris - en, Let your joy - ous prais - es ring.
REFRAIN
If ye then be ris - en ris - en With the King of love, Look not to the things that per - ish, Seek those things a - bove.

# THERE SHALL BE SHOWERS OF BLESSING 872

*There shall be showers of blessing.* Ezek. 34:26. *I am the vine, ye are the branches . . . without Me ye can do nothing.* Jn. 15:5.

SHOWERS OF BLESSINGS 8.7.8.7. with Ref.
M.M. 126
Daniel W. Whittle, 1840-1901
James McGranahan, 1840-1907
1. "There shall be show-ers of bless - ing:" This is the prom-ise of love;
2. "There shall be show-ers of bless - ing:" Pre-cious, re - viv - ing a - gain;
3. "There shall be show-ers of bless - ing:" Send them up-on us, O Lord!
4. "There shall be show-ers of bless - ing:" O that to-day they might fall,
5. "There shall be show-ers of bless - ing," If we but trust and o - bey;
There shall be sea - sons re - fresh - ing, Sent from the Sav - ior a - bove.
O - ver the hills and the val - leys, Sound of a - bun-dance of rain.
Grant to us now a re - fresh - ing; Come, and now hon - or Thy word.
Now as to God we're con - fess - ing, Now as on Je - sus we call!
There shall be sea - sons re - fresh - ing, When we let Him have His way.
CHORUS
Show - - - ers of bless - ing, Show - ers of bless - ing we need;
Show - ers, show - ers of bless - ing,
Mer - cy-drops round us are fall - ing, But for the show-ers we plead.

# 873 LORD, GIVE US A VISION

*Where there is no vision, the people perish.* Prov. 29:18. *I was not disobedient unto the heavenly vision.* Acts 26:19.

VISION 11.8.11.8.
M.M. 108
O. S. Davis
O. S. Davis
1. Lord, give us a vi-sion of souls gone a-stray, Out on the cold
2. The har-vest is great and the lab-'rers are few, The har-vest time
3. Lord, give us a vi-sion of work to be done, Of du-ties neg-
moun-tains of sin; Help us to be work-ing while yet it is day,
soon will be o'er; The Mas-ter is call-ing to me and to you,
lect-ed each day; Re-new our lost vi-sion of souls to be won,
For soon the judg-ment will be-gin.
Go work and be i-dle no more.
Lord, give us a vi-sion we pray.
Refrain
Lord, give us a vi-sion we pray, ......... Help us Thy call to o-bey;.......... Come
of lost souls we pray, to o-bey;
in-to our heart and make it a-new, Lord, give us a vi-sion to-day.

# BACK TO THE BIBLE 874

*And Hilkiah the high priest said unto Shaphan the scribe, I have found the book of the law in the house of the Lord . . . And it came to pass, when the king had heard the words of the book of the law, that he rent his clothes.*
II Kings 22:8, 11.

BACK TO BETHEL 10.10.10.9. with Ref.
M.M. 80

Benjamin Baylus McKinney, 1886-1952 — Benjamin Baylus McKinney

1. Back to the Bi - ble, the true Liv - ing Word, Sweet-est old sto - ry that
2. Back to the beau - ti - ful path I once trod, Back to the church and the
3. Back to the giv - ing of mon - ey and time, Back to the life of con-
4. Back to the prayer-life in Christ I once knew, Back to its beau - ti - ful
ev - er was heard; Back to the joy - life my soul longs to know,
peo - ple of God. Out of the cold world of sin and its woe,
tent - ment sub - lime, Back to pro - tec - tion the world can - not know,
life - cleans - ing dew, Back to help oth - ers to con - quer each foe,
Beth - el is call - ing, and I must go.
CHORUS
Back to Beth - el I must go, Back where the riv - ers of sweet wa - ters flow, Back to the
true life my soul longs to know, Beth-el is call - ing, and I m

# 875 RISE YE CHILDREN OF SALVATION

*Behold, now is the day of salvation.* II Cor. 6:2. *I will wait for the God of my salvation.* Mic. 7:7. *Shew forth from day to day His salvation.* I Chron. 16:23.

Justus Falckner, 1697 (1672-1723)
Auf ihr Christen, Christi Glieder
Tr. Emma Frances Bevan, c. 1858 (b. 1827)
RISE YE CHILDREN 8.7.8.7. with Ref.
M.M. 72
James McGranahan, 1840-1907
Arr. by Compiler, 1970
1. Rise, ye chil-dren of sal - va - tion, All who cleave to Christ the Head;
2. Saints and he-roes long be - fore us Firm-ly on this ground have stood;
3. Death-less, we are all un - fear - ing, Life laid up with Christ in God;
4. Soon we all shall stand be - fore Him, See and know our glo-rious Lord;
Wake, a - rise! O might - y na - tion, Ere the foe on Zi - on tread.
See their ban-ners wav - ing o'er us, Con-quer-ors through Je-sus' blood.
In the morn of His ap - pear - ing Flow-eth forth a glo - ry flood.
Soon in joy and light a - dore Him, Each re-ceiv - ing his re - ward.
CHORUS
Pour it forth . . a might - y
Pour it forth a might- y an - them, pour it forth,
an - them, Like the thun - ders of the sea; . . Thro' the
might- y an - them, Like the thun - ders of the sea;

blood of Christ our ran-som, More than con-quer-ors are we, . . . More than
Through the blood of Christ our ran-som, More than con -

con - quer-ors are we, . . . More than con - quer-ors are
con-quer-ors, con-quer-ors, than con-quer-ors are we, More than con-quer-ors, con-quer-ors, than

we; Thro' the blood of Christ our ran-som, More than con-quer-ors are we.
con-quer-ors are we;

## RISE YE CHILDREN (Alternate Refrain) 876

*Salvation belongeth unto the Lord. Ps. 3:8.*

Justus Falckner, 1697 (1672-1723)
*Auf ihr Christen, Christi Glieder*
Tr. Emma Frances Bevan, c. 1858 (b. 1827)

ÜBERWINDER 8.7.8.7.
M.M. 72

Anon.
Arr. John J. Overholt, 1970

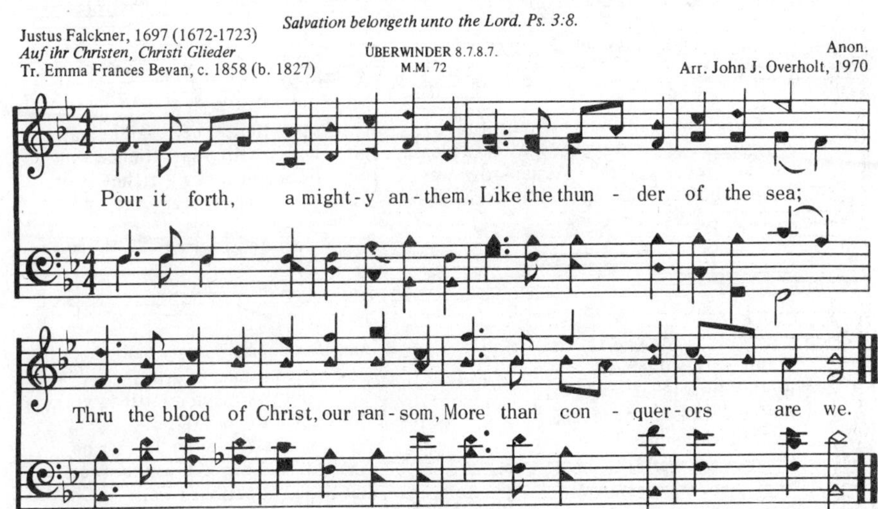
Pour it forth, a might-y an-them, Like the thun - der of the sea;
Thru the blood of Christ, our ran-som, More than con - quer-ors are we.

# 877 YOU WEARY PILGRIMS ROAMING HERE

*Wait for His Son from heaven, whom He raised from the dead, even Jesus.* I Thess. 1:10. *We look not at the things which are seen, but at the things which are not seen . . . which are . . . eternal.* II Cor. 4:18.

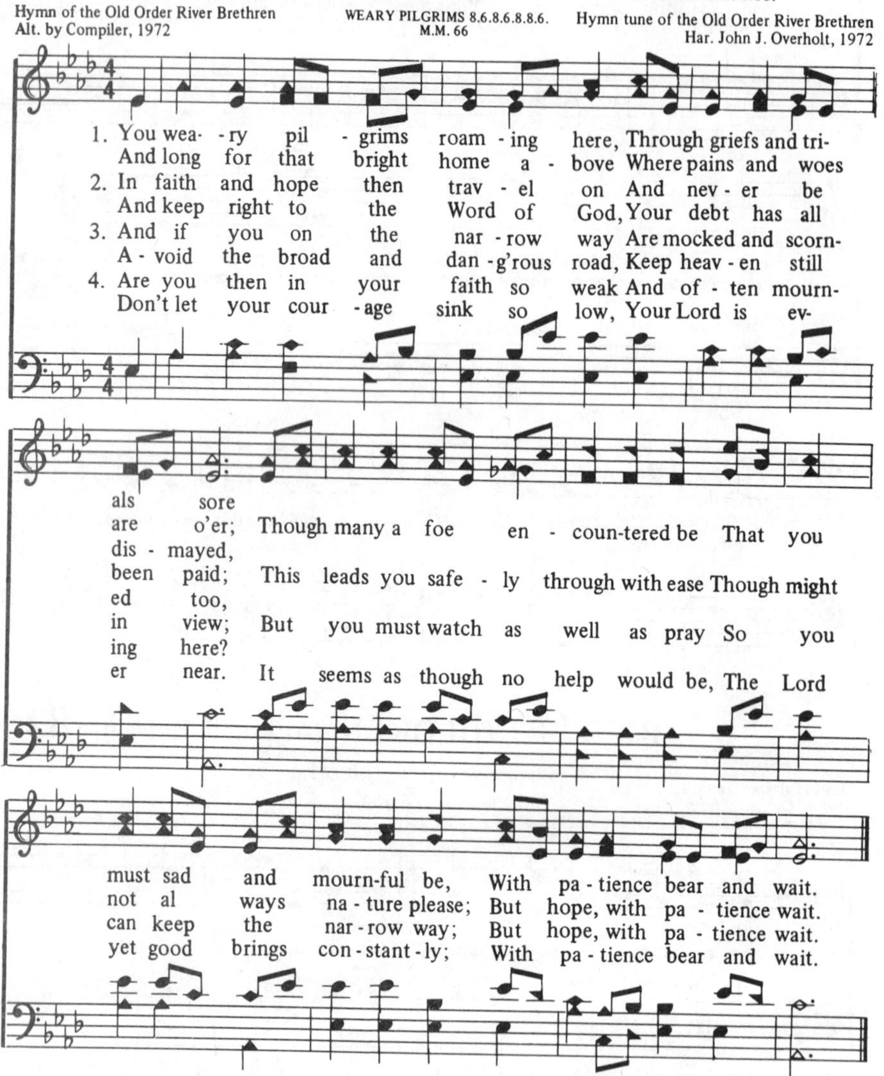
Hymn of the Old Order River Brethren
Alt. by Compiler, 1972
WEARY PILGRIMS 8.6.8.6.8.8.6.
M.M. 66
Hymn tune of the Old Order River Brethren
Har. John J. Overholt, 1972
1. You wea - ry pil - grims roam - ing here, Through griefs and tri-
And long for that bright home a - bove Where pains and woes
2. In faith and hope then trav - el on And nev - er be
And keep right to the Word of God, Your debt has all
3. And if you on the nar - row way Are mocked and scorn-
A - void the broad and dan - g'rous road, Keep heav - en still
4. Are you then in your faith so weak And of - ten mourn-
Don't let your cour - age sink so low, Your Lord is ev-
als sore
are o'er; Though many a foe en - coun-tered be That you
dis - mayed,
been paid; This leads you safe - ly through with ease Though might
ed too,
in view; But you must watch as well as pray So you
ing here?
er near. It seems as though no help would be, The Lord
must sad and mourn-ful be, With pa - tience bear and wait.
not al ways na - ture please; But hope, with pa - tience wait.
can keep the nar - row way; But hope, with pa - tience wait.
yet good brings con - stant - ly; With pa - tience bear and wait.

5. Your Lord leads you so wonderfully
In this dark wilderness,
By this He wishes to reveal
What you in heart possess;
By this we learn, and find we must
Forsake the world, in Jesus trust,
In patience bear and wait.

6. And if it seems so very hard
To bear your load of grief,
Just keep your Saviour still in view,
He'll come to your relief;
And you shall like the Saviour be,
Who suffered anguish you to free;
But hope, in patience wait.

# COME, COME, YE SAINTS 878

*Wherefore gird up the loins of your mind, be sober, and hope to the end for the grace that is to be brought unto you at the revelation of Jesus Christ.* I Pet. 1:13.

William Clayton, 1814-1879
Alt. Joseph F. Green, b. 1924

ALL IS WELL 10.6.10.6.8.8.8.6.
M.M. 63

J. T. White's *Sacred Harp*, 1844

1. Come, come, ye saints, no toil nor la - bor fear; But with joy wend your way. Though hard to you the jour - ney may ap - pear, Grace shall be as your day. We have a liv - ing Lord to guide, And we can trust Him to pro- vide; Do this, and joy your hearts will swell: All is well! All is well!
2. The world of care is with us ev - 'ry day; Let it not this ob-scure: Here we can serve the Mas - ter on the way, And in Him be se - cure. Gird up your loins; fresh cour - age take; Our God will nev - er us for - sake; And so our song no fear can quell: All is well! All is well!
3. We'll find the rest which God for us pre - pared, When at last He will call; Where none will come to hurt or make a - fraid, He will reign o - ver all. We will make the air with mu - sic ring, Shout prais-es to our God and King; O how we'll make the cho-rus swell: All is well! All is well!

# 879 I LOVE THY KINGDOM, LORD

*And he [Paul] . . . spake boldly for the space of three months, disputing and persuading the things concerning the kingdom of God.* Acts 19:8. *The kingdom of God is within you.* Lk. 17:21. *Behold, I have graven thee upon the palms of My hands.* Is. 49:16.

Timothy Dwight, 1800 (1752-1817)
BEALOTH S.M.D. 6.6.8.6.D.
M.M. 72
Lowell Mason, 1792-1872

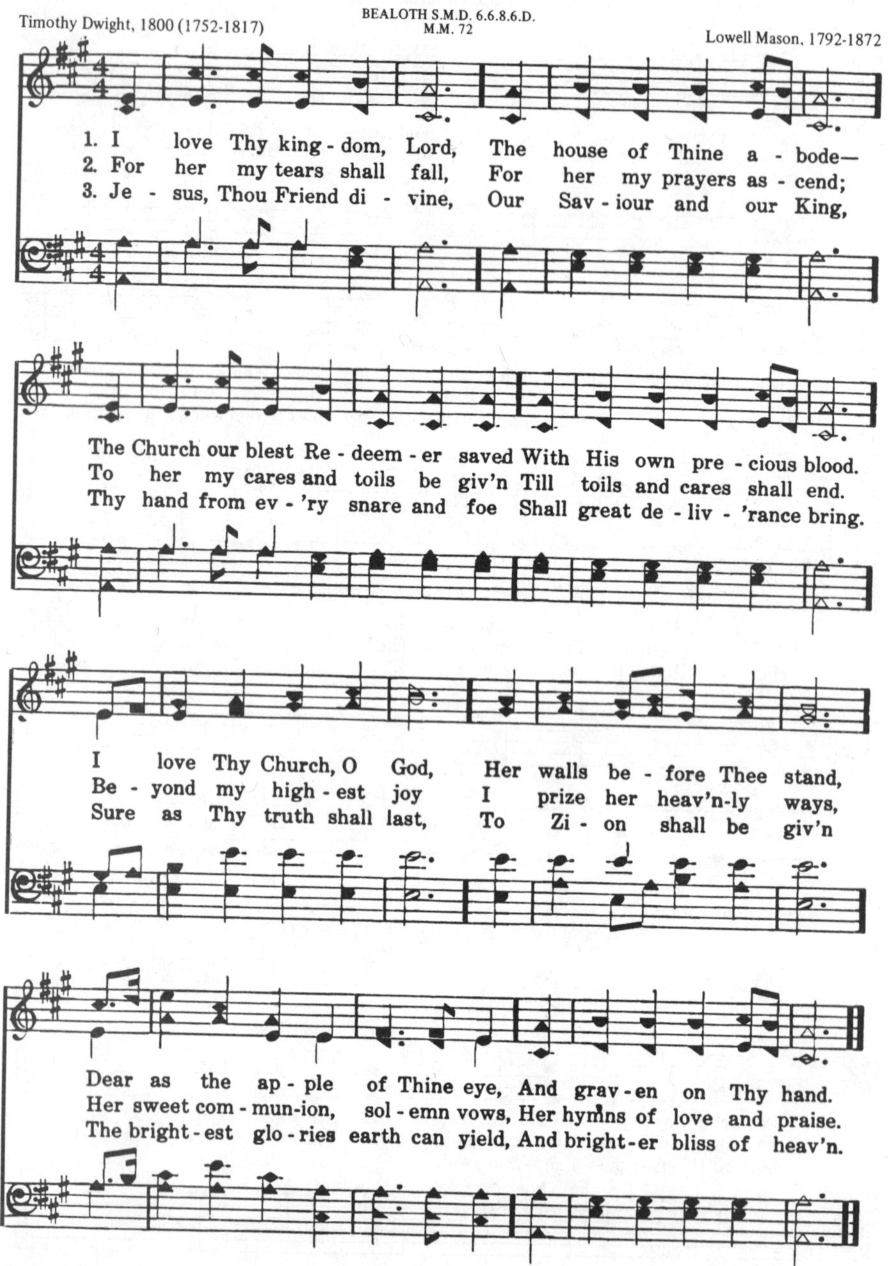
1. I love Thy king - dom, Lord, The house of Thine a - bode—
2. For her my tears shall fall, For her my prayers as - cend;
3. Je - sus, Thou Friend di - vine, Our Sav - iour and our King,
The Church our blest Re - deem - er saved With His own pre - cious blood.
To her my cares and toils be giv'n Till toils and cares shall end.
Thy hand from ev - 'ry snare and foe Shall great de - liv - 'rance bring.
I love Thy Church, O God, Her walls be - fore Thee stand,
Be - yond my high - est joy I prize her heav'n-ly ways,
Sure as Thy truth shall last, To Zi - on shall be giv'n
Dear as the ap - ple of Thine eye, And grav - en on Thy hand.
Her sweet com - mun-ion, sol - emn vows, Her hymns of love and praise.
The bright - est glo - ries earth can yield, And bright - er bliss of heav'n.

# ON JORDAN'S STORMY BANKS I STAND 880

*These all died in faith . . . and confessed that they were strangers and pilgrims on the earth.* Heb. 11:13.

I'M BOUND FOR THE PROMISED LAND C.M. 8.6.8.6. with Ref.
M.M. 69

Samuel Stennet, 1727-1795

American Folk Hymn
Arr. Rigdon M. McIntosh, 1836-1899

1. On Jor-dan's storm-y banks I stand, And cast a wish-ful eye
2. All o'er those wide-ex-tend-ed plains Shines one e-ter-nal day;
3. No chill-ing winds nor poi-s'nous breath Can reach that health-ful shore;
4. When shall I reach that hap-py place, And be for-ev-er blest?
To Ca-naan's fair and hap-py land, Where my pos-ses-sions lie.
There God the Son for-ev-er reigns And scat-ters night a-way.
Sick-ness and sor-row, pain and death Are felt and feared no more.
When shall I see my Fa-ther's face, And in His bos-om rest?
Refrain
I am bound for the prom-ised land, . . . I am bound for the prom-ised land;
O who will come and go with me? I am bound for the prom-ised land.

# 881 HERE SO MANY ARE BREAKING TRADITIONS

*Therefore, brethren, stand fast, and hold the traditions which ye have been taught, whether by word, or our epistle.* II Thess. 2:15.

Albert E. Brumley, b. 1905

ANCIENT LANDMARK 10.9.10.9.D.
M.M. 96

Albert E. Brumley

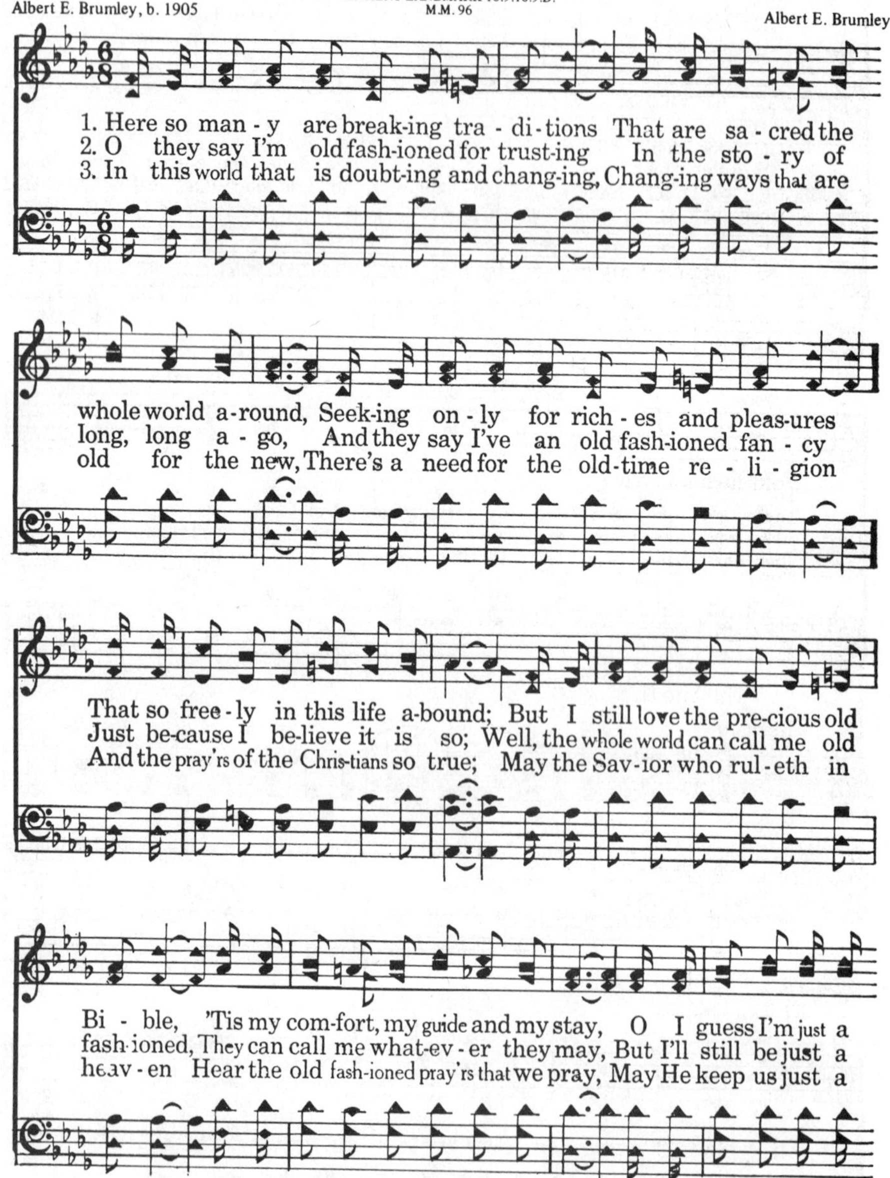
1. Here so man - y are break-ing tra - di - tions That are sa - cred the whole world a-round, Seek-ing on - ly for rich - es and pleas-ures That so free - ly in this life a-bound; But I still love the pre-cious old Bi - ble, 'Tis my com-fort, my guide and my stay, O I guess I'm just a
2. O they say I'm old fash-ioned for trust-ing In the sto - ry of long, long a - go, And they say I've an old fash-ioned fan - cy Just be-cause I be-lieve it is so; Well, the whole world can call me old fash-ioned, They can call me what-ev - er they may, But I'll still be just a
3. In this world that is doubt-ing and chang-ing, Chang-ing ways that are old for the new, There's a need for the old-time re - li - gion And the pray'rs of the Chris-tians so true; May the Sav-ior who rul - eth in heav - en Hear the old fash-ioned pray'rs that we pray, May He keep us just a

lit - tle old fash-ioned But I still love the old fash-ioned way.
lit - tle old fash-ioned For I still love the old fash-ioned way.
lit - tle old fash-ioned For I still love the old fash-ioned way.
CHORUS
O I guess I'm just a lit-tle old fash-ioned, But I still love the
old fash-ioned way, Lord, I care not for the world and its glo - ry,
Or the life that is mod-ern and gay; But I still love the songs a-bout
Je-sus And I still love the Bi-ble so true; O I guess I'm just a
lit - tle old fash-ioned, But my Sav-ior was old fash-ioned, too.

# 882 THERE'S A FOUNTAIN THAT FLOWS

*And He shewed me a pure river of water of life, clear as crystal, proceeding out of the throne of God and of the Lamb.* Rev. 22:1.

H. F. Page FOUNTAIN OF LOVE 6.6.9.6.6.9. M.M. 56 H. F. Page

1. There's a foun-tain that flows Where the light ever glows, In the beau-ti - ful land of the skies; 'Tis the foun-tain of love In the re-gions a-bove, And the gleam on its stream never dies.
2. From the great throne of God Flows this soul cleansing flood, Gliding on in its pla - cid re - pose; They who drink of its tide Shall in peace e'er abide, Saved from sin and re-deemed from its woes.
3. When the heav-ens shall rend And the Lord shall de-scend To re-ceive all its ransomed a-bove, O the glo-ri-ous time, As the home bells shall chime, And we meet 'round that fountain of love.
REFRAIN:
Fountain of life, Fountain of life, Fountain of love, Fountain of love,
Je-sus in-vites to the soul-cleansing flood; Fountain of life, Fountain of life,
Fountain of love, Fountian of love, Open to all who will come thro' His blood.
3

# JESUS CAME FROM GLORY TO DIE 883

*Ye shall be witnesses unto me both in Jerusalem, and in all Judea, and in Samaria, and unto the uttermost part of the earth.* Acts 1:8.

SPREAD THE GOOD NEWS 10.6.10.6. with Ref.
M.M. 69

B. B. Edmiasten

Samuel W. Beazley, 1873-1944

1. Je-sus came from glo-ry to die for all, Spread the news, glad good news;
2. Let the soul that heareth bid others come,
3. "Who-so-ev-er will let him come today, Spread the news, glad good news;
Bid the sin-bound souls hear redemption's call, Spread the news, glad good news.
Speak in word and deed of the heav'nly home,
Fill the earth with joy, drive the gloom away, Spread the news, glad good news.
REFRAIN:
Spread the good news, ............ Spread the good news .................. To the
all a - round, far and wide,
wea - ry and the sad; ............ Spread the good news, ........... Spread the
wea-ry and the sad; all a - round.
good news, ................. It will make the whole world glad.
far and wide, the whole world glad.

# 884 GO OUT AND GATHER THE GOLDEN GRAIN

*The harvest truly is plentious.* Mt. 9:37. *He that winneth souls is wise.* Prov. 11:30.

Mrs. E. W. Chapman

GATHER THE GOLDEN GRAIN 9.7.9.7. with Ref.
M.M. 69

Frank M. Davis, 1839-1896

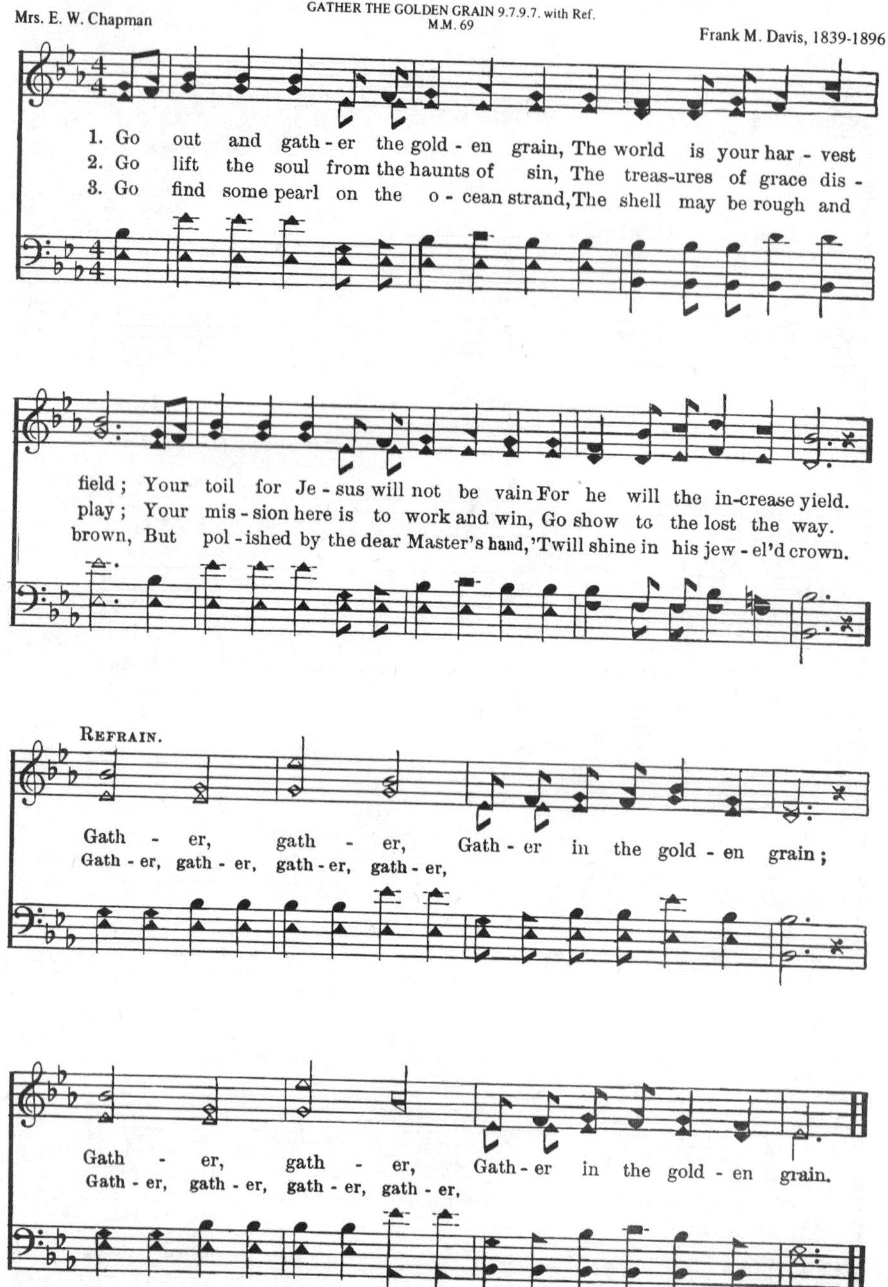
1. Go out and gath - er the gold - en grain, The world is your har - vest field; Your toil for Je - sus will not be vain For he will the in-crease yield.
2. Go lift the soul from the haunts of sin, The treas-ures of grace dis - play; Your mis - sion here is to work and win, Go show to the lost the way.
3. Go find some pearl on the o - cean strand, The shell may be rough and brown, But pol - ished by the dear Master's hand, 'Twill shine in his jew - el'd crown.
REFRAIN.
Gath - er, gath - er, Gath - er in the gold - en grain;
Gath - er, gath - er, gath - er, gath - er,
Gath - er, gath - er, Gath - er in the gold - en grain.
Gath - er, gath - er, gath - er, gath - er,

# THE TIME OF THE HARVEST IS NIGH 885

*The harvest truly is great.* Lk. 10:2. *The fields . . . are white already to harvest.* Jn. 4:35. *Others save with fear, pulling them out of the fire.* Jude 23.

THE LABORERS ARE FEW 8.8.4.5.8. with Ref.
M.M. 120

R. A. Evilsizer

J. Henry Showalter, 1864-1947

1. The time of the har-vest is nigh, All rip-ened the wait-ing fields lie;
2. The Lord of the har-vest needs you — There's work that you on - ly can do;
3. Oh, broth - er, the la - bor is blest, And af - ter the toil com - eth rest;
The la-b'rers are few, Christ call-eth for you To glean for his gar-ner on high.
Then do not de - lay, But has-ten a - way And glean where the toil-ers are few.
Your Saviour and Lord Will rich-ly re-ward, If you will but heed his re - quest.
Refrain
The la - b'rers are few; Christ call - eth for you; . Then
The lab'rers, the lab'rers are few, are few, Christ calleth, he call - eth for you, for you; Then
has - ten a - way, . The Lord of the har-vest o - bey. ( to-day )
has-ten, oh, has - ten a - way, a-way, The Lord of the har - vest o - bey. ( to-day.)

# 886 THERE WERE NINETY AND NINE

*Doth he not leave the ninety and nine, and goeth into the mountains, and seeketh that which is gone astray?* Mt. 18:12.

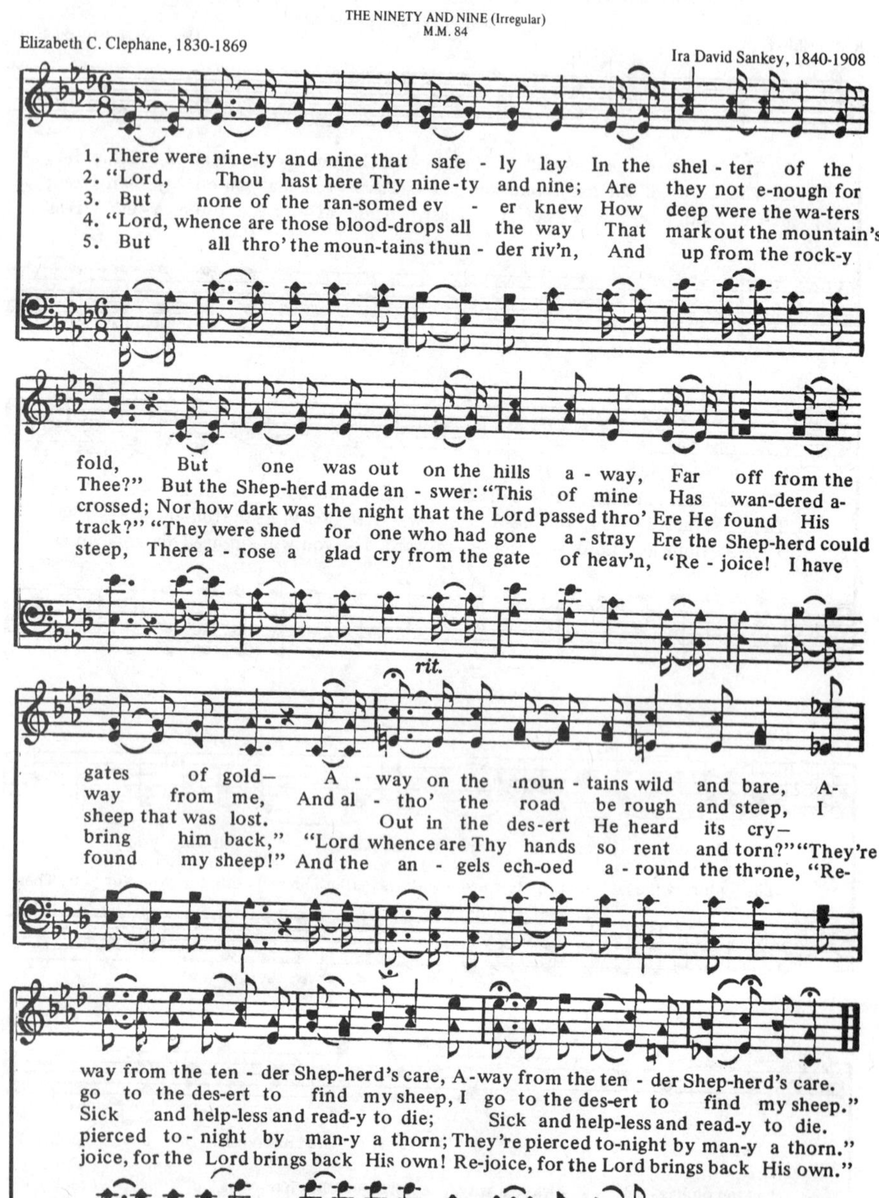
THE NINETY AND NINE (Irregular)
M.M. 84
Elizabeth C. Clephane, 1830-1869
Ira David Sankey, 1840-1908
1. There were nine-ty and nine that safe - ly lay In the shel - ter of the
2. "Lord, Thou hast here Thy nine-ty and nine; Are they not e-nough for
3. But none of the ran-somed ev - er knew How deep were the wa-ters
4. "Lord, whence are those blood-drops all the way That mark out the mountain's
5. But all thro' the moun-tains thun - der riv'n, And up from the rock-y
fold, But one was out on the hills a - way, Far off from the
Thee?" But the Shep-herd made an - swer: "This of mine Has wan-dered a-
crossed; Nor how dark was the night that the Lord passed thro' Ere He found His
track?" "They were shed for one who had gone a - stray Ere the Shep-herd could
steep, There a - rose a glad cry from the gate of heav'n, "Re - joice! I have
rit.
gates of gold— A - way on the moun - tains wild and bare, A-
way from me, And al - tho' the road be rough and steep, I
sheep that was lost. Out in the des-ert He heard its cry—
bring him back," "Lord whence are Thy hands so rent and torn?" "They're
found my sheep!" And the an - gels ech-oed a - round the throne, "Re-
way from the ten - der Shep-herd's care, A-way from the ten - der Shep-herd's care.
go to the des-ert to find my sheep, I go to the des-ert to find my sheep."
Sick and help-less and read-y to die; Sick and help-less and read-y to die.
pierced to-night by man-y a thorn; They're pierced to-night by man-y a thorn."
joice, for the Lord brings back His own! Re-joice, for the Lord brings back His own."

# THE NINETY-NINE WITHIN THE FOLD 887

*My people hath been lost sheep: their shepherds have caused them to go astray, they have turned them away on the mountains.* Jer. 50:6. *For ye were as sheep going astray; but are now returned.* I Pet. 2:25.

William G. Schell, (b. 1869) — THE NINETY-NINE L.M. 8.8.8.8 with Ref. M.M. 60 — B. Elliot Warren, 1867-1951

1. The nine - ty - nine with - in the fold, Are safe from fears and storms of night,
2. The nine - ty - nine are safe to - day, They're all at home, so ful - ly blest,
3. The nine - ty - nine with care are fed, And rest with-in the Shepherd's fold;
4. The Shepherd dear, a - loud doth weep Be - cause one lamb a - far doth roam;
But one is on the moun-tains cold, 'Twill per-ish there—how sad the sight!
But one is wand-'ring far a - way, Up - on the mountain's snow-y crest.
But one is starv - ing, near - ly dead, Up - on the mountains bare and cold.
The nine - ty-nine He'll safe - ly keep,—We'll seek that lamb and bring it home.
REFRAIN
Go search it out, and bring it home, No more in dark - ness let it roam:
You'll find it there in dread-ful plight, Oh! go and bring it back to-night.

# 888 TO THE WORK! TO THE WORK!

*Go work today in my vineyard.* Mt. 21:28. *This we commanded you, that if any would not work, neither should he eat.* II Thess. 3:10.

Anon. TO THE WORK 12.12.12.12. with Ref. M.M. 69 William H. Doane, 1832-1915

1. To the work! to the work! we are serv-ants of God, Let us fol - low the
2. To the work! to the work! let the hun - gry be fed; To the foun-tain of
3. To the work! to the work! there is lab - or for all, For the king-dom of
4. To the work! to the work! in the strength of the Lord, And a robe and a
path that our Mas-ter has trod; With the balm of His coun - sel our strength to renew,
Life let the wea - ry be led; In the cross and its ban - ner our glo - ry shall be,
dark-ness and er-ror shall fall, And the name of Je - ho - vah ex - alt - ed shall be
crown shall our la-bor reward; When the home of the faith-ful our dwell-ing shall be,
CHORUS
Let us do with our might what our hands find to do. Toil-ing on,
While we her-ald the ti-dings, "Sal - va - tion is free!"
In the loud swell-ing cho - rus "Sal - va - tion is free!"
And we shout with the ransomed, "Sal - va - tion is free!"
Toil-ing on,
toil - ing on, Toil - ing on, toil - ing on,
toil - ing on Toil-ing on toil - ing on,
Let us hope, let us watch, And la - bor till the Mas - ter comes.
and trust, and pray,

# O LAND OF REST, FOR THEE I SIGH 889

*The people had a mind to work.* Neh. 4:6. *Work: for I am with you.* Hag. 2:4.

WE'LL WORK TILL JESUS COMES C.M. 8.6.8.6. with Ref.
M.M. 72

Elizabeth K. Mills, 1805-1829 — William Miller, 1801-1878

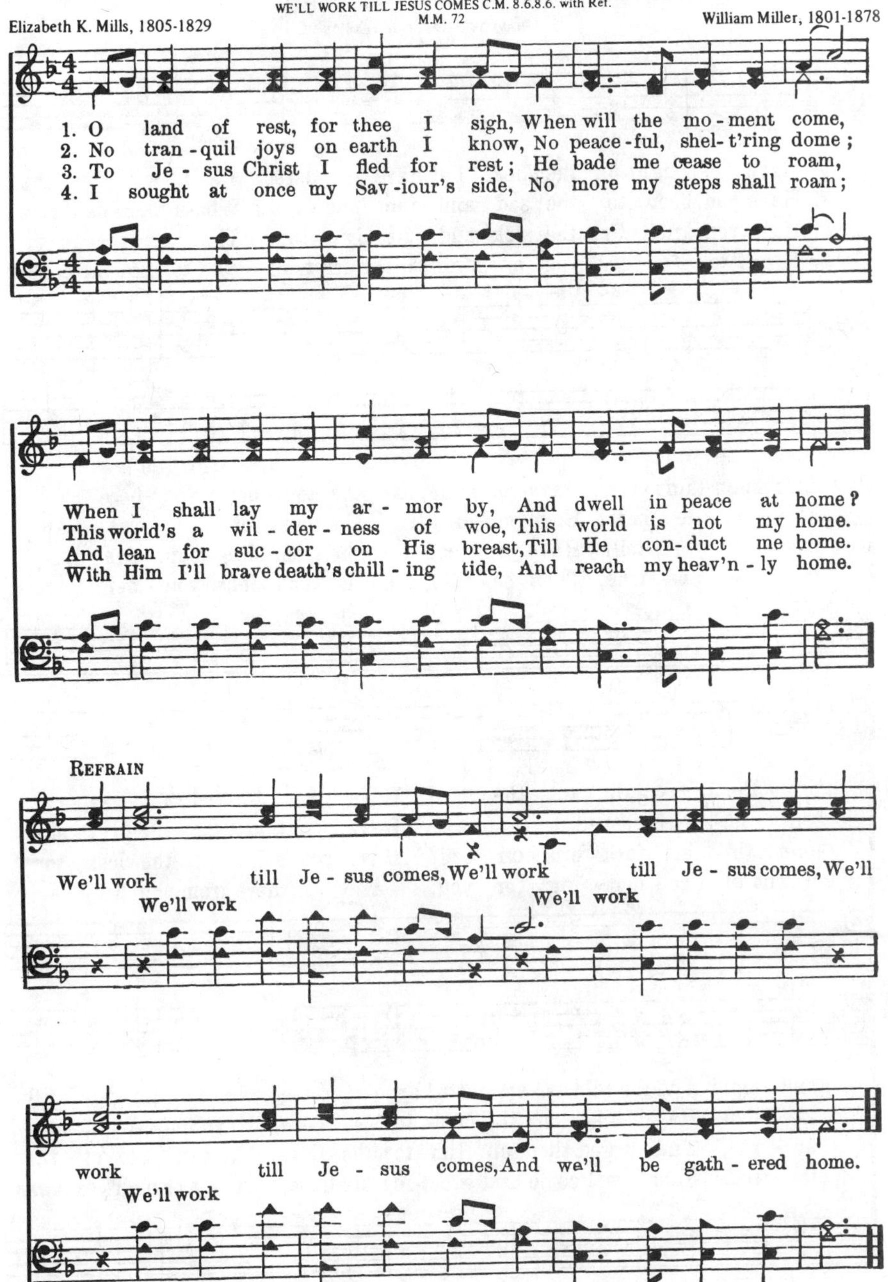
1. O land of rest, for thee I sigh, When will the mo - ment come,
2. No tran - quil joys on earth I know, No peace - ful, shel - t'ring dome;
3. To Je - sus Christ I fled for rest; He bade me cease to roam,
4. I sought at once my Sav - iour's side, No more my steps shall roam;
When I shall lay my ar - mor by, And dwell in peace at home?
This world's a wil - der - ness of woe, This world is not my home.
And lean for suc - cor on His breast, Till He con - duct me home.
With Him I'll brave death's chill - ing tide, And reach my heav'n - ly home.
REFRAIN
We'll work till Je - sus comes, We'll work till Je - sus comes, We'll
We'll work
We'll work
work till Je - sus comes, And we'll be gath - ered home.
We'll work

# 890 HAVE YOU SOUGHT FOR THE SHEEP

*My sheep wandered through all the mountains . . . My flock was scattered upon all the face of the earth, and none did search or seek after them.* Ezek. 34:6.

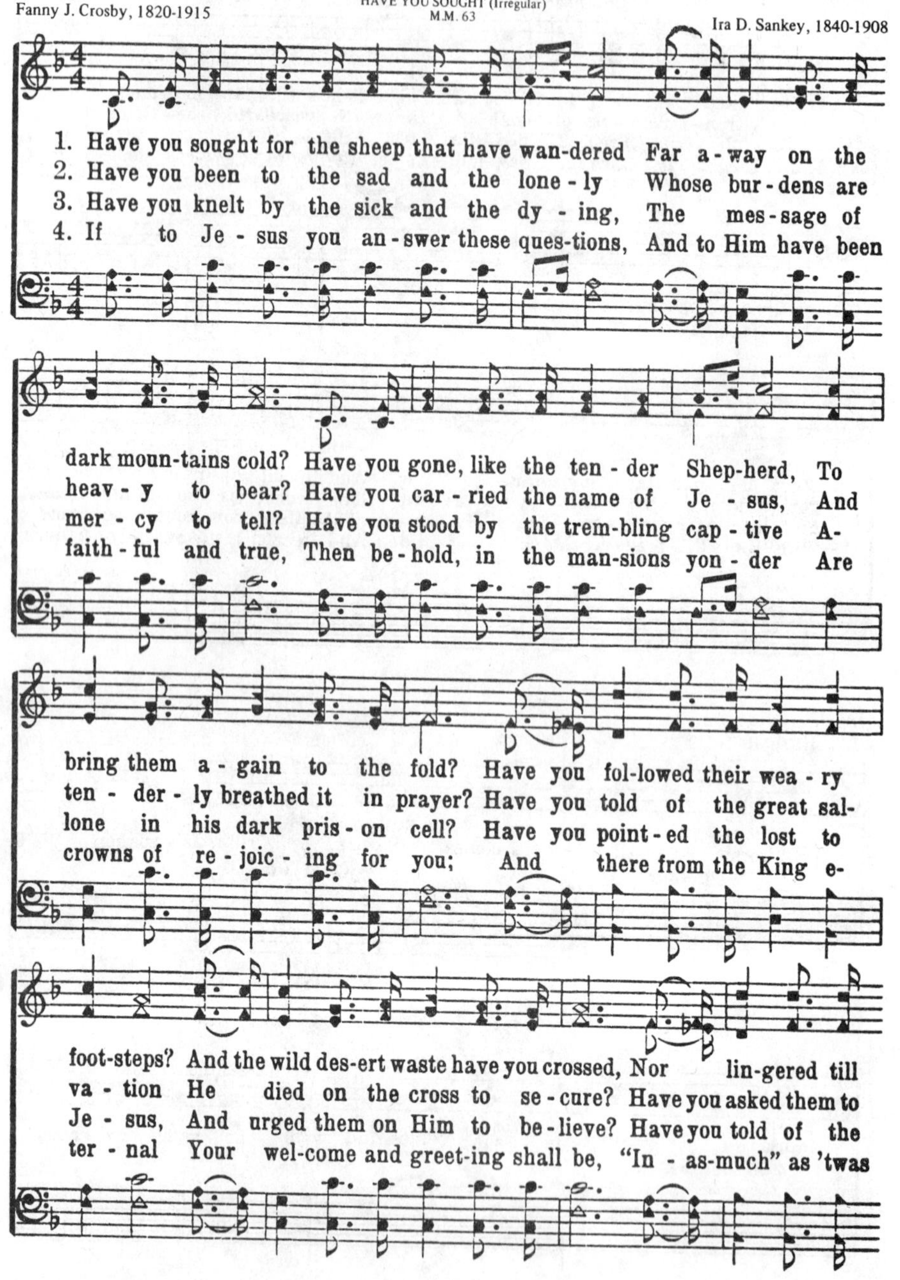
Fanny J. Crosby, 1820-1915
HAVE YOU SOUGHT (Irregular)
M.M. 63
Ira D. Sankey, 1840-1908
1. Have you sought for the sheep that have wan-dered Far a-way on the
2. Have you been to the sad and the lone-ly Whose bur-dens are
3. Have you knelt by the sick and the dy-ing, The mes-sage of
4. If to Je-sus you an-swer these ques-tions, And to Him have been
dark moun-tains cold? Have you gone, like the ten-der Shep-herd, To
heav-y to bear? Have you car-ried the name of Je-sus, And
mer-cy to tell? Have you stood by the trem-bling cap-tive A-
faith-ful and true, Then be-hold, in the man-sions yon-der Are
bring them a-gain to the fold? Have you fol-lowed their wea-ry
ten-der-ly breathed it in prayer? Have you told of the great sal-
lone in his dark pris-on cell? Have you point-ed the lost to
crowns of re-joic-ing for you; And there from the King e-
foot-steps? And the wild des-ert waste have you crossed, Nor lin-gered till
va-tion He died on the cross to se-cure? Have you asked them to
Je-sus, And urged them on Him to be-lieve? Have you told of the
ter-nal Your wel-come and greet-ing shall be, "In-as-much" as 'twas

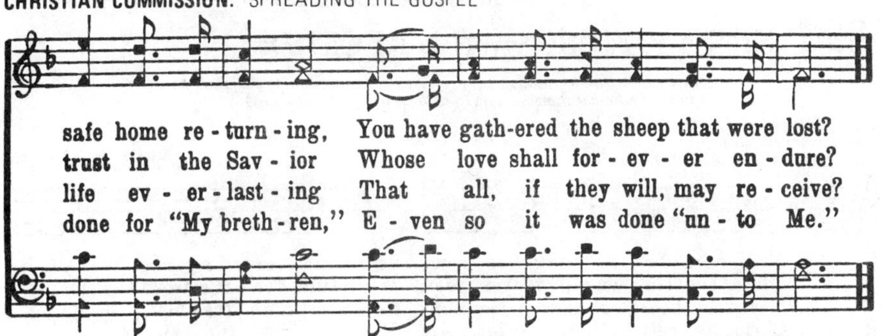
safe home re - turn - ing, You have gath-ered the sheep that were lost?
trust in the Sav - ior Whose love shall for - ev - er en - dure?
life ev - er - last - ing That all, if they will, may re - ceive?
done for "My breth - ren," E - ven so it was done "un - to Me."

# HARK! 'TIS THE SHEPHERD'S VOICE 891

*He shall feed His flock like a shepherd.* Is. 40:11. *Go ye therefore into the highways, and as many as ye shall find, bid to the marriage.* Mt. 22:9.

BRING THEM IN L.M. 8.8.8.8. with Ref.
M.M. 76

Alexcenah Thomas

William A. Ogden, 1841-1897

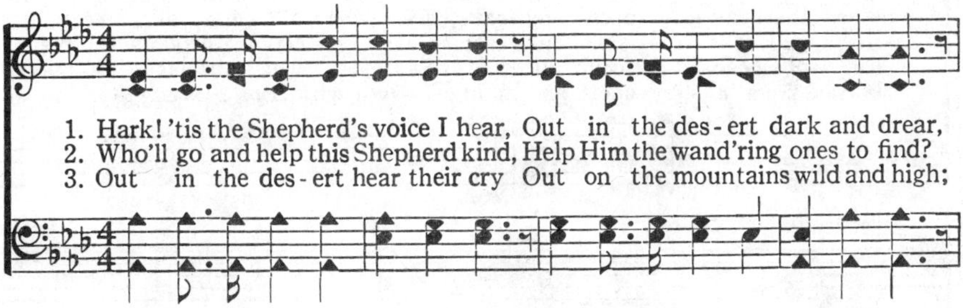

1. Hark! 'tis the Shepherd's voice I hear, Out in the des - ert dark and drear,
2. Who'll go and help this Shepherd kind, Help Him the wand'ring ones to find?
3. Out in the des - ert hear their cry Out on the mountains wild and high;

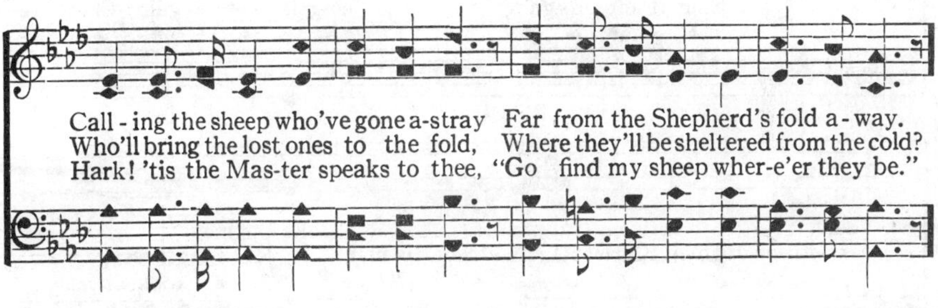

Call - ing the sheep who've gone a-stray Far from the Shepherd's fold a - way.
Who'll bring the lost ones to the fold, Where they'll be sheltered from the cold?
Hark! 'tis the Mas-ter speaks to thee, "Go find my sheep wher-e'er they be."

**Chorus**

1 2

Bring them in, bring them in, Bring them in from the fields of sin;
Bring them in, bring them in, Bring the wand'ring ones to (*Omit* . . . .) Je - sus.

# 892 SINNERS JESUS WILL RECEIVE

*This man receiveth sinners.* Lk. 15:2. *He that cometh to Me shall never hunger . . . him that cometh to Me I will in no wise cast out.* Jn. 6:35, 37.

Erdman Neumeister, 1671-1756
*Jesus nimmt die Sünder an*
Tr. Emma F. Bevan, 1827-1909

CHRIST RECEIVETH SINFUL MEN 7.7.7.7. with Ref.
M.M. 60

James McGranahan, 1840-1907

1. Sin - ners Je - sus will re - ceive; Sound this word of grace to all
2. Come, and He will give you rest; Trust Him, for His word is plain;
3. Now my heart con-demns me not, Pure be - fore the law I stand;
4. Christ re - ceiv - eth sin - ful men, E - ven me with all my sin;
Who the heav'n-ly path - way leave, All who lin - ger, all who fall.
He will take the sin - ful - est; Christ re - ceiv - eth sin - ful men.
He who cleansed me from all spot, Sat - is - fied its last de - mand.
Purged from ev - 'ry spot and stain, Heav'n with Him I en - ter in.
REFRAIN
Sing it o'er............ and o'er a - gain;........... Christ re-
Sing it o'er a - gain, sing it o'er a - gain; Christ re-
ceiv - - eth sin - ful men;........... Make the mes - - sage
ceiv-eth sin-ful men, Christ re-ceiv-eth sin-ful men; Make the message plain,
clear and plain:............. Christ re - ceiv - eth sin - ful men.
make the message plain:

# I WILL SING THE WONDROUS STORY 893

*Deliver me from bloodguiltiness, O God, thou God of my salvation: and my tongue shall sing aloud of Thy righteousness.* Ps. 51:14.

Francis H. Rowley, 1886 (1854-1952)
Alt. by Ira David Sankey, 1887 (1840-1908)

THE WONDROUS STORY 8.7.8.7. with Ref.
M.M. 72

Peter P. Bilhorn, 1886 (1865-1936)

1. I will sing the won-drous sto-ry Of the Christ who died for me,
2. I was lost, but Je-sus found me, Found the sheep that went a-stray,
3. I was bruised, but Je-sus healed me; Faint was I from many a fall;
4. Days of dark-ness still come o'er me, Sor-row's paths I of-ten tread,
5. He will keep me till the riv-er Rolls its wa-ters at my feet;
How He left His home in glo-ry For the cross of Cal-va-ry.
Threw His lov-ing arms a-round me, Drew me back in-to His way.
Sight was gone, and fears pos-sessed me, But He freed me from them all.
But the Sav-ior still is with me; By His hand I'm safe-ly led.
Then He'll bear me safe-ly o-ver, Where the loved ones I shall meet.
CHORUS
Yes, I'll sing . . . the won-drous sto - - - ry Of the
Yes, I'll sing the won-drous sto-ry
Christ . . . who died for me, . . . . . Sing it with . . . the saints in
Of the Christ who died for me, Sing it with
glo - - - ry, Gath-ered by . . . the crys-tal sea. . . . . .
the saints in glo-ry, Gath-ered by the crys-tal sea.

# 894 COME YE SINNERS, POOR AND NEEDY

*And the Spirit and the bride say, Come. And let him that heareth say, Come.* Rev. 22:17.

Arr. Joseph Hart, 1712-1768
KOMMT IHR SÜNDER 8.7.8.7.D.
M.M. 72
Unknown German Source
Arr. John J. Overholt, 1965
1. Come, ye sin - ners, poor and need - y, Weak and wound-ed, sick and sore,
2. Let not con-science make you lin - ger, Nor of fit - ness fond - ly dream;
3. Ag - o - ni - zing in the gar - den, Lo, your Sav - iour pros-trate lies!
4. Lo! the ris - ing Lord as - cend - ing, Pleads the vir - tue of his blood;
5. Saints and an - gels, joined in con - cert, Voice the prais - es of the Lamb,
Je - sus rea - dy stands to save you, Full of pit - y, love, and pow'r;
All the fit - ness he re - quir - eth Is to feel your need of him;
On the blood - y tree be - hold him! Hear him cry be - fore he dies:
Ven - ture on him, ven - ture free - ly, Let no oth - er trust in - trude;
While the bliss - ful seats of heav - en Sweet-ly ech - o with his name;
He is a - ble, he is a - ble, He is will - ing doubt no more;
Grace he gives you, grace he gives you, 'Tis the Sav - iour's balm for sin
"It is fin - ished, it is fin-ished!" Sinners, will not this suf-fice?
None but Je - sus, none but Je - sus Can do help - less sin-ners good;
Hal - le - lu - jah! Hal - le - lu - jah! Saints on earth may do the same;
He is a - ble, he is a - ble, He is will - ing doubt no more.
Grace he gives you, grace he gives you, 'Tis the Sav - iour's balm for sin
"It is fin - ished, it is fin - ished!" Sinners, will not this suf - fice?
None but Je - sus, none but Je - sus Can do help - less sin - ners good.
Hal - le - lu - jah! hal - le - lu - jah! Saints on earth may do the same.

# WERE YOU THERE 895

*And they crucified Him.* Mt. 27:35.

WERE YOU THERE (Irregular)
M.M. 60

Anon. Anon.

1. Were you there when they cru - ci - fied my Lord? (Were you there)
2. Were you there when they nailed Him to the tree? (Were you there)
3. Were you there when they pierced Him in the side? (Were you there)
4. Were you there when they laid Him in the tomb? (Were you there)
5. Were you there when He rose up from the grave? (Were you there)

Were you there when they cru - ci - fied my Lord? (Were you there)
Were you there when they nailed Him to the tree? (Were you there)
Were you there when they pierced Him in the side? (Were you there)
Were you there when they laid Him in the tomb? (Were you there)
Were you there when He rose up from the grave? (Were you there)

1-4. Oh! . . . . . . . . . Some-times it caus - es me to trem-ble, tremble, tremble,
5. Oh! . . . . . . . . . No more it caus - es me to trem-ble, tremble, tremble,

Were you there when they cru - ci - fied my Lord? (Were you there)
Were you there when they nailed Him to the tree? (Were you there)
Were you there when they pierced Him in the side? (Were you there)
Were you there when they laid Him in the tomb? (Were you there)
Were you there when He rose up from the grave? (Were you there)

# 896 O, DO NOT LET THE WORD DEPART

*For if we sin wilfully after that we have received the knowledge of the truth, there remaineth no more sacrifice for sins, But a certain fearful looking for of judgment.* Heb. 10:26, 27.

O WHY NOT TONIGHT 8.8.8.5. with Ref.
M.M. 60

Horatius Bonar, 1808-1889 | J. Calvin Bushey

1. Oh, do not let the Word de-part, And close thine eyes a-gainst the
2. To-mor-row's sun may nev-er rise To bless thy long de-lud-ed
3. Our Lord in pit-y lin-gers still: And wilt thou thus His love re-
4. Our bless-ed Lord re-fus-es none Who would to Him their souls u-
light; Poor sin-ner, hard-en not your heart, Be saved, oh, to-night.
sight; This is the time, oh, then be wise, Be saved, oh, to-night.
quite? Re-nounce at once thy stub-born will, Be saved, oh, to-night.
nite. Be-lieve, o-bey, the work is done, Be saved, oh, to-night.
REFRAIN
Oh, why not to-night? Oh, why not to-
Oh, why not to-night? Why not to-night? Why not to-night?
night? Wilt thou be saved? Then why not to-night?
Why not to-night? Wilt thou be saved, wilt thou be saved, Then why not, oh, why not to-night?

# THERE IS A GATE THAT STANDS AJAR 897

*Having therefore, brethren, boldness to enter into the holiest by the blood of Jesus, Let us draw near with a true heart in full assurance of faith.* Heb. 10:19, 22.

THE GATE AJAR 8.7.8.7. with Ref.
M.M. 108

Lydia Baxter, 1809-1874

Silas Jonas Vail, 1818-1884

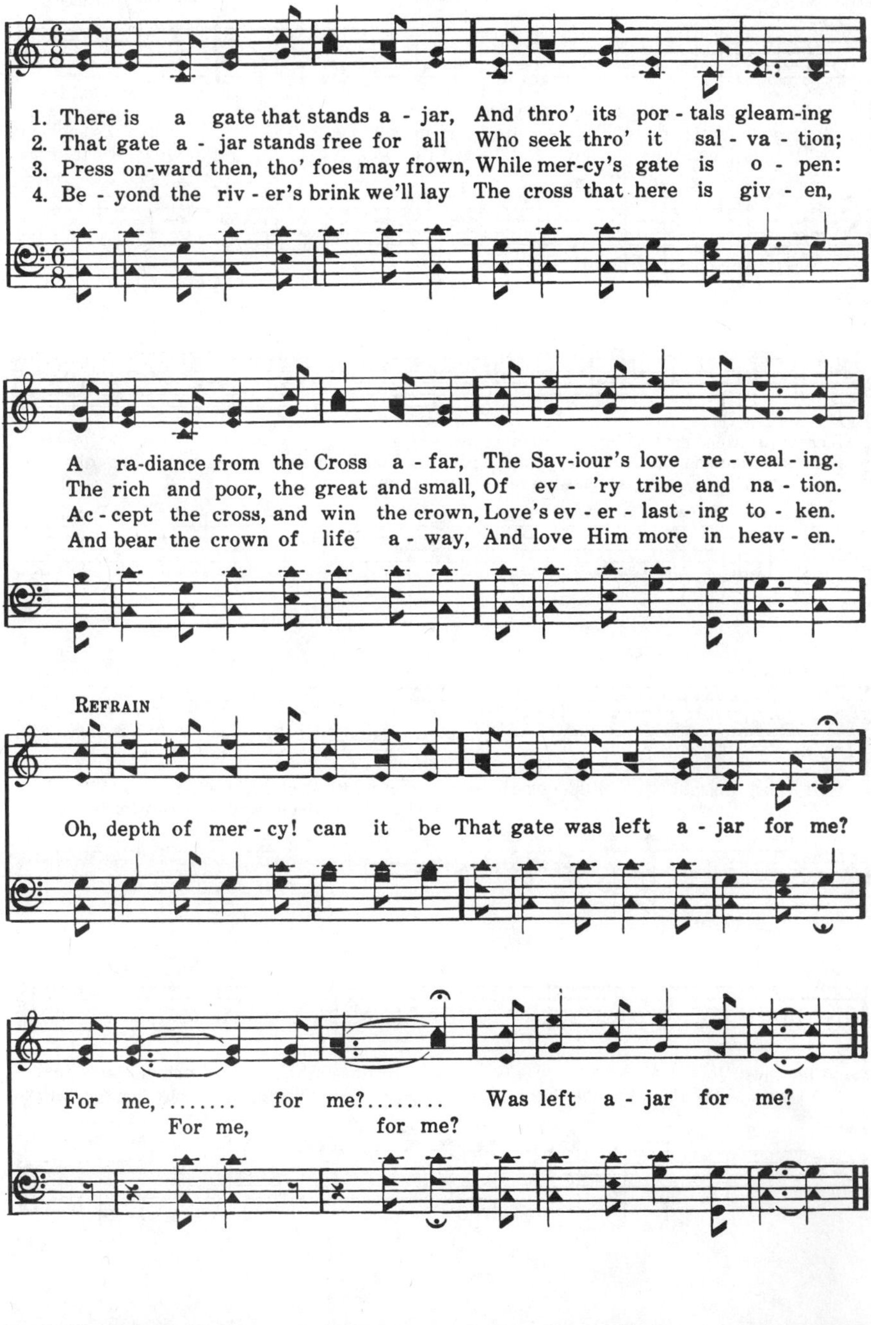

1. There is a gate that stands a - jar, And thro' its por - tals gleam-ing
A ra-diance from the Cross a - far, The Sav-iour's love re - veal - ing.

2. That gate a - jar stands free for all Who seek thro' it sal - va - tion;
The rich and poor, the great and small, Of ev - 'ry tribe and na - tion.

3. Press on-ward then, tho' foes may frown, While mer-cy's gate is o - pen:
Ac - cept the cross, and win the crown, Love's ev - er - last - ing to - ken.

4. Be - yond the riv - er's brink we'll lay The cross that here is giv - en,
And bear the crown of life a - way, And love Him more in heav - en.

REFRAIN

Oh, depth of mer - cy! can it be That gate was left a - jar for me?
For me, ....... for me?........ Was left a - jar for me?
For me, for me?

# 898 HAVE YOU WANDERED AWAY

*The younger son gathered all together, and took his journey into a far country, and there wasted his substance with riotous living . . . And he arose, and came to his father. But when he was yet a great way off, his father saw him, and had compassion, and ran, and fell on his neck, and kissed him.* Lk. 15:13, 20.

CHILD COME HOME 11.9.11.9. with Ref.
M.M. 66

Kem G. Bottorf

Kem G. Bottorf
Arr. John J. Overholt, 1970

1. Have you wan-dered a - way from your Fa-ther's care, Hea-vy heart-ed and sad do you roam?
2. Is your frail bark a - drift on life's rag-ing sea, Are you tossed on its bil-lows and foam?
3. He is plead-ing to - day, heed His gen-tle voice, As He bids you no long-er to roam,
There's a sweet gen-tle voice call-ing now to you,
There's a safe har-bor home now wait-ing for you, Wan-d'ring child, wan-d'ring child, O come home.
To that dear Fa-ther's house haste with-out de-lay,
Child, come home, child, come home, Wan-d'ring child, why long-er roam?
Child, come home child, come home Wan-d'ring child why long-er roam?
'Tis thy Fa - ther en - treats, Wan-d'ring child, O come home.
'Tis thy Fa - ther now en - treats, Wan-d'ring child, come home, come home.

# SOFTLY AND TENDERLY JESUS IS CALLING 899

*Behold, I stand at the door, and knock: if any man hear my voice and open the door, I will come in to him, and will sup with him, and he with Me.* Rev. 3:20.

SOFTLY AND TENDERLY 11.7.11.7. with Ref.
M.M. 84

Will L. Thompson, 1847-1909 — Will L. Thompson

1. Soft-ly and ten-der-ly Je-sus is call-ing, Call-ing for you and for me;
2. Why should we tarry when Jesus is pleading, Plead-ing for you and for me;
3. Time is now fleeting, the moments are passing, Passing for you and for me;
4. Oh! for the won-der-ful love He has promised, Promised for you and for me;
See, on the por-tals He's watching and waiting, Watch-ing for you and for me.
Why should we lin-ger and heed not His mer-cies, Mer-cies for you and for me.
Shad-ows are gath-er-ing, death beds are com-ing, Com-ing for you and for me.
Tho' we have sinned, He has mer-cy and par-don, Par - don for you and for me.
REFRAIN
Come home,.... come home,.... Ye who are wea-ry, come home!....
Come home, come home,
rit.
Ear-nest-ly, ten-der-ly, Je-sus is call-ing, Call-ing, O sin-ner, come home!

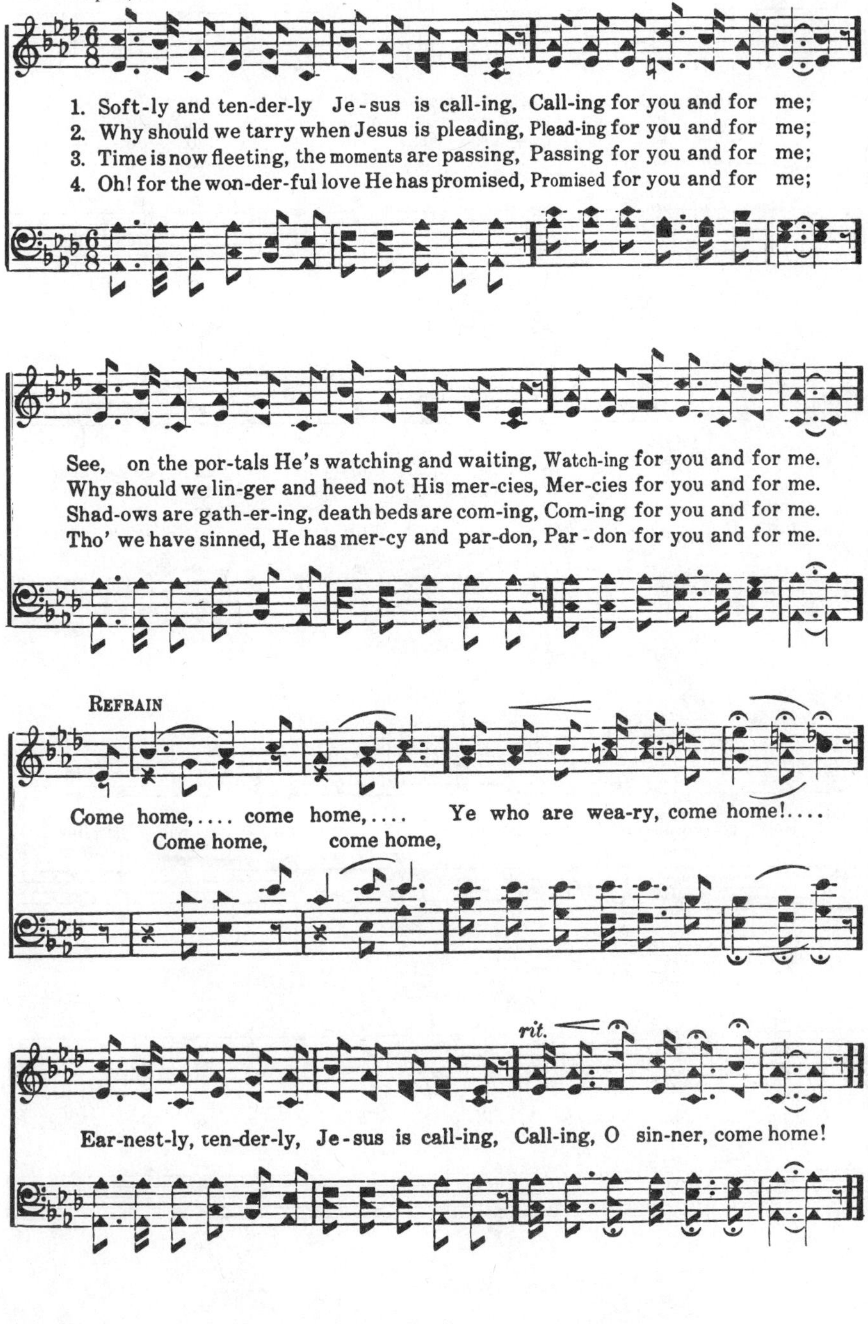

# 900 WANDERER IN SINFUL WAYS

*All things are ready: come unto the marriage.* Mt. 22:4.

WILL YOU GO TO JESUS 7.6.7.6. with Ref.
M.M. 138

Eden Reeder Latta, b. 1839

Jacob M. Showalter
Arr. Joseph S. Overholt, c. 1926 (1876-1937)

1. Wan - der - er in sin - ful ways, Will you go to Je - sus?
2. Wan - der - er on bar - ren ground, Will you go to Je - sus?
3. Wan - der - er, be - fore too late, Will you go to Je - sus?
4. Wan - der - er, do not de - lay! Will you go to Je - sus?
He will save you by his grace, Will you go to Je - sus?
On - ly so can peace be found, Will you go to Je - sus?
Death may seal your aw - ful fate, Will you go to Je - sus?
Start for heav - en—Start to - day! Will you go to Je - sus?
REFRAIN.
He is wait - ing to re - ceive, If you on - ly will be - lieve,
And to him your heart will give, Will you go to Je - sus?

# GOD IS CALLING THE PRODIGAL 901

*Seek ye the Lord while He may be found, call ye upon Him while He is near.* Is. 55:6.

Charles H. Gabriel, 1856-1932 | GOD IS CALLING 13.11.13.8. with Ref. M.M. 152 | Charles H. Gabriel

1. God is call-ing the prod-i-gal: come with-out de-lay; Hear, O hear Him calling, call-ing now for thee; Tho' you've wandered so far from His presence, come today;
2. Pa - tient, lov-ing, and ten-der-ly still the Fa-ther pleads; Hear, O hear Him calling, call-ing now for thee; O re-turn while the Spir-it in mer-cy in-ter-cedes;
3. Come, there's bread in the house of thy Father, and to spare; Hear, O hear Him calling, call-ing now for thee; Lo! the ta-ble is spread and the feast is waiting there;
for thee;
Hear His loving voice calling still....... calling still.
CHORUS
Call - - ing now for thee,........ Calling now for thee, Calling now for thee,
O wea - - ry prod-i-gal, come;.......... Wea-ry prod-i-gal, come, wea-ry prodigal, come;
Call - - ing now for thee,........ Calling now for thee, Calling now for thee,
O wea - - ry prod-i-gal, come........... Weary prodigal, come, wea-ry prodigal, come.

# 902 O COME TODAY TO THE FOUNTAIN

*Let the wicked forsake his way and the unrighteous man his thoughts: and let him return unto the Lord, and He will have mercy upon him; and to our God for He will abundantly pardon.* Is. 55:7.

John J. Overholt, 1971 — WHISPERING HOPE M.M. 112 — Alice Hawthorne, Arr. John J. Overholt, 1971

1. O, come to - day to the foun-tain, Drawn from Im-man - u - el's veins,
2. O sin - ner, look un-to Je - sus, Who conquered death, sin and grave;
3. O, come to - day to the foun-tain, Flow - ing for sin's mis-er - y;
His blood on Cal - va-ry's moun-tain Cleanses from sin and it's stains;
He bids you come to the foun-tain, His blood has pow - er to save;
Come, and be cleansed in its flood - tide Flow-ing from Mt. Cal - va - ry;
O sin-ner, burdened with sor-row, How sweet the message, how free;
Why will you wan-der in dark-ness? Why to the world will you cling?
O sin - ner, burdened with sor - row, How sweet the message for thee:
Par - don and hope for the mor-row, Life and sal- va - tion for thee.
O, come and plunge in the fountain, You can be freed from all sin.
Come to the blood of Im-man-uel; Come, leave your sins and be free!

**CHRISTIAN COMMISSION:** INVITING MEN TO CHRIST

Come to the foun - - - - tain of blood

Come to the foun - tain of blood shed for thee, Come to the

shed for thee, Je - - - - - sus for -

foun - tain of blood shed for thee, Je - sus for - gives, cleans-es

gives, cleans-es sin, and sets free.

Cleans-es sin and sets free.

sin and sets free, Je - sus for-gives, cleans-es sin and sets free.

# 903 ARE YOU LIVING NOW IN SIN

*For whosoever shall call upon the name of the Lord shall be saved.* Rom. 10:13.

CALL ON HIS NAME 7.7.10.7.7.9. with Ref.
M.M. 66

Finis C. Ashmore — Finis C. Ashmore

1. Are you liv - ing now in sin, Hav-ing naught of God with-in? Call on
2. Are you out in sin's dark night, Drift-ing far-ther from the light? Call on
3. If your path-way grows more dim, Turn to Christ and fol-low Him, Call on
4. O He loves you, sin-ner, friend, And will keep you to the end, Call on
Je - sus' name, call on Je - sus' name; Leav-ing doubt and fears be-hind,
Je - sus' name, call on Je - sus' name; He will bright-en up the way,
Je - sus' name, call on Je - sus' name; He will make your path-way bright,
Je - sus' name, call on Je - sus' name; If you hear His lov - ing voice,
Peace and com - fort you will find, If you call on Je-sus' name to - day.
Change the dark-est night to day, If you call on Je-sus' name to - day.
Make your heav - y bur-dens light, If you call on Je-sus' name to - day.
He will make your heart re-joice, If you call on Je-sus' name to - day.
FINE.
CHORUS.
D.S.—call on Je-sus' name to - day.
Call on His name, O call on His
Call on His name, Call on His name, Call on His name,
name, He will re-claim, Then
Call on His name, He will re-claim, He will re-claim, Then
D. S.

# OH, MY BROTHER, DO YOU KNOW THE SAVIOR 904

*This is a faithful saying, and worthy of all acceptation, that Christ Jesus came into the world to save sinners.* I Tim. 1:15.

F. A. Graves
Arr. Joseph Overholt, 1968

HONEY IN THE ROCK 10.9.9.8. with Ref.
M.M. 88

F. A. Graves

1. Oh, my brother, do you know the Sav-ior, Who is won-drous kind and true? He's the "Rock of your sal-va-tion!"
2. Have you "tast-ed that the Lord is gra-cious?" Do you walk in the way that's new? Have you drank from the liv-ing fount-ain?
3. Do you pray un-to God the Fa-ther, "What wilt thou have me to do?" Nev-er fear, He will sure-ly an-swer,
4. Then go out thro' the streets and by-ways, Preach the word to the ma-ny or few; Say to ev-'ry fall-en broth-er,
CHORUS.
There's hon-ey in the Rock for you. O there's hon-ey in the Rock, my brother,...... There's hon-ey in the Rock for you; Leave your sins for the blood to cov-er, There's honey in the Rock for you.
my broth-er
for you;
for you.
Jesus Christ can make you new! Je-sus Christ sat-is-fies, my broth-er, Jesus Christ sat-is-fies the soul; Leave your sins for the blood to co-ver, Jesus Christ can make you whole!
3. Ac-cept my sal-va-tion true!
rit.

# 905 HAVE YOU HEARD ABOUT THE STONE

*Thou sawest till that a stone was cut out without hands, which smote the image upon his feet that were of iron and clay, and brake them to pieces. And in the days of these kings shall the God of heaven set up a kingdom, which shall never be destroyed.* Dan. 2:34, 44.

Anon.
Arr. by Compiler, 1965

FELSEN 7.8.7.8.7.8.10. with Ref.
M.M. 66

Anon. American folk melody
Arr. John J. Overholt, 1965, 1972

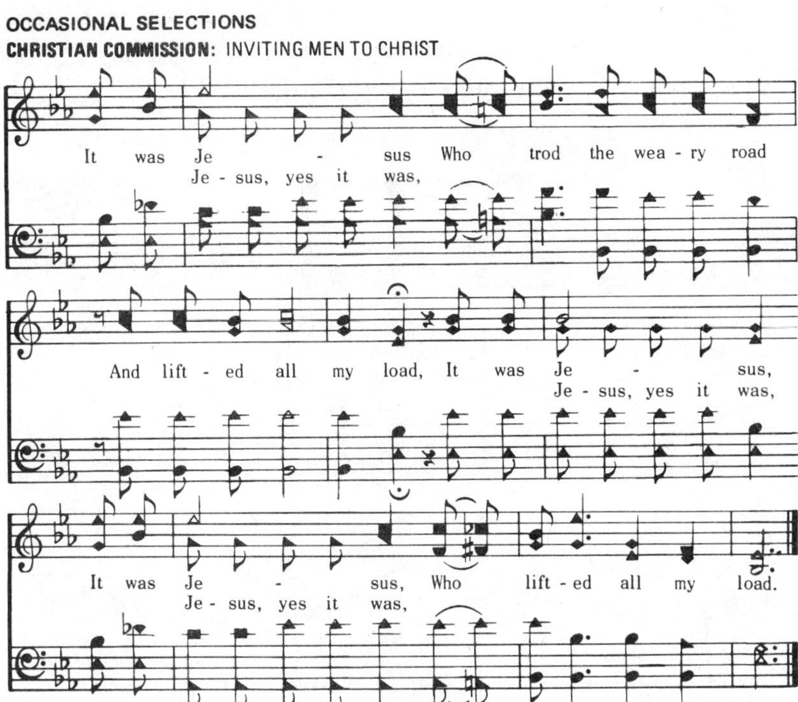
It was Je - sus Who trod the wea - ry road
Je - sus, yes it was,
And lift - ed all my load, It was Je - sus,
Je - sus, yes it was,
It was Je - sus, Who lift - ed all my load.
Je - sus, yes it was,

# COME, EVERY SOUL BY SIN OPPRESSED 906

*And I, if I be lifted up from the earth, will draw all men unto Me.* Jn. 12:32. *Come unto Me, all ye that labour and are heavy laden, and I will give you rest.* Mt. 11:28.

ONLY TRUST HIM C.M. 8.6.8.6. with Ref.
M.M. 66

John H. Stockton, 1813-1877 — John H. Stockton

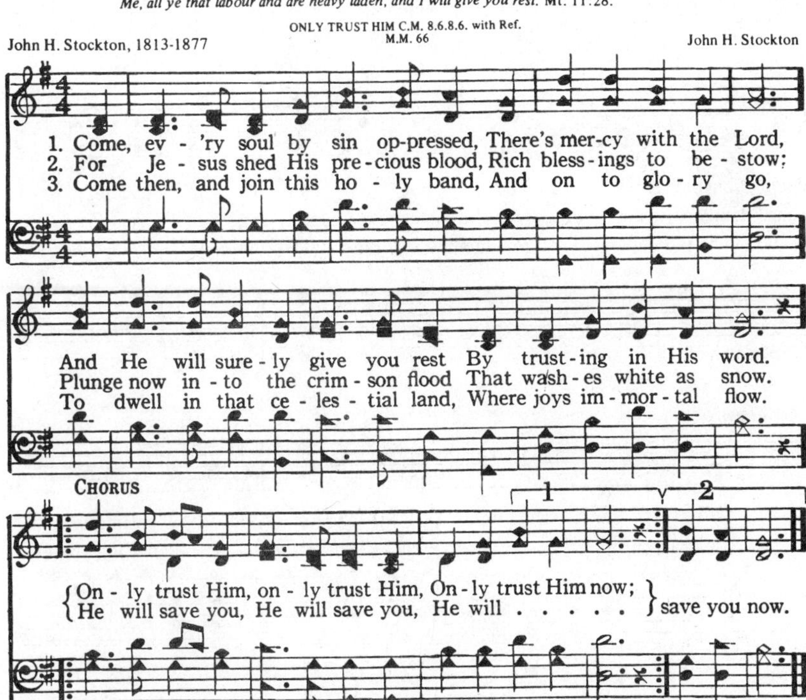
1. Come, ev - 'ry soul by sin op-pressed, There's mer-cy with the Lord,
2. For Je - sus shed His pre-cious blood, Rich bless-ings to be - stow;
3. Come then, and join this ho - ly band, And on to glo - ry go,
And He will sure - ly give you rest By trust-ing in His word.
Plunge now in - to the crim - son flood That wash - es white as snow.
To dwell in that ce - les - tial land, Where joys im - mor - tal flow.
CHORUS
On - ly trust Him, on - ly trust Him, On - ly trust Him now;
He will save you, He will save you, He will . . . . . save you now.
1
2

# 907 HAVE YOU COUNTED THE COST

*And how I kept back nothing that was profitable unto you, but have shewed you, and have taught you publickly, and from house to house.* Acts 20:20.

Steve Matovich, 1971
Alt. John J. Overholt, 1971

NEARING THE PORT 6.6.9.12.9. with Ref.
M.M. 126

Charles Edward Pollock, b. 1853
Har. John J. Overholt

1. Have you count – ed the cost that a soul should be lost, Since
2. Have you thought on dis – may that the sin – ner must pay, Since
3. Had you count – ed the price of the Lord's sac – ri – fice, When

you didn't go call–ing to – day? Have you count–ed the sin, and the
you didn't go call–ing to – day? Have you failed to re–gard what is
you didn't go call–ing to – day? Did you think to o – bey, when the

souls you didn't win, Since you did not go call – ing to – day?
your lost re – ward, Since you did not go call—ing to – day?
Lord had to pay That you might go out call – ing to – day?

REFRAIN

Call – ing for Je – sus, Let us all go out calling to –
Call – ing for Je – sus, ev–er call – ing for Him Let us all go out calling, ev–er

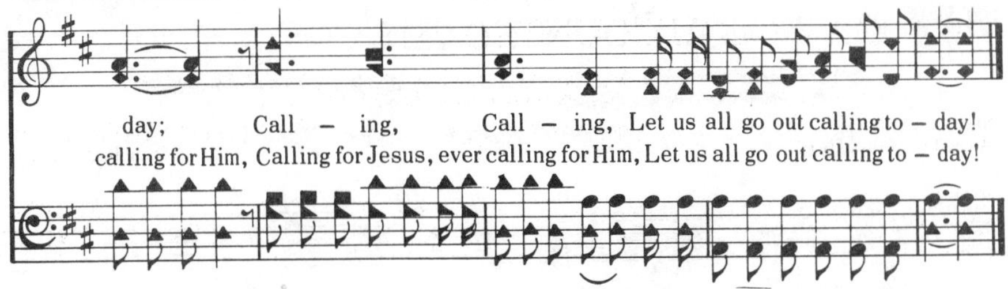
day; Call – ing, Call – ing, Let us all go out calling to – day!
calling for Him, Calling for Jesus, ever calling for Him, Let us all go out calling to – day!

# LORD, SPEAK TO ME 908

*Let him know, that he which converteth the sinner from the error of his way, shall save a soul from death, and shall hide a multitude of sins.* Jas. 5:20.

Frances Ridley Havergal, 1872 (1836-1879)

HOLLY 8.8.8.8.
M.M. 72

George Hews, 1835 (1806-1873)

1. Lord, speak to me that I may speak In liv-ing ech-oes of Thy tone;
2. O strength-en me, that while I stand Firm on the Rock and strong in Thee,
3. O teach me, Lord, that I may teach The pre-cious things Thou dost im-part;
4. O fill me with Thy full-ness, Lord, Un-til my ver-y heart o'er-flow;
As Thou has sought, so let me seek Thine err-ing chil-dren, lost and lone.
I may stretch out a lov-ing hand To wres-tlers with the trou-bled sea.
And wing my words that they may reach The hid-den depths of many a heart.
In kin-dling tho't and glow-ing word, Thy love to tell, Thy praise to show.

5. O lead me, Lord, that I may lead The wandering and the wavering feet;
O feed me, Lord, that I may feed Thine hungering ones with manna sweet.

6. O grant enabling grace to me, That I may speak with soothing power
A word in season, as from Thee, To weary ones in needful hour.

7. O use me, Lord, use even me, Just as Thou wilt, and when, and where;
Until Thy blessed face I see, Thy rest, Thy joy, Thy glory share.

**CHRISTIAN COMMISSION:** EDIFICATION, ENCOURAGEMENT, TESTIMONY

# 909 IT'S NOT AN EASY ROAD

*Strive to enter in at the strait gate: for many, I say unto you, will seek to enter it, and shall not be able.* Lk. 13:24.

IT'S NOT AN EASY ROAD 13.9.13.9. with Ref.
M.M. 88

John W. Peterson, b. 1921 | John W. Peterson

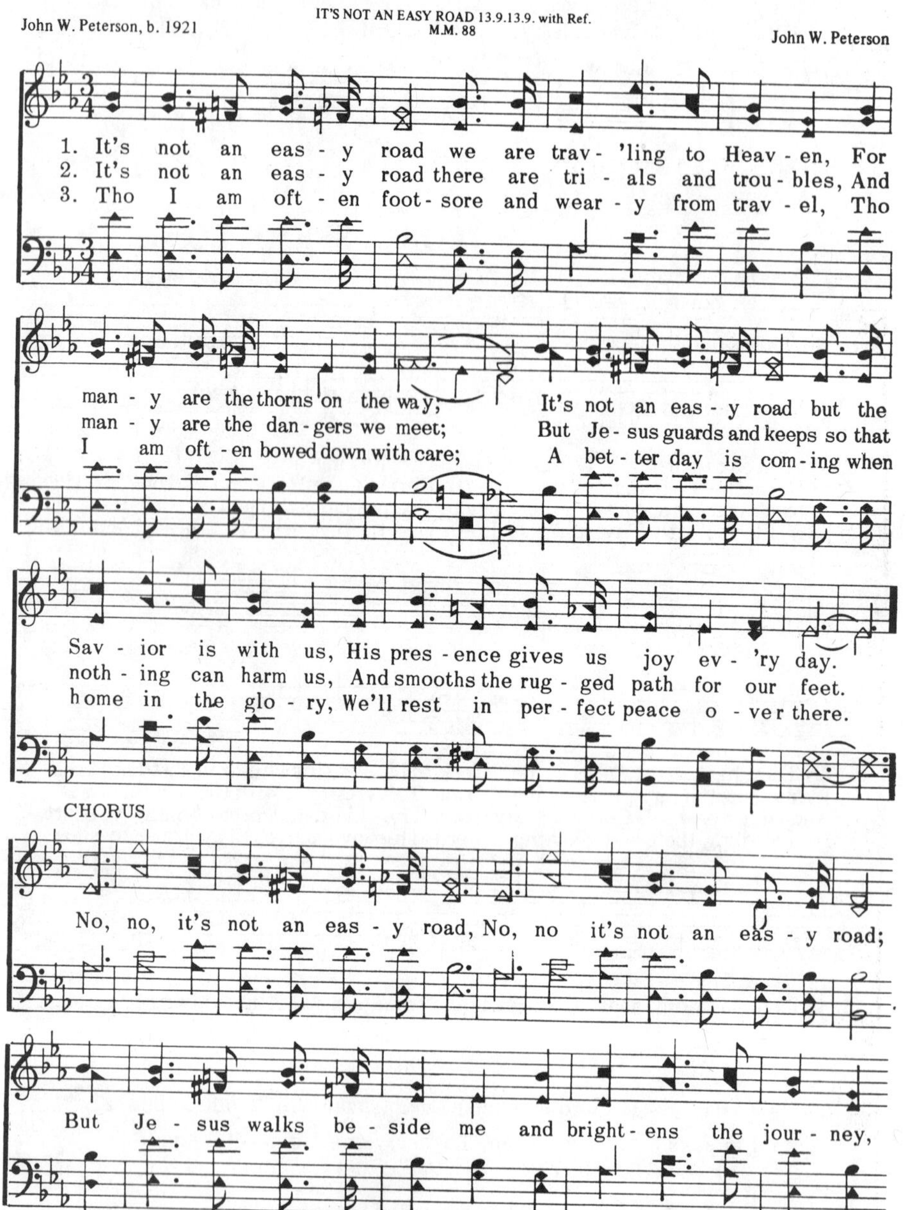

1. It's not an eas - y road we are trav - 'ling to Heav - en, For man - y are the thorns on the way; It's not an eas - y road but the Sav - ior is with us, His pres - ence gives us joy ev - 'ry day.
2. It's not an eas - y road there are tri - als and trou - bles, And man - y are the dan - gers we meet; But Je - sus guards and keeps so that noth - ing can harm us, And smooths the rug - ged path for our feet.
3. Tho I am oft - en foot - sore and wear - y from trav - el, Tho I am oft - en bowed down with care; A bet - ter day is com - ing when home in the glo - ry, We'll rest in per - fect peace o - ver there.
CHORUS
No, no, it's not an eas - y road, No, no it's not an eas - y road;
But Je - sus walks be - side me and bright - ens the jour - ney,

And light - ens ev - 'ry heav - y load.

# WHEN SAINTS OF GOD IN DANGER STOOD 910

*He answered and said, Lo, I see four men loose, walking in the midst of the fire, and they have no hurt; and the form of the fourth is like the Son of God.* Dan. 3:25.

H. J. Zelley, 1859-1942
Cho. alt. by Compiler, 1972

VARINA 8.6.8.6.D.
M.M. 72

Geo. F. Root, 1820-1895

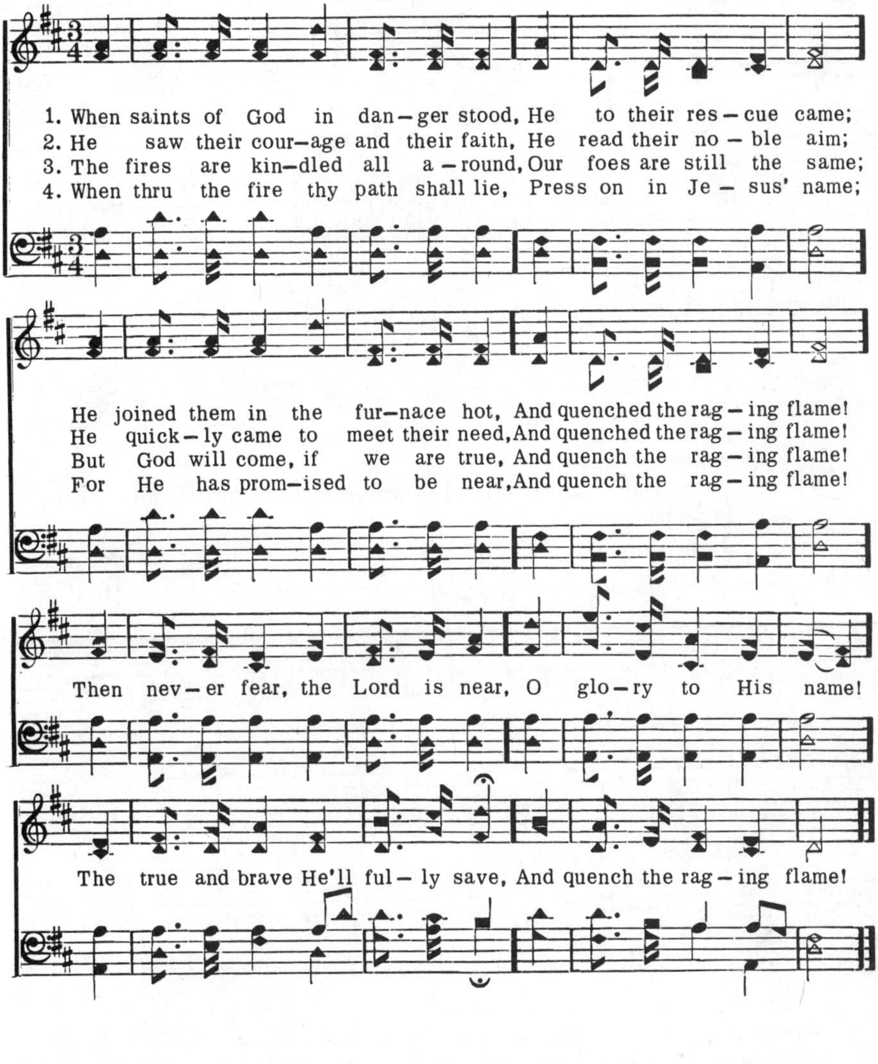

1. When saints of God in dan–ger stood, He to their res–cue came;
He joined them in the fur–nace hot, And quenched the rag–ing flame!

2. He saw their cour–age and their faith, He read their no–ble aim;
He quick–ly came to meet their need, And quenched the rag–ing flame!

3. The fires are kin–dled all a–round, Our foes are still the same;
But God will come, if we are true, And quench the rag–ing flame!

4. When thru the fire thy path shall lie, Press on in Je–sus' name;
For He has prom–ised to be near, And quench the rag–ing flame!

Then nev–er fear, the Lord is near, O glo–ry to His name!
The true and brave He'll ful–ly save, And quench the rag–ing flame!

# 911 A PILGRIM WAS I AND A-WAND'RING

*Surely goodness and mercy shall follow me all the days of my life: and I will dwell in the house of the Lord forever.* Ps. 23:6.

John W. Peterson, b. 1921
SURELY GOODNESS AND MERCY 9.9.9.8. with Ref.
M.M. 100
John W. Peterson
Alfred B. Smith
1. A pil-grim was I and a-wand'ring, In the cold night of sin I did roam; When Je-sus the kind Shepherd found me, And now I am on my way home.
2. He re-stor-eth my soul when I'm wear-y, He giv-eth me strength day by day; He leads me be-side the still wa-ters, He guards me each step of the way.
3. When I walk thru that dark lonesome val-ley, My Sav-iour will walk with me there; And safe-ly His great hand will lead me To the mansions He's gone to pre-pare.
CHORUS
Sure-ly good-ness and mer-cy shall fol-low me All the days, all the days of my life,.......... Sure-ly
Good-ness and mer-cy shall fol-low me All the days, all the
8
©1958 by Singspiration, Inc. All rights reserved. Used by permission.

FINE
Opt. Coda
days of my life. And I shall dwell in the house of the Lord for-
D.S. al FINE
ev - er, And I will feast at the ta - ble spred for me. Sure - ly

## "COME YE APART!" IT IS THE LORD 912

*And He said unto them, Come ye yourselves apart into a desert place, and rest awhile.* Mk. 6:31.

CHISHOLM 11.10.11.10.
M.M. 69

Thomas O. Chisholm, b. 1866 — George Coles Stebbins, 1846-1945

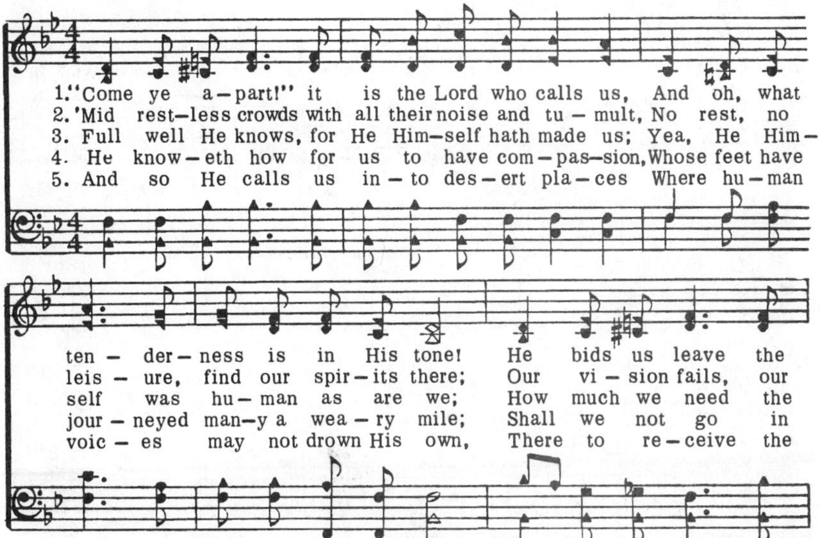

1."Come ye a–part!" it is the Lord who calls us, And oh, what
2.'Mid rest–less crowds with all their noise and tu – mult, No rest, no
3. Full well He knows, for He Him–self hath made us; Yea, He Him–
4. He know–eth how for us to have com–pas–sion, Whose feet have
5. And so He calls us in–to des–ert pla–ces Where hu–man

ten – der – ness is in His tone! He bids us leave the
leis – ure, find our spir – its there; Our vi – sion fails, our
self was hu – man as are we; How much we need the
jour – neyed man–y a wea – ry mile; Shall we not go in
voic – es may not drown His own, There to re – ceive the

bus – y world be–hind us And draw a–part a–while with Him a – lone.
sense of life's pro–por–tion, Un–less we seek the qui – et place of prayer.
calm of sweet com–mun–ion, New strength to gain for bat–tles yet to be.
an – swer to His bid–ding: "Come ye your-selves a–part and rest a–while?"
full – er rev – e – la–tion He makes to those who wait with Him a – lone.

# 913 OFTEN WEARY AND WORN

*That they may rest from their labours.* Rev. 14:13.

REST BY AND BY 11.12.11.12. with Ref.
M.M. 76

W. F. Cosner

Charles Edward Pollock, b. 1853

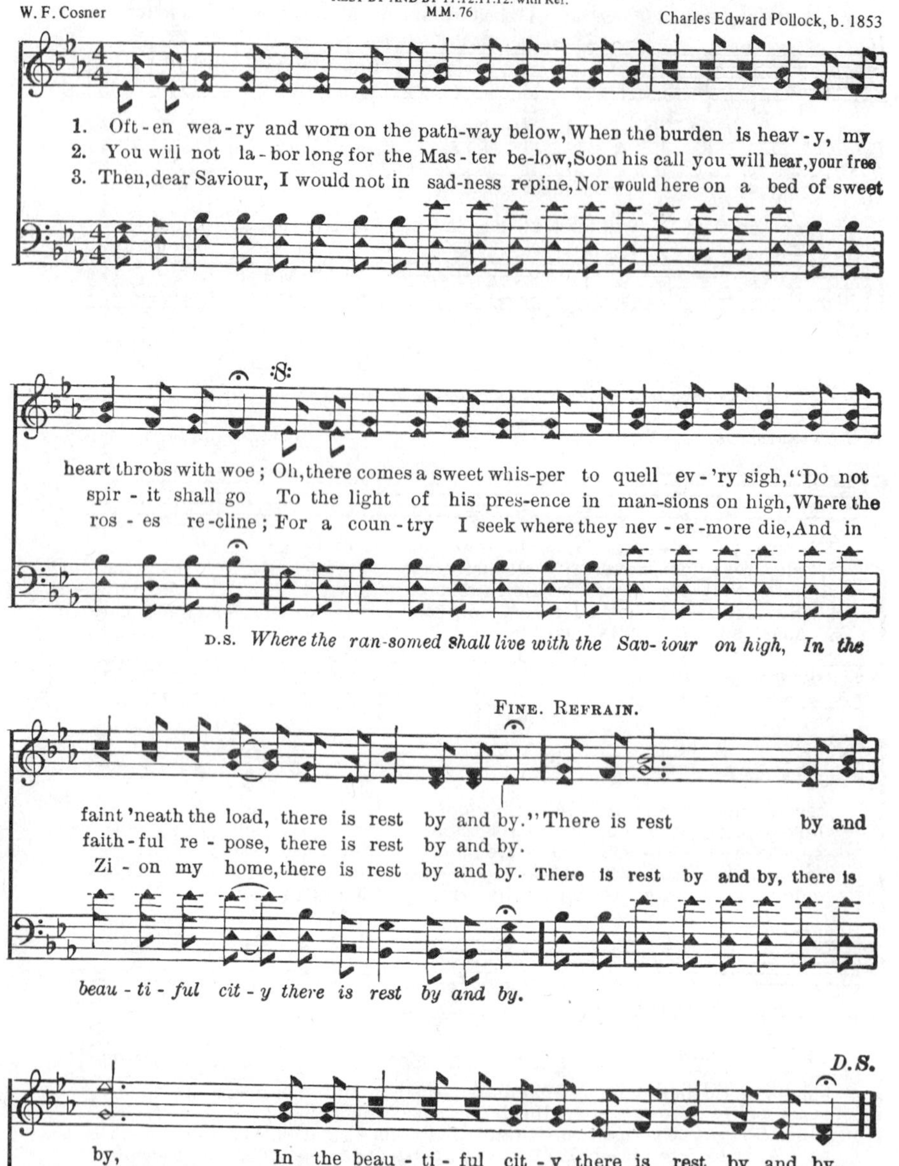
1. Oft-en wea-ry and worn on the path-way below, When the burden is heav-y, my heart throbs with woe; Oh, there comes a sweet whis-per to quell ev-'ry sigh, "Do not faint 'neath the load, there is rest by and by."
2. You will not la-bor long for the Mas-ter be-low, Soon his call you will hear, your free spir-it shall go To the light of his pres-ence in man-sions on high, Where the faith-ful re-pose, there is rest by and by.
3. Then, dear Saviour, I would not in sad-ness repine, Nor would here on a bed of sweet ros-es re-cline; For a coun-try I seek where they nev-er-more die, And in Zi-on my home, there is rest by and by.
D.S. Where the ran-somed shall live with the Sav-iour on high, In the beau-ti-ful cit-y there is rest by and by.
FINE. REFRAIN.
There is rest by and by, In the beau-ti-ful cit-y there is rest by and by.
There is rest by and by, there is rest by and by,
D.S.

# THO DREARISOME SHADOWS MAY HANG 914

*The Lord is my light and my salvation; whom shall I fear? the Lord is the strength of my life; of whom shall I be afraid?* Ps. 27:1.

THE LORD IS MY LIGHT 11.11.11.11. with Ref.
M.M. 88

Alfred Barrat, b. 1879

M. R. Quarles

1. Tho drear-i-some shad-ows may hang o'er my way, The light of the gos-pel shines clear-ly and bright; My steps can-not fal-ter nor wan-der a-stray,
2. The Lord is my Guard-ian, my Lead-er and Guide, And noth-ing can ev-er my spir-it af-fright; My hope is un-fail-ing with Him by my side,
3. My spir-it is res-cued from doubt and de-spair, His pres-ence is fill-ing my soul with de-light; In love He is wait-ing my bur-dens to share,
4. The light of my Sav-iour is shin-ing for me, 'Tis lead-ing my foot-steps in path-ways of right; 'Twill shine till I an-chor be-yond the dark sea,
The Lord is my Ban-ner, the Lord is my Light.
FINE
CHORUS
The Lord is my Ban-ner, the Lord is my Light, And noth-ing can ev-er my spir-it af-fright; His love-light is shin-ing by day and by night,
D. S.

# 915 BY THE CROWD OF WORSHIPPERS

*And Jesus said unto her, Neither do I condemn thee: go, and sin no more.* Jn. 8:11.

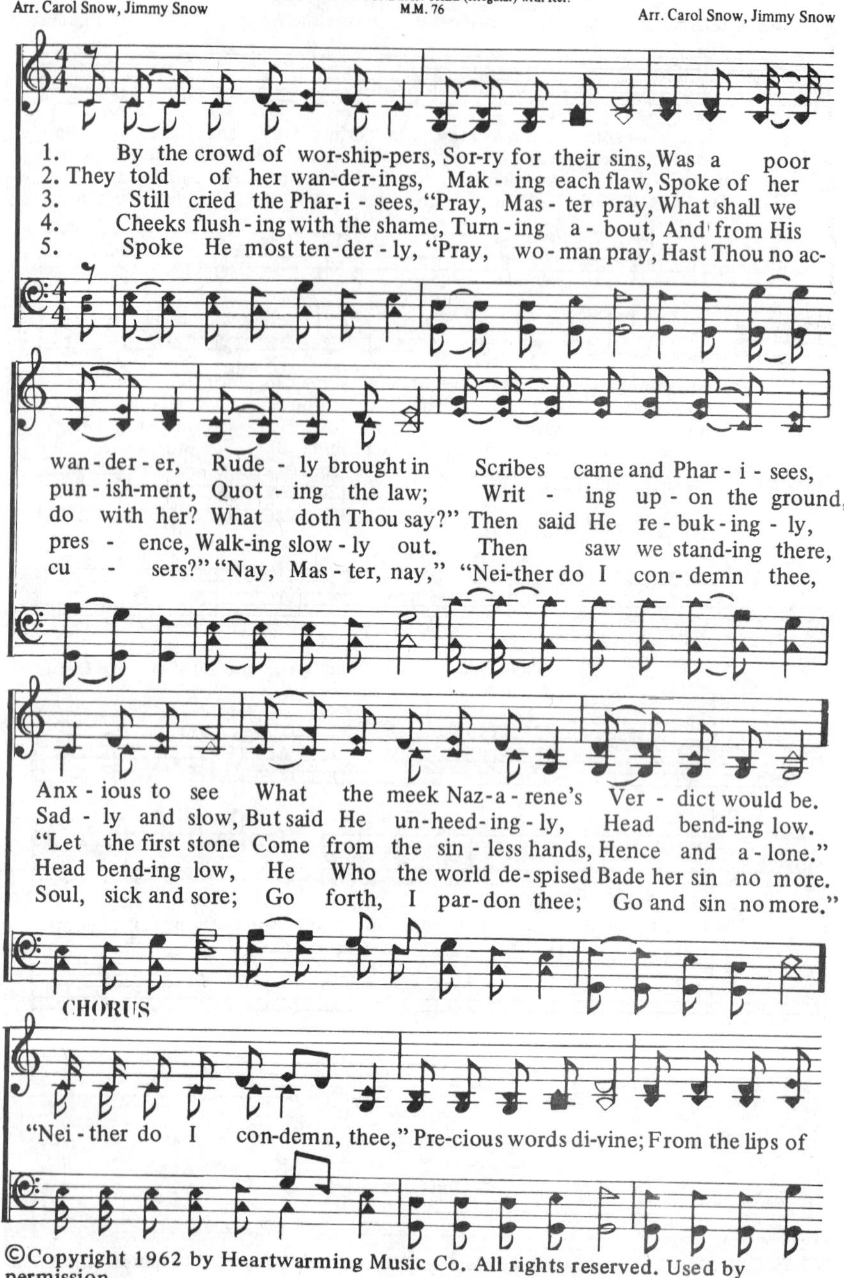
NEITHER DO I CONDEMN THEE (Irregular) with Ref.
M.M. 76
Arr. Carol Snow, Jimmy Snow
Arr. Carol Snow, Jimmy Snow
1. By the crowd of wor-ship-pers, Sor-ry for their sins, Was a poor wan-der-er, Rude - ly brought in Scribes came and Phar - i - sees, Anx - ious to see What the meek Naz-a - rene's Ver - dict would be.
2. They told of her wan-der-ings, Mak - ing each flaw, Spoke of her pun - ish-ment, Quot - ing the law; Writ - ing up - on the ground, Sad - ly and slow, But said He un-heed-ing - ly, Head bend-ing low.
3. Still cried the Phar-i - sees, "Pray, Mas - ter pray, What shall we do with her? What doth Thou say?" Then said He re - buk-ing - ly, "Let the first stone Come from the sin - less hands, Hence and a - lone."
4. Cheeks flush - ing with the shame, Turn - ing a - bout, And from His pres - ence, Walk-ing slow - ly out. Then saw we stand-ing there, Head bend-ing low, He Who the world de - spised Bade her sin no more.
5. Spoke He most ten-der - ly, "Pray, wo - man pray, Hast Thou no ac - cu - sers?" "Nay, Mas - ter, nay," "Nei-ther do I con - demn thee, Soul, sick and sore; Go forth, I par - don thee; Go and sin no more."
CHORUS
"Nei - ther do I con-demn, thee," Pre-cious words di-vine; From the lips of

mer - cy Like the sweet - est chimes. Won-der-ful words of Je - sus,
Sing them o'er and o'er; "Nei-ther do I con-demn thee, Go and sin no more."

# 916

## SOMETIMES WHEN THE SHADOWS ARE GATHERING

*Who shall separate us from the love of Christ? shall tribulation, or distress, or persecution, or famine, or nakedness, or peril, or sword?* Rom. 8:35.

THE LOVE OF THE SAVIOUR 10.8.11.8. with Ref.
M.M. 88

G. W. Cornell — W. H. Williams

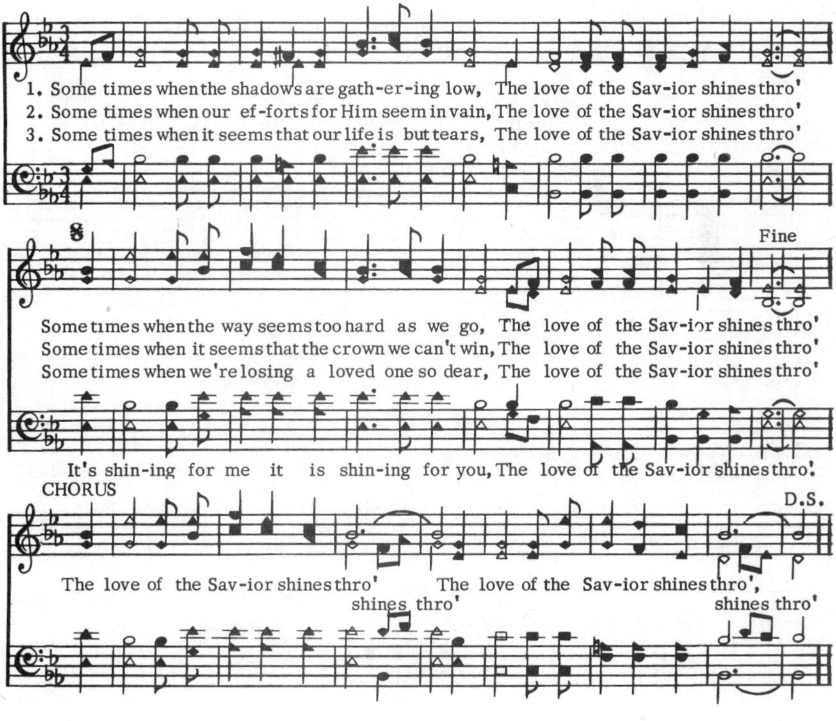

1. Some times when the shadows are gath-er-ing low, The love of the Sav-ior shines thro'
2. Some times when our ef-forts for Him seem in vain, The love of the Sav-ior shines thro'
3. Some times when it seems that our life is but tears, The love of the Sav-ior shines thro'

Some times when the way seems too hard as we go, The love of the Sav-ior shines thro'
Some times when it seems that the crown we can't win, The love of the Sav-ior shines thro'
Some times when we're losing a loved one so dear, The love of the Sav-ior shines thro'

Fine

It's shin-ing for me it is shin-ing for you, The love of the Sav-ior shines thro'.

CHORUS

The love of the Sav-ior shines thro' shines thro' The love of the Sav-ior shines thro', shines thro'

D.S.

**CHRISTIAN COMMISSION:** EDIFICATION, ENCOURAGEMENT, TESTIMONY

# 917 FAR AWAY THE NOISE OF STRIFE

*Thou shalt no more be termed Forsaken; neither shall thy land any more be termed Desolate: but thou shalt be called Hephzibah, and thy land Beulah: for the Lord delighteth in thee, and thy land shall be married.* Is. 62:4.

C. Austin Miles, 1868-1946

DWELLING IN BEULAH LAND 14.13.14.10. with Ref.
M.M. 92

C. Austin Miles

1. Far a-way the noise of strife up-on my ear is fall-ing, Then I know the
2. Far be-low the storm of doubt up-on the world is beat-ing, Sons of men in
3. Let the storm-y breez-es blow, their cry cannot a-larm me; I am safe-ly
4. Viewing here the works of God, I sink in con-tem-pla-tion, Hear-ing now His
sins of earth be-set on ev-'ry hand; Doubt and fear and things of earth in
bat-tle long the en-e-my with-stand; Safe am I with-in the cas-tle
sheltered here, pro-tect-ed by God's hand; Here the sun is al-ways shin-ing,
bless-ed voice, I see the way He planned; Dwell-ing in the Spir-it, here I
vain to me are call-ing, None of these shall move me from Beu-lah Land.
of God's word re-treat-ing, Nothing then can reach me-'tis Beu-lah Land.
here there's naught can harm me, I am safe for-ev-er in Beu-lah Land.
learn of true sal-va-tion, Glad-ly will I tar-ry in Beu-lah Land.
CHORUS
I'm liv-ing on the moun-tain, un-der-neath a cloud-less sky, I'm
Praise God!
drink-ing at the foun-tain that nev-er shall run dry; O yes! I'm feast-ing on the

man-na from a boun-ti-ful sup-ply, For I am dwell-ing in Beu - lah Land.

## I CANNOT TELL, I DO NOT KNOW 918

*And we know that all things work together for good to them that love God, to them who are the called according to His purpose.* Rom. 8:28.

GOD PLANS THE BEST L.M. 8.8.8.8. with Ref.
M.M. 63

Anon. Anon.

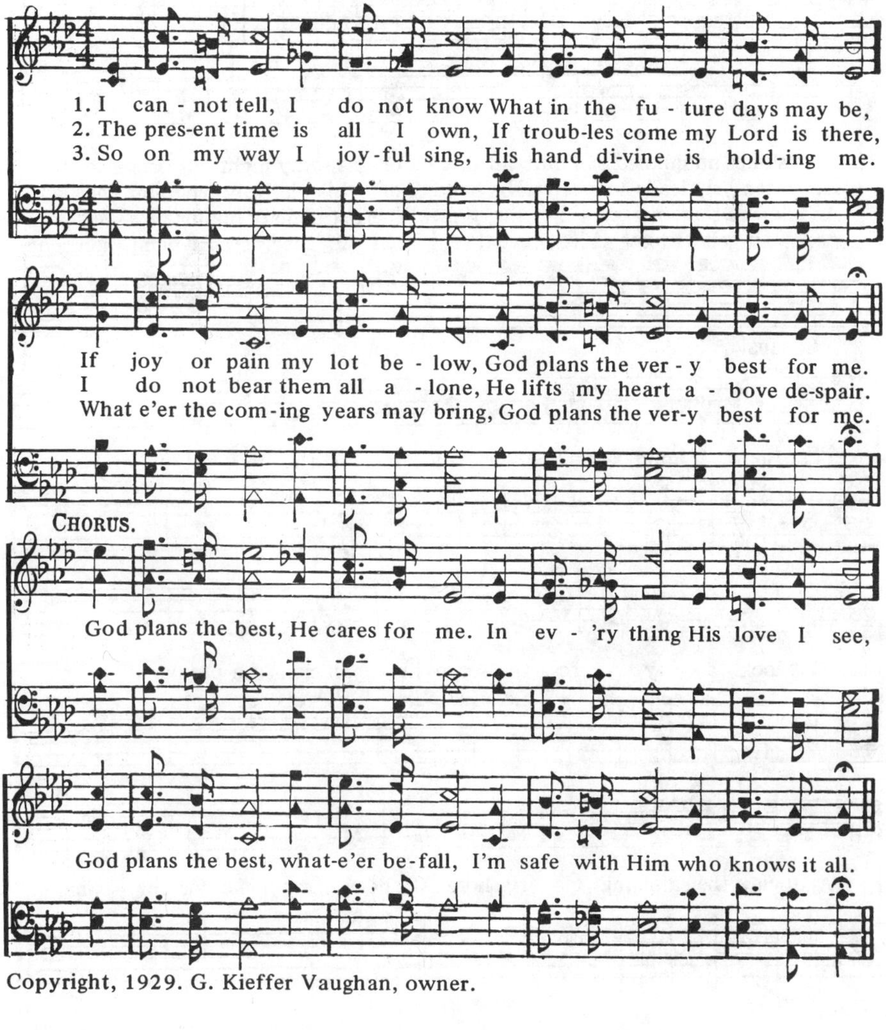

1. I can - not tell, I do not know What in the fu - ture days may be,
If joy or pain my lot be - low, God plans the ver - y best for me.

2. The pres-ent time is all I own, If troub-les come my Lord is there,
I do not bear them all a - lone, He lifts my heart a - bove de-spair.

3. So on my way I joy-ful sing, His hand di-vine is hold-ing me.
What e'er the com-ing years may bring, God plans the ver-y best for me.

CHORUS.

God plans the best, He cares for me. In ev - 'ry thing His love I see,
God plans the best, what-e'er be-fall, I'm safe with Him who knows it all.

# 919 I'VE REACHED THE LAND

*The pastures are clothed with flocks; the valleys also are covered over with corn; they shout for joy, they also sing.* Ps. 65:13.

BEULAH LAND L.M. 8.8.8.8. with Ref.
M.M. 69

Edgar Page — John R. Sweney, 1837-1899

1. I've reached the land of corn and wine, And all its rich - es free - ly mine;
2. My Sav - ior comes and walks with me, And sweet com - mun - ion here have we;
3. A sweet per - fume up - on the breeze Is borne from ev - er - ver - nal trees,
4. The zeph - yrs seem to float to me, Sweet sounds of heav - en's mel - o - dy,
Here shines undimmed one bliss - ful day, For all my night has passed a - way.
He gen - tly leads me by His hand, For this is heav - en's bor - der - land.
And flow'rs that, nev - er - fad - ing, grow Where streams of life for ev - er flow.
As an - gels with the white - robed throng Join in the sweet Re - demp - tion song.
CHORUS
O Beu - lah Land, sweet Beu - lah Land, As on thy high - est mount I stand,
I look a - way a - cross the sea, Where man - sions are pre - pared for me,
And view the shin - ing glo - ry - shore, My heav'n, my home for ev - er - more!

## YE SONS AND DAUGHTERS OF THE KING 920

*He is not here, but is risen.* Lk. 24:6.

Author unknown, c. 1600
Tr. John M. Neale, 1851

GELOBT SEI GOTT 8.8.8. with Alleluias
M.M. 96

Melchior Vulpius, 1609

1. Ye sons and daugh - ters of the King, Whom heav'nly hosts in glo - ry sing, To - day the grave hath lost its sting:
2. On that first morn - ing of the week, Be - fore the day be - gan to break, The Ma - rys went their Lord to seek:
3. An an - gel bade their sor - row flee, For thus he spake un - to the three: "Your Lord is gone to Gal - i - lee:"
Al - le - lu - ia! . . . Al - le - lu - ia! . . . Al - le - lu - ia!
Al - le - lu - ia! . . . Al - le - lu - ia! . . . Al - le - lu - ia!
Al - le - lu - ia! . . . Al - le - lu - ia! . . . Al - le - lu - ia! A - men.

## O SOUL, DO NOT DELAY 921

*Wherewith shall I come before the Lord, and bow myself before the high God? . . . with thousands of rams, or with ten thousands of rivers of oil? shall I give my firstborn for my transgression, the fruit of my body for the sin of my soul? He hath shewed thee, O man, what is good; and what doth the Lord require of thee, but to do justly, and to love mercy, and to walk humbly with thy God?* Mic. 6:6-8.

John Fretz Funk, 1835-1930
*O Seele, säume nicht*
Tr. John J. Overholt, 1972

DENNIS S.M. 6.6.8.6.
M.M. 72

Johann Georg Nägeli, 1832 (1773-1836)
Arr. Lowell Mason, 1845 (1792-1872)

1. O soul, do not delay!
Thy Saviour calleth thee:
I am the Light, come, take my way
And e'er thy light I'll be.

2. O soul, do not delay!
Come sorr'wing, brokenly!
Jesus as Saviour, own, obey
And serve Him faithfully.

3. O soul, do not delay!
Sin leave which thee enticed;
Disown the world, and thy own way,
And follow after Christ!

1. O Seele, säume nicht!
Dein Heiland rufet dir:
Komm her zu mir, ich bin das Licht,
Ich leucht dir für und für.

2. O Seele, säume nicht!
O komm mit Leid und Reu!
Nimm Jesus dein'n Erlöser an
Und diene Ihm getreu.

3. O Seele, säume nicht!
Verlass die Sünde doch;
Verleugne Welt und auch dich selbst,
Und folge Jesus nach!

Note: this text is to be sung with the tune Dennis, No. 706, "Blest Be the Tie That Binds."

# 922 OFTEN WHEN WE SIT AND PONDER

*But straightway Jesus spake unto them, saying, Be of good cheer; it is I; be not afraid.* Mt. 14:27.

LOOK TO JESUS 8.7.8.7.8.7.9.7.
M.M. 76

Harry Showalter, 1914 (b. 1889)

Harry Showalter
Har. John J. Overholt, 1970

1. Of - ten when we sit and pon - der o'er the cares that life may bring,
2. While mis - takes are ev - er near us, and our mo - tives miss their aim,
3. Dis - ap - point-ments may sur - round us, chast - en - ings may come se - vere,
4. In our up - ward, pil - grim jour - ney, may we to each oth - er show
We can on - ly look to Je - sus, our Re - deem - er and our King;
We should not be-come dis-cour-aged, but be - lieve that Christ, the same;
But we have the bless - ed prom - ise that a com - fort - er is near;
Love un - change-a - ble, un - fad - ing, that in peace we on - ward go;
Tho sore tri - als may sur - round us, or our way may be more smooth,
Yes - ter - day, to - day, to - mor - row, will for - give us if we come
Whom the Lord loves He will chast-en, and He scourg - eth ev - 'ry son
Till the sum - mons at death's por - tals shall our wea - ry eye - lids close,
'Tis by these bless-ings or af - flic-tions that He doth our mo - tives prove.
With hearts pos - sess-ing god - ly sor - row and an hon - est, plead-ing tongue.
Whom He re - ceiv - eth in - to glo - ry, ev - er say, "His will be done."
Then may we meet those gone, im - mor - tal, who are free from cares and woes.

# NOT TO THE STRONG IS THE BATTLE 923

*And all this assembly shall know that the Lord saveth not with sword and spear: for the battle is the Lord's.* I Sam. 17:47.

NOT TO THE STRONG 8.7.8.7.8.7.10.7.
M.M. 132

Harry Showalter, 1957 (b. 1889)

Harry Showalter
Har. John J. Overholt, 1970

1. Not to the strong is the bat-tle, nor to the swift is the race,
But to the true and the faith-ful, vic-t'ry is prom-ised through grace;
Grace, 'tis the gift of the Fa-ther, sent to the world through His Son,
Oh, it is grace, it is won-der-ful grace, through which the vic-t'ry is won.

2. Not to the wise is the call-ing, nor to the no-ble and great,
But un-to those poor in spir-it, bless-ings of Je-sus a-wait;
Bless-ings of Je-sus, how pre-cious, bless-ings of God through His Son,
Oh, it is grace, it is mar-vel-ous grace, through which sal-va-tion is won.

3. Not to the rich is the King-dom, nor to the men of re-nown,
Those un-to death that are faith-ful, Je-sus has prom-ised a crown;
Crown in the King-dom of heav-en, crown in the man-sions a-bove,
Oh, it is grace, it is fath-om-less grace, grace, the pure gift of God's love.

# 924 I OPENED MY HEART TO THE WORD

*Christ liveth in me: and the life which I now live in the flesh I live by the faith of the Son of God, Who loved me, and gave Himself for me.* Gal. 2:20.

Benjamin J. Coblentz, 1968 (b. 1922)
Alt. by Compiler, 1968

CHRIST IS ALIVE 10.10.10.9. with Ref.
M.M. 120

Benjamin J. Coblentz
Arr. John J. Overholt, 1968

1. I o-pened my heart to the Word di-vine, And searched in the Scrip-tures from line to line; Con-fess-ing my sin and my need with-in, I turned from e-vil and Christ moved in!

2. I was born in sin un-der A-dam's curse, I had need of Christ and a-noth-er birth; From an e-vil heart and an emp-ty soul through Christ a-lone could I be whole!

3. I re-ceived my Christ with a child-like faith I be-lieved his Word and re-ceived his grace; New life with-in, born from heav'n a-bove, Christ brought to me with meas-ure-less love!

4. Christ is far great-er who reigns with-in, Than all the world with its lust and sin; In him now I shall al-ways live and reign, To me Christ is life and to die is gain!

CHORUS

Christ is a-live in my heart to-day, Yes, he's my life and my walk al-way; My heart is his tem-ple, He reigns as King, He makes my whole be-ing re-joice and sing!

Christ is a - live in my heart to - day, Yes he's my life and my walk al - way!

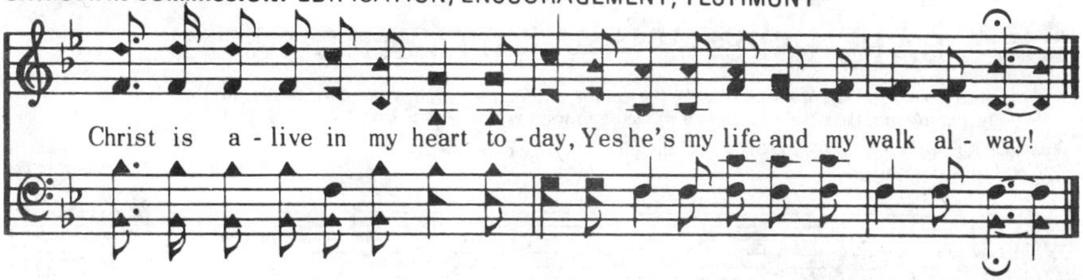

# MY FATHER IS RICH 925

*The same Lord over all is rich unto all that call upon Him.* Rom. 10:12.

A CHILD OF THE KING 10.11.11.11. with Ref.
M.M. 88

Harriet E. Buell, 1834-1910

John B. Sumner, 1838-1918

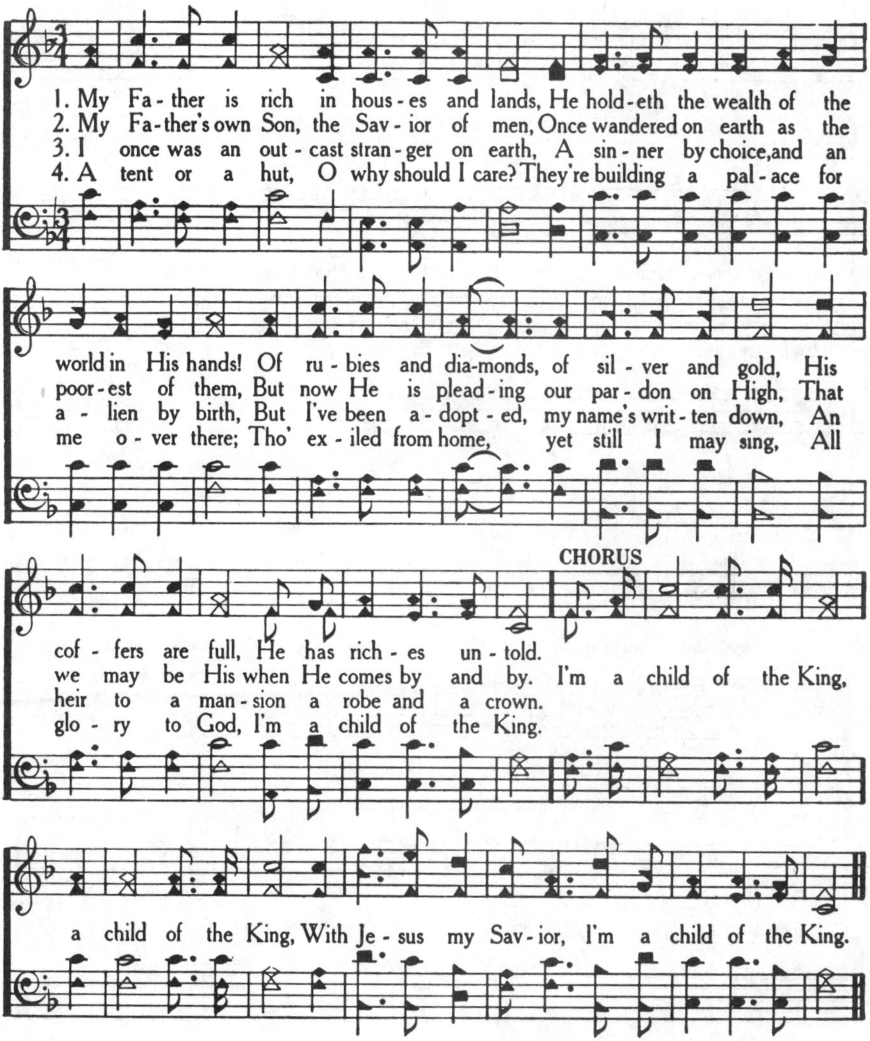

1. My Fa - ther is rich in hous - es and lands, He hold - eth the wealth of the
2. My Fa - ther's own Son, the Sav - ior of men, Once wandered on earth as the
3. I once was an out - cast stran - ger on earth, A sin - ner by choice, and an
4. A tent or a hut, O why should I care? They're building a pal - ace for

world in His hands! Of ru - bies and dia - monds, of sil - ver and gold, His
poor - est of them, But now He is plead - ing our par - don on High, That
a - lien by birth, But I've been a - dopt - ed, my name's writ - ten down, An
me o - ver there; Tho' ex - iled from home, yet still I may sing, All

cof - fers are full, He has rich - es un - told.
we may be His when He comes by and by.
heir to a man - sion a robe and a crown.
glo - ry to God, I'm a child of the King.

CHORUS

I'm a child of the King,
a child of the King, With Je - sus my Sav - ior, I'm a child of the King.

# 926 YEARS I SPENT IN VANITY AND PRIDE

*Who was before a blasphemer, and a persecutor, and injurious: but I obtained mercy, because I did it ignorantly in unbelief. And the grace of our Lord was exceeding abundant.* I Tim. 1:13, 14.

AT CALVARY 9.9.9.4. with Ref.
M.M. 80

William R. Newell, 1868-1956 — Daniel B. Towner, 1850-1919

1. Years I spent in van - i - ty and pride, Car - ing not my Lord was
2. By God's word at last my sin I learned; Then I trem-bled at the
3. Now I've giv'n to Je - sus ev - 'ry - thing, Now I glad - ly own him
4. Oh! the love that drew sal - va - tion's plan, Oh! the grace that brought it
cru - ci - fied, Know- ing not it was for me he died On Cal - va - ry.
law I'd spurned, Till my guilt - y soul im- plor- ing, turned To Cal - va - ry.
as my King, Now my rap-tured soul can on - ly sing Of Cal - va - ry.
down to man, Oh! the might-y gulf that God did span At Cal - va - ry.
REFRAIN.
Mer - cy there was great and grace was free, Par - don there was mul - ti -
plied to me, There my burdened soul found lib - er - ty, At Cal - va - ry.

# I WILL SING OF MY REDEEMER 927

*The Redeemer shall come to Zion.* Is. 59:20. *I the Lord am thy . . . Redeemer.* Is. 49:26. *Thou . . . hast redeemed us to God.* Rev. 5:9.

Philip Paul Bliss, 1876 (1838-1876)
MY REDEEMER 8.7.8.7. with Ref.
M.M. 132
James McGranahan, 1877 (1840-1907)

1. I will sing of my Re-deem-er, And His won-drous love to me;
2. I will tell the won-drous sto-ry, How my lost es-tate to save,
3. I will praise my dear Re-deem-er, His tri - um-phant pow'r I'll tell,
4. I will sing of my Re-deem-er, And His heav'n-ly love to me;
On the cru - el cross He suf-fered, From the curse to set me free.
In His boundless love and mer - cy, He the ran - som free - ly gave.
How the vic - to - ry He giv - eth O - ver sin, and death, and hell.
He from death to life hath brought me, Son of God, with Him to be.
CHORUS
Sing, O sing . . . . of my Re-deem - er! With His
Sing, O sing of my Re-deem-er, Sing, O sing of my Re-deem-er;
blood . . . He purchased me; . . . On the cross . . . He sealed my
He purchased me, With His blood He purchased me, He sealed my pardon, On the
par - don, Paid the debt . . . . and made me free. . . . . .
cross He sealed my pardon, Paid the debt and made me free, and made me free.

# 928 JUST LEAN UPON THE ARMS

*And He took them up in His arms, put His hands upon them, and blessed them.* Mk. 10:16.

LEAN ON HIS ARMS 9.9.9.6. with Ref.
M.M. 76

Lewis E. Jones, 1865-1936

Lewis E. Jones

1. Just lean up-on the arms of Je - sus, He'll help you a - long, help you a - long; If you will trust His love un - fail - ing, He'll fill your heart with song.
2. Just lean up-on the arms of Je - sus, He'll bright-en the way, bright-en the way; Just fol - low glad - ly where he lead - eth, His gen - tle voice o - bey.
3. Just lean up-on the arms of Je - sus, O bring ev - 'ry care, bring ev - 'ry care! The bur - den that has seemed so heav - y, Take to the Lord in pray'r.
4. Just lean up-on the arms of Je - sus, Then leave all to him, leave all to him; His heart is full of love and mer - cy, His eyes are nev - er dim.
REFRAIN.
Lean on his arms, trust-ing in his love;
Lean up-on his arms, ful-ly trust-ing in his love;
Lean on his arms, all his mer-cies prove; Lean on his arms, look-ing home a-bove, Just lean on the Sav-iour's arms!
Lean up-on his arms and all his mer-cies prove; Lean up-on his arms, ev-er

# FOR GOD SO LOVED THIS SINFUL WORLD 929

*For God so loved the world, that He gave His only begotten Son, that whosoever believeth in Him should not perish, but have everlasting life.* Jn. 3:16.

I KNOW GOD'S PROMISE IS TRUE C.M. 8.6.8.6. with Ref.
M.M. 108

Mrs. C. H. Morris, 1862-1929 — Mrs. C. H. Morris

1. For God so loved this sin - ful world, His Son He free - ly gave,
2. I was a way - ward, wand'ring child, A slave to sin and fear,
3. The "who - so - ev - er" of the Lord, I trust - ed was for me;
4. E - ter - nal life, be - gun be - low, Now fills my heart and soul;
That who - so - ev - er would be - lieve, E - ter - nal life should have.
Un - til this bless - ed prom - ise fell Like mu - sic on my ear.
I took Him at His gra - cious word, From sin He set me free.
I'll sing His praise for - ev - er - more, Who has re-deemed my soul.
Refrain
'Tis true, oh, yes, 'tis true, . . . . . . . . God's won-der-ful prom-ise is true;
the prom-ise is true, 'tis true;
For I've trusted, and test-ed, and tried it, And I know God's promise is true. . . . . .
'tis true.

# 930 THERE'S A CLEFT IN THE ROCK

*For in the time of trouble He shall hide me in His pavilion: in the secret of His tabernacle shall He hide me: He shall set me up upon a rock.* Ps. 27:5.

THE CLEFT OF THE ROCK (Irregular)
M.M. 72

Samuel E. Good, 1905 (1878-1905)

Samuel E. Good

1. There's a cleft in the Rock of A - ges, Where my soul may
2. There is peace for the soul that hid - eth In the Rock that is
3. Oh, soul, thou who now art wea - ry, To the Rock do
safe - ly hide While the storms of life are rag - ing And the
high - er than I, For the soul that on - ly con - fid - eth And the
come for rest, Come to Him who on - ly can cheer thee, To the
bil - lows roll o'er the tide.
cleft of the Rock will try.
dear lov-ing Saviour's breast.
Refrain
Oh, the cleft of the Rock,
Oh, the cleft of the Rock, Oh, the cleft of the Rock,
Where my soul may hide,
Where my soul may se - cure - ly, may se - cure - ly hide,
While the storms of life are rag - ing, And the bil - lows roll o'er the tide.

# MY SOUL IN SAD EXILE 931

*He bringeth them unto their desired haven.* Ps. 107:30.

Henry L. Gilmour, 1836-1920

THE HAVEN OF REST 11.8.11.8. with Ref.
M.M. 72

George D. Moore

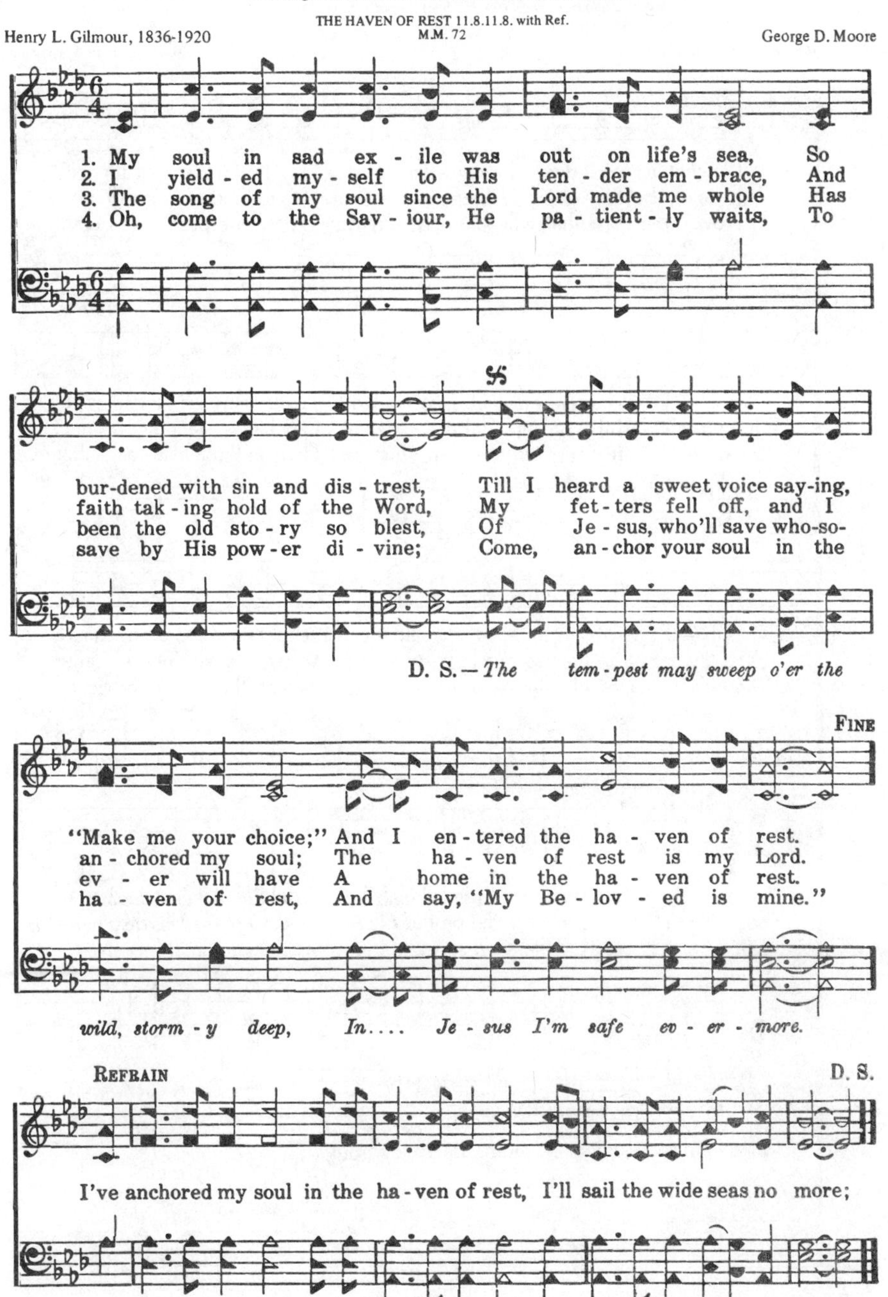
1. My soul in sad ex - ile was out on life's sea, So
2. I yield - ed my - self to His ten - der em - brace, And
3. The song of my soul since the Lord made me whole Has
4. Oh, come to the Sav - iour, He pa - tient - ly waits, To
bur-dened with sin and dis - trest, Till I heard a sweet voice say-ing,
faith tak - ing hold of the Word, My fet - ters fell off, and I
been the old sto - ry so blest, Of Je - sus, who'll save who-so-
save by His pow - er di - vine; Come, an - chor your soul in the
D. S.—The tem - pest may sweep o'er the
FINE
"Make me your choice;" And I en - tered the ha - ven of rest.
an - chored my soul; The ha - ven of rest is my Lord.
ev - er will have A home in the ha - ven of rest.
ha - ven of rest, And say, "My Be - lov - ed is mine."
wild, storm - y deep, In.... Je - sus I'm safe ev - er - more.
REFRAIN
D. S.
I've anchored my soul in the ha - ven of rest, I'll sail the wide seas no more;

# 932 O WHAT A WONDERFUL, WONDERFUL DAY

*At midday, O king, I saw in the way a light from heaven, above the brightness of the sun, shining round about me and them which journeyed with me.* Acts 26:13.

HEAVEN CAME DOWN 10.7.10.7.D. with Ref.
M.M. 120

John W. Peterson, b. 1921 — John W. Peterson

1. O what a won-der-ful, won-der-ful day, Day I will nev-er for-get;
2. Born of the Spir-it with life from a-bove In-to God's fam'ly di-vine;
3. Now I've a hope that will sure-ly en-dure After the pass-ing of time;
Aft-er I'd wan-dered in dark-ness a-way, Je-sus my Sav-ior I met.
Jus-ti-fied ful-ly thru Cal-va-ry's love, O what a standing is mine!
I have a fu-ture in heav-en for sure, There in those mansions sublime.
O what a ten-der com-pas-sion-ate friend He met the need of my heart;
And the trans-ac-tion so quick-ly was made, When as a sin-ner I came,
And it's be-cause of that won-der-ful day When at the cross I be-lieved;
Shadows dispel-ling, With joy I am telling, He made all the darkness depart!
Took of the offer Of grace He did proffer He saved me, O praise His dear name!
Riches e-ter-nal And blessings supernal From His precious hand I received.
CHORUS
Heav-en came down and glo-ry filled my soul, filled my soul,

When at the cross the Sav-ior made me whole; My
made me whole;
sins were washed a -way And my night was turned to day
Heav -en came down and glo -ry filled my soul!
filled my soul!

## UNDER AN EASTERN SKY 933

*Wherefore Jesus also, that He might sanctify the people with His own blood, suffered without the gate.* Heb. 13:12.

John Long | FOR ME 6.6.6.4. M.M. 72 | I. H. Meredith, b. 1872

Slowly
cres.
p rall.
pp
1. Un - der an east - ern sky, A - mid a rab - ble's cry....
2. Thorn-crowned His bless-ed head, Blood-stained His ev - 'ry tread;
3. Pierc - ed His hands and feet, Three hours o'er Him beat
4. Thus wert Thou made all mine; Lord, make me whol - ly Thine;
5. In thought and word and deed, Thy will to do, O lead
A Man went forth to die,...... For me, (for me,) for me.
Cross - la - den, on He sped..... For me, (for me,) for me.
Fierce rays of noon - tide heat,..... For me, (for me,) for me.
Grant grace and strength di - vine...... To me, (to me,) to me.
My soul, e'en though it bleed,.... To Thee, (to Thee,) to Thee.

# 934 AND CAN IT BE THAT I SHOULD GAIN

*For when we were yet without strength, in due time Christ died for the ungodly.* Rom. 5:6.

AND CAN IT BE 8.8.8.8.8.8. with Ref.
M.M. 54

Charles Wesley, 1707-1788 | Thomas Campbell, 1777-1844

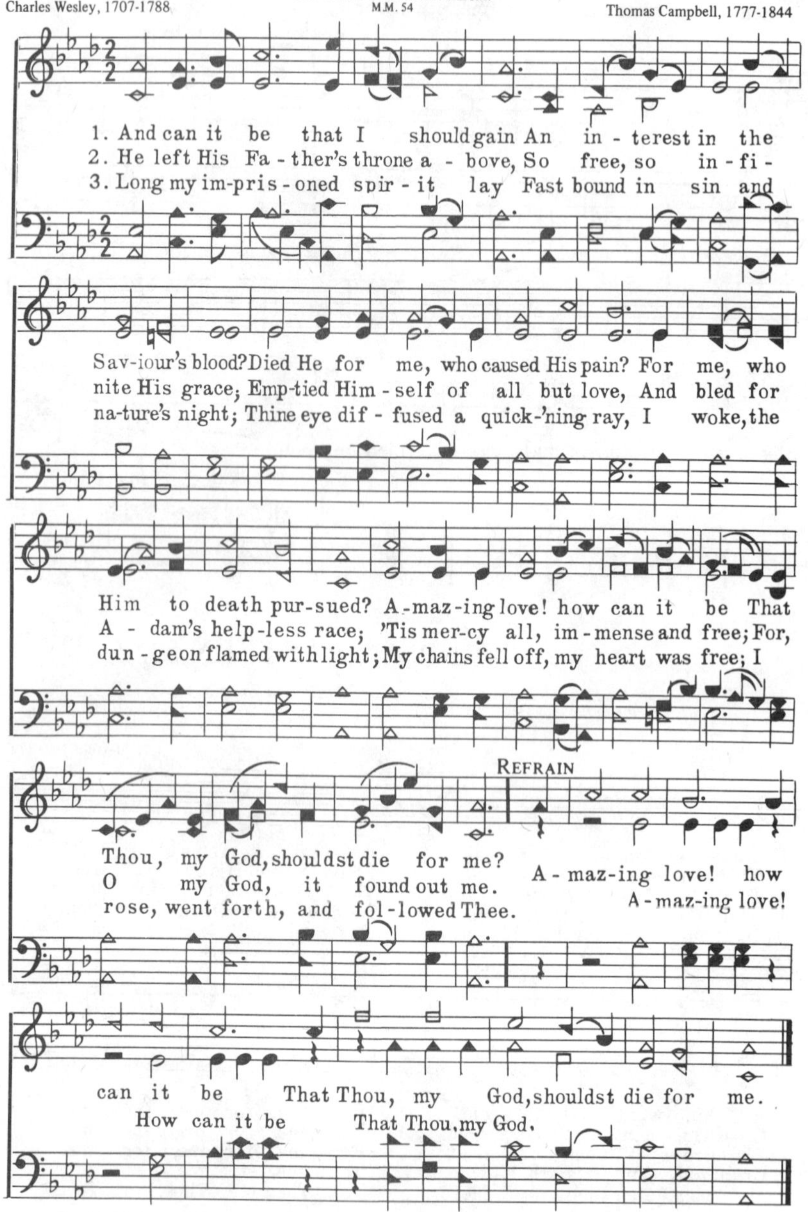
1. And can it be that I should gain An in - terest in the
2. He left His Fa - ther's throne a - bove, So free, so in - fi -
3. Long my im-pris - oned spir - it lay Fast bound in sin and
Sav-iour's blood? Died He for me, who caused His pain? For me, who
nite His grace; Emp-tied Him - self of all but love, And bled for
na-ture's night; Thine eye dif - fused a quick-'ning ray, I woke, the
Him to death pur-sued? A-maz-ing love! how can it be That
A - dam's help-less race; 'Tis mer-cy all, im - mense and free; For,
dun - geon flamed with light; My chains fell off, my heart was free; I
Thou, my God, shouldst die for me?
O my God, it found out me.
rose, went forth, and fol-lowed Thee.
REFRAIN
A - maz-ing love! how
A - maz-ing love!
can it be That Thou, my God, shouldst die for me.
How can it be That Thou, my God,

4. No condemnation now I dread; Jesus, and all in Him, is mine!
Alive in Him, my living Head, And clothed in righteousness Divine,
Bold I approach the eternal throne, And claim the crown, through Christ my own.

# GOD IS LOVE, HIS MERCY BRIGHTENS 935

*In this was manifested the love of God toward us, because that God sent His only begotten Son into the world, that we might live through Him.* I Jn. 4:9.

John Bowring, 1825 — EFFIE 8.7.8.7. M.M. 63 — D. M. Click

1. God is love, His mer-cy bright-ens All the path in which we move;
2. Chance and change are bus-y ev - er; Worlds de-cay, and a - ges move;
3. E'en the hour that dark-est seem-eth Will His changeless good-ness prove;
4. He with earth-ly cares en-twin-eth Hope and com-fort from a - bove;
Bliss He forms, and woe He light-ens; God is light, and God is love.
But His mer - cy wan-eth nev - er; God is light, and God is love.
From the mist His bright-ness streameth; God is light, and God is love.
Ev - 'ry-where His glo - ry shin - eth; God is light, and God is love.

# 'TIS THE OLD-TIME RELIGION 936

*He that spared not His own Son, but delivered Him up for us all, how shall He not with Him also freely give us all things.* Rom. 8:32.

Anon. — OLD TIME RELIGION 7.7.7.7. M.M. 69 — Anon. Arr. by Compiler, 1972

1. 'Tis the old - time re - lig - ion, 'Tis the old - time re - lig - ion,
2. Makes me love ev - 'ry - bod - y, Makes me love ev - 'ry - bod - y,
3. It was good for Paul and Si - las, It was good for Paul and Si - las,
(Verse 1 for Chorus)
'Tis the old - time re - lig - ion, And it's good e - nough for me.
Makes me love ev - 'ry - bod - y, And it's good e - nough for me.
It was good for Paul and Si - las, And it's good e - nough for me.

4. It was good for our mothers,
   And it's good enough for me.
5. It has saved our fathers,
   And it's good enough for me.
6. Makes me love the precious Bible,
   And it's good enough for me.
7. It will lead all men to Jesus,
   And it's good enough for me.
8. It will do when I am dying,
   And it's good enough for me.
9. It will take us all to heaven,
   And it's good enough for me.

# 937 HEAVEN IS A HOLY PLACE

*And there shall in no wise enter into it any thing that defileth, neither whatsoever worketh abomination, or maketh a lie: but they which are written in the Lamb's book of life.* Rev. 21:27.

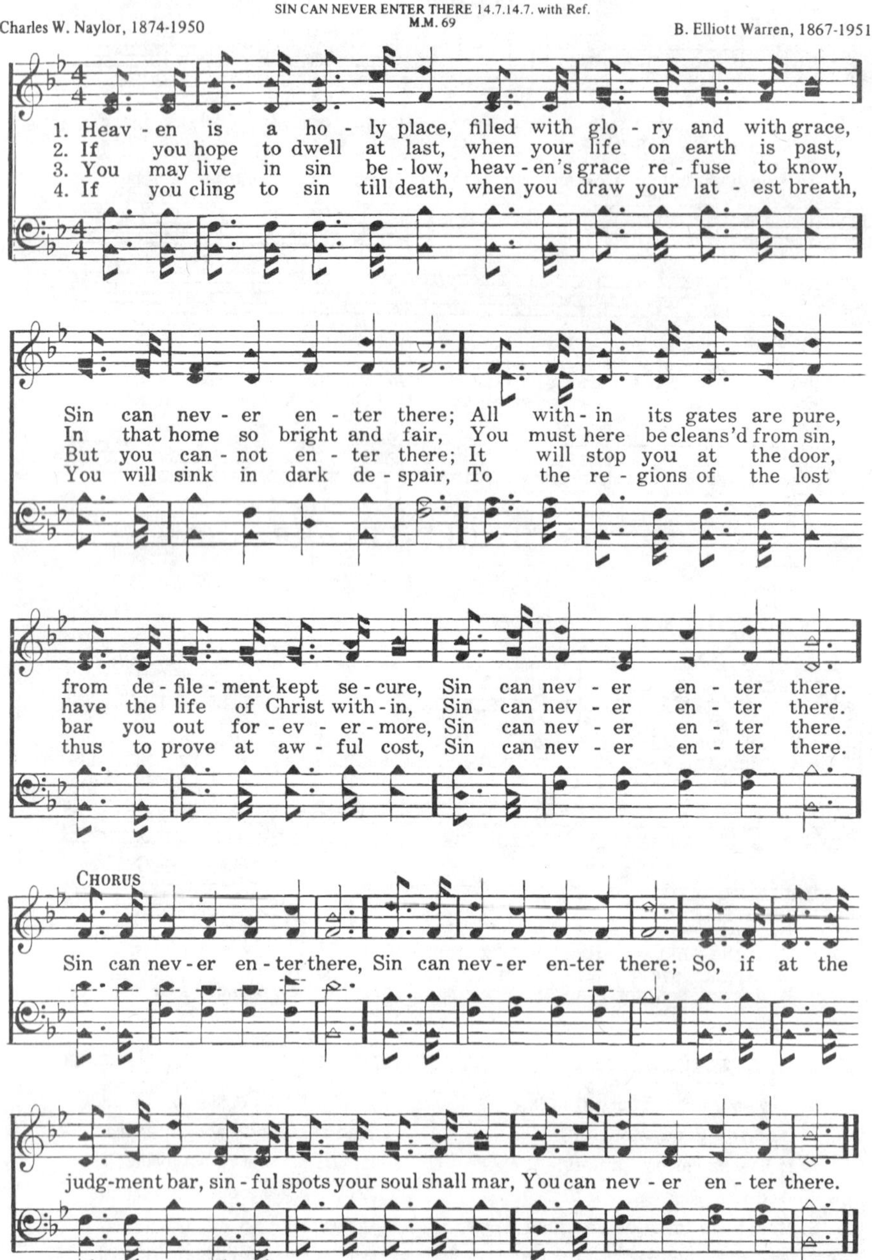
SIN CAN NEVER ENTER THERE 14.7.14.7. with Ref.
M.M. 69
Charles W. Naylor, 1874-1950
B. Elliott Warren, 1867-1951
1. Heav - en is a ho - ly place, filled with glo - ry and with grace,
2. If you hope to dwell at last, when your life on earth is past,
3. You may live in sin be - low, heav - en's grace re - fuse to know,
4. If you cling to sin till death, when you draw your lat - est breath,
Sin can nev - er en - ter there; All with - in its gates are pure,
In that home so bright and fair, You must here be cleans'd from sin,
But you can - not en - ter there; It will stop you at the door,
You will sink in dark de - spair, To the re - gions of the lost
from de - file - ment kept se - cure, Sin can nev - er en - ter there.
have the life of Christ with - in, Sin can nev - er en - ter there.
bar you out for - ev - er - more, Sin can nev - er en - ter there.
thus to prove at aw - ful cost, Sin can nev - er en - ter there.
CHORUS
Sin can nev - er en - ter there, Sin can nev - er en - ter there; So, if at the
judg - ment bar, sin - ful spots your soul shall mar, You can nev - er en - ter there.

# IF I GAINED THE WORLD 938

*For what is a man profited, if he shall gain the whole world, and lose his own soul? or what shall a man give in exchange for his soul?* Mt. 16:26.

Anna Ölander, 1904 (1861-1939)
Tr. Composite

OM JAG ÄGDE ALLT 10.9.10.9.D.
M.M. 69

Trad. Swedish

1. If I gained the world, but lost the Sav - ior, Were my life worth liv - ing
2. Had I wealth and love in full - est meas-ure, And a name re - vered both
3. O what emp - ti - ness! with-out the Sav - ior 'Mid the sins and sor - rows
4. O the joy of hav - ing all in Je - sus! What a balm the bro - ken
for a day? Could my yearn-ing heart find rest and com - fort In the
far and near, Yet no hope be - yond, no har - bor wait - ing, Where my
here be - low! And e - ter - ni - ty, how dark with - out Him! On - ly
heart to heal! Ne'er a sin so great, but He'll for - give it, Nor a
things that soon must pass a - way? If I gained the world, but lost the
storm-tossed ves - sel I could steer; If I gained the world, but lost the
night and tears and end - less woe! What, tho' I might live with-out the
sor - row that He does not feel! If I have but Je - sus, on - ly
Sav - ior, Would my gain be worth the life - long strife? Are all earth - ly
Sav - ior, Who en - dured the cross and died for me, Could then all the
Sav - ior, When I come to die, how would it be? O to face the
Je - sus, Noth - ing else in all the world be - side O then ev - 'ry-
pleas - ures worth com - par - ing For a mo - ment with a Christ-filled life?
world af - ford a ref - uge, Whith - er, in my an - guish, I might flee?
val - ley's gloom with - out Him! And with - out Him all e - ter - ni - ty!
thing is mine in Je - sus; For my needs and more He will pro - vide.

# 939 IN THE DAY OF ALL DAYS

*For we must all appear before the judgment seat of Christ; that every one may receive the things done in his body . . . whether it be good or bad.* II Cor. 5:10.

AT THE SAVIOUR'S RIGHT HAND 12.12.12.12. with Ref.
M.M. 104

Eden R. Latta, b. 1839

George B. Holsinger, 1857-1908

1. In the day of all days, when the world shall be judged, And the chaff from the wheat shall be thor-ough-ly fanned, Then the righteous shall shine as the stars in the sky, And their pla - ces shall be at the Sav-iour's right hand.
2. But the wick - ed who will not re - pent and be - lieve, And will nev - er live up to the Mas-ter's command, Shall be placed on the left, as un - wor - thy to be With the chil - dren of God at the Sav-iour's right hand.
3. We are jour - ney - ing on to e - ter - ni - ty now, On the bank of death's Jor-dan we sometime shall stand! Shall we fear to pass o - ver the dark roll - ing flood, Lest our por - tion be not at the Sav-iour's right hand?
4. If our Shep - herd He is, and we fol - low His call, He will lead us safe home, to that beau - ti - ful land; And, with crowns on our brows, and with branch - es of palm, We shall ev - er a - bide at the Sav-iour's right hand.
REFRAIN
Let me . . . . find a place . . with that . . . hap-py band, . .
Let me find a place with that hap - py band, Let me find a place with that hap - py band,
Who shall ev - - er a - bide, . . . . A-bide at the Saviour's right hand. . .
Who shall ev - er a - bide at the Saviour's right hand, right hand.

# FLEE AS A BIRD TO YOUR MOUNTAIN 940

*Who hath warned you to flee from the wrath to come? Bring forth therefore fruits meet for repentance.* Mt. 3:7, 8.

FLEE AS A BIRD 8.7.8.7.8.8.8.8.8.
M.M. 63

Mary S. B. Dana, 1840

Spanish Air

1. Flee as a bird to your moun-tain, Thou who art weary of sin; Go to the
2. He will pro-tect thee for ev - er, Wipe ev-'ry fall-ing tear; He will for-
clear flow-ing foun-tain Where you may wash and be clean. Fly, for th'a-ven-ger is
sake thee, O nev - er, Shel-tered so ten-der-ly there. Haste, then, the hours are
near thee; Call, and the Sav-ior will hear thee; He on His bos-om will
fly - ing, Spend not the mo-ments in sigh - ing, Cease from your sor-row and
bear thee, O thou who art wea-ry of sin, O thou who art wea - ry of sin.
cry - ing: The Sav-ior will wipe ev-'ry tear, The Sav-ior will wipe ev-'ry tear.

3. He is the bountiful Giver, Now unto Him draw near;
Peace then shall flow as a river, Thou shalt be saved from thy fear.
Hark! 'tis thy Saviour calling, Haste, for the twilight is falling,
Flee! for the night is appalling, And thou shalt be saved from thy fear,
And thou shalt be saved from thy fear.

# WHEN THE SUN OF YOUR LIFE HAS GONE DOWN

*If therefore the light that is in thee be darkness, how great is that darkness!* Mt. 6:23.

IF THE LIGHT HAS GONE OUT 9.9.9.9. with Ref.
M.M. 66

Curtis J. Williams — Curtis J. Williams

1. When the sun of your life has gone down And the clouds in the
2. When you come to the end of the way, And life's sto - ry for
3. When be - fore judg-ment's bar you shall stand, And the deeds that have
west turn to gold, (turn to gold,) End-less night then to you will have
you has been told, (has been told,) O how sad all to you will ap-
here had con-trol, (had con-trol) Good and e - vil ap - pear, O what
come, If the light has gone out in your soul.
pear, If the light has gone out in your soul.
then, If the light has gone out in your soul?
Fine
D.S.–still! (how still!) When the light has gone out in your soul.
Chorus
O just think how in death you will feel, you will feel, With the
light grow-ing dim in your soul; in your soul: O how lone-ly 'twill be! O how
D.S.

# SAY NOW, YE LOVELY SOCIAL BAND 942

*Seek ye the Lord while He may be found, call ye upon Him while He is near: Let the wicked forsake his way, and the unrighteous man his thoughts: and let him return unto the Lord.* Is. 55:6, 7.

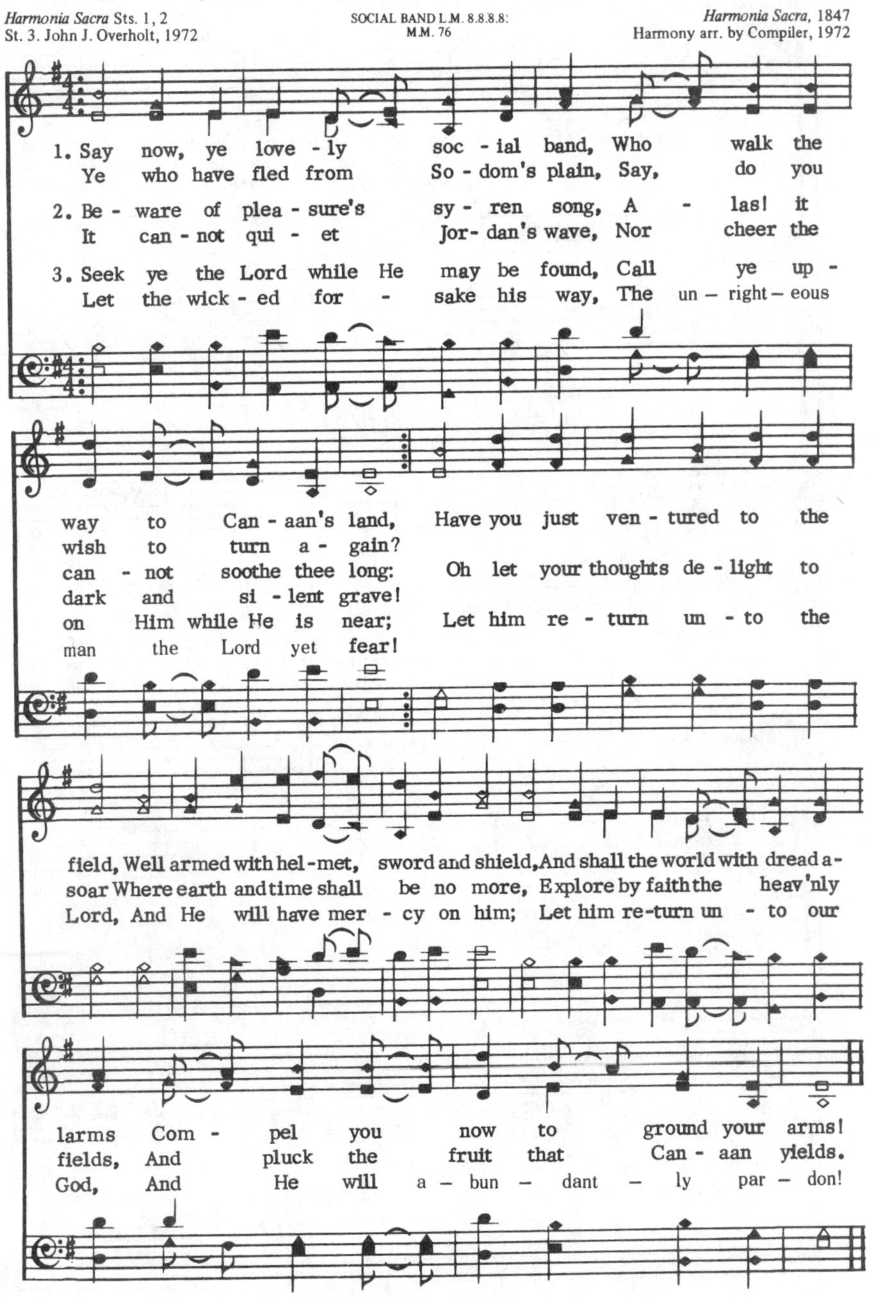
*Harmonia Sacra* Sts. 1, 2
St. 3. John J. Overholt, 1972
SOCIAL BAND L.M. 8.8.8.8.
M.M. 76
*Harmonia Sacra,* 1847
Harmony arr. by Compiler, 1972
1. Say now, ye love - ly soc - ial band, Who walk the way to Can - aan's land, Have you just ven - tured to the field, Well armed with hel - met, sword and shield, And shall the world with dread a - larms Com - pel you now to ground your arms!
Ye who have fled from So - dom's plain, Say, do you wish to turn a - gain?
2. Be - ware of plea - sure's sy - ren song, A - las! it can - not soothe thee long: Oh let your thoughts de - light to soar Where earth and time shall be no more, Explore by faith the heav'nly fields, And pluck the fruit that Can - aan yields.
It can - not qui - et Jor - dan's wave, Nor cheer the dark and si - lent grave!
3. Seek ye the Lord while He may be found, Call ye up - on Him while He is near; Let him re - turn un - to the Lord, And He will have mer - cy on him; Let him re - turn un - to our God, And He will a - bun - dant - ly par - don!
Let the wick - ed for - sake his way, The un - right - eous man the Lord yet fear!

# 943 AS YOU JOURNEY THROUGH THIS WORLD

*The dead were judged out of those things which were written in the books, according to their works.* Rev. 20:12.

YOUR DEEDS ARE RECORDED 14.14.14.14. with Ref.
M.M. 69
Bernard Bates Edmiaston, 1881-1964
Samuel W. Beazley, 1873-1944
1. As you jour - ney thro' this world are you do - ing deeds of love, Are you
2. Are you liv - ing for the Lord, or in self - ish-ness and ease, Do you
3. Pon-der you the ques-tion well, check the deeds of ev-'ry day With the
tell - ing saddened hearts of the joy like that a-bove, Are you help-ing wea-ry
sac-ri - fice for right, hu-man suff'ring to ap-pease? There are books for records
standard of the Lord-He's the Truth, the Light, the Way; When you're called, account to
souls here to bear the heav-y load, Are you send-ing heaven's light out a-
true, ev - 'ry deed is writ - ten there; Will your showing bring to you life e-
give, and the books are opened wide, With your record written there will your
REFRAIN:
long the darksome road? Your deeds are re-corded, don't you know it?....................
ter-nal or de-spair?
don't you know it?
soul be sat - is - fied?
Can you face that record to-day? Your deeds are recorded, don't you
as it stands?

know it? (don't you know it?) Can you face the rec-ord as it stands? (today?)

# THERE ARE LOVED ONES IN THE GLORY 944

*So shall it be at the end of the world: the angels shall come forth, and sever the wicked from among the just.* Mt. 13:49. *He shall separate them one from another.* Mt. 25:32. *Between us and you there is a great gulf fixed.* Lk. 16:26.

WILL THE CIRCLE BE UNBROKEN 8.7.8.7. with Ref.
M.M. 63

Ada Habershon — Charles H. Gabriel, 1856-1932

1. There are loved ones in the glo - ry, Whose dear forms you of - ten miss:
2. In the joy - ous days of child-hood, Oft they told of won-drous love,
3. You can pic - ture hap - py gath-'rings Round the fire - side long a - go,
4. One by one their seats were emp-tied, One by one they went a - way;

When you close your earth - ly sto - ry, Will you join them in their bliss?
Point-ed to the dy - ing Sav - ior – Now they dwell with Him a - bove.
And you think of tear-ful part - ings, When they left you here be - low:
Here the cir - cle has been brok - en – Will it be com-plete one day?

**CHORUS**

Will the cir - cle be un-brok - en By and by, by and by?
In a bet - ter home a - wait - ing In the sky, in the sky?

# 945 I AM LOOKING FOR THE CITY

*For he looked for a city which hath foundations, whose builder and maker is God.* Heb. 11:10.

GLORY GATES 11.7.11.7. with Ref.
M.M. 80

G. P. Hott — G. P. Hott

1. I am look-ing for the cit-y built of God, Where the man-y man-sions be;
2. Thro' the val-ley of the shadow I may go, But his grace shall be my stay;
3. 'Tis the glo-ry now that fills and thrills my soul, As I walk the nar-row way;
I am walk-ing now the path that Je-sus trod, And his face I soon shall see.
Tho' the path be dark and dan-ger-ous, I know He will guide me all the way.
I am look-ing for the heav'nly light to dawn, That shall rise in end-less day.
REFRAIN.
Oh, the glo-ry gates are ev-er o-pen wide, In-vit-ing the world to come;
Oh, the glo-ry gates are ev-er o-pen wide, To wel-come the wea-ry home!

# DEATH SHALL NOT DESTROY MY COMFORT 946

*Knowing that shortly I must put off this my tabernacle, even as our Lord Jesus Christ hath shewed me.* II Pet. 1:14.

HAPPY SPIRITS 8.7.8.7. with Ref.
M.M. 80

Anon. J. C. Burkett

1. Death shall not de-stroy my com-fort, Christ shall guide me thro' the gloom;
2. Jor-dan's streams shall not o'er-flow me While my Sav-iour's by my side;
3. Smil-ing an-gels now sur-round me, Troops re-splen-dent fill the skies;
4. Je-sus, clad in daz-zling splen-dor, Now, me-thinks, ap-pears in view!
Down he'll send some an-gel con-voy To con-vey my spir-it home.
Ca-naan, Ca-naan lies be-fore me, Rise, and cross the swell-ing tide.
Glo-ry shin-ing all a-round me While my hap-py spir-it flies.
Breth-ren, could you see my Je-sus, You would love and serve him, too.
REFRAIN.
Soon with an-gels I'll be march-ing With bright glo-ry on my brow;
Who will share my bliss-ful por-tion, Who will love my Sav-iour now?

# 947 THE HEAVENS ARE LOWERING OVER CAST

*My soul thirsteth for God, for the living God: when shall I come and appear before God?* Ps. 42:2.

From *Deutsches Lieder und Melodienbuch*
*Der Himmel hängt voll Wolken schwer*
Tr. John J. Overholt, 1965

ICH GINGE GERN L.M. 8.8.8.8. with Ref.
M.M. 72

From *Deutsches Lieder und Melodienbuch*

1. The heav'ns are low-ering o - ver-cast, I hard - ly see blue can - o - py, Yet bright and clear oe'r storm-y mass, My Sav - iour's kind-ly eye I see.
2. The storm is rag - ing fear - ful - ly, And Sa - tan sore my soul intrigues; Tho' night be dark'ning cheerless- ly, I know that my Re - deem-er lives!
3. My Fath-er's House of bless-ed-ness, Not earth - ly storms, my soul would see; Lord, I would find e - ter - nal rest In Thee, willt Thou my soul re - ceive?
4. The sink-ing earth is soon no more, It trem-bles like a skiff in strand; But I, se - cure on heav-en's shore, Can view ce - les - tial prom-ised land.

CHORUS

I'll glad - ly come, glad - ly to Thee, But if Thou dost to stay de - cree, In storm and la - bour

(I'll glad - ly) come, I'll come, I'll glad-ly come I'll come, I'll glad - ly come to Thee But if Thou dost a long-er stay de - cree, a longer stay decree; In storm and labour I will stand In

"I'll Gladly Come", (Ich Ginge Gern), is dedicated to the memory of the arranger's father, the late Joseph S. Overholt (1876-1937), who was a great lover of hymn and song. While on a visit to Canada he became aquainted with the German melody, "Ich Ginge Gern". The writer remembers with fond recollection the singing of this Gospel song since childhood in his father's home.

I will stand, My soul's in thy O'er - shad - owing hand.
storm and labour I will stand My soul's in thy o'ershadowing hand My soul's in thy o'ershadowing hand.
Bass: In thy o'ershadowing hand.

1. Der Himmel hängt voll Wolken schwer,
Ich seh' das blaue Zelt kaum mehr,
Doch über Wolken hell und klar
Nehm ich ein freundlich Auge wahr.

2. Es tobt der Sturm mit wilder Macht
Sie wird so dunkel oft, die Nacht,
Doch wenn auch meine Seele bebt,
Sie weiss, dass dort ihr Heiland lebt.

Ich gin - ge gern, So gern zu Dir,
Ich ginge gern, so gern zu Dir, Ich ginge gern, so gern zu Dir,

Doch wenn Du mich noch län - ger hier,
Doch wenn Du mich noch länger hier, Doch wenn Du mich noch länger hier,

In Sturm und Ar - beit ste - hen läss't,
In Sturm und Arbeit stehen läss't, In Sturm und Arbeit stehen läss't,

So halt Du mei-ne See - le fest.
So halt Du meine Seele fest, So halt Du meine Seele fest.

# COME, COME, SWEET DEATH 948

*For I am now ready to be offered, and the time of my departure is at hand.* II Tim. 4:6.

YEARNING FOR HOME 8.9.8.11.
M.M. 58

Zion's Harp | Zion's Harp

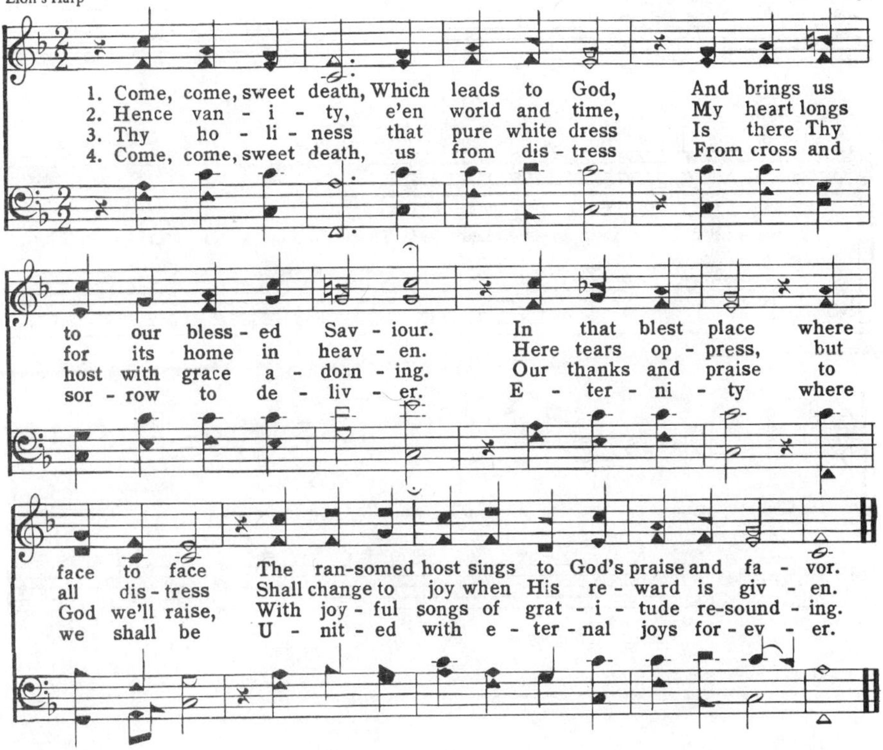

1. Come, come, sweet death, Which leads to God, And brings us
2. Hence van - i - ty, e'en world and time, My heart longs
3. Thy ho - li - ness that pure white dress Is there Thy
4. Come, come, sweet death, us from dis - tress From cross and

to our bless - ed Sav - iour. In that blest place where
for its home in heav - en. Here tears op - press, but
host with grace a - dorn - ing. Our thanks and praise to
sor - row to de - liv - er. E - ter - ni - ty where

face to face The ran-somed host sings to God's praise and fa - vor.
all dis - tress Shall change to joy when His re - ward is giv - en.
God we'll raise, With joy - ful songs of grat - i - tude re-sound - ing.
we shall be U - nit - ed with e - ter - nal joys for - ev - er.

# 949 SHADOWS NEVER DARKEN HEAVEN

*And the city had no need of the sun, neither of the moon, to shine in it: for the glory of the Lord did lighten it, and the Lamb is the light thereof.* Rev. 21:23. *And there shall be no night there.* Rev. 22:5

NO NIGHT IN HEAVEN 8.7.8.7. with Ref.
M.M. 66

Christian K. Hostetler, 1865-1935

Anon.
Arr. Abram B. Kolb, 1862-1925

1. Shad - ows nev - er dark - en heav - en, End - less day shall ban - ish night;
2. In that land of gold - en sun - light, We shall meet those gone be - fore,
3. Nei - ther pain nor death nor sor - row E'er shall reach that land on high,
Dark-ness ne'er can cross its por - tals, For the Lamb shall be the light.
And shall join in that glad cho - rus, Prais - ing God for ev - er - more.
And the ran - somed shall be gath - ered To that home be - yond the sky.
Refrain.
There shall be no night in heav - en, There shall be no dark - ness there;
Glo - ry, glo - ry, be to Je - sus For his sun-shine ev - 'ry - where.

# WHEN THE TRUMPET OF THE LORD 950

*For the Lord Himself shall descend from heaven with a shout . . . and with the trump of God . . . Then we which are alive and remain shall be caught up . . . to meet the Lord in the air.* I Thess. 4:16, 17.

WHEN THE ROLL IS CALLED 15.11.15.11. with Ref.
M.M. 84

James M. Black, 1856-1938 — James M. Black

1. When the trump-et of the Lord shall sound and time shall be no more, And the
2. On that bright and cloudless morning when the dead in Christ shall rise, And the
3. Let us la - bor for the Mas-ter from the dawn till set - ting sun, Let us
morning breaks e-ter-nal, bright and fair; When the saved of earth shall gath-er
glo - ry of His res - ur - rec-tion share; When His cho - sen ones shall gath-er
talk of all His wondrous love and care; Then when all of life is o - ver
o - ver on the oth - er shore, And the roll is called up yon-der, I'll be there.
to their home beyond the skies, And the roll is called up yon-der, I'll be there.
and our work on earth is done, And the roll is called up yon-der, I'll be there.
FINE
D. S.—roll is called up yon - der, I'll be there.
CHORUS
When the roll . . . . is called up yon - der, When the roll . . . . is
When the roll is called up yonder I'll be there, When the roll is
called up yon - der, When the roll . . . . is called up yon-der, When the
called up yonder I'll be there, When the roll is called up yon-der,
D. S.

# 951 THERE'S A LAND THAT IS FAIRER THAN DAY

*A land which the Lord thy God careth for.* Deut. 11:12. *Blessed are they that do His commandments, that they may have right to the tree of life, and may enter in through the gates into the city.* Rev. 22:14.

S. Fillmore Bennet, 1867 (1836-1898)
SWEET BY AND BY 9.9.9.9. with Ref.
M.M. 76
Joseph P. Webster, 1867 (1819-1875)
1. There's a land that is fair - er than day, And by faith we can
2. We shall sing on that beau - ti - ful shore The me - lo - di - ous
3. To our boun - ti - ful Fa - ther a - bove, We will of - fer the
see it a - far; For the Fa - ther waits o - ver the way, To pre-
songs of the blest, And our spir - its shall sor - row no more, Not a
trib - ute of praise For the glo - ri - ous gift of His love, And the
pare us a dwell - ing - place there.
sigh for the bless - ing of rest.
bless - ings that hal - low our days.
CHORUS
In the sweet by and by, We shall meet on that beau - ti - ful shore; In the sweet by and by, We shall meet on that beau - ti - ful shore.
In the sweet by and by, by and by; In the sweet by and by,

# WE MAY TARRY AWHILE HERE AS STRANGERS 952

*And they that be wise shall shine as the brightness of the firmament; and they that turn many to righteousness as the stars forever and ever.* Dan. 12:3.

WE SHALL SHINE AS THE STARS
M.M. 96

J. W. Van Deventer

J. W. Van Deventer
Arr. Amanda Jarret

1. We may tar-ry a while here as strangers, Unnoticed by those who pass by;
2. We may nev-er be rich in earth's treasures, Nor rise on the lad-der of fame;
3. We may live in a tent or a cot-tage, And die in se-clu-sion un-known;
But the Sav-iour will crown us in glo-ry, To shine as the stars of the sky.
But the Saints will at last be re-ward-ed, Made rich in Imman-u-el's name.
But the Fa-ther who see-eth in se-cret, Re-mem-bers each one of His own.
CHORUS
We shall shine as the stars of the morning, With Jesus the cru-ci-fied one;
We shall rise to be like Him for-ev-er, E - ter-nal - ly shine as the sun.

# 953 SOME DAY THE SILVER CORD WILL BREAK

*Or ever the silver cord be loosed . . . because man goeth to his long home.* Eccles. 12:6-5.

Fanny J. Crosby, 1820-1915
SAVED BY GRACE L.M. 8.8.8.8. with Ref.
M.M. 69
George C. Stebbins, 1846-1945
Stanza Har. arr. by John J. Overholt, 1965
1. Some day the sil - ver cord will break, And I no more as now shall sing;
2. Some day my earth - ly house will fall, I can-not tell how soon 'twill be,
3. Some day, when fades the gold - en sun Be - neath the ro - sy tint - ed west,
4. Some day; till then I'll watch and wait, My lamp all trimmed and burn - ing bright,
But, O, the joy when I shall wake With - in the pal - ace of the King!
But this I know—my All in All Has now a place in heav'n for me.
My bless-ed Lord shalt say, "Well done!" And I shall en - ter in - to rest.
That when my Sav - iour ope's the gate, My soul to him may take its flight.
CHORUS
And I shall see him face to face, And tell the sto - ry Saved by grace;
shall see to face,
rit.
And I shall see Him face to face, And tell the sto - ry Saved by grace.
shall see to face,

# WHEN MY LIFE WORK IS ENDED 954

*For now we see through a glass, darkly; but then face to face: now I know in part; but then shall I know even as also I am known.* I Cor. 13:12.

MY SAVIOUR FIRST OF ALL 14.11.14.11. with Ref.
M.M. 69
Fanny J. Crosby, 1820-1915
John R. Sweney, 1837-1899
1. When my life work is ended, and I cross the swelling tide, When the bright and glorious morning I shall see, I shall know my Redeemer when I reach the other side, And his smile will be the first to welcome me.
2. Oh, the soul-thrilling rapture when I view his bless-ed face, And the luster of his kindly beaming eye; How my full heart will praise him for the mercy, love and grace That prepared for me a mansion in the sky.
3. Oh, the dear ones in glory, how they beckon me to come; And our parting at the river I recall; To the sweet vales of Eden they will sing my welcome home; But I long to see my Saviour first of all.
4. Thro' the gates to the city in a robe of spotless white He will lead me where no tears will ever fall; In the glad song of ages I shall mingle with delight; But I long to see my Saviour first of all.
REFRAIN.
I shall know him, I shall know him, And redeem'd by his side I shall stand,
I shall know him,
I shall know him, I shall know him By the prints of the nails in his hand.
I shall know him,

# 955 WHEN THE RANSOMED GET HOME

*And the ransomed of the Lord shall return, and come to Zion with songs and everlasting joy upon their heads: they shall obtain joy and gladness, and sorrow and sighing shall flee away.* Is. 35:10.

Samuel W. Beazley, 1873-1944

WHEN THE RANSOMED GET HOME 6.6.6.6.D. with Ref.
M.M. 120

Samuel W. Beazley

Not fast.
1. When the ransom'd get home ... to that land fair and bright, ... Where the lov'd ones now wait ... 'mid the scenes of de-light, ... What a joy it will be ... to be numbered up there, ... With the faith-ful and true, ... in that home bright and
2. When the ransom'd shall rise ... to the glo - ri - ous bliss, ... Of that land far a - way, ... fair - er, bright-er than this; ... What a shout - ing will sound ... thro' heav-en's fair dome, ... On that beau-ti - ful shore, ... when the ransom'd get
3. When the ransom'd cross o'er ... to the bright gold-en plains, ... What a beau-ti - ful song, ... what mel-o - di - ous strains, ... Will be waft - ed a-way ... 'mid the domes of the sky, ... When the ransom'd get home ... in the sweet by and
1. When the ransom'd get home. to that land fair and bright, Where the lov'd ones now wait 'mid the scenes of de-light, What a joy it will be to be numbered up there, With the faith-ful and true,

REFRAIN:

fair. ........................... When the ransom'd get home,
home. ...........................
by. ........................... When the ransom'd get home, ...................................
in that home bright and fair.

what a joy it will be, To be gath-ered up
what a joy it will be, ...................................

there, ........................... bless-ed Sav-iour, with thee, ...........................
to be gathered up there, blessed Saviour, with thee;

Where no part-ings e'er come,
Where no partings e'er come, ................................... and we nev - er - more

And we nev-er-more roam; In that beau-ti - ful land, ...........................
roam; ................................ In that beautiful land,

when the ran - som'd get home. ...................................................
when the ran - som'd get home.

# 956 ON THE HAPPY, GOLDEN SHORE

*And if I go and prepare a place for you, I will come again, and receive you unto myself; that where I am, there ye may be also.* Jn. 14:3.

MEET ME THERE 7.7.7.3.D. with Ref.
M.M. 69

Henrietta E. Blair — William J. Kirkpatrick, 1838-1921

1. On the hap - py, gold-en shore, Where the faith-ful part no more, When the storms of life are o'er, Meet me there, Where the night dissolves a - way In - to pure and per - fect day, I am go - ing home to stay, Meet me there.
2. Here our fond-est hopes are vain, Dear - est links are rent in twain, But in heav'n no throb of pain, Meet me there, By the riv - er sparkling bright, In the cit - y of de - light, Where our faith is lost in sight, Meet me there.
3. Where the harps of an - gels ring, And the blest for - ev - er sing, In the pal - ace of the King, Meet me there, Where in sweet communion blend Heart with heart, and friend with friend, In a world that ne'er shall end, Meet me there.
D. S.—storms of life are o'er, On the hap - py, gold - en shore, Where the faith - ful part no more, Meet me there.
FINE
REFRAIN
Meet me there, Meet me there, Meet me there, Meet me there, Where the tree of life is bloom-ing, Meet me there, Meet me there, When the
D. S.

# LIFE AT BEST IS VERY BRIEF 957

*We spend our years as a tale that is told.* Ps. 90:9.

MEET ME THERE 7.7.7.3.D. with Ref.
M.M. 66

Anon. William J. Kirkpatrick, 1838-1921

1. Life at best is very brief, Like the falling of a leaf,
Like the binding of a sheaf, Be in time!
Fleeting days are telling fast That the die will soon be cast,
And the fatal line be passed, Be in time!

Refrain: Be in time,(Be in time), Be in time,(Be in time),
While the voice of Jesus calls you, Be in time, (Be in time),
If in sin you longer wait, You may find no open gate,
And your cry be just too late, Be in time!

2. Fairest flowers soon decay, Youth and beauty pass away,
Oh, you have not long to stay, Be in time!
While God's Spirit bids you come, Sinner, do no longer roam,
Lest you seal your hopeless doom, Be in time!

3. Time is gliding swiftly by, Death and judgment draweth nigh,
To the arms of Jesus fly, Be in time!
Oh, I pray you count the cost, Ere the fatal line be crossed,
And your soul in hell be lost, Be in time!

4. Sinner, heed the warning voice, Make the Lord your final choice,
Then all heaven will rejoice, Be in time!
Come from darkness into light, Come, let Jesus make you right,
Come, and start for heaven tonight, Be in time!

# WE'LL WALK IN THE LIGHT 958

*And I saw no temple therein: for the Lord God Almighty and the Lamb are the temple of it.* Rev. 21:22.

WE'LL WALK IN THE LIGHT 9.10.10.7.
M.M. 132

John J. Overholt, 1970 J. V. C.

We'll walk in the light, beautiful light, Dwelling in heaven in pure raiment
white; There with our Saviour to ever abide, Jesus, our Master, and Lord.

# 959 AT THE SOUNDING OF THE TRUMPET

*After this I beheld, and, lo, a great multitude, which no man could number, of all nations, and kindreds, and people, and tongues, stood before the throne, and before the Lamb, clothed with white robes, and palms in their hands.* Rev. 7:9.

J. H. Kurzenknabe

WHAT A GATHERING 15.11.15.11. with Ref.
M.M. 80

J. H. Kurzenknabe
Arranged by Compiler, 1972

1. At the sound-ing of the trum-pet, when the saints are gath-ered home, We will
2. When the an-gel of the Lord pro-claims that time shall be no more, We shall
3. At the great and fi-nal judg-ment, when the hid-den comes to light, When the
greet each oth-er by the crys-tal sea (crys-tal sea), With the friends and all the
gath-er and the saved and ransomed see (ransomed see); Then to meet a-gain to-
Lord in all His glo-ry we shall see (we shall see); At the bid-ding of our
loved ones there a-wait-ing us to come, What a gath-'ring of the faith-ful that will be!
geth-er on the bright ce-les-tial shore, What a gath-'ring of the faith-ful that will be!
Sav-ior, "Come, ye bless-ed to my right," What a gath-'ring of the faith-ful that will be!
FINE
CHORUS
What a gath---'ring, gath---'ring, At the sounding of the
What a gath'ring of the loved ones when we'll meet with one another,
glo-rious ju-bi-lee! What a gath--'ring, gath--'ring,
ju-bi-lee! What a gath'ring when the friends and all the dear ones meet each other,
D.S.

# WHAT A HAPPY MEETING 960

*A great multitude . . . clothed with white robes, and palms in their hands; and cried with a loud voice, saying, Salvation to our God.* Rev. 7:9, 10.

ON THAT CLOUDLESS MORNING 11.9.11.9. with Ref.
M.M. 69

Will H. Ruebush

Samuel Beazley, 1873-1944

1. What a hap - py meet-ing when the saints shall come To the shin - ing por - tals up on high; There with earth's redeemed ones to be crowned at home,
2. Then the saints their spotless robes of white shall wear, Hal-le - lu - jah to the Lamb shall cry; On that glo-rious dawning we their joy shall share,
3. To the Lamb once of - fered but who lives a - gain, To the One who came to earth to die, We shall join the ran-somed in a glad re-frain,
On that cloudless morning, by and by.
REFRAIN:
On that cloudless morning when the saints shall rise, I'll be there, I'll be there;
I'll be there, I'll be there:
In that land of beau-ty far a-bove the skies, I'll be there, I'll be there.
I'll be there I'll be there.

# 961 I AM NEARING THE PORT

*Knowing that shortly I must put off this my tabernacle, even as our Lord Jesus Christ hath shewed me.* II Pet. 1:14.

W. T. Dale | NEARING THE PORT 12.9.12.9. with Ref. M.M. 104 | Charles Edward Pollock, c. 1902, Arr. by Compiler, 1965

1. "I am near - ing the port," I will soon be at home, And the
2. "I am near - ing the port," I will soon be at rest, I will
3. "I am near - ing the port," for the land is in sight, And the
4. "I am near - ing the port," see, the bless - ed have come, And are
5. "I am an - chored in port," I have reached the bright strand, And the
voy - age of life will be o'er; And be - neath the high arch - es of
an - chor in peace on the strand, I will stand on that shore 'mid the
moun-tains in gran - deur are seen; And the land-scape of E - den I
gath - 'ring a - long on the shore; Now they watch to re - ceive me and
voy - age of life is now past; With my Sav - iour I'll dwell in that
heav - en's bright dome I shall dwell with my friends gone be - fore
throng of the blest, I will dwell in that beau - ti - ful land
hail with de - light, And the plains that are cov - ered with green.
wel - come me home, Where we'll part nev - er, no, nev - er - more.
beau - ti - ful land, And with rap - ture I'll shout, "Home at last!"
REFRAIN
I am near - ing, yes, near - ing, I am nearing, yes, nearing the
I am nearing, yes, nearing, I am nearing the port, I am nearing, yes, nearing, I am

port; Near - ing, Near - ing, I am nearing, yes, nearing the port.
nearing, the port; Nearing, yes, nearing, I am nearing, yes, nearing,

## WE ARE CLIMBING JACOB'S LADDER 962

*And he dreamed, and behold a ladder . . . reached to heaven . . . And, behold, the Lord stood above it.* Gen. 28:12, 13.

Anon. — JACOB'S LADDER 8.8.8.5. M.M. 72 — Anon.

1. We are climb - ing Ja-cob's lad-der, We are climb-ing Ja - cob's
2. Ev - 'ry round goes high - er, high-er, Ev - 'ry round goes high - er,
3. Sin - ner, will you love my Je - sus? Sin - ner, will you love my
4. If you love Him, why not serve Him? If you love Him, why not
5. We are climb - ing high - er, high - er; We are climb - ing high - er,

lad - der, We are climb-ing Jac-ob's lad - der, Sol-diers of the Cross.
high - er; Ev - 'ry round goes high-er, high - er, Sol-diers of the Cross.
Je - sus? Sin - ner will you love my Je - sus? Sol-diers of the Cross.
serve Him? If you love Him, why not serve Him? Sol-diers of the Cross.
high - er; We are climb - ing high-er, high-er, Sol-diers of the Cross.

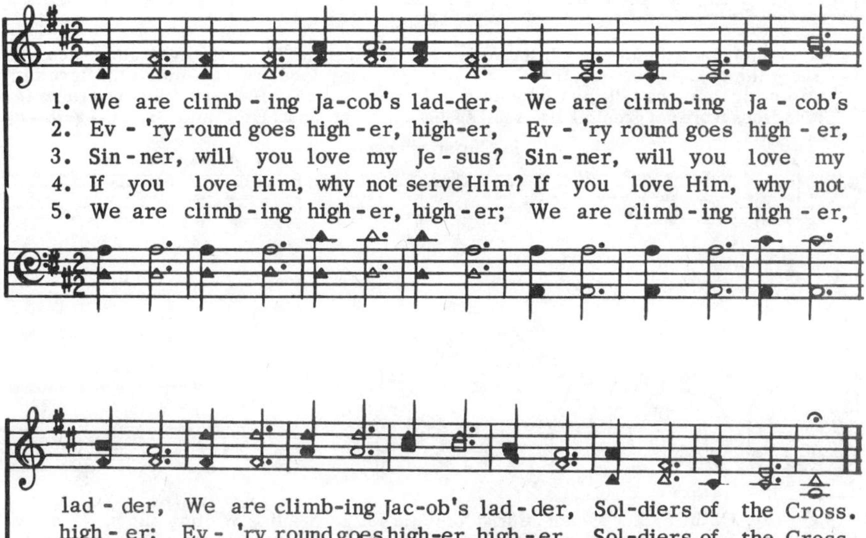

# 963 'MIDST THE DARKNESS, STORM, AND SORROW

*Eye hath not seen, nor ear heard, neither have entered into the heart of man, the things which God hath prepared for them that love Him.* I Cor. 2:9.

Gerhard Tersteegen, 1697-1769
Tr. Unknown

TERSTEEGEN 8.5.8.5.D.
M.M. 66

Clara H. Scott, 1841-1897

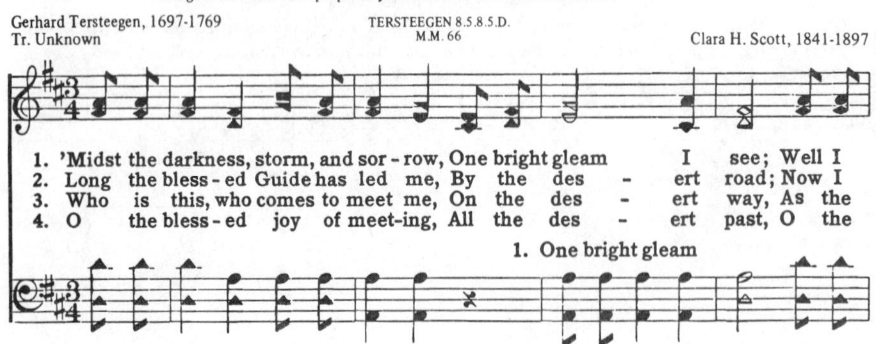
1. 'Midst the darkness, storm, and sor - row, One bright gleam I see; Well I
2. Long the bless - ed Guide has led me, By the des - ert road; Now I
3. Who is this, who comes to meet me, On the des - ert way, As the
4. O the bless - ed joy of meet-ing, All the des - ert past, O the
1. One bright gleam

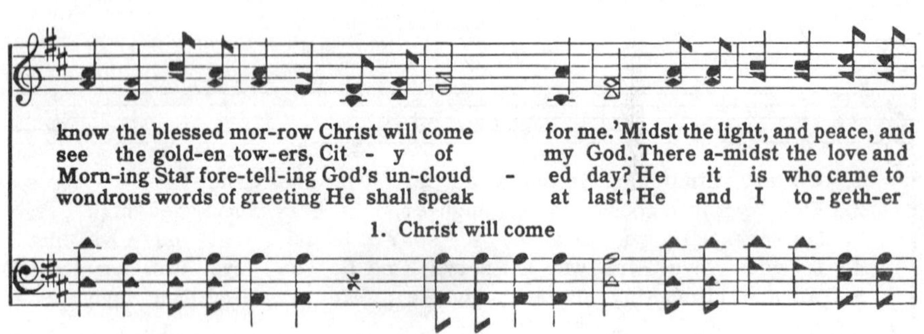
know the blessed mor-row Christ will come for me.'Midst the light, and peace, and
see the gold-en tow-ers, Cit - y of my God. There a-midst the love and
Morn-ing Star fore-tell-ing God's un-cloud - ed day? He it is who came to
wondrous words of greeting He shall speak at last! He and I to - geth-er
1. Christ will come

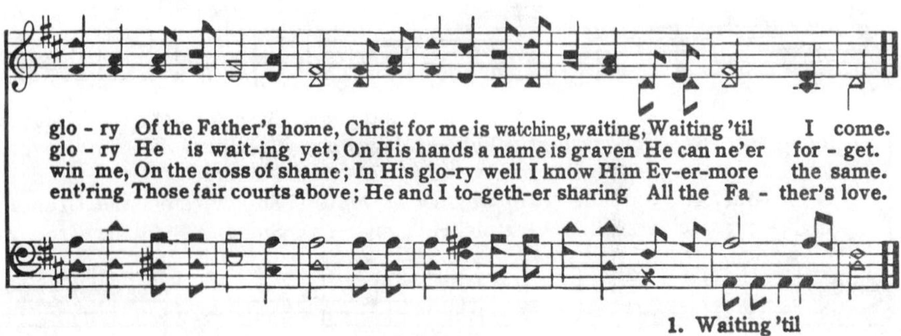
glo - ry Of the Father's home, Christ for me is watching, waiting, Waiting 'til I come.
glo - ry He is wait-ing yet; On His hands a name is graven He can ne'er for - get.
win me, On the cross of shame; In His glo-ry well I know Him Ev-er-more the same.
ent'ring Those fair courts above; He and I to-geth-er sharing All the Fa - ther's love.
1. Waiting 'til

# WHEN ALL MY LABORS AND TRIALS ARE O'ER 964

*Then shall ye also appear with Him in glory.* Col. 3:4. *The glory that shall be revealed.* I Pet. 5:1.

GLORY SONG 10.10.10.10. with Ref.
M.M. 108

Charles H. Gabriel, 1856-1932 — Charles H. Gabriel

1. When all my la-bors and tri-als are o'er, And I am safe on that beau-ti-ful shore, Just to be near the dear Lord I a-dore Will thro' the a-ges be glo-ry for me. . . .
2. When, by the gift of His in-fi-nite grace, I am ac-cord-ed in heav-en a place, Just to be there and to look on His face
3. Friends will be there I have loved long a-go; Joy like a riv-er a-round me will flow; Yet just a smile from my Sav-ior I know
rit.
CHORUS
O that will be glo-ry for me, Glo-ry for me, glo-ry for me; When by His grace I shall look on His face, That will be glo-ry, be glo-ry for me.
O . . . . . . . . that will be glo-ry for me, Glo-ry for me, glo-ry for me; . . . . .
rit.

# 965 IN THE LAND OF FADELESS DAY

*And the city lieth foursquare.* Rev. 21:16. *There shall be no night there.* Rev. 21:25. *And God shall wipe away all tears from their eyes; and there shall be no more death, neither sorrow, nor crying, neither shall there be anymore pain.* Rev. 21:4.

NO NIGHT THERE 7.6.7.6. with Ref.
M.M. 69

John R. Clements, 1868-1946 — H. P. Danks

1. In the land of fade-less day Lies the cit-y four-square;
2. All the gates of pearl are made In the cit-y four-square;
3. And the gates shall nev-er close To the cit-y four-square;
4. There they need no sun-shine bright, In the cit-y four-square;
It shall nev-er pass a-way, And there is no night there.
All the streets with gold are laid, And there is no night there.
There life's crys-tal riv-er flows, And there is no night there.
For the Lamb is all the light, And there is no night there.
CHORUS
God shall wipe a-way all tears; There's no death, no pain, nor fears;
God shall wipe a-way all tears; There's no death, no pain, nor fears;
f
dim.
mf
And they count not time by years, . . For there is no night there.
And they count not time by years, by years, For there is no night . . there.

# THERE'S A LAND WHERE ALL ARE BLEST 966

*Charity never faileth . . . For we know in part, and we prophesy in part. But when that which is perfect is come, then that which is in part shall be done away.* I Cor. 13:8-10.

LAND OF LOVE 7.3.7.3.7.7.7.3. with Ref.
M.M. 69
Daniel Henry Bender, 1866-1945
John Martin Shank, 1880 - 1945
1. There's a land where all are blest, Land of love, Where redeemed ones are at rest.
2. There amid ce-les - tial green, Land of love, Viewing glories here unseen,
3. With the ransomed gone before, Land of love, Gathered on the golden shore,
o-ver there,
Land of love; There we'll sing our Saviour's praise, In transcendent, joyful lays,
Land of love, We shall cease from toil and care, Bask in genial, fragrant air,
Land of love, We shall sit at Jesus' feet, And love's tribute oft repeat;
o-ver there;
D. S.—In transcendent, joyful lays, We will sing our Saviour's praise,
FINE. REFRAIN:
Thro'-out ceaseless, heav'nly days, Land of love. Land of love,
Dwell with an - gels bright and fair, Land of love.
There our rest will be complete, Land of love.
o-ver there. o-ver there,
Thro'-out cease-less, heav'n-ly days, Land of love. (o-ver there.)
D. S.
Land of love, Thro'-out ceaseless, heav'nly, days, Land of love,
o-ver there o-ver there,

# 967 I THINK OF A CITY

*And I John saw the holy city, new Jerusalem, coming down from God out of heaven, prepared as a bride adorned for her husband.* Rev. 21:2.

THE UNSEEN CITY 10.8.10.8.D. with Ref.
M.M. 60
Emma Tuttle
Clark
Arr. W. E. M. Hackleman
Very slowly
1. I think of a cit - y I have not seen Ex - cept in my hours of dream - ing; Where the feet of mor - tals have nev - er been To dark - en its soft, soft gleam - ing: A glim - mer of pearl, and a glint of gold, And a breath from the souls of ro - ses; And glo - ry and
2. I think of that cit - y, for oh, how oft My heart has been wrung at part - ing; With friends all pale who with foot - fall soft To its air - y heights were start - ing: I see them a - gain in their rai - ment white, In the blue, blue dis - tance dwell - ing; And I hear their
3. That beau - ti - ful cit - y is home to me, My lov'd ones are go - ing thith - er, And they who al - read - y have cross'd the sea Are call - ing to me, "Come hith - er;" The ten - der eyes that I cher-ished here, From the gold - en heights be - hold me; And their songs en -

beau - ty all un - told, Steal o - ver my calm re - po - ses.
prais - es in calm de - light, Come down to the breez - es swell - ing.
trance my rap - tured ear When the wings of slum - ber fold me.

REFRAIN:

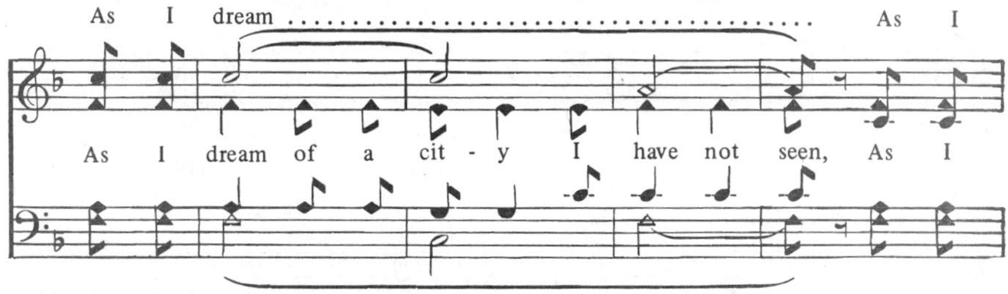
As I dream ........................................ As I
As I dream of a cit - y I have not seen, As I

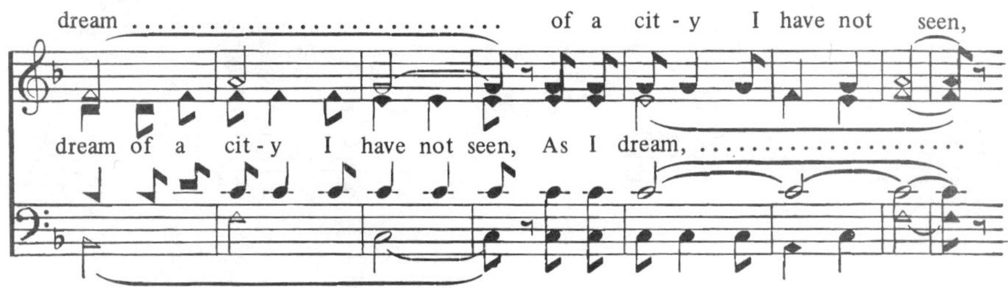
dream .............................. of a cit - y I have not seen,
dream of a cit - y I have not seen, As I dream, ..................

As I dream ........................................
As I dream of a cit - y I have not seen, As I

dream ..............................
dream of a cit - y I have not seen, Of a cit - y I have not seen.

# 968 BEAUTIFUL VALLEY OF EDEN

*For the Lord shall comfort Zion . . . and He will make her wilderness like Eden, and her desert like the garden of the Lord; joy and gladness shall be found therein, thanksgiving, and the voice of melody.* Is. 51:3.

BEAUTIFUL VALLEY OF EDEN S.M. 6.6.8.6.
M.M. 108
William O. Cushing, 1823-1902
William F. Sherwin, 1826-1888
1. Beau - ti - ful val - ley of E - den! Sweet is thy noon-tide calm;
2. O - ver the heart of the mourn - er Shin - eth thy gold - en day,
3. There is the home of my Sav - iour; There, with the blood-washed throng,
O - ver the hearts of the wea - ry Breath-ing thy waves of balm.
Waft-ing the songs of the an - gels Down from the far a - way.
O - ver the high-lands of glo - ry Roll - eth the great, new song.
REFRAIN
Beau - ti - ful val - ley of E - den, Home of the pure and blest, . . . .
the pure and blest,
rit.
How oft - en a - mid the wild bil - lows I dream of thy rest—sweet rest!

# THERE'S A MANSION IN GLORY 969

*In my Father's house are many mansions: if it were not so, I would have told you. I go to prepare a place for you.* Jn. 14:2.

MANSION IN GLORY 7.7.9.6.7.8.
M.M. 112

Harry R. Showalter, 1972 (b. 1889)

Harry R. Showalter
Har. John J. Overholt, 1972

1. There's a mansion in glory, What a wonderful story, How that Jesus has gone to prepare For those that believe Him, He will gladly receive them, In that city that's built four-square.
2. Its streets are of gold And its walls are of jasper, There are twelve gates of glistening pearl; They will never be closed So that pilgrims may enter Where the Lord will His glory unfurl.
3. There's no need for the sun Nor the moon in that city, For all darkness will vanish away, Where the light of the Lamb will shine forth in its beauty, In that place where 'twill always be day.
4. There'll be no pain nor sorrow In the world of tomorrow, If today we take heed to God's call; But to those who take pleasure In the follies of Satan, In perdition together they'll fall.
CHORUS
Shall we meet in that place so fair, And together its glories share? With the throng of the blest, In that mansion of rest, What a joy if we're numbered up there.

# 970 JERUSALEM THE GOLDEN

*But Jerusalem which is above is free, which is the mother of us all.* Gal. 4:26. *And the city was pure gold.* Rev. 21:18.

Bernard of Cluny, 1145
Tr. John Mason Neale, 1845 (1818-1866)

EWING 7.6.7.6.D.
M.M. 88

Alexander C. Ewing, 1853 (1830-1895)

1. Je - ru - sa - lem the gold - en, With milk and hon - ey blest,
2. They stand, those halls of Si - on, All ju - bi - lant with song,
3. There, is the throne of Da - vid; And there, from care re - leased,
4. O sweet and bless - ed coun - try, The home of God's e - lect!
Be - neath thy con - tem - pla - tion Sink heart and voice op - prest;
And bright with many an an - gel, And all the mar - tyr throng:
The shout of them that tri - umph, The song of them that feast.
O sweet and bless - ed coun - try, That ea - ger hearts ex - pect!
I know not, O I know not, What joys a - wait us there;
The Prince is ev - er in them, The day - light is se - rene;
And they who, with their Lead - er, Have con-quered in the fight,
Je - sus, in mer - cy bring us To that dear land of rest!
What ra - dian - cy of glo - ry, What bliss be - yond com - pare.
The pas - tures of the bless - ed Are decked in glo - rious sheen.
For - ev - er and for - ev - er Are clad in robes of white.
Who art, with God the Fa - ther, And Spir - it, ev - er blest. A-MEN.

# JERUSALEM THE GOLDEN 971

*For here have we no continuing city, but we seek one to come.* Heb. 13:14.

Bernard of Cluny, 1145
Tr. John Mason Neale, 1845 (1818-1866)

JERUSALEM THE GOLDEN 7.6.7.6.D.
M.M. 80

Anthony J. Showalter, 1858-1924

1. Je - ru - sa - lem, the gold - en, With milk and hon-ey blest, Be-neath thy
2. They stand, those halls of Zi - on, All ju - bi-lant with song, And bright with
3. There is the throne of Da - vid; And there from care released, The shout of
con - tem - pla - tion Sink heart and voice oppress; I know not, O I know not,
many an an - gel, And all the mar-tyr throng; The Prince is ev-er in them,
them that tri-umph, The song of them that feast; And they who, with their Leader,
What social joys are there, What ra-dian-cy of glo-ry, What light beyond compare.
The day-light is se-rene; The pastures of the blessed Are decked in glorious sheen.
Have conquered in the fight, For ev - er and for ev - er Are clad in robes of white.

4. O sweet and blessed country, The home of God's elect!
O sweet and blessed country, That eager hearts expect!
Jesus, in mercy bring us To that dear land of rest!
Who art, with God the Father, And Spirit, ever blest. Amen.

# 972 PEACEFULLY LAY HIM DOWN TO REST

*For dust thou art, and unto dust shalt thou return.* Gen. 3:19. *I am distressed for thee, my brother Jonathan: very pleasant hast thou been unto me: thy love to me was wonderful, passing the love of women.* II Sam. 1:26.

SLEEP TILL THAT MORNING 8.8.8.9. with Ref.
M.M. 88

Anon. B. F. Showalter

1. Peace-ful - ly lay (her/him) down to rest; Place the turf kind- ly o'er (her/his) breast;
2. Close to (her/his) lone and nar - row house, Grace-ful - ly wave, ye wil- low boughs;
3. Qui - et - ly sleep, be - lov - ed one, Rest from thy toil, thy la - bor's done;

Sweet be the slum - ber 'neath the sod, While the pure soul is rest-ing with God.
Flow'rs of the wild- wood o - dors shed O - ver the ho - ly, beau-ti - ful dead.
Rest till the trump from th' op'ning skies Bids thee from dust to glo - ry a - rise.

REFRAIN.

Peace - - ful - ly sleep,........ Sleep............ till that
Peace - ful - ly, peace - ful - ly, sweet - ly sleep, Peace - ful - ly sleep till that

morn - ing, Yes, peace - - - ful - ly sleep................
morn - ing, Yes, peace - ful - ly, peace - ful - ly, peace - ful - ly sleep.

# COME, YE DISCONSOLATE 973

*That ye sorrow not, even as others which have no hope.* I Thess. 4:13.

Thomas Moore, 1816 (1779-1852)
Alt. Thomas Hastings, 1784-1872

COME YE DISCONSOLATE 11.10.11.10. with Ref.
M.M. 84

Samuel Webbe, 1740-1816

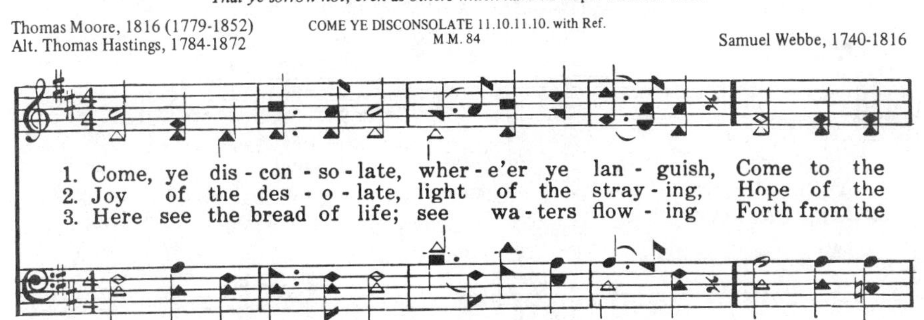
1. Come, ye dis - con - so - late, wher - e'er ye lan - guish, Come to the
2. Joy of the des - o - late, light of the stray - ing, Hope of the
3. Here see the bread of life; see wa - ters flow - ing Forth from the

mer - cy - seat, fer - vent - ly kneel; Here bring your wound - ed hearts,
pen - i - tent, fade - less and pure; Here speaks the Com - fort - er,
throne of God, pure from a - bove; Come to the feast of love;

here tell your an - guish; Earth has no sor - row that heav'n can-not heal.
ten - der - ly say - ing, "Earth has no sor - row that heav'n can-not cure."
come, ev - er know-ing, Earth has no sor - row but heav'n can re - move.

# 974 SOME SWEET DAY WHEN LIFE IS O'ER

*But we know that, when He shall appear, we shall be like Him; for we shall see Him as He is.* I Jn. 3:2.

S. H. Chord | SOME SWEET DAY 7.5.7.5 with Ref. M.M. 69 | S. H. Chord

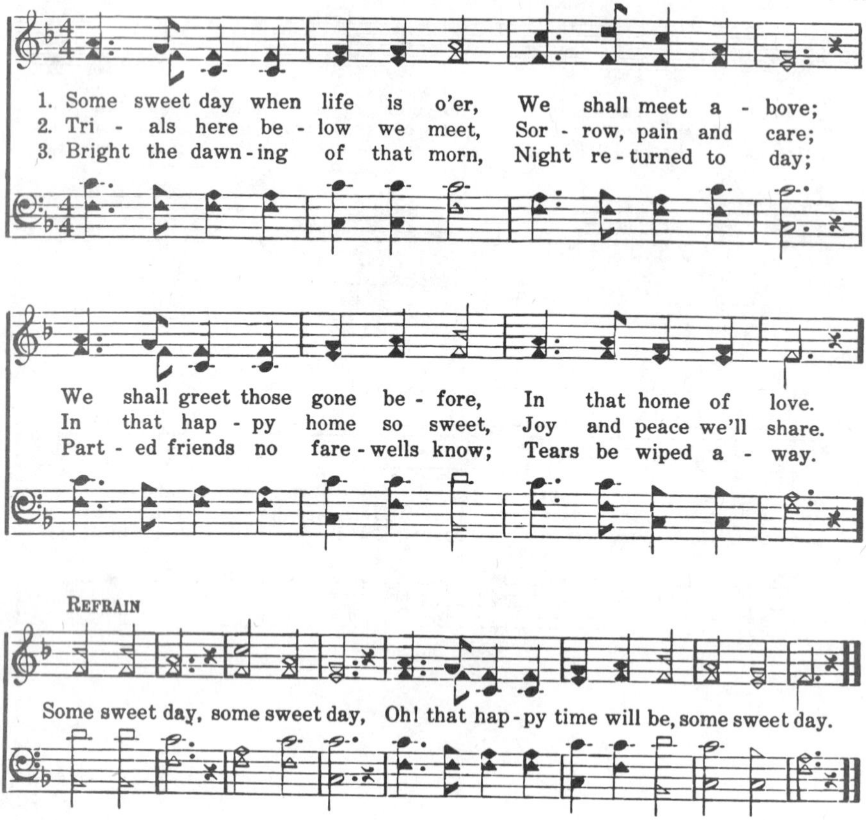

1. Some sweet day when life is o'er, We shall meet a - bove;
2. Tri - als here be - low we meet, Sor - row, pain and care;
3. Bright the dawn - ing of that morn, Night re - turned to day;

We shall greet those gone be - fore, In that home of love.
In that hap - py home so sweet, Joy and peace we'll share.
Part - ed friends no fare - wells know; Tears be wiped a - way.

**Refrain**

Some sweet day, some sweet day, Oh! that hap - py time will be, some sweet day.

# 975 SUNSET AND EVENING STAR

*And they shall see His face.* Rev. 22:4.

Alfred Tennyson, 1809-1892
Adapted by Mrs. Joseph Cook

WORDEN 6.6.8.6.8.6.
M.M. 63

B. T. Worden

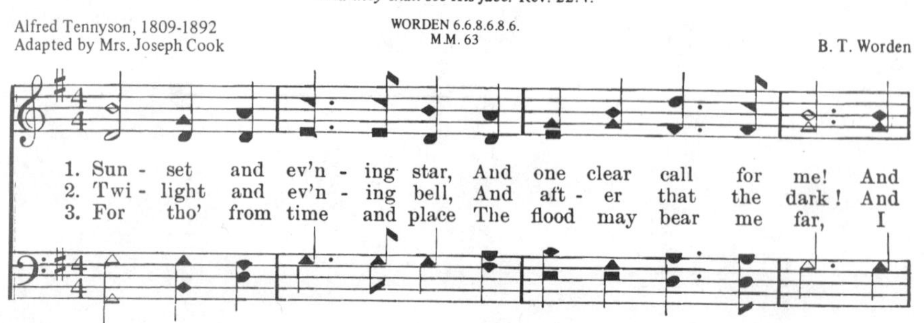
1. Sun - set and ev'n - ing star, And one clear call for me! And
2. Twi - light and ev'n - ing bell, And aft - er that the dark! And
3. For tho' from time and place The flood may bear me far, I

may there be no moan - ing bar When I put out to sea, And
may there be no sad fare-well When I at last em - bark, And
hope to see my Pi - lot's face When I have crossed the bar, I
may there be no moan-ing bar When I put out to sea.
may there be no sad fare - well When I at last em - bark.
hope to see my Pi - lot's face When I have crossed the bar.

# SUNSET AND EVENING STAR 976

*Who can count the dust of Jacob, and the number of the fourth part of Israel? Let me die the death of the righteous, and let my last end be like his!* Num. 23:10.

Alfred Tennyson, 1809-1892
Adapted by Mrs. Joseph Cook

CROSSING THE BAR 6.6.8.6.
M.M. 56

George Frederick Root, 1820-1895

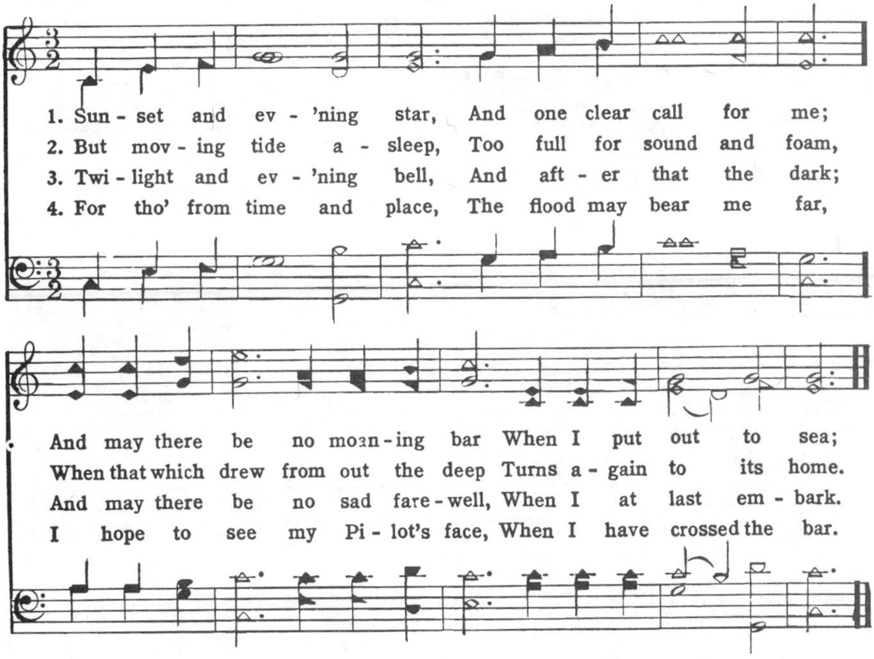

1. Sun - set and ev - 'ning star, And one clear call for me;
2. But mov - ing tide a - sleep, Too full for sound and foam,
3. Twi - light and ev - 'ning bell, And aft - er that the dark;
4. For tho' from time and place, The flood may bear me far,

And may there be no moan - ing bar When I put out to sea;
When that which drew from out the deep Turns a - gain to its home.
And may there be no sad fare - well, When I at last em - bark.
I hope to see my Pi - lot's face, When I have crossed the bar.

# 977 BEYOND THE SUNSET

*The righteous hath hope in his death.* Prov. 14:32. *Mark the perfect man, and behold the upright: for the end of that man is peace.* Ps. 37:37.

BEYOND THE SUNSET 10.9.10.9.
M.M. 58
Virgil P. Brock
Blanche Kerr Brock
1 Be - yond the sun - set, O bliss - ful morn - ing, When with our
2. Be - yond the sun - set no clouds will gath - er, No storms will
3. Be - yond the sun - set a hand will guide me To God, the
4. Be - yond the sun - set, O glad re - un - ion, With our dear
(1.) Be-yond the sun-set,
Sav - ior heav'n is be - gun; Earth's toil-ing end - ed, O glo-rious
threat - en, no fears an - noy; O day of glad - ness, O day un-
Fa - ther, whom I a - dore; His glo-rious pres - ence, His words of
loved ones who've gone be - fore; In that fair home - land we'll know no
(1.) Earth's toil-ing end-ed,
rit.
dawn - ing, Be - yond the sun - set, when day is done.
end - ing, Be - yond the sun - set, e - ter - nal joy!
wel - come, Will be my por - tion on that fair shore.
part - ing; Be - yond the sun - set for ev - er - more.

# NOT NOW, BUT WHEN 'TIS GOD'S SWEET WILL 978

*But then shall I know even as also I am known.* I Cor. 13:12.

WE'LL SURELY KNOW 8.8.8.8. with Ref.
M.M. 66

Harriet E. Jones, (b. 1824)

Arthur B. Coffman, 1842-1879

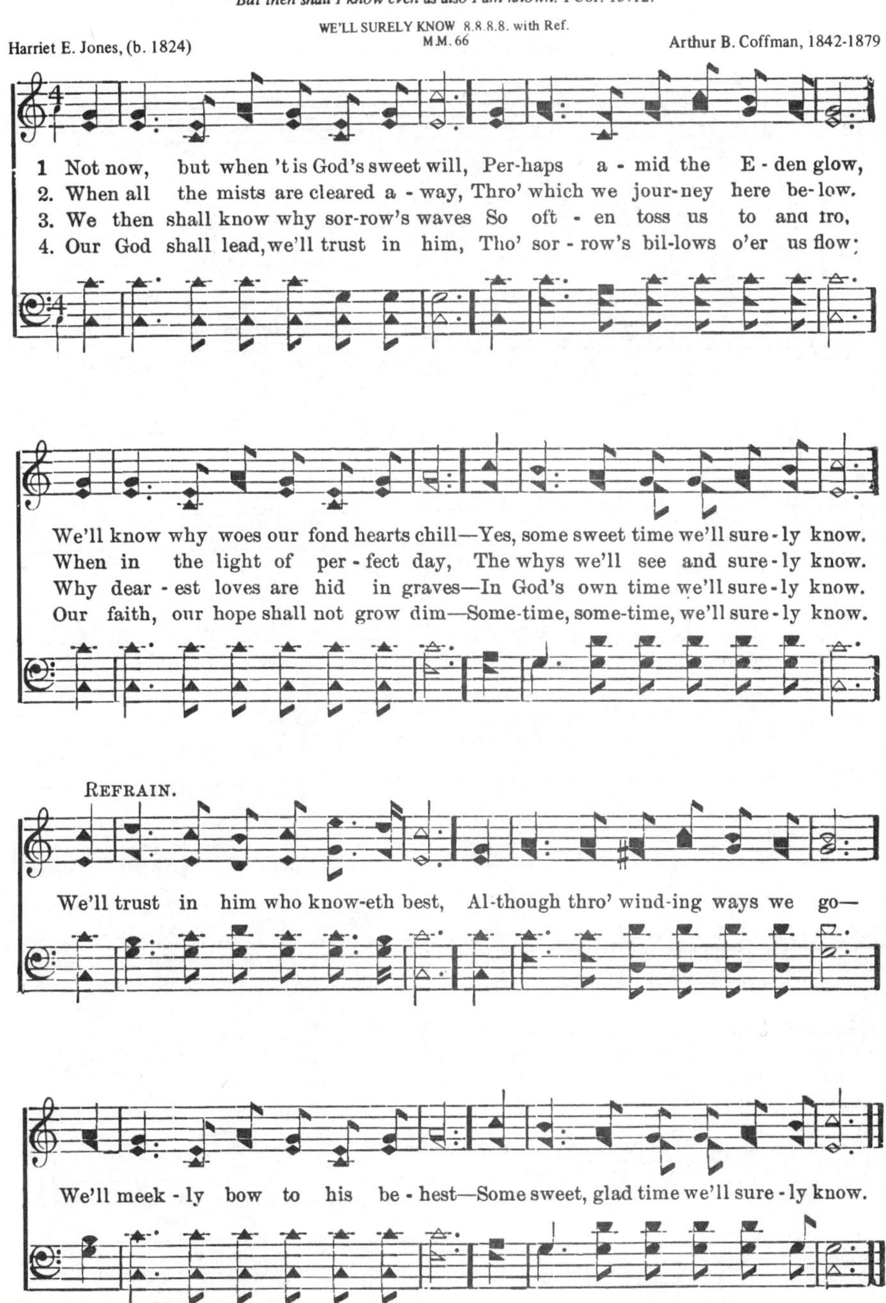
1 Not now, but when 't is God's sweet will, Per-haps a - mid the E - den glow,
2. When all the mists are cleared a - way, Thro' which we jour-ney here be-low.
3. We then shall know why sor-row's waves So oft - en toss us to and fro,
4. Our God shall lead, we'll trust in him, Tho' sor - row's bil-lows o'er us flow;
We'll know why woes our fond hearts chill—Yes, some sweet time we'll sure - ly know.
When in the light of per - fect day, The whys we'll see and sure - ly know.
Why dear - est loves are hid in graves—In God's own time we'll sure - ly know.
Our faith, our hope shall not grow dim—Some-time, some-time, we'll sure - ly know.
REFRAIN.
We'll trust in him who know-eth best, Al-though thro' wind-ing ways we go—
We'll meek - ly bow to his be - hest—Some sweet, glad time we'll sure - ly know.

# 979 THE LORD'S MY SHEPHERD

*The Lord is my shepherd; I shall not want.* Ps. 23:1. *We love Him, because He first loved us.* I Jn. 4:19.

Psalter
Cho. Joseph Overholt, 1968

O HOW LOVE I THE LORD 8 6.8.6. with Ref.
M.M 132

James McGranahan, 1840-1907

1. The Lord's my shep–herd, I'll not want; He makes me down to lie
2. My soul He doth re–store a–gain; And me to walk doth make
3. Yea, though I walk thro' death's dark vale, Yet will I fear no ill;
4. My ta–ble Thou hast fur–nish–ed In pres–ence of my foes;
5. Good–ness and mer–cy all my life Shall sure–ly fol–low me;
In pas–tures green; He lead–eth me The qui–et wa–ters by.
With–in the paths of right–eous–ness E'en for His own name's sake.
For Thou art with me, and Thy rod, And staff me com–fort still.
My head Thou dost with oil an–noint, And my cup o–ver–flows.
And in God's house for–ev–er–more My dwell–ing place shall be.
CHORUS
Oh, how love I the Lord, O how love I the Lord; He is my med–i–ta–tion all (all) the day; Oh, how love I the Lord, O how love I the Lord; He is my med–i–ta–tion all the day (all the day).
rit.

# I COME TO THE GARDEN ALONE 980

*And they heard the voice of the Lord God walking in the garden in the cool of the day.* Gen. 3:8.

IN THE GARDEN 8.9.5.5.7. with Ref.
M.M. 100

C. Austin Miles, 1868-1946 — C. Austin Miles

1. I come to the gar-den a - lone, While the dew is still on the ros - es; And the voice I hear, Fall-ing on my ear, The Son of God dis-clos - es.
2. He speaks, and the sound of His voice Is so sweet the birds hush their sing - ing; And the mel - o - dy That He gave to me, With-in my heart is ring - ing.
3. I'd stay in the gar-den with Him, Tho' the night a-round me be fall - ing, But He bids me go: Thro' the voice of woe His voice to me is call - ing.
CHORUS
And He walks with me, and He talks with me, And He tells me I am His own; And the joy we share as we tar - ry there, None oth-er has ev - er known.

# 981 I GRIEVED MY LORD FROM DAY TO DAY

*Pray without ceasing.* I Thess. 5:17.

PRAYERS L.M. 8.8.8.8. with Ref.
M.M. 63

Lizzie DeArmond

B. D. Ackley, 1872-1958

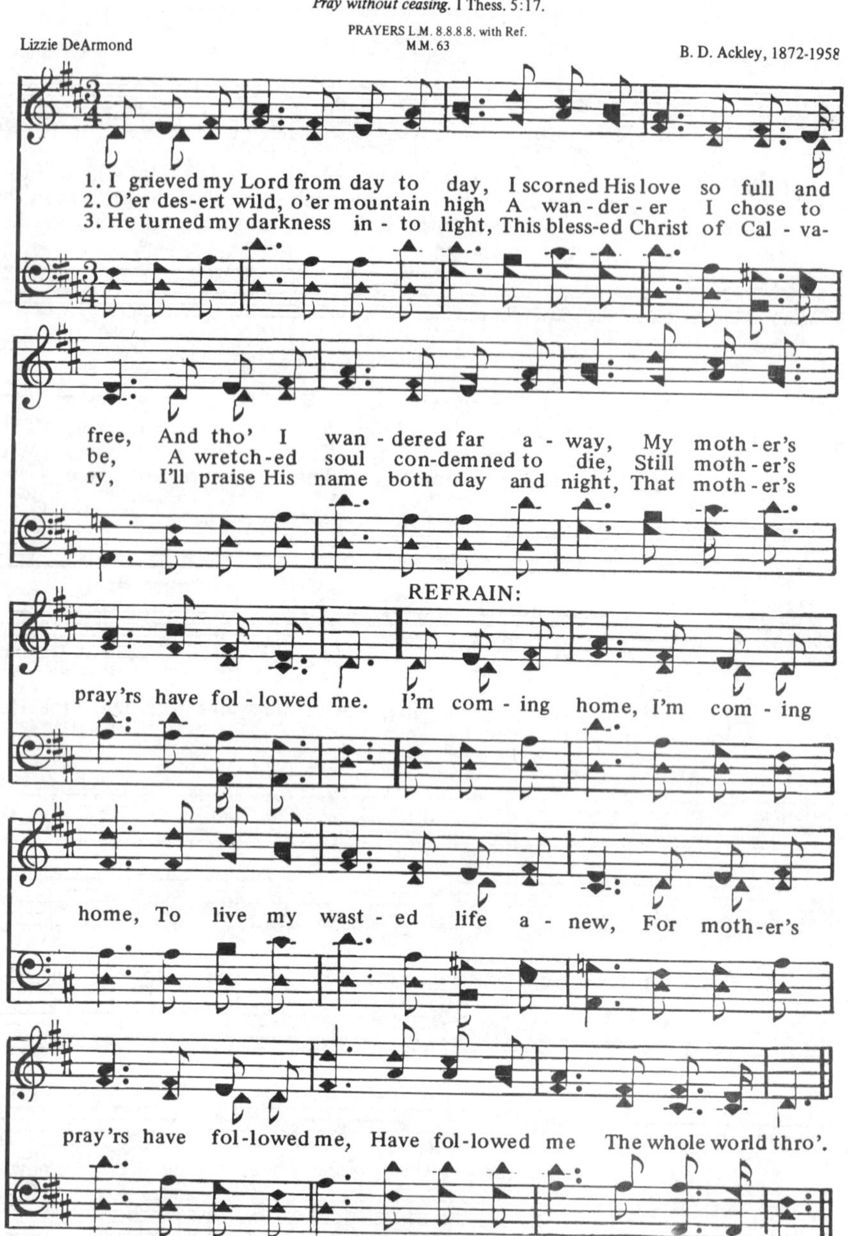
1. I grieved my Lord from day to day, I scorned His love so full and free, And tho' I wan-dered far a-way, My moth-er's pray'rs have fol-lowed me.
2. O'er des-ert wild, o'er mountain high A wan-der-er I chose to be, A wretch-ed soul con-demned to die, Still moth-er's
3. He turned my darkness in-to light, This bless-ed Christ of Cal-va-ry, I'll praise His name both day and night, That moth-er's
REFRAIN:
I'm com-ing home, I'm com-ing home, To live my wast-ed life a-new, For moth-er's pray'rs have fol-lowed me, Have fol-lowed me The whole world thro'.

"Father's prayers" may be substituted above.

# MY SAVIOUR ONCE FOR ALL 982

*And being in an agony He prayed more earnestly: and His sweat was as it were great drops of blood falling down to the ground.* Lk. 22:44.

MY SAVIOUR ONCE FOR ALL (Irregular)
M.M. 66
Anon.
Anon.
Arr. John J. Overholt, 1971
1. My Sav-iour once for all, In the gar-den, He did pray;
2. With lan-terns and with torch-es, With wea-pons for the fight;
3. There were no dear ones with Him, The disciples had all fled;
Drops of blood rolled down, Oh take this cup a-way;
They came and took my Je-sus Up-on that lone-ly night;
Bur-dened with the cross Up the hill-side He was led;
"Not my will, but Thine," These words He plain-ly said
They mocked Him, and they scoffed Him, My Lord so good and true;
The nails were then sent crush-ing Through nerve, flesh, and bone;
For He knew that on the mor-row, He'd be num-bered with the dead.
He bore it all with patience, Oh sin-ner, it was for you.
Oh sin-ner, won't you hear Him, Or is your heart of stone?

# 983

## THE SERVICE OF JESUS TRUE PLEASURE AFFORDS

*When Christ . . . shall appear, then shall ye also appear with Him in glory.* Col. 3:4. *Godliness . . . having promise of the life that now is, and of that which is to come.* I Tim. 4:8.

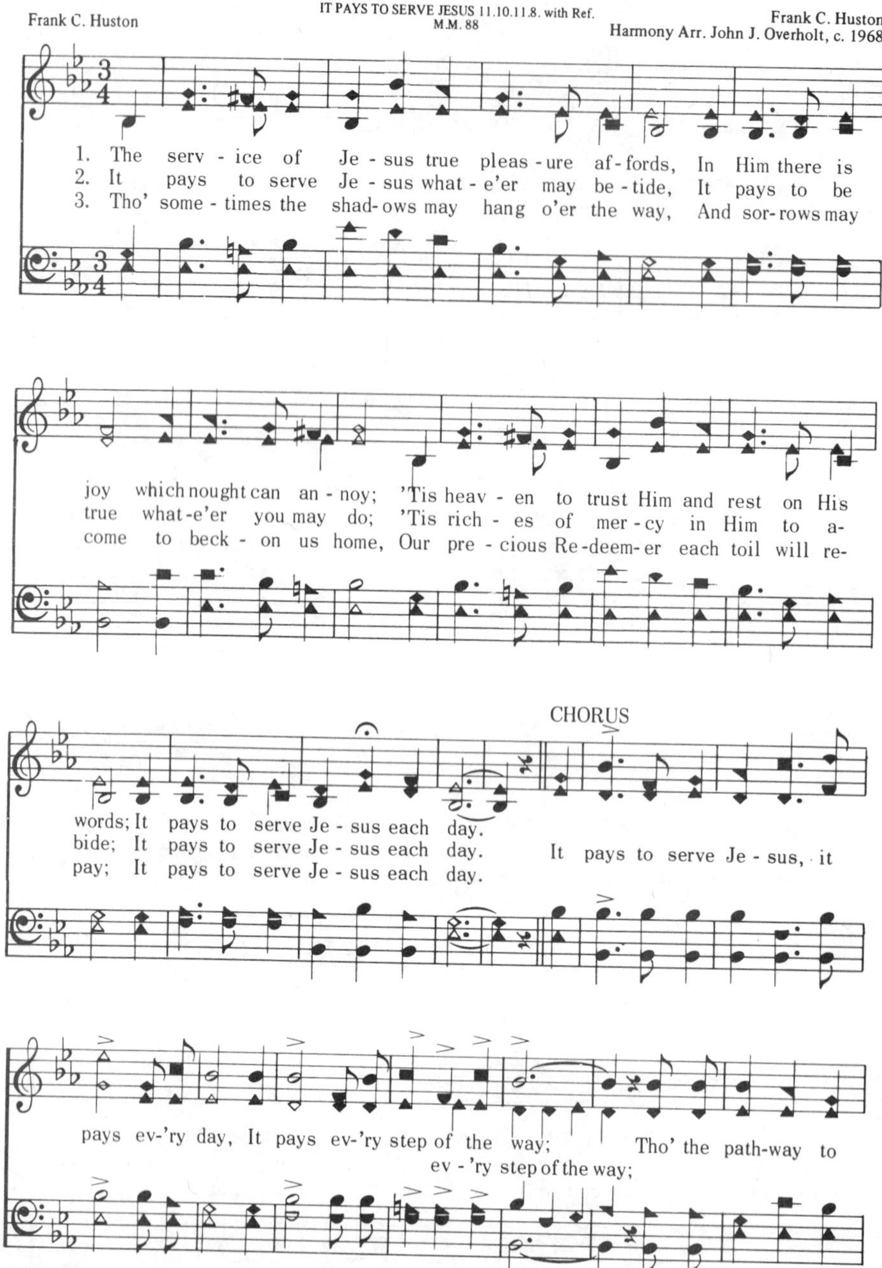
Frank C. Huston
IT PAYS TO SERVE JESUS 11.10.11.8. with Ref.
M.M. 88
Frank C. Huston
Harmony Arr. John J. Overholt, c. 1968
1. The serv - ice of Je - sus true pleas - ure af - fords, In Him there is
2. It pays to serve Je - sus what - e'er may be - tide, It pays to be
3. Tho' some - times the shad- ows may hang o'er the way, And sor- rows may
joy which nought can an - noy; 'Tis heav - en to trust Him and rest on His
true what-e'er you may do; 'Tis rich - es of mer - cy in Him to a-
come to beck - on us home, Our pre - cious Re - deem- er each toil will re-
words; It pays to serve Je - sus each day.
bide; It pays to serve Je - sus each day.
pay; It pays to serve Je - sus each day.
CHORUS
It pays to serve Je - sus, it
pays ev-'ry day, It pays ev-'ry step of the way;
ev - 'ry step of the way;
Tho' the path-way to

glo - ry may sometimes be drear, You'll be hap - py each step of the way.

# FOR BALMY SUNSHINE 984

*We thank Thee . . . for all things come of Thee.* I Chron. 29:13, 14.

FOR BALMY SUNSHINE 5.5.9.5.5.9.5.
M.M. 69

Anon. | Anon. Arr. John J. Overholt, 1971

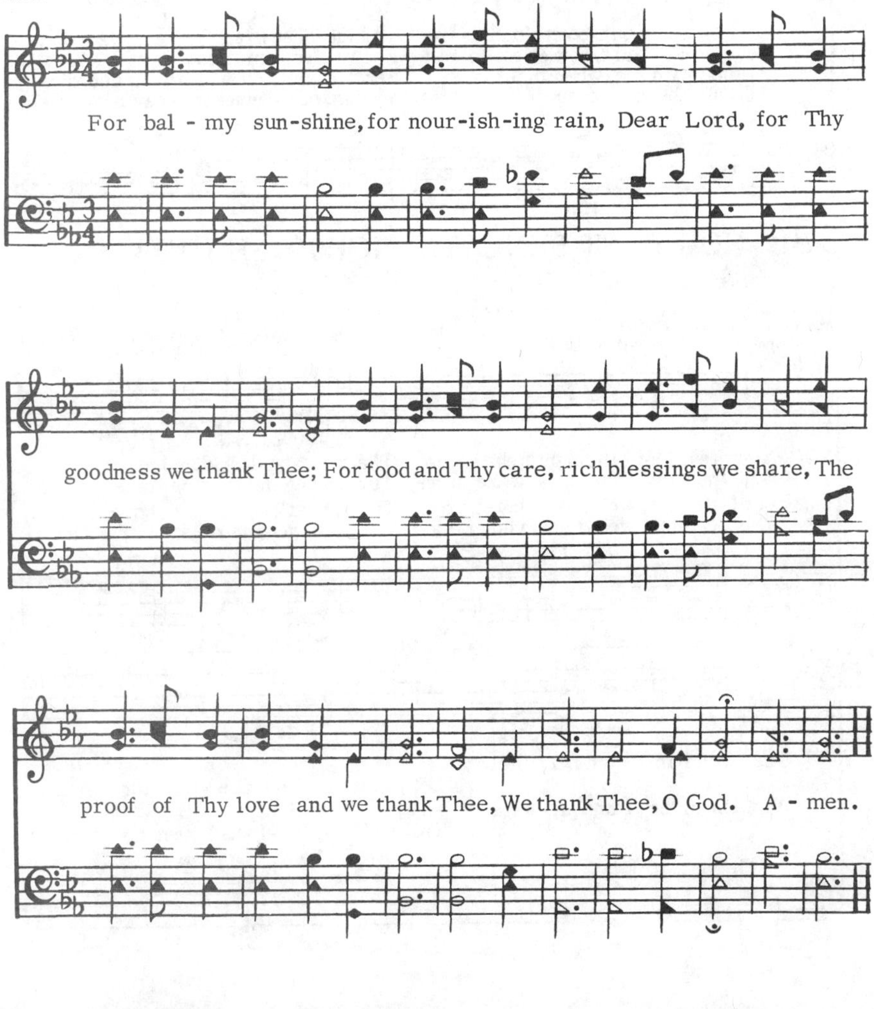

For bal - my sun-shine, for nour-ish-ing rain, Dear Lord, for Thy

goodness we thank Thee; For food and Thy care, rich blessings we share, The

proof of Thy love and we thank Thee, We thank Thee, O God. A - men.

# 985 SUN OF MY SOUL

*Until the day dawn, and the day star arise in your hearts.* II Pet. 1:19.

John Keble, 1820 (1792-1866)
HURSLEY L.M. 8.8.8.8.
M.M. 69
Peter Ritter, 1760-1846

1. Sun of my soul, Thou Sav - ior dear, It is not night if Thou be near;
2. When the soft dews of kind - ly sleep My wea-ried eye - lids gen - tly steep,
3. A - bide with me from morn till eve, For with-out Thee I can - not live;
4. Come near and bless us when we wake, Ere thro' the world our way we take;
O may no earth-born cloud a - rise To hide Thee from Thy serv-ant's eyes.
Be my last tho't, how sweet to rest For ev - er on my Sav-ior's breast.
A - bide with me when night is nigh, For with-out Thee I dare not die.
Till, in the o - cean of Thy love, We lose our - selves in heav'n a - bove.

# 986 NOW REST BENEATH NIGHT'S SHADOW

*I will both lay me down in peace, and sleep: for thou, Lord, only makest me dwell in safety.* Ps. 4:8.

Paul Gerhardt, 1607-1676
*Nun ruhen alle Wälder*
Tr. Catherine Winkworth, 1829-1878
O WELT ICH MUSS DICH LASSEN 7.7.6.7.7.8.
M.M. 66
Heinrich Isaac, c. 1455-1517
Arr. Johann Sebastian Bach, 1685-1750

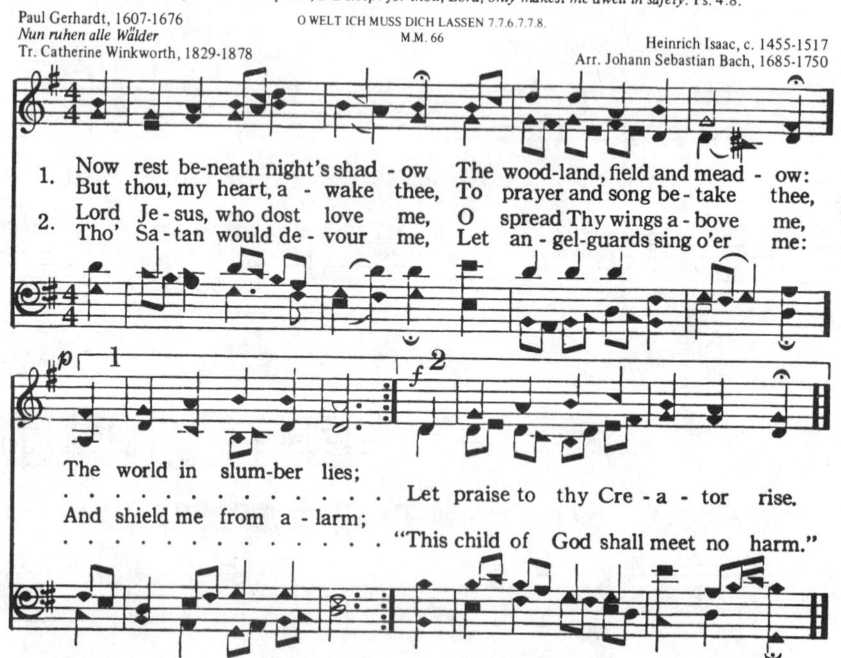
1. Now rest be-neath night's shad - ow The wood-land, field and mead - ow:
But thou, my heart, a - wake thee, To prayer and song be - take thee,
2. Lord Je - sus, who dost love me, O spread Thy wings a - bove me,
Tho' Sa - tan would de - vour me, Let an - gel-guards sing o'er me:
The world in slum-ber lies;
. . . . . . . . . . . . . . Let praise to thy Cre - a - tor rise.
And shield me from a - larm;
. . . . . . . . . . . . . . "This child of God shall meet no harm."

# FATHER ETERNAL, GREAT GOD OF CREATION 987

*Now unto God and our Father be glory forever and ever. Amen.* Phil. 4:20.

LUX FIAT 11.10.11.10.10.10.
M.M. 84
John J. Overholt, 1972
Charles F. Gounod, d. 1893
1. Fa–ther e – ter – nal, great God of cre – a – tion, Whom we with
2. Send forth Thy Spir – it with pow'r that men hear Thee; Send forth sal –
3. Fa–ther e – ter – nal, grant mer – cy and par – don, Thy dear for –
heart and voice would e're a – dore; Do Thou in mer – cy now
va – tion's grace thru Christ, our Lord; Send forth Thy light and Thy
give–ness may it be our own; Our sore trans–gres–sions, our
hear sup–pli – ca – tion, Grant boun–teous grace and fa – vor, we im –
truth that men seek Thee; Grant wis – dom, knowl–edge, faith, thru Thy sure
sins that e're hard – en, Wilt Thou in Je – sus, Thy dear Son, de –
plore; Thou art ex – alt – ed; Thou reign–est ev – er;
Word; Thou art the Giv – er; Thou lov – est ev – er;
throne; Thou art com – pas – sion; Thou chang–est nev – er;
Thy name we laud, we praise Thee ev – er – more!
Thy name be praised and ev – er – more a – dored!
Thy name we praise and laud at Thy great throne! A – men.

# 988 O GOD, TO THEE I LIFT MY JOYFUL VOICE

*I will sing yea, I will sing praises unto the Lord.* Ps. 27:6. *O come, let us sing unto the Lord.* Ps. 95:1.

Vera Sommers Overholt, 1968
John J. Overholt, 1968
O DASS ICH TAUSEND ZUNGEN HÄTTE 9.8.9.8.8.8.
M.M. 69
W. Baumgartner
1. O God, to thee I lift my joy-ful voice, To thee lift
2. O God, to thee I lift my joy-ful voice! Oh give to
3. O God, to thee I lift my joy-ful voice, Lord Je-sus,
4. O God, to thee I lift my joy-ful voice, To thee my
up my voice and sing! I sing to thee in hymns of
me a heart like thine! O may my thoughts be pure and
cleanse my heart and hands, O cleanse me from all sin and
hymns of wor-ship bring! O take my life and voice for-
rap-ture, The joy which Christ's sal-va-tion brings!
love-ly; Just, true, and hon-est, good, di-vine!
self-life, That in thy pre-sence I may stand;
ev-er, May I thy praise for-ev-er sing!
REFRAIN
To thee we
sing (and prais-es bring) To thee we
To Thee we sing and prais-es bring,

sing (and prais - es bring) To thee, Lord
To Thee we sing and prais - es bring
Je - sus, sing we hymns, and praise and grat - i - tude we bring!

# O THAT A THOUSAND TONGUES I'D TREASURE 989

*When the Lord turned again the captivity of Zion, we were like them that dream. Then was our mouth filled with laughter, and our tongue with singing.* Ps. 126:1, 2. *Every tongue shall confess to God.* Rom. 14:11. *And that every tongue should confess that Jesus Christ is Lord.* Phil. 2:11.

(Written on the occasion of his house burning down)
Johann Mentzer, 1704 (1658-1734)
*O dass ich tausend Zungen hätte*
Tr. John J. Overholt, 1972

O DASS ICH TAUSEND ZUNGEN HÄTTE 9.8.9.8.8.8.
M.M. 69

W. Baumgartner

1. O that a thousand tongues I'd treasure
And mouth and voice a thousandfold,
Therewith I'd tune with deepest pleasure,
And sing with zeal most manifold,
A song of praise continually
Of great things God has done for me!

2. O that my voice might be resounding
To where the sun in grandeur stands;
O that my blood be praises sounding,
While it supplies my life's demands,
O were each pulse in thanks employed
And every breath in song o'erjoyed!

3. Why are ye still, my pow'rs of being?
Awake, awake, your strength upraise,
And vig'rously with zeal, agreeing
To God, my Lord, now offer praise;
My soul and body, wake, express
Your heart–felt praise, your God to bless!

1. O dass ich tausend Zungen hätte
Und einen tausendfachen Mund,
So stimmt ich damit um die Wette
Vom allertiefsten Herzensgrund,
Ein Loblied nach dem andern an
Von dem, was Gott an mir getan!

2. O dass doch meine Stimme schallte
Bis dahin, wo die Sonne steht,
O dass mein Blut mit Jauchzen wallte,
Solang es noch im Laufe geht;
Ach wär ein jeder Puls ein Dank
Und jeder Odem ein Gesang!

3. Was schweigt ihr denn, ihr meine Kräfte?
Auf, auf, braucht allen euren Fleiss
Und stehet munter im Geschäfte
Zu Gottes, meines Herren, Preis;
Mein Leib und Seele, schicke dich
Und lobe Gott herzinniglich!

Note: No. 832, "I know that my Redeemer liveth", may also be sung with the above melody. Refrain arranged by Joseph Overholt.

Refrain: I know, I know that Jesus lives, And on the earth again shall stand!
I know, I know that life He gives, That grace and power are in His hand!

# 990 HOLY GOD, WE PRAISE THY NAME

*Praise waiteth for Thee, O God, in Sion: and unto Thee shall the vow be performed.* Ps. 65:1.

Late 4th century
*Te Deum laudamus*
Tr. Clarence Augustus Walworth, 1853 (1820-1900)

GROSSER GOTT, WIR LOBEN DICH 7.8.7.8.7.7.
M.M. 84

. . . *Gesangbuch,* Vienna, 1776

1 Ho - ly God, we praise Thy name; Lord of all, we bow be - fore Thee;
2 Hark, the loud ce-les - tial hymn, An - gel choirs a - bove are rais - ing;
3 Lo! the ap - os-tol - ic train Join Thy sa - cred name to hal - low;
4 Ho - ly Fa - ther, Ho - ly Son, Ho - ly Spir - it, three we name Thee;
All on earth Thy scep - ter claim, All in heav'n a - bove a - dore Thee.
Cher - u - bim and ser - a - phim, In un - ceas - ing cho - rus prais - ing,
Proph-ets swell the glad re - frain, And the white-robed mar - tyrs fol - low;
Though in es - sence on - ly one, Un - di - vid - ed God we claim Thee,
In - fi - nite Thy vast do-main, Ev - er - last - ing is Thy reign.
Fill the heav'ns with sweet ac-cord: Ho - ly, ho - ly, ho - ly Lord.
And, from morn till set of sun, Through the church the song goes on.
And a - dor - ing bend the knee, While we own the mys - ter - y. A - men.

Tr. Ignaz Franz, 1771

1 Grosser Gott, wir loben dich!
  Herr, wir preisen deine Stärke!
Vor dir neigt die Erde sich
  und bewundert deine Werke.
Wie du warst vor aller Zeit,
  so bleibst du in Ewigkeit.

2 Alles, was dich preisen kann,
  Cherubim und Seraphinen,
stimmen dir ein Loblied an,
  alle Engel, die dir dienen,
rufen dir stets ohne Ruh:
  Heilig, heilig, heilig zu.

3 Auf dem ganzen Erdenkreis
  loben Grosse und auch Kleine
dich, Gott Vater; dir zum Preis
  singt die heilige Gemeine,
sie verehrt auf seinem Thron
  deinen eingebornen Sohn.

4 Stehe denn, o Herr, uns bei,
  die wir dich in Demut bitten,
die dein Blut dort machte frei,
  als du für uns hast gelitten.
Nimm uns nach vollbrachtem Lauf
  zu dir in den Himmel auf.

# BLESSED SAVIOR, WE ADORE THEE 991

*Who is like unto Thee, O Lord, among the gods? who is like Thee, glorious in holiness . . . ?* Ex. 15:11.
*Blessed be Thy glorious name.* Neh. 9:5. *A Saviour, which is Christ the Lord.* Lk. 2:11.

GLORIOUS NAME 8.7.8.7. with Ref.
M.M. 84
Benjamin Baylus McKinney, 1942 (1886-1952)
Benjamin Baylus McKinney
1 Bless - ed Sav - ior, we a - dore Thee, We Thy love and grace pro - claim;
2 Great Re - deem - er, Lord and Mas - ter, Light of all e - ter - nal days;
3 From the throne of heav - en's glo - ry To the cross of sin and shame,
4 Come, O come, im - mor - tal Sav - ior, Come and take Thy roy - al throne;
Thou art might - y, Thou art ho - ly, Glo - rious is Thy match - less name!
Let the saints of ev - ery na - tion Sing Thy just and end - less praise!
Thou didst come to die a ran - som, Guilt - y sin - ners to re - claim!
Come, and reign, and reign for - ev - er. Be the king - dom all Thine own!
REFRAIN
Glo - - - - ri - ous, Glo - - - - ri - ous.
Glo - rious is Thy name, O Lord! Glo - rious is Thy name, O Lord!
Glo - rious is Thy name, O Lord! Glo - - - - ri - ous,
Glo - rious is Thy name, O Lord!
Glo - - - - ri - ous. Glo - rious is Thy name, O Lord!
Glo - rious is Thy name, O Lord!

# 992 I WILL SING OF THE MERCIES OF THE LORD

*I will sing of the mercies of the Lord forever: with my mouth will I make known Thy faithfulness to all generations.* Ps. 89:1.

Anon.
Based on Psalm 89

I WILL SING OF THE MERCIES (Irregular)
M.M. 76

Anon.

I will sing of the mer - cies of the Lord for -
ev - er, I will sing, I will sing. I will
sing of the mer - cies of the Lord for -
ev - er, I will sing of the mer - cies of the
Lord. With my mouth will I make known

Thy faith - ful - ness, Thy faith - ful - ness, With
my mouth will I make known Thy faith - ful -
ness to all gen - er - a - tions. I will sing
of the mer - cies of the Lord for - ev - er,
I will sing of the mer - cies of the Lord.

# 993 WHEN GOD FORMED THE EARTH

*And God saw everything that He had made, and, behold, it was very good.* Gen. 1:31. *And I will put enmity between thee and the woman, and between thy seed and her seed; it shall bruise thy head, and thou shalt bruise his heel.* Gen. 3:15.

THE CREATION STORY 12.11.12.11.D.
M.M. 100

Harry Showalter, 1972 (b. 1889)

Harry Showalter, 1972
Har. John J. Overholt, 1972

1. When God formed the earth at the dawn of cre - a - tion,
2. To crown this great work He made man in His like - ness,
3. But God through His in - fi - nite love and com - pass - ion,
At first it was void of div - is - ions that be;
The im - age of God with a liv - ing, pure soul;
Not will - ing that man be e - ter - nal - ly lost,
He placed sun and moon and the stars in their or - bit
O'er the work of His hand he was giv – en do – min – ion,
Gave prom - ise to Eve that her seed in the fu - ture,
To light up the world that all na - ture might see.
The rule of all crea - tures, he had full con - trol.
The head of the ser - pent would bruise at great cost.

He made all the seas, and the plains, and the des - ert;
But Sa - tan, that an - gel once cast out of heav - en,
Now Je - sus has died for the sins of all peo - ple,
The herb - bear - ing seed and all fruits of their kind;
Be - guiled them to sin in truth mixed with a lie;
That all who be - lieve and o - bey His com - mand,
The birds of the air and the fish in the wa - ter,
They took of the fruit that was strict - ly for - bid - den,
He'll pil - ot them through the cold wa - ters of Jor - dan,
The gems in the earth that man dig - geth to find.
Ig - nor - ing God's warn - ing, they sure - ly must die.
Where they shall a - bide at the Sav - iour's right hand.

# 994 SO LET OUR LIVES AND LIPS EXPRESS

*My little children, let us not love in word, neither in tongue, but in deed and in truth.* I Jn. 3:18.

Isaac Watts, c. 1707 (1674-1748) | UXBRIDGE L.M. 8.8.8.8. M.M. 56 | Lowell Mason, 1830 (1792-1872)

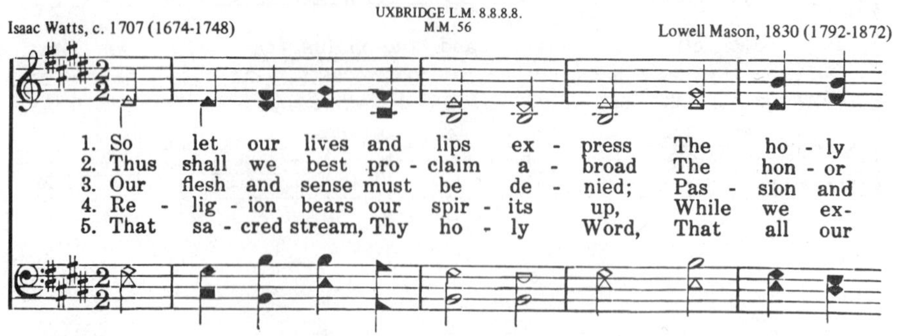
1. So let our lives and lips ex - press The ho - ly
2. Thus shall we best pro - claim a - broad The hon - or
3. Our flesh and sense must be de - nied; Pas - sion and
4. Re - lig - ion bears our spir - its up, While we ex-
5. That sa - cred stream, Thy ho - ly Word, That all our

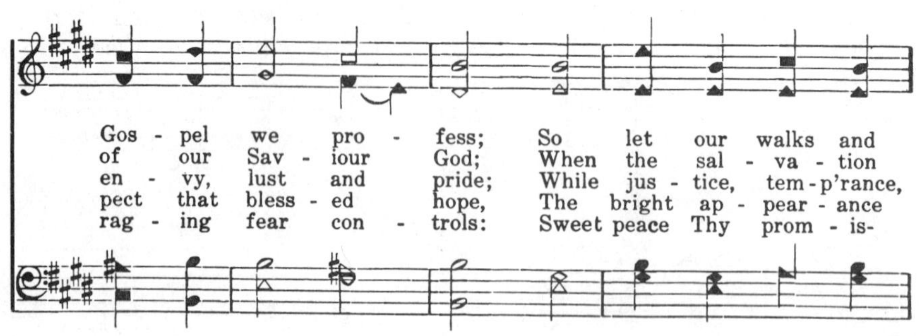
Gos - pel we pro - fess; So let our walks and
of our Sav - iour God; When the sal - va - tion
en - vy, lust and pride; While jus - tice, tem - p'rance,
pect that bless - ed hope, The bright ap - pear - ance
rag - ing fear con - trols: Sweet peace Thy prom - is-

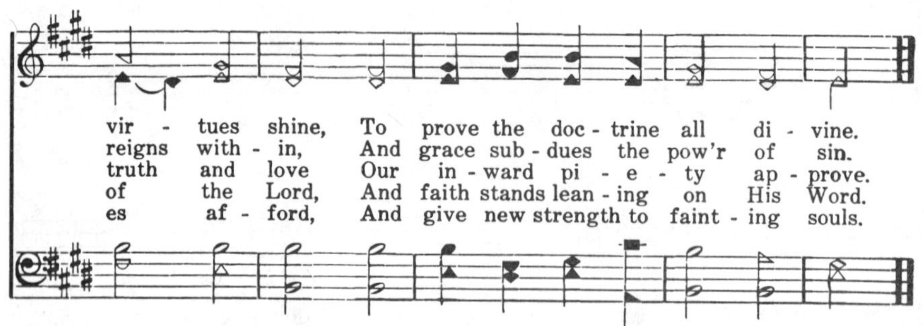
vir - tues shine, To prove the doc - trine all di - vine.
reigns with - in, And grace sub - dues the pow'r of sin.
truth and love Our in - ward pi - e - ty ap - prove.
of the Lord, And faith stands lean - ing on His Word.
es af - ford, And give new strength to faint - ing souls.

# TAKE THE NAME OF JESUS WITH YOU 995

*The name of the Lord is a strong tower: the righteous runneth into it, and is safe.* Prov. 18:10.

PRECIOUS NAME 8.7.8.7.
M.M. 69
Mrs. Lydia Baxter, 1809-1874
William Howard Doane, 1831-1915
1. Take the name of Je - sus with you, Child of sor-row and of woe;
2. Take the name of Je - sus ev - er, As a shield from ev-'ry snare;
3. O the pre-cious name of Je - sus! How it thrills our souls with joy,
4. At the name of Je - sus bow - ing, Fall - ing pros-trate at His feet,
It will joy and com-fort give you: Take it then wher-e'er you go.
If temp-ta-tions round you gath - er Breathe that ho - ly name in prayer.
When His lov - ing arms re - ceive us, And His songs our tongues em-ploy!
King of kings in heav'n we'll crown Him, When our jour - ney is com - plete.
CHORUS
Pre-cious name, O how sweet! Hope of earth and joy of heav'n;
Pre-cious name, O how sweet!
Pre-cious name, O how sweet! . . Hope of earth and joy of heav'n.
Precious name, O how sweet, how sweet!

# 996 GOD BE WITH YOU TILL WE MEET AGAIN

*Now the God of peace be with you all. Amen.* Rom. 15:33. *The Lord bless thee, and keep thee: the Lord make His face to shine upon thee, and be gracious unto Thee: the Lord lift up His countenance upon thee, and give thee peace.* Num. 6:24-26.

GOD BE WITH YOU 9.8.8.9. with Ref.
M.M. 66

Jeremiah Eames Rankin, 1880 (1828-1904)

William Gould Tomer, 1880 (1833-1896)

1. God be with you till we meet a - gain, By His counsels guide, up-hold you,
2. God be with you till we meet a - gain, 'Neath His wings protecting hide you,
3. God be with you till we meet a - gain, When life's perils thick confound you,
4. God be with you till we meet a - gain, Keep love's banner floating o'er you,
With His sheep se - cure-ly fold you: God be with you till we meet a - gain.
Dai - ly man - na still pro-vide you: God be with you till we meet a - gain.
Put His arms un - fail-ing round you: God be with you till we meet a - gain.
Smite death's threat'ning wave before you: God be with you till we meet a - gain.
REFRAIN
Till we meet, .......... till we meet,
Till we meet, till we meet,
Till we meet at Je - sus' feet;
till we meet;
Till we meet, ......... till we
Till we meet,
meet,
till we meet,
God be with you till we meet a - gain.

# O SAVIOUR, BLESS US ERE WE GO 997

*And he said . . . I will not let thee go, except thou bless me.* Gen. 32:26.

Frederick William Faber, 1814-1863

STELLA L.M. 8.8.8.8. with Ref.
M.M. 76

Old English Air

1. O Sav–iour, bless us ere we go; Thy Word in–to our minds in–still,
2. Grant us, dear Lord, from e–vil ways Thy sweet for–give–ness and re–lease;
3. Do more than par–don: give us joy, Sweet fear, and so–ber lib – er – ty,
And make our lukewarm hearts to glow With low–ly love and fer–vant will.
And bless us, more than in past days, With pu – ri – ty and in–ward peace.
And lov–ing hearts in Thy em–ploy That on – ly long to be like Thee.
REFRAIN
Thro' life's long day, and death's dark night, O gen–tle Sav–iour, be our light.

# 998 LORD, AT THIS CLOSING HOUR

*Now unto the King Eternal, immortal, invisible, the only wise God, be honor and glory forever and ever. Amen.* I Tim. 1:17.

SHIRLAND S.M. 6.6.8.6.
M.M. 56

Eleazar Thompson Fitch, 1791-1871

*Harmonia Sacra,* 1847
Arr. by Compiler, 1972

1. Lord, at this clos - ing hour Es - tab - lish ev - 'ry
2. Peace to our breth - ren give; Fill all our hearts with
3. Thro' changes bright or drear, We would Thy will pur -
4. To God the On - ly Wise, In ev - 'ry age a -

heart Up - on Thy Word of truth and
love; In faith and pa - tience may we
sue; And toil to spread Thy king - dom
dored, Let glo - ry from the church a -

pow'r, To keep us when we part.
live, And seek our rest a - bove.
here, Till we its glo - ry view.
rise Thro' Je - sus Christ, our Lord. A - men.

# 999 NOW MAY THE GOD OF PEACE AND LOVE

*Now the God of peace, that brought again from the dead our Lord Jesus, that great Shepherd of the sheep through the blood of the everlasting covenant, Make you perfect in every good work to do His will, working in you that which is well pleasing in His sight, through Jesus Christ; to Whom be glory forever and ever. Amen.* Heb. 13:20, 21.

TALLIS' ORDINAL C.M. 8.6.8.6.
M.M. 66

Thomas Gibbons, 1784

Thomas Tallis, c. 1567 (1505-1585)

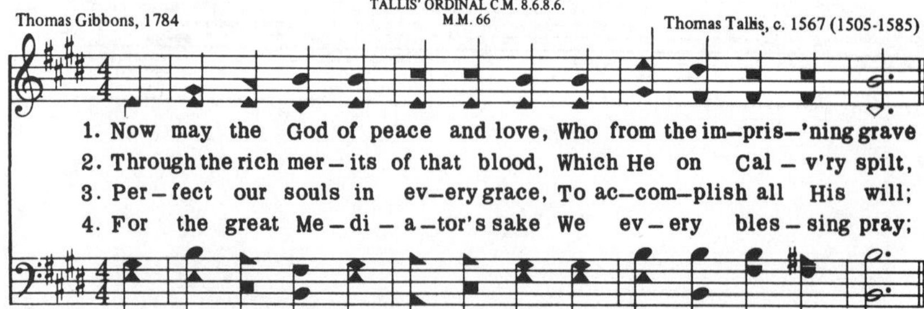
1. Now may the God of peace and love, Who from the im–pris–'ning grave
2. Through the rich mer – its of that blood, Which He on Cal – v'ry spilt,
3. Per – fect our souls in ev–ery grace, To ac–com–plish all His will;
4. For the great Me – di – a–tor's sake We ev – ery bles – sing pray;

Re–stored the Shep–herd of the sheep, Om – nip – o–tent to save.
To make the e–ter–nal cov'nant sure On which our hopes are built.
And all that's pleas–ing in His sight, In–spire us to ful – fil.
With glo–ry let His name be crown'd, Through heaven's eternal day. A–men.

## THE GRACE OF OUR LORD JESUS CHRIST 1000

*The grace of the Lord Jesus Christ, and the love of God, and the communion of the Holy Ghost, be with you all.* II Cor. 13:14.

*Deutsches Lieder und Melodienbuch,* 1895
Tr. John J. Overholt, 1972

DIE GNADE UNSRES HERREN JESU CHRISTI
8.8.10.4.5.
M.M. 60

*Deutsches Lieder und Melodienbuch,* 1895
Arr. John J. Overholt, 1972

The grace of our Lord Je - sus Christ, And the
Die Gna - de un-sres Her-ren Je - su Chri-sti, Und die

love of God the Fa - ther, And the Com - mu - nion
Lie - be Got - - tes, Und die Ge - mein - schaft des

of the Ho - ly Ghost Be with us all,
hei - li - gen Gei - stes Sei mit uns al - len,

*pp*

Be with us all, With us all, A - men, A - men.
Sei mit uns al - len, Mit uns al - len, A - men, A - men.

# Introduction to Rudiments of Music

Notes in written music are *figures or symbols representing distinct sounds or tones* in the tune or melody of a given hymn, and in this sense are similar to the ABC's of the alphabet.

Since the object of singing for the Christian believer is to worship and to glorify God, it is of the utmost importance that a *proper balance* in emphasis of text or words of the hymn, and the music or vehicle be held while singing.

For the Christian, the music or tune, as the *vehicle* of the words or text must be *subordinate* and given far less stress and emphasis than the words being sung.

To engage in singing "with the Spirit" in worship, and to achieve and maintain proper balance of words and tune, text and vehicle, it is very important that *preoccupation* with the music and with the musical notes be kept at a *minimum,* and that the text be *understood* and *experienced.*

This can be done readily with the use of *shaped notes* where seven distinct shapes represent seven syllables or tones of the musical scale. A very *thorough knowledge* of these seven shapes and their *relationship* to each other on the musical scale will facilitate and develop proficiency in sight reading of music, which, comparable to and similar to the reading of written language, will *focus attention* on the *total text* which the symbols and notes convey and articulate, and not on the symbols themselves.

A thorough knowledge of, and actual overlearning of the notes is the key to minimizing effort and preoccupation with music, and to the achieving of balance, so that by the aid of the Holy Spirit the sentiment of the written text may be properly *comprehended* and *experienced in worship.*

The following sight singing exercises are introduced for this purpose.

EXERCISE ONE

## EXERCISE TWO

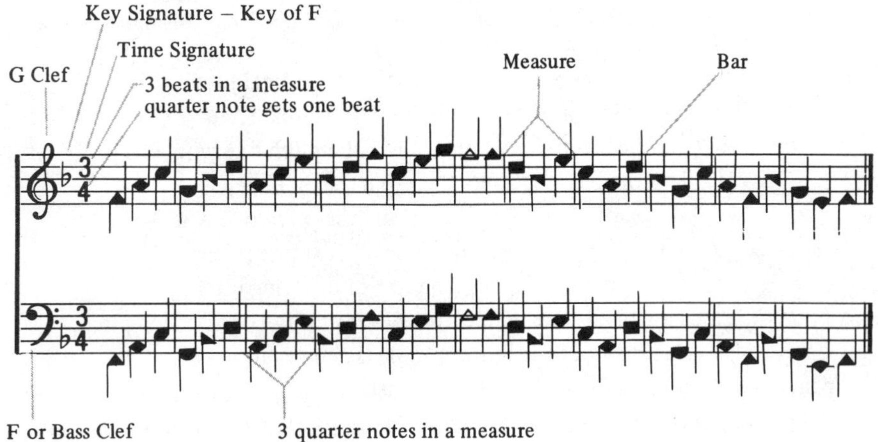


## EXERCISE THREE

| | *Notes* | *Rests* |
|---|---|---|
| Whole | | |
| Half | | |
| Quarter | | |
| Eighth | | |
| Sixteenth | | |

flag
stem

*Time Signatures*

| | Simple | | | Compound | | |
|---|---|---|---|---|---|---|
| Double | $\frac{2}{2}$ | $\frac{2}{4}$ | $\frac{2}{8}$ | $\frac{6}{2}$ | $\frac{6}{4}$ | $\frac{6}{8}$ |
| Triple | $\frac{3}{2}$ | $\frac{3}{4}$ | $\frac{3}{8}$ | $\frac{9}{2}$ | $\frac{9}{4}$ | $\frac{9}{8}$ |
| Quadruple | $\frac{4}{2}$ | $\frac{4}{4}$ | $\frac{4}{8}$ | $\frac{12}{2}$ | $\frac{12}{4}$ | $\frac{12}{8}$ |

*Key Signatures:* One sharp is key of G; one flat is key of F.
(Memorize the following)
Sharps: Good Deeds Are Ever Bearing Fruit (The last sharp on the right is ti.)
Flats: Faithful Brethren Encourage And Dispense Goodwill (The last flat on the right is fa.)

## EXERCISE FOUR

Definition and Explanation of Terms

1. *Accidentals* are sharps, flats, and naturals used other than in the key signature and continue their effect of raising or lowering the pitch throughout the measure in which they occur.
2. A *natural* ♮ placed before a note restores it to its original pitch.
3. A *sharp* ♯ placed before a note raises the pitch one-half step.
4. A *double sharp* x placed before a note raises the pitch one whole step.
5. A *flat* ♭ placed before a note lowers the pitch one-half step.
6. A *double flat* ♭♭ placed before a note lowers the pitch one whole step.
7. A *tie* is a curved line connecting notes of the same pitch.
8. A *slur* is a curved line connecting notes of differing pitch.
9. A *beam* is a straight line connecting notes of same or differing pitch.
10. A *dot* · placed after a note adds one-half of its time value.
11. Singing in *unison* occurs when all sing one part.
12. *A cappella* singing is without the accompaniment of musical instruments.
13. A *hold* 𝄐 permits the songleader to hold a word for effect at his discretion.
14. Music for *soprano* and *alto* voices is written on the upper or G clef.
15. Music for *tenor* and *bass* voices is written on the lower or F clef.

## EXERCISE FIVE

Chromatic Scale

## EXERCISE SIX

### Accidentals

# Index of Hymn Topics

# Index of Hymn Topics Alphabetically Arranged

# Index of Acknowledgments

The publisher acknowledges with gratefulness and appreciation the use of the copyrighted and uncopyrighted matter contained in this collection. A careful effort has been made to determine the copyright status of all material compiled. Any oversight brought to our attention will be corrected in future editions. In keeping with the objectives and purposes for publishing this *Hymnary,* the publisher prohibits the use of any original or arranged material that is covered by the publisher's copyright, for use in historical or any other productions of drama, oratorios, and the like. No part of this book may be copied or reproduced photostatically or otherwise without written permission from the publisher.

The following material is covered by the publisher's copyright: *(With the exception of numbers underlined)*

*Translations by Compiler:* 1, 53, 54, 281, 311, 313, 398, 404, 408, 409, 410, 412, 413, 414, 415, 416, 417, 418, 419, 420, 421, 425, 522, 544, 666, 689, 795, 818, 921, 947, 989, 1000

*Complete Texts by Compiler:* 2, 18, 47, 49, 64, 65, 90, 108, 137, 162, 214, 231, 317, 395, 477, 523, 682, 692, 734, 902, 958, 987

*Partial Texts, Recasts, Alterations by Compiler:* 3, 4, 5, 8, 13, 15, 17, 20, 31, 38, 39, 43, 45, 48, 50, 56, 61, 67, 81, **83**, 84, 90, 91, **95**, 109, 112, 114, 116, 117, 120, 125, 126, 136, 137, 152, 161, 162, 169, 176, 201, 202, 213, 220, 225, 233, 234, 237, 240, 241, 242, 243, 248, 249, 254, 256, 262, 263, 265, 266, 284, 286, 297, 299, 304, 318, 324, 343, 350, 351, 353, 355, 377, 378, 384, 388, 389, 390, 393, 394, 396, 405, 407, 424, 426, 427, 428, 430, 433, 437, 438, 444, 447, 449, 451, 454, 456, 457, 458, 459, 460, 461, 462, 463, 464, 471, 474, 475, 478, 483, 485, 518, 536, 563, 580, 588, 609, 612, 613, 631, 634, 646, 647, 648, 649, 650, 652, 653, 661, **664**, 665, 668, 669, 670, 671, 674, 679, 684, 686, **691**, 693, 694, 696, 700, 702, 716, 718, 726, 728, 732, 735, 737, 761, 762, 784, 809, 839, 842, 877, 902, 905, 907, 910, 924, 942, 988

*Compositions of Music by Compiler:* 18, 64, 65, 90, 202, 214, 223, 317, 570

*Music Arrangements and Harmonizations by Compiler:* (Selections underlined are copyright property of others) 1, 2, 3, 13, 15, 20, 31, **39**, 42, 46, 48, 49, 50, 53, 54, 61, 79, 83, 84, **85**, 90, 114, 128, 130, 131, 133, 140, 142, 159, 162, 193, 202, 220, 224, 231, 237, 241, 247, 256, 258, 279, 299, 304, 312, 324, 340, 398, 399, 405, 409, 410, 411, 413, 414, 415, 416, 417, 418, 419, 422, 423, 424, 426, 427, 444, 456, 468, 476, 477, 483, 485, 510, 511, 518, 536, 547, 563, 568, 580, **581**, 588, 617, 654, **659**, 660, 666, 683, 685, 688, 693, 696, 697, 698, **701**, 714, 718, 720, **722**, 726, 728, 730, 732, 735, 741, 761, 762, 770, 774, 787, 795, 799, 804, 809, 814, **828**, 839, 862, 875, 876, 877, 894, 898, 902, 905, 907, 920, 922, 923, 924, 936, 942, 947, 953, 959, 961, 969, 982, **983**, 984, 993, 998, 1000

*Various Texts, Compositions, and Arrangements:* 194, 736, 741, 757, 900, 988

The Publisher gratefully acknowledges permission for use of the following materials:

6. Descant copyright, Eden Publishing House. Used by permission.

11. Text of hymn and arrangement of harmony copyright, 1972 by John D. Martin and John J. Overholt. Used by permission.

20. Music from R. D. Wetzel. Arranged by permission.

32. Text of hymn by permission of J. Curwen & Sons, Ltd. Music from *The English Hymnal* by permission of Oxford University Press.

39. Music from *The English Hymnal* by permission of Oxford University Press.

45. Text of hymn altered by permission of the Fannie Kreider heirs. Arranged by permission.

55. Translation by permission of Lester Hostetler. Music from *Gesangbuch der Mennoniten* by permission of Faith and Life Press. International copyright, 1965.

59. Text of hymn and music arrangement copyright by Wilmer D. Swope. Used by permission.

62. Text of hymn copyright by Wilmer D. Swope. Music copyright by John Huebert. Used by permission.

67. Descant copyright, Eden Publishing House. Used by permission.

83. Text of hymn from *The Yattendon Hymnal* (edited by Robert Bridges and H. Ellis Wooldridge) by permission of Oxford University Press. Altered by permission.

85. Music from *The English Hymnal* by permission of Oxford University Press. Arranged by permission.

93. Text of hymn for stanzas 1, 2, and 3 from *Youth Hymnary* by permission of Faith and Life Press. Copyright 1956. Words for stanza 4 and refrain from *The Hymnbook* of the Mennonite Brethren Church of Canada.

94. Translation property of Eden Publishing House. Used by permission.

95. Text of hymn from the *Service Book and Hymnal* (Lutheran) by permission of the Commission on the Liturgy and the Hymnal. Composite arranged by permission.

100. Copyright 1923. Renewal 1951 by W. M. Runyan. Assigned to Hope Publishing Co. All Rights Reserved. Used by Permission.

134. Copyright, 1935. Renewal 1963 by W. M. Runyan. Hope Publishing Company, Owner. All Rights Reserved. Used by Permission.

146. Text of hymn from *Hymns of the Russian Church* by permission of Oxford University Press.

166. Copyright, Renewal 1951 by W. M. Runyan. Assigned to Hope Publishing Co. All Rights Reserved. Used by Permission.

169. Text of hymn copyright by Wilmer D. Swope and John J. Overholt. Used by permission.

204. Copyright 1940 by The Rodeheaver Co. © Ren. 1968. The Rodeheaver Co., Owner. All Rights Reserved. Used by Permission.

211. Text of hymn and music from the *Service Book and Hymnal* (Lutheran) by permission of the Commission on the Liturgy and the Hymnal.

233. Text of hymn copyright by Wilmer D. Swope and John J. Overholt. Used by permission.

238. Text of hymn and music copyright by Dora Deanie Nauman. Used by permission.

259. Text of hymn copyright by Elva Yoder. Used by permission.

268. Copyright 1948 by Stamps-Baxter Music and Printing Co. in "Silver Tones." All rights reserved. Used by permission.

287. Music from *The English Hymnal* by permission of Oxford University Press.

303. Text of hymn copyright by Pickering & Inglis, Ltd., Glasgow. Used by permission.

305. Text of hymn copyright by Eden Publishing House. Used by permission.

312. Music copyright by Wilmer D. Swope and John J. Overholt. Used by permission.

314. Arrangement copyright by Inter-Varsity Christian Fellowship. Arranged by Paul Beckwith. Used by permission.

316. © Copyright 1926 by Robert H. Coleman. Renewal 1953, Broadman Press. Used by permission.

324. Music, courtesy of Zoltán Séra. Arrangement copyright John J. Overholt, 1972. Used by permission.

355. Descant Copyright 1935, Renewal 1963 by Hope Publishing Co. All Rights Reserved. Used by Permission.

357. Copyright 1924 and 1927. Renewed 1952 and 1955 by H. D. Clark. Assigned to Hope Publishing Co. All Rights Reserved. Used by Permission.

390. Text of hymn copyright by Wilmer D. Swope and John J. Overholt. Used by permission.

396. Text of hymn copyright by Wilmer D. Swope and John J. Overholt. Used by permission.

422. Text of hymn from THE COMPLETE WRITINGS OF MENNO SIMONS, edited by John Christian Wenger. Copyright 1956 by Mennonite Publishing House, Scottdale, Pa. Used by permission.

423. Text of hymn from THE COMPLETE WRITINGS OF MENNO SIMONS, edited by John Christian Wenger. Copyright 1956 by Mennonite Publishing House, Scottdale, Pa. Used by permission.

424. Text of hymn from THE COMPLETE WRITINGS OF MENNO SIMONS, edited by John Christian Wenger. Copyright 1956 by Mennonite Publishing House, Scottdale, Pa. Used by permission. Sts. 8, 11, altered by permission.

428. Text of hymn copyright by Wilmer D. Swope and John J. Overholt. Used by permission.

430. Text of hymn arrangement copyright by Sanford G. Shetler and John J. Overholt. Used by permission.

437. Text of hymn copyright by Wilmer D. Swope and John J. Overholt. Used by permission.

438. Text of hymn copyright by Wilmer D. Swope and John J. Overholt. Used by permission.

467. Text of hymn arrangement copyright by Wilmer D. Swope. Used by permission.

475. Text of hymn copyright by Wilmer D. Swope and John J. Overholt. Used by permission.

476. Text of hymn by Margaret Horst. Used by permission.

482. Text of hymn by Jacob D. Toews. Used by permission.

485. Text of hymn and music copyright by Joseph E. Martin and John J. Overholt. Used by permission.

489. Text of hymn and music copyright by Mennonite Publishing House. Used by permission.

508. Copyright 1952 by John M. Moore. Assigned to Singspiration, Inc. All rights reserved. Used by permission.

510. Text of hymn and music copyright by Harry Showalter and John J. Overholt. Used by permission.

518. Text of hymn and music arrangement copyright by Adam M. Baer and John J. Overholt. Used by permission.

521. Text of hymn arrangement copyright by Wilmer D. Swope. Used by permission.

532. Copyright 1923. Renewed 1951 by Lillenas Publishing Co. Used by permission.

534. Paraphrase and music arrangement copyright by Joseph Overholt. Used by permission.

540. Music by permission of Independent Press. Ltd. London.

548. Text of hymn used by permission of Gospel Publishers, Moundridge.

586. Text of hymn by Jacob D. Toews. Used by permission.

639. Music by permission of Breitkopf & Härtel, Wiesbaden.

640. Music from *Gesangbuch der Mennoniten* by permission of Faith and Life Press. International copyright. 1965.

643. Copyright ©1940 by Stamps-Baxter Music & Ptg. Co. in "Golden Key." Copyright © Renewed 1968. All rights reserved.

653. © Copyright 1949, Broadman Press. All rights reserved. Used by permission.

659. Copyright 1911 by Chas. H. Gabriel. The Rodeheaver Co., Owner. © Ren. 1939 (extended). The Rodeheaver Co., Owner. Used by permission. Arr. ©1972 by the Rodeheaver Co.

664. Text of hymn by permission of Albert Frederick Bayly. Altered with permission.

688. Text of hymn and music arrangement copyright by Wilmer D. Swope and John J. Overholt. Used by permission.

691. From Five New Student Hymns, copyright 1955 by The Hymn Society of America. Used by permission.

696. Text of hymn and music arrangement copyright by Wilmer D. Swope and John J. Overholt. Used by permission.

698. Text of hymn and music copyright by John D. Martin and Marvin Charles Martin. Used by permission.

701. From *Junior Hymns.* Copyright 1947 by Herald Press, Scottdale, Pa. 15683. Used by permission. Four-part harmonization by permission of Publishers.

703. Text of hymn by permission of Tne Hymn Society of America.

705. From *Cantate Domino* by permission.

719. Text and music composed by Herbert Buffum, Jr. and copyrighted by The Buffum Music Co. Used by permission.

722. Copyright Dora Deanie Nauman. Used by permission.

723. Text and music by Ruth and Willard Buxton. Used by permission.

724. Copyright as "My Prayer," 1931, by David H. Johnson. The Evangelical Alliance Mission, owner. Used by permission.

725. Copyright, 1936. Renewal 1964 by W. Loveless. Assigned to Hope Publishing Co. All rights reserved. Used by permission.

727. Text and music copyright by Clarence Fretz. Used by permission.

729. Used by permission of Paul B. Smith.

730. Text and music copyright by John D. Martin and John J. Overholt. Used by permission.

733. By permission of Lillian Plankenhorn.

734. Music arrangement copyright by John Henry Miller. Used by permission.

738. Used by permission of the National Christian Education Council.

743. Text and music copyright by Elva Yoder. Used by permission.

746. Text copyright by Elva Yoder. Used by permission.

763. Copyright, 1927. Renewal, 1955 by H. Clarke. Assigned to Hope Publishing Co. All rights reserved. Used by permission.

771. ©Copyright 1955 by Manna Music, Inc. 1328 N. Highland Ave., Hollywood, Calif. 90028. International Copyright Secured. Printed in U.S.A. All rights reserved including the right of public performance for profit.

774. Text of hymn and music copyright by John D. Martin and John J. Overholt. Used by permission.

779. Copyright 1917. Renewed 1945 by Nazarene Publishing House. Used by permission.

780. Copyright 1944 Renewal. Stamps-Baxter Music & Printing Co., Owner. All rights reserved. Used by permission.

782. Used by permission of Niemann A. Brunk.

783. Used by permission of Niemann A. Brunk.

792. Copyright © 1959 by Lillenas Publishing Company. International copyright secured. All rights reserved. Used by permission.

794. Copyright 1921. Renewal 1949 by W. K. Woodruff. Assigned to Hope Publishing Co. All Rights Reserved. Used by Permission.

798. Not copyrighted. Let no one do so. May this song ever be free to be published for the glory of God, is the desire of the authors.

801. Copyright 1917. Renewal 1944 in "Praiseworthy" by G. J. Excell Loftus. Assigned to Hope Publishing Co. All rights reserved.

806. Used by permission of Mrs. Austin Hazelwood.

808. Copyright 1950 by James Murray Spiers. Used by permission.

814. Used by permission of Ruth Emswiler. Not copyrighted. Let no one do so. May this song ever be free to be published for the glory of God, is the desire of the authors.

817. Copyright 1910. Renewal, 1938, by A. P. Towner. Assigned to Hope Publishing Company. All Rights Reserved. Used by Permission.

821. Text of hymn copyright by Wilmer D. Swope. Used by permission.

825. Copyright USA 1953 in Jewels Four by John T. Benson, Jr. International copyright secured. Used by permission.

828. Copyright 1913. Renewed 1941 by Lillenas Publishing Co. Used by permission.

836. Copyright 1932 by Homer A. Rodeheaver. © Ren. 1950. The Rodeheaver Co., Owner. All rights reserved. Used by permission.

838. Used by permission of Herbert Buffum, Jr.

839. Text of hymn copyright by Brownie May Burkholder. Music harmonization copyright by John J. Overholt. Used by permission.

847. Copyright 1906 by Lorenz Publishing Co. Re-

newal secured. International copyright. Used by permission.

855. Copyright 1952 by Stamps-Baxter Music & Printing Company in *Songs of Cheer.* All rights reserved. Used by permission.

857. Text of hymn by permission of The Hymn Society of America.

858. Text of hymn and music arrangement by permission of Richard D. Wetzel.

859. Copyright, 1949, by Thompson Music Co., in "Perfect Melodies." Used by permission.

862. Text of hymn and music copyright by Harry Showalter and John J. Overholt. Used by permission.

866. Text of hymn by permission of Ernest Merril.

873. Copyright 1947, by Thompson Music Co. Used by permission.

874. © Copyright 1924 by Robert H. Coleman. Renewal 1959, Broadman Press. Used by permission.

878. © Copyright 1970 Broadman Press. All rights reserved. International copyright secured. Used by permission.

881. Copyright 1938 by Stamps-Baxter Music & Printing Co. in "Matchless Gift." All rights reserved. Used by permission.

904. Arranged by Joseph Overholt. Used by permission.

909. Copyright 1952 by Singspiration, Inc. All rights reserved. Used by permission.

911. © 1958 by Singspiration, Inc. All rights reserved. Used by permission.

912. Copyright 1927. Renewal 1955 by Hope Publishing Co. All rights reserved. Used by permission.

914. Copyright 1949 by Stamps-Baxter Music & Printing Company in "Boundless Love." All rights reserved. Used by permission.

915. © Copyright 1962 by Heartwarming Music Co. All rights reserved. Used by permission.

918. Copyright 1929. G. Kieffer Vaughan, owner. Used by permission.

922. Text of hymn and music copyright by Harry Showalter and John J. Overholt. Used by permission.

923. Text of hymn and music copyright by Harry Showalter and John J. Overholt. Used by permission.

924. Text and music copyright by Benjamin J. Coblentz. Used by permission.

932. © 1961 by Singspiration, Inc. All rights reserved. Used by permission.

944. Copyright 1907. The Rodeheaver Co., Owner. © Ren. 1935 (extended) The Rodeheaver Co. Used by permission.

952. © Copyright 1961 in Inspiration #4 by John T. Benson, Jr. All rights reserved. Used by permission.

969. Text and music copyright by Harry Showalter and John J. Overholt. Used by permission.

977. Copyright 1936 by The Rodeheaver Co. © Ren. 1964. The Rodeheaver Co., Owner. All rights reserved. Used by permission.

979. Arrangement Copyright by Joseph Overholt. Used by permission.

980. Copyright 1912 by Hall-Mack Co. The Rodeheaver Co., Owner. © Ren. 1940 (extended). The Rodeheaver Co. All rights reserved. Used by permission.

981. Copyright 1912 by B. D. Ackley. The Rodeheaver Co., Owner. © Ren. 1940 (extended). The Rodeheaver Co. Used by permission.

983. © 1937, Renewal, Standard Publishing Co., Cincinnati, Ohio. Used by permission. Harmony arranged by permission.

988. By permission of Verlag Friedrich Hänssler.

989. Alternate refrain arranged by Joseph Overholt. Used by permission.

991. © Copyright 1942. Renewal 1970 Broadman Press. All rights reserved. Used by permission.

993. Text and music copyright by Harry Showalter and John J. Overholt. Used by permission.

# Index of Scripture Texts Used with Hymns

# Index of Authors of Hymns

# Index of Alterers, Recasters, Adapters, Sources

# Index of Translators of Hymns

# Index of Composers of Hymn Tunes

# Index of Arrangers, Harmonizers, Adapters, Sources

# Index of Hymn Tunes Arranged Alphabetically

# Index of Hymn Tunes Arranged Metrically

COMMON METER DOUBLE
with Refrain



LONG METER
L.M. 8.8.8.8.



LONG METER
with Alleluias



LONG METER
with Refrain



LONG METER DOUBLE
L.M.D. 8.8.8.8.D.



5.5.7.4.



5.5.7.5.5.8.



5,5.8.8.5.5.



5.5.9.5.5.9.5.



5.5.11.



5.6.8.5.5.9.



5.8.8.8.12.7.7.



6.4.6.4.D.



6.4.6.4.
with Refrain



6.4.6.4.6.6.4.



6.4.6.4.6.6.4.4.



6.4.6.4.6.6.6.4.



6.4.12.D.
with Refrain



6.5.6.4.
with Refrain



6.5.6.5.D.

# Index of Descants, Obligatos

# Index of Miscellany



*Definition of Meter*

The term *meter* is used to indicate, 1) the syllabic pattern and number of word syllables to a line in a given stanza; 2a) the music rhythm, time or pulse measurement pattern, and, 2b) the lyric (or word) rhythm pattern that a given hymn is written in.

As an example of 1) in hymn No. 127, we have the following typical Long Meter 8.8.8.8. pattern:

When I sur-vey the won-drous cross On which the Prince of glo-ry died,
1 2 3 4 5 6 7 8 1 2 3 4 5 6 7 8

My rich-est gain I count but loss, And pour con-tempt on all my pride.
1 2 3 4 5 6 7 8 1 2 3 4 5 6 7 8

An example of metric pattern 2a) may be noticed in hymn No. 5. Here the meter signature or measure sign (also called time signature), indicates that there are three beats or pulses in a measure (for measure see p. 871), and that a quarter note gets one beat.

The first note in every measure following the measure bar receives the *accent* beat, and the notes that follow in each measure are weaker. This can be illustrated in $\frac{3}{4}$ time as 123, 123, 123 and in $\frac{4}{4}$ times as 1234, 1234, 1234. The measure bar therefore becomes a symbol of the regular recurrence and repetition of accent.

Since double $\frac{2}{4}\ \frac{2}{8}\ \frac{2}{2}$ and triple $\frac{3}{4}\ \frac{3}{8}\ \frac{3}{2}$ meters are the primary and basic meters, all other meters are combined and compounded from them and are called *compound meter.* This quadruple meter $\frac{4}{2}\ \frac{4}{4}\ \frac{4}{8}$ is formed by combinding two measures of double (duple) meter $\frac{2}{2}\ \frac{2}{4}\ \frac{2}{8}$. Sextuple meter $\frac{6}{2}\ \frac{6}{4}\ \frac{6}{8}$ is formed by combining two measures of triple meter $\frac{3}{2}\ \frac{3}{4}\ \frac{3}{8}$ (see p. 871).

Meter, then *which organizes musical time into measures,* is the deciding factor in the rhythmic organization of music. Whereas rhythm proper organizes time values within the measure, and tempo, musical pace, pulse, or speed determines the speed and consequently the character or mood of the measures, meter is the controlling organizational structure.

In hymn No. 240 an example of 2b) lyric rhythm organization and measurement may be noticed. This hymn is written in iambic meter and the stress pronunciation is noted beneath the text as follows:

O come, Thou wound-ed Lamb of God! Come, wash us in Thy cleans-ing blood;
ta-TUM ta - TUM ta -TUM ta - TUM ta - TUM ta-TUM ta - TUM ta - TUM

There are four common metric *feet* or units of measurement of lyric rhythm (or *flow,* original Greek root), as the following Chart suggests:

| NAME | CHARACTERISTIC | EXAMPLE | STRESS | HYMN EXAMPLES |
|---|---|---|---|---|
| Iamb | Unaccent-accent | *Repeat* | ta-TUM | 620, 685, 570, 521 |
| Trochee (troke) | Accent-unaccent | *Worship* | TUM-ta | 846, 393, 398, 160 |
| Anapest | Unaccent, unaccent, accent | *Apprehend* | ta-ta-TUM | 239, 190, 533, 955 |
| Dactyl | Accent, unaccent, unaccent | *Happily* | TUM-ta-ta | 581, 584, 628, 643 |
| | | Combined dactylic-iambic meter: | | 158, 229, 503, 500 |
| | | Combined anapestic-iambic meter: | | 888 |
| | | Combined dactylic-trochaic meter: | | 713 |

In summary, meter can be defined as *syllabic meter* organizing and measuring word syllables; and *rhythmic meter,* organizing and measuring the flow of rhythm in music and/or lyrics (words in a given stanza line.

# Index of German and Miscellaneous First Lines

# Index of First Lines

# I HEAR THE SAVIOUR SAY

*Ye were not redeemed with corruptible things . . . but with the precious blood of Christ.* I Pet. 1:18, 19.

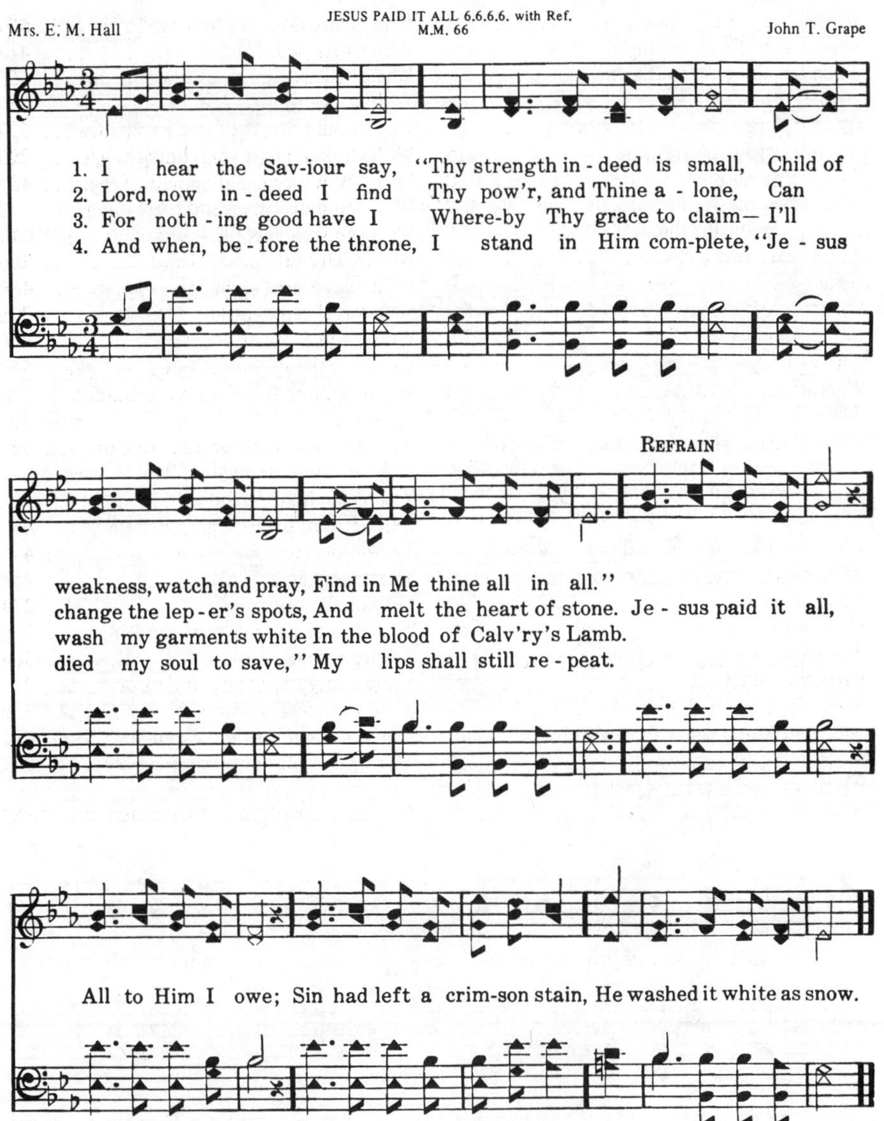
JESUS PAID IT ALL 6.6.6.6. with Ref.
M.M. 66
Mrs. E. M. Hall
John T. Grape
1. I hear the Sav-iour say, "Thy strength in - deed is small, Child of
2. Lord, now in - deed I find Thy pow'r, and Thine a - lone, Can
3. For noth - ing good have I Where-by Thy grace to claim— I'll
4. And when, be - fore the throne, I stand in Him com-plete, "Je - sus
weakness, watch and pray, Find in Me thine all in all."
change the lep - er's spots, And melt the heart of stone.
wash my garments white In the blood of Calv'ry's Lamb.
died my soul to save," My lips shall still re - peat.
Refrain
Je - sus paid it all,
All to Him I owe; Sin had left a crim-son stain, He washed it white as snow.

# THERE WAITS FOR ME A GLAD TOMORROW

*Arise ye, and let us go up to Zion unto the Lord our God.* Jer. 31:6.

James Allen Crutchfield

ZION'S HILL 9.8.9.8. with Ref.
M.M. 66

James Allen Crutchfield
Arr. Haldor Lillenas

1. There waits for me a glad to - mor - row, Where gates of pearl swing o - pen wide,
2. Some day I'll hear the an - gels sing - ing, Be - yond the shadows of the tomb;
3. Some day my la - bors will be end - ed, And all my wand'rings will be o'er,
4. Some day the dark clouds will be rift - ed, And all the night of gloom be past;
And when I've passed this vale of sor - row, I'll camp up - on the oth - er side.
And all the bells of heav - en ring - ing, While saints are singing, "Home, sweet home."
And all earth's broken ties be mend - ed, And I shall sigh and weep no more.
And all life's bur - dens will be lift - ed, The day of rest shall dawn at last.
Some day be - yond the reach of mor - tal ken, Some day, God
on - ly knows just where and when, The wheels of mor - tal life shall
all stand still, And I shall go to dwell on Zi - on's hill.

# PARDON ME, O MY GOD

## (Invocation to Martyrs' Mirror)

From *Martyrs' Mirror*
Tieleman Jansz van Braght, 1625-1664
*Klimt op uw' gulden Hoogtt'*
Tr. J. F. Sohm, 1886
Recast, John J. Overholt, 1975

ANRUFUNG 8.8.10.8. with Ref.

John J. Overholt, 1975

DESCANT
1. Par - don me, O my God, That I, dust, ash-es ap - proach Thee,
The cru-el death of Thy mar-tyrs, De-fense-less lambs, al- to - geth - er,
2. How-e'er I joy con-tem-plat-ed, As I their con-fi - dence see - ing,
Ah! how I oft - en did wish then, To be a par-tak - er with them,
3. Pa-tient-ly bear, I be-sought them, With-out gain-say-ing or flinch - ing;
Scaf-fold and stake, say-ing to them, Fight val-iant-ly, sis - ters, breth - ren,
Yet that which caused my tears to flow Was the re - mem-brance of suf-f'ring;
In-no - cent, led to the wa-ter and fire, To the sword and beast's de-vour-ing;
In Thy great grace as they fought val-iant-ly Thru the strait gate all for-see-ing
My soul went with them to pris-on and then In the tri - bu - nal I stayed them,
Suf-fer the sen-tence of death urg-ing them At the place of ex - e - cu - tion,
The crown awaits you—and died thus with them, So great my love bound up with them,
REFRAIN
There to suf-fer and there to die For Thy name's sake most ho - ly;
There to suf-fer and there to die, For Thy name's sake, O my God!

**These two hymns by van Braght were arranged to commemorate the 450th Anniversary of the founding of the Anabaptist-Mennonite Church (1525-1975).**

# CLIMB UP YOUR GOLDEN HEIGHT

## (Accolade to a Champion)

From *Martyrs' Mirror*
Tieleman Jansz van Braght, 1625-1664
Tr. J. F. Sohm, 1886
Recast, John J. Overholt, 1975
RITTERSCHLAG 6.6.6.6. with Ref.
John J. Overholt, 1975
DESCANT
1. Climb up your gold-en height, Cham-pion of the band
2. God's ban - ner red in blood, Op-pres - sion mis - er - y,
3. The dread - ful burn-ing fires, The shin-ing stakes a - light,
4. Nor makes it them a - shamed To bear the name of Christ,
Of hol - y souls a - light Who fol - lowed Christ's com-mand.
Where smoke and va - por stood, Burnt sac - ri - fi - cial - ly.
The shame which Zi - on bears, God's peo-ple ne'er af - fright!
Un - til they are con-sumed And meet the Lord they prized!
REFRAIN
1. This he - ro went be-fore them, He did fight his way
2. The sac - ri - fi - cial fire As - cend - ing to the skies
3. O Sav - iour, Lord of heav'n, Of earth, and sky, and sea,
4. Lord, our thanks for blood of mar - tyrs And for proph - ets slain;
Thru the straight gate to heav - en Thru Christ's liv - ing way!
Of dread - ful hu-man of - f'rings Who there won the prize!
Thanks for e'er that us is giv'n this Her - it - age from Thee!
This, Thy her - it - age still of - fers Christ's e - ter - nal gain!

The above tribute was paid by Van Braght to the martyr, Gerardus, who for the testimony of Jesus Christ went singing before his companions, five other men, two women, and a girl, on the way to burning at the stake in Cologne, Germany, A. D. 1163.